Kimber-Gray-Stackpole's
ANATOMY AND PHYSIOLOGY

Kimber-Gray-Stackpole's

ANATOMY and PHYSIOLOGY

16th edition

BY

Marjorie A. Miller, M.S.

Associate Professor (Nursing),
Cornell University–New York Hospital School of Nursing, New York
Formerly, Associate Professor (Science),
Cornell University–New York Hospital School of Nursing;
Instructor of Nursing Education (Physiology),
Teachers College, Columbia University, New York

Lutie C. Leavell, M.A., M.S.

Professor Emeritus of Nursing Education,
Teachers College, Columbia University, New York
Formerly, Consultant, College of Nursing, University of Iowa, Iowa City;
and Lecturer, School of Nursing, University of Pennsylvania, Philadelphia

MACMILLAN PUBLISHING CO., INC.
NEW YORK

COLLIER MACMILLAN PUBLISHERS
LONDON

Earlier Editions: Text-book of Anatomy and Physiology for Nurses *by Kimber, copyright,* 1893, *by Macmillan Publishing Co., Inc., and copyright,* 1902, *by Macmillan Publishing Co., Inc.;* Text-book of Anatomy and Physiology for Nurses *by Kimber and Gray, copyright* 1909, 1914, 1918, *by Macmillan Publishing Co., Inc.;* Text-book of Anatomy and Physiology *by Kimber and Gray, copyright,* 1923, 1926, *by Macmillan Publishing Co., Inc.;* Textbook of Anatomy and Physiology *by Kimber and Gray, copyright,* 1931, *by Macmillan Publishing Co., Inc.;* Textbook of Anatomy and Physiology *by Kimber, Gray, and Stackpole, copyright,* 1934, 1938, 1942, *by Macmillan Publishing Co., Inc.;* Textbook of Anatomy and Physiology *by Kimber, Gray, Stackpole, and Leavell, copyright,* 1948, 1955, *by Macmillan Publishing Co., Inc.;* Anatomy and Physiology *by Kimber, Gray, Stackpole, and Leavell,* © 1961, *by Macmillan Publishing Co., Inc.;* Anatomy and Physiology *by Kimber, Gray, Stackpole, Leavell, and Miller,* © *copyright* 1966, *by Macmillan Publishing Co., Inc.*

Copyright renewed: 1930, 1937, *by Mary J. Kimber;* 1946, 1951, 1954, 1959, *by Theresa Buell;* 1962, 1966, 1970, *by Lutie C. Leavell.*

MACMILLAN PUBLISHING CO., INC.
866 Third Avenue, New York, New York 10022

COLLIER-MACMILLAN CANADA, LTD., Toronto, Ontario

Library of Congress catalog card number: 79–158067

PRINTING 4 5 6 7 8 9 0 YEAR 4 5 6 7 8 9 0

PREFACE TO THE SIXTEENTH EDITION

The scope and organization of *Anatomy and Physiology* reflect the authors' belief that the student should thoroughly read assigned chapters out of class, learning at his/her own rate, and that class time (formal and laboratory) is best spent not in repeating this information but in clarifying difficult concepts and in expanding areas of interest to a particular teacher or student group. Because the principal users of the book are students of nursing and various paramedical disciplines, who require greater depth of knowledge in some areas, there is considerable emphasis on acid-base balance, cardiac action, and other subjects of clinical interest. In incorporating advances in scientific knowledge the authors have tried to de-emphasize the elementary material now comprising introductory science courses without sacrificing necessary basic concepts.

A more cohesive integration of anatomy and physiology is evident throughout this sixteenth edition. Such an arrangement is particularly noticeable in Unit II, where circulation and nerve supply are unified with the muscles of body movement, and in other sections where circulation is integrated with appropriate functional areas. This regional approach should facilitate learning and effect a more meaningful comprehension of the structure and function of the body parts. Total content is now divided into seven units, which necessitated considerable reorganization. The greatest changes are to be found in Unit II ("Locomotion and Support: The Organs—Their Structure and Activity"), Unit IV ("Means of Distributing Materials to and from Cells"), and Unit VI ("Maintaining Homeostasis of Body Fluids"). Charts and tables are used to present salient characteristics and detailed information in a simple fashion—most noticeably in the discussions of tissues and of the skeleton and muscles.

The terminology used throughout is based on the third edition of *Nomina Anatomica*. Questions for thought and discussion by students are located at the end of each chapter; references helpful to instructors are listed in the revised *Teacher's Guide*. A revised *Test Manual* supplements the textbook, as does the *Workbook and Laboratory Manual* by Drakontides, Miller, and Leavell.

The authors are particularly grateful to the illustrator, Mrs. Barbara Finneson, for the quality of the line cuts (many of which are reproduced in two, three, and four colors), wash drawings, and cover illustration—integral parts of the textbook. They also wish to thank Dr. James L. German, III, of Cornell University Medical College, who supplied the chromosome map; Dr. George Palade, of Rockefeller University, who provided the electron micrographs of the cell; Dr. Thomas F. DeCaro, of PMC Colleges, who supplied the electron micrograph of skeletal muscle; medical-school faculty members who reviewed the total manuscript and offered constructive comments and criticism; and our students, past and present, who have been a constant source of inspiration. The authors are particularly indebted to Miss Joan C. Zulch, medical editor of The Macmillan Company, for her continued loyal support and help.

M. A. M.
L. C. L.

CONTENTS

UNIT IV
Means of Distributing Materials to and from Cells

UNIT V
Materials to Be Distributed to and from Cells

UNIT VI
Maintaining Homeostasis of Body Fluids

UNIT VII
Structural and Functional Relationships for Human Reproduction and Development

Kimber-Gray-Stackpole's
ANATOMY AND PHYSIOLOGY

UNIT I

The Body as a Whole: Structural and Functional Relationships

The human organism is able to perceive his environment and its changes, to respond purposefully on an unconscious as well as a conscious level, and to think and make judgments based on his perceptions. The specialized function of each organ of the body depends on the organization of tissues within that organ and on the cells which make up each tissue. How these life processes are brought about on the cellular level is the subject of this textbook.

CHAPTER

I

GENERAL STRUCTURE OF THE BODY

Basic Terminology, Cavities, Regions, Systems, and Functional Units

Understanding one's self and others is an important part of healthy enjoyment of life. Since the structure and function of the body are integral parts of this understanding, the study of anatomy and physiology can help those in every walk of life. More particularly—as a basis for understanding the sick individual, what is wrong, and what can be done to help him return to his normal, healthy state—the study of anatomy and physiology is a necessity for those in the medical sciences.

Both anatomy and physiology are divisions of a larger science, biology, which deals with the acquisition and organization of knowledge about living things, plant and animal. *Anatomy* is the study of the parts of the living organism and their relationship to each other; *physiology* is the study of the way these parts accomplish their functions—the multiple activities involved in the life of the organism. It is impossible to separate completely these two areas of study and the fullest understanding of each comes from an understanding of the other.

Anatomy belongs to that group of biological sciences known as *morphology*, the group which deals with structure and spatial relationships, the way bodies are built, the kinds of material used, and the architecture of the entire organism. There are many specialties, for example:

Gross anatomy is the science of macroscopic structure, that which can be seen with the unaided eye.

Comparative anatomy is the study of animal structure, the similarities and differences among various orders or species of animals.

Developmental anatomy is the study of the embryonic and later development of body structures. In its widest sense *embryology* means the science of growth from the one-cell stage to the adult, but the term frequently is restricted to mean the period of growth and development before birth. This period is followed by the postnatal development of infancy, childhood, adolescence, and early, middle, and late maturity. Development can be studied much more vigorously from the standpoint of physiology.

Pathological anatomy has to do with structural changes in disease, their location, and their regional effects. The term *pathology* may be used in connection with anatomy, histology, physiology, etc., and is concerned with deviations from the normal state.

Histology is the study of the minute structure that can be seen only with the aid of lenses, and therefore is often called *microscopic anatomy*, or microanatomy. It makes clear the structure and activities of cells, their arrangement in tissues, and the manner in which tissues are built into organs.

Similar to anatomy, the science of physiology has many specialties, two of which are of interest here.

Human physiology gives attention to all the functions and activities occurring in the human.

Cellular physiology is the study of the individual cells themselves, as they live out on a small scale all the activities that characterize the larger organism—respiration, excretion, absorption of food, movement, etc.

These sciences and others, including psychology and sociology, can be grouped as the *biological sciences*, having to do with living things, as contrasted with the *physical sciences*, represented by mathematics, physics, and the like. The branches of science are closely related and tend to overlap, particularly as more knowledge is gathered in each.

GENERAL STRUCTURE OF THE BODY

An anatomical characteristic of all vertebrate animals is the vertebral column which supports the body. In actuality the body is a tube (the body wall) enclosing a tube (the gastrointestinal tract), the cavity between the two tubes being the body cavity, or celom.

Cavities. There are several cavities within the body. The thoracic and abdominal cavities are separated by the diaphragm; the dorsal cavity lies within the dorsal body wall, and the ventral cavity lies in front of it. Some of the cavities are more open, such as the orbital, nasal, and buccal cavities.

The celom, or body cavity, is a ventral

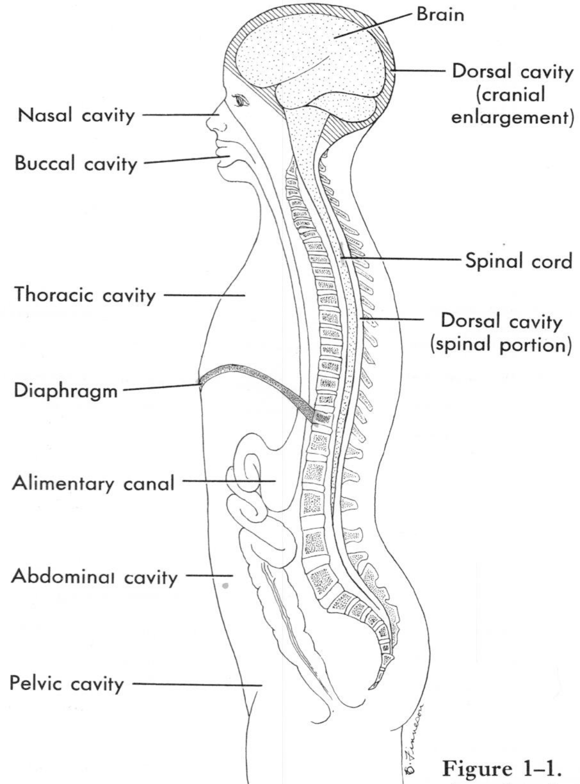

Figure 1–1. Longitudinal section of body to show dorsal and ventral body cavities.

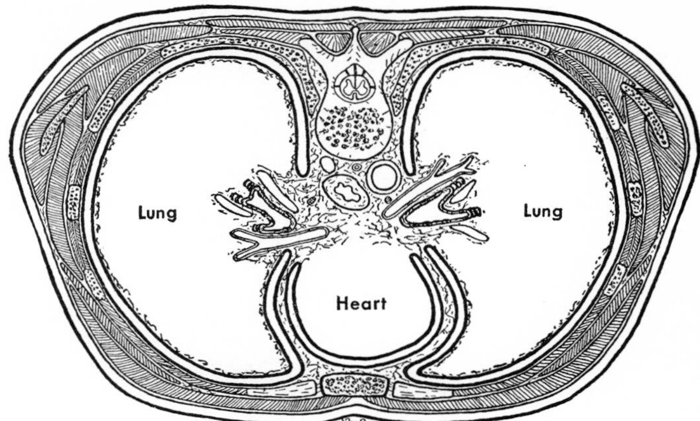

Figure 1–2. Diagram of a cross section of the body in the thoracic region. The mediastinum occupies the space between the lungs and extends from the sternum to the vertebrae. (Modified from Toldt.)

cavity, enclosed by the body wall. This wall is composed of skin, connective tissues, bone, muscles, and serous membrane. In mammals, during embryonic life this cavity becomes subdivided by a dome-shaped partition, the diaphragm, into the thoracic and abdominal cavities. The pericardial cavity also develops embryologically from the celom.

The *thoracic cavity*, or chest, contains the trachea, the bronchi, the lungs, the esophagus, nerves, the heart, and the great blood and lymph vessels connected with the heart. It also contains lymph nodes and the thymus gland.

The thoracic cavity is divided into right and left cavities, each containing a lung. The other thoracic organs lie in the mediastinum between these (Figure 1–2). Each lung is covered by a thin membrane, the *pleura*, which extends to and lines the inner surface

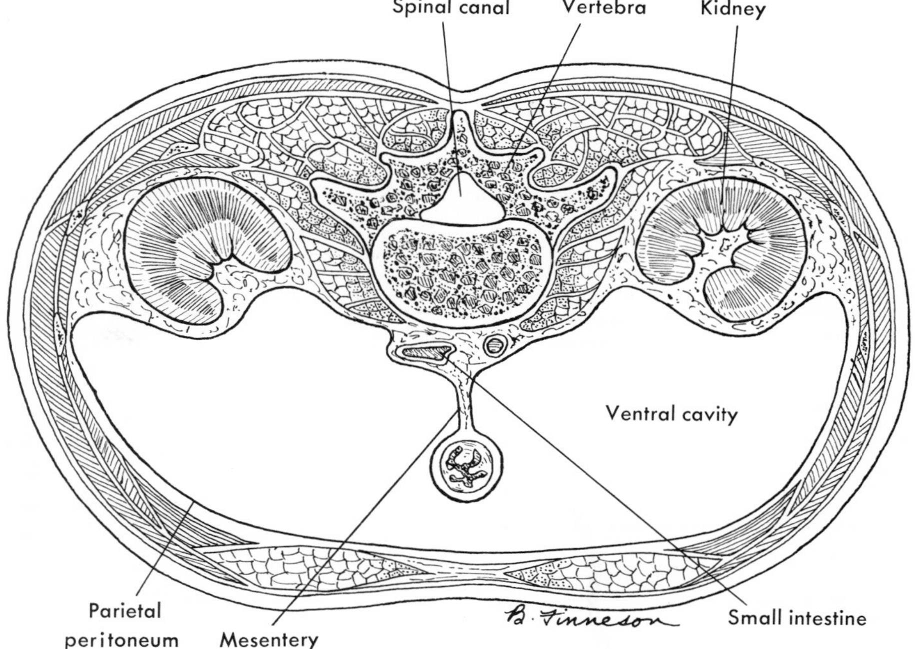

Figure 1–3. Diagrammatic transverse section of the body to show abdominal part of ventral cavity and spinal part of dorsal cavity.

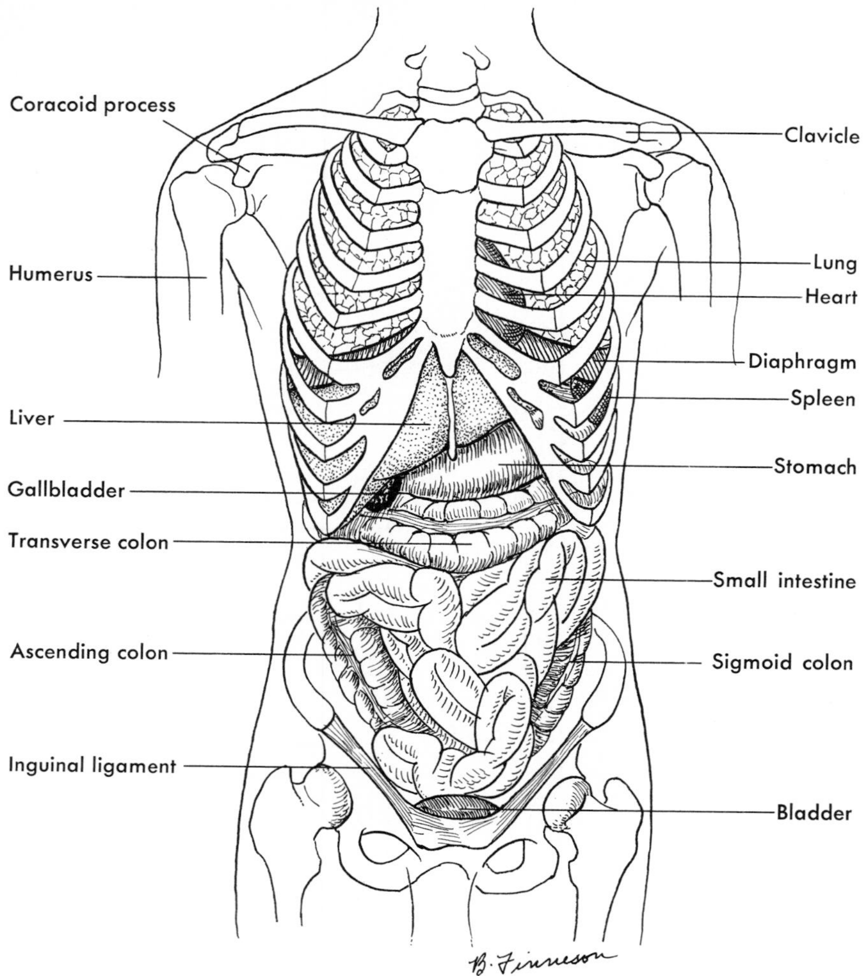

Figure 1–4. Diagram to illustrate the thoracic and abdominal viscera in their normal position and their relationship to the skeleton. Anterior view.

of the chest wall. The *pleural cavity* thus formed is a potential space since the two layers of pleura are in contact.

The *abdominal cavity* contains the stomach, liver, gallbladder, pancreas, spleen, kidneys, and small and large intestines. It may be divided into nine regions, as seen in Figure 1–7.

The *peritoneal cavity*, a potential space like the pleural cavity, lies within the abdomen and is formed by two layers of membrane—that covering the abdominal organs and that covering the inner surface of the abdominal wall.

The *pelvic cavity* is that portion of the abdominal cavity lying below an imaginary line drawn across the prominent crests of the hip bones. It is more completely bounded by bony walls than the rest of the abdominal cavity. It is divided by a narrow bony ring, the pelvic inlet, into the greater, or false, pelvis above and the lesser, or true, pelvis below. The greater, or false, pelvic cavity contains parts of the small and large intestines. The lesser, or true, pelvis contains the bladder, the rectum, and some of the reproductive organs. Study Figures 1–4, 1–5, and 1–6.

The *dorsal cavity* is within the *dorsal body wall*. It contains the brain and spinal cord. The dorsal cavity is a continuous bony

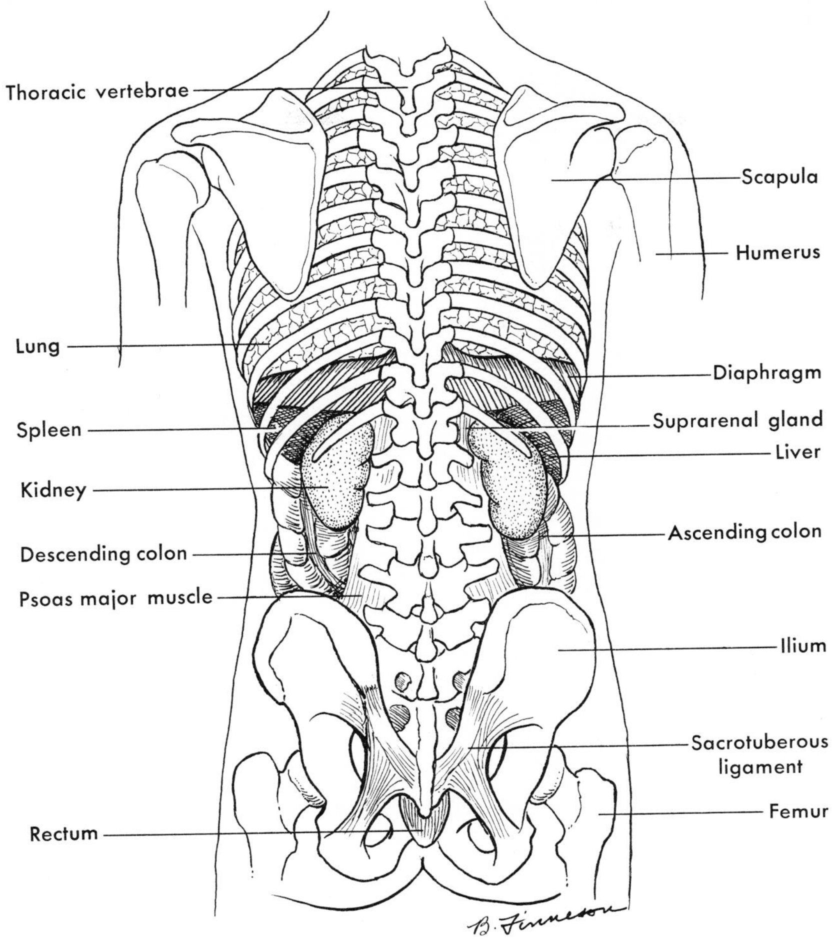

Figure 1–5. Diagram to illustrate the thoracic and abdominal viscera in their normal position and their relationship to the skeleton. Posterior view.

cavity formed by the cranial bones and the vertebrae, and it is lined by the meninges of the brain and spinal cord.

A survey of the skeleton shows small cavities in the skull, in addition to the cranial cavity, which, for the sake of simplicity in study, are included here.

The *orbital cavities* contain the eyes, the optic nerves, the muscles of the eyeballs, and the lacrimal apparatus.

The *nasal cavity* contains the structures forming the nose (page 369).

The *buccal cavity*, or *mouth cavity*, contains the tongue and teeth.

GENERAL ANATOMICAL TERMS

Owing to the fact that man walks erect and the majority of other mammals go on all fours, confusion may arise in the use of terms which describe corresponding parts of man and other animals. To avoid this confusion, anatomists have arbitrarily defined these terms.[1]

[1] *Nomina Anatomica,* 3rd ed. New York: Excerpta Medica Foundation, 1968.

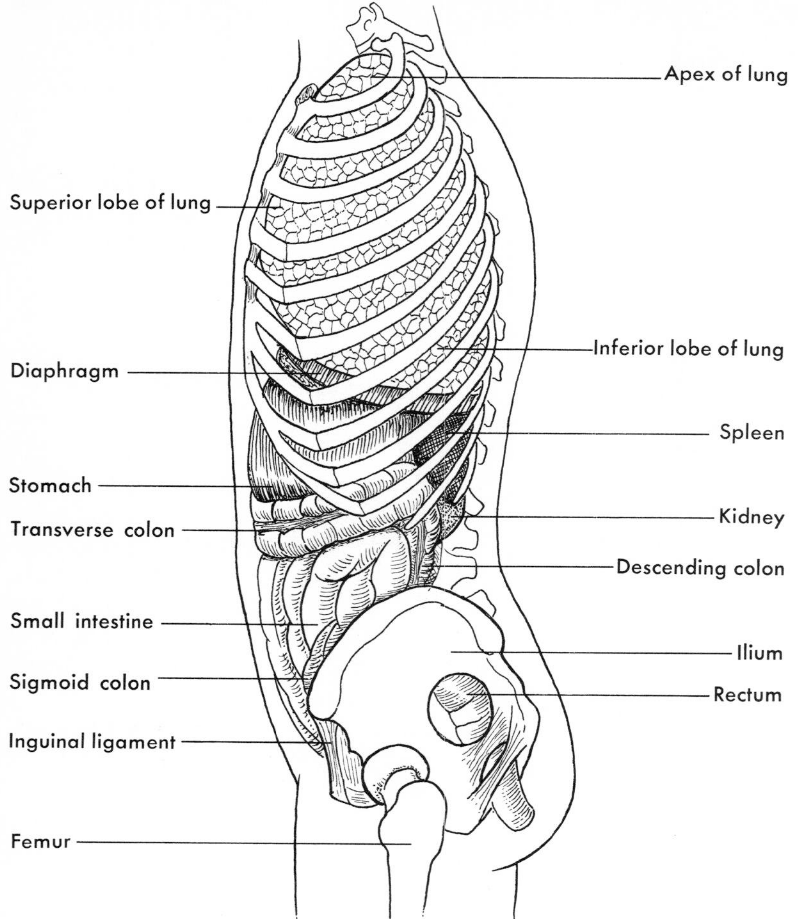

Figure 1–6. Diagram to illustrate the thoracic and abdominal viscera in their normal position and their relationship to the skeleton. Side view.

The Anatomical Position. In describing the body, anatomists always consider it to be in the erect position with the face toward the observer, the arms hanging at the sides, and the palms of the hands turned forward. All references to location of parts assume the body to be in this position.

Textbooks of human anatomy use both *dorsal* and *posterior* for the side containing the backbone, and *ventral* or *anterior* for the opposite side. (Comparative anatomists call the head end of an animal *anterior*, the opposite end *posterior*.) The head end is spoken of as *cranial* and the opposite end as *caudal*. A part above another is described as *superior* to it; a part below another is said to be *inferior*. The term *soma* refers to the body walls and extremities—the body exterior as opposed to the interior. *Viscera* refers to the organs within the body cavities.

Sagittal plane is the dorsoventral plane dividing the body into right and left sides. It is usually used in the sense of a *midsagittal plane* dividing the body into right and left halves. A *coronal* or *frontal plane* divides the body into ventral and dorsal parts. A *transverse plane* divides the body into cranial and caudal parts. The parts nearest the midsagittal plane are *medial* (mesial); those farthest from this plane are *lateral*. A *horizontal plane* is parallel to the horizon, and the term should be used only in relating the individual to his environment. If the term is used solely in relation to the individual, it indicates a transverse plane, since the individual is supposed to be in the anatomical position.

Internal and *external* are reserved almost entirely for describing the walls of cavities or of hollow viscera.

Proximal describes a position near the origin of any part. *Distal* describes a position distant, or farthest away, from the source of any part. Thus we speak of the proximal end or of the distal end of a finger.

Parietal (Latin, *paries*, a wall) is used to describe the wall enclosing a body cavity or surrounding the organs.

Visceral (Latin, *viscus*, an organ) is applied to the organs within the body cavities.

Peripheral pertains to the outside or surface of a body or an organ.

SYSTEMS

The cell is the structural and physiological, as well as the developmental, unit of the body. It is desirable, however, to begin the study of the body with an analysis of its component parts—the systems, organs, tissues, unit patterns, and cells.

A system is an arrangement of organs closely allied to one another and concerned with the same functions.

The skeletal system consists of bones of the body and connective tissues which bind them together.

Main functions: support, protection, and motion.

The muscular system consists of striated muscles (e.g., biceps muscle) and nonstriated muscles (e.g., muscle coats of the stomach).

Main functions: to cause movement by contracting and to maintain static skeletal and postural support.

The nervous system consists of the brain, the spinal cord, ganglia, nerve fibers, and their sensory and motor terminals (e.g., motor end-plates on striated muscle). These are grouped into two integrated systems—the *somatic* and the *visceral* systems.

Main functions: to correlate the nerve impulses in the sensory centers and to coordinate the nerve impulses in the motor centers, thus acquainting the organism with the environment and integrating the nerve impulses into appropriate or adaptive responses.

The vascular, or **circulatory**, **system** consists of the heart, the blood vessels and blood, and the lymphatic vessels and lymph.

Main functions: to supply necessary nutrients and to remove cell secretions and excretions, thus helping to maintain the constancy of fluids around and inside all cells at all times (homeostasis).

The endocrine system includes the thyroid gland, parathyroids, pituitary body, adrenals, the thymus gland, portions of the glands with ducts, such as the islands of Langerhans in the pancreas, and portions of the ovaries and testes.

Main function: to contribute to the body fluids specific substances which affect the activity of other cells and organs.

The respiratory system consists of the nose, pharynx, larynx, trachea, bronchi, and lungs.

Main functions: to provide oxygen and get rid of excess carbon dioxide.

The digestive system consists of the alimentary canal and the accessory glands, i.e., the salivary glands, the pancreas, and the liver.

Main functions: to receive, digest, and absorb food, and eliminate some wastes.

The excretory system consists of the urinary organs, i.e., the kidneys, ureters, bladder, urethra, and the respiratory and digestive systems and the skin.

Main function: to eliminate the waste products that result from cell activity.

The reproductive system consists of the testes, seminal vesicles, penis, urethra, prostate, and bulbourethral glands in the male; the ovaries, uterine tubes, uterus, vagina, and vulva in the female.

All these systems are closely interrelated and dependent on each other. Although each forms a unit especially adapted for the performance of some function, that function cannot be performed without the cooperative activity of the other systems; for instance, the skeleton does not support unless assisted by the muscular, nervous, circulatory, and other systems. It is the function of the endocrine and the nervous systems to integrate the work of the systems.

An organ is a member of a system and is composed of tissues associated in performing some special function for which it is especially adapted. For example, the urinary system consists of the following organs: (1) two kidneys, which form the urine from the blood; (2) two ureters, ducts which convey the urine from the kidneys to the bladder; (3) the bladder, a reservoir for the reception of urine; and (4) the urethra, a tube through which the urine passes from the bladder and is finally voided. The interdependence of these organs is obvious.

Tissues. The organs are composed of component tissues. For example, the stomach is composed of columnar epithelial tissue, smooth-muscle tissue, connective tissue, serous tissue, nerves, blood, and lymph.

Microscopic study of tissues reveals that they are made up of smaller units, or cells. Each tissue is a group of cells with more or less intercellular material. The intercellular material varies in amount and in composition and in many cases determines the nature of the tissue, as, for instance, in the case of bone.

Unit Pattern. Study of the tissues that compose the organs shows that the tissues are arranged in an orderly way.

A *unit pattern*, or *functional unit*, can be defined approximately as the smallest aggregate of cells which, when repeated many times, composes an organ. If the liver is studied in this way, it will be seen that the lobules (smallest macroscopic units) are composed of *chains of cells* with their definite supply paths of blood and lymph and bile capillaries. This arrangement gives an *enormous area*, for the volume of cells and body fluid concerned, over which the cells and

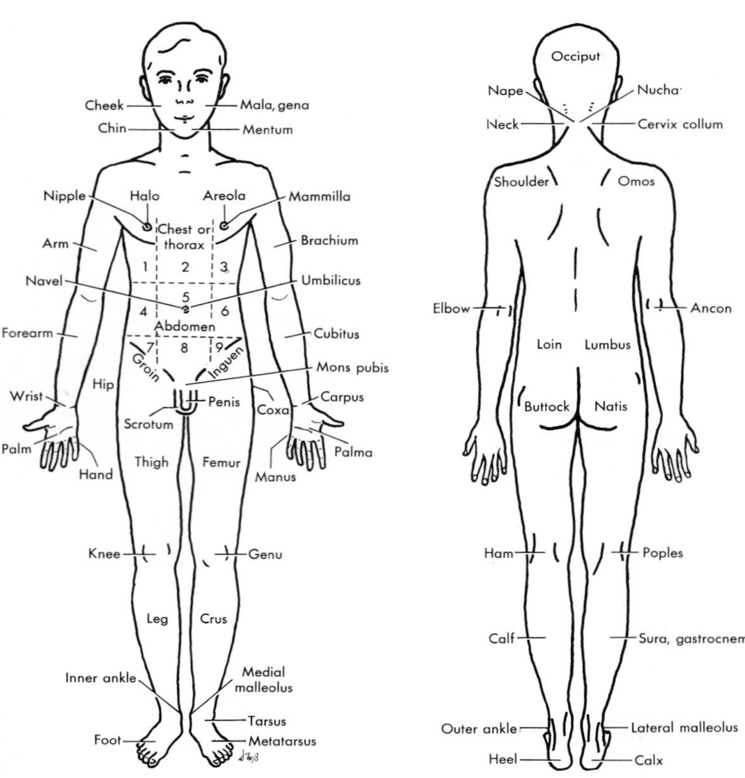

Figure 1–7. The anatomical position and regional names. Latin on one side and English on the other side. Surface lines of the front of thorax and abdomen. (*1* and *3*) Hypochondriac regions; (*2*) epigastric region; (*4* and *6*) lumbar regions, (*5*) umbilical region; (*7* and *9*) iliac regions; (*8*) hypogastric region.

circulatory fluids can be brought into diffusion relations and shows an orderly arrangement of blood and lymph vessels and nerve fibers throughout the organ.

The unit pattern may also be a *functional unit*, such as the reflex arc in the nervous system. This arc includes a sensory neuron (nerve cell) which perceives a stimulus (e.g., pain) and transmits it to one or more connecting cells in the spinal cord, which in turn transmits the impulse to a motor neuron which effects an appropriate response, e.g., muscle contraction. Thus the reflex arc contains at least three cells and is the basic unit comprising the nervous system.

Today we are far from understanding completely the interrelationship between the cell's structure and its functioning and the manner in which this structure controls development of the cell, the organ, and the organism. However, our knowledge has greatly increased in the past decade as a result of scientific advances such as the phase and electron microscopes and others in the field of electronics, and advances in understanding the chemical reactions within the cell.

QUESTIONS FOR DISCUSSION

1. Stand in the anatomical position and use each of the following terms correctly in relation to parts of the body:

   ventrodorsal
   caudal-cranial
   external-internal
   superior-inferior
   parietal-visceral
   proximal-distal

2. Name the body cavities and list the organs in each cavity.
3. Mary Ann is sitting before the mirror carefully combing her hair, turning her head from side to side. Her brother is in the kitchen mopping up the milk he accidentally spilled. What systems of the body are involved in these activities?
4. Which systems are interrelated in their functioning? Explain.

SUMMARY

Biological Sciences Deal with Living Things (Science is organized or classified knowledge)
- Morphology, or structure
  - Anatomy or macroscopic structure
  - Histology or microscopic structure
- Physiology, or function
- Development, or growth
  - Morphological
  - Physiological
  - Embryological or early growth and development

Anatomy
- Human
- Comparative
- Developmental
- Pathological

Histology
- Functional, or physiological
- Pathological
- Comparative

Physiology
- Human
- Comparative
- Cellular

Embryology
- Morphological
- Physiological

- **Human Body**
  - **Ventral cavity**
    - 1. **Thoracic cavity**
      - Esophagus, trachea, lungs, heart, blood and lymph vessels, thymus gland
    - Right and left **thoracic cavities**; each contains a lung
    - The *mediastinum* between the thoracic cavities contains thymus, trachea, bronchi, lymph nodes and vessels, nerves, esophagus, heart, and large blood vessels
    - Pleural cavities, containing serum
    - The *diaphragm* separates the thoracic and abdominal cavities.
    - 2. **Abdominal cavity**
      - Stomach, spleen, pancreas, liver, gallbladder, kidneys, large and small intestines
      - **Pelvic cavity** (Lower portion abdominal cavity)
        - 1. Greater, or false, pelvis
        - 2. Lesser, or true, pelvis: bladder, rectum, some of the reproductive organs
    - **Peritoneal cavity**, lined with peritoneum, contains serum
  - **Dorsal cavity**
    - 1. **Cranial cavity**—brain
    - 2. **Spinal canal**—spinal cord
  - **Facial aspect of skull**
    - 1. **Orbital cavities**
      - Eyes, optic nerves, muscles of the eyeballs, lacrimal apparatus
    - 2. **Nasal cavity**—structures forming the nose
    - 3. **Buccal cavity**
      - Tongue, teeth

- **Body Regions**
  - **Anatomical position and terms**
    - Definition, Dorsal, Ventral, Anterior, Posterior
    - Superior, Inferior, Cranial, Caudal
    - Soma, Viscera
  - **Anatomical planes**
    - Medial (mesial, mesal, mesad)
    - Lateral
    - Sagittal and midsagittal plane
    - Coronal (frontal) plane
    - Transverse plane

System. An arrangement of organs, closely allied and concerned with the same function
Systems found in the human body:

Skeletal	Endocrine
Muscular	Respiratory
Nervous	Digestive
Vascular, or circulatory	Excretory
Reproductive	

Organ. A physiological unit composed of two or more tissues associated in performing some special function

Tissue. A group of cells with varying amounts of intercellular materials

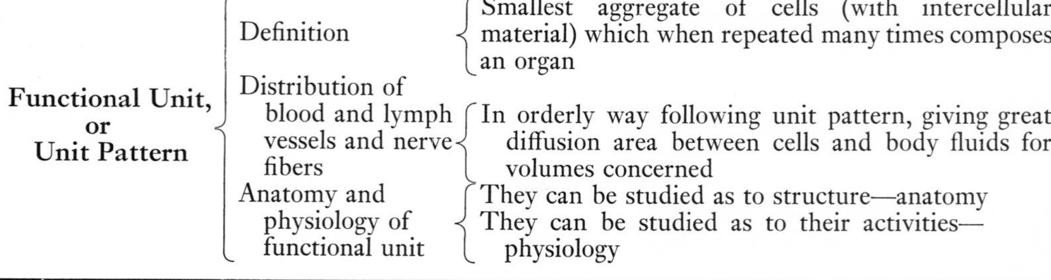

- **Functional Unit, or Unit Pattern**
  - Definition
    - Smallest aggregate of cells (with intercellular material) which when repeated many times composes an organ
  - Distribution of blood and lymph vessels and nerve fibers
    - In orderly way following unit pattern, giving great diffusion area between cells and body fluids for volumes concerned
  - Anatomy and physiology of functional unit
    - They can be studied as to structure—anatomy
    - They can be studied as to their activities—physiology

CHAPTER

2

THE CELL

Structure and Function

The human being may be described as a multicellular animal consisting of an enormous number of cells and intercellular material which the cells have made. In multicellular animals, individual cells are often remote from air, food, and the excreting organs and must rely upon the circulating fluids to carry oxygen and food to them and waste matters from them.

Cells are in contact with one another and with the blood stream, in some cases very intimately and tightly packed together as with muscle cells. At other times the arrangement is rather loose with relatively much material between the cells, or between the cells and the capillaries—the tiny blood vessels from which materials move to the cells, and to which cell excretions move.

Form or Shape of Cells. Cells differ (markedly in some cases) in their size and shape; however, they are in general extremely minute and not visible to the naked eye.

As a generalization, it can be said that for a *given volume* spherical cells have least surface area, and that the more irregular the cell, the greater is its surface area. For example, irregular connective-tissue cells and nerve cells expose an enormous surface area to body fluids (for a given volume of cell content) as compared with cylindrical or columnar cells, or the disk-shaped red blood cells.

The surface area–volume ratio in cells of various shapes is conspicuous as it concerns nerve cells, which contain relatively little metaplasm (e.g., stored food) and may have very long, exceedingly fine processes (fibers); this means an enormous area in relation to the volume of protoplasm concerned. This surface area is in contact with circulating lymph in the perineural lymph spaces, and hence the protoplasm of the cell has abundant opportunity to get supplies (e.g., food) in relation to its need. Or consider a *piece* of nerve fiber 25 mm long and less than 0.01 mm in diameter in terms of surface area–volume ratio!

Size of Cells. The factors that determine the sizes of cells are unknown, though much experimental work has been done in this field, and several theories have been proposed. The average diameter of a red blood cell is about 0.0075 mm, and it is about one fourth as thick. A striated muscle cell may be an inch or more long, but the diameter is seldom over 0.05 mm. The total length of the peripheral and central processes of a spinal sensory nerve fiber may reach from the toe to the medulla. In a tall person, then, it may be more than 4 or 5 ft long, but the diameter of the nerve fiber would probably be less than 0.01 mm. If all the processes of this nerve cell, divested of their sheaths, were wrapped closely around the cell body, the total volume of the cell would still be minute.

Figure 2–1 shows cells of various shapes. *A* is a "shapeless" cell—the ameba. At the right, outlines of an ameba in pseudopodial motion are

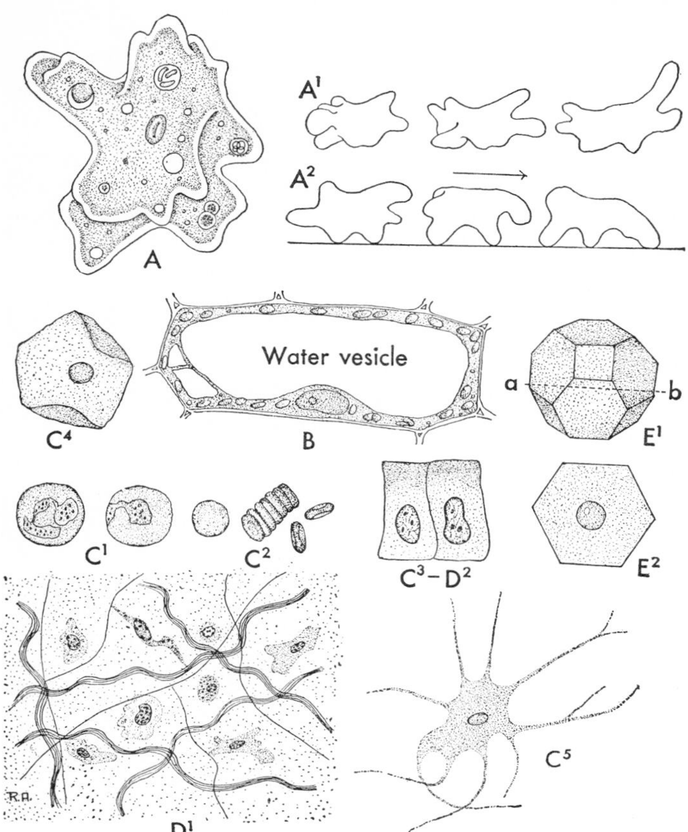

Figure 2–1. Diagrams of cells of many shapes as they would appear under the microscope. Description in text. The cells are not drawn to any scale.

shown, in A^1 from above and in A^2 from the side; the straight line represents the *edge* of a microscope slide. *B* shows a typical plant cell with a cell wall of cellulose giving it fixed shape, with somewhat angled corners.

C^1 shows a spherical white blood cell, at left seen in face view, at right in profile view. C^2 shows at left a face view of a red blood cell; at right, edge views of a few red cells. C^3 shows side views of two cylindrical cells. C^4 shows a surface view of a flat (squamous) cell, the folded-over edge showing its thickness. C^5 shows a very irregular cell.

D^1 shows an abundance of intercellular material between cells (as seen in areolar connective tissue); D^2 shows two cells with very little intercellular material between the cells (represented by the black line).

E^1 shows the shape which soft living cells (e.g., fat cells) assume when lightly pressed together (as in adipose connective tissue); E^2 shows how the microscope would show this cell if focused at plane *a . . . b*.

The ratio of nuclear volume to cytoplasmic volume is in many cells the same, the volume of the nucleus being from about $\frac{1}{25}$ to $\frac{1}{50}$ the volume of the cytoplasm. In young cells with a high metabolic rate, the nucleus is relatively large. In position the nucleus is usually near the most active (chemically) part of the cell. This seems to indicate that the activities of the cell can be carried on only within certain small limits of size. Since the surface area of the nucleus increases only in

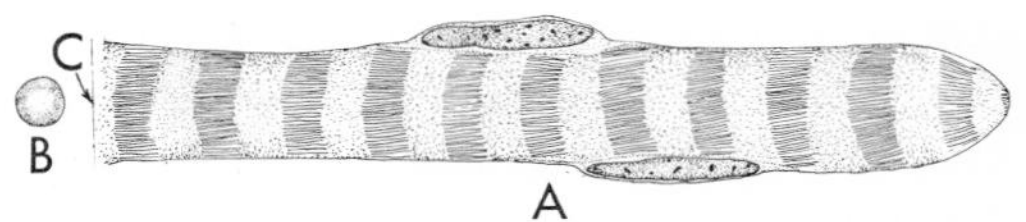

Figure 2–2. Size of cells. (*A*) Voluntary muscle cell magnified in width 200 times and represented as cut off at *C*. At this magnification it would be about 200 in. long. (*B*) Red blood cell, also magnified about 200 times.

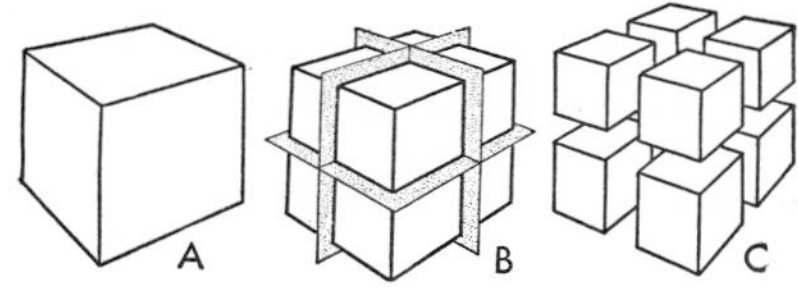

Figure 2–3. Diagrams to illustrate increased proportion of total surface area to total volume on fragmenting an object. *A* is a cube 2 in. on a side. *B* shows planes in which it may be cut to produce the eight cubes shown in *C*. Each of these eight cubes is 1 in. on a side. The total area of *A* is 24 sq in. The total area of the eight cubes in *C* is 48 sq in. The volume of material in *A* and *C* is the same, 8 cu in.

a ratio of the square, whereas the cell volume of cytoplasm and the nucleus increase in a cubic ratio, the area of contact between nucleus and cytoplasm does not keep pace with their growth in volume; hence, the efficiency of the nucleus in relation to cell activities decreases markedly. This may be one of the important factors in limiting the sizes of cells.

Structure of the Cell. A cell is a microscopic unit of *protoplasm* contained within a double-layered envelope, the *cell membrane*, or *plasma membrane*. The membrane has long been of interest since through it must pass all the materials the cell needs as well as any secretions of the cell; yet it must be of sufficient consistency to retain the *cytoplasm*, the protoplasm outside the nucleus. It is thought to be composed of lipid and protein molecules arranged in a double layer with the protein molecules outside. Recent studies indicate that animal cells, like vegetable cells, have a cell "coat" which separates them from other cells, the coat being composed of a protein-carbohydrate compound.

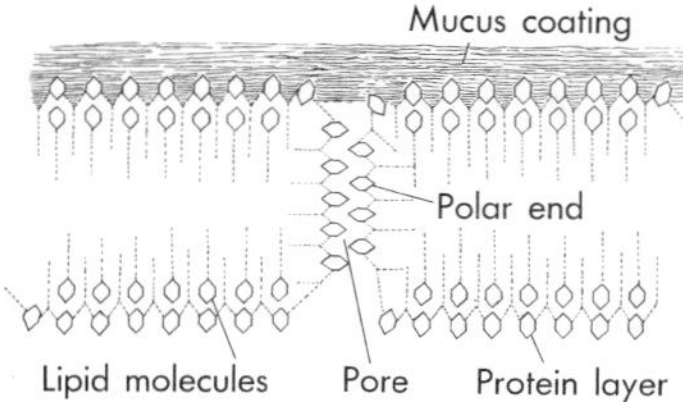

Figure 2–4. Diagram of molecular arrangement of cell membrane.

Cytoplasm contains a variety of structures —*organelles*, organized living material, and *inclusions*, lifeless and often temporary material, such as pigment granules, secretory granules, and nutrients such as protein and carbohydrate particles—material which will be utilized by the cell in its life processes, or excreted.

The organelles comprise the *mitochondria*, the *Golgi complex* or *apparatus*, the *centrioles*, *endoplasmic reticulum* and *ribosomes*, *lysosomes*, and in some cells *fibrils*.

Mitochondria vary in number from a few to several hundred. Depending on the type of cell, they appear as rod-shaped or round structures which change shape as cell activity varies. They are concentrated in areas of greatest cell activity, e.g., near the surface of actively secreting gland cells, in muscle cells near the motor end-plates, and in nerve cells near the nodes. The mitochondrial surface is a double-layered membrane, whose inner surface is extensively infolded. The mitochondria contain a variety of enzymes for energy-releasing chemical reactions in the cell, and for synthesis of materials such as amino acids.

The Golgi apparatus, most noticeable in secretory cells, appears as a stacked arrangement of flattened membrane, somewhat like an accordion, lying between the nucleus and the cell surface. As protein material is synthesized in the endoplasmic reticulum it moves away, surrounded by a portion of its membrane, which then fuses with the membrane at the base of the Golgi stack, and the protein droplet is discharged into the Golgi apparatus. In the case of glycoproteins such as are found in mucus, the carbohydrate portion is added to the protein molecule by the Golgi apparatus, and it is then discharged from the top of the stack, again surrounded by membrane from the Golgi apparatus. When the secretory vesicle is discharged from the cell, the membrane coat remains as part of the cell membrane. Thus it appears that the Golgi apparatus is a dynamic membrane —being continuously removed at one end and re-formed at the other.

The *centrioles* are two in number, cylindrical

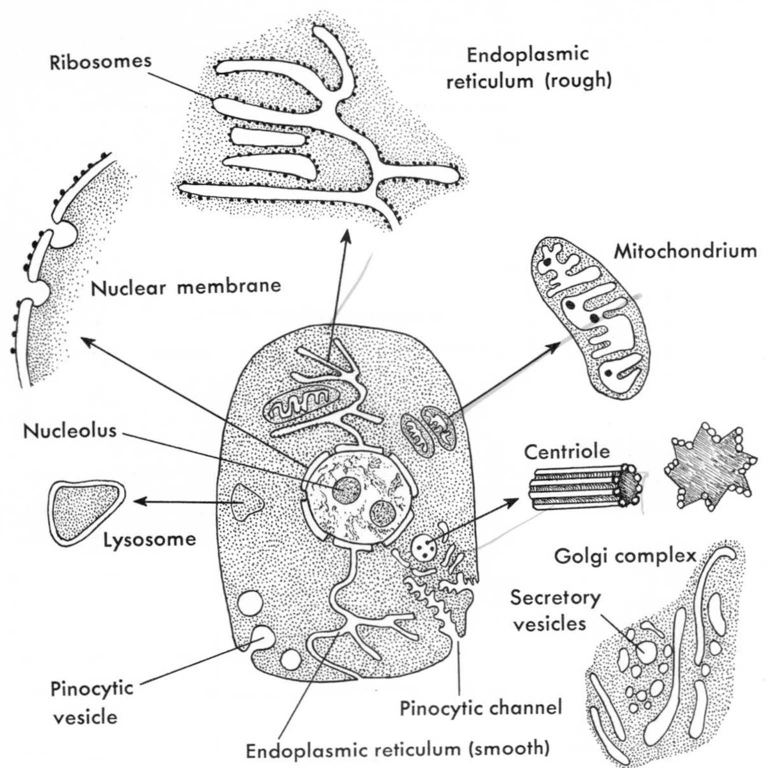

Figure 2–5. Diagram of typical cell showing structures visible under electron microscope.

in shape, lying near the nucleus, and are doubled in the early stage of cell division. By means of the microtubules ("spindle," see Figure 2–5) they form, the centrioles serve to separate one of each pair of chromosomes, so that each daughter cell receives identical chromosomes. The centriole is cylindrical in appearance with nine longitudinally arranged bundles, each bundle being composed of two or three tubules. (It is of interest that this same arrangement of nine fibers is found in cilia and the tail of spermatozoa.)

Endoplasmic reticulum (ER) is found in variable amounts in all cells and is in two forms, rough and smooth. *Smooth* ER appears under the microscope as a network of tubules. Its probable function is metabolism of certain cholesterol-containing hormones (it is prominent in the adrenal cortex) and of glycogen (it is prominent in liver and striated muscle). *Rough* ER appears microscopically as a series of flattened bags. The granules along its surface giving it a rough appearance are the *ribosomes*, sites of protein synthesis. The term *microsome* refers to small fragments of endoplasmic reticulum.

Lysosomes are seen as "droplets" within the cell which are of different consistency from the rest of the cytoplasm. Separation of these droplets by centrifugation and chemical analysis indicates that various digestive enzymes are contained within the lysosomal membrane at the edge of the "droplet." Thus, cytoplasm is protected from digestion by the enzymes; at the same time ingested nutrients coming into contact with the lysosome can be acted on. Larger molecules are broken down to smaller ones which the cell can use. Distinct granules termed *microbodies* are found in liver and kidney cells. Their exact function is not understood, but they are known to contain certain enzymes (e.g., catalase, which causes the release of oxygen from hydrogen peroxide).

Fibrils are found in many cells and are prominent in muscle and nerve cells. The myofibrils in muscle cells are contracting units. Neurofibrils (neurofilaments) are hair-like processes arranged in a network throughout nerve cell bodies and processes. It is possible that they lend support to the cell; other function is not known.

The most noticeable structure within the cell is the *nucleus*—usually one in each cell, although some liver cells contain two, and skeletal muscle cells contain multiple numbers. Protoplasm of the nucleus is given a special name, *karyoplasm*; it is surrounded by a nuclear membrane—a double-layered membrane which has openings or pores at intervals, through which materials pass from the nucleus to the cytoplasm and vice versa. The nucleus contains a more densely staining particle called the *nucleolus*, which is very large in growing cells and disappears entirely during the process of cell division. The ribonucleic acid (RNA) which makes up the ribosomes is formed in the nucleoli. In addition to the nucleoli, the nucleus contains *chromatin*—a combination of protein and deoxyribonucleic acid (DNA). The chromatin is transformed during cell division from its granular arrangement to one of long strands, called *chromosomes*—the particles within cells that control the transmission of characteristics from parent to child, or from one cell to daughter cells. The protein portion serves as support for the chromosome and also to suppress the action of the DNA.

Nucleic acids derive their name from the fact that they were first identified in the nucleus; however, they are found in the cytoplasm as well. These molecules are immense in relation to others, e.g., a molecule of water or of sugar. Like a coiled ladder, the nucleic acid molecule is made up of repeating units that are basically almost identical. The unit is termed a nucleotide, each of which contains a sugar (with five carbon atoms), a phosphate group, and one of the following organic substances called nitrogenous "bases": adenine, guanine, cytosine, thymine, and uracil. In the case of DNA the sugar is deoxyribose; the bases are adenine, guanine, cytosine, and thymine. In RNA the sugar is ribose; the bases are adenine, guanine, cytosine, and uracil. The nucleotides are fastened to each other in a particular fashion—the phosphate group of one attaching to the sugar of the next, forming the backbone of the molecule with the "bases" projecting outward from it. A DNA molecule contains a double array of these backbones, and the bases from each half attach to the bases of the other half—thus the base attachments form the steps of the ladder and the sugar-phosphate links form the sides. The size of the molecule and the spatial arrangement of its atoms make it possible for the "bases" to pair selectively: adenine on either side always combines with thymine on the other; cytosine combines with guanine. A sequence of four different bases on one side will give a complementary sequence on the other.

Current biochemical experiments with bacteria indicate that it is the sequence of bases in DNA—the order in which they are arranged—which contains the genetic information and is responsible for transmission of this information. Prior to cell division, the DNA molecule separates—each half synthesizing its opposite half so that two DNA molecules result. In fact, the entire chromosome, including the protein portion, doubles. Certain drugs used in the treatment of cancer act by preventing the normal synthesis of DNA molecules.

RNA differs from DNA in that it is a single strand and is characteristically found in the cytoplasm, although lesser, varying amounts are found in the nucleus, depending on the activity of the cell. There are three types of RNA—some much smaller than others. All RNA is formed in the nucleus under the direction of DNA. As the new DNA molecules are formed prior to cell division, the bases in DNA match with the

DNA		RNA
Guanine	:	Cytosine
Thymine	:	Adenine
Cytosine	:	Guanine
Adenine	:	Uracil[1]

[1] Note that RNA contains no thymine.

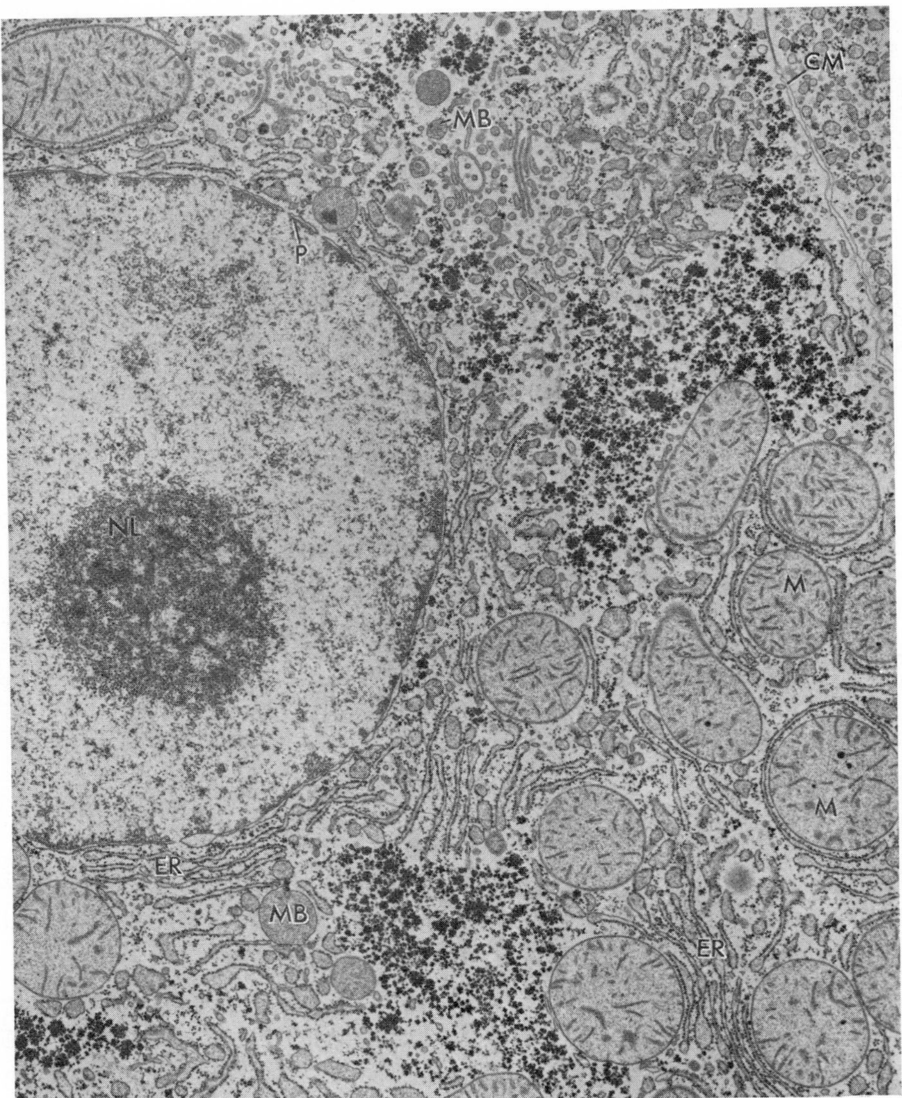

Figure 2–6. Liver cells of newborn rat showing nucleolus (*NL*); nucleus and nuclear membrane with several pores, one of which is labelled *P*; endoplasmic reticulum (*ER*); microbodies (*MB*); several mitochondria at lower right, two of which are labelled *M*; glycogen particles, which are visible as aggregated black dots. A portion of the cell membrane (*CM*) is visible at upper right. × 8,400. (Courtesy of Dr. George Palade, Rockefeller University, New York.)

appropriate RNA base. This formation is termed "transcription."

Ribosomal RNA is formed in small units within the nucleoli, which then move to the cytoplasm and attach to the endoplasmic reticulum. It is thought that loops of DNA enter the nucleolus in order to direct this formation.

Messenger RNA is synthesized in the nucleus, moves out into the cytoplasm, and usually attaches to the ribosomes, where it acts as a template, or plan for formation of a particular type of protein. In some cells the RNA does not attach to ribosomes but is free within the cytoplasm. *Transfer RNA* is a small molecule which attaches to amino

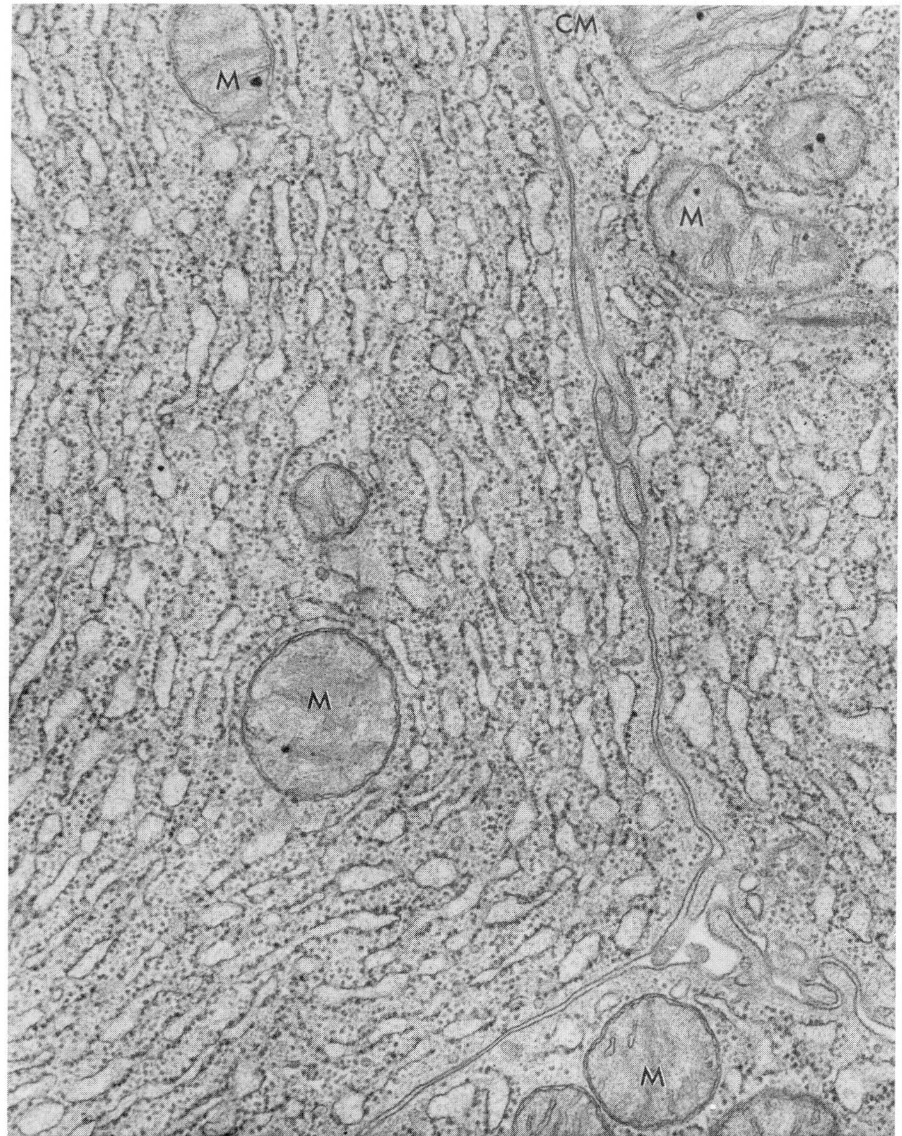

Figure 2–7. Portion of pancreatic exocrine cell (guinea pig) with cell membrane (*CM*) separating it from two adjacent cells visible to the right and in the lower right-hand corner. Endoplasmic reticulum is shown; several mitochondria (*M*) are seen in cross section. × 32,000. (Courtesy of Dr. George Palade, Rockefeller University, New York.)

acids present in the cytoplasm and aids in their transfer to the ribosome and in the attachment of the amino acid in its appropriate position so that the particular protein molecule will be formed. (There is a transfer RNA specific for each of the 20 amino acids found in human tissue.) Formation of such a larger molecule from smaller ones requires energy, and the amino acids acquire energy prior to their transfer to the ribosome. This energy is obtained from adenosine triphosphate (see page 466).

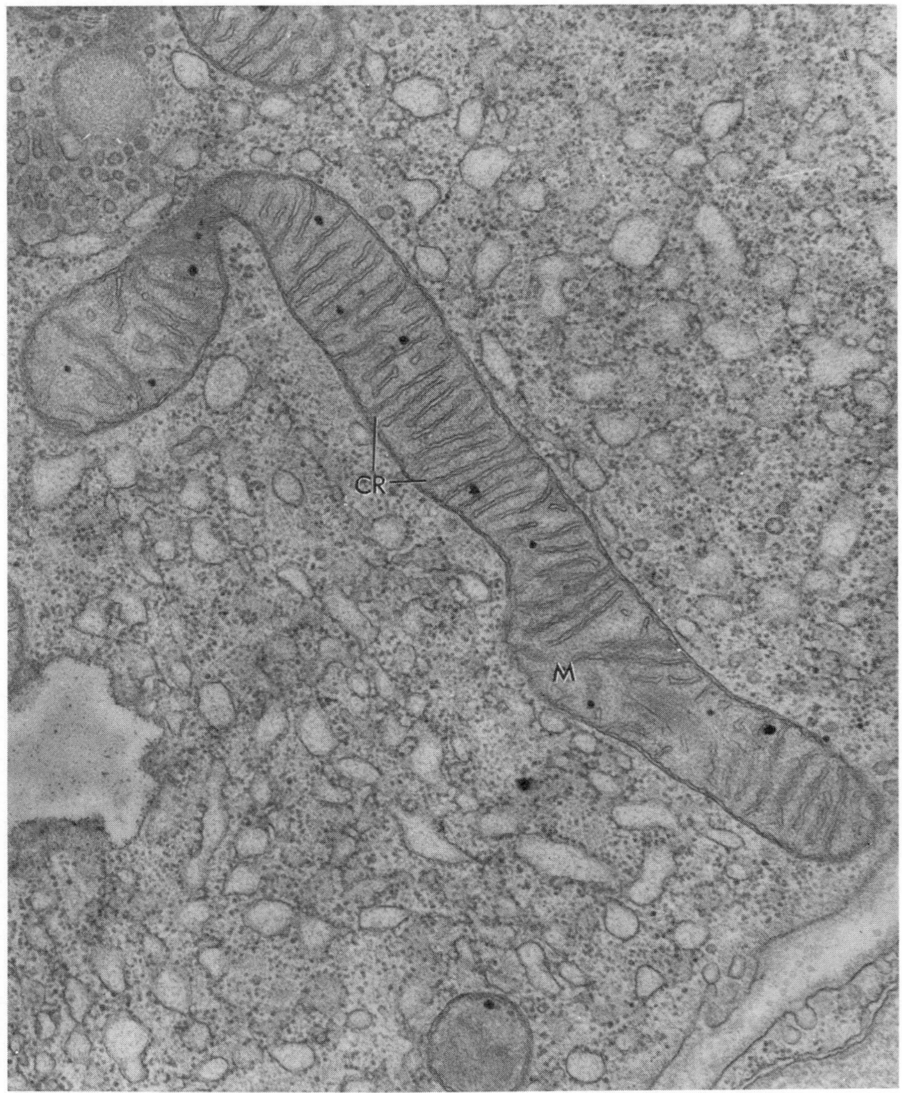

Figure 2–8. Mitochondrion (*M*) of pancreatic exocrine cell (guinea pig), seen longitudinally. Note infolding of inner membrane to form cristae (*CR*). × 30,000. (Courtesy of Dr. George Palade, Rockefeller University, New York.)

Elucidation of DNA structure of the chromosome has brought us closer to answering the question "What is the gene?"

Proteins differ from each other in the number and kind of amino acids they contain and in the sequence of these amino acids. The sequence of three bases in messenger RNA, which in turn matches with the specific three bases of a transfer RNA to which a particular amino acid is attached, means that the amino acids which make up a protein must be lined up in a particular order. Thus distinctive proteins are formed. Since the enzymes within the cell are protein the cell activity is directly determined by the sequence of bases (in groups of three, called *codons*) within the DNA molecule. The pigment which gives color to the skin and the ability (or inability) of the liver cell to metabolize certain products are examples of gene action.

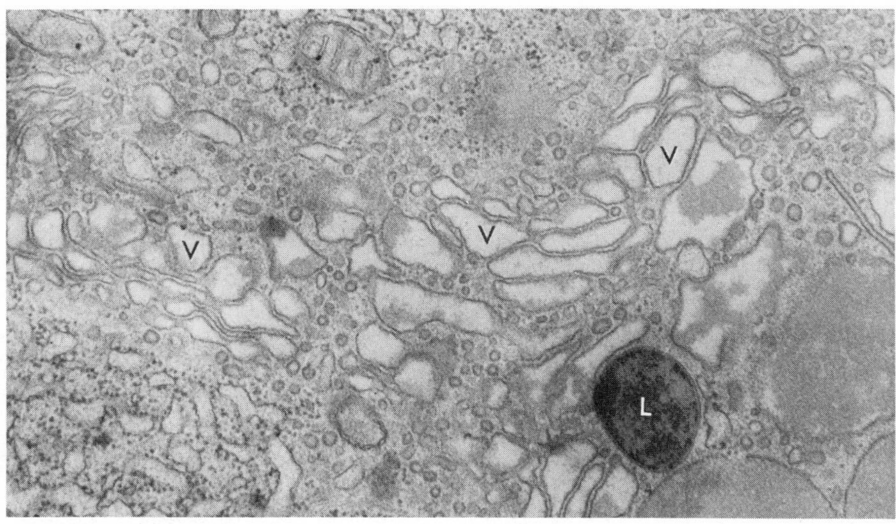

Figure 2–9. Golgi region of pancreatic exocrine cell (guinea pig). Clear areas are large vacuoles (*V*). A lysosome is visible as the dark granular body (*L*). × 30,500. (Courtesy of Dr. George Palade, Rockefeller University, New York.)

Thus it seems that the gene might properly today be termed that group of codons which direct formation of a particular molecule.

Activities of Cells. Living cells are active—performing a variety of chemical reactions as well as being physically active. Activities exhibited by cells are:

1. Motion. This involves two forms of movement:

a. Ameboid movement consists in the pushing outward by the cell of protoplasmic processes, called *pseudopodia*. These pseudopodia may be slowly retracted, they may be bent, or the contents of the cell may flow slowly or rapidly into them and change both the shape and position of the cell. By a repetition of this process, the cell may move slowly about, so that an actual locomotion takes place, e.g., ameboid or pseudopodial movement of white blood cells.

b. Ciliary movement is the whipping motion exhibited by short, protoplasmic processes called *cilia*, which project from the surface of some epithelial cells. This motion serves to propel particles and secretions along the surface of the membrane, e.g., secretions in the respiratory tract.

2. Irritability. Irritability is that property which enables a cell to respond to a stimulus (change in its environment). If the stimulus received by a cell is strong enough, it is conducted throughout the protoplasm of the cell, and the cell responds. The response may take the form of an increase of some kind of activity, such as motion, or growth, or it may take the form of a decrease of these activities. If the response is an increased activity, the protoplasm is said to be *excited*; if the response is a decreased activity, the protoplasm is said to be *inhibited*.

3. Respiration. Each cell coming in contact with oxygen absorbs it. During this absorption some of the cell contents are oxidized, and, as a result of this oxidation, energy is liberated, and carbon dioxide is formed and given off by the cell to its liquid environment. This is known as cellular respiration.

4. Circulation. This consists of a "streaming" of the protoplasm within the cell. By this means nutritive material and oxygen may be distributed gradually to all parts of the protoplasm, and the waste substances are gradually brought to the surface of the cell for elimination.

5. Use of Nutrients. Each cell can absorb and convert into its own protoplasm certain materials (foods) that are nonliving;

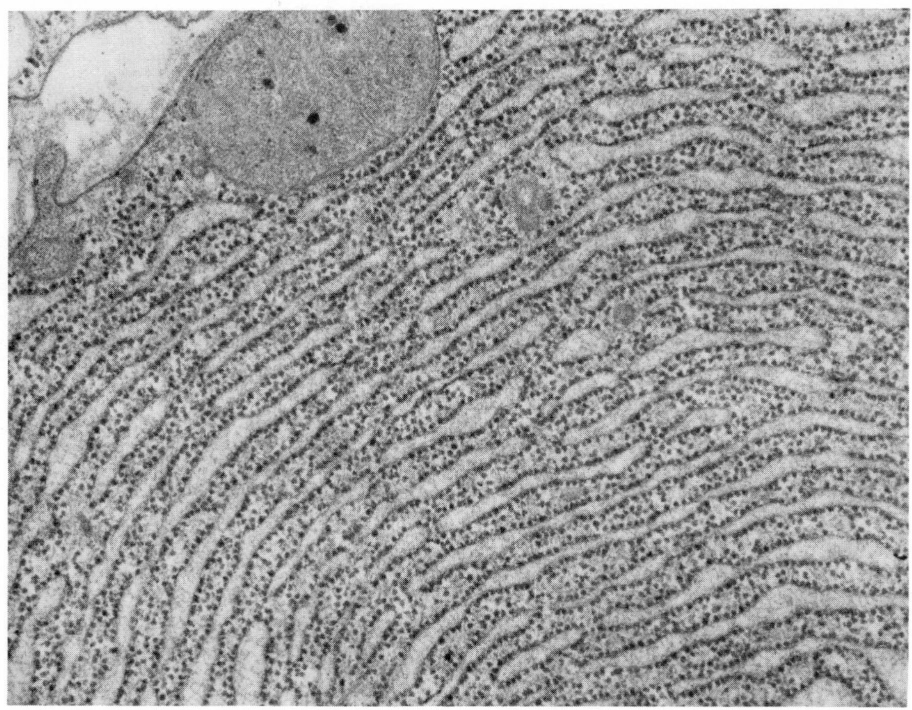

Figure 2–10. Endoplasmic reticulum of pancreatic exocrine cell (guinea pig). Ribosomes are seen as dark "beads" along the membranes as well as lying free and unattached. ×41,500. (Courtesy of Dr. George Palade, Rockefeller University, New York.)

in this way the protoplasm is maintained and may undergo repair, and the cell grows. Foods can also be oxidized to yield energy and to regulate body functions. The general term *metabolism* summarizes the activities each living cell carries on. The changes that involve the building up of living material within the cell have received the general name of *anabolic* changes, or *anabolism*; those that involve the breaking down of such material into other and simpler products are known as *catabolic* changes, or *catabolism*; the sum of all the anabolic and catabolic changes proceeding within the cell is spoken of as the *metabolism* of the cell. These chemical changes are always more marked as the activity of the cell is hastened by warmth, hormonal stimulation, or the action of certain drugs.

6. *Excretion and Secretion.* Excretion refers to the ability of the cell to extrude waste products from within. If the extruded material is a useful substance such as a hormone or gastric juice, it is termed a secretion. The process may be by diffusion or by the functioning of excretory vacuoles in some cells, such as in the pancreas.

7. *Cell Division.* In all living organisms, each cell grows and produces other cells. Since the cells of the body are constantly wearing out and leaving the body in the excretions, the need for constant reproduction of cells is apparent. Cells usually divide by indirect cell division, called *mitosis.* In mitosis the nucleus passes through a series of changes, illustrated in Figure 2–12. It will be noted that the chromatin, which at first (*A*) exists as granules in the nucleus, becomes (*C*) definite bodies, the chromosomes. Each chromosome duplicates itself during interphase and separates (*E*), and one of each pair of chromosomes thus formed moves to the poles of the spindles (*F* and *G*) so that when the cell divides, each daughter

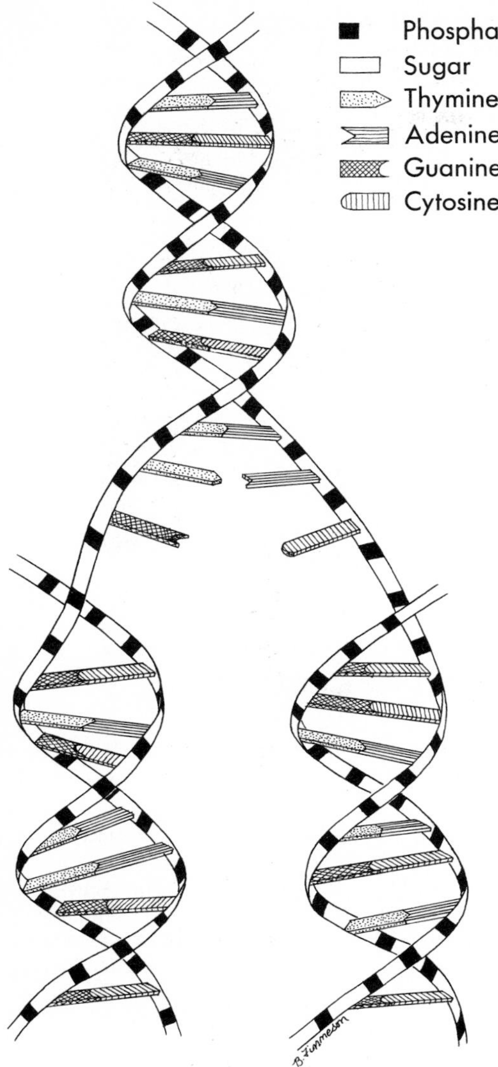

Figure 2–11. Diagram of DNA molecule showing replication.

cell has a complete set of chromosomes. The chromosomes in the daughter cells unwind, so that the daughter cells are like the parent cell except in size. As indicated earlier in the chapter, the nucleic acid portion of the chromosome is responsible for transmission of genetic information from one generation to the next. During the resting stage between cell divisions, the chromosomes double so that the cell will be prepared for the next division.

Cancer is a disease in which the chromosomes are altered (by unknown means) and genetic control of cell division and growth is lost. The resulting malignant cells retain some characteristics of the cell from which they originated, but seem to devote energy primarily to growth rather than to the specialized function of that cell type. Abnormality in structure is seen in the large size of the nucleus, multiplicity of nuclei per cell, and changes in staining characteristics. Obviously any chromosomal change will be transmitted to succeeding generations; and unless eradicated, the malignancy grows and spreads.

The Constituents of Protoplasm. Chemical analysis of the human body has shown that it contains the following *chemical elements*:

Element	Symbol		%
Oxygen	(O)	Form 96% of total weight of body	65.0%
Carbon	(C)		18.0
Hydrogen	(H)		10.0
Nitrogen	(N)		3.0
Sulfur	(S)		0.25
Calcium	(Ca)		2.2
Phosphorus	(P)		0.8–1.2
Potassium	(K)		0.35
Chlorine	(Cl)		0.15
Sodium	(Na)		0.15
Magnesium	(Mg)		0.05
Iron	(Fe)		0.004
Iodine	(I)		0.00004
Silicon	(Si)	Very minute amounts	
Fluorine	(F)		

Traces of Cu, Mn, Co; perhaps traces of Ni, Ba, Li

In the human body free oxygen, hydrogen, and nitrogen have been found in the blood and intestines, but the bulk of these elements, as well as of all the others, exists in the form of complex compounds which are constituents of the cells and body fluids. The compounds are divided into two classes, organic and inorganic.

The *inorganic compounds* exist in cells partly as dissolved salts and partly in combination with the organic compounds. In chemical analyses of cells, the *mineral elements* remain either wholly or largely in

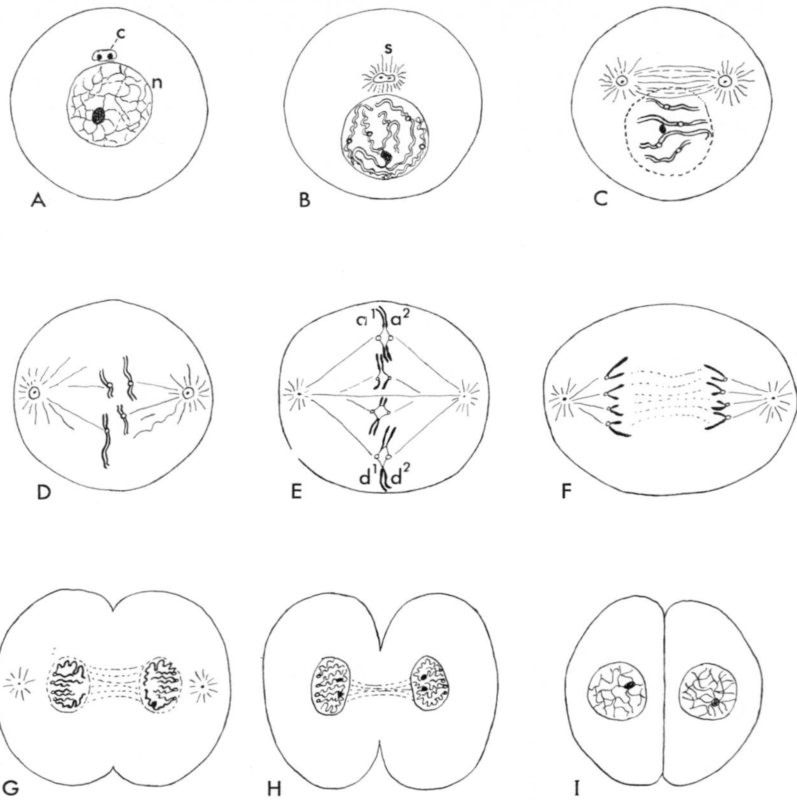

Figure 2–12. Diagrams to show mitosis. The cell is presumed to have four chromosomes. (*A*) Resting cell with nucleus (*n*) and centrosome (*c*); a nucleolus and network of chromatin are shown in the nucleus. (*B*) Spindle fibers (*s*) forming; a chromatin thread, or *spireme*, is breaking into chromosomes. (*C*) Nuclear membrane disappearing, *chromosomes* shown dividing *lengthwise* into halves. (*D*) Chromosomes shorter and thicker, staining power increased. (*E*) Chromosomes arranged on the *spindle*, the two halves of each chromosome opposite each other at a^1 and a^2, d^1 and d^2, etc. (*F*) Chromosomes moving toward the poles of the spindle. (*G*) Cell beginning to divide. (*H*) Cell division continued. (*I*) Cell division complete. *A-C* called prophase; *C-D* called metaphase; *E-G* called anaphase; *G-I* called telophase. (Modified from *The Cell in Development and Heredity*, by E. G. Wilson, The Macmillan Company.)

the ash when the cells are incinerated; hence, they are grouped as the *ash constituents*. Only small amounts of these elements are needed, but they are essential parts of cells.

The *organic compounds* found in protoplasm are proteins, carbohydrates, and lipids. Wherever found in living organisms, these compounds are fundamentally similar.

In addition to this universal similarity, the proteins, carbohydrates, and lipids of each species of plant or animal possess distinctive characteristics. The essential chemical elements are present in varying absolute quantities, in varying relative quantities, and in varying combinations. The essential elements in proteins are carbon, hydrogen, oxygen, and nitrogen, and in some also sulfur and phosphorus; in carbohydrates and lipids the essential elements are carbon, hydrogen, and oxygen. The body ingests these proteins, carbohydrates, and lipids. They are split into simpler compounds (i.e., carbohydrates into simple sugars, lipids into an alcohol and fatty acids, proteins into amino acids), which are carried by the blood and lymph to the cells, where they are reconverted into carbohydrates, lipids, and proteins having the distinctive characteristics of those found in the human body. These may then be stored in the cells, or utilized for making protoplasm or for supplying energy. A more complete discussion will be found in Chapters 21 and 22.

Water is the most abundant constituent of tissues and constitutes about two thirds of body weight and more than 70 to 75 per cent of nonbony body weight. It is difficult to obtain the normal water content of an isolated living cell. One estimate gives it at from 85 to 92 per cent of the weight of the cell. It is evident that water is by far the predominant constituent of protoplasm.

Physical Characteristics

With the exception of dense connective tissue and bone, the intercellular, or interstitial, material is a viscous solution which is in general similar to cytoplasm—containing inorganic chemicals, proteins, carbohydrates, and lipids—the primary difference being one of kind of protein present and of amounts of the various chemicals present. The accompanying table illustrates the difference in mineral makeup between the fluid within the cell and that without the cell. In some tissues fibers are embedded within the *matrix*, or background substance of intercellular material.

Concentration of Major Electrolytes in Cellular and Interstitial Fluid

	Cell Fluid	*Tissue Fluid*
Na^+	10 mEq/l	146 mEq/L
K^+	150	4
Ca^{++}	40	2.5
Mg^{++}	40	1.5
HCO_3^-		30
Cl^-		115
HPO_4^-	140	2
SO_4^-		1
Organic acids$^-$		5
Protein$^-$	40	1

Physically cytoplasm and intercellular material are emulsions containing *ions* (electrically charged particles) and noncharged particles dissolved or suspended in water. Several advantages accrue from the fact that water is the universal solvent in animal tissue.

1. The solvent power of water is great. No other substance can compare with water in relation to the kinds of substances which can be dissolved in it and the great and varied concentrations that can be obtained.
2. The ionizing power of water is high; hence, the great number and many kinds of solute molecules yield large numbers of varied ions.
3. Water has a high specific heat. This means that it can hold more heat with less change of temperature than most substances; hence, the heat produced by cell metabolism makes comparatively little change in the temperature of the cell.
4. The heat-conducting power of water is high (for fluids). This means that the heat produced in the cells can pass to body fluids even if the temperature of the cell is barely above that of the fluid around the cell, which likewise can hold this heat with comparatively little rise in temperature and pass it on with little change in temperature to the blood and finally to the skin.
5. The latent heat of evaporation of water is high. Owing to the high latent heat of evaporation, a maximum of heat is taken from the skin for the evaporation of perspiration—about 0.5 large calorie per gram of water evaporated.
6. Water has a high surface tension. Because of this any immiscible liquid with which it comes in contact must expose to it the minimum of surface. The substances which dissolve in water lower its surface tension, since dilute concentrations especially have a tendency to lower surface tensions, and because of the great solvent capacity of water, the surface tension of water can be lowered greatly and by a great variety of substances. This permits the area of contact of the immiscible liquids to be enormously increased. Also, it is known that any dissolved substances which do lower surface tension will accumulate or be *adsorbed* at the surface of contact of the immiscible liquids.

The particles of material dispersed throughout protoplasm vary in size and may be dissolved, as in the case of glucose, or merely suspended in the case of fat droplets in the cytoplasm. Particles with diameters less than 0.1 mμ are dissolved in water and are said to form true solutions; whereas particles 0.1 to 1 mμ in diameter are termed colloidal particles and form colloidal solutions. Colloids may be individual molecules of large size, e.g., protein, or groups of molecules. Other characteristics of colloids that are important in cell physiology include:

1. They can take up large quantities of water and hold it within the cell.
2. Owing to their large size they do not diffuse readily.
3. They absorb other substances at their interphase, or surface.
4. They possess electrical charges which contribute to chemical activity.

Sometimes in experimental work cells behave as *sols*, that is, as solutions in which the continuous phase is water, the colloidal particles of proteins and lipoids being dispersed in it. Sometimes they behave as *gels*, in which the protein molecules form networks enclosing areas of water between them. It has been said of protoplasm that its characteristics are like those of a reversible sol-gel colloidal system.

The cell is regarded as a highly organized unit engaged in ceaseless chemical activities. These activities are dependent on the continuous reception of substances from the so-called *internal environment* (tissue fluid) and the continuous elimination of substances to this tissue fluid. The circulatory liquids continually bring substances from the supply organs, which obtain them from the *external environment*, and continuously take eliminated substances to the eliminating organs for final removal to the external environment. Keeping the cell environment constant, within a narrow range, as regards oxygen, nutrients, acidity, and temperature is critical for optimum cell functioning. The term *homeostasis* was coined by Walter B. Cannon[2] and refers to the overall processes of maintaining optimum internal environmental conditions.

The physical processes that govern the movement of materials across the cell membrane are only partially understood at present. However, four processes seem to be important—diffusion, osmosis, active transport, and pinocytosis.

Diffusion. The term *diffusion* is applied to the spreading or scattering of molecules of gases or liquids. When two gases are brought into contact, the continual movement of the molecules of gas will soon produce a uniform mixture. If a solution of salt is placed in a receptacle and a layer of water poured over it, there will be a mingling of salt molecules and

[2] Walter B. Cannon, American physiologist (1871–1945).

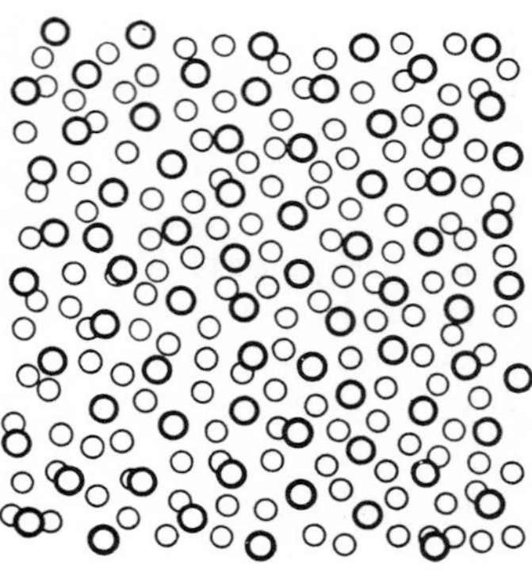

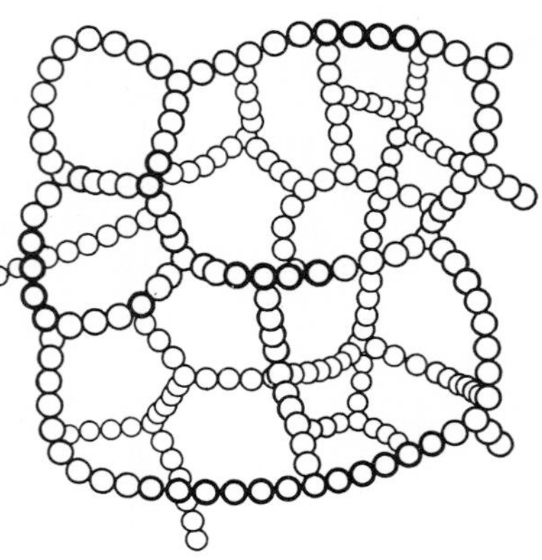

Figure 2–13. Colloidal particles of the sol state (*left*) are separated from one another like islands in a lake. Such a sol is therefore a continuous liquid and flows easily. When the particles stick together in interlacing strands in the gel state (*right*), the mass is more comparable to lakes separated by strips of land. Such a gel, then, is a spongy solid and, though soft, holds its shape. (Courtesy of Dr. Ralph W. Gerard and Harper and Row.)

water molecules, producing a solution of uniform composition.

Molecular movement of particles is random; however, they will move in greater number toward the area where they are fewer in number, that is, from an area of greater concentration to one of lesser concentration (of that particular substance). Eventually an equilibrium will be reached in which all areas of the solution are identical. In the case of the salt solution, there will be the same number of salt molecules relative to water molecules in all parts of the solution. Oxygen moves from the blood into the fluid around the cell and into the cell as a result of diffusion. The amount of oxygen in the blood is much greater than that in the cell. Therefore, it moves to the area of lesser concentration. In this instance a static equilibrium is never reached, but a dynamic equilibrium is kept constant. Oxygen supply to the cell is continually replenished owing to movement of blood through the lungs and the circulatory system; the oxygen is continually used in metabolic processes once it enters the cell.

Osmosis. The usual definition of osmosis is the movement of solvent particles, such as water molecules, through a membrane. If a saline solution and water are separated by a membrane permeable to water, the water molecules will pass through the membrane to the salt solution, thereby raising the level of the latter. Theoretically, molecules of liquid are constantly in motion, a permeable membrane offering no resistance to their passage, and therefore the movement of water particles is in both directions; but the water molecules will travel in greater numbers per unit of time from the place where their number is highest to where it is lowest. If the number of the water particles on both sides of the membrane is the same, in a given time equal numbers of particles will travel in each direction, and equilibrium will be reached. Pressure is exerted by the flow of these water molecules across the membrane and may be expressed as millimeters of mercury (mm Hg). Every solution then has a potential osmotic pressure.

Osmotic pressure is determined by the *number* of particles of solute dissolved in a particular solution. The more particles in solution, the greater the *osmolality* of that solution and the greater is its "pull" for water. In other words, water moves toward the area of greater osmolality. It is important to remember that the particles in solution are the critical factor in determining osmotic pressure. A solution made from an ionizing substance (e.g., sodium chloride) will have a greater osmolality than the one containing an equal amount of nonionizing substance such as glucose.

In physiology the osmotic characteristics of different solutions are often determined by the way in which they affect the red cells of the blood. That is, their effect is compared with that of the blood serum. If red cells are subjected to contact with any fluid other than normal serum, they may remain unchanged or they may shrink or swell. If they remain unchanged, the solution is said to have the same osmotic characteristics as the blood serum and is called *isotonic*. If they shrink, the solution has higher osmotic characteristics than that of the blood serum and is called *hypertonic*. If they swell, the solution has lower osmotic characteristics than that of the blood serum and is called *hypotonic*.

Sometimes the word *dialysis* is used for the diffusion of molecules of the soluble constituents (solutes) through a permeable membrane. If two solutions of unequal concentration are separated by a membrane which is permeable to the solute, a greater number of solute particles will pass from the more concentrated solution to the less concentrated, per unit of time. The diffusing particles may be ions, molecules, or small molecular aggregates.

Active Transport. It is obvious that diffusion and osmosis alone cannot explain entirely the movement of particles into the cell. Clearly the cell membrane controls selectively which materials enter and whether or not they remain inside. When materials are transported across the cell membrane against a concentration gradient, that is, in a direction opposite to what would be expected from the principles of diffusion and osmosis, energy is utilized and oxygen is consumed by the cell. This process is therefore termed active transport of the substance, as opposed to *passive* transport as in diffusion or osmosis during which cell energy is not expended. It is possible that there are carriers to aid in transportation of certain materials into the cell, or out of the cell, as in the case of sodium which is present in large amounts outside the cell but not inside. Support for this theory is based on the fact that certain enzymes are known to be present just inside the cell membrane.

Pinocytosis. Material enters cells by the process of pinocytosis—indentation of cell membrane and cytoplasm so that channels form, permitting entrance of molecules and minute droplets of fluid from the exterior. The channel seals off, forming small vacuoles within the cytoplasm.

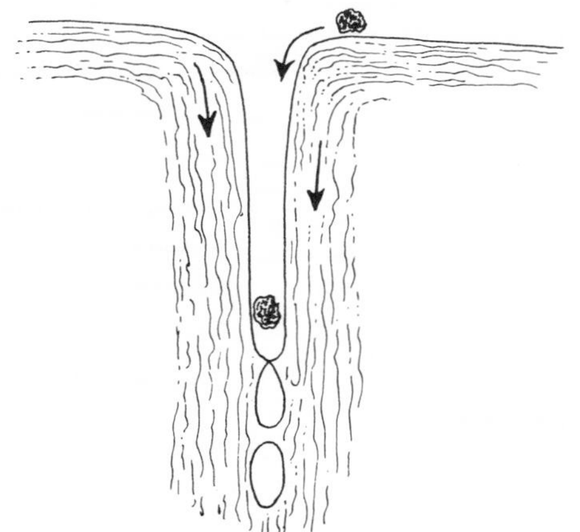

Figure 2–14. Diagram of pinocytosis. Particle is adherent to infolded portion of cell membrane and moves through it into the cytoplasm.

When a substance moves across the cell membrane, the membrane is said to be permeable to that particular substance. Size of the particle is important—if it is too large (over 7 angstrom units[3]), it cannot enter and the cell is impermeable to it. This leads to the belief that there are pores in the membrane too small for the electron microscope to identify. Ionic charge also influences cell permeability. The positive charge on the outside of the membrane tends to repel positively charged ions.

Enzyme Action. Materials that enter the cytoplasm have potential value to the cell (1) as a source of energy, (2) as building blocks for the parts of the cell itself, if it is growing or dividing, and (3) as building blocks for cell secretions, e.g., hormones and digestive enzymes.

Utilization of nutrients is possible only through chemical reactions—the step-by-step breaking down of large molecules to smaller, or building small molecules into larger ones. These chemical reactions are many and varied and require the presence of enzymes, termed *endoenzymes*, to differentiate them from enzymes which are secreted from the cell and act outside the cell (exoenzymes), e.g., the digestive enzymes.

Characteristics of Enzyme Action. In general, all enzymes are influenced by temperature, pH, and the presence of the appropriate *substrate*, or initial substance which is being changed in the chemical reaction. When the temperature or pH of the fluid in which the enzyme is found is not at optimum levels, the enzyme action is slowed down, or it may be completely ineffective. Endoenzymes act best at body temperature and at the pH of the cytoplasm and body fluids. A given enzyme can catalyze only one type of reaction, or sometimes only one particular reaction. For the metabolic reaction to occur, the substrate molecule must come into contact with the specific enzyme. It is believed that there is a specific configuration for each enzyme and its substrate. Thus a particular enzyme and its substrate must possess shapes that complement each other. Inhibitors of enzymes, such as certain metals, act by interfering with this complementary shape, or by attaching to the site on the molecule which will react, e.g., to accept the hydrogen atom in the case of dehydrogenases.

The accompanying chart lists important classes of enzymes and their actions. Many of the biological reactions are reversible, the

[3] One angstrom unit equals 1/10,000,000 of a millimeter.

ENDOENZYME CLASSIFICATION

Name	Action
I. Hydrolases:	Split molecules into smaller ones through utilization of H_2O
(a) Esterases:	Split ester linkages of acids and alcohols
cholinesterase	Split acetylcholine to acetic acid and choline
lipases	Split fats to fatty acids and glycerol
phosphatases	Split phosphate group from phosphoric acid esters
pyrophosphatases	Split phosphate group from high-energy phosphate compounds
nucleases	Split nucleic acids to nucleotides
(b) Carbohydrases:	Break down polysaccharides and other compounds with similar chemical bonding
amylases	Split glycogen to glucose Split starch to maltose, then to glucose
hyaluronidase	Splits hyaluronic acid, intercellular material
(c) Proteases:	Split peptide linkages of proteins and peptides
carboxypeptidases	Split terminal peptide bond to free amino acids from protein
proteinases	Split proteins by attacking interior peptide bonds
II. Phosphorylases:	Split molecule by addition of phosphate radical
muscle phosphorylase	Phosphate + glycogen $\rightleftarrows$ glucose phosphate
III. Oxidation-reduction enzymes	
(a) Dehydrogenases	Oxidation of a compound by removal of $2H^+$
(b) Oxidases	Addition of oxygen to a compound
(c) Catalases	Remove atomic oxygen from H_2O_2; associated with cytochrome systems of mitochondria.
IV. Transferases	Transfer a radical from one compound to another
(a) Transaminases	Transfer NH_2^-
(b) Hexokinases	Transfer phosphate from adenosine triphosphate to glucose
V. Decarboxylases	Remove CO_2 from a compound without oxidation
(a) Carbonic anhydrase	Carbonic acid $\rightleftarrows$ CO_2 and H_2O
VI. Hydrases	Remove H_2O from a molecule
VII. Isomerases	Move radical from one part of molecule to another
VIII. Condensing enzymes	Transfer acetyl radical from acetyl coenzyme A into the citric acid cycle

Note that the -ase ending indicates an enzyme and the prefix indicates its action (e.g., transaminase) or its substrate (e.g. amylase).

enzyme influencing the speed of both the forward and the reverse reaction, operating to bring about equilibrium.

Endoenzymes are found in the active form within the cell. This is not true of *exoenzymes*, those that act outside the cell, for these are usually secreted in an inactive form and must be activated by another substance or the pH of the environment before they can catalyze the particular chemical reaction. The inactive form is known as *zymogen* or *proenzyme*. Activation of the proenzyme is believed to involve a chemical change, such as the removal of a small group from the molecule and exposure of the active site of the enzyme.

In some cases the action of an enzyme is helped by, or perhaps is dependent upon, the presence of some other substance. An example of this activity is the interaction of bile salts and lipase on fat digestion. The bile salts emulsify fat droplets, thereby increasing the surface area available for enzyme activity. These cases of *coactivity* are to be distinguished from activation by the fact that the combination may be made or unmade. For example, in a mixture of bile salts and lipase, the bile salts may be removed by dialysis. In activation, on the contrary, the active enzyme cannot be changed back to the inactive zymogen.

Nature of Enzymes. Most enzymes are proteins of high molecular weight, hence cannot diffuse across cell membranes. Some enzymes, such as pepsin and trypsin, appear to be simple proteins; others resemble the conjugated proteins in that they function with a nonprotein component known as a *coenzyme*. The importance of vitamins is becoming increasingly evident as more is learned about enzyme activity within the cells. The B-complex vitamins in particular are known to form parts of the molecules of various enzymes involved in energy release. These are discussed more fully in Chapter 21.

The Cells and Tissue Fluid

All cells lie in a liquid environment called tissue fluid. This fluid serves as the only medium of exchange between blood plasma and the cells. Substances needed by cells for maintenance, growth, and repair diffuse from the plasma to the tissue fluid and on into the cell. The products of cell metabolism or other cell activity diffuse into the tissue fluid and enter either the blood or lymph capillaries.

The name *tissue fluid* covers all fluids *not* in the blood vascular system, the lymph vascular system, the great spaces of the body, or the cells themselves.

Points of view differ in regard to classifying the liquids concerned in the exchange of material between the blood and the tissue cells. In general, the lymph vessels form a closed system, and the name *lymph* should be applied to the fluid within the vessels only; the fluid outside the vessels, in the tissue spaces, should be called *tissue fluid*. In the different spaces of the body, e.g., the pericardial, pleural, and peritoneal cavities, it is serous; in the spaces of the cerebrum and spinal cord it is cerebrospinal fluid, and in joints it is synovial fluid. Lacteals are lymph vessels in the small intestine. During digestion, they are filled with *chyle*, a milk-white fluid composed mainly of emulsified fat.

Sources of Tissue Fluid. The walls of the capillaries are thin, and some of the fluid passes out into the spaces between the tissue cells. *Tissue fluid* is derived from the plasma of the blood mainly by diffusion and by capillary hydrostatic pressure. There is difference in pressure within the blood capillary and in the tissue spaces surrounding the capillary. For instance, at the arterial end of the capillary the hydrostatic pressure is about 30 mm Hg and in the tissue spaces surrounding the capillary the pressure is much lower. Since the pressure is highest within the capillary, fluid and other substances are driven from the capillary into the tissue spaces. Another force that must be considered is the protein osmotic pressure formed by the plasma proteins, which act as a "pulling" force to hold fluids within the vessels as well as to "attract fluids in." This opposing force prevents undue loss of fluid from the capillaries.

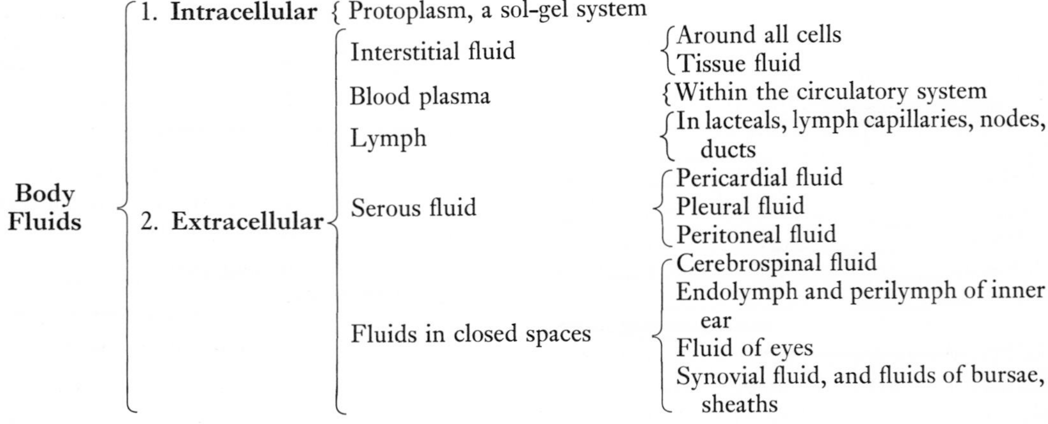

Body Fluids

- 1. **Intracellular**
  - Protoplasm, a sol-gel system
- 2. **Extracellular**
  - Interstitial fluid
    - Around all cells
    - Tissue fluid
  - Blood plasma
    - Within the circulatory system
  - Lymph
    - In lacteals, lymph capillaries, nodes, ducts
  - Serous fluid
    - Pericardial fluid
    - Pleural fluid
    - Peritoneal fluid
  - Fluids in closed spaces
    - Cerebrospinal fluid
    - Endolymph and perilymph of inner ear
    - Fluid of eyes
    - Synovial fluid, and fluids of bursae, sheaths

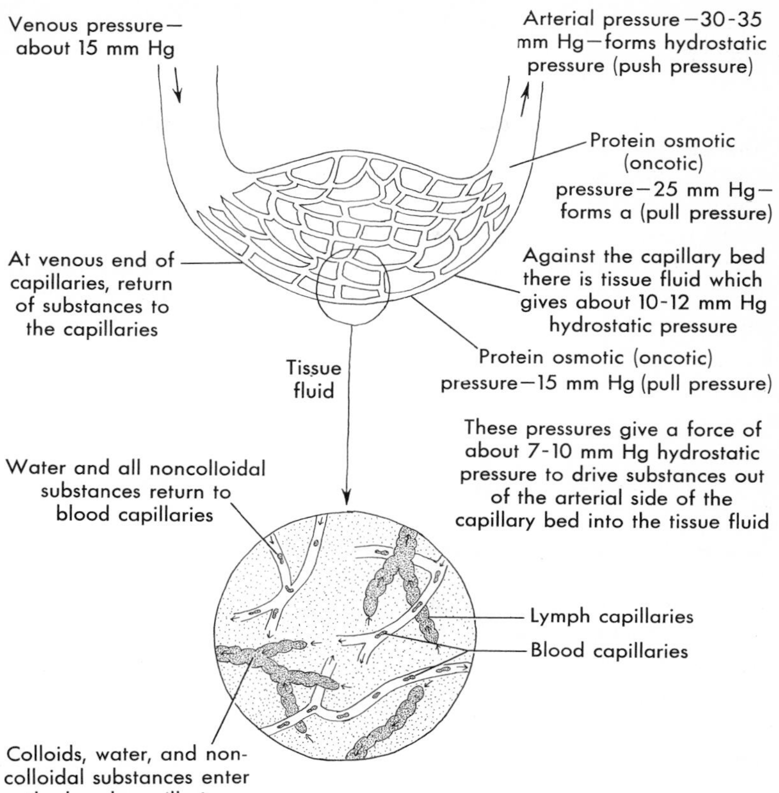

Figure 2–15. Detail of capillary bed showing relationship of blood capillaries to lymph capillaries and return of substances to the blood stream. By this process the amount of tissue fluid is kept constant. Since all lymph vessels eventually enter lymph nodes before emptying into the blood stream, what would occur if the returning lymph could not reach the blood stream? What might be some of the causes?

At the venous end of the capillary, hydrostatic pressure is about 15 mm Hg. This means that the difference in pressure within the capillary and in the tissue spaces is not as great as at the arterial end. As blood moves through the capillary network and fluid is lost to the tissue spaces, plasma protein concentration is slightly raised, and hence the "pulling force" is increased so that water and crystalloids re-enter the capillaries readily. Colloids, along with water and crystalloids, enter the lymph capillaries. Increases in hydrostatic pressure within the capillaries from any cause will interfere with return of materials to capillaries and will result in excess accumulation of tissue fluid, or edema.

There are two important exceptions to the capillary pressure figures used in the preceding discussion. These exceptions are the capillaries of the lungs and of the kidneys. Hydrostatic pressure in the lung capillaries is approximately 6 mm Hg; thus fluid does not move out of the capillary as it does in other tissue of the body. In the kidney, glomerular hydrostatic pressure is 60–70 mm Hg, which acts to force an increased amount of fluid from the capillary in the first step of urine formation.

The composition of tissue fluid is similar to that of blood plasma. It is a colorless or yellowish fluid possessing an alkaline reaction, a salty taste, and a faint odor. When examined under the microscope, it is seen to consist of cells floating in a clear liquid. Its resemblance to the plasma is indicated in the table following. In consequence of varying needs and wastes of different tissues at different times, both the tissue fluid and blood must vary in composition in different parts of the body. But the loss and gain are so fairly balanced that the average composition is constantly maintained.

Function of Tissue Fluid. The tissue fluid bathes all cells of the body. It delivers to the cells the material they need to maintain functional activity and picks up and returns

Comparison of Blood and Tissue Fluid

Blood	Tissue Fluid
Specific gravity about 1.055*	Specific gravity varies between 1.015 and 1.023
Contains erythrocytes	May contain a few erythrocytes
Contains white cells	Granulocyte count lower, lymphocyte count higher
Contains blood platelets	Does not contain blood platelets
A high content of blood proteins	A lower content of blood proteins
A low content of waste products	A higher content of waste products
A high content of nutrients	A lower content of nutrients
Normally—clots quickly and firmly	Clots slowly, and clot is not firm
Relatively high in colloidal protein	Relatively low in colloidal protein; globulin practically absent
Water, glucose, salts, same concentration in both	

* The specific gravity of a liquid is the ratio of the weight of the liquid (blood, urine, etc.) compared with the weight of an equal volume of distilled water at 15°C (60°F), the weight of water being considered 1.000.

to the blood the products of this activity. These products may be simple waste or materials capable of being made use of by some other tissue. There is thus a continual interchange going on between the blood and the tissue fluid. This interchange is effected by means of *diffusion*. Some of the constituents of the blood pass into the tissue fluid; some of the constituents of the tissue fluid pass into the blood directly, and some into the lymphatics. Water and noncolloidal substances are returned to the blood capillaries; colloidal substances as well as water and noncolloidal substances enter the lymphatics. Diffusion of this kind is dependent on differences in concentration of diffusible particles of any substance at the two surfaces of the diffusion membranes.

As cells become active, varying needs must be met in relation to supplies and the products of metabolism. Experimental work has shown that as use of oxygen increases, the number of open capillaries in the muscle increases, the capillary diameter increases, the total area of the capillary bed increases, the volume of blood in the muscle increases, the distance of the farthest cell from a capillary decreases, and the difference in oxygen pressure inside and outside the capillary decreases. There are also other changes, such as increased temperature, and velocity of blood flow.

Since cellular metabolism is increased when muscular effort is increased, there is produced in the cells an increased quantity of metabolites, carbon dioxide, and other substances to be eliminated, as well as pH[4] change. Thus the chemical activity of the muscle cells may be the chief factor controlling the amount and distribution of blood through the muscle. This is an automatic control—the graded need to get and to give off brings about the graded means (variable blood flow) to do so accurately. If maximum blood supply does not bring sufficient oxygen and remove metabolites fast enough, oxygen hunger, followed by fatigue, results.

This automatic control for optimum distribution of blood in relation to muscular effort involves adjustment of pulse rate, pulse volume, general and local peripheral resistance, respiratory rate, and respiratory volume, and, in fact, an adjustment of all body functions. This control is brought about by the effects of variations in chemical equilibrium on the tissues themselves, or by the local changes in chemical equilibrium and the influence of the nervous system on the distant organs concerned.

This indicates the relative functions of

[4] pH is the measure of the relative acidity of a solution. Substances having a pH of 7 are *neutral*; above, from 7 to 14, are increasingly *alkaline*; and below, from 7 to 1, are increasingly *acid*. (See Chapter 25.)

blood plasma and tissue fluid. The blood brings (and takes away) substances. The volume of blood per minute in the muscle, the capillary area for diffusion, etc., are constantly varied. To the muscle cells the blood is the source of supplies, kept relatively high in concentration because circulation keeps blood in motion. Blood and tissue fluid are also the place of disappearance of products of metabolism, which are thus kept relatively low in concentration.

In the cells the supplies are used and wastes produced.

The tissue fluid stands between the two. It is a fluid that moves very slowly and is separated both from the blood and from the cell contents, which it closely resembles chemically and physically, by diffusion membranes. In the cell the rate of change of chemical equilibriums, controlled by catalysts, constantly uses supplies and produces wastes; the blood constantly brings supplies and carries off wastes. The tissue fluid mediates this transfer and makes it possible for large amounts of substances to be transported and used with relatively small differences in concentration of soluble constituents in any of the body fluids.

This, together with the fact that blood returning from all tissues is *mixed in the heart* and hence all tissues receive the same blood, is probably the basis of all *physiological integration*.

QUESTIONS FOR DISCUSSION

1. Contrast the physiological activities of the human body and those of the individual cell.
2. How does cell activity influence the growth and development of a child?
3. Explain the structure and functions of DNA and RNA.
4. What are organelles? Name them and give their function.
5. Discuss the relationship between cells and tissue fluid and explain how tissue fluid is formed.
6. What are the characteristics of water and colloids that make them so important in physiology?
7. Differentiate between protein osmotic and hydrostatic pressure.
8. What is the difference between active and passive transport across cell membranes?
9. Name the classes of endoenzymes and discuss their function.
10. Is osmolality of a solution the same as concentration?

SUMMARY

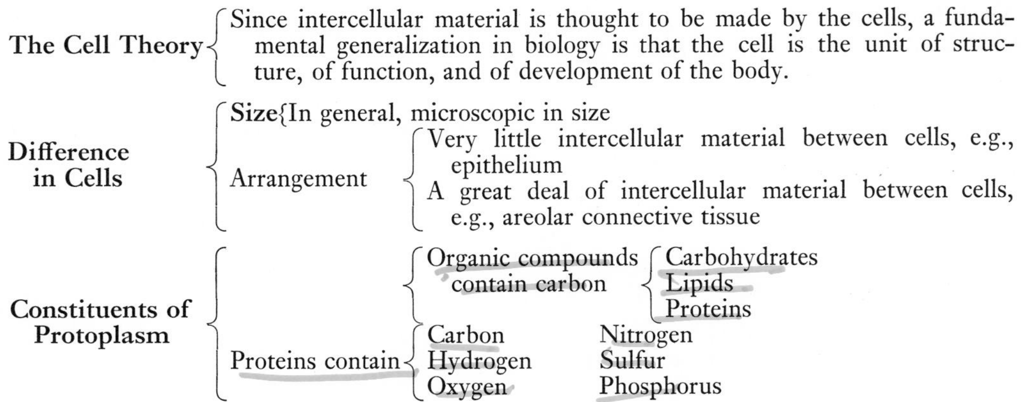

The Cell Theory — Since intercellular material is thought to be made by the cells, a fundamental generalization in biology is that the cell is the unit of structure, of function, and of development of the body.

Difference in Cells
- Size — In general, microscopic in size
- Arrangement
  - Very little intercellular material between cells, e.g., epithelium
  - A great deal of intercellular material between cells, e.g., areolar connective tissue

Constituents of Protoplasm
- Organic compounds contain carbon
  - Carbohydrates
  - Lipids
  - Proteins
- Proteins contain
  - Carbon
  - Hydrogen
  - Oxygen
  - Nitrogen
  - Sulfur
  - Phosphorus

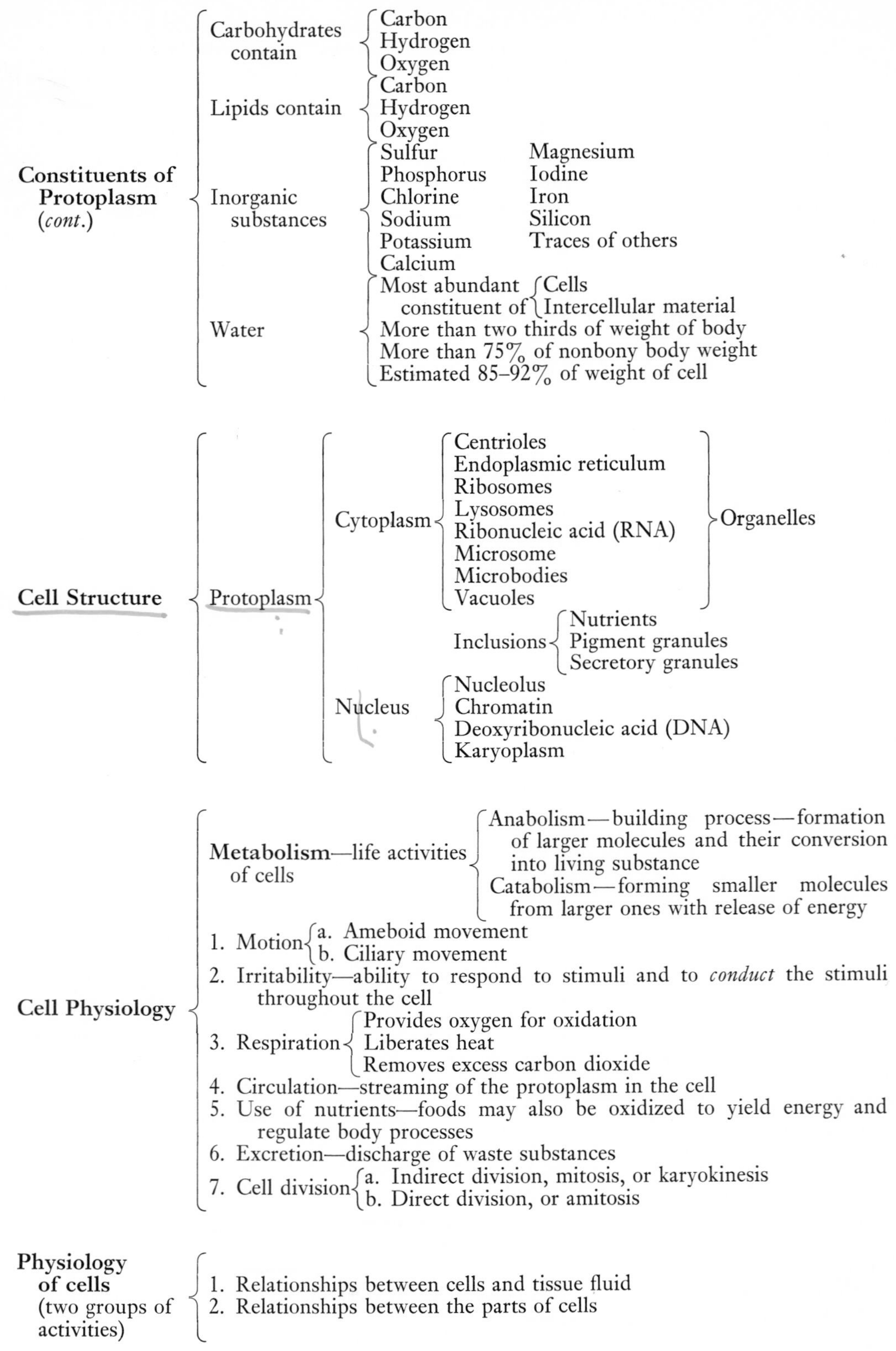

- **Constituents of Protoplasm** (*cont.*)
  - Carbohydrates contain
    - Carbon
    - Hydrogen
    - Oxygen
  - Lipids contain
    - Carbon
    - Hydrogen
    - Oxygen
  - Inorganic substances
    - Sulfur
    - Phosphorus
    - Chlorine
    - Sodium
    - Potassium
    - Calcium
    - Magnesium
    - Iodine
    - Iron
    - Silicon
    - Traces of others
  - Water
    - Most abundant constituent of
      - Cells
      - Intercellular material
    - More than two thirds of weight of body
    - More than 75% of nonbony body weight
    - Estimated 85–92% of weight of cell

- **Cell Structure**
  - Protoplasm
    - Cytoplasm
      - Organelles
        - Centrioles
        - Endoplasmic reticulum
        - Ribosomes
        - Lysosomes
        - Ribonucleic acid (RNA)
        - Microsome
        - Microbodies
        - Vacuoles
      - Inclusions
        - Nutrients
        - Pigment granules
        - Secretory granules
    - Nucleus
      - Nucleolus
      - Chromatin
      - Deoxyribonucleic acid (DNA)
      - Karyoplasm

- **Cell Physiology**
  - **Metabolism**—life activities of cells
    - Anabolism—building process—formation of larger molecules and their conversion into living substance
    - Catabolism—forming smaller molecules from larger ones with release of energy
  1. Motion
     - a. Ameboid movement
     - b. Ciliary movement
  2. Irritability—ability to respond to stimuli and to *conduct* the stimuli throughout the cell
  3. Respiration
     - Provides oxygen for oxidation
     - Liberates heat
     - Removes excess carbon dioxide
  4. Circulation—streaming of the protoplasm in the cell
  5. Use of nutrients—foods may also be oxidized to yield energy and regulate body processes
  6. Excretion—discharge of waste substances
  7. Cell division
     - a. Indirect division, mitosis, or karyokinesis
     - b. Direct division, or amitosis

- **Physiology of cells** (two groups of activities)
  1. Relationships between cells and tissue fluid
  2. Relationships between the parts of cells

- **Constituents of Protoplasm**
  - Water
    - Some physical characteristics having physiological significance
      - Solvent power is high
        - As to kinds of solutes
        - As to variable and high concentration of solutes
      - Ionizing power is high
      - Surface tension is high
      - Specific heat is high
      - Thermal conductivity (for liquids) is high
      - Latent heat of evaporation is high
  - Colloids
    - Importance in physiology
      - Protoplasm is an emulsion of colloids
      - Ability to take up large quantities of water
      - Holds water within the cell
      - Adsorb other substances at interphase
      - Process electrical charges which contribute to chemical activity
  - Cell organization
    - Cells may act like liquids (sols)
    - Cells may act like semisolids (gels)
    - Body cells organized close to line of demarcation between sol and gel

- **Absorption**
  - Mechanism
    - Diffusion
    - Osmosis
    - Dialysis
    - Pinocytosis
  - Relationships (if experiments are standardized and conditions kept the same throughout)
    - Relationship between area of membrane and amount of a substance diffused
    - Relationship between time duration and amount of a substance diffused
    - Relationship between difference in concentration of a diffusible substance on the two sides of the membrane and amount of this substance diffused
    - Relationship between temperature change and amount of a substance diffused

- **Cell Metabolism** (chemical activities in cells)
  - The place of disappearance of supplies diffusing into it; the source of wastes diffusing out
  - In relation to slow, continuous diffusion
  - Relations of cell, water, colloids, adsorption, enzymes to cell activities
  - Organization of protoplasm exceedingly complex
  - Activities of cells are studied by isolation of synthesis of known cellular constituents and their physical and chemical characteristics, e.g., vitamins, hormones

- **Enzymes**
  - Definition
    - Substances produced in living cells which act by catalysis
  - Classification
    - Endoenzymes—substances found within cells which promote chemical reactions in the cell. For classification of endoenzymes see page 29
    - Exoenzymes—secreted in an inactive form—activated by another substance—function outside of the cell
  - Nature of
    - Are proteins of high molecular weight
    - Highly specific in action
    - Vitamins important in chemical structure of enzymes
    - Inhibitors of enzymes are possible
  - Characteristics of
    - Act best at body temperature
    - Require medium of definite pH
    - Action is specific and may be reversible

- **Body Fluids**
  1. Intracellular fluid
     - Protoplasm, a sol-gel system
  2. Extracellular fluid
     - Interstitial fluid
       - Around all cells
       - Tissue fluid

Body Fluids (*cont.*)

- 2. Extracellular fluid (*cont.*)
  - Blood plasma
    - Within the circulatory system
  - Lymph
    - In lacteals, lymph capillaries, nodes, ducts
  - Serous fluid
    - Pericardial fluid
    - Pleural fluid
    - Peritoneal fluid
  - Fluids in closed spaces
    - Cerebrospinal fluid
    - Endolymph and perilymph of inner ear
    - Fluid of eyes
    - Synovial fluid, and fluids of bursae, sheaths
- **Location**
  - Surrounding all cells
  - Occupies the spaces of loose (areolar) connective tissue and all other tissues
- **Source**
  - Diffused from blood plasma
  - Diffused from cellular materials
  - Cell membrane is a two-way filtering and diffusion membrane between all cells and tissue fluid, including capillary cells
- **Composition**
  - Chemically and physically similar to blood plasma and protoplasm
- **Function**
  - Go-between for blood and lymph and cells

CHAPTER

3

THE TISSUES OF THE BODY

EPITHELIAL TISSUES

Characteristics, Location, and Function

Formation of Exocrine Glands and Membranes

Skin and Its Structure

CELLS OF THE NERVOUS SYSTEM

CONNECTIVE TISSUES

Characteristics, Location, and Function

Cartilage, Bone

MUSCLE TISSUE

TISSUE REPAIR

Microscopic anatomy refers to the study of any structure under the microscope. *Histology* limits microscopic anatomy to the study of tissues. It is concerned with structural characteristics of cells and groups of cells as arranged to form tissues; hence a knowledge of the structure and activities of cells forms the basis of histology. The structure and function of tissues are closely related. An understanding of structure will clarify function and help to build the foundation for physiology.

The kinds of tissues of which the body is formed are comparatively few, and some of these, although apparently distinct, have so much in common in their structure and origin that only five distinct tissues are usually recognized.

The five distinct tissues usually recognized include the epithelial tissues, the connective tissues, the muscle tissues, the nervous tissue, and the embryonal tissues.

Epithelial tissues may be classified as:

Squamous
- Simple: epithelium, endothelium, mesothelium
- Stratified

Columnar
- Transitional
- Plain } With or without goblet cells
- Ciliated }

Neuroepithelium

From a functional point of view these may be classified as (1) forming membranes, covering, and lining; and (2) forming glandular tissue.

Connective tissues are classified as:

Connective tissues proper

Loose	Elastic
Adipose	Fibrous
Reticuloendothelial	Liquid (see Chapter 14)

Compact tissues, sometimes called *dense* tissues:

Cartilage: Hyaline, Elastic, Fibrous

Bone: Compact, Cancellous

Embryonal tissue develops in the embryo (see Chapter 27) and is a stage in what will become adult-type connective tissue. It is rich in a semifluid intercellular substance which may contain large amounts of mucin.

The *muscle tissues* include striated (skeletal), smooth (visceral), and cardiac muscle.

For ease of grasping essential characteristics of the tissues, they have been placed in chart form.

EPITHELIAL TISSUES

Epithelial tissues are composed of cells held firmly together by a viscous intercellular substance containing hyaluronic acid. The cells are arranged so as to form a membrane covering the external surfaces and lining the internal parts of the body. They are devoid of blood vessels and are nourished by intercellular substance. The general functions are protection, secretion, and absorption.

NAME	CHARACTERISTICS, LOCATION, AND FUNCTION
Simple squamous epithelium derived from the ectoderm and entoderm	Consists of one layer of flattened scalelike cells. Edges are serrated and fitted together to form a mosaic. Nucleus centrally located, oval or spherical, causing bulging of cytoplasm. Lining the alveoli of the lungs, crystalline lens of the eye, membranous labyrinth of the inner ear, and portions of the uriniferous tubule and rete testis.
Endothelium	Similar in structure to epithelium, lines the heart, blood vessels, and lymph vessels and forms capillary networks, derived from mesoderm. 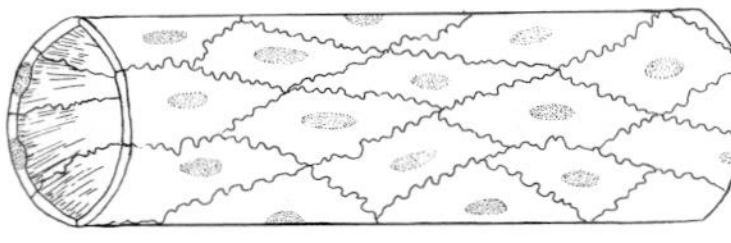 **Figure 3–1.** Diagram of endothelium, surface and sectional views. Seen in the wall of a capillary.
Mesothelium	Called *mesothelium* where it lines serous cavities and covers visceral organs.
Mesenchyme	Is similar in structure and lines the perilymph chambers of the ear, cavities of the eyeball, and spaces between the dura and the pia of the brain and cord.
Stratified squamous epithelium. Many layers of cells. Derived from ectoderm	The deeper cells of this membrane are separated by a system of channels which are bridged by numerous protoplasmic threads. This layer is constantly multiplying by mitosis. As new cells are produced, the deeper parts increase in size, become compressed and push outward, become dehydrated, shrink, and grow harder as they are forced away from body fluids; superficial cells are continually rubbed off. They have great capacity for repair. Protective tissue forms epidermis and is found whenever the ectoderm folds in from outside, e.g., mouth, nose, anus. It prevents loss of body fluids and contains structures for the reception of stimuli.

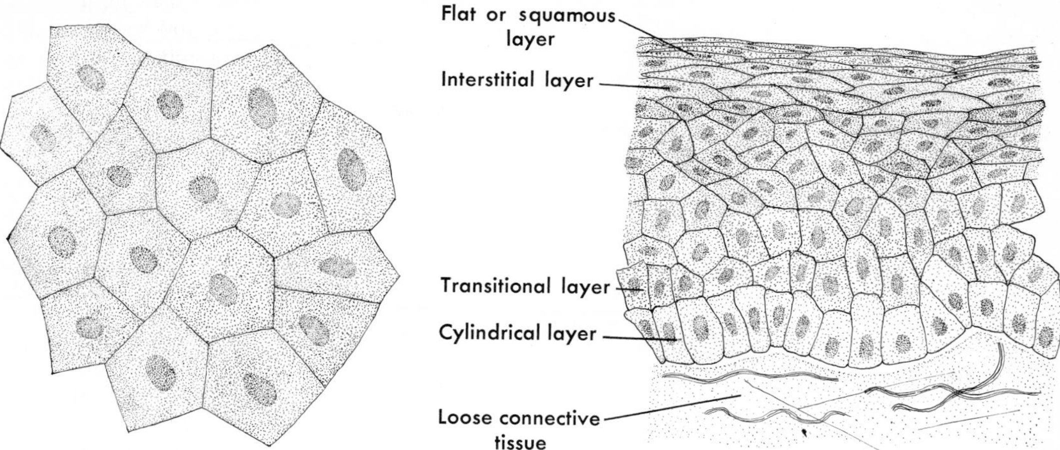

Figure 3–2. Stratified squamous epithelium, surface view.

Figure 3–3. Stratified squamous epithelium, sectional view, as seen in the skin. Note loose connective tissue beneath it.

Transitional	The cells are soft and pliable and adjust to environmental influences, which either *increase* or *decrease* the surface area. The membrane adjusts to the content of the organ. When the bladder is empty, five or six layers of cells are evident; when it is distended, two or three layers are evident. Pelvis of kidney, ureter, bladder, part of the urethra. Forms membrane of these organs.
Columnar epithelium plain, derived from *entoderm*	Cells are cylindrical and are set upright on the surface. The broad base rests on basement membrane. Nucleus oval and located near base of cell. Cytoplasm contains numerous mitochondria. Golgi apparatus prominent. The distal part of these cells contains inclusions such as zymogen granules. Found in its most characteristic form, lining the stomach, small intestine, large intestine, digestive glands, and gallbladder. In the liver they are more cuboidal. Chief functions are secretion of digestive fluids and absorption of digested food and fluids.

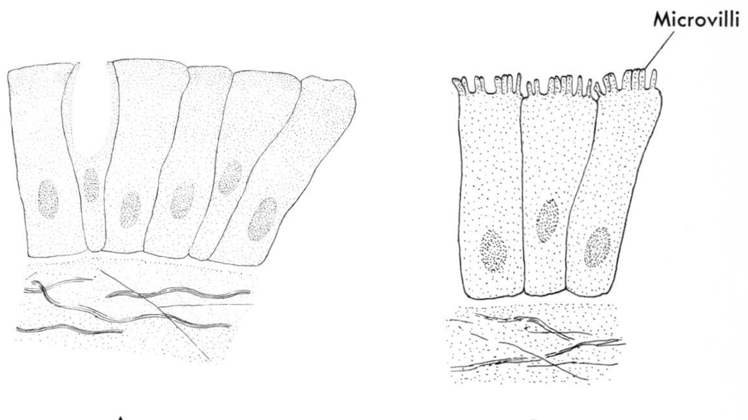

Figure 3–4. (*A*) Columnar epithelium, sectional view; note one goblet cell. (*B*) Columnar cell showing microvilli.

Goblet cells

Modification of columnar epithelium, goblet cells are columnar and assume a chalice form resulting from accumulation of mucoid secretion. After discharge of secretion, the cell repeats its secretory activity. Numerous in the mucosa of the small and large intestine and respiratory tract. The mucoid secretion protects the membrane in many ways.

Microvilli

In the intestine, the epithelial cells show a marked surface modification, which gives the appearance of a striated border. The electron micrographs show that this border is composed of minute protoplasmic extensions known as *microvilli.* They greatly increase the surface area which aids in their absorptive function. (The *brush border* cells in the proximal convoluted tubule of the kidney also have microvilli.)

Columnar Epithelium Forms Glands

Glands are groups of cells which take certain materials from tissue fluid and make new substances of them. All cells in the body take, from the surrounding fluid, substances essential for their nutrition and give off products of their metabolism. Certain cells of the body also manufacture specific substances, not for their own use, but to be extruded from the cell and used elsewhere in

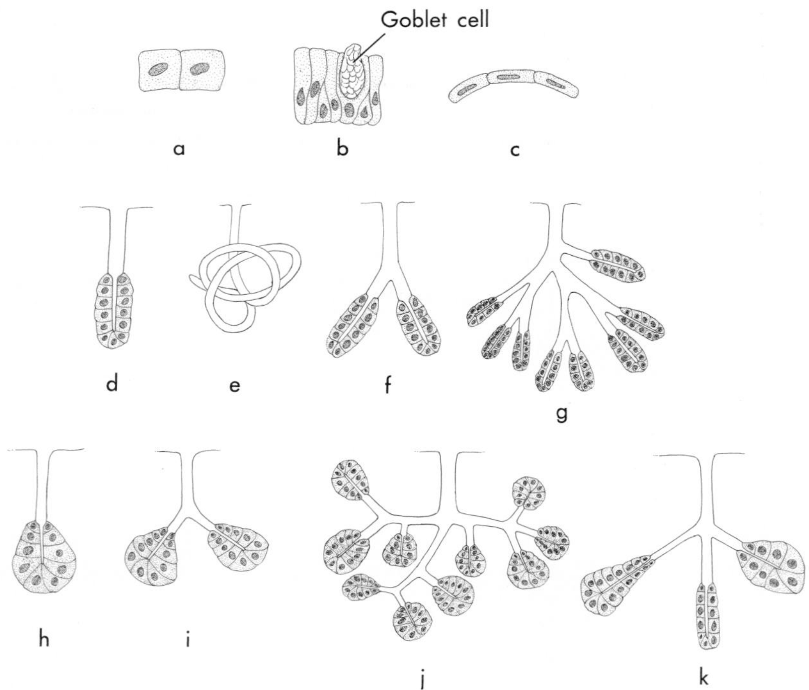

Figure 3–5. Diagram illustrating types of glands formed by columnar epithelium. (*a*) Plain cuboidal secreting cells, (*b*) plain columnar secreting cells, one of which is a "goblet gland," (*c*) plain flat secreting cells, (*d, e, f, g*) tubular glands: simple, twisted, branched, and several times branched. (*h, i, j*) Saccular or alveolar glands: (*h*) simple, (*i*) branched, (*j*) much-branched. (*k*) Compound tubuloalveolar gland.

the body, such as, for example, *secretions* of the gastrointestinal tract. Other cells form substances that are called excretions, such as sweat. These cells are known as *gland cells,* or glandular epithelium. A group of such cells that have definite structure for the specific purpose of either secretion or excretion is called a *gland.*

Classification. Columnar epithelium forms exocrine, or duct, glands which secrete into a cavity or on the body surface; hence they are called glands of external secretion. Cells from surface epithelium grow down into the underlying tissue forming epithelial cords, called tubules. The cords separate and form a duct. The deepest cells become secretory. It is the arrangement of cells in the secretory portion that determines the type of exocrine gland. The secretory cells become highly specialized.

These glands may be classed according to structure:

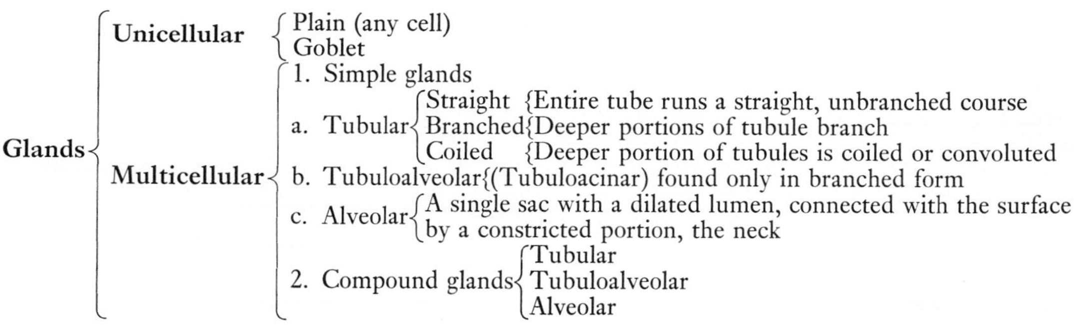

- **Glands**
  - **Unicellular**
    - Plain (any cell)
    - Goblet
  - **Multicellular**
    - 1. Simple glands
      - a. Tubular
        - Straight {Entire tube runs a straight, unbranched course
        - Branched {Deeper portions of tubule branch
        - Coiled {Deeper portion of tubules is coiled or convoluted
      - b. Tubuloalveolar {(Tubuloacinar) found only in branched form
      - c. Alveolar {A single sac with a dilated lumen, connected with the surface by a constricted portion, the neck
    - 2. Compound glands
      - Tubular
      - Tubuloalveolar
      - Alveolar

The Simple Glands. The simple tubular glands are divided in relation to the structure of the fundus into straight, branched, and coiled. The *straight* tubular glands are found in the large intestine; the *branched* glands may have several branches and are found in the gastric and uterine mucosa; the *coiled* tubular glands are found in the skin (the sweat glands).

The Compound Glands. The compound glands may be tubular, tubuloalveolar, or alveolar. The *compound tubular* glands have a large number of distinct duct systems, which eventually open into a main or common excretory duct. The liver, kidneys, and testes are good examples of these glands.

THE COMPOUND TUBULOALVEOLAR GLANDS. These glands are numerous, and although the general principle of structure is about the same in all of them, there is considerable variation in their minute structure. These glands also have many distinct duct systems which eventually open into a common duct. All the salivary glands, the pancreas and some of the larger glands of the esophagus, the seromucous glands of the respiratory pathway, and many of the duodenal glands belong in this group.

THE COMPOUND ALVEOLAR GLANDS. These glands are very much like the other compound glands in general structure; however, the terminal ducts end in alveoli with a dilated saclike form. The mammary glands are good examples of this kind of gland.

NAME	CHARACTERISTICS, LOCATION, AND FUNCTION
Ciliated epithelium derived from entoderm	The cells are columnar in shape with many threadlike processes called cilia on their free surface. The cilia are prolongations of the cell protoplasm. The motion of an individual cilium may be compared to the lashlike motion of a short-handled whip, the cilium bending rapidly in one direction and recovering slowly. Motion is performed in regular succession, giving rise to the appearance of a series of waves traveling along the surface. Since all motion is in one direction, a current of much power is produced.

Cilia are seen in the respiratory tract from nose to bronchial tubes (except pharynx and vocal folds), and in the uterine tubes, upper part of the uterus, and efferent ducts of the testes. Function of the cilia is motion to impel secreted fluids and other materials along the surfaces from which they extend and prevent the entrance of foreign matter into cavities.

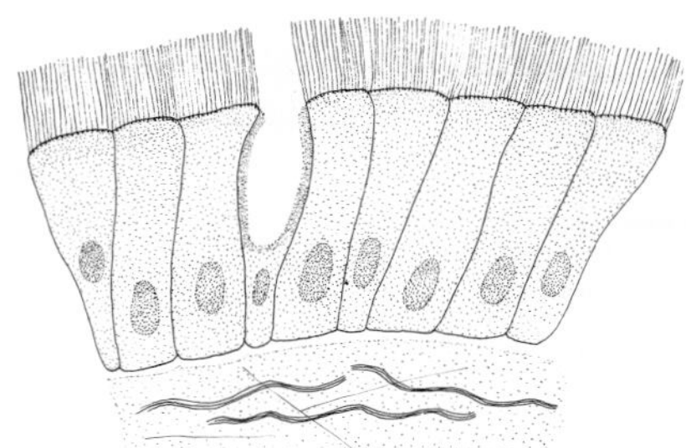

Figure 3–6. Ciliated columnar epithelium, sectional view. Note one goblet cell.

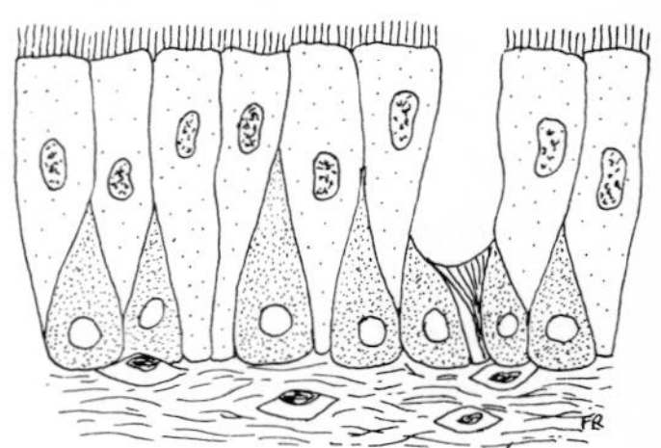

Figure 3–7. Pseudostratified ciliated epithelium. All the cells reach the basement membrane; some cells do not reach the free surface. One goblet cell is shown.

Pseudostratified ciliated epithelium

Between the tall, narrow, ciliated cells there is a layer of nonciliated cells that does not reach the surface. These nonciliated cells function in the repair of ciliated epithelium. Numerous mucus-secreting goblet cells are found in all ciliated epithelium. This type of ciliated epithelium is found in the trachea and large bronchi.

Reticular tissue

A variety of loose connective tissue with a network or reticulum of fibrous fibers. The cells are thin and flat and are wrapped around fibers, more like a meshwork of stellate cells forming minute cavities in which lymph cells are found. Forms framework of lymphoid tissue.

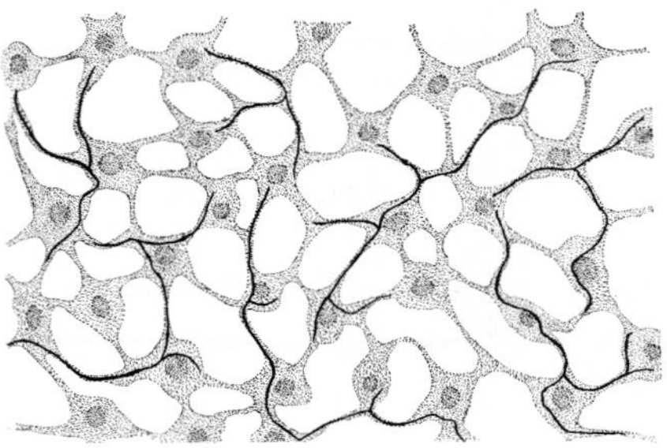

Figure 3–8. Diagram of reticular tissue as seen in a thin section of a portion of lymph node. (Highly magnified.) This tissue forms the framework of lymph tissue.

Lymphoid or adenoid tissue

It is a reticular tissue in which the meshes of the network are occupied by lymph cells. It forms a supporting framework in lymph nodes, bone marrow, spleen, lungs, liver, kidneys, and mucous membranes of the gastrointestinal tract.

Neuroepithelium (sensory) derived from ectoderm

The epithelial membrane of the nose has two kinds of cells—olfactory and supporting cells. The olfactory cells send their axons into the brain where they come into relation with other neurons of the olfactory tract. The olfactory epithelium is thus a neuroepithelium; its sensory cells are nerve cells. The cells of the organ of Corti, the taste buds, and the retina are other examples of neuroepithelium. The function is sensation. These cells contain end organs of nerve fibers with surrounding supporting cells.

MEMBRANES

In combination with the underlying connective tissue, epithelium forms *membranes*. The word *membrane* in its broadest sense is used to designate any thin expansion of tissues. In the commonest sense, the word *membrane* is used to denote an *envelope* or *lining* made up of tissues. The underlying connective tissue forms a stratum of closely woven fibers which permits a variable amount of stretching but prevents an expansion which may separate the epithelial cells.

Classification of Membranes

The chief membranes of the body are classified as serous, synovial, mucous, and cutaneous.

Serous membranes are thin, transparent, strong, and elastic. The surfaces are moistened by a self-secreted serous fluid. They consist of simple squamous epithelium and a layer of areolar connective tissue which serves as a base. Since the epithelium is derived from mesoderm, it is called *mesothelium*.

Serous membranes are found (1) lining the body cavities and covering the organs which lie in them, and (2) forming the fascia bulbi and part of the membranous labyrinth of the ear.

Lining the Body Cavities and Covering the Organs Which Lie in Them. With one exception, these membranes form closed sacs, one part of which is closely adherent to the walls of the cavity it lines—the *parietal* portion—whereas the other is reflected over the surface of the organ or organs contained in the cavity and is named the *visceral* portion of the membrane. The viscera are not contained within the sac cavity proper, but are really placed outside it; and some of the organs (e.g., lung) may receive a complete, and others (e.g., kidney) receive only a partial, investment.

The free surface of a serous membrane is smooth and lubricated; the free surface of one part is applied to the corresponding free surface of some other part, with only a small quantity of fluid being interposed between the surfaces. The organs situated in a cavity lined by a serous membrane, being themselves also covered by it, can thus glide easily against the walls of the cavity or upon each other, their motions being rendered smoother by the lubricating fluid.

This class of serous membranes includes (1) the two *pleurae*, which cover the lungs and line the chest cavity, (2) the *pericardium*, which covers the heart and lines the inner surface of the fibrous pericardium, and (3) the *peritoneum*, which lines the abdominal cavity and covers its contained viscera and the upper abdominal surface of some of the pelvic viscera.

Lining the Vascular System. This is the internal membrane of the heart, blood vessels, and lymph vessels. It is called endothelium.

Forming the Fasci Bulbi of the Eye and Part of the Membranous Labyrinth of the Ear. (1) Between the pad of fat in the back of the orbit and the eyeball is a serous sac—the fascia bulbi—which envelops the eyeball from the optic nerve to the ciliary region and separates the eyeball from the bed of fat on which it rests. (2) The membranous labyrinth of the ear has somewhat the same general form as the bony cavities in which it is contained.

Function. The function of the membranes is mainly protective, by secreting a serous fluid which covers its surface and supplying the lubrication for organs as they move over each other.

Synovial membranes are associated with the bones and muscles. They consist of an outer layer of fibrous tissue and an inner layer of areolar connective tissue with loosely arranged collagenous and elastic fibers, connective tissue cells, and fat cells. There is no definite cellular layer at the inner surface. Synovial membranes secrete *synovia.*

They are divided into three classes: (1) articular, (2) mucous sheaths, and (3) bursae mucosae.

1. *Articular synovial membranes* line the articular capsules of the freely movable joints.

2. *Synovial sheaths* (mucous sheaths) are elongated closed sacs which form sheaths for the tendons of some of the muscles, particularly the flexor and the extensor muscles of the fingers and toes. They facilitate the gliding of the tendons in the fibro-osseous canals.

3. *Synovial bursae* (bursae mucosae) are simple sacs interposed to prevent friction between two surfaces which move upon each other. They may be subcutaneous, submuscular, subfascial, or subtendinous. The large bursa situated over the patella is an example of a subcutaneous bursa. Similar, though smaller, bursae are found over the olecranon, the malleoli, the knuckles, and other prominent parts.

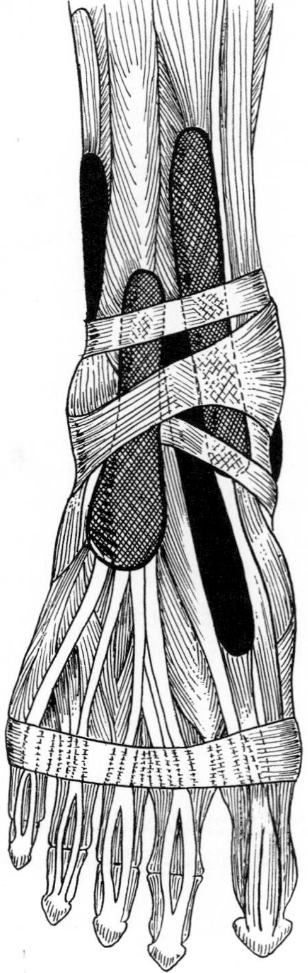

Figure 3–9. The anterior annular ligament of the ankle and synovial membranes of the tendons beneath it. Artificially distended.

Synovial fluid is an ultrafiltrate of blood (as is tissue fluid) plus some mucin, a variable number of white blood cells, and hyaluronic acid, and it has an electrolytic pattern similar to that of tissue fluid. Synovial fluid is the major source of nutrition for articular cartilage. Synovial membranes are richly supplied with blood capillaries, lymphatics, and nerves.

The function of synovial membranes is the same as that of serous membranes. Both the serous and the synovial membranes are derived from the mesoderm.

The Mucous Membranes. The mucous membranes may be grouped in two divisions: (1) gastropulmonary and (2) genitourinary. Mucous membranes secrete mucus, a watery fluid containing mucin (a glycoprotein), salts, and other substances.

The Gastropulmonary Mucous Membrane. This lines the alimentary canal, the air passages, and the cavities communicating with them. It is continuous from the edges of the lips and nostrils and extends through the mouth and nose to the throat, throughout the length of the alimentary canal to the anus. At its origin and termination it is continuous with the external skin. It also extends throughout the trachea, bronchial tubes, and air sacs. From the interior of the nose the membrane extends into the frontal, ethmoid, sphenoid, and maxillary sinuses, into the lacrimal passages, and also becoming the conjunctival membrane over the forepart of the eyeball and inside of the eyelids on the edges of which it meets the skin. A prolongation of this membrane extends on each side of the upper and back part of the pharynx, forming the lining of the auditory (eustachian[1]) tube. This membrane also lines the salivary, pancreatic, and biliary ducts and the gallbladder.

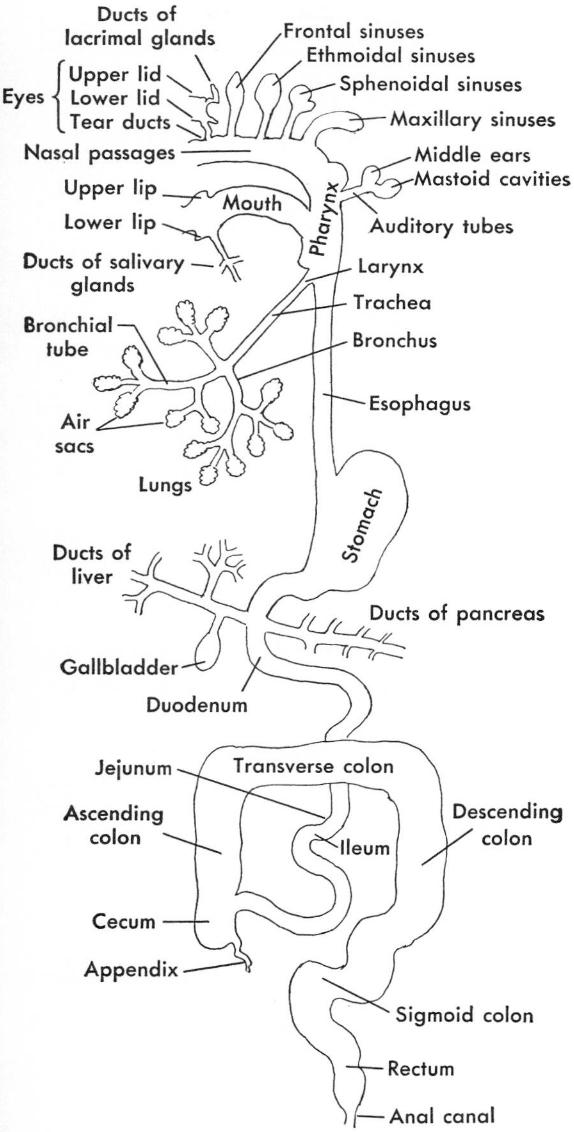

Figure 3–10. Diagram showing continuity of the gastropulmonary mucous membrane.

The Genitourinary Mucous Membrane. This lines the bladder and the urinary tract from the interior of the kidneys to the orifice of the urethra; it lines the ducts of the testes, epididymis, and seminal vesicles; it lines the vagina, uterus, and uterine (fallopian[2]) tubes.

A study of Figures 3–11 and 3–12 will make this plain.

Structure of Mucous Membrane. A mucous membrane is usually composed of three layers of tissue: (1) epithelium, (2) a supporting lamina propria, and (3) a thin, usually double, layer of smooth muscle.

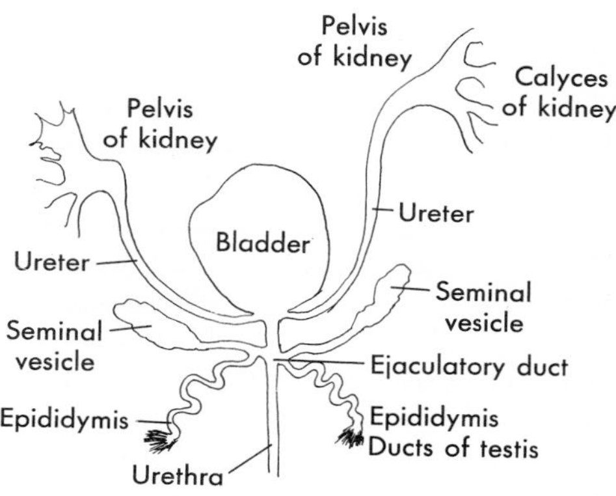

Figure 3–11. Diagram showing continuity of mucous membrane in the male genitourinary pathway.

[1] Bartolommeo Eustacchio, Italian anatomist (1520–1574).

[2] Gabriel Falloppius, Italian anatomist (1523–1562).

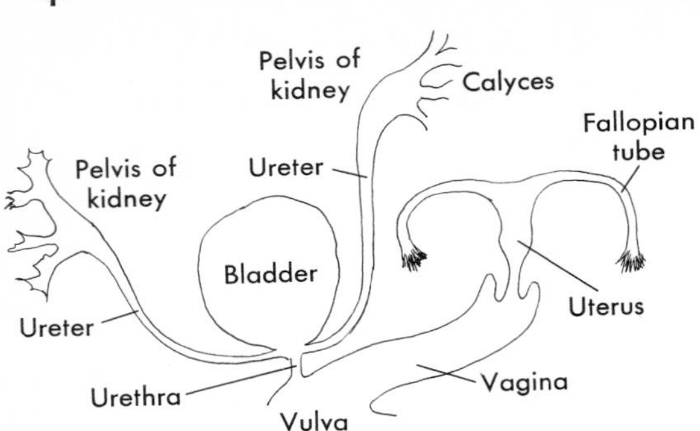

Figure 3–12. Diagram showing continuity of mucous membrane in the female genitourinary pathway.

1. EPITHELIUM. Epithelium is the surface layer. It may be stratified squamous, as in the throat; columnar, as in the stomach and intestine where it is secretory or absorptive; or ciliated, as in the respiratory tract.

2. THE LAMINA PROPRIA. This is formed by connective tissue with fine interlacing fibers. It contains fibroblasts and macrophages. It may contain plasma cells and lymphocytes; many blood and lymph capillaries are present. It *supports* the epithelium and connects it with the muscularis layer.

3. THE MUSCULARIS MUCOSAE. This is usually a double layer of smooth-muscle fibers held together by elastic tissue. The muscle fibers of the inner layer are circularly arranged, and in the outer layer, longitudinally. This layer is not present in the trachea.

The mucous membranes are attached to the parts beneath them by loose connective tissue, in this case called *submucous* connective tissue. This differs greatly in quantity as well as in consistency in different parts. The connection is in some cases close and firm, as in the cavity of the nose. In other instances, especially in cavities subject to frequent variations in capacity, like the esophagus and the stomach, it is lax. When such a cavity is narrowed by contraction of its outer coats, the mucous membrane is thrown into folds, or *rugae,* which disappear again when the cavity is distended. In certain parts the mucous membrane forms permanent folds that cannot be effaced, and these project conspicuously into the cavity it lines. The best example of these folds is seen in the small intestine, where they are called *circular folds* (valvulae conniventes), which increase the area of absorbing surface for the products of digestion. In some locations the free surface of mucous membrane contains minute glands or is covered with papillae or villi.

Functions of Mucous Membranes. The functions of mucous membranes are protection, support of blood vessels and lymphatics, and provision of a large amount of surface for secretion and absorption.

A mucous membrane protects by forming a lining for all the passages that communicate with the exterior, i.e., those passages subject to contact with foreign substances which are introduced into the body and with waste materials which are expelled from the body. The mucus secreted is a thicker and more viscid liquid than either serum or synovia and, by coating the surface, lessens the irritation from food, waste materials, or secreted substances. This is especially true in the stomach and duodenum, where mucus protects the membrane against the highly acid secretion of hydrochloric acid. The cilia of the respiratory tract also assist in protection.

The redness of mucous membranes is due to their abundant supply of blood. The small blood vessels which convey blood to the mucous membranes divide in the submucous tissues and send smaller branches into the corium, where they form a network of capillaries just under the basement membrane. The lymphatics also form networks in the corium and communicate with larger vessels in the submucous tissue below.

The projections of mucous membrane, such as the circular folds, covered with glands and villi as they are, increase enormously the surface area of the membrane for secretion and absorption and enable the membrane to carry more blood vessels and lymphatics.

Cutaneous membrane or integument refers to membrane that covers the body and is commonly spoken of as skin.

THE SKIN AND APPENDAGES

Most of our contacts with the environment are through the skin. Since living cells must be surrounded with fluid, the contact of the body with the air is made by means of dead cells. These dead cells form a protective covering for the living cells. The living cells of the inner layers of the skin are constantly pushed to the outside, shrinking and undergoing progressive chemical changes which cement them firmly together and render them waterproof. In this way a tissue-fluid environment is maintained for living cells although man lives in an air environment.

The Skin

The skin has many functions. It covers the body and protects the deeper tissues from drying and injury. It protects from invasion by infectious organisms. It is important in many ways in temperature regulation. It contains end organs of many of the sensory nerve fibers by means of which one becomes aware of the environment. It also acts as an accessory mechanism for tactile and pressure corpuscles. In the skin fat, glucose, water, salts such as sodium chloride, and fluid accumulate in the tissues. The skin has excretory functions, eliminating water with the various salts which compose perspiration, and the dead cells themselves become an important way of eliminating many salts. It is an important light screen for the underlying living cells. It also has absorbing powers. It will absorb oily materials placed in contact with it.

The rule of nine gives the relative distribution of total body surface area.

Head and neck	9%
Anterior trunk	18%
Posterior trunk	18%
Upper extremity (9 × 2)	18%
Lower extremity (18 × 2)	36%
Perineum	1%
Total 100%	

Skin consists of two distinct layers: (1) epidermis, cuticle; (2) dermis, corium, or cutis vera.

The epidermis is stratified squamous epithelium, consisting of a variable number of layers of cells. It varies in thickness in different parts of the body, being thickest on the palms of the hands and on the soles of the feet, where the skin is most exposed to friction, and thinnest on the ventral surface of the trunk and the inner surfaces of the limbs. It forms a protective covering over every part of the true skin and is closely molded on the papillary layer of the corium. The external surface of the epidermis is marked by a network of ridges caused by the size and arrangement of the papillae beneath. Some of these ridges are large and correspond to the

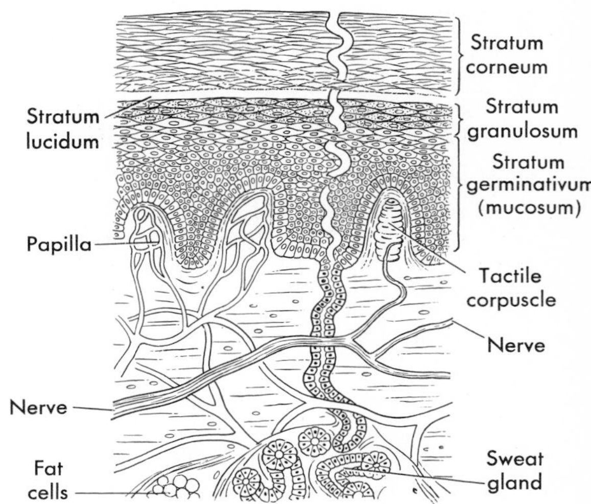

Figure 3–13. Diagram of a section of the skin to show its structure. The epidermis consists of the strata corneum, lucidum, granulosum, and germinativum (mucosum). The corium lies below the epidermis.

folds produced by movements, e.g., at the joints; others are fine and intersect at various angles, e.g., upon the back of the hand. Upon the palmar surface of the fingers and hands and the soles of the feet, the ridges serve to increase resistance between contact surfaces and therefore prevent slipping. On the tips of the fingers and thumbs these ridges form distinct patterns which are peculiar to the individual and practically never change, hence the use of fingerprints for purposes of identification.

From without inward four regions of the epidermis are named: the *stratum corneum*, the *stratum lucidum*, the *stratum granulosum*, and the *stratum germinativum* (*mucosum*).

The three outer layers consist of cells which are constantly being shed and renewed from the cells of the *stratum germinativum*. In the *stratum corneum* the protoplasm of the cells has become changed into a protein substance called *keratin*, which acts as a waterproof covering. The reaction is acid; and many kinds of organisms, when placed upon the skin, are destroyed, presumably by the effect of the acidity. Underneath this is the *stratum lucidum*, a few layers of clear cells.

The *stratum granulosum* is formed by two or three layers of flattened cells that are cells in transition between the stratum germinativum and the horny cells of the superficial layers.

The *stratum germinativum* consists of several layers of cells. The cells of the deepest layer are columnar and are called the *stratum mucosum*. The growth of the epidermis is by multiplication of the cells of the germinative layer. As they multiply, the cells previously formed are pushed upward toward the surface. In their upward progress these cells undergo a chemical transformation, and the soft protoplasmic cells become converted into the flat scales which are constantly being rubbed off the surface of the skin. The pigment in the skin is found in greatest amount in the cells of the stratum germinativum. No blood vessels pass into the epidermis, but fine nerve fibers lie between the cells of the inner layers.

The *corium* (*derma*) is a highly sensitive and vascular layer of connective tissue. It contains numerous blood vessels, lymph vessels, nerves, glands, hair follicles, and papillae and is described as consisting of two layers: the *papillary*, or *superficial*, *layer*, and the *reticular*, or *deeper*, *layer*.

The surface of the *papillary*, or *superficial*, layer is increased by small conical elevations, called papillae, whence this layer derives its name. They project up into the epidermis, which is molded over them. The papillae consist of small bundles of fibrillated tissue, the fibrils being arranged parallel to the long axis of the papillae. Within this tissue is a loop of capillaries, and some papillae, especially those of the palmar surface of the hands and fingers, contain *tactile corpuscles*, which are numerous where the sense of touch is acute.

The *reticular*, or *deeper*, layer consists of strong bands of fibrous tissue and some fibers of elastic tissue. These bands interlace, and the tiny spaces formed by their interlacement are occupied by adipose tissue and sweat glands. The reticular layer is attached to the parts beneath by a subcutaneous layer of areolar connective tissue, which, except in a few places, contains fat. In some parts, as on the front of the neck, the connection is loose and movable; in other parts, as on the palmar surface of the hands and the soles of the feet, the connection is close and firm. In youth the skin is both extensile and elastic, so that it can be stretched and wrinkled and return to its normal condition of smoothness. As age advances, the elasticity is lessened, and the wrinkles tend to become permanent.

Blood Vessels and Lymphatics. The arteries which supply the skin form a network in the subcutaneous connective tissue and send branches to the papillae, the hair follicles, and the sudoriferous glands. The capillaries of the skin are so numerous that when distended, they are capable of holding a large proportion of the blood contained in the body. The amount of blood they contain is dependent on their caliber, which is regulated largely by the vasomotor nerve fibers.

There is a superficial and a deep network of lymphatics in the skin. These communicate with each other and with the lymphatics of the subcutaneous connective tissue.

Nerves. The skin contains the peripheral terminations of many nerve fibers and receptors. These fibers may be classified as follows:

1. Motor nerve fibers, including the vasoconstrictors and vasodilators distributed to the blood vessels, and motor nerve fibers distributed to the arrector muscles (arrectores pilorum) of the hair follicles.
2. Receptors concerned with the temperature sense, which terminate in *cold receptors* (end organs of Krause) and *receptors for warmth* (possibly the end organs of Ruffini).
3. Receptors concerned with touch and pressure, which terminate in *touch* (Meissner's corpuscles and free nerve endings around hairs and skin) and *pressure receptors* (pacinian corpuscles).

The Appendages of the Skin

The appendages of the skin are the nails, the hairs, the sebaceous glands, the sudoriferous, or sweat, glands, and their ducts.

The Nails. The nails (ungues) are composed of clear, horny cells of the epidermis, joined so as to form a solid, continuous plate upon the dorsal surface of the terminal phalanges. Each nail is closely adherent to the underlying corium, which is modified to form what is called the bed, or *matrix*. The body of the nail is the part that shows. The hidden part, in the nail groove, is called the root. The *lunule* is the crescent-shaped white area which can be seen on the part nearest the root. The nails appear pink except at the *lunule* because blood in the capillary bed shows through.

The nails grow in length by multiplication of the soft cells in the stratum germinativum. The cells are transformed into hard, dry scales, which unite to form a solid plate; and the nail, constantly receiving additions, slides forward over its bed and projects beyond the end of the finger. When a nail is thrown off by suppuration or torn off by violence, a new one will grow in its place provided any of the cells of the stratum germinativum are left.

The Hairs. The hairs (pili) are growths of the epidermis, developed in the hair follicles, which extend downward into the subcutaneous tissue. The part which lies within the follicle is known as the root, and that portion which projects beyond the surface of the skin is called the shaft. The hair is composed of:

Cuticle, a single layer of scalelike cells which overlap.

Cortex, a middle portion, which constitutes the chief part of the shaft, formed of elongated cells united to form flattened fibers which contain pigment granules in dark hair and air in white hair.

Medulla, an inner layer composed of rows of many-sided cells, which frequently contain air spaces. The fine hairs covering the surface of the body and the hairs of the head do not have this layer.

The root of the hair is enlarged at the bottom of the follicle into a bulb which is composed of growing cells and fits over a vascular papilla which projects into the follicle. Hair has no blood vessels but receives nourishment from the blood vessels of the papilla.

Growth of Hair. Hair grows from the papilla by multiplication of its cells (matrix cells). These cells become elongated to form the fibers of the fibrous portion, and as they are pushed to the surface, they become flattened and form the cuticle. If the scalp is thick, pliable, and moves freely over the skull, it is favorable to the growth of hair. A thin scalp that is drawn tightly over the skull tends to constrict the blood vessels, lessen the supply of blood, and cause atrophy of the roots of the hair by pressure; in such cases massage of the head loosens the scalp, improves the circulation of the blood, and usually stimulates the growth of the hair. The hairs are constantly falling out and constantly being replaced. In youth and early adult life not only may hairs be replaced, but there may be an increase in the number of hairs by development of new follicles. When the matrix cells lose their vitality, new hairs will not develop.

With the exceptions of the palms of the

hands, the soles of the feet, and the last phalanges of the fingers and toes, the whole skin is studded with hairs. The hair of the scalp is long and coarse, but most of the hair is fine and extends only a little beyond the hair follicle.

Arrector (Arrectores Pilorum) Muscles. The follicles containing the hairs are narrow pits which slant obliquely upward, so that the hairs they contain lie slanting on the surface of the body. Connected with each follicle are small bundles of involuntary muscle fibers called the *arrector muscles.* They arise from the papillary layer of the corium and are inserted into the hair follicle below the entrance of the duct of a sebaceous gland. These muscles are situated on the side toward which the hairs slope, and when they contract, as they will under the influence of cold or fright, they straighten the follicles and elevate the hairs, producing the roughened condition of the skin known as "gooseflesh." Since the sebaceous gland is situated in the angle between the hair follicle and the muscle, contraction of the muscle squeezes the sebaceous secretion out from the duct of the gland. This secretion aids in preventing too great heat loss.

Glands in the Skin. *Sebaceous Glands.* These occur everywhere over the skin surface with the exception of the palms of the hands and the soles of the feet. They are abundant in the scalp and face and are numerous around the apertures of the nose, mouth, external ears, and anus. Each gland is composed of a number of epithelial cells and is filled with larger cells containing fat. These cells are cast off bodily, their detritus forms the secretion, and new cells are continuously formed. Occasionally the ducts open upon the surface of the skin, but more frequently they open into the hair follicles. In the latter case, the secretion from the gland passes out to the skin along the hair. Their size is not regulated by the length of the hair.

The largest sebaceous glands are found on the nose and other parts of the face, where they may become enlarged with accumulated secretion. This retained secretion often becomes discolored, giving rise to the condition commonly known as blackheads. It also provides a medium for the growth of pus-producing organisms and consequently is a common source of pimples and boils.

SEBUM. Sebum is the secretion of the sebaceous glands. It contains fats, soaps, cholesterol, albuminous material, remnants of epithelial cells, and inorganic salts. It serves to protect the hairs from becoming too dry and brittle, as well as from becoming too easily saturated with moisture. Upon the surface of the skin it forms a thin protective layer, which serves to prevent undue absorption or evaporation of water from the skin. This secretion keeps the skin soft and pliable. An accumulation of this sebaceous matter upon the skin of the fetus furnishes the thick, cheesy, oily substance called the *vernix caseosa.*

Sudoriferous, or Sweat, Glands. These are abundant over the whole skin but are largest and most numerous in the axillae, the palms of the hands, the soles of the feet, and the forehead. Each gland consists of a single tube, with a blind, coiled end which is lodged in the subcutaneous tissue. From the coiled end, the tube is continued as the excretory duct of the gland up through the corium and epidermis and finally opens on the surface by a pore. Each tube is lined with secreting epithelium. The coiled end is closely invested by capillaries, and the blood

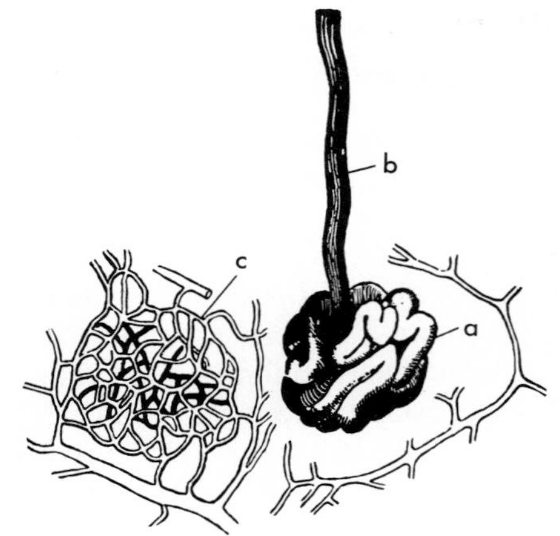

Figure 3–14. Coiled end of a sweat gland. (*a*) The coiled end, (*b*) the duct, (*c*) network of capillaries, inside which the sweat gland lies.

in the capillaries is separated from the cavity of the glandular tube by the thin membranes which form their respective walls.

PERSPIRATION, OR SWEAT. Pure sweat is very dilute and practically neutral. When gathered from the skin, it contains fragments of cells and sebum and has a pH range of 5.2 to 6.75. Perspiration contains the same inorganic constituents as the blood, but in lower concentration. The chief salt is sodium chloride. The organic constituents in sweat include urea, uric acid, amino acids, ammonia, sugar, lactic acid, and ascorbic acid. Any factor which affects the composition of blood may also alter the composition of sweat. Sulfonamides are present after administration. Immune substances may also be present.

Under ordinary circumstances, the perspiration that the body is continually throwing off evaporates from the surface of the body without one's becoming aware of it and is called *insensible perspiration.* When more sweat is poured upon the surface of the body than can be removed at once by evaporation, it appears on the skin in the form of drops and is then spoken of as *sensible perspiration.*

The amount secreted during 24 hours varies greatly. It is estimated to average about 480 to 600 ml, but may be increased to such an extent that even more than this may be secreted in an hour.

ACTIVITY OF THE SWEAT GLANDS. Special secretory nerve fibers are supplied to the glandular epithelium of the sweat glands. The activity of these glands is supposed to be the result either of direct stimulation of the nerve endings in the glands or of indirect stimulation through the sensory fibers of the skin. The usual cause of profuse sweating is a high external temperature or muscular exercise. It is known that the high temperature acts upon the sensory cutaneous nerves, possibly the heat fibers, and stimulates the sweat fibers indirectly.

PHYSIOLOGY OF THE SWEAT GLANDS. Although perspiration is an excretion, its value lies not so much in the elimination of waste matter as in the loss of body heat by the evaporation of water. Each gram of water requires about 0.5 Cal for evaporation, and this heat comes largely from the body. This loss of heat helps to balance the production of heat that is constantly taking place. When the kidneys are not functioning properly, and the blood contains an excessive amount of waste material, the sweat glands will excrete some of the latter, particularly if their activity is stimulated. In the condition known as uremia, when the kidneys secrete little or no urine, the percentage of urea in perspiration rises.

Ceruminous Glands. The skin lining the external auditory canal contains modified sweat glands called *ceruminous* glands. They secrete a yellow, pasty substance resembling wax, which is called *cerumen.* An accumulation of cerumen deep in the auditory canal may interfere with hearing.

NERVOUS TISSUE

Nerve tissue

Nerve tissue, like other tissue is composed of cells, but these cells (called neurons) differ from other cells in both structure and function. The unique functional aspects of neurons are (1) irritability (excitability) or the ability to respond to changes in their environment, (2) conductivity, the ability to transmit nerve impulses to other cells.

Neuron

A neuron consists of a cell body and long and short cytoplasmic processes. The long process is termed the axon. Short processes, variable in number depending on location of the nerve cell, are termed dendrites. Depending on the number of processes, the neuron may be called multipolar, bipolar, or unipolar.

The cell body

The cell body consists of granular cytoplasm surrounding a nucleus. The nucleus, usually centrally placed, is spherical with a well-defined membrane. The cytoplasm contains mitochondria, a Golgi apparatus, and chromophilic granules (called Nissl substance). These granules contain ribonucleic acid; the quantity is variable, depending on the fatigue of the cell. Neurofibrils form a reticulum within the cell body, projecting into the dendrites and axons as well.

Size

The bodies of nerve cells vary greatly in size. The granule cells of the cerebellum have a diameter of 4 or 5 μ, whereas the large motor cells of the ventral column of the spinal cord may be 125 to 130 μ in diameter.

Cell processes

Dendrites are usually short, rather thick protoplasmic projections of the cell body. They have a *rough* outline and branch in a treelike manner. *Axons* (sometimes called "fibers") are long, slender protoplasmic projections of the cell body and may attain a length equal to more than half that of the whole body. They have a *smooth* outline, diminishing very little in caliber. Axons give off one or more branches called *collaterals*. Usually, a neuron has one axon which may become surrounded with a sheath called *myelin*.

Myelinated fibers

Myelinated fibers appear white. If fibers lack a myelin sheath, they are called nonmyelinated and appear gray. They consist of three parts. (1) The central core or axis cylinder is the cell process containing cytoplasm or axoplasm surrounded by the nerve cell membrane. Mitochondria are abundant. (2) The myelin sheath is a semifluid fatty substance that surrounds the axis cylinder, and is composed of cholesterol and phospholipids. It is arranged in concentric rings, separated by the flattened layers of cell membrane, from the cytoplasmic extensions of a Schwann or sheath cell. (3) The neurilemma.

Neurilemma

Neurilemma surrounds the myelin sheath, forming a thin membrane. It actually is the outer coil of cytoplasm of the Schwann cell.

Nodes of Ranvier[3]

At regular intervals along myelinated nerve fibers the myelin sheath is interrupted and the neurilemma is brought close to the axis cylinder. These constrictions (some 50 to 200 μ apart) are the nodes of Ranvier. It is at these nodes that branching of the axon occurs. Interruption of the myelin sheath at the nodes forms sites for exchange of materials between the extracellular fluid and the axoplasm. The nodes are indispensable for the transmission of the nerve impulse. Myelinated fibers within the brain and cord do *not* contain neurilemma.

Nonmyelinated nerve fibers (fibers of Remak[4])

These fibers have little or no myelin sheath, the fiber being directly invested with the neurilemma.

Function of the neuron

Neurons generate the nerve impulse when suitably stimulated and convey this impulse to other cells. Neurons which carry impulses from the spinal cord up to the brain, or from the periphery to the

[3] Louis Antoine Ranvier, French histologist (1835–1922).
[4] Robert Remak, German physiologist (1815–1865).

central nervous system, are called *afferent*, or *sensory*. Neurons which carry impulses down the spinal cord, or from the central nervous system to the periphery, are called *efferent*, or *motor*, or *secretory* (if they cause secretion).

Neuroglial tissue	Neuroglial tissue consists of cells called glial cells, which give off numerous processes that extend in every direction and intertwine among the neurons forming a *supporting* and *protective framework* throughout the brain and cord.
Types of neuroglia	(1) The *protoplasmic* astrocytes found in gray matter have large nuclei, abundant cytoplasm, and many processes. They are found attached to blood vessels and to the membranous tissue at the brain surface. Some lie close to the bodies of neurons and are called *satellite* cells. (2) The *fibrous* astrocytes are found in white matter, have long, thin unbranched processes, and are also found attached to blood vessels. (3) *Oligodendrocytes* are smaller than astrocytes with fewer processes and do not branch. They are found in rows along nerve fibers and surrounding the nerve cells.
Microglial cells	These small multipolar cells are found in both gray and white matter of the nervous system. They function as phagocytic cells when nerve tissue is damaged or infected.

CONNECTIVE TISSUES

These tissues differ in appearance, but are alike in that the cellular elements are relatively few and the intercellular material relatively abundant. They serve to connect and support the other tissues of the body and with few exceptions are highly vascular. The intercellular substances determine the physical characteristics of the tissue.

NAME	CHARACTERISTICS, LOCATION, AND FUNCTION
Loose connective tissue	This tissue has a semifluid ground substance, or matrix, in which lie an irregular network of silvery white collagenous fibers and light elastic fibers which are the predominant characteristic of the tissue. Many cells are found in this tissue. It (1) is important in the repair

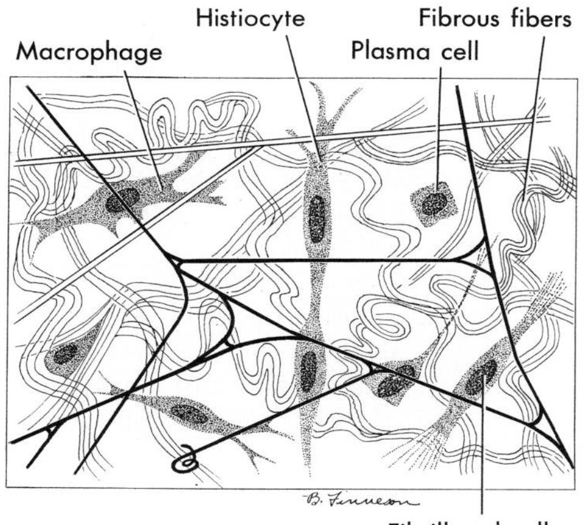

Figure 3–15. Loose connective tissue (highly magnified). The fibrous fibers are in wavy bundles; the elastic fibers form an open network. The ground substance, or matrix, in which the cells and fibers lie is tissue fluid. About 11 per cent of the body fluid lies in this tissue.

of all tissue, (2) has the capacity to hold water in the tissues, and (3) is an important factor for changes in viscosity and permeability of the ground substance in the tissue. The matrix of this tissue is called tissue fluid. It is continuous throughout the body, under the skin, and in all mucous membranes around all blood vessels and nerves. This tissue forms the "internal environment of the body," delivers all substances to the cells, delivers products of metabolism to blood and lymph, and stores water, salts, and glucose temporarily.

Fibers of loose connective tissue

The collagenous fiber is composed of an albuminoid protein called *collagen,* which, when boiled, yields gelatin. Each fiber is composed of minute wavy fibrils lying parallel and held together by "cement." The fibrils frequently separate into groups, extending in different directions. They are flexible but possess great tensile strength. Elastic fibers are homogeneous, branch freely, and are composed of a protein called *elastin*.

Cells of loose connective tissue (*fibrocytes*, fibroblasts)

These are most numerous and are large, flat branching cells with many processes. After tissue injury these cells enlarge and become active in forming collagenous fibers. They play an important role in the formation of collagenous fibers and perhaps also form ground substance.

Macrophages

These are irregularly shaped cells with short processes. Found in the sinusoids of the liver, lymph organs, and bone marrow. They are phagocytic and function in normal physiological processes. They have great phagocytic capacity under such conditions as inflammatory processes.

Plasma cells

These are small round or irregular-shaped cells. There is evidence that they may be derived from special cells in the thymus and are distributed to other tissues shortly after birth. Found in greatest numbers in all connective tissue, especially of the alimentary mucosa and great omentum. Plasma cells are the actual formers of circulating antibodies.

Mast cells

They form the anticoagulant *heparin. Histamine* is also liberated from these cells in allergic and inflammatory reactions. Mast cells contain serotonin, which functions as a vasoconstrictor at the site of injury. They are most numerous along blood vessel beds.

Blood cells

Lymphocytes, neutrophils, monocytes, and eosinophils from the blood and lymph move in and out of this tissue.

Adipose connective tissue

This is loose connective tissue in which many of the cells are filled with fat. It exists throughout the body wherever loose connective tissue is found. It is an important reserve of food which may be oxidized, thus producing energy. It is a poor conductor of heat, thus reduces heat loss through the skin. Supports and protects various organs. Found generally throughout the body, under skin, in the subcutaneous layers. Large amount around the kidneys, covering the base and filling up furrows on the surface of the heart. Padding around joints. In marrow of long bones.

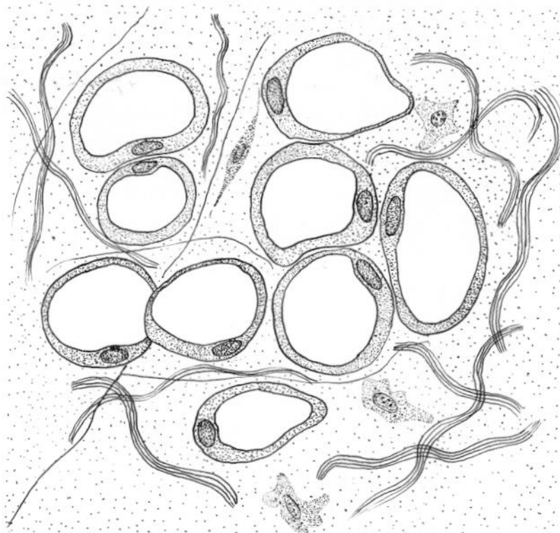

Figure 3–16. Diagram of a thin section of adipose connective tissue (highly magnified). Note adipose cells, matrix, fibrous fibers, elastic fibers, connective tissue. The white centers of the adipose cells represent fat. Excess fat adds to the work of the heart.

Elastic connective tissue

Elastic connective tissue is loose connective tissue in which the elastic fibers predominate. It consists of a ground substance containing cells with a few fibrous fibers and a predominance of elastic fibers which branch freely. They give it a yellowish color. Elastic tissue is extensile and elastic. It is found entering into the formation of the lungs and uniting the cartilages of the larynx. In the walls of arteries, trachea, bronchial tubes, and vocal folds; and in a few elastic ligaments and between the laminae of adjacent vertebrae (ligamenta flava, ligamentum nuchae).

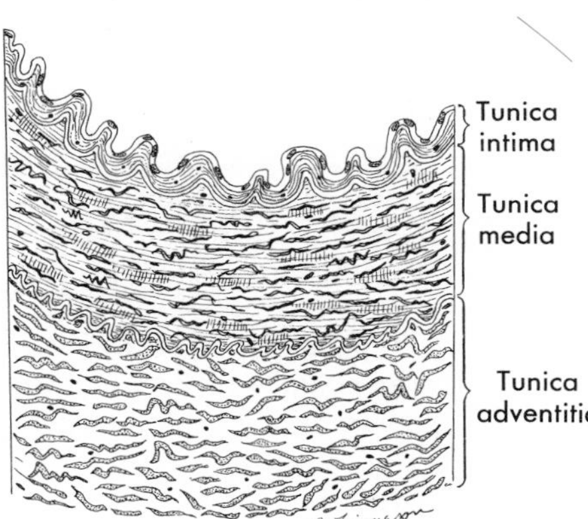

Figure 3–17. Elastic connective tissue as seen in a thin section of the wall of a large artery (highly magnified). The elastic fibers appear as short, black lines in the tunica media

Fibrous connective tissue

This tissue is loose connective tissue in which fibrous fibers predominate. It consists of a ground substance in which there are cells and wavy collagenous fibers, which cohere very closely and are arranged side by side in bundles which have an undulating outline. The matrix between the bundles contains cells arranged in rows but the cells are not a prominent feature of the tissue. The tissue is silvery white and tough, yet pliant; it is almost devoid of extensibility and is very sparingly supplied with nerves and blood vessels. This tissue is part of the supporting framework of the body. It forms: (1) *Ligaments*, strong flexible bands or cords that help to hold the bones together at the joints. (2) *Tendons*, white glistening cords or bands which attach the muscles to the bones. (3) *Aponeuroses*, flat, wide bands which connect one muscle with another or with periosteum of bone. (4) *Membranes*, containing fibrous tissue found investing and protecting different organs of the body, e.g., the heart and the kidneys. (5) *Fasciae* (*fascia*, in Latin, means a band or bandage). It is found as sheets of fibrous connective tissue which are wrapped around muscles and serve to hold them in place. There are two groups: superficial fascia and deep fascia. Infection of superficial fascia is called *cellulitis*.

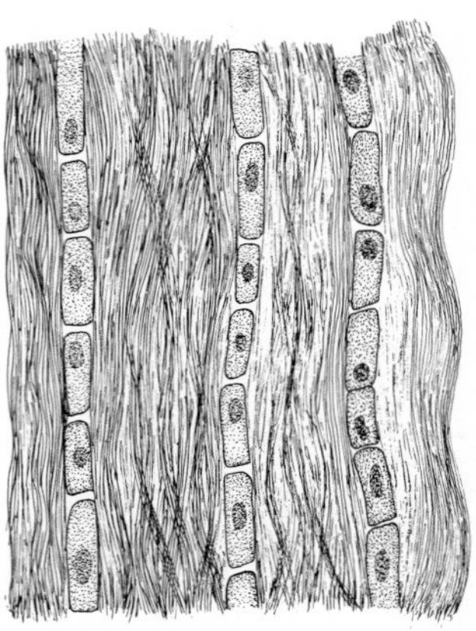

Figure 3–18. Fibrous connective tissue as seen in a thin, longitudinal section of a tendon (highly magnified). Fibrous fibers and cells lying in a matrix (white).

CARTILAGE

NAME	CHARACTERISTICS, LOCATION, AND FUNCTION
	Cartilage is firm, tough, and flexible. It consists of groups of cells in a mass of intercellular substance called matrix. Depending upon the texture of the intercellular substance three principal varieties can be distinguished: hyaline, fibrous, and elastic.
Hyaline cartilage	Comparatively few cells lying in fluid spaces or lacunae embedded in an abundant quantity of intercellular substance. This substance appears as a bluish white, glossy, or homogeneous mass. It is made up of collagenous fibrils forming a feltlike matrix. Hyaline cartilage covers the ends of the bones at the joints forming articular cartilage; it forms the ventral ends of the ribs as the costal cartilage. It is frequently described as skeletal cartilage since it is in immediate

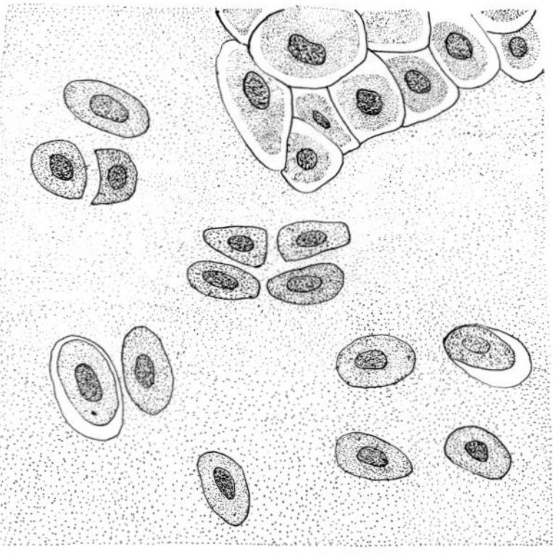

Figure 3–19. Hyaline cartilage as seen in a thin section (highly magnified). Some cells are shrunken to show that they lie in fluid spaces. Matrix is stippled.

connection with bone and may be said to form part of the skeleton. Hyaline cartilage enters into the formation of the nose, larynx, trachea, bronchi, and bronchial tubes. In covering the ends of the bones at the joints, it provides the joints with a thick, springy coating which gives ease to motion. In forming part of the bony framework of the thorax, the costal cartilages impart flexibility to its walls. In the embryo, a type of hyaline cartilage known as embryonal cartilage forms the matrix in which most of the bones are developed.

Fibrous cartilage

The intercellular substance is pervaded with bundles of white fibers, between which are scattered cartilage cells. The encapsulated cells frequently lie in rows with bundles of collagenous fibers between them. Fibrous cartilage closely resembles fibrous tissue. It is found joining bones together as in the round disks or symphyses of fibrocartilage connecting the bodies of the vertebrae and symphysis pubis between the pubic bones. In these cases the part in contact with the bone is always hyaline cartilage which changes gradually into fibrocartilage. In the center of the intervertebral disks there is a soft mass called the *nucleus pulposus*. Herniation of this mass may occur into the spinal canal. Fibrocartilage serves as a strong, flexible connecting material between bones and is found whenever great strength combined with a certain amount of rigidity is required.

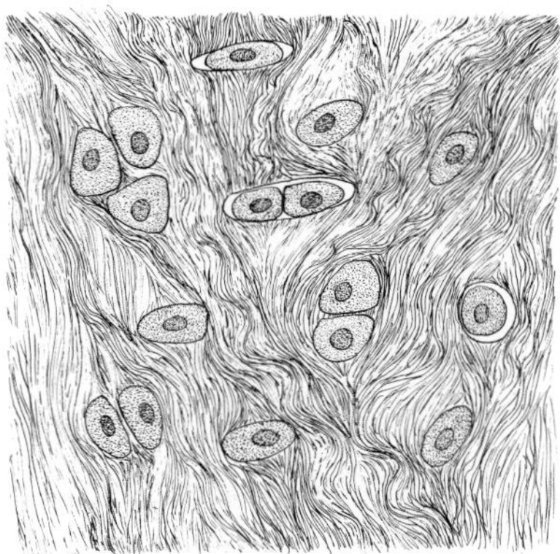

Figure 3–20. Fibrous cartilage as seen in a thin section (highly magnified).

Elastic cartilage

The intercellular substance is pervaded with a large number of elastic fibers which form a network. In the meshes of the network the cartilage cells are located. This form of cartilage is found in the

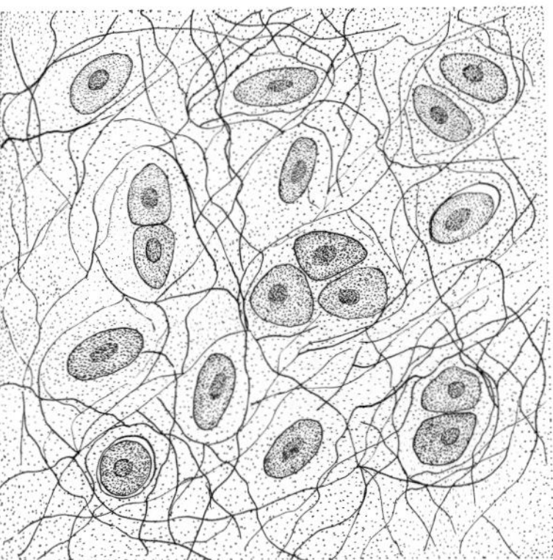

Figure 3–21. Elastic cartilage as seen in a thin section (highly magnified).

epiglottis, the larynx, the auditory tube, and the external ear. It strengthens and maintains the shape of these organs and yet allows a certain amount of change in shape.

Nerve and blood supply
Repair
Aging

Cartilage is not supplied with nerves and very rarely with blood vessels. *Perichondrium*, a moderately vascular fibrous membrane, covers and nourishes cartilage except where it forms articular surfaces. Perichondrium also functions in the repair process of injured cartilage. When injured, the area is invaded by perichondrial tissues, which is gradually changed to cartilage. With the aging process, cartilage loses its translucency and bluish-white color and appears cloudy. Calcification may occur, with degenerating changes of the cartilage cells.

BONE, OR OSSEOUS TISSUE

Bone is connective tissue in which the intercellular substance is rendered hard by being impregnated with mineral salts, chiefly calcium phosphate and calcium carbonate. This inorganic matter constitutes about two thirds of the weight of bone. Organic matter consisting of cells, blood vessels, and cartilaginous substance constitutes about one third. Bone freed from inorganic matter is called decalcified. It is a tough, flexible, elastic substance that can be tied in a knot. Bone free from organic matter is white and so brittle that it can be crushed in the fingers.

Forms of bony tissue

1. Cancellous or spongy — Has larger cavities and more slender intervening bony partitions and is found in the interior of a bone.
2. Compact — This bone has fewer spaces and is always found on the exterior of a bone. The relative quantity of spongy and compact bone varies in different bones and in different parts of the same bone, depending on the need for strength or lightness.

Structure of compact bone — The haversian[5] system consists of a canal containing blood vessels, lymph vessels, and nerves, surrounded by concentric rings or *lamellae*, *canaliculi*, and *lacunae*.

Lamellae — These are concentric rings formed by fibers which encircle the haversian canal.

Canaliculi — A system of tiny canals which extend from one lacuna to another and to the surfaces of bone where there are many capillaries. They contain the processes of the osteocytes and form the "lifeline" of nutrition to bone cells.

Lacunae — These are "little lakes" or spaces which contain the osteocyte. Study Figure 3–23.

Red marrow — Consists of connective tissue that acts as a support for a large number of blood vessels and marrow cells: (1) *Myelocytes*, which resemble white blood cells; and a small number of fat cells. (2) *Erythroblasts*, from which red blood cells are derived. Giant cells called (3) *osteoclasts* are found in both red and yellow marrow. Red marrow is found in the articular ends of long bones and in cancellous tissue. (See Chapter 14 for red and white blood cell formation.)

[5] Clopton Havers, English anatomist (1650–1702).

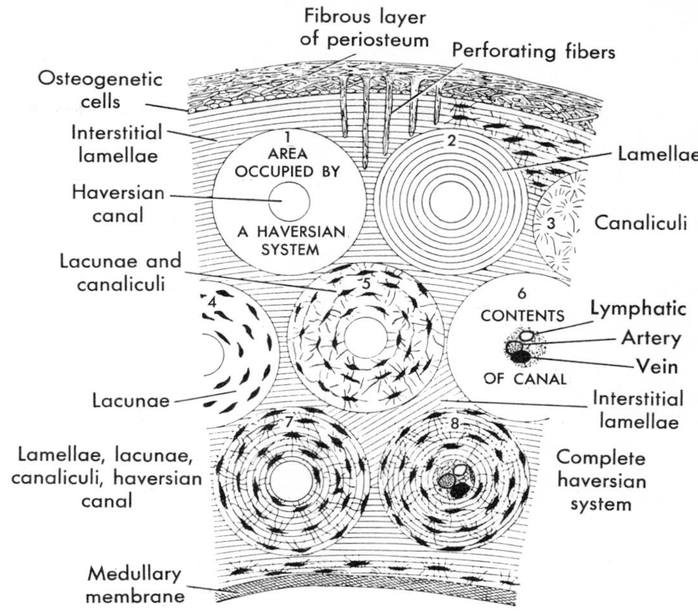

Figure 3–22. Diagram of a cross section of osseous tissue. Details are drawn to a very much larger scale than the complete drawing. A small part of a *transverse section* of a long bone is shown. At the uppermost part is the periosteum, covering the outside of the bone; at the lowermost part is the medullary membrane, lining the marrow cavity. Between these is compact tissue, consisting largely of a series of haversian systems, each being circular in outline and perforated by a central canal, left blank in the canals of five of the systems in this illustration. The *first* circle shows the area occupied by a system. The *second* shows the layers of bony tissue, or lamellae, arranged around the central canal. In the *third*, fine, dark radiating lines represent canaliculi, or lymph channels. In the *fourth*, dark spots arranged in circles between the lamellae represent lymph spaces, or lacunae, which contain the bone cells. In the *fifth*, the central canal, lacunae, and canaliculi, which connect the lacunae with each other and with the central canal, are shown. The *sixth* shows the contents of the canal: artery, veins, lymphatics, and areolar tissue. The *seventh* shows the lamellae, lacunae, canaliculi, and haversian canal. The *eighth* shows a complete haversian system.

Between the systems are interstitial lamellae, only a few of which show lacunae. The periosteum is made up of an outer fibrous layer and an inner osteogenetic layer, so called because it contains bone-forming cells, or osteoblasts. (Modified from Gerrish.)

Yellow marrow	Consists of connective tissue containing many blood vessels and cells. Most of the cells are fat cells; a few are myelocytes. It is found in the medullary canals of long bones and extends into the spaces of the cancellous tissue and haversian canals.
Periosteum	Bones are covered, except at their cartilaginous extremities, by a membrane called *periosteum*. It consists of an outer layer of connective tissue and an inner layer of fine fibers which form dense networks. In young bones, periosteum is thick, vascular, and closely connected with the epiphyseal cartilages. Later in life it is thinner and less vascular.
Endosteum	The marrow cavities and haversian canals are lined with a membrane called endosteum. Beneath it lies a layer of osteoblasts. After growth ceases, injury is the stimulus which activates the osteoblasts.
Blood vessels of bone	Bones are plentifully supplied with blood vessels which enter and leave the bones through canals (Volkmann).[6] These blood vessels proceed from the periosteum to join the haversian canals. The *lamellae* lie around the haversian canals, and arranged in circles are found the *lacunae*, which contain the bone cells. See Figure 3–22.

[6] Alfred Wilhelm Volkmann, German physiologist (1800–1877).

Bone cells or osteocytes

Are found in the almond-shaped cell spaces, or lacunae. Their cytoplasmic processes project into the canaliculi. Before imprisonment in the lacunae, they were the osteoblasts, or bone-forming cells of the matrix. Osteoclasts are arranged in single rows on surfaces of growing bone. They are found on surfaces of bone where reabsorption takes place. They contain numerous mitochondria.

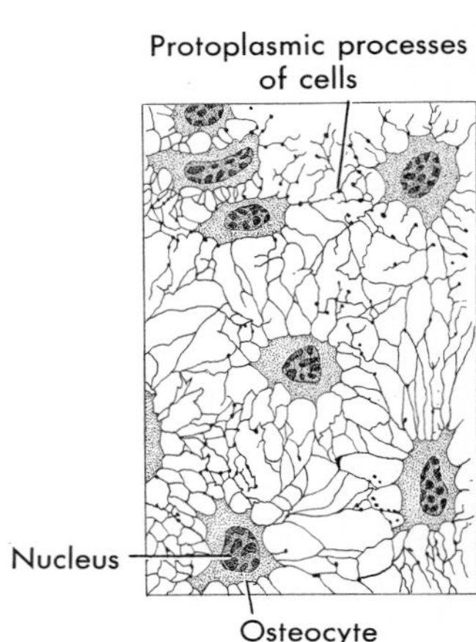

Figure 3–23. Diagram of a thin cross section of compact bone, showing osteocytes, which lie in the lacuna, and their protoplasmic processes which occupy the canaliculi.

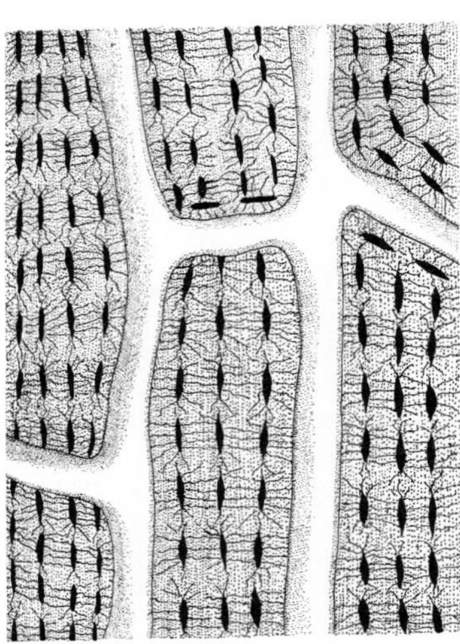

Figure 3–24. Bony tissue as seen in a thin longitudinal section of a bone (highly magnified). Haversian canals light in color, lacunae and canaliculi black.

Arteries to bone

The marrow of long bone is supplied by the medullary or nutrient arteries which enter the bone at the nutrient foramen, located in most cases near the center of the body, and perforate the compact tissue obliquely. Its branches ramify in all directions in the marrow and bony tissue. The twigs of these vessels anastomose with arteries of compact and cancellous tissue. Veins emerge with or apart from the arteries.

Lymphatic vessels

Have been traced into the substance of bone and accompany the blood vessels in the haversian canals.

Nerve supply

The periosteum is well-supplied with nerves, which accompany the arteries into bone. These nerve fibers form a plexus around the blood vessels. The nerve fibers include *afferent* myelinated and autonomic unmyelinated fibers.

Medullary canal

The shafts of long bone are formed almost entirely of compact bone, except where they are hollowed out to form the *medullary canal*, which is lined by a vascular tissue called medullary membrane and filled with bone marrow.

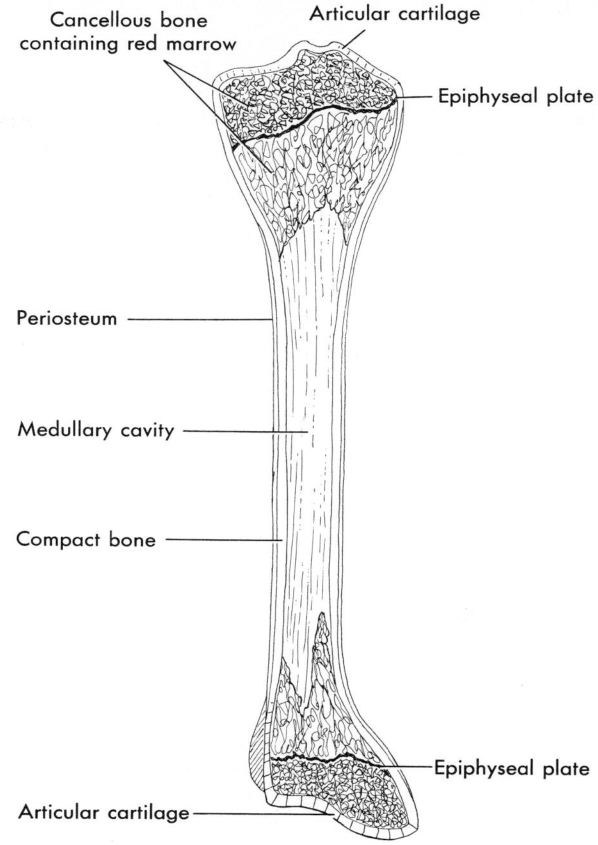

Figure 3–25. Diagram of longitudinal section of a long bone. Note the cancellous tissue at the ends of the epiphyseal plates.

Development of bone

In the early embryo the bones forming the roof and sides of the skull are preformed in membrane. Others are preformed in cartilage.

Intramembranous ossification

Before the cranial bones are formed the brain is covered by inner meningeal membranes, a middle fibrous membrane, and an outer layer of skin. Periosteum and bone are formed from the middle fibrous membrane. It is composed of fibers and bone-forming cells called osteoblasts in a matrix or ground substance. When bone begins to form, a network of *spicules* radiates from a point or center of ossification. The spicules develop into fibers. Calcium salts are deposited in the fibers and matrix, enclosing some of the osteoblasts in the lacunae. As the fibers grow out they continue to calcify and give rise to fresh bone spicules. Thus, a network of bone is formed. Successive layers of bony tissue are deposited under the periosteum, so that bone increases in thickness and presents the structure of compact bone on the outer and inner surfaces.

Diploe

With a layer of soft, spongy cancellous tissue between, the cancellous tissue between the layers of the skull is called the *diploe.*

Ossification of bones of the skull is not complete at birth. At the site of the future union of two or more bones, membranous areas called *fontanelles* persist.

Intracartilaginous or endochondrial ossification

The skeleton of the embryo is preformed in cartilage by the end of the second month. Soon after this, ossification begins. Cartilage cells at the center of ossification enlarge and become arranged in rows. Then calcium salts are deposited in the matrix between the cells, first separating them and later surrounding them so that all nutriment is cut off, resulting in their atrophy and disappearance. *Perichondrium*, the membrane which covers the cartilage, assumes the character of periosteum. From this membrane cells grow which are deposited in the spaces left by the atrophy of the cartilage cells. The two processes, destruction of cartilage cells and the formation of bone cells to replace them, continue until ossification is complete. The number of centers of ossification varies in differently shaped bones.

Ossification centers

In long bones, the center of ossification for the body is called *diaphysis* and one or more centers for each extremity are called *epiphyses*. Ossification proceeds from the diaphysis toward the epiphyses. As each new portion is ossified, thin layers of cartilage continue to develop between the diaphysis and epiphyses; during the period of growth these outstrip ossification. When this ceases, growth of bone stops. Normal, healthy bone is under constant change as it is reabsorbed and repaired continuously.

Nutritional needs

Growth of bones is dependent upon (1) adequate amounts of calcium and phosphorus in the food, (2) chemical substances which enable the bone cells to utilize calcium and phosphorus, such as vitamins from foods, and (3) hormones. Low calcium content of blood may be caused by inadequate calcium in the diet, poor absorption of calcium, or too rapid excretion in the feces.

Hormonal Influences on Bone. *Somatotropin* (STH) influences growth of all tissues, especially bone growth. When the epiphyses of the long bones have united with the bone shafts, growth of bone ceases.

Thyroxin increases osteoclastic activity more than it increases osteoblastic activity.

Hyperactivity of *adrenocortical hormones* will cause protein mobilization from the organic matrix of bone, thereby decreasing it.

Parathyroid hormone is essential for normal osteoclastic activity and the deposition of calcium and phosphate in bone tissue.

Estrogens cause increased osteoblastic activity—for this reason, after puberty, bone rate of growth becomes rapid for several years. They also cause rapid uniting of the epiphyses with the shafts of long bone. Estrogens have a broadening effect on the pelvis.

Testosterone causes bones to thicken and deposit calcium salts, thereby increasing the total quantity of the matrix.

Ossification begins soon after the second month of intrauterine life and continues well into adult life. The sternum, the sacrum, and the hip bones do not unite to form single bones until the individual is well beyond 21 years of age.

The bones of the newborn infant are soft and largely composed of cartilage; since the process of ossification is going on continually, the proper shape of the cartilage should be preserved in order that the shape of the future bone may be normal. Therefore, it is obvious that a young baby's back should be supported, and a child should always rest in a horizontal position. The facility with which bones may be molded and become misshapen is seen in the bowlegs of children. However, the softness of the skeleton of a child accounts for the fact that the many jars and tumbles experienced in early life are not as injurious to the cartilaginous frame as they would be to a harder structure.

Rickets. Rickets is a condition in which the mineral metabolism is disturbed so that calcification of the bones does not take place normally. The bones remain soft and become misshapen, resulting in bowlegs and malformations of the head, chest, and pelvis. Liberal amounts of calcium and phosphorus in food, and vitamin D, found in fish-liver oils and in significant amounts in egg yolk, whole milk, butter, fresh vegetables, etc., are important factors in the cure and prevention of rickets. Exposure to sunshine, especially irradiation of the skin, helps also in the optimal use of calcium and phosphorus in the body.

Three types of rickets are recognized as due to chemical deficiency of the blood. The first, or so-called low-phosphorus rickets, is caused by a subnormal content of phosphate ions in the blood related to a lack of dietary vitamin D. This is the commonest type, sometimes called true rickets, and is characterized by histological changes resulting in large joints, deformed bones of the cranium, chest, and spine, and a condition in which beadlike deposits occur at the ends of the ribs. The second type is characterized by deformed bones of the head, trunk, and limbs and is frequently accompanied by tonic muscular spasms (tetany) lasting for considerable periods of time. It is sometimes called low-calcium rickets or a "ricketslike condition." The third type is one in which both calcium and phosphorus are below normal and is characterized by progressive porosity of the bones. A deficiency of vitamin C interferes with the function of the osteoblasts and their formation of organic intercellular substance. Individuals, especially women past middle life, frequently suffer from impaired skeletal maintenance, and the bones become relatively more fragile. This condition is called *osteoporosis*. There is some evidence that certain hormones may in part contribute to the condition.

Fracture. Fracture is a term applied to the breaking of a bone. It may be either partial or complete. As a result of the greater amount of organic matter in the bones of children, they are flexible, bend easily, and do not break readily. In some cases the bone bends like a bough of green wood. Some of the fibers may break, but not the whole bone, hence the name *green-stick fracture*. The greater amount of inorganic matter in the bones of the aged renders the bones more brittle, so that they break easily and heal with difficulty.

Regeneration of Bone. A fracture is usually accompanied by injury to the periosteum and tissues causing hemorrhage and destruction of tissue.

Fibroblasts and capillaries grow into the blood clot, forming granulation tissue. The plasma and white cells from the blood exude into the tissues and form a viscid substance, which sticks the ends of the bone together. This exudate into which the fibroblasts and capillaries grow is called *callus*. Usually bone cells from the periosteum and calcium salts are gradually deposited in the callus, which eventually becomes hardened and forms new bone. Occasionally the callus does not ossify, and a condition known as *fibrous union* results. The periosteum is largely concerned in the process of repair. If a portion of the periosteum is stripped off, the subjacent bone may die, whereas if a large part of the whole of a bone is removed and the periosteum at the same time is left intact, the bone will wholly or in great measure be regenerated.

MUSCLE TISSUE

Muscle tissue is composed of cells and intercellular substance. The cells become elongated and are called fibers. The intercellular material consists of a small amount of intercellular substance which holds the cells to the framework of loose connective tissue in which they are embedded.

NAME	CHARACTERISTICS, LOCATION, AND FUNCTION
Striated muscle tissue Structure	Striated muscle tissue is called striated because of the cross stripes, or *striae*; *skeletal* because it forms the muscles which are attached to the skeleton: *somatic* because it helps to form the body wall; and

voluntary because movements are under conscious control. It is capable of rapid powerful contraction and can maintain long states of partially sustained contraction. The function of all muscle tissue is dependent on blood and nerve supply. Spindle-shaped fibers or cells—1 to 40 mm in length, 0.01 to 0.15 mm in diameter, in a tubular sheath, or *sarcolemma*—enclose a soft, contractile substance. Many nuclei are located on the inner surface of the sarcolemma.

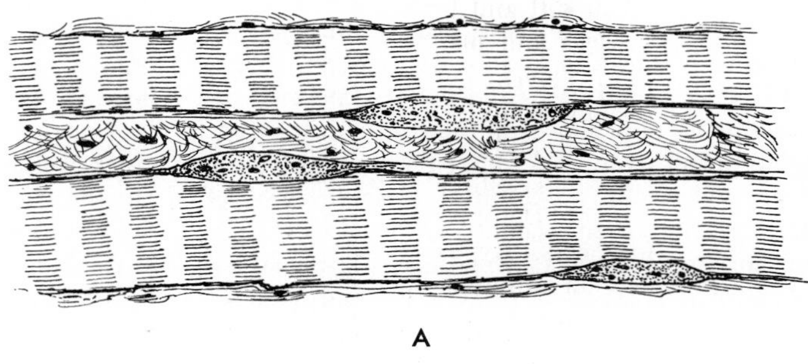

A

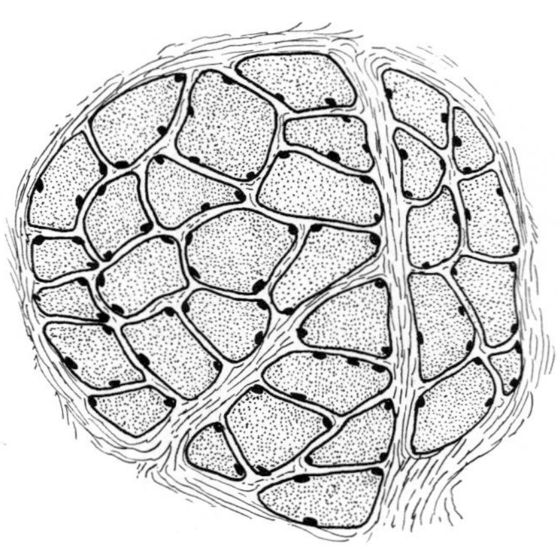

B

Figure 3–26. Striated muscle cells. (*A*) Parts of two cells seen in longitudinal section showing sarcolemma nuclei, cross striations. Note that each cell lies in connective tissue. (*B*) Three bundles (fasciculi) of cells seen in cross section. Note sarcolemma, nuclei, connective tissue between cells and around fasciculi.

Myofibrils

Myofibrils are closely packed together and run lengthwise through the entire fiber.

Sarcoplasm

The fluid material that surrounds the myofibrils. It contains a Golgi complex, numerous mitochondria, endoplasmic reticulum, ribosomes, and glycogen. The mitochondria are located beneath the sarcolemma, around the nuclei, beneath the myofibrils, and in the neuromuscular junctions.

Bands of striated muscle

The fibers vary in length, width, number of nuclei, and relative amount of myofibrils and sarcoplasm present. Myofibrils are marked by alternating light and dark bands. Dark bands are called

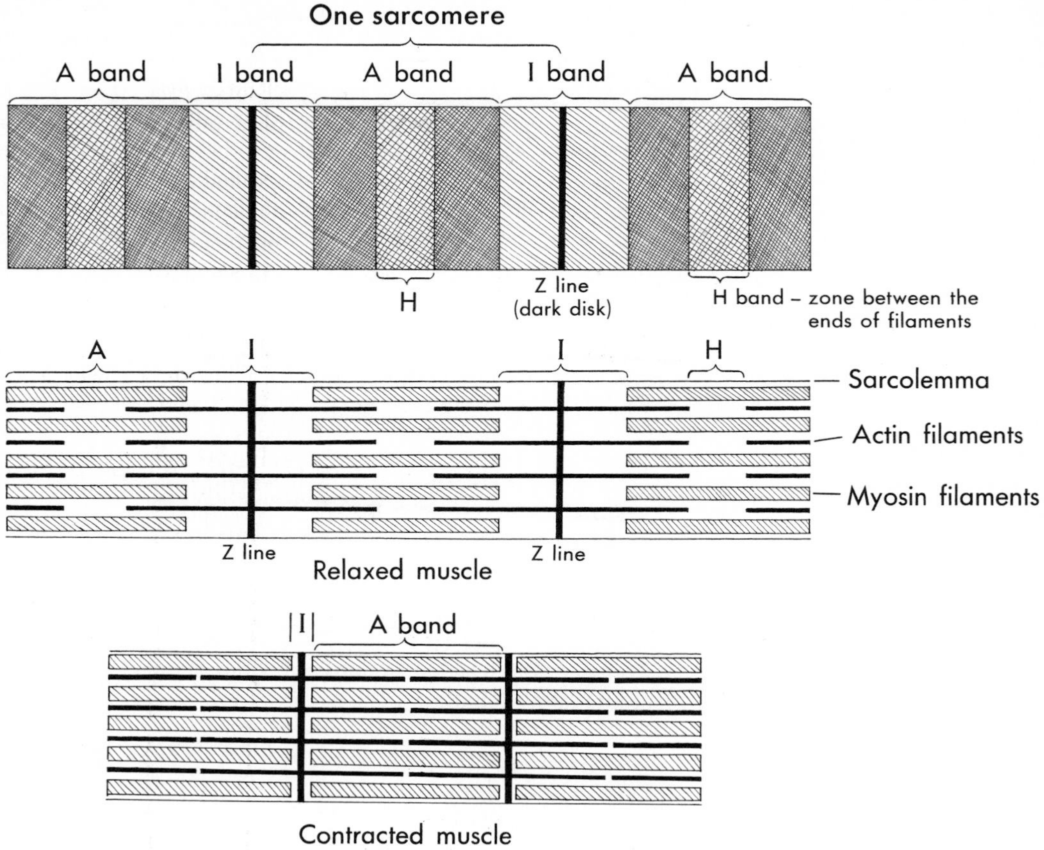

One sarcomere
A band
I band
A band
I band
A band
H
Z line
(dark disk)
H band – zone between the
ends of filaments
A
I
I
H
Sarcolemma
Actin filaments
Myosin filaments
Z line
Relaxed muscle
Z line
I
A band
Contracted muscle

Figure 3–27. Diagram illustrating details of structure of skeletal muscles and changes that occur during contraction. Note that the I band shortens considerably during contraction.

One sarcomere
H
Z
A

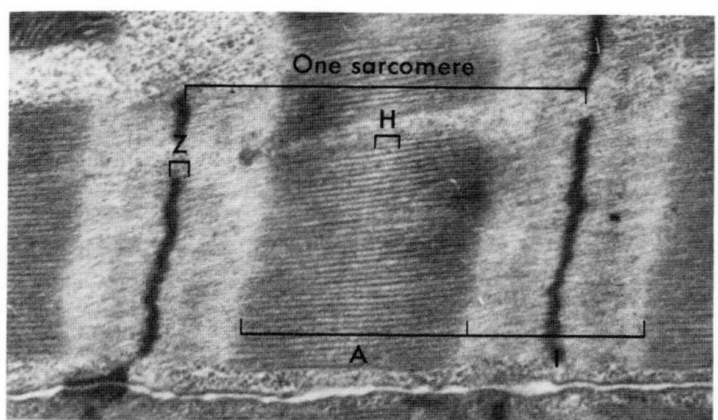

Figure 3–28. An electron micrograph of the fine structural detail of striated muscle fibrils in longitudinal section. Note the distribution of the thick myosin and thin actin filaments. Letters correspond to those of Figure 3–27. (Courtesy of Dr. Thomas F. De Caro, PMC Colleges.)

anisotropic, *A bands*; light bands are called *isotropic*, *I bands*. Each band is bisected by a thin, dark disk or line called the *Z line*.

The sarcomere

The combination of an A and I band is called a *sarcomere*. The H band is the zone between the ends of the filaments. Contraction of the muscle fiber is based on the sliding together of the myofilaments in the sarcomeres. The muscle fiber becomes shorter and broader, but the total length of the A band remains constant except in extreme contractions, when it shortens, producing thick myosin filaments against the Z band. The I band shortens markedly during contraction. See Figure 3–27.

Composition of myofibrils

Each one is composed of *myosin* and *actin*. Another protein, tropomyosin, is bound with actin to form actin-tropomyosin. These molecules are responsible for muscle contraction.

Types of fibers

Red

Each skeletal muscle contains some fibers of each type; in general the slower movements are executed by the red fibers.

White

Rapid movements are carried out by muscles in which white fibers predominate.

Arrangement of primary bundles

Muscle fibers are closely packed forming primary bundles or *fasciculi*. Loose connective tissue forms a supporting framework between the fibers and surrounding the small bundles, grouping them into larger bundles.

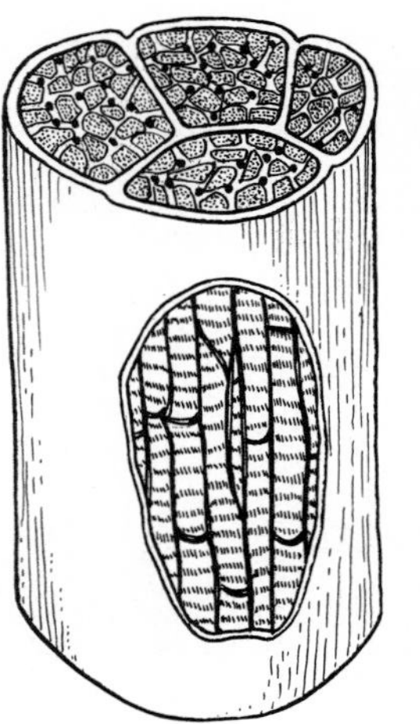

Figure 3–29. (*A*) Section of a voluntary muscle composed of fasciculi covered with fascia. (*B*) A single fasciculus of striated muscle, in one area the fascia is removed to show muscle fibers and part of the capillary network surrounding fibers.

Fascia

Surrounds the larger bundles and forms a covering for the entire muscle.

Blood vessels
Lymph vessels
Nerves

The connective tissue around the bundles contains an intricate network of blood, lymph vessels, and nerves, so that each muscle fiber is supplied with nerve endings and is surrounded by tissue fluid.

Epimysium

Each skeletal muscle is a separate organ having its own sheath of connective tissue called *epimysium*.

Perimysium

Each primary bundle of muscle fibers is enveloped by a fibrous sheath called *perimysium.*

Endomysium

Each muscle fiber is surrounded by a fibrous sheath called *endomysium.*

Muscle length
Origin and insertion

Muscles vary in length from about 1 mm to 60 cm (24 in.) and are diverse in form. Their trunks are broad, flattened, and expanded, forming the walls of the cavities they enclose. In the limbs they are more or less elongated. A muscle consists of a body and two extremities. Skeletal muscles usually pass over joints, some of which are movable, some immovable. If the joint is movable the muscle has an *origin* and an *insertion.* The *origin* is attached to the *less movable* bone; the *insertion*, to a bone *moving* in the ordinary activity of the body. A muscle increases in diameter as it contracts lengthwise, pulling the attachments at each end nearer to each other.

Tendons and aponeuroses

Attach muscles to bones. Near the end of a muscle, the connective-tissue framework of the muscle increases in quantity and extends beyond the muscle fibers as a dense, white cord, or *tendon*, or as a flattened tendon, or *aponeurosis.* Tendons are cable-like, exceedingly strong, inextensible yet flexible.

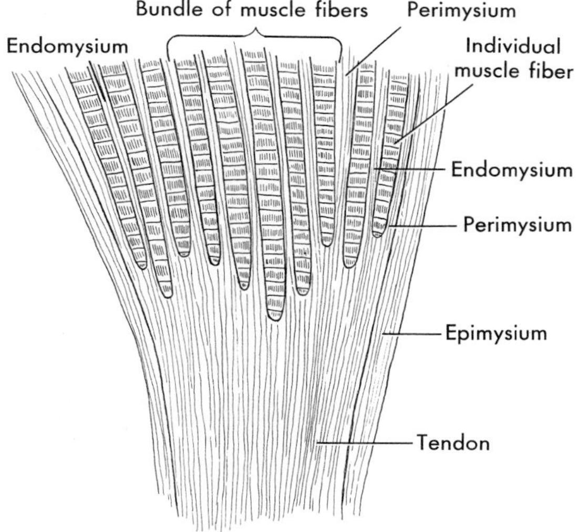

Figure 3–30. Diagram of a muscle-tendon junction.

Fasciae

Are sheets of connective tissue by which most muscles are covered. They envelop and bind down the muscles into separate groups. The muscle groups are named according to the part of the body where they are found—cervical fascia, thoracic fascia, abdominal fascia, pelvic fascia. Individual fasciae are frequently given the names of the muscles they envelop and bind down, e.g., pectoral fascia.

Annular ligaments

In the area of the wrist and ankle, fascia is blended into tight transverse bands, or *annular* ligaments, which bind down the tendons close to the bones. The function of skeletal muscle is to operate the bones of the body, thereby producing motion.

Nonstriated or smooth-muscle tissue

It is called smooth because it does not exhibit cross strips, or striae; visceral because it forms the muscular portion of visceral organs. Cells are usually arranged in two main layers: the inner, thick, circular coat and the outer, thin, longitudinal coat. Motion caused by smooth muscle is unconscious and involuntary. The tissue is composed of spindle-shaped cells about 0.015 to 0.5 mm long and 0.002 to 0.02 mm in diameter. Each cell has a single *large nucleus.* The coats are surrounded by a network of connective tissue which carries blood lymph vessels and nerves. Smooth muscle contracts slowly and relaxes much more slowly than skeletal muscle. It possesses greater extensibility and maintains a state of contraction or a tonus (page 117). Nerve endings are found about smooth-muscle cells, but motor end-plates have not been demonstrated. In general, smooth muscle is innervated by both sympathetic and parasympathetic fibers. It is not under precise nerve control. Impulses are probably transmitted by a chemical agent or by mechanical pull exerted by one cell in contraction serving as a stimulus for other cells. The walls of all visceral organs including blood vessels

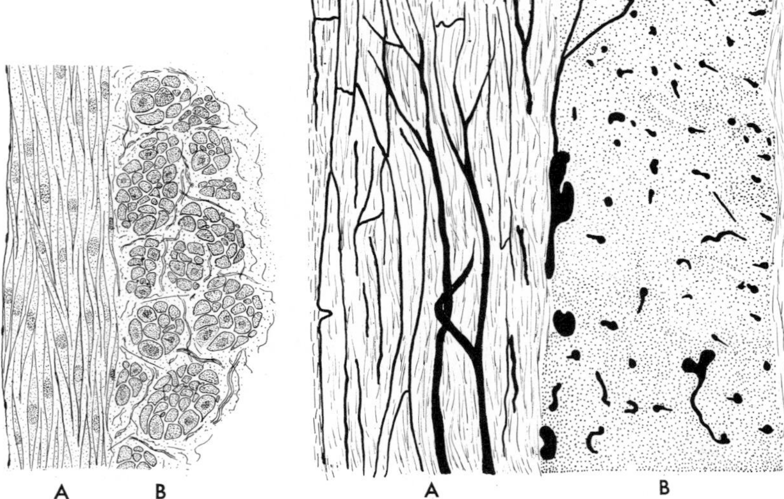

Figure 3–31. Longitudinal section of a visceral organ to show smooth muscle tissue. (*A*) In longitudinal section. (*B*) In cross section. Note that there is a little connective tissue between the cells and that the cells are arranged in bundles.

Figure 3–32. An injected longitudinal section of the wall of a visceral organ to show blood vessels. (*A*) In longitudinal section. (*B*) In cross section. Note that the blood vessels run in the same general direction as the muscle fibers. In *B* the blood vessels are in groups lying between the muscle bundles rather than between the muscle cells.

contain smooth-muscle cells. Their function is to produce changes in shape and size as occur in these organs. An example is peristalsis of the alimentary canal.

Cardiac muscle

This tissue forms the heart. The myofibrils are similar to skeletal muscle, but transverse striations are less distinct. The cells are smaller, the mitochondria more abundant. Each cell has a large, oval, centrally placed nucleus. Cardiac muscle is composed of elongated branching cells which are irregular at their junctions. See Chapter 16.

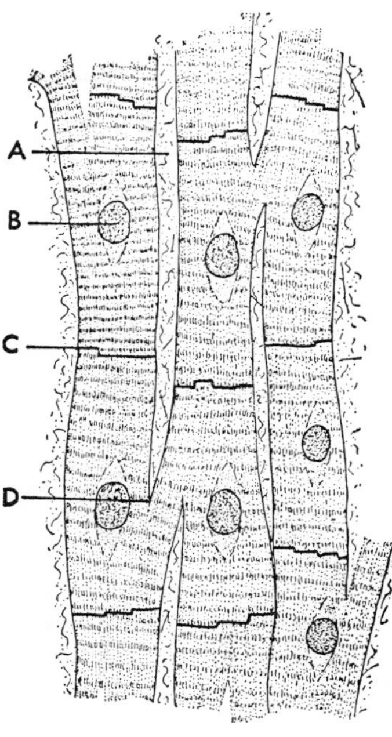

Figure 3–33. Diagram of a thin section of cardiac muscle tissue. (*A*) Connective tissue between cells, (*B*) nucleus, (*C*) dark-stained bands, (*D*) branching of a cell.

Intercalated disks

Are dark-stained cross bands located at the cell junctions of heart muscle. Their irregular course gives a "step formation" appearance. They are the membranes of adjacent cells. The cells are surrounded by a network of fine collagenous fibers, blood, and lymph capillaries. The rhythm of the heartbeat is presumably preserved by means of this "network" nature of cardiac muscle over which impulses may pass. Cardiac muscle has little or no capacity for regeneration of fibers. After injury, healing is accomplished by scar formation.

TISSUE REPAIR

Repair of tissues takes place continually under the normal process of living. Some tissues are subject to more wear and tear than others, such as, for example, those in the skin. The stratified squamous epithelium of the skin is constantly being subjected to varying degrees of friction and will respond to meet immediate needs. This might be shown by thickening, callus formation, or a blister, depending on the rapidity of the friction. When subjected to greater friction, sudden contact with sharp, dull, or blunt objects, the tissues are damaged or there may be tissue loss.

Some tissues are repaired easily and quickly, such as surface epithelium, connective tissue, and liver cells. Others repair more slowly; others, as typified by bone, must have parts kept in alignment and immobilized until repair is completed. Periosteum must be present for bone regeneration, muscle tissue has least ability for repair, and nerve cells destroyed by injury or infection do not regenerate.

Repair of Epithelial Tissues. Both the epithelial cells and underlying connective-tissue cells have capacity for cell division and repair. The response to injury depends on the extent of the injured surface. There is usually rapid cell multiplication of the surface layer. Mitosis is decreased for the first few days but soon exceeds the normal rate. When injury is more extensive, the underlying tissue cells divide and migrate by a sort of ameboid movement into the injured area. There is formation of tonguelike processes which grow into the area and finally the surface layer of cells multiplies and they migrate over the injured surface, re-forming the surface layer of cells.

Primary Repair. Primary repair takes place in "clean" wounds, such as, for instance, incisions, cuts, and the like, when infection is not present. If the injury simply involves the skin, the deep layer of stratified squamous epithelium divides longitudinally, the cells "push up," and the wound is rapidly and completely restored to normal. If the area is larger, the underlying connective-tissue cells, the fibroblasts, take part in the repair process.

If the area of skin loss is great, fluid exudes from the capillaries; it dries and seals the open tissue, and a "scab" forms. Epithelial cells proliferate at the edges and continue to grow over the area until it is covered. If skin loss involves a large area, skin grafting is done to hasten the process.

When the deeper tissues are involved, if the edges of the wound are brought together with sutures, as, for example, in operative incisions, there is outpouring of serous fluid into the wound, and a coagulum is formed which seals the wound. The coagulum contains leukocytes and tissue fragments. In 24 to 36 hours, fibroblasts of connective tissue and the *endothelial* cells of the capillaries are multiplying rapidly. The newly formed cells remain along the edges of the wound, and by the third day new vascular buds are present. These grow across the wound along with connective-tissue formation.

By the fourth or fifth day, fibroblast activity is markedly evident. Collagenous fibers are rapidly formed, and capillaries sprout and extend across the wound, holding the edges firmly together. Later the fibers shorten and scar tissue is reduced to a minimum.

Secondary Repair. In large open wounds with more or less tissue loss, the area is filled in by a process of building up "granulation tissue." Each granulation represents a minute vascular area consisting of newly formed, vertically upstanding blood vessels which are surrounded by young connective tissue and wandering cells of different kinds.

The surface has a characteristic pebbly appearance. The connective-tissue cells, the fibroblasts, increase in number; collagenous fibers are proliferated by them, and eventually the wound closes.

Granulation tissue secretes a fluid which has definite bactericidal properties. Its defense characteristics include hyperemia, which is more or less marked, active exudation, and marked local leukocytosis.

The amount of scar tissue formed is in relation to tissue damage. It is important that parts of the body undergoing extensive tissue repair (such as, for example, burned areas involving the chest and neck, the chest after breast removal, and the like) be kept in alignment, immobile at first, and in some instances stretched. Active movement should be encouraged early so that, as new tissues are formed, contracture from scar formation will not result. Every effort should be directed toward preventing or minimizing disfigurement.

At times, as when large areas of skin are destroyed by burns, considerable blood plasma is lost, with its contained proteins, electrolytes, and other substances. This may result in disturbance of fluid balance. It is, therefore, important that fluids be replaced by artificial means until the tissues themselves can prevent such loss by coagulation and initial wound healing response.

It is known that glucocorticoids have an anti-inflammatory action. However, the exact mechanism of action is not understood. If given in large doses, they diminish the inflammatory process and inhibit the formation of granulation tissue.

Conditions Favorable to Wound Healing. Nutrition plays an important role in the healing process. The tissues need plenty of protein for repair, hence the need for protein-rich diets.

The vitamins play an important part in wound healing, as well as in resistance to and prevention of infection. It is believed that *vitamin A* is important for repair of epithelial tissues, especially the maintenance of epithelial integrity of the respiratory pathway. There is no conclusive evidence that vitamin A has anti-infective or wound-healing properties when applied in ointments. However, reports of controlled experiments on animals show that ointments containing vitamins A and D shortened the healing time.

Vitamin B. Thiamine, nicotinic acid, and riboflavin are important from the viewpoint of the general well-being of the individual as a whole, and specifically in relation to metabolism, vigor, appetite, relief of pain in some instances, and integrity of selective epithelial areas.

Vitamin C. The normal production and maintenance of intercellular substance as well as cement substances of the connective tissues, especially collagen formations and the integrity of capillary walls, are directly dependent upon vitamin C. In wound healing by granulation, new capillaries must sprout and fibroblasts must grow; to meet the increased demands, vitamin C is essential.

Vitamin D. Vitamin D is essential for the normal absorption of calcium from the intestine; so possibly it aids in the healing of fractures. A low serum calcium level stimulates parathormone production, which increases excretion of phosphorus by the kidney and tends to raise serum calcium.

Vitamin K. Vitamin K functions in wound healing from the viewpoint of helping to maintain the normal coagulability of the blood.

On the whole, tissues heal faster and leave less visible scars in the young than in the aged. This perhaps is due to the fact that in the young the tissues are soft, pliable, and in a constant state of growth; and in comparison to the aged or older age group cells multiply more rapidly.

Normally tissue repair takes place so readily and is so commonplace that thought is not given to it. Tissues may remain dormant for years, then suddenly become actively growing tissues in a response to stimulus. It is believed the stimulus is almost certainly chemical in nature, a substance liberated by the degenerating cells. When part of a tissue is removed, this in itself initiates regeneration and forms the basis of the theory that disturbance of *spatial equilibrium* is an important factor. Another theory suggests the coaptation theory—that cells of a tissue have common affinity due to highly specialized specific stereochemical bonds which exist at cell surfaces. If the bonds are disrupted, it provides a stimulus for proliferation of tissue activity.

The *leukocytes* have a specific function in relation to tissue repair. They are attracted to areas of injury, perhaps in response to the chemical liberated. The monocytes are especially active in the repair of tissue, possibly providing nutritive and building materials of protein and lipoid character.

Tissue Transplants. In the human, transplants of tissue from one part of the body to another are accepted because they are part of the same body and are said to be *autologous.* The tissues of identical twins are also autologous because they are from the same fertilized egg so that the tissues have the same tissue proteins. The transplanted cells survive only when nutrients and oxygen can reach the cells from the surrounding tissue fluid. Fraternal twins do not come from the same fertilized ovum and are genetically different; hence each has different tissue proteins and they are said to be *homologous.*

Each individual has a different genetic structure and therefore different protein structure so that when tissues are transplanted from one person to another, *antibodies* are formed in the *recipient* against the foreign tissue proteins which are antigenic, and destruction of the cells of the transplant results. However, the many tissues used for transplants from "tissue banks" such as bone, tendons, blood vessels, nerves, and fascia survive because of the large amount of connective tissue and the relatively small numbers of cells. The transplanted tissue serves as a temporary bridge which functions as a substitute for the destroyed tissue and stimulates regeneration of tissue in the recipient. In some instances the recipient for fresh tissue transplants is subjected to radiation to destroy his ability to form antibodies against the donor's tissue proteins. Antibody-blocking drugs, antimetabolites, and glucocorticoids are also used to prevent antibody formation by the recipient.

Successful corneal transplants have been done for many years. It has been thought that since the cornea is normally avascular and does not contain lymphocytes, it is different from other tissues. Recent studies show that the surface epithelium is regenerated by the recipient so that the transplanted cornea is covered in a few days. Regeneration of the endothelium takes longer, and the connective-tissue cells are slowly replaced. Research today is vigorous in relation to *organ* transplants, and a certain degree of success is reported in the transplantation of the kidney and heart.

SUMMARY—TISSUE REPAIR

Name of Tissue	*Repair Process*
Stratified squamous epithelium	Thickens in response to slow friction. Forms blister in response to rapid friction. Readily repaired. Basal layer of cells divides by mitosis, the cells migrate upward, forming a tonguelike process which grows over the denuded area. If large areas are denuded, skin grafts may be necessary.
Modified forms	
Cornea	When injured, the cells of the cornea form scar tissue.
Conjunctiva	Conjunctiva is repaired readily.
Simple squamous	Considerable ability for repair.
In kidney and small ducts	Repair in some areas may result in abnormal shape of cells.
Mesothelium In serous cavities	Destruction by inflammatory processes frequently results in the formation of fibroblasts which form scar tissue.
Endothelium All blood vessels and lymphatic capillaries	In capillaries, cells have ability to multiply rapidly. In all tissue repair, capillaries are formed by an outgrowth of former capillaries.
Plain columnar epithelium Glands of stomach and intestine Ducts of many glands	Secretory cells are replaced occasionally. They multiply or the underlying cells replace surface cells. If large areas are destroyed, scar tissue results.
Goblet cells	Readily replaced.
Cuboidal cells of liver	Liver cells have great power of regeneration.
Ciliated columnar epithelium	Small injuries are repaired by mitotic division. Large areas repaired by underlying cell layers or connective-tissue cells.
Loose connective tissue	Blood oozes or flows into wound; clot forms, edges of wound are glued together, capillaries sprout, fibroblasts multiply rapidly. Collagenous and elastic fibers are formed quickly and invade area.
Adipose tissue	Regeneration rapid.
Elastic connective tissue	Good blood supply to tissue. Tissue repaired by fibroblasts and invasion of elastic and fibrous fibers.
Fibrous connective tissue Ligaments, tendons, and fascial sheaths	Scant blood supply to tissue except in fibrous membranes. Repair process slow but complete. Periosteum and dura mater—blood supply good, repair depends on the connective tissue.
Muscle	Repair limited to a few cells.
Striated	Regeneration limited, healing takes place by scar formation.
Smooth	In pregnant uterus cells increase in size. Limited cell multiplication.
Cardiac	Do not regenerate. Repair by scar tissue.
Cartilage Hyaline Elastic Fibrous	Healing of cartilage is by repair of the surrounding connective tissue called perichondrium. Degenerative changes frequently occur as age advances.
Bone	All bone is surrounded by periosteum, which is richly supplied with blood, lymph, and nerves. Bone is readily repaired if the periosteum is present. Deformations will not occur if good approximation is maintained. Cells under the periosteum proliferate and form a splint of

	cartilage around the fractured ends. Cells at the edges become osteoblasts and form bone.
Nerve tissue	Nerve cells when injured are *not* replaced. Nerve fibers when severed from the cell body die. Myelinated nerve fibers will grow into the sheath if the neurilemma is present.

QUESTIONS FOR DISCUSSION

1. Mr. X. had second-degree burns of all of his chest, abdomen, and arms and first-degree burns of all of his face and neck. Orders included: give plasma, 1,000 ml, and electrolytes with dextrose by vein; record fluid intake and output each hour; give medication ordered for pain; and apply dressings; Foley catheter is to be kept in place.
   a. What percentage of the body received first-degree burns? Second-degree burns?
   b. What receptors are involved? What is the reason for so much pain?
   c. What fluids are being lost from the body? How do you know?
   d. Give reasons for giving each of the fluids by vein.
   e. Are the sweat glands involved?
   f. What problems must the nurse be alert for during the healing process of the skin before and after skin grafting is done?
   g. Why must fluid intake and output be measured each hour? Why must the catheter be kept in place?
   h. One pint of blood was ordered on the fifth day. Explain why.
2. Explain the relationship between tissue repair and nutrition.
3. Discuss the tissues of the body and indicate how their respective anatomy correlates with their specific functions and body needs.
4. Compare the types of muscle and indicate how their structure correlates well with their function.
5. Discuss bone healing in a young child as contrasted to an old person. In which is the healing slower? In which is a fracture more dangerous? What might be some of the complications, in both, of healing, immobilization, or future capabilities of the affected area?

SUMMARY

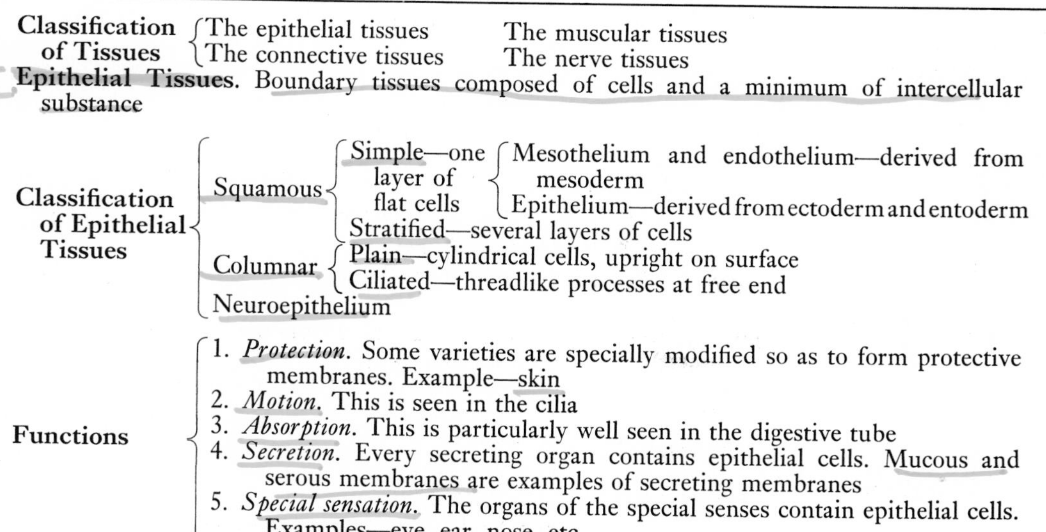

Classification of Tissues
- The epithelial tissues
- The connective tissues
- The muscular tissues
- The nerve tissues

Epithelial Tissues. Boundary tissues composed of cells and a minimum of intercellular substance

Classification of Epithelial Tissues
- Squamous
  - Simple—one layer of flat cells
    - Mesothelium and endothelium—derived from mesoderm
    - Epithelium—derived from ectoderm and entoderm
  - Stratified—several layers of cells
- Columnar
  - Plain—cylindrical cells, upright on surface
  - Ciliated—threadlike processes at free end
- Neuroepithelium

Functions
1. *Protection.* Some varieties are specially modified so as to form protective membranes. Example—skin
2. *Motion.* This is seen in the cilia
3. *Absorption.* This is particularly well seen in the digestive tube
4. *Secretion.* Every secreting organ contains epithelial cells. Mucous and serous membranes are examples of secreting membranes
5. *Special sensation.* The organs of the special senses contain epithelial cells. Examples—eye, ear, nose, etc.

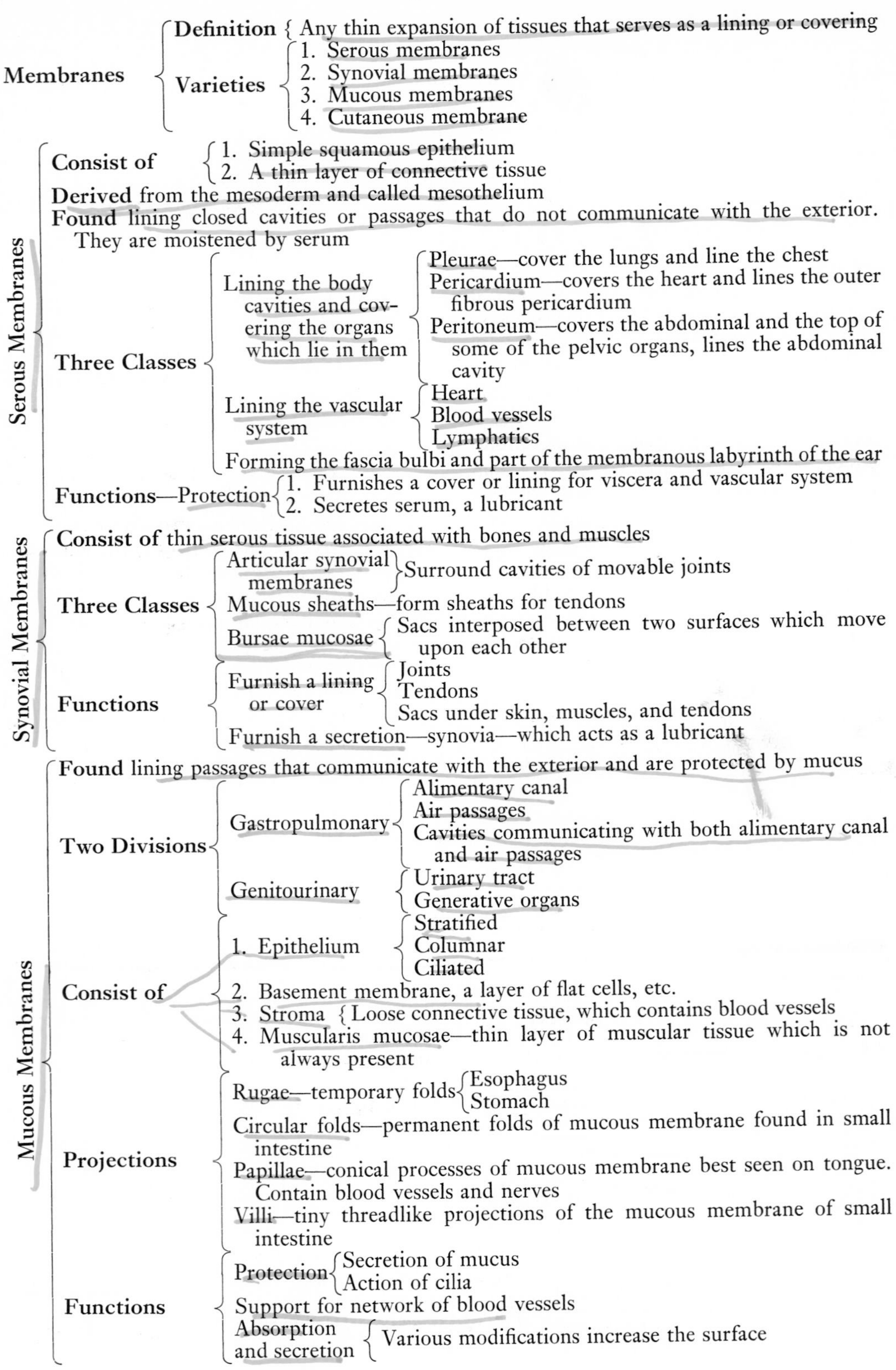

- **Membranes**
  - **Definition** — Any thin expansion of tissues that serves as a lining or covering
  - **Varieties**
    1. Serous membranes
    2. Synovial membranes
    3. Mucous membranes
    4. Cutaneous membrane

- **Serous Membranes**
  - **Consist of**
    1. Simple squamous epithelium
    2. A thin layer of connective tissue
  - **Derived** from the mesoderm and called mesothelium
  - **Found** lining closed cavities or passages that do not communicate with the exterior. They are moistened by serum
  - **Three Classes**
    - Lining the body cavities and covering the organs which lie in them
      - Pleurae—cover the lungs and line the chest
      - Pericardium—covers the heart and lines the outer fibrous pericardium
      - Peritoneum—covers the abdominal and the top of some of the pelvic organs, lines the abdominal cavity
    - Lining the vascular system
      - Heart
      - Blood vessels
      - Lymphatics
    - Forming the fascia bulbi and part of the membranous labyrinth of the ear
  - **Functions**—Protection
    1. Furnishes a cover or lining for viscera and vascular system
    2. Secretes serum, a lubricant

- **Synovial Membranes**
  - **Consist of** thin serous tissue associated with bones and muscles
  - **Three Classes**
    - Articular synovial membranes — Surround cavities of movable joints
    - Mucous sheaths—form sheaths for tendons
    - Bursae mucosae — Sacs interposed between two surfaces which move upon each other
  - **Functions**
    - Furnish a lining or cover
      - Joints
      - Tendons
      - Sacs under skin, muscles, and tendons
    - Furnish a secretion—synovia—which acts as a lubricant

- **Mucous Membranes**
  - **Found** lining passages that communicate with the exterior and are protected by mucus
  - **Two Divisions**
    - Gastropulmonary
      - Alimentary canal
      - Air passages
      - Cavities communicating with both alimentary canal and air passages
    - Genitourinary
      - Urinary tract
      - Generative organs
  - **Consist of**
    1. Epithelium
       - Stratified
       - Columnar
       - Ciliated
    2. Basement membrane, a layer of flat cells, etc.
    3. Stroma — Loose connective tissue, which contains blood vessels
    4. Muscularis mucosae—thin layer of muscular tissue which is not always present
  - **Projections**
    - Rugae—temporary folds
      - Esophagus
      - Stomach
    - Circular folds—permanent folds of mucous membrane found in small intestine
    - Papillae—conical processes of mucous membrane best seen on tongue. Contain blood vessels and nerves
    - Villi—tiny threadlike projections of the mucous membrane of small intestine
  - **Functions**
    - Protection
      - Secretion of mucus
      - Action of cilia
    - Support for network of blood vessels
    - Absorption and secretion — Various modifications increase the surface

- **Cutaneous Membrane**
  - Forms the skin
  - Covers the body
  - Serves to protect underlying tissues
  - Prevents loss of body fluids
  - Contains structures for the reception of stimuli
- **Skin**
  - **Functions**
    1. Covers the body
    2. Protects the deeper tissues from
       - Drying, injury
       - Invasion by infectious organisms
    3. Important factor in heat regulation
    4. Contains the end organs of many sensory nerves
    5. It has limited excretory and absorbing power
  - **Consists of**
    - **Epidermis** is a stratified epithelium
      1. Stratum corneum
      2. Stratum lucidum
      3. Stratum granulosum
         - (1–3) Practically dead cells being constantly shed and renewed from the stratum germinativum
      4. Stratum germinativum
         - Soft protoplasmic cells that are constantly multiplying by cell division
    - **Corium** is a layer of connective tissue
      1. Papillary layer—papillae are minute conical elevations of the corium. They contain looped capillaries, and some contain termination of nerve fibers called tactile corpuscle
      2. Reticular layer
         - Bands of fibrous and elastic tissue which interlace, leaving tiny spaces which are occupied by adipose tissue and sweat glands
  - **Blood vessels.** The arteries form a network in the subcutaneous tissue and send branches to papillae and glands of skin. Capable of holding a large proportion of total amount of blood in body
  - **Lymphatics.** There is a superficial and a deep network of lymphatics in the skin
  - **Nerve fibers**
    1. Motor fibers to blood vessels and arrector muscles
    2. Fibers concerned with temperature sense
    3. Fibers concerned with sense of touch and pressure
    4. Fibers stimulated by pain
    5. Secretory fibers which are distributed to the glands
  - **Appendages**
    - Nails, hairs
    - Sebaceous glands, sudoriferous glands
- **Nails**
  - Consist of clear, horny cells of epidermis
  - Corium forms a bed, or matrix, for nail
  - Root of nail is lodged in a deep fold of the skin
  - Nails grow in length from soft cells in stratum germinativum at root
- **Hairs (Pili)**
  - The hairs grow from the roots
  - The roots are bulbs of soft, growing cells contained in the hair follicles
  - Hair follicles are little pits developed in the corium
  - Stems of hair extend beyond the surface of the skin, consist of three layers of cells: (1) cuticle, (2) cortex, and (3) medulla
  - Found all over body, except
    - Palms of the hands
    - Soles of the feet
    - Last phalanges of the fingers and toes
  - Arrector muscles are attached to corium and to each hair follicle. Contraction pulls hair up straight, drags follicles upward, forces secretion of sebaceous glands to surface, and forces blood to interior
- **Sebaceous Glands**
  - Compound alveolar glands, the ducts of which usually open into a hair follicle but may discharge separately on the surface of the skin
  - Lie between arrector muscles and hairs
  - Found over entire skin surface except
    - Palms of hands
    - Soles of feet
  - Secrete *sebum*, a fatty, oily substance, which keeps the hair from becoming too dry and brittle, the skin flexible, forms a protective layer on surface of skin, and prevents undue absorption or evaporation of water from the skin

Sweat Glands
- Tubular glands, consist of single tubes with the blind ends coiled in balls, lodged in subcutaneous tissue, and surrounded by a capillary plexus. Secrete sweat and discharge it by means of ducts which open exteriorly

Sweat
- Watery, colorless, turbid liquid, salty taste, distinctive odor, and usually an acid reaction: pH is 5.2 to 6.75
- Contains the same inorganic constituents as the blood but in lower concentration
- Average quantity, at least 500 ml in 24 hours
- Amount increased by
  1. Increased temperature or humidity of the atmosphere
  2. Dilute condition of blood
  3. Exercise
  4. Pain
  5. Nausea
  6. Mental excitement or nervousness
  7. Dyspnea
  8. Use of diaphoretics, e.g., pilocarpine, physostigmine, nicotine
  9. Various diseases, such as tuberculosis, acute rheumatism, and malaria
- Amount decreased by
  1. Cold
  2. Voiding a large quantity of urine
  3. Diarrhea
  4. Certain drugs, e.g., atropine and morphine
  5. Certain diseases

Activity of Sweat Glands due to
1. Direct stimulation of nerve ending in sweat glands
2. Indirect stimulation through sensory nerves of the skin
3. Influenced by external heat, dyspnea, muscular exercise, strong emotions, and the action of various drugs

Function of Sweat
- Importance not in elimination of waste substances in perspiration, but elimination of *heat* needed to cause evaporation of perspiration
- When kidneys are not functioning properly, sweat glands will excrete waste substances, particularly if stimulated

Ceruminous Glands
- Modified sweat glands
- Found in skin of external auditory canal
- Secrete cerumen, a yellow, pasty substance, like wax

Nervous Tissue
- Neuron—cell body
- Size of cells variable
- Myelinated fibers, thickness related to speed of impulse
- Neurilemma, necessary for regeneration
- Nodes of Ranvier
- Function—to receive and transmit nerve impulses

Connective Tissues. Tissues composed of cells with much intercellular substance, which is derived from the cells

Characteristics
- Cellular element at a minimum, intercellular element abundant
- Intercellular material determines characteristic of the tissue
- Serves to connect and support other tissues
- With the exception of cartilage, they are highly vascular

Varieties
- Connective tissue proper
  1. Loose connective
  2. Adipose
  3. Liquid
  4. Reticular
  5. Elastic
  6. Fibrous
- Cartilage
- Bone

Embryonal Tissues. Develop in the embryo and become adult-type connective tissue

A. Connective Tissue Proper

Loose Connective Tissue. Formed by interlacing of wavy bundles of fibrous fibers and some straight elastic fibers with cells lying in the ground substance

Function. Connects, insulates, forms protecting sheaths, and is continuous throughout the whole body

Fluid matrix is called tissue fluid

Fluid matrix, often called internal environment, serves as a medium for transfer of supplies from blood and lymph vessels to cells, and wastes from cells to blood and lymph. Stores water, salts, glucose, etc.

Adipose Tissue. Modification of areolar tissue, with cells filled with fat. Distribution quite general but not uniform

Function
1. Forms a reserve food to be drawn upon in time of need
2. Prevents the too rapid loss of heat
3. Serves to protect and support delicate organs

Liquid Tissues. Cells in a liquid intercellular substance, e.g., blood and lymph

Reticular Tissue. Areolar tissue with a network of fibrous fibers. Cells wrapped around fibers.

Lymphoid Tissue. Reticular tissue with meshes of network occupied by lymph cells

Function. Reticular tissue forms a supporting framework in many organs, e.g., lymph nodes, bone marrow, and muscular tissue. Reticular tissue is present in the spleen, mucous membrane of the gastrointestinal tract, lungs, liver, and kidneys

Elastic Tissue. Consists of cells with few fibrous fibers and a predominance of elastic fibers

Function. It is extensile and elastic. Found in blood vessels, air tubes, larynx, vocal folds, and lungs, ligamenta flava, ligamentum nuchae

Fibrous Tissue. Formed by wavy bundles of fibrous fibers only, with cells in rows between bundles; very strong and tough but pliant

Function. Is found in form of ligaments, tendons, aponeuroses, protecting sheaths, and fasciae

B. **Cartilage.** Cartilage consists of a group of cells in a matrix. It is firm, tough, and elastic, covered and nourished by perichondrium

Varieties
1. **Hyaline cartilage**
   - Articular } Skeletal
   - Costal } Skeletal
2. **Fibrocartilage**
3. **Elastic cartilage**

C. **Bone, or Osseous Tissue.** Bone is connective tissue in which the intercellular substance derived from the cells is rendered hard by being impregnated with mineral salts

Bone or Osseous Tissue

- **Composition**
  - *Inorganic matter about 67%*
    - Calcium phosphate
    - Calcium carbonate
    - Calcium fluoride
    - Magnesium phosphate
    - Sodium chloride
  - *Organic matter about 33%*
    - Cells
    - Blood vessels
    - Gelatinous substance
- **Varieties**
  - Cancellous, or spongy
  - Dense, or compact, like ivory
- **Canals**
  - Medullary—red and yellow marrow
  - Haversian
    - Blood vessels
    - Lymphatics
- **Haversian System**
  - Haversian canals are surrounded by lamellae, lacunae, and canaliculi
  - Lamellae—bony fibers arranged in rings around haversian canals
  - Lacunae—hollow spaces between lamellae occupied by bone cells
  - Canaliculi—canals which radiate from one lacuna to another and toward the haversian canals
- **Medullary Membrane.** A vascular tissue that lines the medullary canal
- **Marrow**
  - **Red**: Consists of connective tissue supporting blood vessels, myelocytes, fat cells, erythroblasts from which red blood cells are derived, and giant cells. Found in the marrow cavity at the ends of long bones and in cancellous tissue
  - **Yellow**: Contains more connective tissue and fat cells than red marrow, fewer myelocytes, few if any red cells, and fewer giant cells. White cells of blood and lymph are derived from its myelocytes. Found in the medullary canals of the long bones

Periosteum. A vascular fibrous membrane that covers the bones except at their cartilaginous extremities and serves to nourish them. Important in the reunion of broken bone and growth of new bone

Blood Vessels. Twigs of nutrient artery in medullary canal anastomose with twigs from haversian canals, and these in turn anastomose with others which enter from periosteum. Nerves accompany arteries into bone

Development of Bone
- In the embryo bones are preformed in membrane and in cartilage
- **Ossification**
  - Intramembranous
  - Intracartilaginous, or endochondral
- **Dependent on**
  - Adequate amounts of calcium and phosphorus in food
  - Vitamins and hormones

Rickets
- **A disturbance** of mineral metabolism
- **Prophylaxis, or Prevention**
  - Adequate amounts of calcium and phosphorus in food. Vitamin D supplied by fish oils, egg yolk, milk, butter, fresh vegetables, direct sunlight
- **Types**
  - True rickets
  - "Ricketslike condition"
  - Sometimes called osteoporosis

Muscle
- Striated
- Smooth
- Cardiac

Muscular Tissue
1. Striated, skeletal
2. Nonstriated, visceral
3. Indistinctly striated, cardiac

Classification
- Cells become elongated and are called fibers
- Intercellular substance between fibers
- Connective tissue—supporting framework
- Well supplied with nerves and blood and lymph vessels

Striated { **Cross-striped**, **Skeletal** }
1. Marked with transverse striae
2. Movements accomplished by it are voluntary
3. Attached to skeleton
4. Muscle fibers are long and spindle-shaped
5. Connective-tissue framework carries blood vessels and nerves
6. Origin—more fixed attachment
7. Insertion—more movable attachment
8. Origin in periosteum of bone or intervening tendon
9. Insertion either by tendons or aponeuroses
10. Muscles closely covered by sheets of fasciae
11. Deep fasciae form annular ligaments in vicinity of wrist and ankle

Function. To operate the bones of the body, producing motion

Nonstriated { **Smooth**, **Visceral** }
1. Not marked with transverse striae
2. Movements accomplished by it are involuntary
3. Found in walls of blood vessels and viscera
4. Composed of spindle-shaped cells that contain one large nucleus, cells held together by fibrils
5. Connective-tissue framework carries blood vessels and nerves

Function. To cause visceral motion

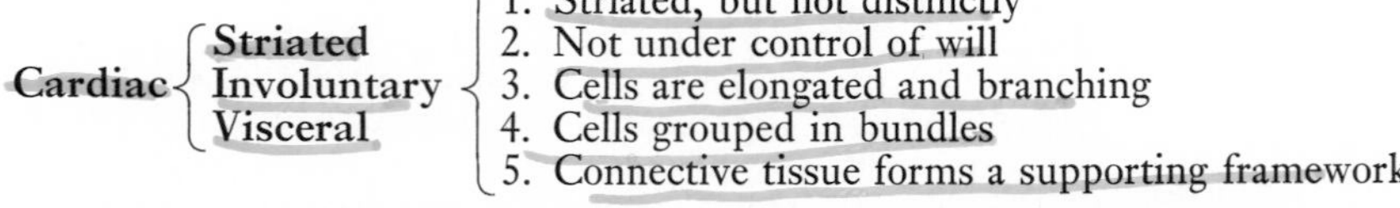

Cardiac { **Striated**, **Involuntary**, **Visceral** }
1. Striated, but not distinctly
2. Not under control of will
3. Cells are elongated and branching
4. Cells grouped in bundles
5. Connective tissue forms a supporting framework

Function. To cause contraction, thereby ejecting blood from the heart

UNIT II

Locomotion and Support: The Organs—Their Structure and Activity

Body movement is in essence movement of bones at their articulating surfaces as a result of skeletal muscle contraction. A muscle contracts when stimulated by its nerve and when adequately nourished, i.e., when the blood supply is normal. Unit II describes bone-joint-muscle-nerve interrelationships.

CHAPTER

4

THE SKELETON

Bones and Sinuses of Head, Trunk, Extremities

The bones are the principal organs of support and the passive instruments of locomotion. They form a framework of hard material to which the skeletal muscles are attached. This framework affords attachment for the soft parts, maintains them in position, shelters them, helps to control and direct varying internal pressures, gives stability to the whole body, and preserves its shape. The bones form joints which may be movable. Here the bones act as levers for movement. Certain blood cells are formed in red bone marrow.

The adult skeleton consists of 206 named bones.

Cranium	8	
Face	14	
Ear: Malleus 2, Incus 2, Stapes 2	6	
Hyoid	1	206
The spine, or vertebral column (sacrum and coccyx included)	26	
Sternum and ribs	25	
Upper extremities	64	
Lower extremities	62	

This list does not include the sesamoid[1] and wormian[2] bones. Sesamoid bones are found embedded in the tendons covering the bones of the knee, hand, and foot. Wormian bones are small isolated bones which occur in cranial sutures, most frequently the lambdoid suture.

Classification. The bones may be classified according to their shape into four groups: (1) *long*, (2) *short*, (3) *flat*, and (4) *irregular*.

A *long bone* consists of a shaft and two extremities. The shaft is formed mainly of compact bone tissue, the compact tissue being thickest in the middle, where the bone is most slender and the strain greatest, and it is hollowed out in the interior to form the *medullary canal*. The extremities are made of cancellous tissue, with a thin coating of compact tissue, and are more or less expanded for greater convenience of mutual connection and to afford a broad surface for muscular attachment. All long bones are more or less curved, which gives them greater strength. They are found in the arms and legs, e.g., humerus.

The *short bones* are irregularly shaped. Their texture is spongy throughout, except at their surface, where there is a thin layer of compact tissue. The short bones are the 16 bones of the carpus, the 14 bones of the tarsus, and the two patellae.

Where *flat bones* are found there is need for extensive protection or the provision of broad surfaces for muscular attachment. The bony tissue expands into broad or elongated flat plates which are composed of two thin layers of compact tissue, enclosing between them a variable quantity of cancellous tissue, e.g., occipital bone.

[1] Ses′amoid (Greek *sesamon*, a "seed of the sesamum," and *eidos*, "form," "resemblance").

[2] Olaus Wormius, Danish anatomist (1588–1654).

The *irregular bones*, because of their peculiar shape, cannot be grouped under any of the preceding heads. A vertebra is a good example. The bones of the ear are so small that they are described as *ossicles*.

Processes and Depressions. The surface of bones shows projections, or *processes*, and depressions, called *fossae* or *cavities*. Qualifying adjectives or special names may be used to describe them. Both processes and depressions are classified as (1) *articular*—those serving for connection of bones to form joints, and (2) *nonarticular*—those serving for the attachment of ligaments and muscles.

PROCESSES

Process. Any marked bony prominence	*Crest.* A narrow ridge of bone
Condyle. A rounded or knucklelike process	*Spine*, or *spinous process.* A sharp, slender process
Tubercle. A small rounded process	*Head.* A portion supported on a constricted part, or *neck*
Tuberosity. A large rounded process	
Trochanter. A very large process	

CAVITIES

Fissure. A narrow slit
Foramen. A hole or orifice through which blood vessels, nerves, and ligaments pass
Meatus, or *canal.* A long, tubelike passageway
Sinus[3] and *antrum.* Applied to cavities within certain bones
Groove, or *sulcus.* A furrow
Fossa. A depression in or upon a bone

[3] The term *sinus* is also used in surgery to denote a narrow tract through tissues, leading from the surface down to a cavity, and sometimes it refers to a large vein.

DIVISIONS OF THE SKELETON

The bones of the body may be divided into two main groups:

The Axial Skeleton	1. Head or skull	Cranium	8
		Face	14
	2. Hyoid		1
	3. Trunk	Vertebrae—child 33, adult 26	
		Sternum	1
		Ribs	24
Appendicular Skeleton	4. Upper		64
	5. Lower		62

The head, or skull, rests upon the spinal column and is composed of the cranial and facial bones. It is divisible into *cranium*, or *brain case*, and *anterior region*, or *face*.

The Skull as a Whole. The cranium is a firm case, or covering, for the brain. Four of the eight bones (occipital, two parietal, and frontal) which form this bony covering are flat bones and consist of two layers of compact tissue, the outer one thick and tough, the inner one thinner and more brittle. The base of the skull is much thicker and stronger than the walls and roof; it presents a number of openings, or foramina, for the passage of the cranial nerves, blood vessels, and other structures.

The bones of the cranium develop in early fetal life. Ossification of these bones is gradual and takes place from ossification centers, generally near the center of the

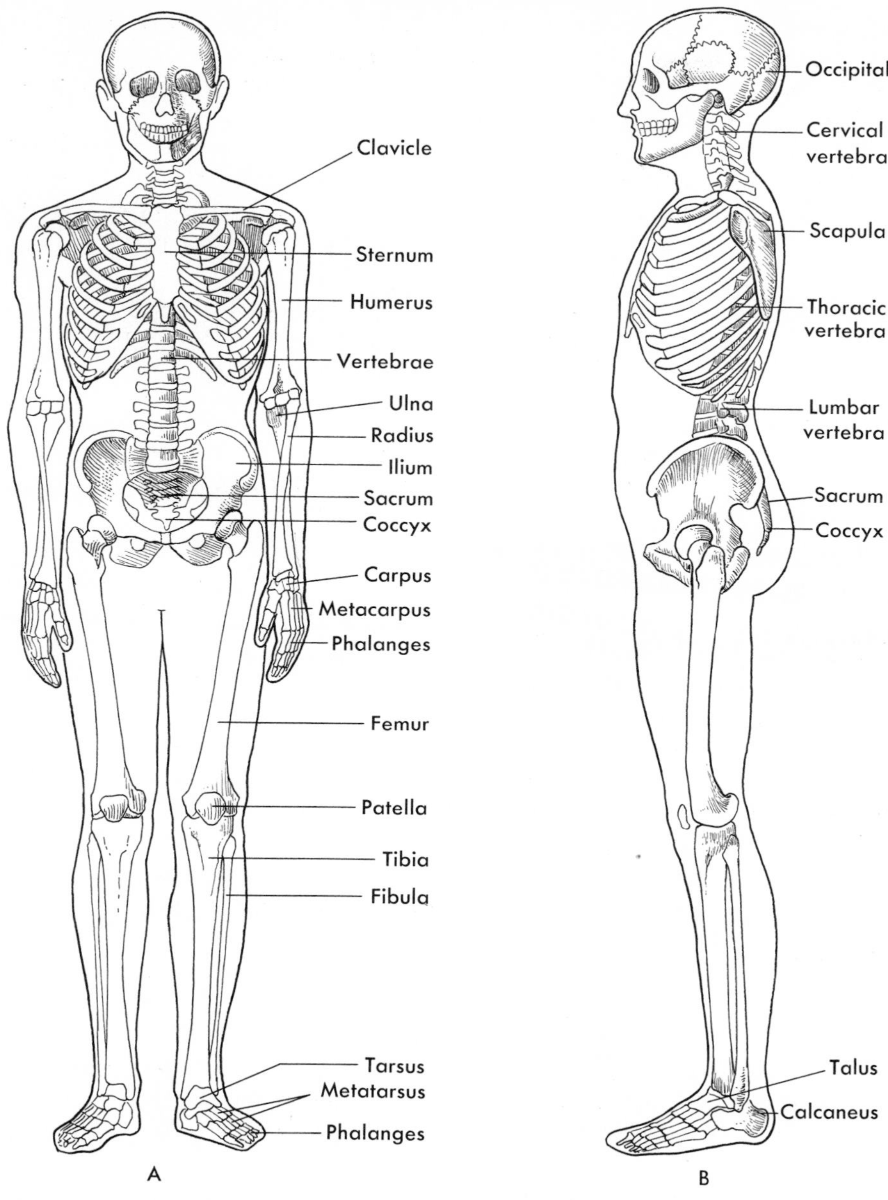

Figure 4–1. (*A*) The human skeleton, front view. (*B*) The human skeleton, side view.

completed bones. Ossification is not complete at birth; hence, membrane-filled spaces are found between the bones. These spaces are called fontanelles.

The Fontanelles. At birth there may be many of these fontanelles. The shape and location of six of them are quite constant.

The *anterior*, or *bregmatic*, is the largest and is a lozenge-shaped space between the angles of the two parietal bones and the two segments of the frontal bone. Normally this fontanelle closes at about 18 months of age.

In abnormal conditions the fontanelle may close much earlier or much later. In cases of retarded brain growth, called microcephalus, it closes early. In hydrocephalus the increased internal pressure may cause it to remain open.

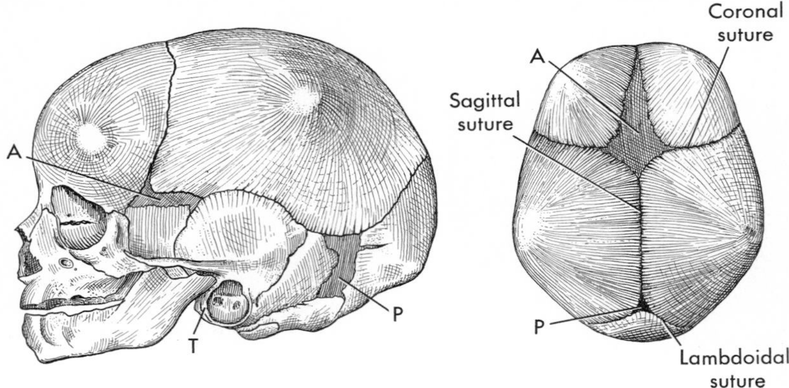

Figure 4–2. (*Left*) Skull of newborn infant, side view. (*A*) Anterolateral fontanelle, (*P*) posterolateral fontanelle, (*T*) tympanic ring. (Modified from Toldt.) (*Right*) Same, seen from above. Anterior fontanelle, (*P*) posterior fontanelle. (Modified from Toldt.)

In rickets and cretinism which are not yielding to treatment it may not close until much later.

The *posterior* (or *occipital*) *fontanelle* is much smaller and is a triangular space between the occipital and two parietal bones. Usually this closes a few months after birth.

There are two *sphenoidal fontanelles* at the junction of the frontal, parietal, temporal, and sphenoid bones. They are quite small and usually close by the second month after birth.

There are two *mastoid fontanelles* at the junction of the parietal, occipital, and temporal bones. They decrease in size and usually close one or two months after birth.

Figure 4–3. Base of skull, exterior view.

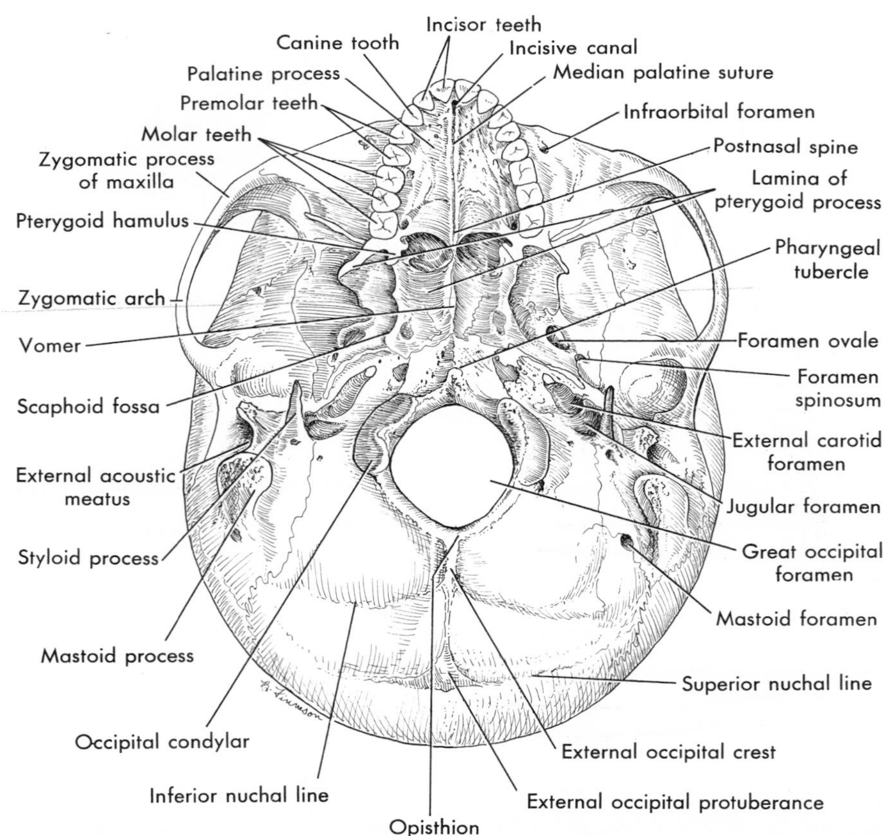

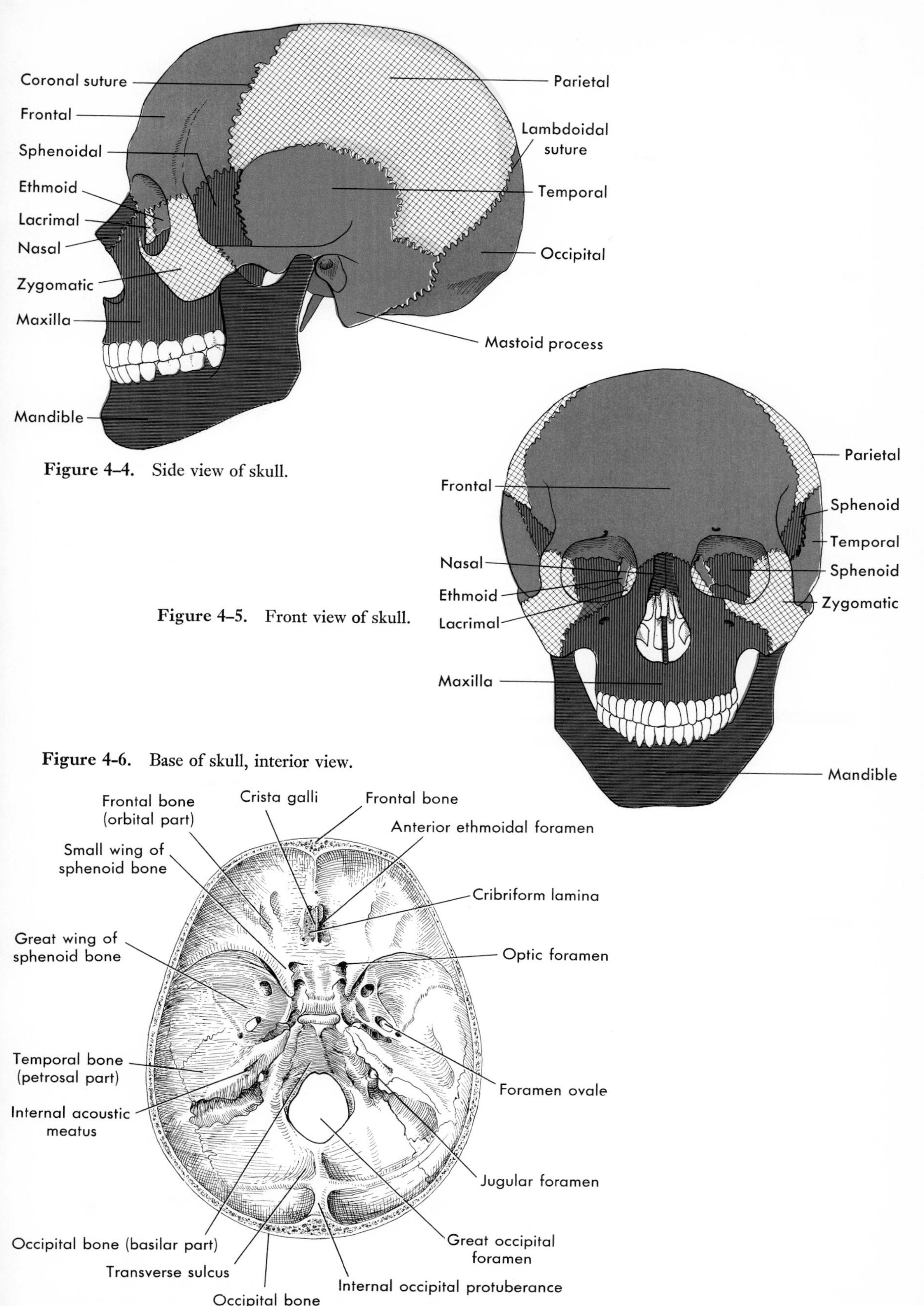

Figure 4–4. Side view of skull.

Figure 4–5. Front view of skull.

Figure 4-6. Base of skull, interior view.

The membranous tissue between the cranial bones at the sutures and fontanelles allows more or less overlapping during birth processes, thus reducing the diameters of the skull. This is called *molding* and accounts for the elongated shape of the head of a newborn infant, particularly if the labor has been long.

NAME OF BONE	DESCRIPTION
BONES OF THE SKULL	
Occipital (os occipitale)	Is situated at the back and base of skull. *Internal surface* is concave and presents many eminences and depressions for parts of the brain. *External surface* is convex. The *external occipital protuberance* is a projection which can be felt through the scalp. From this median ridge the external occipital crest leads to the *foramen magnum*, the largest opening in the inferior part of the bone for the transmission of the *medulla oblongata*, where it narrows to join the spinal cord. The protuberances and crest give attachment for the ligamentum nuchae. Other muscles are attached to the expanded plate of the bone. At the sides of the foramen magnum on the external surface, there are two processes called condyles, which articulate with the atlas.
Parietal bone, right and left (os parietale)	By their union they form the greater part of the sides and roof of the skull. The *external* surface is smooth and convex. The *internal* surface is concave and presents many eminences and depressions for reception of the convolutions of the brain and many furrows for the ramifications of arteries which supply blood to the dura mater, which covers the brain.
Frontal bone (os frontale)	Forms the forehead, part of the roof of the orbits, and the nasal cavity. The *supraorbital margin* is the arch formed by the part of the bone over the eyes. Just above the supraorbital margins are hollow spaces within the bone called the *frontal sinuses*, which are filled with air and open into the nose. The *lacrimal fossae* are located in the upper outer angle of each orbit in which lie the *lacrimal glands*, which secrete tears. At birth the bone consists of two parts, which become united soon after birth.
Temporal bones, right and left (os temporale)	Are situated at the sides and base of the skull. They are divided into five parts: 1. *The squama*, a thin expanded portion, forms the anterior and upper part of the bone. The supramastoid crest runs backward and upward across its posterior part. The *zygomatic process*, which projects from the lower part, articulates with the temporal process of the zygomatic bone. 2. *The petrous portion* is shaped like a pyramid and is wedged in at the base of the skull between the sphenoid and occipital bones. The internal ear, the essential part of the organ of hearing, is contained in a series of cavities in the petrous portion. Between the squamous and the petrous portion is a socket, the *mandibular fossa*, for the reception of the condyle of the mandible. 3. *Mastoid portion* projects downward behind the opening of the meatus. It is filled with numerous connected spaces called

mastoid cells[4] or sinuses which contain air. These cells communicate with the middle ear.

4. *Tympanic portion* is a curved plate of bone below the squama and in front of the mastoid portion. It forms a part of the external acoustic meatus leading to the middle ear.
5. *The styloid* is a slender, pointed process that projects downward from the undersurface of the temporal bone. Some muscles and ligaments of the tongue are attached to its distal part.

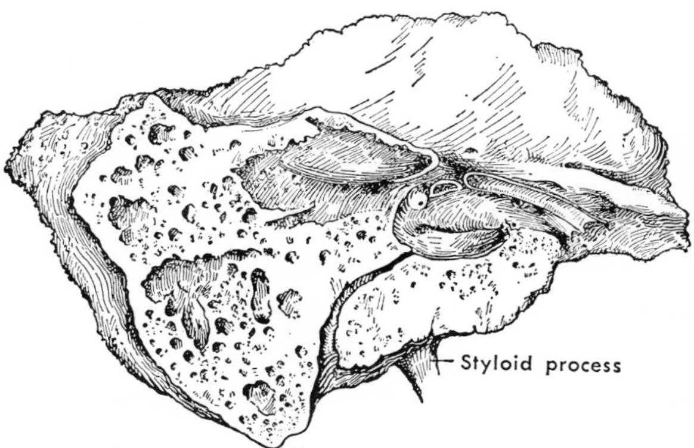

Figure 4–7. Right temporal bone, sectioned to show mastoid cells.

The ethmoid bone (os ethmoidale)

Is a light cancellous bone consisting of a cribriform (horizontal) plate, a perpendicular plate, and two lateral masses or *labyrinths*. The cribriform plate forms the roof of the nasal cavity and closes the anterior part of the base of the cranium. There are many foramina through which *olfactory fibers* pass from the mucous membrane of the nose to the *olfactory bulb*. Projecting upward from the horizontal plate is a smooth, triangular process called the *crista galli* which forms an attachment of the *falx cerebri* (page 204). The perpendicular plate, descending from the horizontal plate, helps to form the upper part of the nasal septum. On either side the lateral masses form part of the orbit and nasal cavity. The lateral masses contain many thin-walled cavities, the sinuses of the ethmoid, which communicate with the nasal cavity. On either side of the septum are two thin processes of thin, cancellous bony tissue, the superior and middle conchae.

Superior and middle conchae

The sphenoid bone (os sphenoidale)

Is an important bone situated at the anterior part of the base of the skull which binds the other cranial bones together. It resembles an airplane with extended wings and consists of a body, two great and two small wings which extend transversely from the sides of the body, and two pterygoid processes (hamuli) which project downward. The body is joined to the ethmoid in front and the occipital behind.

[4] *Cells*. Histologically, the word *cell* refers to one of the component units of the body, such as an epithelial cell. Occasionally it refers to such minute chambers as mastoid cells.

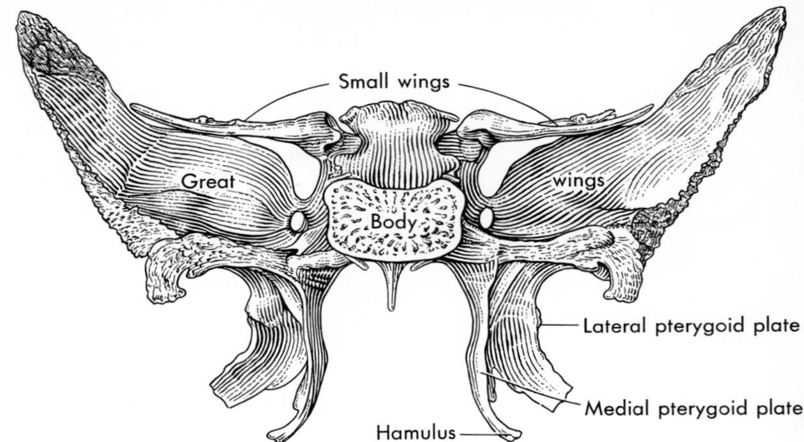

Figure 4–8. The sphenoid bone, seen from behind.

Sinuses of the sphenoid

The bone contains cavities called the sphenoidal sinuses which communicate with the nasopharynx.

Sella turcica

The upper portion of the body presents a *fossa* with anterior and posterior eminences. This is called the *sella turcica*. The *hypophysis cerebri* is contained in the *sella turcica*.

BONES OF THE FACE

Nasal bones (os nasalia)

Are two small oblong bones placed side by side at the middle and upper part of the face, forming by their junction the upper part of the bridge of the nose. The lower part of the nose is formed by cartilage.

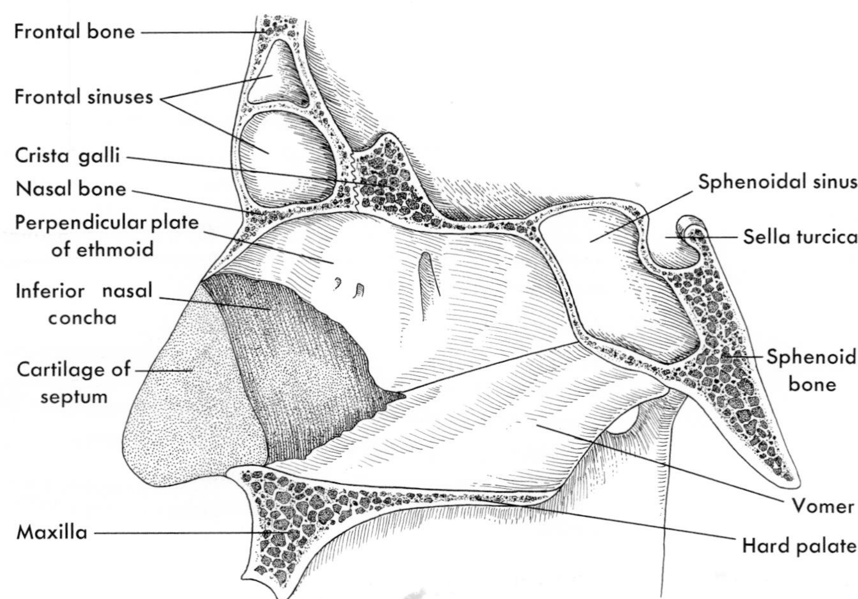

Figure 4–9. Bones and cartilage of the septum of nose, left side. (Modified from Gray's *Anatomy*.)

Vomer	A single bone located at the lower and back part of the nasal cavity, forming part of the central septum of the nasal cavity. It is thin and may be deviated to one side, thus making the nasal chambers of unequal size.
Inferior nasal conchae	Are located on the outer wall of the nasal cavity. They consist of a layer of thin cancellous bone curled upon itself like a scroll. They are below the superior and middle conchae of the ethmoid bone.
Lacrimal bones	Are located at the front part of the inner wall of the orbit and somewhat resemble a fingernail in form, thinness, and size. They contain part of the canal through which the tear ducts run.
Zygomatic malar bones (os zygoma)	These bones form the prominences of the cheeks and part of the outer wall and floor of the orbits. The temporal process (narrow and serrated) projects backward and articulates with the zygomatic process of the temporal bone, forming an arch on each side.
Palatine bones (2) (os palatinum)	These bones are shaped somewhat like an L and have a horizontal part, a vertical part, and three processes, the pyramidal, orbital, and sphenoid. They are situated at the back part of the nasal cavity between the maxillae and pterygoid processes of the sphenoid. They help to form (1) the back part of the roof of the mouth, (2) part of the floor and outer walls of the nasal cavities, and (3) a small part of the floor of the orbit.

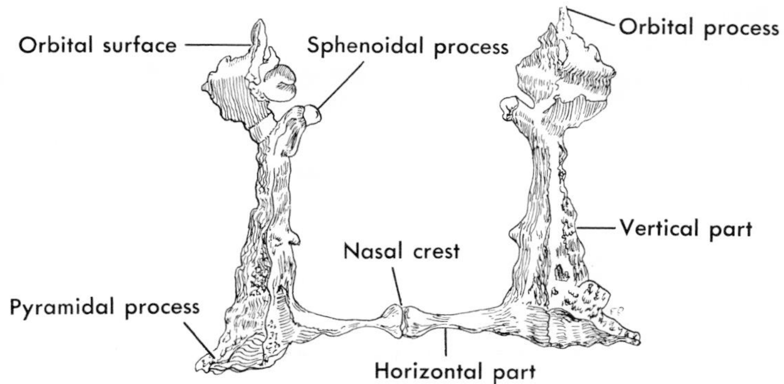

Figure 4–10. The two palatine bones in their natural position, viewed from behind.

Maxillae, or upper jaw bones (2)	Form by their union the whole of the upper jaw. Each bone helps to form (1) part of the floor of the orbit, (2) the floor and lateral walls of the nasal cavities, and (3) the greater part of the roof of the mouth. Each bone contains a large cavity, the *maxillary sinus*, which opens into the nose. The *alveolar* processes are excavated cavities, which vary in depth and size according to the teeth they contain. Before birth these bones unite to form one. When they fail to do so, the condition is known as cleft palate.
The mandible, or lower jaw bone (os mandibula)	Is the largest and strongest bone of the face and consists of a curved horizontal portion, the *body*, and two perpendicular portions, the *rami*. The alveolar process border of the body contains cavities for

the reception of the teeth. Each ramus has a *condyle*, which articulates with the mandibular fossa of the temporal bone, and a *coronoid process*, which gives attachment to the temporal muscle and some fibers of the buccinator. The deep depression between the two processes is called the *mandibular notch*. The *mental foramen*, which is just below the first molar tooth, serves as a passageway for the mental nerve, which is a terminal branch of the inferior dental nerve (of the trigeminal nerve). At birth the mandible consists of two parts which unite at the symphysis in front to form one bone, during the first year.

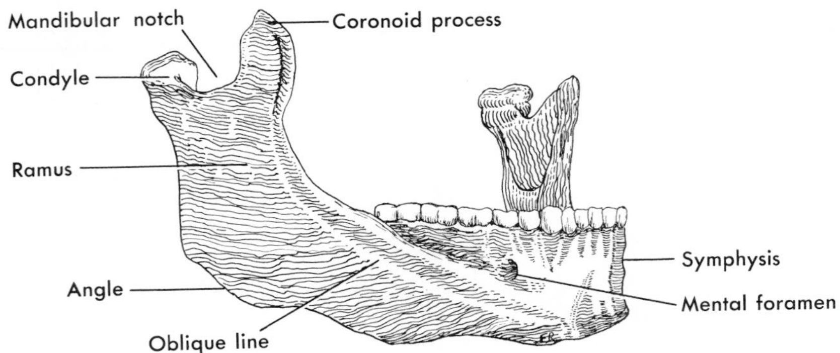

Figure 4–11. The mandible, viewed from the right and a little in front.

The hyoid bone (os hyoideum)

Is shaped like a horseshoe and consists of a body and two projections on each side called the greater and lesser cornua. It is suspended from the styloid processes of the temporal bones and may be felt in the neck just above the laryngeal prominence. It supports the tongue and gives attachment to some of its numerous muscles.

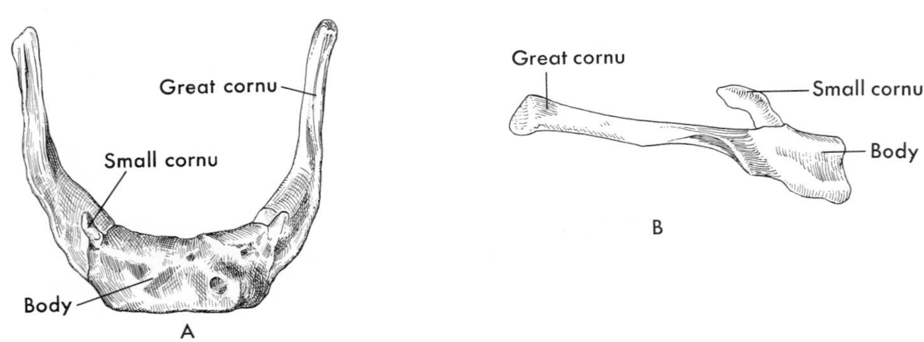

Figure 4–12. (*A*) Hyoid bone seen from above. (*B*) Hyoid bone seen from the side. (Modified from Toldt.)

Sinuses of the head

There are four air sinuses which communicate with each nasal cavity; the *frontal*, the *ethmoidal*, the *sphenoidal*, and the *maxillary*. They are lined with mucous membrane. Inflammation of this membrane is called sinusitis.

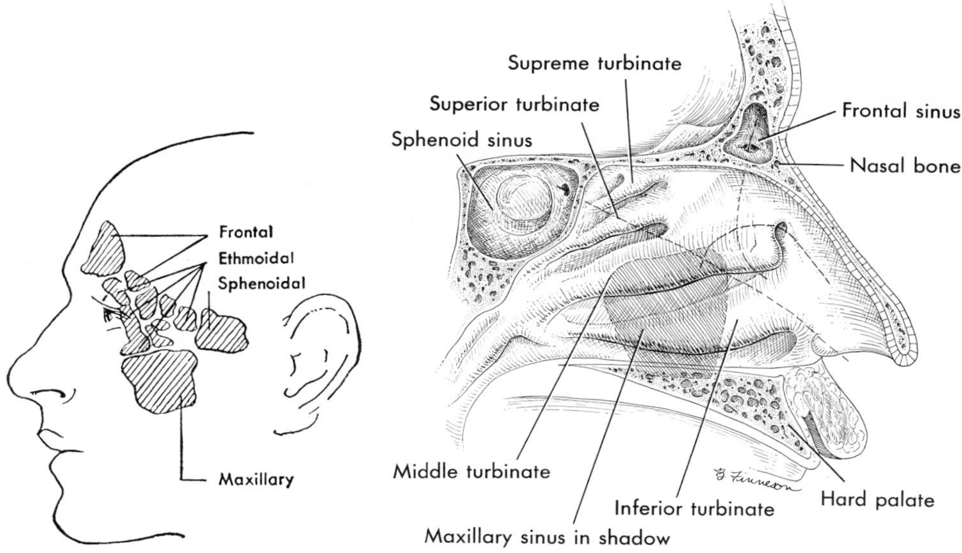

Figure 4–13. Sinuses projected to the surface of the face. All except the maxillary sinus are near the central line of the skull when viewed from the front.

See also Figure 4–7 for mastoid cells.

Figure 4–14. Diagram of sinuses and openings into nasopharynx.

The skull at birth

The skull is proportionately larger than other parts of the skeleton, and the facial portion is small. The small size of the maxillae and mandible, the noneruption of the teeth, and the small size of the sinuses and nasal cavities account for the smallness of the face. With the eruption of the first teeth there is an enlargement of the face and jaws. This enlargement is much more pronounced after the eruption of the second set of teeth. Usually the skull becomes thinner and lighter in old age, but occasionally the inner table hypertrophies, causing an increase in weight and thickness (pachycephalia). The most noticeable feature of the skull in the aged is the decrease in the size of the maxillae and mandible, resulting from the loss of the teeth and the absorption of the alveolar processes.

Bones of the Trunk

The trunk

The bones forming the trunk are the *vertebrae*, *sternum*, and *ribs*.

The vertebral column

Is formed of a series of bones called vertebrae and in a man of average height is about 71 cm long (28 in.). In youth the vertebrae are 33 in number:

Cervical, in the neck	7	Movable, or true, vertebrae
Thoracic, or dorsal, in the thorax	12	
Lumbar, in the loins	5	
Sacral, in the pelvis	5	Fixed, or false, vertebrae
Coccygeal, in the pelvis	4	

In the cervical, thoracic, and lumbar regions the vertebrae are separate and movable throughout life. In the sacral and coccygeal regions they are firmly united in the adult, so that they form two sections, five bones entering into the sacrum and four into the terminal bone, or coccyx.

The vertebrae

Differ in size and shape, but their structure is similar. Seen from above, as in Figure 4–19, page 93, they consist of a body from which two short, thick processes, called the pedicles, project backward, one on each side to join with the laminae which unite posteriorly, thus forming the vertebral, or neural, arch. This arch encloses the spinal foramen. Each vertebra has several processes: four articular, two to connect with the bone above, two to connect

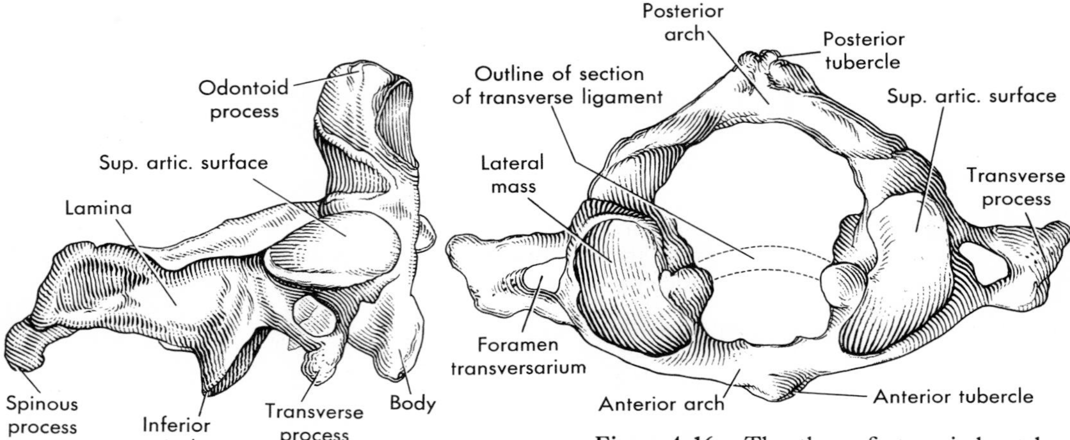

Figure 4–15. The epistropheus, or axis, seen from the right side. (Modified from Gray's *Anatomy*.)

Figure 4–16. The atlas, or first cervical vertebra. (Modified from Gray's *Anatomy*.)

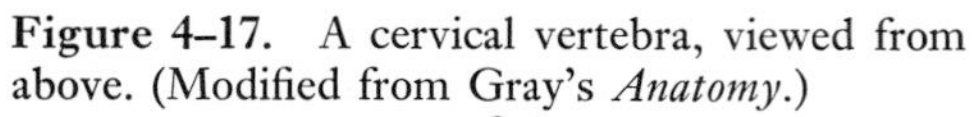

Figure 4–17. A cervical vertebra, viewed from above. (Modified from Gray's *Anatomy*.)

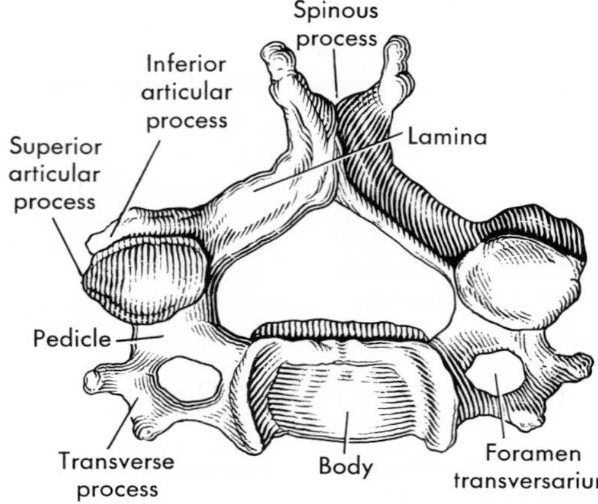

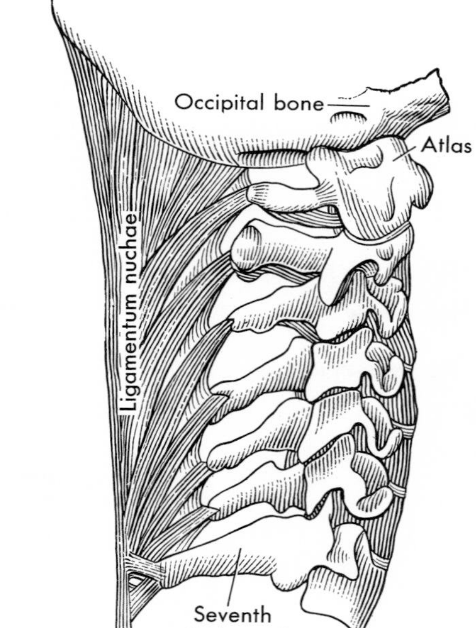

Figure 4–18. The ligamentum nuchae seen from the right side. (Modified from Henle.)

with the bone below; two transverse, one at each side where the pedicle and lamina join; and one spinous process, projecting backward from the junction of the laminae in the midline.

Cervical vertebrae

The bodies of the cervical vertebrae are smaller than the thoracic, but the arches are larger. The spinous processes are short and are often cleft in two, or bifid. Each transverse process is pierced by a foramen (foramen transversarium) through which nerves, a vertebral artery, and a vein pass. As Figures 4–15, 16, 17, indicate, the first and second cervical vertebrae differ from the rest. The first, or *atlas*, so named from supporting the head, is a bony ring consisting of an anterior and posterior arch and two bulky lateral masses. Each has a superior and inferior articular surface. Each superior surface forms a cup for the corresponding condyle of the occipital bone and thus makes possible the backward and forward movements of the head. The bony ring is divided into an anterior and posterior section by a transverse ligament. The posterior section of this bony ring contains the spinal cord, and the anterior, or front, section of the ring contains the bony projection which arises from the upper surface of the body of the second cervical vertebra, the *epistropheus*, or *axis*. This bony projection, the *odontoid* process, forms a pivot; around this pivot the atlas rotates when the head is turned from side to side.

Thoracic, or dorsal, vertebrae

These vertebrae are larger and stronger than those of the cervical and have a facet or demifacet for articulation with the heads of the ribs. The transverse processes are longer and heavier than those of the cervical, and all except those of the eleventh and twelfth vertebrae have facets for articulation with the tubercles of the ribs. The spinous processes are long and are directed downward.

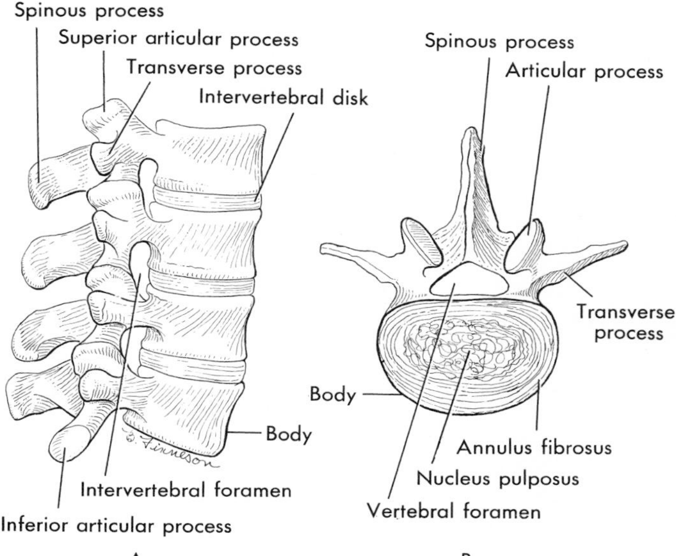

Figure 4–19. (*A*) Diagram of several vertebrae with intervertebral disks between the vertebrae. (*B*) Viewed from above. Note nucleus pulposus.

The lumbar vertebrae The bodies of these vertebrae are the largest and heaviest in the spine. The processes are short, heavy, and thick.

The sacrum Is an important bone of the vertebral column. It is formed by the union of the five sacral vertebrae. It is a large wedge-shaped bone firmly connected with the hip bones. The pelvic side is concave and relatively smooth and the dorsal side is irregular. The sacrum is marked by four transverse ridges. At the ends of the ridges there are four pairs of pelvic sacral foramina which communicate with the four pairs of dorsal foramina through which nerves and blood vessels pass. The sacral canal contains the lower part of the cauda equina of the spinal cord, spinal ligament, and fat.

The coccyx Is usually formed of four small segments of bone and is the most rudimentary part of the vertebral column.

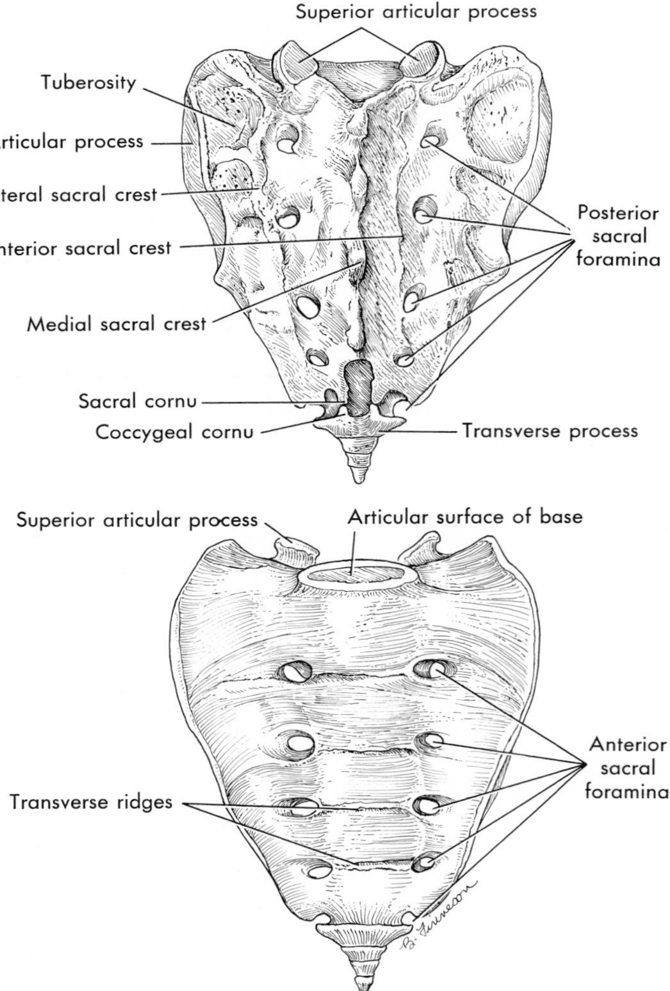

Figure 4–20. The sacral bone. (*A*) Posterior view. (*B*) Anterior view. (Modified from Pansky and House.)

The intervertebral disks — Are disks of fibrocartilage interposed between the bodies of adjacent vertebrae from the axis to the sacrum. They vary in size and thickness in different regions, being thickest in the lumbar region. They are attached below and above by a thin layer of hyaline cartilage which covers the surfaces of the bodies of the vertebrae.

The nucleus pulposus — Is a soft, pulpy, elastic, and compressible substance centrally located within each disk. The disk as a whole permits flexibility of the vertebral column and the nucleus pulposus functions as an important shock absorber.

Structure of Vertebral Column

As a whole — The bodies of the vertebrae are piled one upon another, form a strong, flexible column for the support of the cranium and trunk, and provide articular surfaces for the attachment of the ribs. The arches form a hollow cylinder for the protection of the spinal cord. Viewed from the side, the vertebral column presents four curves, which are alternately convex and concave. The two concave ones, named thoracic and pelvic, are called primary curves because they exist in fetal life and are designed for the accommodation of viscera. The two convex ones, named cervical and lumbar, are called secondary, or compensatory, curves because they are developed after birth. The cervical curve begins its development when the child is able to hold up his head (at about three or four months) and is well formed when he sits upright (at about 19 months). The lumbar develops when the child begins to walk (from 12 to 18 months). The joints between the bodies of the vertebrae are slightly movable, and those between the arches are freely movable. The *bodies* are connected (1) by disks of fibrocartilage placed between the vertebrae; (2) by the *anterior longitudinal ligament*, which extends along the anterior surfaces of the bodies of the vertebrae from the axis to the sacrum; and (3) by the *posterior longitudinal ligament*, which is inside the vertebral canal and extends along the posterior surfaces of the bodies from the axis to the sacrum.

The laminae — Are connected by broad, thin ligaments called the *ligamenta flava* (*ligamenta subflava*).

The spinous processes — Are connected at the apexes by the supraspinal ligament, which extends from the seventh cervical vertebra to the sacrum. It is continued upward as the *ligamentum nuchae*, which extends from the protuberance of the occiput to the spinous process of the seventh cervical vertebra.

Adjacent spinous processes — Are connected by interspinal ligaments which extend from the root to the apex of each process and meet the ligamenta flava in front and the supraspinal ligament behind. The transverse processes are connected by the intertransverse ligaments, which are placed between them.

The spinal curves — Confer springiness and strength upon the spinal column, and the elasticity is further increased by the ligamenta flava and the disks of fibrocartilage. These pads also mitigate the effects of concussion arising from falls or blows. The vertebral column is freely movable, being capable of bending forward freely, backward, and from side

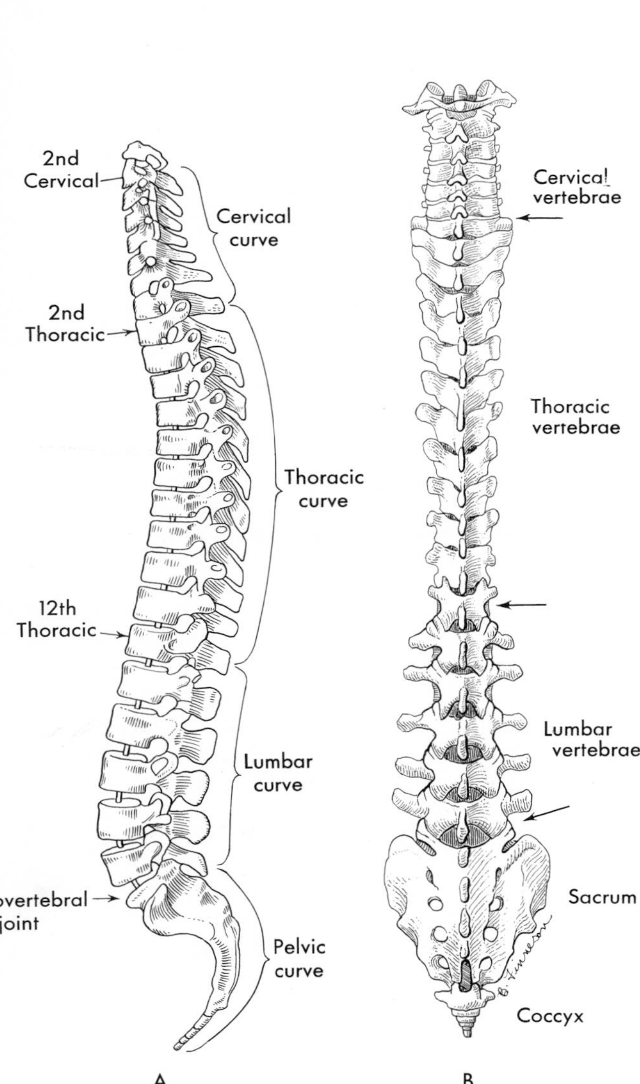

Figure 4–21. The vertebral column. (*A*) Left lateral view showing curves. (*B*) Dorsal view.

Figure 4–22. (*A*) Skeletal form of a person with good body mechanics. (*B*) Skeletal form of a person with poor body mechanics. (Courtesy of the Children's Bureau, U.S. Department of Health, Education, and Welfare.)

to side less freely. Certain exercises increase the flexibility of the spine to a marked degree. In the cervical and thoracic regions a limited amount of rotation is possible.

Posture

The weight of the body should rest evenly on the two hip joints. A perpendicular dropped from the ear should fall through shoulder, hip, and ankle (Figure 4–22). In this position the chest is up, the head is erect, the lower abdominal muscles are retracted, and the body is well balanced and functioning efficiently.

As a result of postural habits, injury, or disease, the normal curves may become exaggerated and are then spoken of as *curvatures*. If the thoracic curve is exaggerated, it is called *kyphosis*, or hump-back; if the exaggeration is in the lumbar region, it is called *lordosis*, or hollow back. If the curvature is lateral, i.e., toward one side, it is called *scoliosis*.

It occasionally happens that the laminae of a vertebra do not unite and a cleft is left in the arch (*spina bifida*). As a result the membranes and the spinal cord itself may protrude, forming a "tumor" on the child's back. This most often occurs in the lumbosacral region, though it may occur in the thoracic or cervical region.

The Thorax

The thorax Is a bony cage formed by the sternum and costal cartilages, the ribs, and the bodies of the thoracic vertebrae. It is cone-shaped, narrow above and broad below, flattened from before backward, and shorter in front than in back. In infancy the chest is rounded, and the width from shoulder to shoulder and the depth from the sternum to the vertebrae are about equal. With growth the width increases more than the depth. The thorax supports the bones of

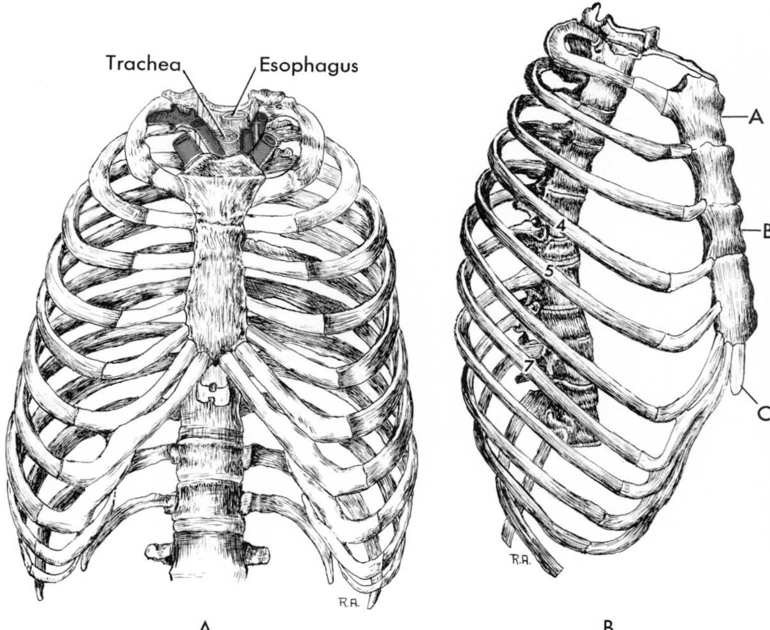

Figure 4–23. (*A*) Bones of thorax, seen from the front. Lying in the superior aperture of the "thoracic basket," note: esophagus (close to vertebral column), trachea, vagus nerves (*yellow*), arteries (*red*), veins (*blue*). (Modified from Toldt.) (*B*) Bones of thorax, seen from right side. Between the fourth and fifth ribs note articulation of the head and tubercle of the seventh rib. (*A*) Manubrium, (*B*) body showing articular notches of ribs and lines of union of parts of body, (*C*) xiphoid process.

the shoulder girdle and upper extremities and contains the principal organs of respiration and circulation.

The sternum

Is a flat, narrow bone about 6 in. long, situated in the median line in the front of the chest. It develops as three separate parts. The upper part, the *manubrium*; the middle and largest part, the *body*, or *gladiolus*; the lowest portion, the *xiphoid* or *ensiform process*. On both the manubrium and body are notches for the reception of the sternal ends of the upper seven costal cartilages. The xiphoid process has no ribs attached to it but affords attachment for some of the abdominal muscles.

At birth the sternum consists of several unossified portions, the body alone developing from four centers. Union of the centers in the body begins at about puberty and proceeds from below upward until at about 25 years of age they are all united. Sometimes by 30 years of age, more often after 40, the xiphoid process becomes joined to the body. In advanced life, the manubrium may become joined to the body by bony tissue. Posture, activity (play, work), and diet have much to do with shaping the sternum and the thoracic cavity.

The ribs (costae)

Twenty-four in number, are situated 12 on each side of the thoracic cavity. They are arches of bone consisting of a body, or shaft, and two extremities, the posterior (or vertebral) and the anterior (or sternal). Each rib is connected with a thoracic vertebra by the head and tubercle of the posterior extremity. The head fits into a facet formed on the body of one vertebra or formed by the adjacent bodies of two vertebrae; the tubercle articulates with the transverse processes. Strong ligaments surround and bind these articulations but permit slight gliding movements.

The heads of the first, tenth, eleventh, and twelfth ribs each articulate with a single vertebra. The heads of the remaining ribs articulate with facets formed by the bodies of two adjacent vertebrae. On the eleventh and twelfth ribs the articulation between the tubercle and the adjacent transverse process is missing.

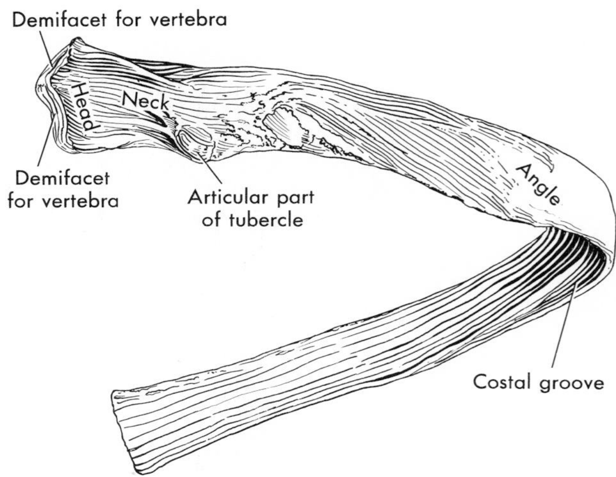

Figure 4–24. A central rib of the right side, viewed from behind. (Modified from Gray's *Anatomy*.)

The anterior extremities of each of the first seven pairs are connected with the sternum in front by bars of hyaline cartilage called costal cartilages. They are called *vertebrosternal* or *true ribs*. The remaining five pairs are termed *false ribs*. The cartilagenous attachment of ribs to sternum permits a degree of movement when pressure is applied. Pressure to the lower third of the sternum compresses the heart, which lies directly beneath and to the left (see Figure 16–1, page 320). Alternate pressure and release in a rhythmic fashion (cardiac "massage") simulates normal pumping action of the heart.

The convexity of the ribs is turned outward, giving roundness to the sides of the chest and increasing the size of its cavity; each rib slopes downward from its posterior attachment, so that its sternal end is considerably lower than its vertebral. The lower border of each rib is grooved for the accommodation of the intercostal nerves and blood vessels. The spaces left between the ribs are called the *intercostal spaces*. The red marrow of the sternum and ribs is one of the principal sites of red blood cell formation.

Bones of the Upper Extremities

The appendicular skeleton — Consists of the upper and lower extremities. The upper extremity consists of the *shoulder girdle* and the *upper limb*.

The shoulder girdle — Is formed by the two clavicles and the two scapulae. It is incomplete in front and behind. The clavicles articulate with the sternum in front but the scapulae are connected to the trunk by muscles. The shoulder girdle serves to attach the bones of the upper extremity to the axial skeleton.

The clavicle — Is a long bone with a double curvature, placed horizontally at the upper and anterior part of the thorax above the first rib. The inner end articulates with the sternum, called the *sternal extremity*. The outer, or *acromial*, end articulates with the scapula.

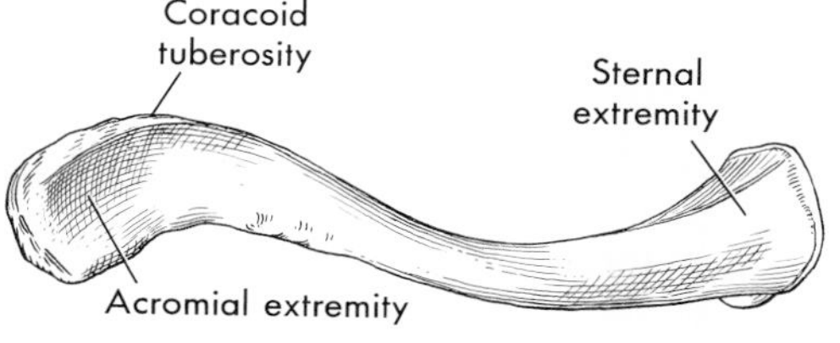

Figure 4–25. The right clavicle, seen from above.

The scapula — Is a large, flat, triangular bone situated on the dorsal aspect of the thorax between the second and seventh ribs. On its dorsal surface there is a prominent ridge, the spine, which terminates in a triangular projection, the *acromion* process, which articulates with the clavicle. Below the acromion, at the end of the shoulder blade is a shallow socket, the *glenoid cavity*, which receives the head of the humerus.

The humerus, or arm bone[5] — Is the longest and largest bone of the upper extremity. The upper end consists of a rounded head, joined to the shaft by a constricted

[5] Anatomically, the word *arm* is reserved for that part of the upper limb which is above the elbow; between the elbow and wrist is the forearm; below the wrist are the hand and fingers.

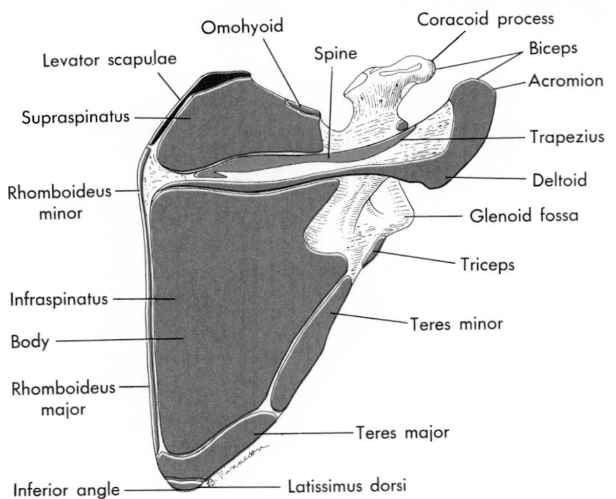

Figure 4–26. The right scapula, dorsal surface. (*Red*) Origin of muscles, (*blue*) insertion of muscles.

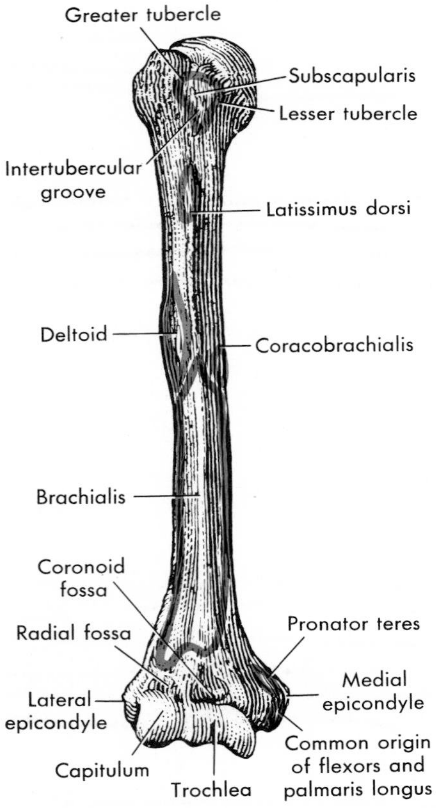

Figure 4–27. The right humerus, or arm bone, ventral view. (*Red*) Muscle origins, (*blue*) insertions.

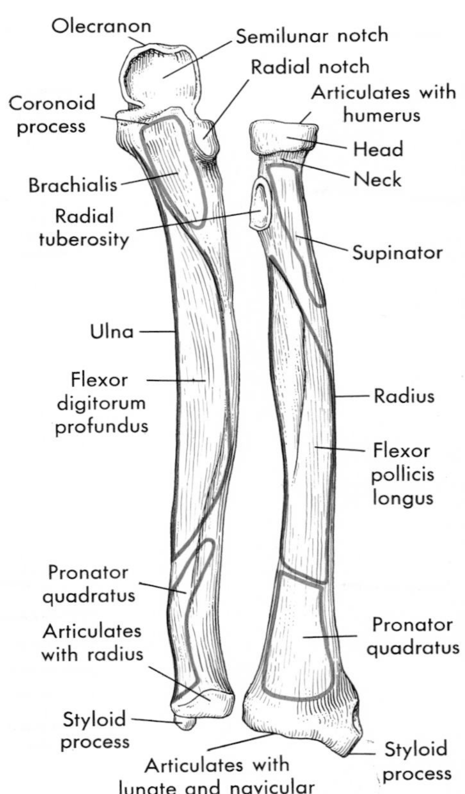

Figure 4–28. Anterior view of the bones of the left forearm. (*Red*) Muscle origins, (*blue*) insertions.

neck and two eminences, the *greater* and *lesser* tubercles, between which is the intertubercular groove.

The anatomical neck

Is the constricted neck above the tubercules.

The surgical neck

Is that part below the tubercules, so called because it is so often fractured. The head articulates with the glenoid cavity of the scapula, the lower end is flattened from before backward and ends below in an articular surface which is divided by a ridge into a lateral eminence called the *capitulum* and a medial portion, the *trochlea*. The capitulum is rounded and articulates with the depression on the head of the radius. The trochlea articulates with the ulna. Above these surfaces on the lateral and medial aspects are projections called *epicondyles*.

The ulna

Is the largest bone of the forearm and is placed at the medial side of the radius. Its upper end shows two processes and two concavities; the larger process, called the *olecranon process*, forms the prominence of the elbow. The smaller process is called the *coronoid process*. The trochlea of the humerus fits into the semilunar notch between these two processes. The radial notch is on the lateral side of the coronoid and articulates with the radius. The lower end of the ulna is small and ends in two eminences; the larger head articulates with the fibrocartilage disk which separates it from the wrist; the smaller is the styloid process, to which a ligament from the wrist joint is attached.

The radius

Is placed on the lateral side of the ulna and is shorter and smaller than the ulna. The upper extremity presents a head, a neck, and a tuberosity. The head (caput radii) is small and rounded and has a shallow, cuplike depression on its upper surface for articulation with the capitulum of the humerus. A prominent ridge surrounds the head, and by means of this it rotates within the radial notch of the ulna. The head is supported on a constricted neck. Beneath the neck on the medial side is an eminence called the *radial tuberosity*, into which the tendon of the biceps brachii muscle is inserted. The lower end has two articular surfaces, one below, which articulates with the scaphoid and lunate bones of the wrist, and the other at the medial side, called the *ulnar notch*, which articulates with the ulna. Fracture of the lower third of the radius is called *Colles'* fracture.[6]

The carpus, or wrist (ossa carpi)

Is composed of eight small bones united by ligaments; they are arranged in *two rows* and are closely joined together, yet by the arrangement of their ligaments allow a certain amount of motion. They afford *origin* by their palmar surface to most of the *short* muscles of the thumb and little finger and are named:

Proximate, or Upper Row		*Distal, or Lower Row*	
1. Scaphoid	1	5. Trapezium	1
2. Lunate	1	6. Trapezoidium	1
3. Triangular	1	7. Capitate	1
4. Pisiform	1	8. Hamate	1

[6] Abraham Colles, Irish surgeon (1773–1843).

The metacarpus, or body of hand

Each metacarpus is formed by five bones (ossa metacarpalia), *numbered* from the lateral side. The bones are convex behind and concave in front. They articulate at their bases with the second row of carpal bones and with each other. The *heads* of the bones *articulate* with the bases of the first row of the phalanges.

The phalanges (phalanges digitorum manus)

The bones of the fingers are 14 in number in each hand, three for each finger, and two for the thumb. The *first* row *articulates* with the metacarpal bones and the second row of phalanges; the *second row* articulates with the *first* and *third*; the *third* articulates with the *second* row.

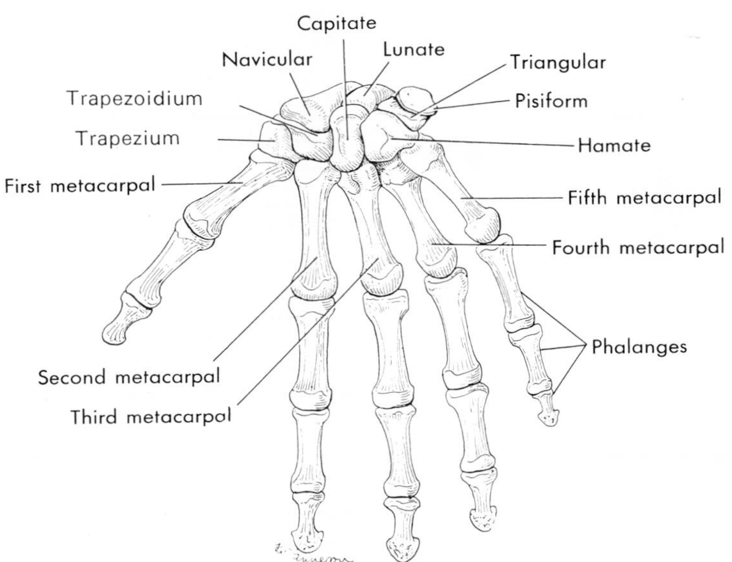

Figure 4–29. Bones of the right hand, volar surface.

Bones of the Lower Extremities

Hip bones, ossa coxae	2	62 (total)
Femur, thigh bone	2	
Patella, knee cap	2	
Tibia, shin bone, 2 } leg / Fibula, small bone of calf, 2 } leg	4	
Tarus, ossa tarsi	14	
Metatarsus, sole and lower instep	10	
Phalanges, 2 in great toe, 3 in others	28	

The two hip bones (os coxae)

Articulate with each other in front, forming an arch called the *pelvic girdle*. The arch is completed behind by the sacrum and the coccyx, forming a rigid and complete ring of bone called the *pelvis*. The pelvis attaches the lower extremities to the axial skeleton. The bones of the lower extremities correspond in general to those of the upper extremities, but their function is different. The lower extremities support the body in the erect position and are more solidly built. They are less movable than those of the upper extremities. The hip bones are large, irregularly shaped bones which form the sides and front wall of the pelvic cavity. In youth the hip bone consists of three separate parts. In the adult these have become united, but it is usual to describe the bone as divisible into three portions: (1) the *ilium* (pl., *ilia*), or upper, expanded portion forming the prominence of the hip; (2) the ischium (pl., *ischia*), or lower, strong portion; (3) the *pubis* (pl., *pubes*), or portion helping to form the front of the pelvis. These three portions of the bone meet and finally ankylose in a deep socket, called the *acetabulum*, into which the head of the femur fits. Processes formed by the projection of the crest of the ilium in front are called the *anterior superior iliac spine* and the *anterior inferior iliac spine*. The largest foramen in the skeleton, called the *obturator foramen*, is situated between the ischium and pubis. The articulation formed by the two pubic bones in front, called the *symphysis pubis*, serves as a convenient landmark in making body measurements.

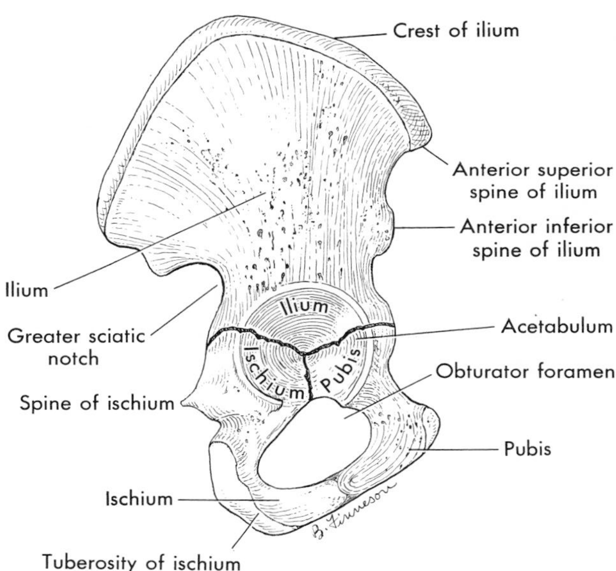

Figure 4–30. The hip bone, showing the union of ilium, ischium, and os pubis in the acetabulum.

The pelvis

Resembles a basin, is strong and massively constructed. It is composed of four bones, the two hip bones forming the sides and front, the sacrum and coccyx completing it behind, and is divided by a narrowed bony ring into the greater, or false, and the lesser, or true, pelvis. The narrowed bony ring which is the dividing line is spoken of as the *brim of the pelvis*.

The greater pelvis is the expanded portion situated above the brim, bounded on either side by the ilium; the front is filled by the walls of the abdomen. *The lesser pelvis* is below and behind the pelvic brim, bounded on the front and sides by the pubes and ischia and behind by the sacrum and coccyx. It consists of an *inlet*, an *outlet*, and a *cavity*. The space included within the brim of the pelvis is called the superior aperture, or inlet; and the space below, between the tip of the coccyx behind and the tuberosities of the ischia on either side, is called the inferior aperture, or outlet. The cavity of the lesser pelvis is a short, curved canal, deeper on the posterior than on its anterior wall. In the adult it contains part of the sigmoid colon, the rectum, bladder, and some of the reproductive organs. The bladder is behind the symphysis pubis; the rectum is in the curve of the sacrum and coccyx. In the female the uterus, tubes, ovaries, and vagina are between the bladder and the rectum.

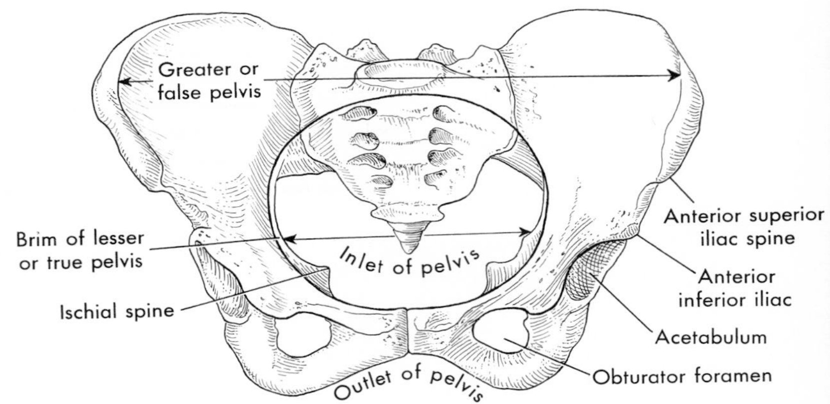

Figure 4–31. The female pelvis, ventral view.

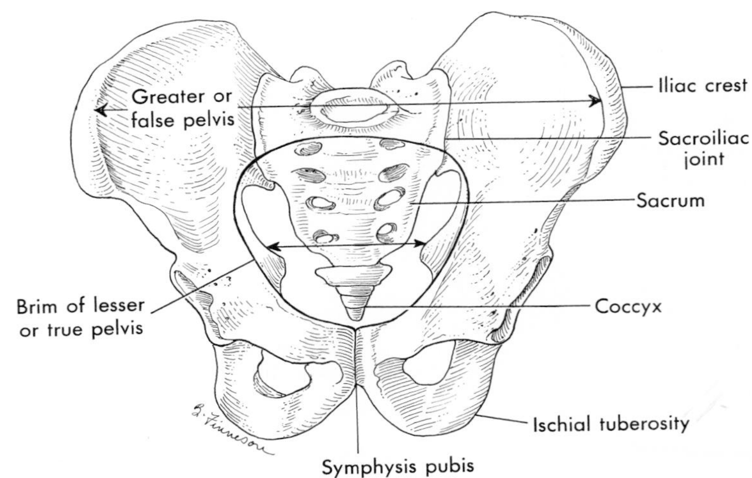

Figure 4–32. The male pelvis, ventral view.

The female pelvis differs from that of the male in those particulars which render it better adapted to pregnancy and parturition. It is more *shallow* than the male pelvis but wider in every direction. The inlet and outlet are larger and more nearly oval, the bones are lighter and smoother, the coccyx is more movable, and the subpubic arch is greater than a right angle. The subpubic angle in a male is less than a right angle.

The femur

Is the longest bone in the body. The upper end has a rounded head with a constricted neck, and two eminences, called the *greater* and *lesser trochanters*. The head articulates with the cavity in the hip bone, called the *acetabulum*. The lower extremity of the femur is larger than the upper, is flattened from before backward, and is divided into two large eminences, or *condyles*, by an intervening notch. The condyles are the lateral and medial, and the intervening notch is the *intercondyloid fossa*. The lower end of the femur articulates with the tibia and the patella. The bone inclines gradually downward and inward, so as to approach its fellow below to bring the knee joint near the line of gravity of the body. The degree of inclination is greater in the female than in the male.

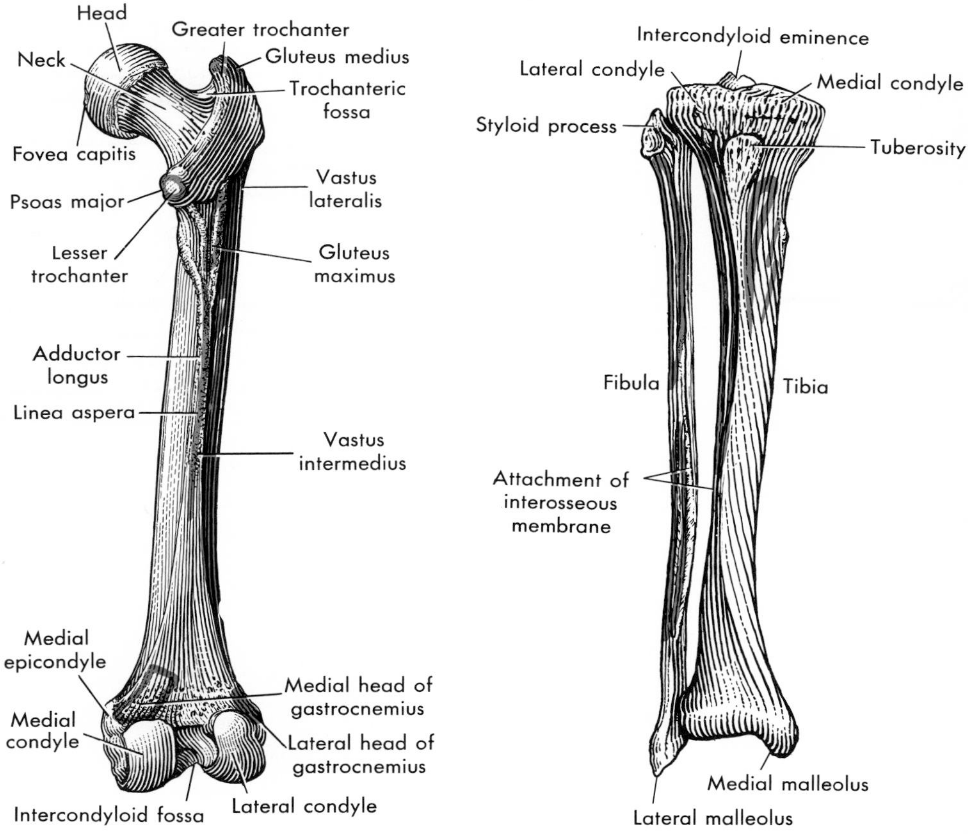

Figure 4–33. The right femur, or thigh bone, dorsal aspect. (*Red*) Muscle origins, (*blue*) muscle insertions.

Figure 4–34. The bones of the right leg, ventral surface. (*Red*) Muscle origins, (*blue*) muscle insertions.

The patella

Small, flat, triangular, sesamoid bone developed in the tendon of the quadriceps femoris muscle and placed in front of the knee joint. It articulates with the femur and is surrounded by large, fluid-filled bursae.

The tibia

Lies at the front and medial side of the leg. The upper extremity is expanded into two condyles, lateral and medial, with the sharp intercondyloid eminence between them. The superior surfaces are concave and receive the condyles of the femur. The lower extremity is smaller than the upper; it is prolonged downward on its medial side into a strong process, the *medial malleolus*, which forms the inner prominence of the ankle. There is also the surface for articulation with the talus, which forms the ankle joint. The tibia also articulates with the lower end of the fibula. In the male the tibia is vertical and parallel with the bone of the opposite side, but in the female it has a slightly oblique direction lateralward, to compensate for the oblique direction of the femur medialward.

The fibula (calf bone)

Is situated on the lateral side of the tibia, parallel with it. It is smaller than the tibia and, in proportion to its length, is the most slender of all the long bones. Its upper extremity consists of an irregular head by means of which it articulates with the tibia, but it does not reach the knee joint. The lower extremity is prolonged downward into a pointed process, the *lateral malleolus*, which lies just beneath the skin and forms the outer ankle bone. The lower extremity articulates with the tibia and the talus. The talus is held between the lateral malleolus of the fibula and the medial malleolus of the tibia. A fracture of the lower end of the fibula with injury of the lower tibial articulation is called a *Pott's*[7] *fracture*.

The tarsus (ossa tarsi)

Is formed by the calcaneus (os calcis), talus, cuboid (os cuboideum), navicular (os naviculare pedis), and the first, second, and third cuneiforms (os cuneiforme). The largest and strongest of the tarsal bones is called the *calcaneus*, or *heel bone*; it serves to transmit the weight of the body to the ground and forms a strong lever for the muscles of the calf of the leg.

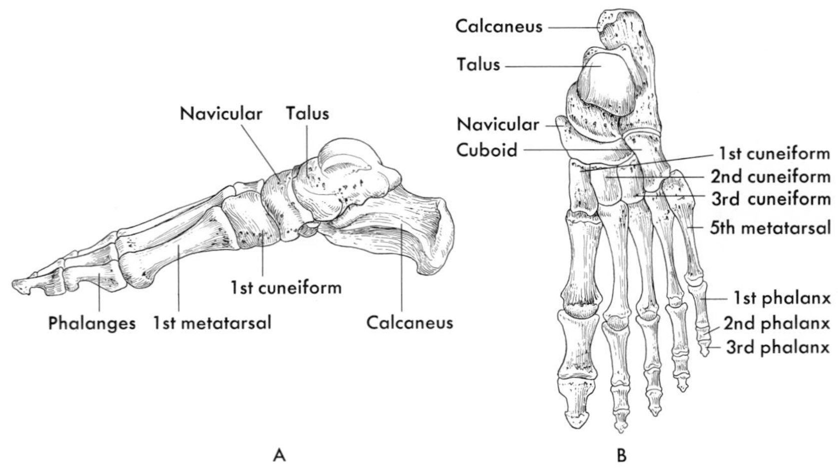

Figure 4–35. (*A*) Inner side of right foot. (*B*) Dorsal surface, bones of left foot.

The metatarsus, or sole and instep of the foot

Is formed by five bones which resemble the metacarpal bones of the hand. Each bone articulates with the tarsal bones by one extremity and by the other with the first row of phalanges.

The tarsal and metatarsal bones are so arranged that they form two distinct arches; the one running from the calcaneus to the heads of the metatarsal bones on the inner (medial) side is called the

[7] Percivall Pott, English surgeon (1714–1788).

longitudinal arch, and the other across the foot in the metatarsal region is called the *transverse arch*. The arches of the foot are completed by strong ligaments and tendons. The foot is strong, flexible, resilient, and able to provide the spring and lift for the activities of the body.

These arches may become weakened and progressively broken down, a condition known as flatfoot. This condition is thought to be due to prenatal conditions, dietary or hormone disturbances, improper posture, weight or fatigue conditions, or the wearing of shoes ill-fitting in last or size.

Phalanges

Both in number and general arrangement they resemble those in the hand, there being two in the great toe and three in each of the other toes

QUESTIONS FOR DISCUSSION

1. What are the functions of the bones?
2. Which bones articulate with the femur, humerus, scapula, and the atlas?
3. What is the anatomical relationship of the nerves, blood vessels, and lymphatics to the skeleton?
4. Discuss the structure and function of the intervertebral disk and nucleus pulposus.
5. Discuss the sternum, its position and flexibility in relation to heart massage.

SUMMARY

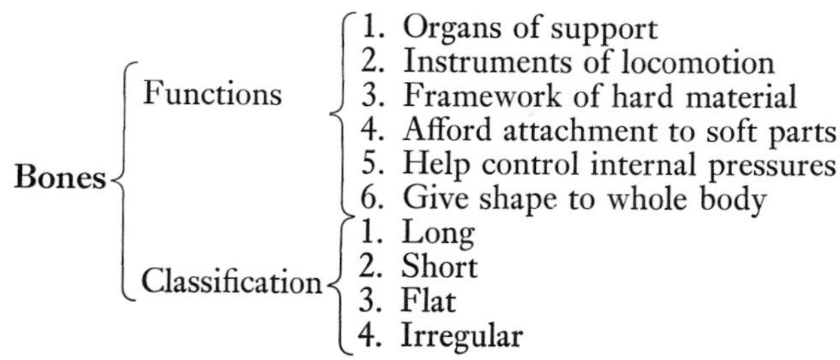

Table of the Bones

BONES OF THE HEAD

Cranium		*Face*	
Occipital	1	Nasal	2
Parietal	2	Vomer	1
Frontal	1	Inferior nasal concha (inf. turb.)	2
Temporal	2	Lacrimal	2
Sphenoid	1	Zygomatic (malar)	2
Ethmoid	1	Palatine (palate)	2
	—	Maxilla	2
	8	Mandible	1
			—
			14

Fontanelles	Anterior	1
	Posterior	1
	Anterolateral	2
	Posterolateral	2
Sinuses Opening into Nasal Cavity	Frontal	
	Ethmoidal	
	Sphenoidal	
	Maxillary	
Ear	Malleus	2
	Incus	2
	Stapes	2
		—
	Described with ear (Chapter 12)	6
	Hyoid bone in the neck	1

Bones of the Trunk

		Child	*Adult*	
Vertebrae	Cervical	7	7	
	Thoracic	12	12	
	Lumbar	5	5	
	Sacral	5	1	
	Coccygeal	4 = 33	1 =	26
Ribs				24
Sternum				1
				—
				51

Intervertebral Disks Disks of fibrocartilage interposed between the bodies of vertebrae from axis to sacrum

Bones of the Upper Extremity

Clavicle	1	Greater multangular (trapezium)	1
Scapula	1	Lesser multangular (trapezoid)	1
Humerus	1	Capitate (os magnum)	1
Ulna	1	Hamate (unciform)	1
Radius	1	Metacarpus	5
Carpus		Phalanges	14
Navicular (scaphoid)	1		—
Lunate (semilunar)	1		32
Triangular (cuneiform)	1		32 × 2 = 64
Pisiform	1		

Bones of the Lower Extremity

Hip bone (os coxae)	1	Third cuneiform (external cuneiform)	1
Femur	1	Second cuneiform (middle cuneiform)	1
Patella	1	First cuneiform (internal cuneiform)	1
Tibia	1	Metatarsus	5
Fibula	1	Phalanges	14
Tarsus			—
Calcaneus (os calcis)	1		31
Talus (astragalus)	1		31 × 2 = 62
Cuboid	1		
Navicular (scaphoid)	1		

Comparison of Female and Male Pelvis

	Female	*Male*
Bones	Slender	Heavier and rough
Sacrum	Broad, less curved	Narrow, more curved
Symphysis	Shallow	Deeper
Major pelvis	Narrow	Wide
Minor pelvis	Shallow and wide, capacity great	Deeper and narrower, capacity less
Great sciatic notches	Wide	Narrow
Superior aperture	Oval	Heart-shaped

CHAPTER

5

JOINTS OR ARTICULATIONS

Classification and Function

All bones have articulating surfaces so that various body movements may be accomplished. These surfaces form joints or articulations, some of which are freely movable, others slightly movable or immovable. All types are important for smooth, coordinated movements of the body.

Structure of Joints. The articulating surfaces of the bones are sometimes separated by a thin membrane, sometimes by strong strands of connective tissue, or fibrocartilage, and in the freely moving joints are completely separated. Strong ligaments extend over the joints or form capsules, which ensheath them. Tendons of muscles also extend over the joints.

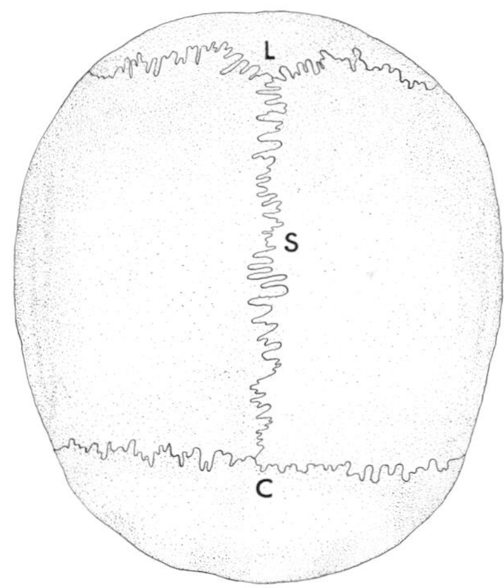

Figure 5–1. A toothed, or sagittal, suture, seen on the top of the skull. (*L*) Lambdoidal suture, (*S*) sagittal suture, (*C*) coronal suture.

Classification. Joints are classified according to the amount of movement of which they are capable and their structural composition:

1. Synarthroses (juncturae fibrosae), or immovable joints.

2. Amphiarthoses (juncturae cartilagenae), or slightly movable articulations.

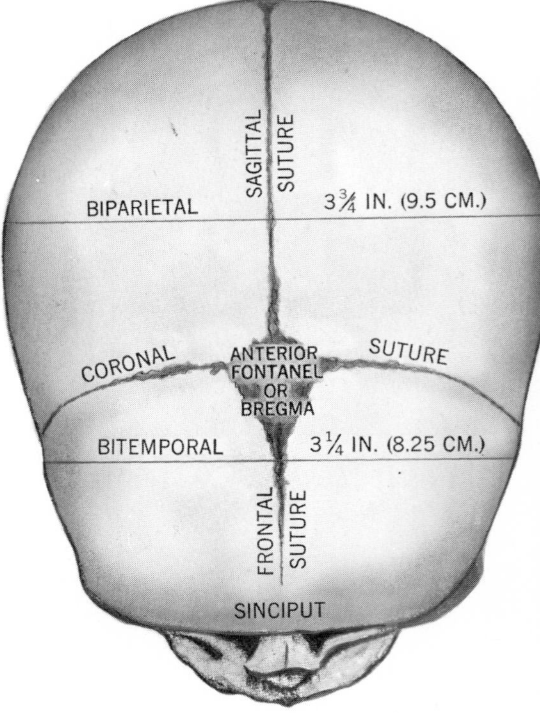

Figure 5–2. Diameters and landmarks of the fetal skull, upper surface. (Modified from Edgar.)

3. Diarthroses (juncturae synoviales) or freely movable articulations.

Synarthroses, or Immovable Joints. The bones are connected by fibrous tissue or cartilage. The bones of the skull and face (with the exception of the mandible) have their adjacent surfaces in direct contact fastened together by a thin layer of fibrous tissue. The union is by a series of interlocking processes and indentations which form sutures. (See summary for list of these sutures.)

Amphiarthroses, or Slightly Movable Joints. These include two varieties: (1) symphysis and (2) synchondrosis. *Symphysis* is a joint where two long bony surfaces are connected by a broad, flat disk of fibrocartilage. *Synchondrosis* is a temporary form of joint. The cartilage is changed to bone before adult life, as found between the epiphysis and bodies of long bone.

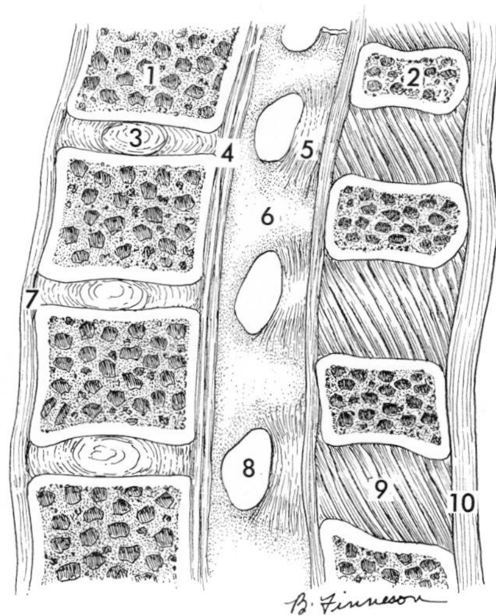

Figure 5–3. Diagram of vertebral symphyses, seen in longitudinal section through four segments of the vertebral column. (*1*) Body of vertebra; (*2*) spinous processes; (*3*) intervertebral cartilaginous disk; (*4*) posterior longitudinal ligament; (*5*) ligamentum flavum; (*6*) spinal canal; (*7*) anterior longitudinal ligament; (*8*) intervertebral foramen; (*9*) interspinus ligament; (*10*) supraspinous ligament.

Diarthroses (Juncturae Synoviales), or Freely Movable Joints. These include most of the joints in the body. The adjacent ends of the bones are covered with hyaline cartilage and are surrounded by a fibrous *articular* capsule which is strengthened by ligaments and lined with synovial membrane except over the articular cartilage. Tendons of muscles pass over these joints and play an important part in stabilizing the joint. The hyaline cartilage provides a smooth surface for the opposing bones, lubricated by synovial fluid (see page 44). Freely movable joints are classified by the kind of motion permitted.

1. Gliding Joints (Articulatio Plana). These joints permit gliding movement only, as in the joints between the carpal bones of the wrist, between the tarsal bones of the ankle, and between the articular processes of the vertebrae. The articular surfaces are nearly flat, or one may be slightly convex and the other slightly concave.

2. Hinge Joints (Ginglymus). Hinge joints allow angular movement in one direction, like a door on its hinges. The articular surfaces are of such shape as to permit motion in the forward-and-backward plane. These movements are called flexion and extension, as may be seen in the joint between the humerus and ulna, in the knee and ankle joints, and in the articulations of the phalanges. Strong collateral ligaments form their chief bond of union. The knee joint is described as a hinge joint, but it is actually much more complicated. There is the articulation between each condyle of the femur and the corresponding meniscus and the condyle of the tibia, and the articulation between the femur and the patella. The bones are held together by the articular capsule and 10 ligaments. (See Figure 5–5.) There are two menisci, the medial and the lateral; they are crescent-shaped structures of fibrocartilage; the surfaces are smooth and covered with synovial membrane. The upper surfaces are concave and in contact with the femur; the lower surfaces are flat and rest on the head of the tibia. The peripheral border of each one is thick and convex and attached to the inside of the joint capsule.

The inner border is thin, concave, and unattached. The *function* of the menisci is to *deepen* the surfaces of the head of the tibia for articulation with the condyles of the femur.

3. CONDYLOID JOINTS (ARTICULATIO ELLIPSOIDEA). These permit an angular movement in two directions, as when an ovoid articular surface or condyle of bone is received into an elliptical cavity, e.g., the wrist joint. Movements permitted in this form of articulation include flexion, extension, adduction, abduction, and circumduction but no axial rotation.

4. SADDLE JOINTS (ARTICULATIO SELLARIS). In this type of joint the articular surface of each of the articular bones is concave in one direction and convex in another. The metacarpal bone of the thumb is articulated with the trapezium bone of the carpus by a saddle joint. The movements at these joints are the same as in condyloid joints.

5. PIVOT JOINTS (TROCHOID). These are joints with a rotary movement in one axis. In this form a ring rotates around a pivot or a pivotlike process rotates within a ring being formed of bone and cartilage. In the articulation of the axis and atlas, the front of the ring is formed by the anterior arch of the atlas and the back by the transverse ligament. The odontoid process of the axis forms a pivot, and around this pivot the ring rotates, carrying the head with it. In the proximal articulation of the radius and ulna, the head of the radius rotates within the ring formed by the radial notch of the ulna and the annular ligament. The hand is attached to the lower end of the radius, and the radius, in rotating, carries the hand with it; thus, the palm of the hand is alternately turned forward and backward. When the palm is turned forward or

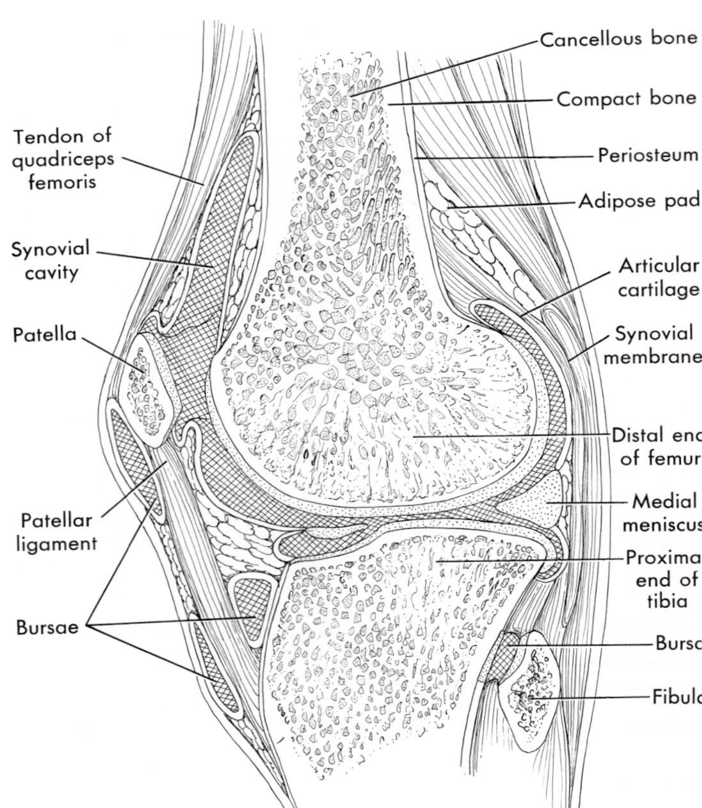

Figure 5–4. Longitudinal section of a hinge joint—the knee. (Modified from Ham.)

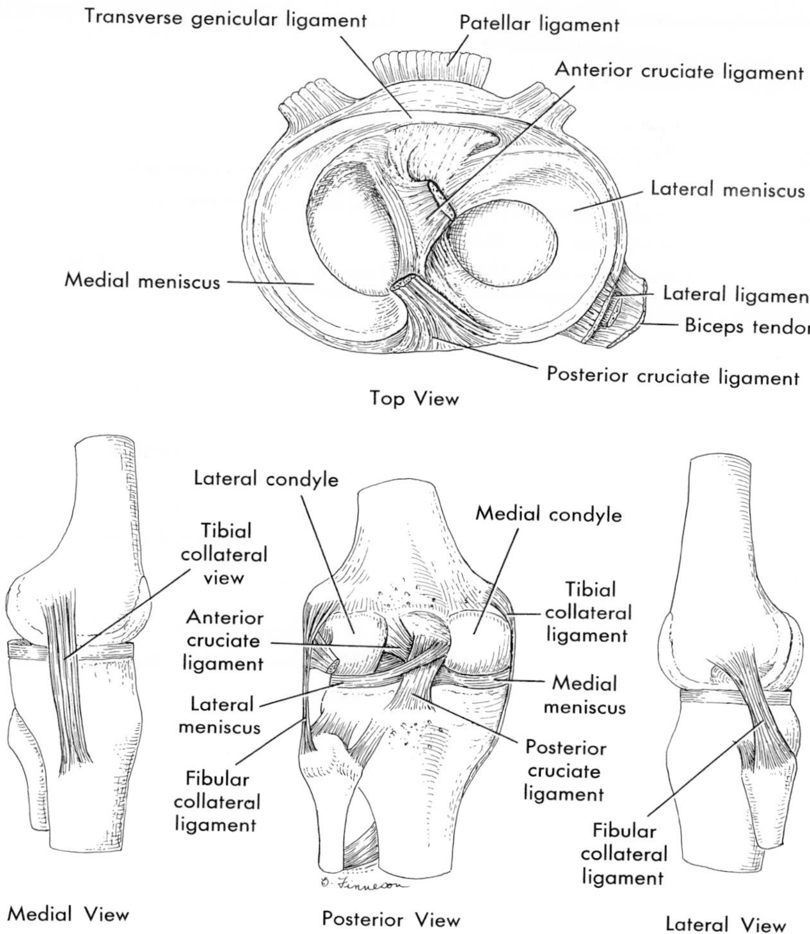

Figure 5–5. Ligaments of the knee. (Modified from Pansky and House.)

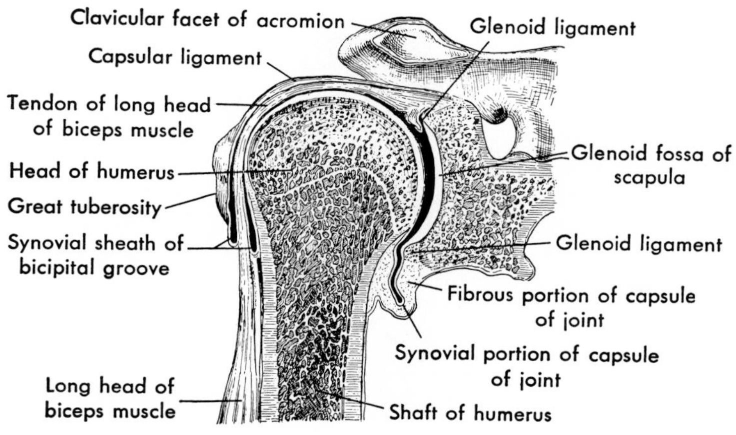

Figure 5–6. Diagram of the shoulder joint. Shallow ball-and-socket joint. (Modified from Toldt.)

upward, the attitude is called *supination*; when backward or downward, *pronation*.

6. BALL-AND-SOCKET JOINTS (SPHEROIDEA ENARTHROSIS). These have an angular movement in all directions and a pivot movement. In this form of joint a more or less rounded head lies in a cuplike cavity, such as the head of the femur in the acetabulum and the head of the humerus in the glenoid cavity of the scapula. The shoulder joint is the most freely movable joint in the body.

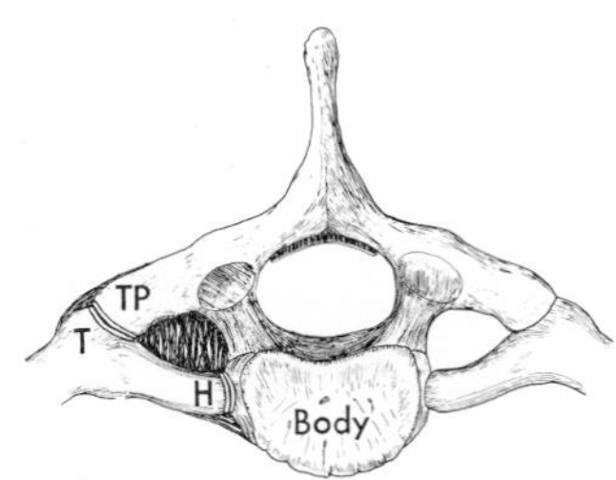

Figure 5–7. Diagram of gliding joints between the head of a rib and the body of a vertebra, and also between the tubercle of a rib and the transverse process of a vertebra. (*H*) Head of rib, (*T*) tubercle of rib, (*TP*) transverse process.

Movement. Bones thus connected are capable of different kinds of movement, which rarely occur singly but usually in combination, thus allowing great variety.

1. Gliding Movement. This is the simplest kind of motion that can take place in a joint, one surface moving over another without any angular or rotatory movement. The costovertebral articulations permit a slight gliding of the heads and tubercles of the ribs on the bodies and transverse processes of the vertebrae.

2. Angular Movement. This occurs only between long bones, and by it the angle between two bones is either increased or diminished. It includes flexion, extension, abduction, and adduction.

A. FLEXION. A limb is flexed when it is bent, e.g., bending the arm at the elbow. The angle between the two bones is *decreased*.

B. EXTENSION. This is the reverse of flexion. The angle between the two bones is *increased*.

C. ABDUCTION. This term means drawn away from the middle line of the body, e.g., lifting the arm away from or at right angles to the body.

D. ADDUCTION. This term means brought to, or nearer, the middle line of the body, e.g., bringing the arm to the side of the body.

Both abduction and adduction have a different meaning when used with reference to the fingers and toes. In the hand, abduction and adduction refer to an imaginary line drawn through the middle finger, and in the foot, to an imaginary line drawn through the second toe.

3. Circumduction. This means that form of motion which takes place between the head of a bone and its articular cavity, when the bone is made to circumscribe a conical space

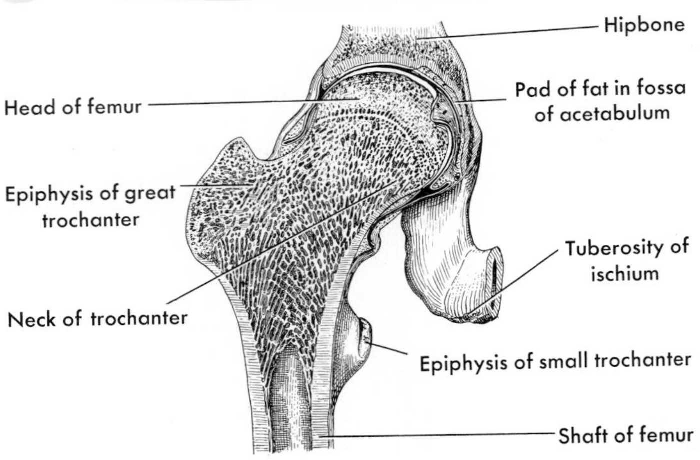

Figure 5–8. Diagram of the hip joint. Section of a ball-and-socket joint. (Modified from Toldt.)

by rotation around an imaginary axis, e.g., swinging the arms or legs.

4. Rotation. This means a form of movement in which a bone moves around a central axis without undergoing any displacement from this axis, e.g., rotation of the atlas around the odontoid process of the axis.

Complete rotation, as of a wheel, is not possible in any joints of the body.

5. Inversion. In movement at the ankle the sole of the foot turns inward.

6. Eversion. In movement at the ankle the sole of the foot turns outward.

Sprain. A wrenching or twisting of a joint accompanied by a stretching or tearing of the ligaments or tendons is called a sprain.

Dislocation. If, in addition to a sprain, a bone of a joint is displaced, the injury is called a dislocation.

Ankylosis. This is immobility and consolidation of a joint.

Frequent Disorders of Joints. *Bursitis.* Bursitis is an acute inflammation of the synovial bursa. It may be caused by excess tension or from some systemic or local inflammatory process. There may be deposits of calcium which interfere with motion. If bursitis becomes chronic, the joint may become stiff even though the joint itself is not involved. Joints most often involved include the shoulder, elbow, and knee joints.

Arthritis. This is an inflammation of joints which is common and painful. There are many varieties. The most common types are:

1. RHEUMATOID ARTHRITIS. This is a systemic disease with widespread involvement of connective tissues. The synovial membrane is thickened and ankylosis results.

2. OSTEOARTHRITIS. This is a degenerative condition which occurs in joints that are subject to a great deal of wear and tear. It usually occurs in individuals after the age of 45 years. The spine and joints of the lower extremity are most frequently involved.

There are softening of the cartilage, separation of fibers, and eventually disintegration of the cartilage. As the cartilage thins, the perichondrium and periosteum are irritated, which in turn stimulates cartilaginous and bony proliferation at the joint margins.

3. GOUTY ARTHRITIS. This is a metabolic disorder due to a disturbance of purine metabolism. Uric acid is elevated in the blood and crystals may be formed in the joints. The joint most frequently involved is the metatarsophalangeal of the great toe.

4. RHEUMATIC FEVER. This is a disease involving the synovial tissues, tendons, and other connective tissues around joints. Cartilage and bone are not involved. It is an acute inflammatory process which does not show residual changes in the articular system, but may leave permanent damage to the valves of the heart which becomes evident in later life.

QUESTIONS FOR DISCUSSION

1. What is the soft spot felt on a baby's head? What is its function? What becomes of this as the baby develops?
2. How are joints classified? Give examples of each.
3. After a knee injury, there may be considerable swelling. Explain. What structures of the knee are affected?
4. A frequent knee injury to football players involves ligaments and the menisci. Explain the menisci and give their location and structure.

SUMMARY

Joints or articulations—connections between bones

- **Immovable Joint, or Synarthrosis**
  - Bones are connected by fibrous tissue or cartilage
    1. *Sutures.* Articulations by processes and indentations interlocked
       - *True sutures*
         - Sutura dentata—toothlike, e.g., sutures between parietal bones
         - Sutura serrata—sawlike, e.g., sutures between two portions of frontal bone
         - Sutura limbosa—in addition to interlocking, the articular surfaces are beveled and overlap, e.g., suture between parietal and frontal bones
       - *False sutures*
         - Sutura squamosa—scalelike, e.g., suture between the temporal and parietal bones
         - Sutura plana—simple apposition of rough surfaces, e.g., articulations between the maxillae
    2. *Schindylesis.* A thin plate of bone is received in a cleft or fissure of another bone, e.g., the reception of the vomer in the fissure between the maxillae and between the palatine bones
    3. *Gomphosis.* A conical process fits into a socket, e.g., roots of teeth into the alveoli of the maxillae and mandible
- **Slightly Movable Joint, or Amphiarthrosis**
  - Bones are connected by disks of cartilage or interosseous ligaments
    1. *Symphysis.* The bones are united by a plate or disk of fibrocartilage of considerable thickness
    2. *Synchondrosis.* Temporary form of joint as the cartilage is changed to bone before adult life, as found between the epiphysis and bodies of long bone
- **Movable Joint, or Diarthrosis**
  - 1. Hyaline cartilage covering adjacent ends of the bones
    2. Fibrous capsule strengthened by ligaments
    3. Synovial membrane lining fibrous capsule
    - 1. *Articulatio plana.* Gliding joint; articulates by surfaces which glide upon each other
      2. *Ginglymus.* Hinge joint; moves backward and forward in one plane
      3. *Articulatio ellipsoidea.* Condyloid joint; ovoid head received into elliptical cavity
      4. *Articulatio sellars.* Saddle joint; articular surfaces are concavoconvex
      5. *Trochoid.* Pivot joint; articulates by a process turning within a ring or by a ring turning around a pivot
      6. *Spheroidea enarthrosis.* Ball-and-socket joint; articulates by a globular head in a cuplike cavity
- **Movement**
  1. Gliding movement
  2. Angular — Flexion, Extension, Adduction, Abduction
  3. Circumduction
  4. Rotation
  5. Inversion
  6. Eversion

CHAPTER

6

PROPERTIES OF MUSCLE TISSUE

Physiology of Contraction

Levers

Skeletal Muscles

Motion is an important activity of the body which is made possible by the special function of contractility in muscle tissue. Motion in this sense includes not only movements of the entire body or parts of the body from place to place, but those of breathing, the beating of the heart, movements of the parts of the alimentary canal and its glands, and movements of the other viscera, including those of the blood and lymph vessels.

All physiological activities are closely related to motion brought about by contraction of muscle. Contraction (change in shape) of the enormous number of muscle cells is intimately related to all the other tissue cells of the body, for example, supplying gland cells with the requisite materials for the manufacture of their secretion; in making it possible for glands to empty their secretion into cavities or into body fluids and in moving tissue fluid about to supply all cells (e.g., nerve cells or the muscle cells themselves) with a continuous source of supplies at low concentration, and removing their wastes constantly.

MUSCULAR TISSUE

In the human, muscular tissue constitutes 40 to 50 per cent of the body weight. Special characteristics of muscle tissue are irritability (excitability), contractility, extensibility, and elasticity. *Irritability*, or *excitability*, is the property of receiving stimuli and responding to them. All cells possess this property. The response of any tissue to stimulation is to perform its special function, which, in the case of muscular tissue, is contraction. *Contractility* is the property which enables muscles to change their shape and become shorter and thicker. This property is characteristic of all protoplasm but is more highly developed in muscular tissue than in any other. *Extensibility* of a living muscle cell means that it can be stretched, or extended, and *elasticity* means that it readily returns to its original form when the stretching force is removed.

Tonus. Tonus is a property of muscle whereby a steady, partial contraction varying in degree is maintained. The fundamental mechanism whereby *tone*, or *tonus*, is produced is not fully understood, but physiologically it is known to be due to nerve impulses. By means of tonic contraction in skeletal muscles, posture is maintained for long periods with little or no evidence of fatigue. Absence of fatigue is brought about mainly by means of different groups of muscle fibers contracting

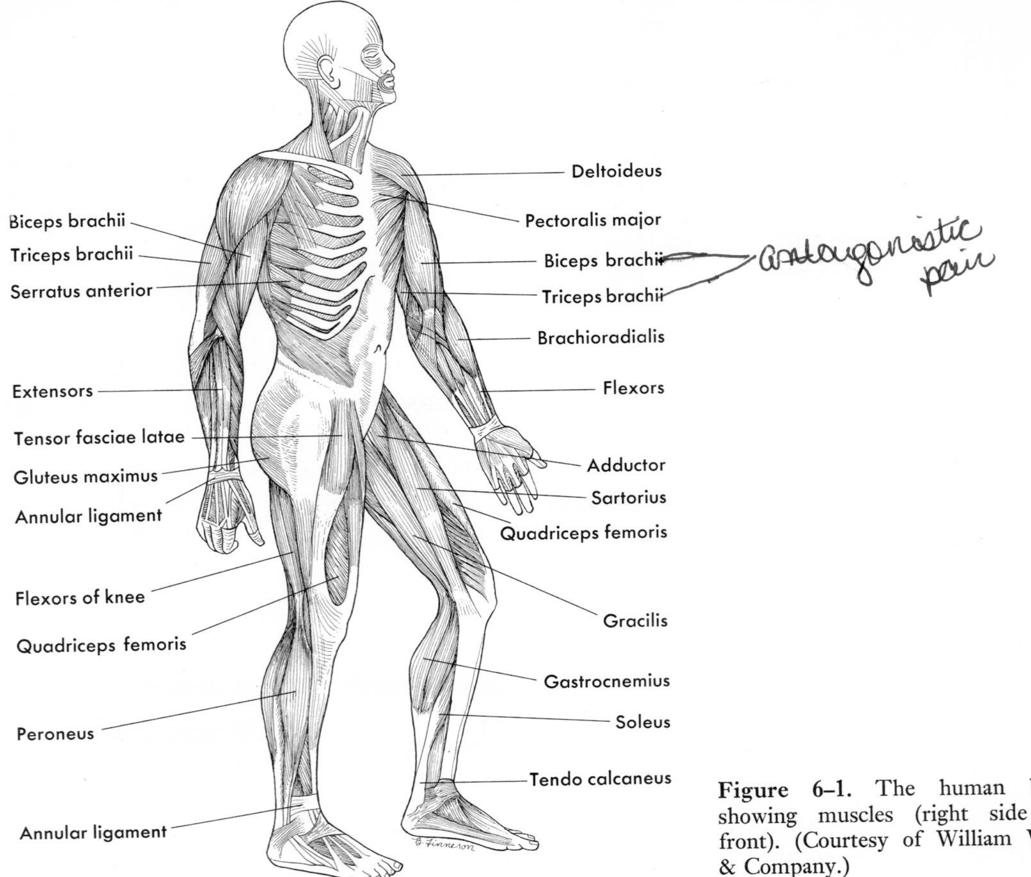

Figure 6–1. The human body, showing muscles (right side and front). (Courtesy of William Wood & Company.)

in relays, giving alternating periods of rest and activity for a given muscle fiber group. In man the antigravity skeletal muscles (retractors of neck, extensors of the back, etc.) exhibit the highest degree of tonus. During sleep, tone is at a minimum.

The tone of skeletal muscles gives a certain firmness and maintains a slight, steady pull upon their attachments; it also functions in the maintenance of a certain pressure upon the contents of the abdominal cavity. Both the rapidity and the smoothness of movement depend on tone. In fractures the overriding of the broken ends of the bone is often due to the contractions of the muscles because of this property of tonicity.

Both visceral and cardiac muscle exhibit tonus even when isolated from the nervous system. This is probably due to the plexuses of nerve cells and fibers distributed through them. The maintenance of normal blood pressure is partly dependent on the tone of the muscles in the walls of the small arteries. Likewise, digestion is dependent on the tone of the muscles of the stomach and intestines. Although the tone of visceral and cardiac muscles is inherent in them, it is probably also under chemical control similar to that for striated muscle.

Muscle contraction is concerned with the tone of the protoplasm of muscle cells, first the tone of individual muscle cells themselves, then the integrated tone of muscle cells in individual muscles. This tone is maintained by the chemical and physical composition of tissue fluids and by the nervous system. The cerebellum makes the final adjustments needed for *muscle groups* to act together, though muscle tone is maintained through centers in the spinal cord or brain.

Excitation (Stimulation). A muscle is excitable because the muscle fibers composing it are excitable. All protoplasm possesses the property of *excitability*. Any force which affects this excitability is called a *stimulus*. Physiologically, a stimulus represents a change in the environment of the muscle cells. Protoplasm also possesses the property of *conductivity*, and when stimulated at one point the response may travel through the cell. The response is the specialized one which is characteristic for the tissue stimulated; in muscles it is contraction. Normally, the muscles are stimulated by impulses conveyed to them by nerve fibers.

As the motor nerve fiber approaches the muscle fiber, it loses its myelin sheath. The unmyelinated fiber divides into terminal ramifications which make profuse and close contact with a specialized part of the muscle sarcoplasm called the neuromuscular junction. When the nerve impulse reaches the nerve terminal, acetylcholine is released and diffuses into the end-plate. (Acetylcholine becomes attached to the end-plate receptor, and local end-plate electrical potential is produced. Eventually the surface membrane of the muscle fiber is depolarized, the muscle fibers set up a propagated muscle action potential, and the muscle responds.) An enzyme cholinesterase also formed in the motor end-plate rapidly destroys acetylcholine at the area of release. Various stimuli may serve to inhibit muscular activity as well as to excite it. (Other forms of stimuli, such as mechanical, thermal, chemical, and electrical, are used in experimental work with muscles and are called *artificial stimuli*. A common source of stimulation is electricity as it is available and convenient, easily controlled as to strength and speed of application, and least destructive to the tissues stimulated. While muscles are within the body or when isolated from the body, they can be excited by artificial stimuli applied to their nerves or to the muscles directly.)

Muscles are supplied with two types of nerve fibers—*sensory* fibers, conveying to the central nervous system the state of contraction of the muscle, and *motor* fibers, conveying impulses from the central nervous system to the muscles, controlling their contraction. If a *motor nerve* is severed or the center in the brain or cord is damaged, no impulse is carried to the muscle, and *its function is lost*. When a sensory nerve is severed, no impulse is carried from the sensory end organ to the central nervous system, and sensation is thereby lost.

Conditions of Contraction. Skeletal muscles contract quickly and relax promptly. In contrast to this, the contractions of visceral muscle coats develop slowly, are maintained for some time, and fade out slowly. The contraction of a skeletal muscle is the result of stimuli discharged by the nerve fibers innervating it. If one of these contractions is analyzed, it will be found that there is a brief period after the muscle is stimulated before it contracts. This is called the *latent period* and is followed by a *period of contraction*, which in turn is followed by a *period of relaxation*. It has been demonstrated experimentally that if electrical stimuli are applied to a muscle, for instance to the gastrocnemius muscle of the frog, and the contractions are recorded on a moving drum, the contractions will vary in strength (in height on the drum record) depending on several factors: (1) the strength of the stimulus, (2) the speed of application of the stimulus, (3) the duration of the stimulus, (4) the weight of the load, and (5) the temperature. In general, the stronger the stimulus, the stronger the contraction will be, i.e., the greater the number of single cells which will contract. Strongest contractions result from stimuli of moderate duration. Some load is necessary in order to get the best response, but increase of load beyond the optimum decreases the height of contraction. Muscles do their best work at a certain optimum temperature. For man this is about 37° C (98.6° F) body temperature. If the temperature is raised much above this, the muscle loses its excitability and becomes functionally depressed, entering finally the state of heat rigor, i.e., a condition of permanent shortening.

Response to Stimuli. It has been found that if the stimulus applied to a single muscle fiber is strong enough to produce a response, it will give a contraction which is maximal, no matter what the strength of the stimulus. This is the all-or-none law. This means that each muscle fiber gives a maximal response or none at all under the conditions of the experiment. Fatigue and varying conditions of nutrition may alter the cell's response, but increasing the strength of the stimulus will not change the response.

The weakest stimulus which when applied over a reasonable period will cause contraction of the fiber under specified conditions is called the *minimal stimulus*. Any stimulus weaker than this is known as *subminimal* (*subliminal*). Two subminimal stimuli (each too weak in itself to cause contraction of the muscle fiber) may, when applied in rapid succession, by their combined forces be equivalent to a minimal stimulus and the cell will respond. This phenomenon is called *summation of stimuli*.

The unit of measure used in studying the excitability or irritability of any tissue is the *chronaxie*. The chronaxie of a cell is the shortest duration of time that a stimulus of twice minimal (rheobasic) strength must be applied to evoke a response.

When a muscle trunk is stimulated to contract many times in succession, the contractions for a time become progressively increased in extent, resulting in a record which shows a staircase effect. This effect is probably determined by an increase in irritability brought about by metabolic wastes formed during the first few contractions. As these metabolic products increase, irritability is decreased, and the contractions diminish progressively in extent until fatigue develops to a point where the muscle fails to respond. From this staircase phenomenon it is judged that activity of muscles is at first physiologically beneficial to the extent that irritability of muscular tissue is thereby increased.

If a second stimulus occurs during the apex of contraction from the first stimulus, the resulting height of contraction will be maximal. This is known as *summation of contractions*. If, however, the second stimulus occurs during a certain period of time after the accomplishment of the first contraction, there will be no second contraction. During this exceedingly brief lapse of time, known as the *absolute refractory period*, the muscle will not respond to any stimulus, however strong. This is followed by the *relative refractory period*, often called the *period of depressed excitability*, during which the muscle gradually regains its irritability.

If stimuli are applied to a muscle in such rapid succession that each occurs before the fibers have relaxed from the one preceding, the cells will remain in a state in which no relaxation is apparent. Such sustained contraction is called *tetanus*. Probably all voluntary acts, even the simplest, have tetanic contractions as their basis, and they are especially to be noted in such continued muscular work as holding the body erect or in carrying a load. Postural tonus is believed to be the result of a slight state of tetanic contraction of skeletal muscles due to fiber summation.

Types of Contractions. When a muscle trunk contracts and a weight is lifted, the muscle becomes shorter and thicker, but its tone remains the same. Since the tone of the fibers is not altered, such contractions are called *isotonic*. If the muscle is compelled to contract against some weight which it cannot lift, the tension in the fibers increases, but the muscle length remains unaltered. Since the length of the fibers is unchanged, such contractions are called *isometric*. Contraction of a skeletal muscle is usually of the isotonic type, but complexities of muscular activity involve the coordinated development of both isometric and isotonic contractions in the different fibers of a muscle trunk.

Contraction in Skeletal Muscles. The height of contraction of a skeletal muscle is in direct proportion to the strength of the stimulus applied. This is not a contradiction of the all-or-none law. It is explained by the fact that voluntary muscle cells are separate units insulated from each other by connective tissue. On account of environmental conditions the minimal stimulus of these separate fibers may vary. Thus, the minimal stimulus of a skeletal muscle trunk is one which evokes contraction from a single fiber; the maximal stimulus is one which will cause the contraction of every fiber present. A skeletal muscle trunk varies in this respect from the heart muscle, which responds as a unit to any stimulus which will contract a single cardiac cell. It will be recalled that cardiac muscle is a "network" of cells and that the rhythmical action of the heart is brought about by the contraction of these cells in unison.

The immediate cause of muscular contraction is not known, although there is evidence that *diffusion* and physical characteristics of *colloidal* conditions may help to explain it. The chemical reactions known to be associated with it seem to follow contraction rather than to produce it.

There are two phases in the contraction of muscle fibers: the *contractile phase* for which energy must be provided, and the *recovery phase* during which the fiber returns to resting state. The direct source of energy for muscle contraction is from reactions involving adenosine triphosphate (ATP), a compound which is rich in chemical energy. During the recovery period this substance is promptly re-formed by reaction with creatine phosphate, which is stored in muscle cells. Both contraction and relaxation of muscle can occur under anaerobic conditions with lactic acid made at the expense of muscle glycogen. However, to maintain adenosine triphosphate and creatine phosphate within the cell, energy is supplied primarily by oxidation of glycogen to carbon dioxide and water through reactions for which oxygen is essential.

Chemical Changes During Muscle Contraction

The active parts of striated muscle are composed of very minute fibers which contain the proteins actin and myosin surrounded by a very thin membrane. In resting muscle this membrane is polarized by the ions distributed on either side of the membrane. When the nerve impulse stimulates the muscle cells, waves of excitation pass over the fibers; the concentrations of potassium, sodium, and chloride ions change; and the muscle contracts. During the recovery period, the cell returns to its resting state. For these activities energy must be supplied within the cell.

Contraction of Muscle. This involves combination of myosin and actin to form a complex known as actomyosin. This complex reacts with adenosine triphosphate (ATP) releasing phosphate in the cell and leaving adenosine diphosphate (ADP). This reaction provides energy for the contraction of muscle.

$$\text{Actomyosin} + \text{ATP} \rightarrow \text{ADP-Actomyosin} + \text{Phosphate} + \text{Energy}$$

Relaxation of Muscle. Relaxation of muscle, which follows contraction, is accompanied by resynthesis of adenosine triphosphate in reaction with creatine phosphate.

$$\text{ADP} + \text{Creatine phosphate} \rightarrow \text{Creatine} + \text{ATP}$$

Some energy must be used in this synthesis. Creatine phosphate, which is stored in muscle cells, is used in the course of muscle activity in direct quantitative relation to the work done by the cell. In fatigued muscle, as the store of creatine phosphate is exhausted, the concentration of adenosine triphosphate is reduced, and the rate of muscle relaxation slows down and finally ceases.

Contraction and relaxation of muscles are also influenced by the varying ion concentrations within the cells and interstitial fluids. Magnesium and calcium are essential for normal response of skeletal muscle fibers to the nerve impulse. A lack of calcium ions increases irritability and may cause tetany (generalized tonic skeletal muscle contraction). Magnesium has a sedative action on the neuromuscular junction. The fibers also respond to changes in hydrogen ion concentration; an increase in hydrogen ions favors relaxation, a decrease favors contraction.

Source of Energy for Muscle Activity. Production of energy in muscle cells utilizes stored glycogen. The initial reactions, which involve the breaking down of the large carbohydrate units to smaller units, pyruvic acid and lactic acid, are known as glycogenolysis. These reactions are catalyzed by enzymes and do not involve oxygen. They result in a small net gain of adenosine triphosphate within the cell. It is believed that lactic acid is transported to the surface of the muscle cell by the sarcoplasmic reticulum. Lactic acid then escapes into the blood stream and is borne to the liver, where it is converted to glycogen and stored. In the muscle cell lactic acid may be used to re-form pyruvic acid, which can be oxidized to carbon dioxide and water.

The major *source* of energy for *resynthesis* of ATP, hence for the activity of muscle cells, comes through the reactions that involve oxygen. When oxygen supply is adequate, the production of lactic acid is inhibited and pyruvic acid enters the citric acid cycle—the common pathway for terminal oxidation of carbohydrate, fat, and amino acids—with the production of carbon dioxide and water. The greater part of the energy product comes from the transfer of electrons from hydrogen to oxygen through the citric acid cycle (page 474) to form water. Much of this energy is captured by enzymes and used in the synthesis of ATP; some energy is liberated as heat. The reactions with oxygen make available from 10 to 12 times as much energy as do the anaerobic reactions. Muscles operating under anaerobic conditions use six to eight times as much glycogen to do the same amount of work as could be accomplished under aerobic conditions.

Heat Formation. Muscles form the major source of body heat. The chemical changes that occur in muscle cells form mechanical energy used for movement and also release heat energy. Heat is liberated by the chemical processes that change the muscle from a relaxed to an active state, regardless of whether the muscle shortens or not.

Summary of Some of the Chemical Changes Taking Place in Muscle Cells in Relation to Contraction

1. ATP-actomyosin → ADP-actomyosin + Phosphate ion + Energy for contraction
2. Phosphocreatine + ADP → Creatine + ATP
3. Glycogen ↗ Pyruvic acid → Carbon dioxide + Water + Energy
   ↓↑
   Glycogen ↘ Lactic acid + Energy
4. Lactic acid → Re-formed into glycogen in liver cells

Oxygen Debt. During moderate exercise little or no lactic acid accumulates in the muscle cells, but with vigorous exercise the oxygen demand may be greater than the oxygen supply to the cells. Lactic acid accumulates in blood and muscle cells. This produces the condition known as *oxygen debt*. The anaerobic process is stimulated, with its attendant demand for glycogen, lessened synthesis of ATP, and depletion of creatine phosphate. This causes fatigue and the physiological demand for rest. The length of time is variable for meeting oxygen needs and restoration to normal concentration of cell components. Almost all reactions in living cells are catalyzed by enzymes; therefore, maintenance of enzymes is of physiological importance. Several members of the vitamin-B group have been identified as essential in the functioning of enzymes and enzyme systems. (See page 439.)

Fatigue and Exercise. In muscles undergoing contraction, the first effect of the formation of carbon dioxide and lactic acid is to increase irritability; but if a muscle is continuously stimulated, the strength of contraction becomes progressively less until the muscle refuses to respond. This is true fatigue and is caused, in part at least, by anoxia and the toxic effects of metabolites (carbon dioxide, acid phosphate, lactic acid) which accumulate during exercise. The loss of nutritive materials may also be a factor in fatigue, but recent conceptions stress the accumulation of metabolites.

In moderate exercise the system is able to eliminate these substances readily. After prolonged contractions a period of rest may be necessary to furnish opportunity for the blood to carry the fatigue substances to the excretory organs and nutritive material and oxygen to the muscle. Probably it is chiefly lactic acid which brings on fatigue by disturbing the hydrogen ion concentration of the cell

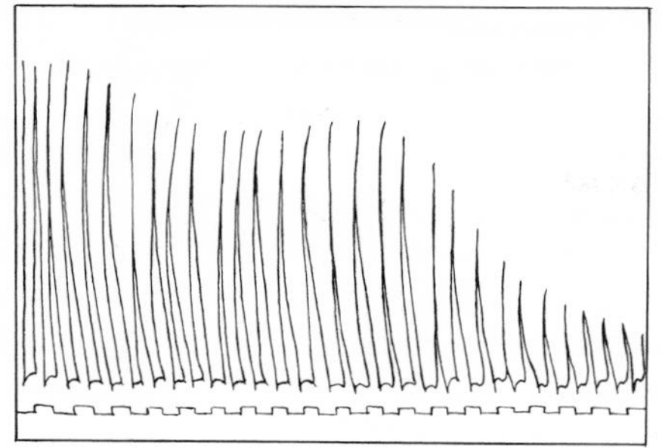

Figure 6–2. Record of muscular fatigue of finger. A weight is lifted by a finger by means of a cord which runs over a pulley. The writing lever is attached to the weight and writes on a moving drum. The apparatus is called an ergograph.

fluids, thus inhibiting the enzyme action which is responsible for further breakdown of glycogen. It has been demonstrated that injection of the blood of a fatigued animal into a rested one will promptly bring on signs of fatigue.

If fatigue is carried on to the point of absolute exhaustion, the cells do not recover. The protein constituents of the fibers coagulate, exhibiting the phenomenon known as *rigor mortis*. Rigor mortis occurs in muscles from 10 minutes to seven hours after death.

The body is susceptible to other fatigue than that of muscles. Most easily fatigued of all are the synapses, next the junctions between nerves and muscle fibers, then the muscles themselves.

Exercise stimulates circulation and thereby brings about a change in conditions for cells in all locations throughout the body. This great stirring-up effect of exercise brings fresh blood via the arterioles, and the local pressure as well as the fluid environment of all cells is changed. Exercise has been shown to increase the size, strength, and tone of the muscle fibers. Massage and passive exercise may, if necessary, be used as a partial substitute for exercise. Although physical recreation is desirable for aiding metabolic processes, continued use of fatigued muscles is injurious if, during such conditions, the muscles exhaust their glycogen supply and utilize the protein of their own cells. Under normal conditions it is the sensation of fatigue which protects us from such extremes.

MUSCLES AND THE BONY LEVERS

Levers. Direct muscular contraction alone is not entirely responsible for bodily motions. Intermediate action of bony levers is also essential. In the body, cooperative functioning of bones and muscles forms levers. A knowledge of levers gives a basis for understanding the principles underlying good posture and the movements of the body.

A *simple lever* is a rigid rod which is free to move about on some fixed point or support

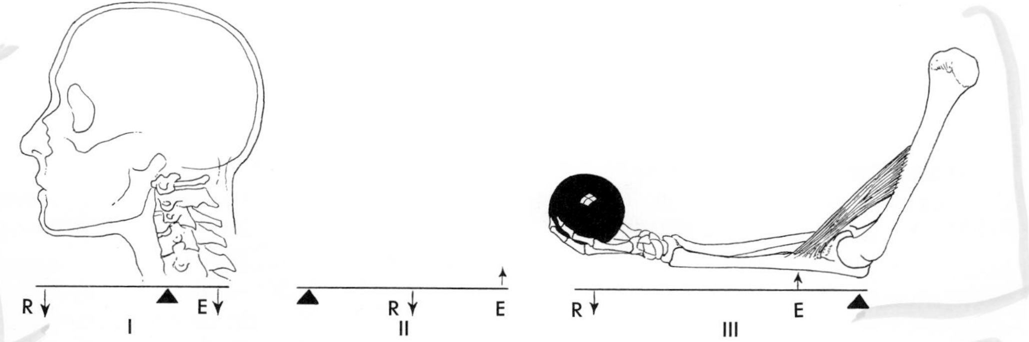

Figure 6–3. Diagram of simple levers. Note insertion of muscle in relation to fulcrum and resistance. The effort is applied at the place of insertion of muscle to the bone. The ▲ represents the fulcrum; *R*, the resistance; *E*, the effort; *arrows*, the direction of motion. There are no levers of the second class in the body. See discussion in text.

called the *fulcrum*. It is acted upon at two different points by (1) the *resistance* (weight), which may be thought of as something to be overcome or balanced, and (2) the *force* (*effort*) which is exerted to overcome the resistance. In the body bones of varying shapes are levers, and the resistance may be a part of the body to be moved or some object to be lifted or both of these. The muscular effort is applied to the bone at the insertion of the muscle and brings about the motion or work.

For example, when the forearm is raised, the elbow is the fulcrum, the weight of the forearm is the resistance, and the pull due to contraction of the biceps muscle is the effort.

Levers act according to a law which may be stated thus: When the lever is in equilibrium, the effort times the effort arm equals the resistance times the resistance arm ($E \times EA = R \times RA$).

The "resistance arm" is the perpendicular distance from the fulcrum to the line of action of the resistance (weight). The "effort arm" is the perpendicular distance from the fulcrum to the line of action of the effort (force.)

For example, if the distance from the effort to the fulcrum is the same as the distance from the resistance to the fulcrum, an effort of 5 lb will balance a resistance of 5 lb.

Levers may be divided into three classes according to the relative position of the fulcrum, the effort, and the resistance. In levers of the *first class* the fulcrum lies between the effort and the resistance, as in a set of scales. In this type of lever the resistance is moved in the opposite direction to that in which the effort is applied. When the head is raised, the facial portion of the skull is the resistance, moving upon the atlanto-occipital joint as a fulcrum, while the muscles of the back produce the effort.

In levers of the *second class* the resistance lies between the fulcrum and the effort and moves, therefore, in the same direction as that in which the effort is applied, as in the raising of a wheelbarrow. There are no levers of the second class in the body.

In levers of the *third class* the effort is exerted between the fulcrum and the resistance. Levers in which the resistance arm is thus longer than the effort arm produce rapid delicate movements wherein the effort used must be greater than the resistance. The flexing of the forearm is a lever of this type, as are most of the levers of the body. The *law of levers* applies in the maintenance of correct posture. The head held erect in correct standing posture rests on the atlas as a fulcrum, with little or no muscular effort being exerted to maintain this position. The head in this position is in the "line of gravity" which passes through the hip joints, knee joints, and the balls of the feet (Figure 4–22, page 96). When the shoulders are stooped and the head is bent forward, constant muscular effort is exerted against the pull of gravity on the head.

SKELETAL MUSCLES

Skeletal muscles are arranged in groups with specific functions to perform: flexion and extension, external and internal rotation, abduction and adduction. For example, in flexing of the elbow, several muscle groups are involved in varying degrees. The *agonists*, or prime movers, give power for flexion; the opposing group, the *antagonists*, contribute to smooth movements by their power to maintain tone yet relax and give way to movement of the flexor group. Other groups of muscles act to hold the arm and shoulder in a suitable position for action and are called *fixation* muscles. The *synergists* are muscles which assist the agonists (prime movers) and reduce undesired action or unnecessary movement. Activity of these opposing muscle groups is coordinated in relation to degree of tension exerted. When tension of the flexor muscles is increased, the tone of the extensor muscles is decreased; movement is controlled and position is maintained against varying degrees of pressures or pulls.

Muscle activity is entirely dependent upon nerve and blood supply. Each muscle has motor and sensory nerve fibers and is well supplied with arteries, capillaries, veins, and lymphatics.

Arteries are blood vessels that convey blood from the heart to the arterioles and capillaries. *Capillaries* are microscopic blood vessels that connect arterioles (smallest arteries) with venules (smallest veins). *Veins* are blood vessels that convey blood from the capillaries, and venules, to the heart.

The synergic units are believed to have a complex reciprocal innervation because they receive both inhibitory and excitatory impulses which effect the muscle tension needed for any specific movement. The cerebellum plays an important role in muscle activity because it regulates muscle tension necessary for the proper maintenance of equilibrium and posture; it coordinates skilled movement initiated at cortical levels and regulates muscular tension essential for all fine muscle movements. This regulation of muscle tension is by means of sensation from the Golgi tendon apparatus and muscle spindles. Stretch of muscle or tendon stimulates the receptor, initiating reflex muscle action.

Almost all the skeletal muscles occur in pairs. A few single muscles situated in the median line represent the fusion of two muscles. Only a few of the more than 600 muscles of the body are included in this unit. They are arranged in relation to function.

Many skeletal muscles bear two names, one Latin and the other English, e.g., obliquus externus abdominis and external abdominal oblique. Sometimes a muscle has more than one Latin name, e.g., psoas magnus and psoas major, vastus intermedius and vastus crureus. Frequently a muscle has no well-known English name, e.g., levatores costarum; sometimes the English name is the one that is best known, e.g., deltoid instead of deltoideus.

QUESTIONS FOR DISCUSSION

1. What is the role of ATP during muscle contraction?
2. Distinguish between isometric and isotonic contraction of striated muscle.
3. Explain how an individual can exercise muscles while lying in bed.
4. What three principles of body mechanics should be observed in bending, lifting, and walking? Explain why.
5. In contraction of the biceps muscle in opening a door, what is occurring in the muscle cells in relation to:
   a. Myosin?
   b. Actin?
   c. The sarcomeres?
   d. Oxygen?
   e. ATP?

SUMMARY

The movements of the body are dependent upon the contractions of muscular tissue

Characteristics of Muscular Tissue
1. Irritability or excitability—property of receiving stimuli and responding to them
2. Contractility—muscle becomes shorter, thicker, because the cells do
3. Extensibility—muscle can be stretched, i.e., property of individual cells
4. Elasticity—muscle readily returns to original shape

Classification
1. Striated, skeletal
2. Nonstriated, visceral
3. Indistinctly striated, cardiac

Muscular Tissue
- Cells become elongated and are called fibers
- Intercellular substance between fibers
- Connective tissue—supporting framework
- Well supplied with nerves and blood and lymph vessels

Striated { **Cross-striped**, **Skeletal** }
1. Marked with transverse striae
2. Movements accomplished by it are voluntary
3. Attached to skeleton
4. Muscle fibers are long and spindle-shaped with many nuclei
5. Connective-tissue framework carries blood vessels and nerves
6. Origin—more fixed attachment
7. Insertion—more movable attachment
8. Origin in periosteum of bone or intervening tendon
9. Insertion either by tendons or aponeuroses
10. Muscles closely covered by sheets of fasciae
11. Deep fasciae form annular ligaments in vicinity of wrist and ankle

Function. To operate the bones of the body, producing motion

Nonstriated { **Smooth**, **Visceral** }
1. Not marked with transverse striae
2. Movements accomplished by it are involuntary
3. Found in walls of blood vessels and viscera
4. Composed of spindle-shaped cells that contain one large nucleus, cells held together by fibrils
5. Connective-tissue framework carries blood vessels and nerves

Function. To cause visceral motion

Cardiac { **Striated**, **Involuntary** }
1. Striated, but not distinctly
2. Not under control of will
3. Cells are elongated and branching, multinucleated
4. Cells grouped in bundles
5. Connective tissue forms a supporting framework

Function. To cause contraction, thereby ejecting blood from the heart

Physiology of Contraction
- **Tonus**
  - Steady, partial contraction existing under normal conditions
  - Gives skeletal muscles firmness and a slight, sustained pull upon attachments
  - Both visceral and cardiac muscle exhibit tonus even when isolated from body
- **Excitation (stimulation)**
  - A property of all protoplasm
  - *Stimulus*—a change in the environment of the cell
  - *Conductivity*—a property of protoplasm by which responses are brought about
  - *Artificial stimuli*—pressure, temperature, electrical, etc.
  - Nerve fibers
    - *Sensory*, convey to central nervous system the state of contraction of a muscle
    - *Motor*, convey impulses from central nervous system to the muscles and control their contraction
- **Contraction periods**
  - *Latent period*—time between stimulation and contraction
  - *Period of contraction*
  - *Period of relaxation*
  - Factors influencing contraction
    1. Strength of stimulus—the stronger (up to a certain maximum) the stimulus, the stronger the contraction of muscle trunk
    2. Duration of stimulus
    3. Weight of load—increase of load decreases the height of contraction
    4. Temperature—optimum is 37° C (98.6° F)

- **Physiology of Contraction** (*cont.*)
  - **Response to stimuli**
    - *All-or-none law*—contraction of muscle cell is maximal or none at all for the conditions
    - *Minimal stimulus*—the weakest stimulus which will give contraction
    - *Subminimal stimulus*—any stimulus weaker than minimal
    - *Summation of stimuli*—the combined forces of subminimal stimuli which result in contraction
    - *Chronaxie*—the shortest duration of time that a stimulus of twice minimal strength must be applied to evoke a response
    - *Summation of contraction*—a maximal contraction resulting from a second stimulus occurring during apex of contraction from the first
    - *Absolute refractory period*—the time between the accomplishment of a contraction and the reception of the next stimulus
    - *Tetanus*—sustained contraction resulting from rapid succession of stimuli
  - **Types of contractions**
    - *Isotonic*—muscle shortens and thickens but its tone is not altered
    - *Isometric*—tension increases but length of muscle is unaltered
  - **Contraction in skeletal muscle**
    - Voluntary muscle cells are separate units, in contrast to heart muscle, which responds as a unit
    - Phases in contraction
      - *Contraction*
        - ATP → ADP + Energy. Oxygen not required
        - Glycogen converted to lactic acid and energy
      - *Recovery*
        - ATP resynthesized from ADP and phosphocreatine. Oxygen needed. Lactic acid oxidized or converted to glycogen by liver cells
        - During contraction changes occur in ionic concentrations of sodium, potassium, chloride, and calcium; magnesium ions also necessary
  - **Fatigue and exercise**
    - Oxygen debt—when oxygen demand exceeds oxygen supply, lactic acid accumulates
    - Formation of carbon dioxide at first increases irritability of muscles
    - Continuous contraction brings about accumulation of waste products, causing fatigue
    - Moderate exercise aids in getting rid of these waste products
    - *Rigor mortis*—fatigue carried to point beyond possible recovery. Protein constituents of muscle fibers coagulate
    - Fatigue is complex
      - Other cells than muscles show fatigue
      - Associated with various mental states
    - Exercise brings change in conditions (new blood, etc.) for all cells of body. May increase size, strength, and tone of muscle fibers
  - **Levers**
    - *Lever*—a rigid rod free to move about on some fixed point, the *fulcrum*
    - Lever acted upon by
      - *Resistance* (weight)—something to be overcome or balanced
      - *Force* (effort)—that which is exerted to overcome the resistance
    - Three types of levers
      1. Fulcrum lies between the effort and the resistance
         Example, raising head
      2. Resistance lies between fulcrum and effort
      3. Effort exerted between fulcrum and resistance
         Example, flexing forearm

CHAPTER

7

MUSCLES OF THE FACE AND HEAD, ABDOMEN, VERTEBRAL COLUMN, AND RESPIRATION

Origin

Insertion

Nerve and Blood Supply

Function

The muscles have been placed in chart form for ease in learning the relationships of nerve and blood supply to muscle function. * Indicates muscles to be emphasized for first-level learning.

MUSCLES OF FACIAL EXPRESSION

Expression	Muscle	Origin	Insertion	Nerve Supply	Function
Surprise	*Epicranius (occipito frontalis) Occipital portion	Occipital bone and mastoid portion of temporal bone	Galea aponeurotica (epicranial part)	Posterior auricular branches of facial nerve	Occipital portion draws scalp backward
	Frontal portion	Epicranial aponeurosis (galea aponeurotica)	Skin above supraorbital line	Temporal branch of facial nerve	Most powerful in raising eyebrows and wrinkling forehead

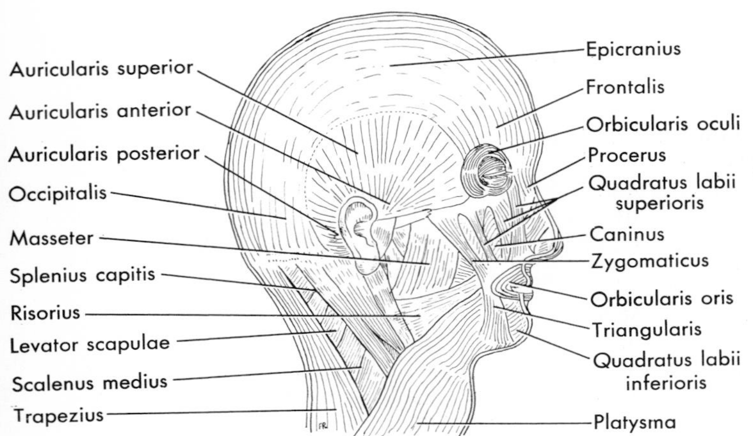

Figure 7–1. The superficial muscles of the head and neck.

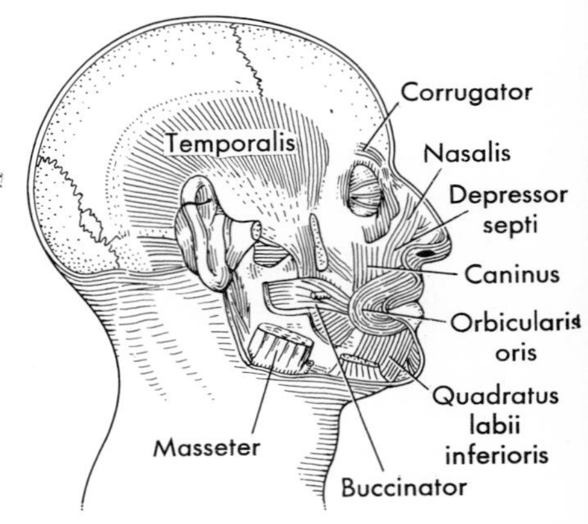

Figure 7–2. The temporal and deep muscles about the mouth.

Expression	Muscle	Origin	Insertion	Nerve Supply	Function
Smiling or laughing	Zygomaticus minor	Zygomatic bone and descends obliquely to its insertion	Upper lip between greater alar cartilage and orbicularis oris muscle	Buccal branches of facial nerve	Draws upper lip upward and outward
Sadness	Levator labii superioris	Below infraorbital foramen of maxilla	Orbicularis oris	Buccal branches of facial nerve	Elevates upper lip
Irony	Depressor labii inferioris	Mandible between symphysis and mental foramen	Integument, lower lip	Mandibular branch of facial nerve	Draws lower lip downward
	*Buccinator	Alveolar processes of the maxilla and mandible	Orbicularis oris at angle of mouth	Motor fibers Buccal branches from facial nerve	Principal muscle of cheek; compresses cheek; important in mastication
Laughing or smiling	Zygomaticus major	Zygomatic bone	Orbicularis oris at angle of mouth	Branches of facial nerve	Pulls angle of mouth upward and backward
Doubt, disdain, contempt	Mentalis	Incisive fossa of the mandible	Skin of chin	Mandibular and buccal branches of facial nerve	Raises and protrudes lower lip
	*Orbicularis oris (ring-shaped muscle of the mouth)	Layers of muscle fibers surrounding the opening of the mouth	Angle of mouth	Buccal branches of facial nerve	Compresses and closes lips
	Depressor anguli oris (triangularis)	Oblique line of mandible	Orbicularis oris muscle	Mandibular, branches of facial nerve	Depresses angle of mouth
Horror	*Platysma (broad sheet muscle)	Skin and fascia covering pectoral and deltoid muscles	Mandible and muscles about angle of mouth	Cervical branch of facial nerve	Draws outer part of lower lip inferiorly and posteriorly, widens aperture at corner of mouth
Strain and tenseness	Risorius	Fascia over masseter muscle	Skin at angle of mouth	Fibers of mandibular and buccal branches of facial nerve	Retracts angle of mouth
Frowning, suffering	Corrugator supercilii	Medial end of superciliary arch (fibers pass upward and lateralward)	Deep surface of skin above supraorbital arch	Branches of temporal and zygomatic branches of facial nerve	Frowning and principal muscle in expressions of suffering
Disdain or contempt	Levator anguli oris (caninus)	Canine fossa below infraorbital foramen	Angle of mouth	Buccal branches of facial nerve	Furrow is deepened into expression of disdain
Muscles of the nose	Nasalis, depressor septi, and procerus	Small muscles of nose cover nasal bones	In skin, lower part of forehead, and nose	Buccal branches of facial nerve	Constrict and enlarge apertures of the nares

MUSCLES OF MASTICATION

Name	Origin	Insertion	Nerve Supply	Function
*Masseter	Zygomatic process of maxilla and zygomatic arch	Superior half of ramus and lateral surface of the mandible	Masseteric nerve from mandibular division of trigeminal nerve	Closes jaws

Figure 7–3. (*A*) Diagram showing distribution of trigeminal nerve of the face. (*B*) Diagram showing distribution of facial nerve.

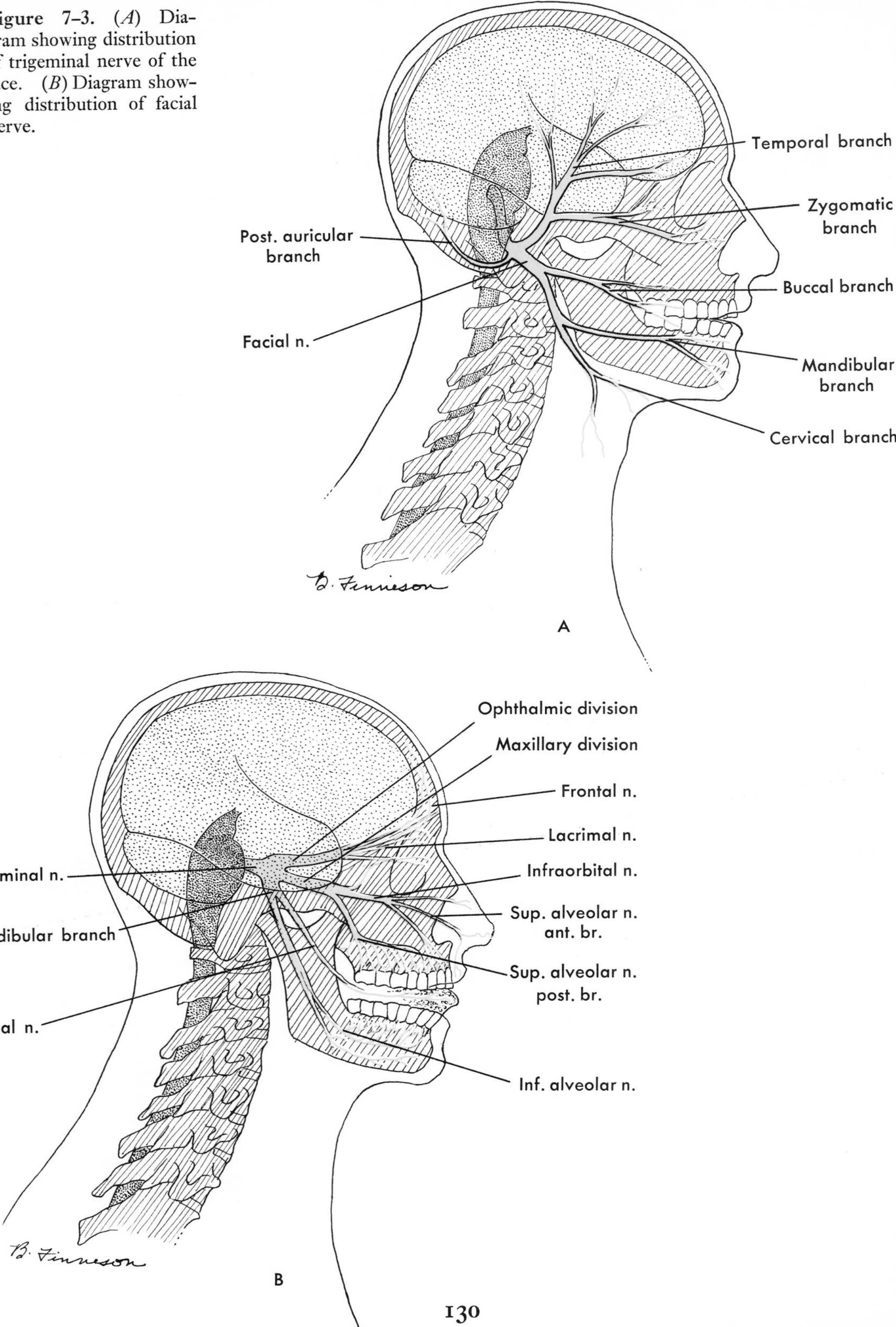

Name	Origin	Insertion	Nerve Supply	Function
Temporalis	Temporal fossa of skull and from deep surface of temporal fascia	Medial surface, apex, and coronoid process of mandible	Deep temporal nerves from mandibular division of trigeminal nerve	Raises mandible and closes mouth, draws mandible backward
Pterygoideus medialis (internal pterygoid)	Medial surface, lateral pterygoid plate; pyramidal process of palatine bone; tuberosity of maxilla	Ramus of mandible Inferior and posterior part of ramus and mandibular foramen	Medial pterygoid, branch of mandibular division of trigeminal nerve	Raises mandible and closes mouth
Pterygoideus lateralis (external pterygoid)	Two heads: upper head from great wing of sphenoid; lower head from lateral surface of pterygoid plate	Upper head: condyle of mandible Lower head: articular disk of temporal mandibular articulation	Lateral pterygoid nerve from mandibular division of trigeminal nerve	Opens jaw; protrudes mandible; moves mandible from side to side

EXTRINSIC MUSCLES OF THE TONGUE

These muscles are concerned with speaking, mastication, and swallowing.

Name	Origin	Insertion	Nerve Supply	Function
Genioglossus	Superior mental spine of mandible	Entire length of undersurface of tongue and, by a thin aponeurosis, upper part of body of hyoid bone	Hypoglossal	Thrusts tongue forward and depresses it
Styloglossus	Styloid process of temporal bone	Whole length of side and under part of tongue	Hypoglossal	Draws tongue upward and backward
Hyoglossus	Side and body of greater cornu of hyoid bone	Fibers pass upward and enter side of tongue between other muscles	Hypoglossal	Depresses tongue and draws down its sides
Stylohyoid (stylohyoideus)	Posterior and lateral surface of styloid process	Body of hyoid bone	Branch of facial nerve	Draws hyoid bone superiorly and posteriorly

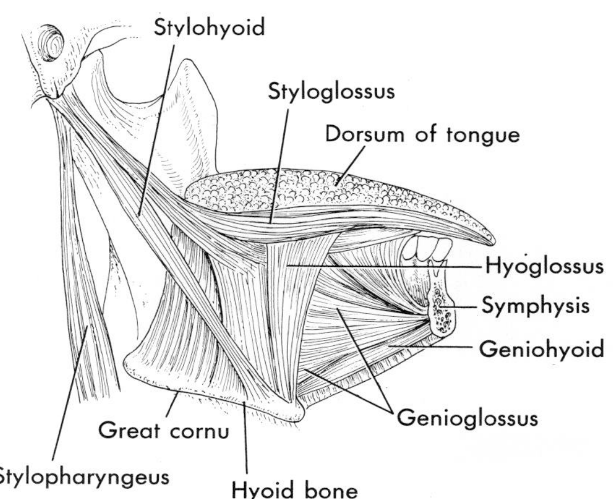

Figure 7–4. The muscles of the tongue viewed from the right side.

Muscles	Origin	Insertion	Nerve Supply	Function
Geniohyoid (geniohyoideus)	Inferior mental spine, inner surface	Anterior surface, body of hyoid bone	Branch of first cervical nerve through hypoglossal	Draws long and hyoid bone anteriorly

MOVEMENT OF THE HEAD

Muscles	Origin	Insertion	Nerve Supply	Function
*Sternocleidomastoideus (two heads)	Upper sternum and inner border of the clavicle	Inserted by a strong tendon into the lateral surface of the mastoid process	Spinal part of the accessory nerve and anterior branches of the second and third cervicals	One side flexes cervical vertebral column laterally and rotates it; both muscles acting together flex cervical vertebral column bringing head ventrally, at the same time elevating chin
Splenius capitis	Lower half ligamentum nuchae and spinous processes of the seven cervical vertebrae and upper four thoracic vertebrae	Outer part of occipital bone and mastoid process of temporal bone	Lateral branches of dorsal division of the middle and lower cervical nerves	When both muscles act together, head is pulled backward; when they act alone, head is rotated to same side
Semispinalis capitis	Series of tendons from transverse processes of first six, or seven thoracic, and seventh cervical vertebrae	Occipital bone	Branches of dorsal primary divisions of middle and lower cervical nerves	Extends head and rotates it to opposite side
Longus capitis	Transverse processes of upper four thoracic vertebrae	Posterior margin of mastoid process	Branches of dorsal division of middle and lower cervical nerves	When both muscles contract, head is extended; when they act alone, head is bent to same side

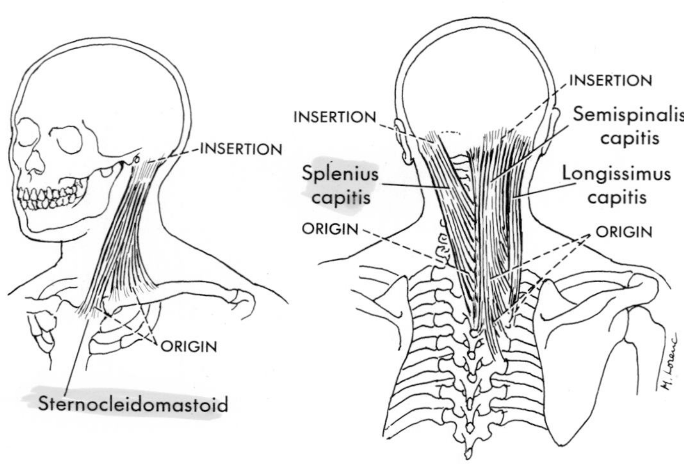

Figure 7–5. The muscles for flexion and extension of the head.

Blood Circulation to Muscles of Head, Face, and Neck

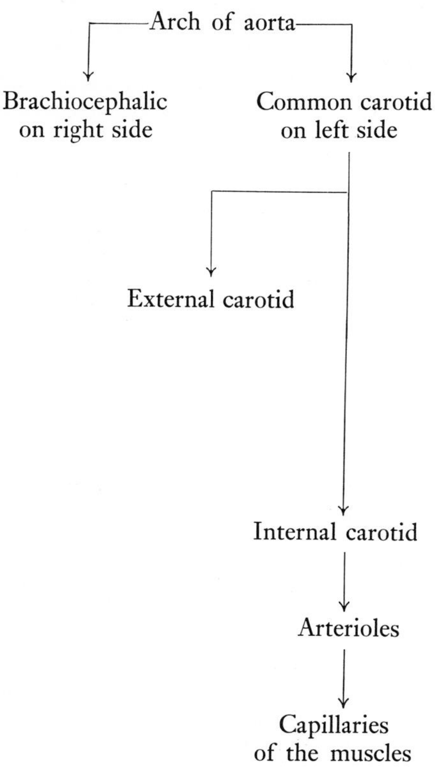

The left common carotid is an inch or two longer than the right. The right common carotid is a division of the brachiocephalic artery. They ascend obliquely on either side of the neck until on a level with the upper border of the thyroid cartilage where they divide into two great branches: (1) the external carotid, and (2) the internal carotid. These subdivide into many branches.

This artery is more superficial. Each side has eight main branches which continue to divide into smaller branches. Each one is usually named in relation to the part supplied. These arteries supply blood to all the muscles of the face, scalp, and tongue and to the thyroid and parathyroid gland.

Each internal carotid has many branches. Important branches are the cerebral, distributed to the brain, and the ophthalmic, which enters the orbit through the optic foramen and distributes branches to the orbit, the muscles, and bulb of the eye.

See Figure 11–7 (page 207).

Venous Return

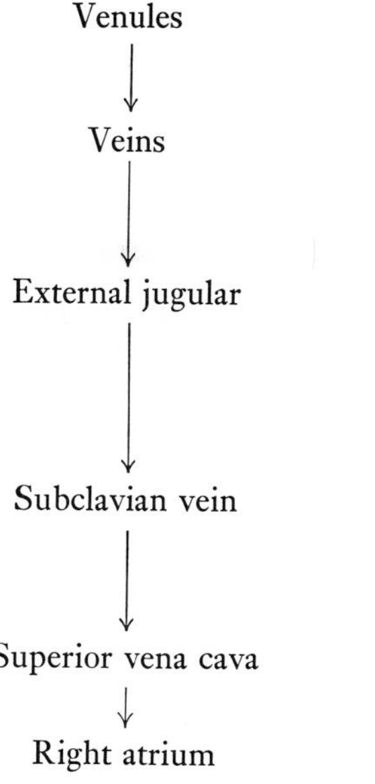

Tributaries to the external jugular veins are usually named in terms of structures from which they receive blood.

The external jugular veins are the chief superficial veins of the neck. They are formed in the substance of the parotid glands by the union of the posterior facial and the posterior auricular veins of each side of the face on a level with the angle of the mandible. Each vein terminates in the subclavian vein. The external jugular receives most of the blood from the greater part of the scalp and deep parts of the face. Blood from the tongue and all other deep structures of the face and neck enters the internal jugular vein → brachiocephalic → superior vena cava → right atrium.

MUSCLES OF ABDOMINAL WALL

Muscle	Origin	Insertion	Nerve Supply	Function
*Obliquus externus (external oblique)	External surfaces and inferior border of lower eight ribs	Anterior half of outer lip of iliac crest; anterior rectus sheath to linea alba	Iliohypogastric ilioinguinal nerve; branches from eighth through twelfth intercostal nerves	Compresses abdominal contents in forced expiration; one side alone bends vertebral column laterally
*Obliquus internus (internal oblique)	Iliac crest; lumbodorsal fascia and inguinal ligament	Costal cartilages of last three or four ribs	Iliohypogastric Ilioinguinal nerve; branches of eighth through twelfth intercostals	Compresses abdominal contents in forced expiration; one side acting alone bends vertebral column laterally
*Transversus abdominis (transversalis)	Lateral third of inguinal ligament and anterior three fourths of inner lip of iliac crest, lumbodorsal fascia, inner surface of cartilages of lower six ribs	Xiphoid process Linea alba and pubis	Iliohypogastric Ilioinguinal nerve; branches of seventh to twelfth intercostals	Constricts abdomen; in forced expiration
*Rectus abdominis	Crest of pubis and ligaments; ventral surface of symphysis pubis	Cartilages of fifth, sixth, and seventh ribs and xiphoid process	Branches of seventh through twelfth intercostal nerves	Flexes vertebral column (lumbar portion); tenses anterior abdominal wall; compresses abdominal contents
*Levator ani	Posterior surface of body of pubic bone, spine of ischium and obturator fascia	Side of coccyx and fibrous band which extends between coccyx and anus	Branches of pudendal plexes; fibers from fourth and sometimes third and fifth sacral nerves	Supports and slightly raises pelvic floor; resists increased intra-abdominal pressure

For arterial blood supply to these muscles and venous return see Figure 7–7.
Weak places in abdominal walls are the inguinal canal (fascia of transverse muscle, between superior spine of ilium and symphysis pubis), femoral ring, and umbilicus.

MOVEMENT OF THE VERTEBRAL COLUMN

Forward and backward movement of the spine is limited in the thoracic region, but movement is free in the lumbar region, particularly between the fourth and fifth lumbar vertebrae.

Muscle	Origin	Insertion	Nerve Supply	Function
*Quadratus lumborum (rectangular muscle)	Iliac crest and iliolumbar ligament	Inferior border of last rib and first four lumbar vertebrae	Branches of twelfth thoracic and first lumbar nerves	Flexes vertebral column laterally; fixes last two ribs in forced expiration

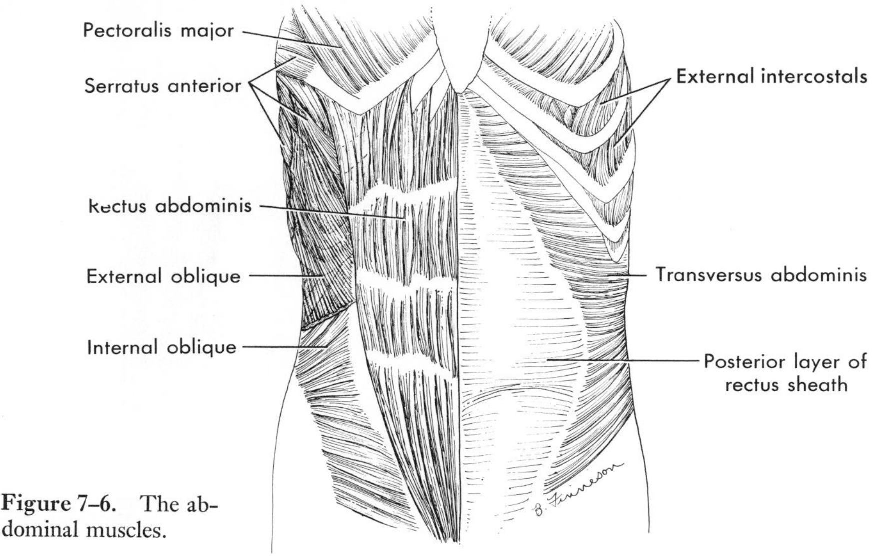

Figure 7–6. The abdominal muscles.

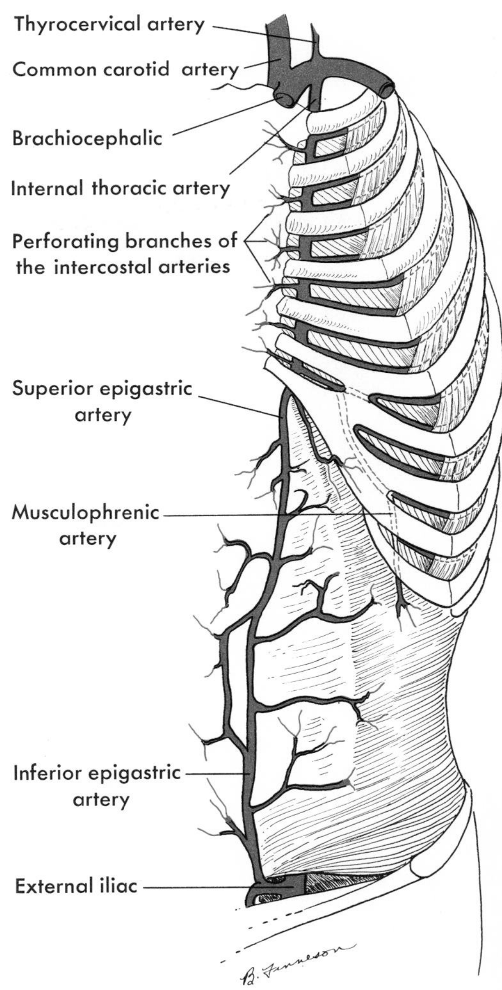

Figure 7–7. Diagram showing blood supply to intercostal muscles and abdominal wall.

Figure 7–9 [Right]. The muscles producing movement of the vertebral column in the lumbar region.

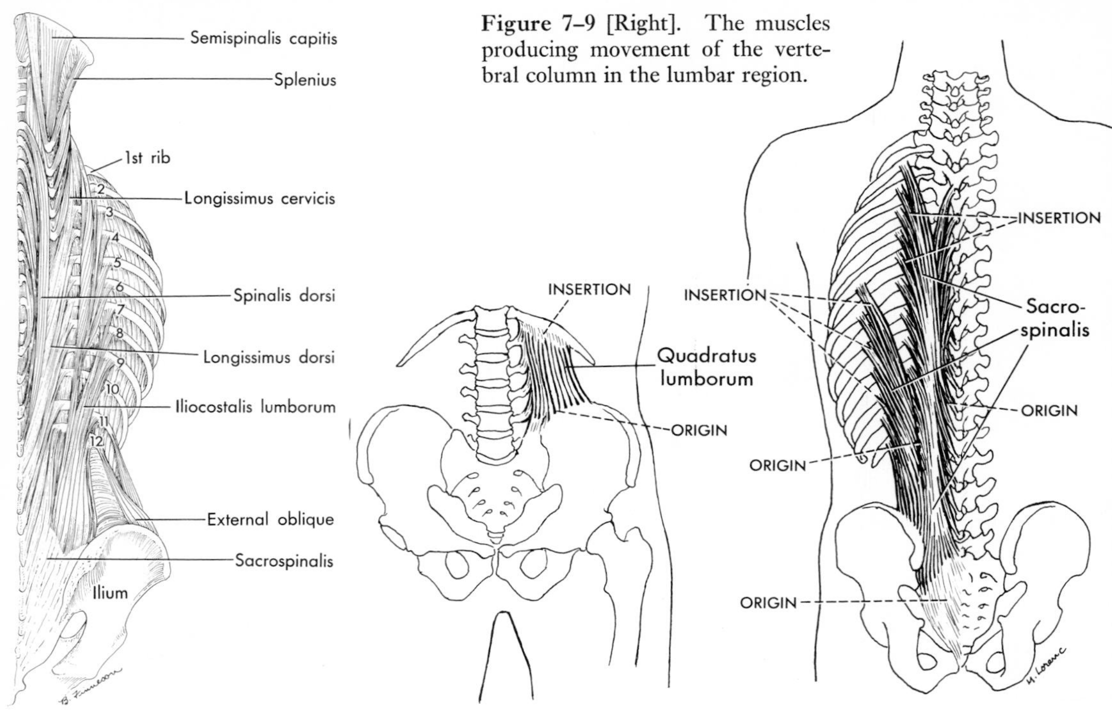

Figure 7–8 [Above]. Diagram showing location of the deep muscles of the back.

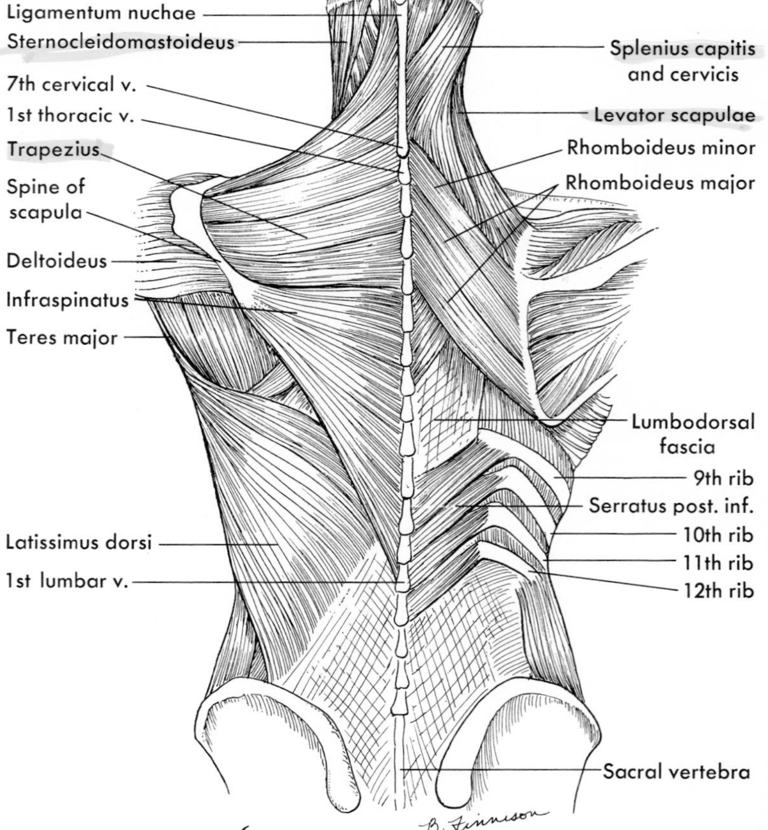

Figure 7–10. Diagram showing anatomical relations of some of the muscles of the shoulders and back. (Modified from *Gray's Anatomy*.)

Muscle	Origin	Insertion	Nerve Supply	Function
*Sacrospinalis	Anterior surface of a broad, thick tendon which is attached to the middle crest of sacrum; spinous processes of lumbar and eleventh and twelfth thoracic vertebrae	Fibers form a large mass of muscular tissue which splits in the upper lumbar region into three columns: 1. Lateral (iliocostalis) 2. Intermediate (longissimus) 3. Medial, the spinalis These are all attached to the ribs and vertebrae at various levels; see Figure 7–9	Lateral branches and posterior divisions of spinal nerves	Maintains vertebral column in erect posture against gravity

MUSCLES OF RESPIRATION

Name	Origin	Insertion	Nerve Supply	Function
*Diaphragm—principal openings: Aortic Vena caval Esophageal	Circumference of thoracic outlet composed of skeletal muscle and dense collagenous connective tissue	Central tendon—muscle fibers converge and become tendinous near central part of diaphragm	Phrenic nerve (derived from third, fourth, and fifth cervical nerves)	Principal muscle of respiration; during inspiration, central tendon pulled downward; vertical diameter (volume) of thoracic cavity increased; pressure in thoracic cavity decreased; air "pulled" into the lungs; pressure in abdominal cavity increased
A series of smaller ones	See page 138			
*External intercostals (11 on either side)	Lower border of rib (caudal aspect); fibers run downward and forward	Upper border of rib below origin (cranial aspect)	Intercostal nerves	During inspiration, lifts ribs, increases volume of thoracic cavity
*Levatores costarum (12 on either side)	Ends of transverse processes of seventh cervical and upper 11 thoracic vertebrae	Outer surface of rib immediately caudal (below) to vertebrae from which it arises	Branches of intercostal nerves	Raises the ribs, increasing thoracic cavity
*Internal intercostals (11 on either side)	Ridge on inner surface of rib and corresponding costal cartilage; fibers run downward and backward	Cranial border of rib below origin	Intercostal nerves	In expiration, draws adjacent ribs together; decreases volume of thoracic cavity
The scaleni, anterior, medial, posterior	Transverse process of cervical and upper second or third thoracic vertebrae	Inserted into first and second ribs	Fourth, fifth, sixth, seventh, and eighth cervical nerves	In forced inspiration, raises first two ribs, increasing thoracic cavity

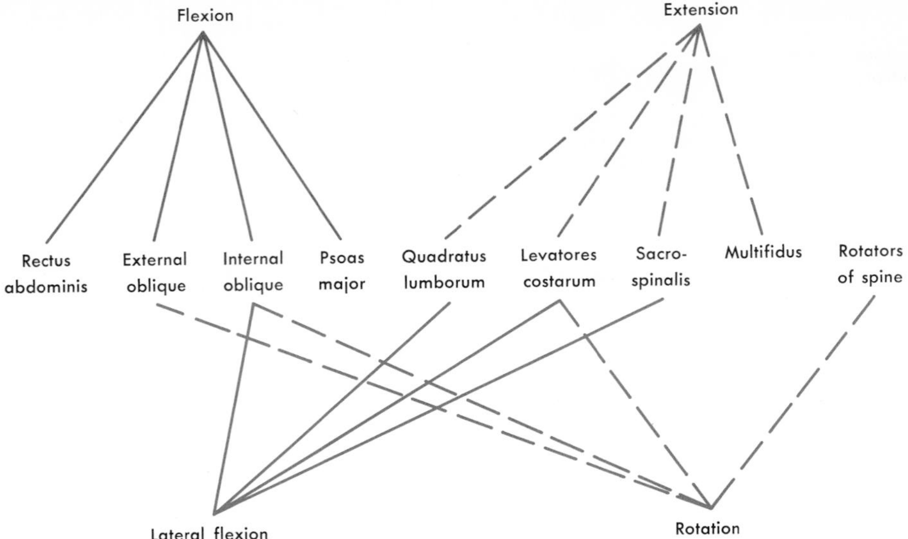

Figure 7–11. Summary of muscle action of the vertebrae.

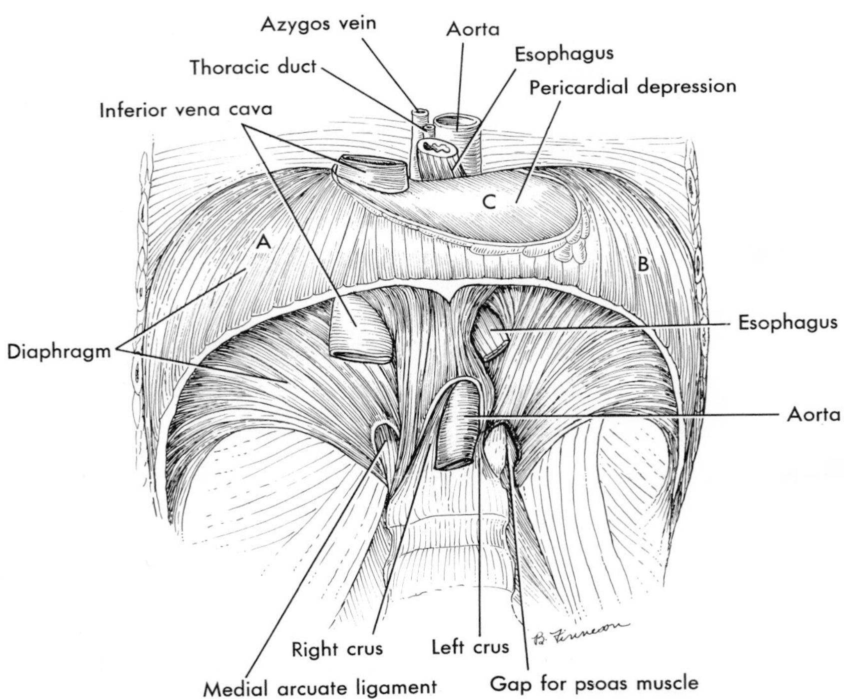

Figure 7–12. Frontal view of the diaphragm. It is slightly elevated at *A* by the liver and at *B* by the stomach.

Name	Origin	Insertion	Nerve Supply	Function
Serratus posterior superior	Caudal part of ligamentum nuchae and spines of seventh and first two thoracic vertebrae	Cranial borders of second, third, fourth, and fifth ribs	Branches of ventral divisions of first four thoracic nerves	Raises ribs, increasing thoracic cavity
Serratus posterior inferior	Spinous processes of last two thoracic and first two or three lumbar vertebrae	Inferior borders of last four ribs	Branches of ventral divisions of ninth to twelfth thoracic nerves	Draws these ribs outward and downward, counteracting inward pull of diaphragm
Transverse thoracic	Inner surface body of sternum, dorsal surface, xiphoid process, sternal ends of costal cartilages of last three or four true ribs	Caudal borders and inner surfaces of costal cartilages of second, third, fourth, fifth, and sixth ribs	Branches of intercostal nerves	Decreases thoracic cavity, draws ventral part of ribs downward

Also see muscles of neck for action in respiration

Blood Circulation to the Muscles of Respiration—Main Blood Vessels

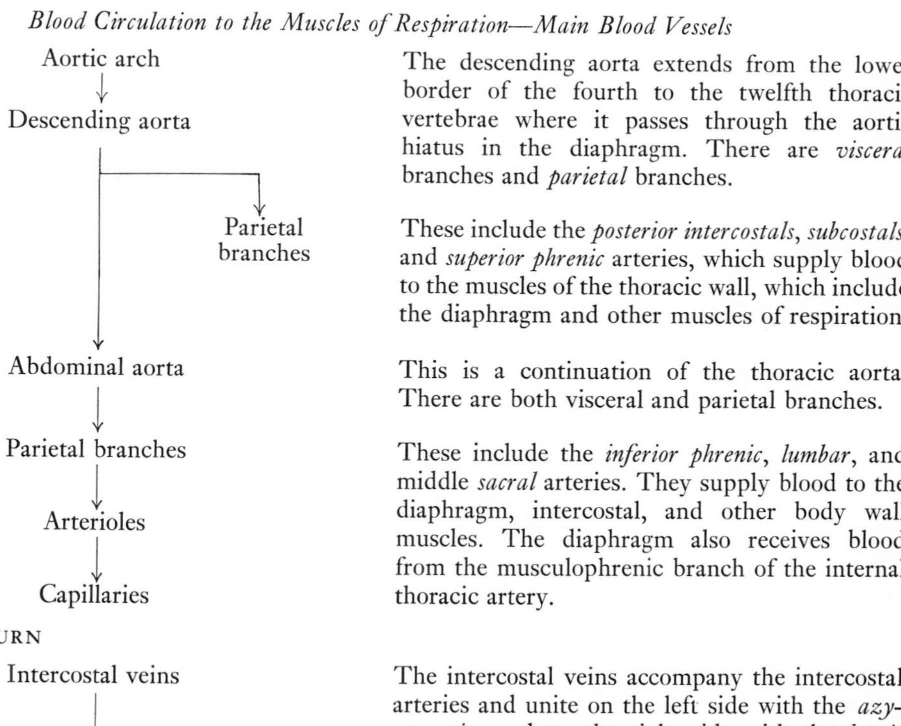

The descending aorta extends from the lower border of the fourth to the twelfth thoracic vertebrae where it passes through the aortic hiatus in the diaphragm. There are *visceral* branches and *parietal* branches.

These include the *posterior intercostals*, *subcostals*, and *superior phrenic* arteries, which supply blood to the muscles of the thoracic wall, which include the diaphragm and other muscles of respiration.

This is a continuation of the thoracic aorta. There are both visceral and parietal branches.

These include the *inferior phrenic*, *lumbar*, and middle *sacral* arteries. They supply blood to the diaphragm, intercostal, and other body wall muscles. The diaphragm also receives blood from the musculophrenic branch of the internal thoracic artery.

VENOUS RETURN

Intercostal veins → Azygos veins → Inferior vena cava → Right atrium

The intercostal veins accompany the intercostal arteries and unite on the left side with the *azygos vein*, and on the right side with the *hemiazygos* and *accessory hemiazygos veins*. (See Figure 15–13, page 310.)

The azygos and hemiazygos veins receive the ascending lumbar veins from the abdominal region. In case of obstruction of the vena cava, the azygos veins form a channel by which blood from the lower part of the body can enter the superior vena cava.

QUESTIONS FOR DISCUSSION

1. a. What is the principal muscle of respiration?
   b. Where are its origin and insertion?
   c. Which spinal nerves form the phrenic nerve?
2. What important anatomical structures pass through the diaphragm? What is their function?
3. Discuss the importance of the muscles of facial expression for the nurse.
4. Which muscles are used in forced respiration?
5. An individual has had a cerebral accident and has lost function of the left side of his face. What nerve or nerves are involved?
6. Discuss the nerve supply to the following structures:
   a. Tongue
   b. Neck
   c. Forehead
   d. Abdominal muscles
   e. Intercostal muscles
   f. Face and head
7. Discuss in detail the blood supply to the head and face.
8. What is the blood supply to the intercostal muscles?

CHAPTER

8

MUSCLES OF THE EXTREMITIES

Origin

Insertion

Nerve and Blood Supply

Function

TABLE OF SPINAL NERVES AND THEIR DISTRIBUTION

The muscles have been placed in chart form for ease in learning the relationships of nerve and blood supply to muscle function. * Indicates muscles to be emphasized for first-level learning.

Figure 8–1 [Left]. Opposing muscle groups that elevate and depress the shoulder girdle.

Figure 8–2 [Right]. Opposing muscles that abduct and adduct the shoulders.

Figure 8–3 [Below]. Summary of muscle action at the shoulder girdle, illustrating multiple functions of muscles.

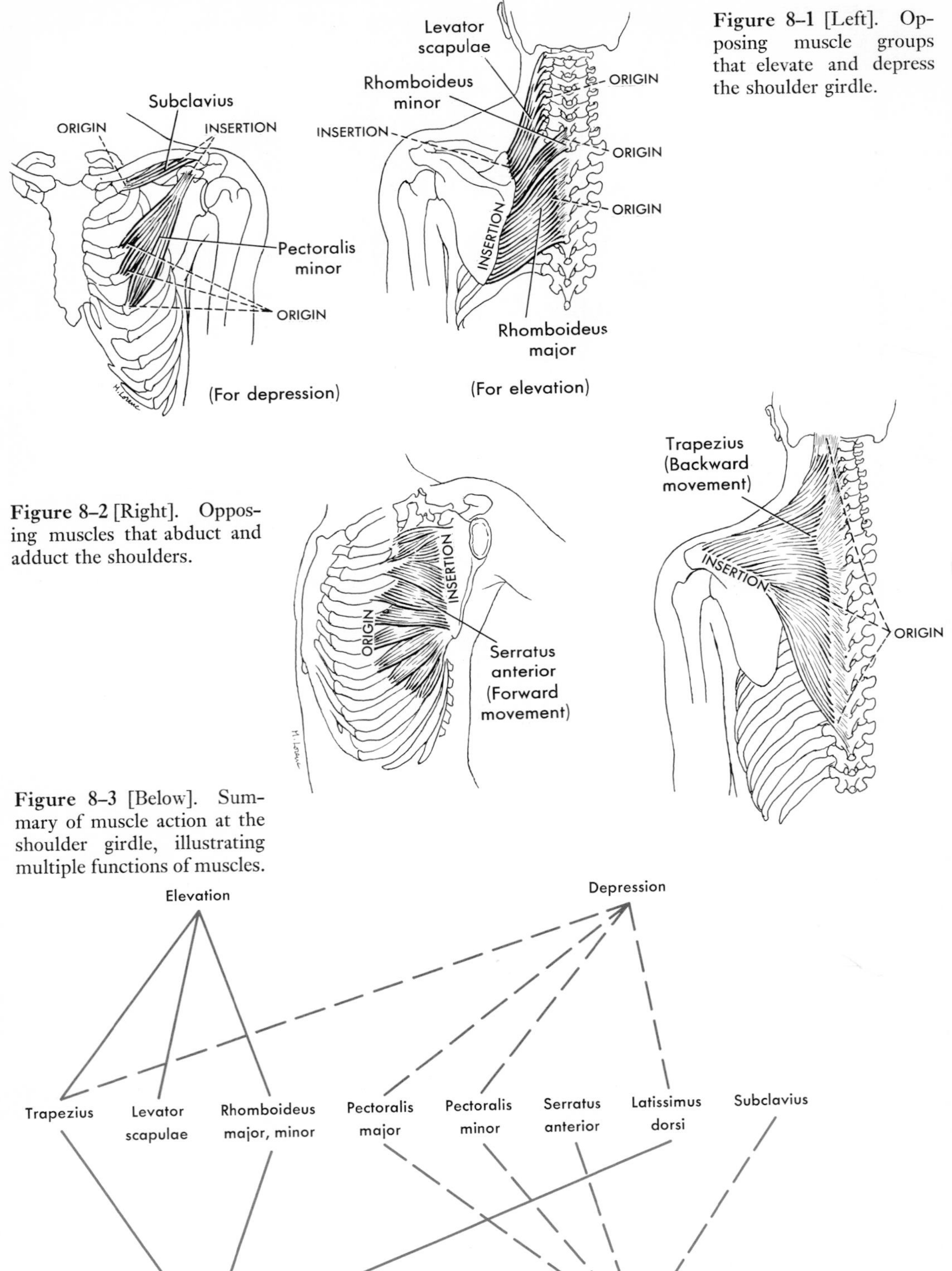

MOVEMENT OF THE SHOULDER GIRDLE

Name	Origin	Insertion	Nerve Supply	Function
FLEXION				
Levator scapulae	Upper four or five cervical vertebrae	Vertebral border of scapula	Dorsal scapular branches of third and fourth cervical nerves	Raises scapula, draws it medially, and rotates it to lower the lateral angle
ADDUCTION				
*Rhomboideus major	Spines of first four or five thoracic vertebrae	Vertebral border of scapula between root of spine and inferior angle of scapula	Dorsal scapula nerve derived from fifth cervical nerve	Moves scapula backward and upward, producing slight rotation
Rhomboideus minor	Inferior part of ligamentum nuchae and spinus processes of seventh cervical and first thoracic vertebrae	Vertebral border of scapula at root of spine	Dorsal scapula derived from fifth cervical nerve	Adducts scapula (backward and upward movement) and assists in adduction of arm
*Trapezius—flat, triangular muscle	Occipital bone, ligamentum nuchae, spinous processes of seventh cervical and spinous processes of all thoracic vertebrae	Acromial process of clavicle and spine of scapula	Spinal accessory and branches of third and fourth cervical nerves	All fibers rotate scapula; lower fiber draws scapula downward; upper fibers of one side draw head toward same side
*Pectoralis minor	Upper margins and outer surfaces of third, fourth, and fifth ribs and aponeuroses covering intercostals	Medial border and superior surface of coracoid process of scapula	Medial pectoral nerve (derived from eighth cervical and first thoracic nerves)	Draws scapula downward and rotates it to lower the lateral angle; raises third, fourth, and fifth ribs in forced inspiration when scapula is fixed
Subclavius	First rib and its cartilage	Groove on inferior surface of the clavicle	A special nerve from lateral trunk of brachial plexus (derived from fifth and sixth cervical nerves)	Draws shoulder forward and downward
*Serratus anterior	Outer surfaces and superior borders of first eight or nine ribs and from intercostals between ribs; see page 142	Ventral surface of medial angle of vertebral border and inferior angle of scapula	Long thoracic nerve (derived from fifth, sixth, and seventh cervical nerves)	Rotates scapula; moves scapula forward as in act of pushing; assists in abduction of arm

MOVEMENT OF ARM AT SHOULDER (BALL-AND-SOCKET JOINT)

Head of humerus fits into shallow glenoid cavity of scapula.

Name	Origin	Insertion	Nerve Supply	Function
FLEXION				
*Coracobrachialis	Coracoid process of scapula	Middle of humerus at medial aspect	Musculocutaneous nerve (derived from sixth and seventh cervical nerves)	Carries arm forward (flexion); assists in adduction of arm
EXTENSION				
Teres major	Dorsal side, axillary border of scapula	Crest of lesser tubercle of humerus	Branches of lower subscapular nerve (derived from fifth and sixth cervical nerves)	Extends humerus and draws it down; helps to adduct and rotate arm medially
ABDUCTION				
*Deltoideus, thick, triangular muscle, covers shoulder joint	Clavicle, acromion process, and posterior border of scapula of spine	Lateral surface of body of humerus	Branches of axillary nerve (derived from fifth and sixth cervical nerves)	Abduction (raises arm from side)
Supraspinatous	Fossa, superior to spine of scapula, passes over shoulder joint	Inserted into highest facet of greater tubercle of humerus	Branches of suprascapular nerve (derived from fifth cervical nerve)	Assists deltoid in abduction of arm
*Pectoralis major, large, fan-shaped muscles	Anterior surface of sternal half of clavicle, ventral surface of sternum, and costal cartilages of ribs two to six	Fibers converge and form a thick mass which is inserted by a flat tendon into crest of greater tubercle of humerus	Lateral and medial pectoral nerves (derived from fifth, sixth, seventh, and eighth cervical, and first thoracic nerves)	Flexes, adducts, and rotates arm medially
ROTATION				
Infraspinatus	Infraspinous fossa on posterior aspect of scapula	Middle facet of greater tubercle of humerus	Suprascapular nerve (derived from fifth and sixth cervical nerves)	Rotates arm outward
Teres minor, long, narrow muscle	Axillary border of scapula	Lowest facet of greater tubercle of humerus	Branches of axillary nerve (derived from fifth cervical nerve)	Functions with infraspinatous to rotate humerus laterally; weakly adducts it
*Latissimus dorsi, large, triangular muscle	Broad aponeurosis which is attached to spinous processes of lower six thoracic vertebrae, spinous processes of lumbar vertebrae, crests of sacrum and posterior part of crest of ilium and outer surface of lower four ribs	Fibers converge to form a flat tendon which is inserted into bottom of intertubercular groove of humerus	Thoracodorsal nerve (derived from sixth, seventh, and eighth cervical nerves)	Rotates arm medially; extends and adducts humerus, draws shoulder downward and backward

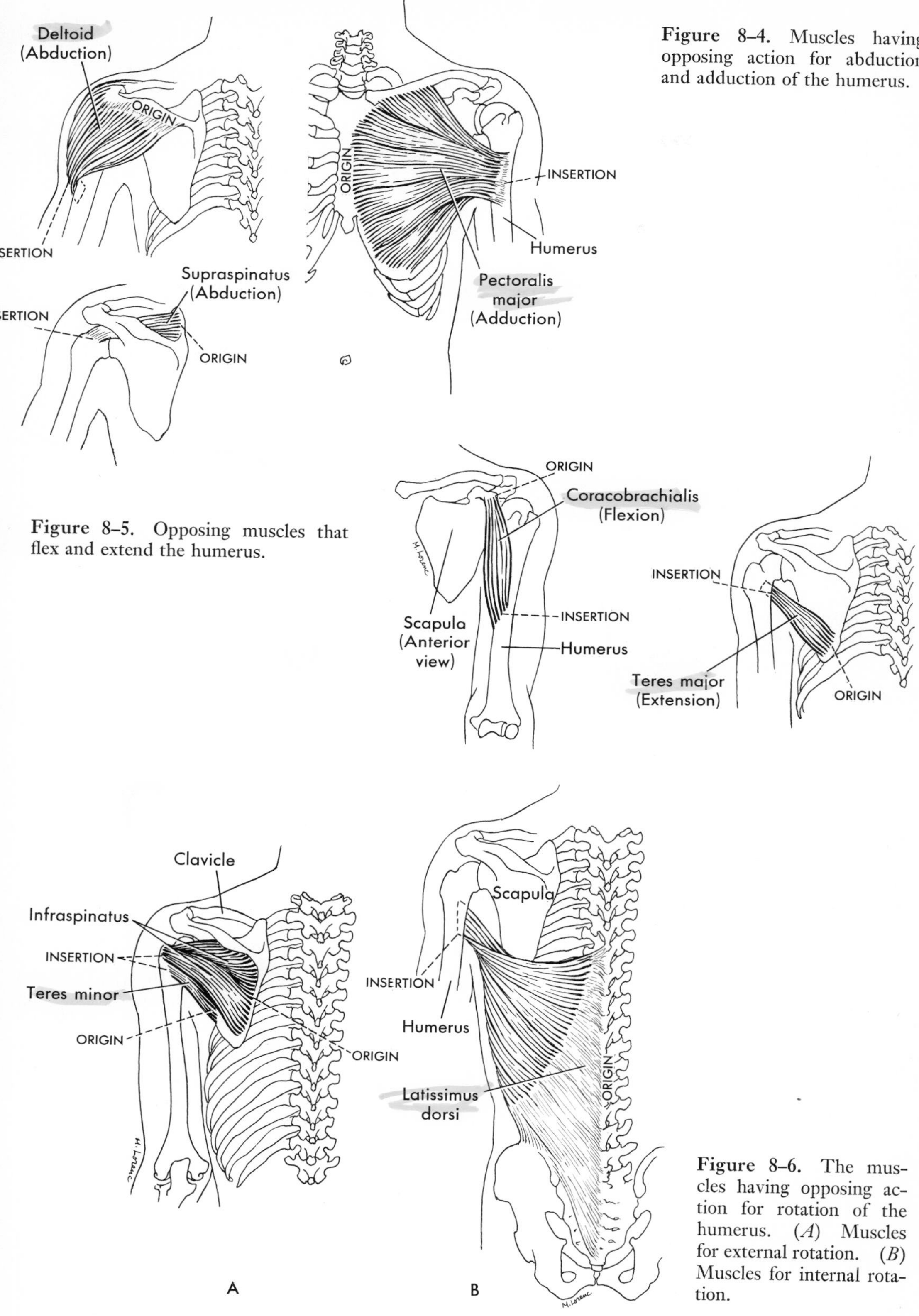

Figure 8–4. Muscles having opposing action for abduction and adduction of the humerus.

Figure 8–5. Opposing muscles that flex and extend the humerus.

Figure 8–6. The muscles having opposing action for rotation of the humerus. (*A*) Muscles for external rotation. (*B*) Muscles for internal rotation.

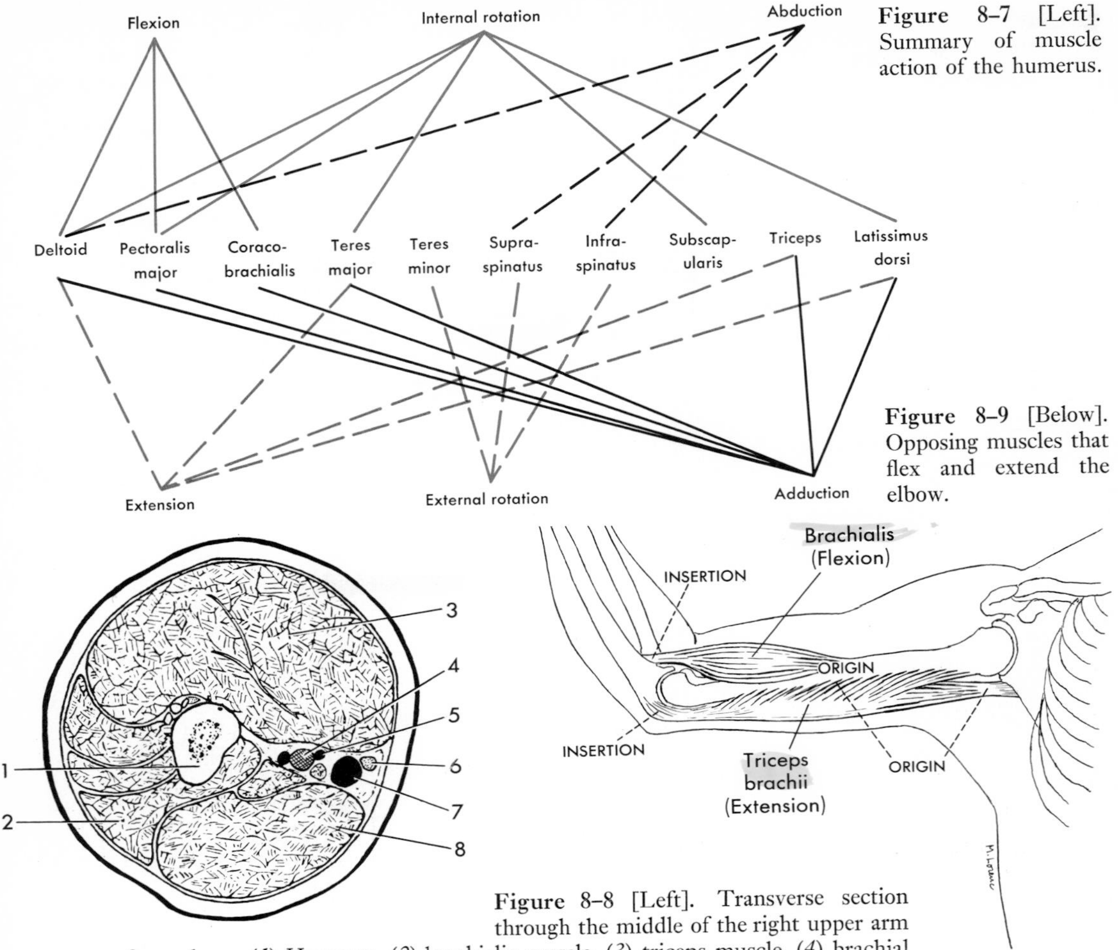

Figure 8–7 [Left]. Summary of muscle action of the humerus.

Figure 8–9 [Below]. Opposing muscles that flex and extend the elbow.

Figure 8–8 [Left]. Transverse section through the middle of the right upper arm as seen from above. (*1*) Humerus, (*2*) brachialis muscle, (*3*) triceps muscle, (*4*) brachial artery, (*5*) companion vein, (*6*) ulnar nerve, (*7*) basilic vein, (*8*) biceps muscle.

Flexion

Extension

Brachialis

Biceps brachii

Brachio-radialis

Triceps brachii

Anconeus

Pronator teres

Pronator quadratus

Supinator

Extensor carpi radialis

Supination

Pronation

Figure 8–10 [Left]. Summary of muscle action at the elbow.

MOVEMENT BETWEEN HUMERUS AND ULNA (ELBOW)

Name	Origin	Insertion	Nerve Supply	Function
*Brachialis	Distal half of anterior aspect of humerus	Tuberosity of ulna and rough depression, anterior surface of coronoid process	Branches of musculocutaneous nerve (derived from fifth and sixth cervical nerves)	Strong flexor of forearm
Triceps brachii (arises by three heads):		All fibers terminate in two aponeurotic laminae which unite above the elbow and are inserted into proximal surface of olecranon of ulna	Branches of radial nerve (derived from seventh and eighth cervical nerves)	Great extensor of forearm; direct antagonist of brachialis; long head extends and adducts arm
Long head	Infraglenoid tuberosity of scapula			
Lateral head	Lateral side and posterior surface of body of humerus above radial groove			
Medial head	Posterior surface of body of humerus below radial groove			
*Biceps brachii				
Long head	Supraglenoid tuberosity at superior margin of glenoidal labrum	Common tendon inserts on rough posterior portion, tuberosity of radius	Branches of musculocutaneous nerve (derived from the fifth and sixth cervical nerves)	Flexes arm, flexes forearm, supinates hand; long head draws humerus toward glenoid fossa
Short head	Thick, flattened tendon from apex coracoid process	As above	As above	As above
Brachioradialis	Lower two thirds, ridge of humerus; lateral supracondyle ridge of humerus	Lateral side, base of styloid process of radius	Branches of radial nerve (derived from fifth and sixth cervical nerves)	Flexes forearm
*Supinator	Lateral epicondyle of humerus and ridge of ulna below medial notch	Anterior and lateral margin of tuberosity and oblique line of radius	Branches of deep radial nerve (derived from fifth, sixth, and seventh cervical nerves)	Supination of hand
*Pronator teres, has two heads: humeral head, ulnar head	Medial epicondyle of humerus and coronoid process of ulna	Middle of lateral surface of body of radius	Branches of median nerve (derived from sixth and seventh cervical nerves)	Pronation of hand
Pronator quadratus	Distal part of volar surface of body of ulna	Volar surface of radius	Anterior interosseous branch of median nerve (derived from eighth cervical and first thoracic nerves)	Pronation of hand

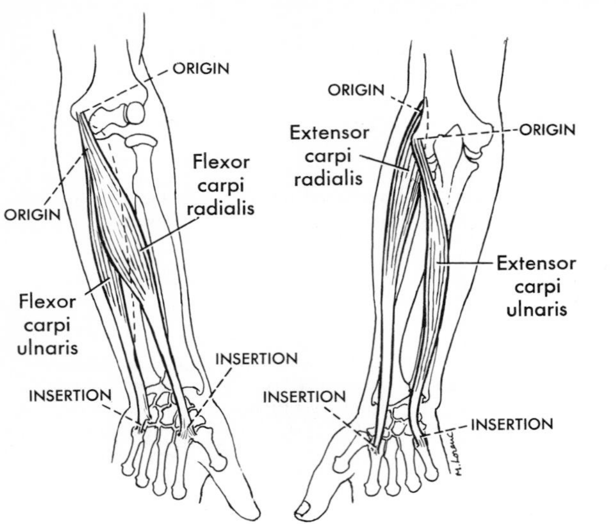

Figure 8–11. Opposing groups of muscles that flex and extend the wrist (left hand.)

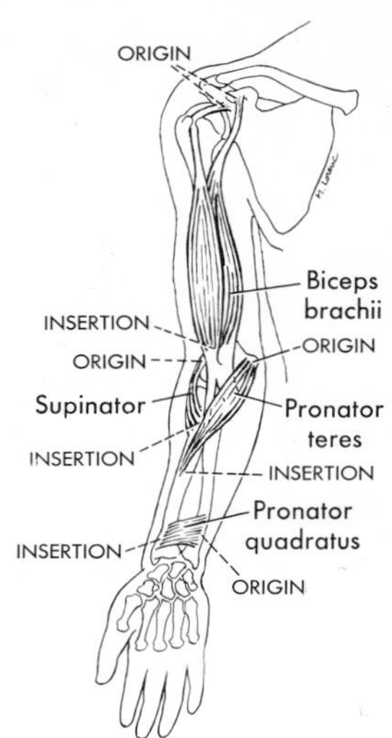

Figure 8–12. Opposing muscles that supinate and pronate the hand (right arm).

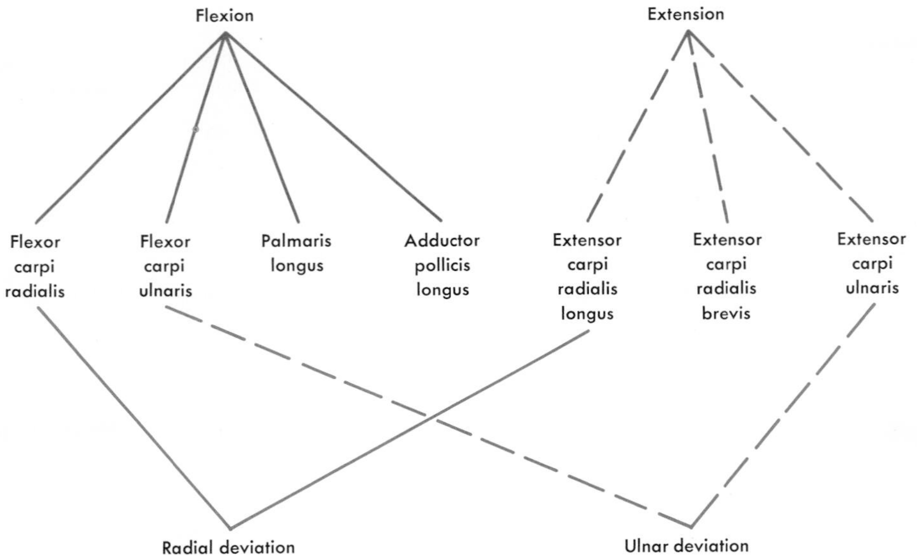

Figure 8–13. Summary of muscle action at the wrist.

MOVEMENT OF THE WRIST

Name	Origin	Insertion	Nerve Supply	Function
*Flexor carpi radialis	Medial epicondyle of humerus	Base of second and third metacarpal bones	Branches of median nerve (derived from sixth and seventh cervical nerves)	Flexion of hand, assists in abduction

Name wrist	Origin	Insertion	Nerve Supply	Function
*Flexor carpi ulnaris	Medial epicondyle of humerus and upper two thirds of dorsal border of ulna	Pisiform, hamate, and fifth metacarpal bones	Branches of ulnar nerve (derived from eighth cervical nerve and first thoracic nerve)	Flexion of hand, assists in adduction of hand
*Extensor carpi radialis longus	Lower third lateral supracondylar ridge of humerus	Dorsal side of base of second metacarpal bone	Branch of radial nerve (derived from sixth and seventh cervical nerves)	Extends and abducts hand
Extensor carpi ulnaris	Lateral epicondyle of humerus and dorsal border of ulna	Ulnar side of base of fifth metacarpal bone	Branch of deep radial nerve (derived from sixth, seventh, and eighth cervical nerves)	Extends and adducts hand
*Extensor carpi radialis brevis	Lateral epicondyle of humerus	Dorsal surface of base of third metacarpal bone, radial side	Branches of radial nerve	Extends and may abduct hand

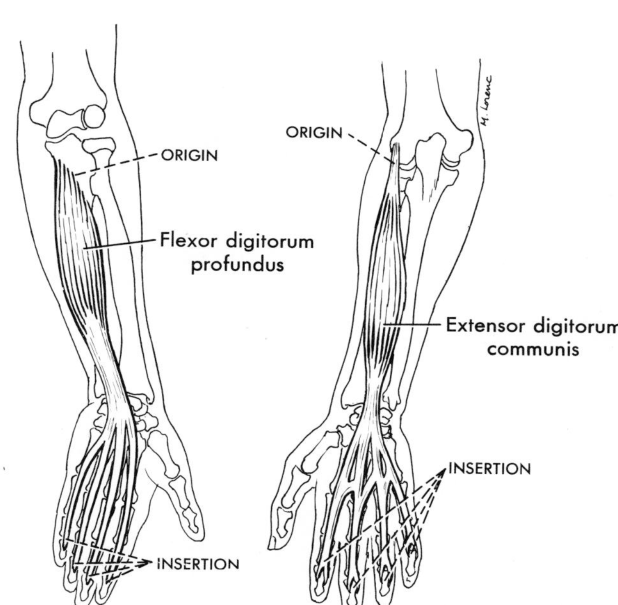

Figure 8–14. Opposing muscles that flex and extend the fingers (left hand).

MOVEMENT OF THE FINGERS

Name	Origin	Insertion	Nerve Supply	Function
*Flexor digitorum profundus	Volar and medial surfaces of body of ulna and interosseous membrane	Bases of last phalanges	Branches of ulnar and median nerves (derived from eighth cervical and first thoracic nerves)	Flexes terminal phalanges of each finger and by continued action flexes other phalanges

Name	Origin	Insertion	Nerve Supply	Function
Flexor digitorum superficialis	Medial epicondyle of humerus and medial side of coronoid process and oblique line of radius	Second phalanges of four fingers	Branches of median nerve (derived from seventh and eighth cervical and first thoracic nerves)	Flexes second phalanx of each finger; flexes hand
Extensor digitorum	Lateral epicondyle of humerus	Second and third phalanges of fingers	Branch of deep radial nerve (derived from sixth, seventh, and eighth cervical nerves)	Extends phalanges, then wrist
*Extensor indicis	Dorsal surface of body of ulna	Into tendon of extensor digitorum to index finger	Branch of deep radial nerve (derived from sixth, seventh, and eighth cervical nerves)	Extends index finger
Extensor digiti minimi	With extensor digitorum	First phalanx of little finger	Branch of deep radial nerve (derived from sixth, seventh, and eighth cervical nerves)	Extends little finger

MOVEMENT OF THE THUMB

Name	Origin	Insertion	Nerve Supply	Function
*Flexor pollicis longus	Volar surface of body of radius	Base of distal phalanx of thumb	Branch of palmar interosseous from median nerve (derived from eighth cervical and first thoracic nerves)	Flexes second phalanx of thumb and by continued action flexes first phalanx
Flexor pollicis brevis	Trapezium bone	Radial sides of and medial base of proximal phalanx of thumb	Branches of median and ulnar nerves (derived from eighth cervical and first thoracic nerves)	Flexes and adducts thumb
*Extensor pollicis longus	Lateral side of dorsal surface of body of ulna	Base of last phalanx of thumb	Branch of deep radial nerve (derived from sixth, seventh, and eighth cervical nerves)	Extends second phalanx of thumb
Extensor pollicis brevis	Dorsal surface of body of radius and interosseous membrane	Base of first phalanx of thumb	Branch of deep radial nerve (derived from sixth and seventh cervical nerves)	Extends first phalanx of thumb
Abductor pollicis longus	Lateral part of dorsal surface of body of ulna and interosseous membrane	Radial side of base of first metacarpal bone	Branch of deep radial nerve (derived from sixth and seventh cervical nerves)	Abducts thumb and by continued action, the wrist

Name	Origin	Insertion	Nerve Supply	Function
Abductor pollicis brevis	Transverse carpal ligament and tuberosity of scaphoid and trapezium	Radial side of first phalanx of thumb	Branch of median nerves (derived from sixth and seventh cervical nerves)	Abducts thumb
Adductor pollicis	Distal two thirds of palmar surface of third metacarpal bone; capitate bone	Ulnar side of base of proximal phalanx of thumb	Branch of the deep palmar branch of ulnar nerve (derived from eighth cervical and first thoracic nerves)	Adducts thumb, brings thumb toward palm
*Opponens pollicis	Ridge of trapezium	Length of metacarpal bone of thumb	Branch of median nerve (derived from sixth and seventh cervical)	Abducts, flexes, and rotates metacarpal bone of thumb

Blood Circulation in the Upper Extremities: Main Branches

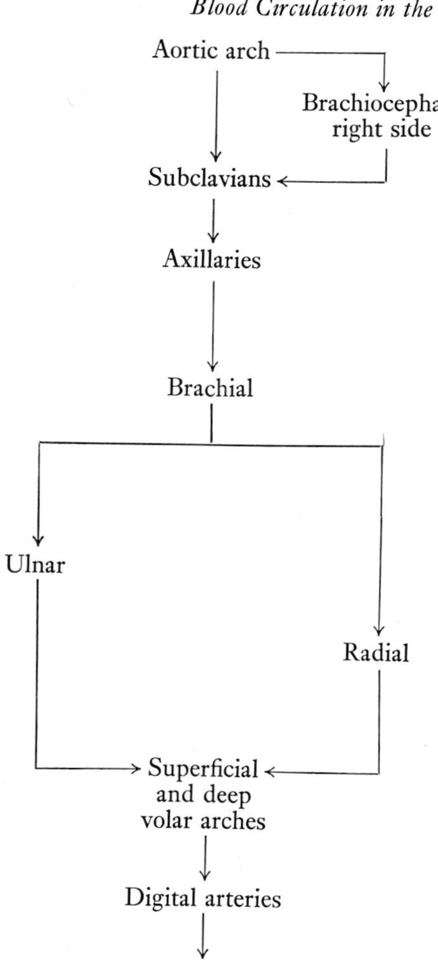

Branches to muscles of scapular region, shoulder, chest, and mammary glands.

These extend from outer border of first rib to lower border of tendon of teres major muscles where they become the brachial. Distribute branches to chest, shoulder, and arm.

Lies in the depression of the inner border of the biceps muscles and divides into two main branches. It distributes many branches to the muscles of the upper arm, both flexors and extensors.

This extends along ulnar border of forearm into the palm of the hand. Supplies flexor and extensor muscles of wrist and hand.

Extends along radial side of forearm. Several branches to muscles of forearm and comes to the surface at wrist—a pulse point.

The ulnar and radial arteries anastomose, forming arches which supply the hand with blood.

These go to each finger.

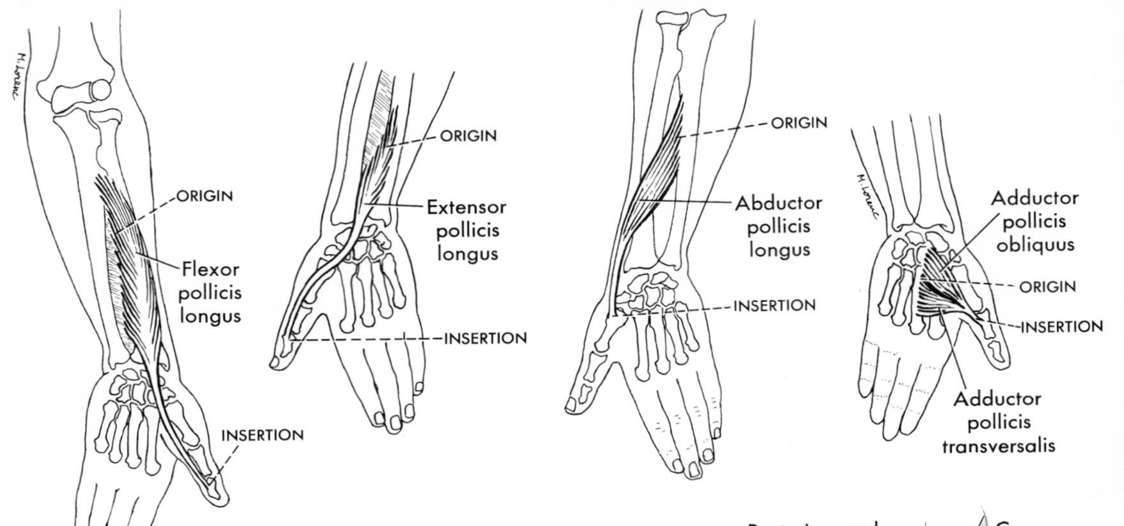

Figure 8–15 [Above]. Opposing muscles that flex and extend the thumbs (left hand).

Figure 8–16 [Above right]. The muscles concerned with adduction and abduction of the thumb (left hand).

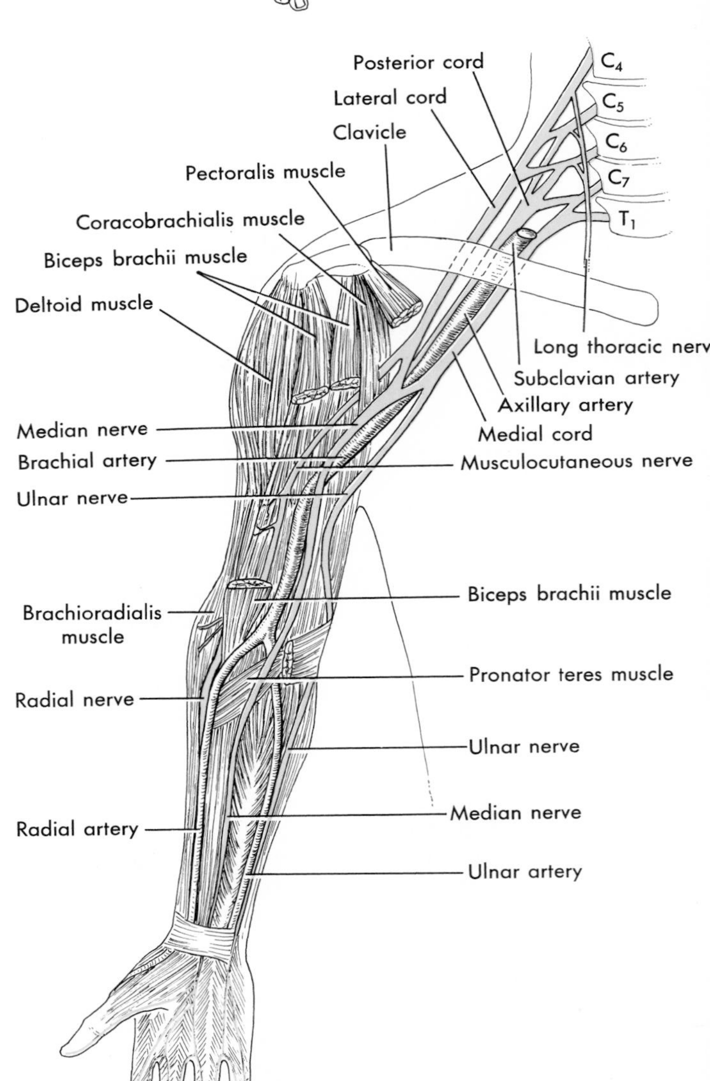

Figure 8–17 [Right]. Diagram illustrating the brachial plexus and distribution of nerves. Note their relation to arteries and to muscles (right arm).

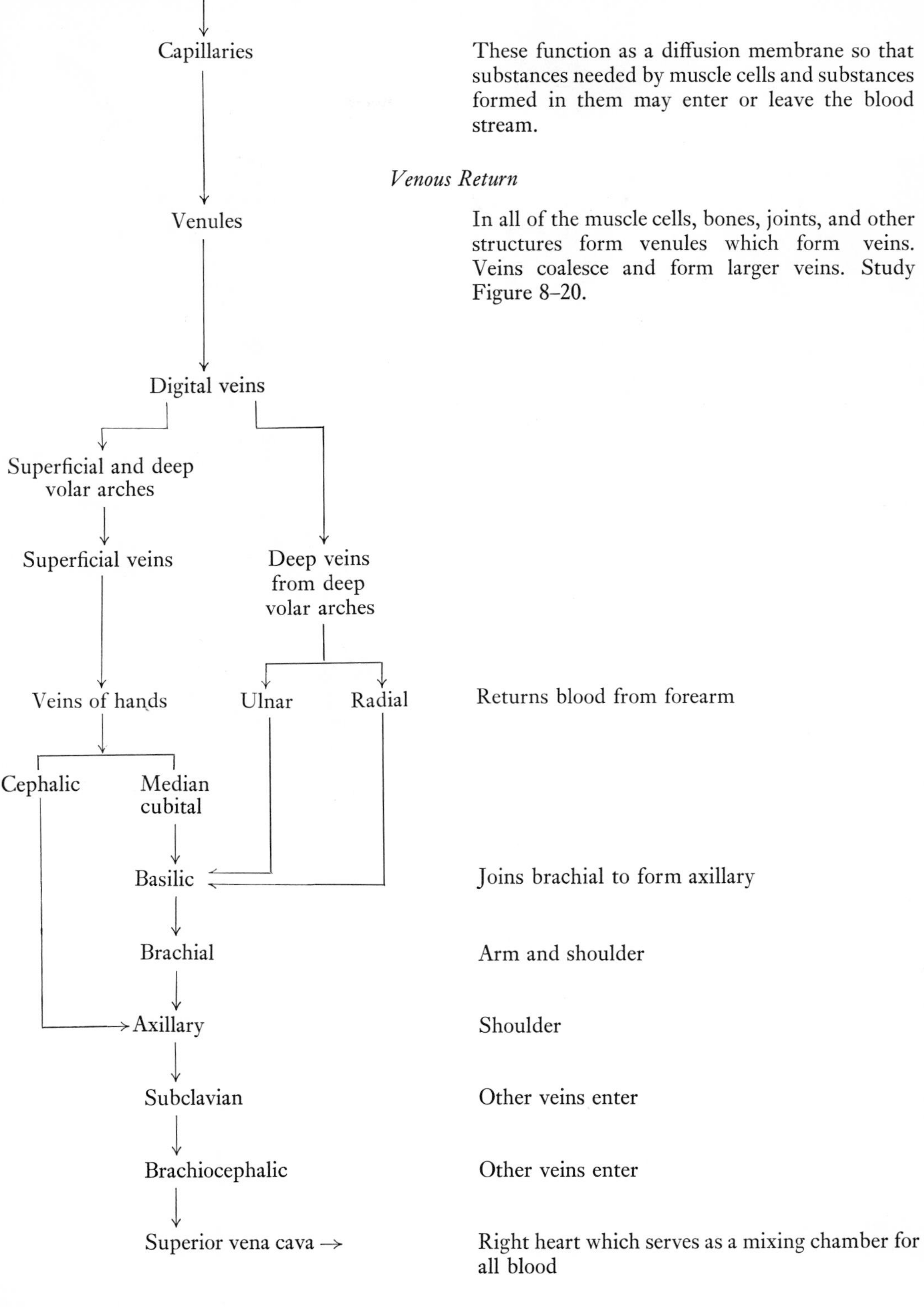
Capillaries
These function as a diffusion membrane so that substances needed by muscle cells and substances formed in them may enter or leave the blood stream.
Venous Return
Venules
In all of the muscle cells, bones, joints, and other structures form venules which form veins. Veins coalesce and form larger veins. Study Figure 8–20.
Digital veins
Superficial and deep volar arches
Superficial veins
Deep veins from deep volar arches
Veins of hands
Ulnar
Radial
Returns blood from forearm
Cephalic
Median cubital
Basilic
Joins brachial to form axillary
Brachial
Arm and shoulder
Axillary
Shoulder
Subclavian
Other veins enter
Brachiocephalic
Other veins enter
Superior vena cava →
Right heart which serves as a mixing chamber for all blood

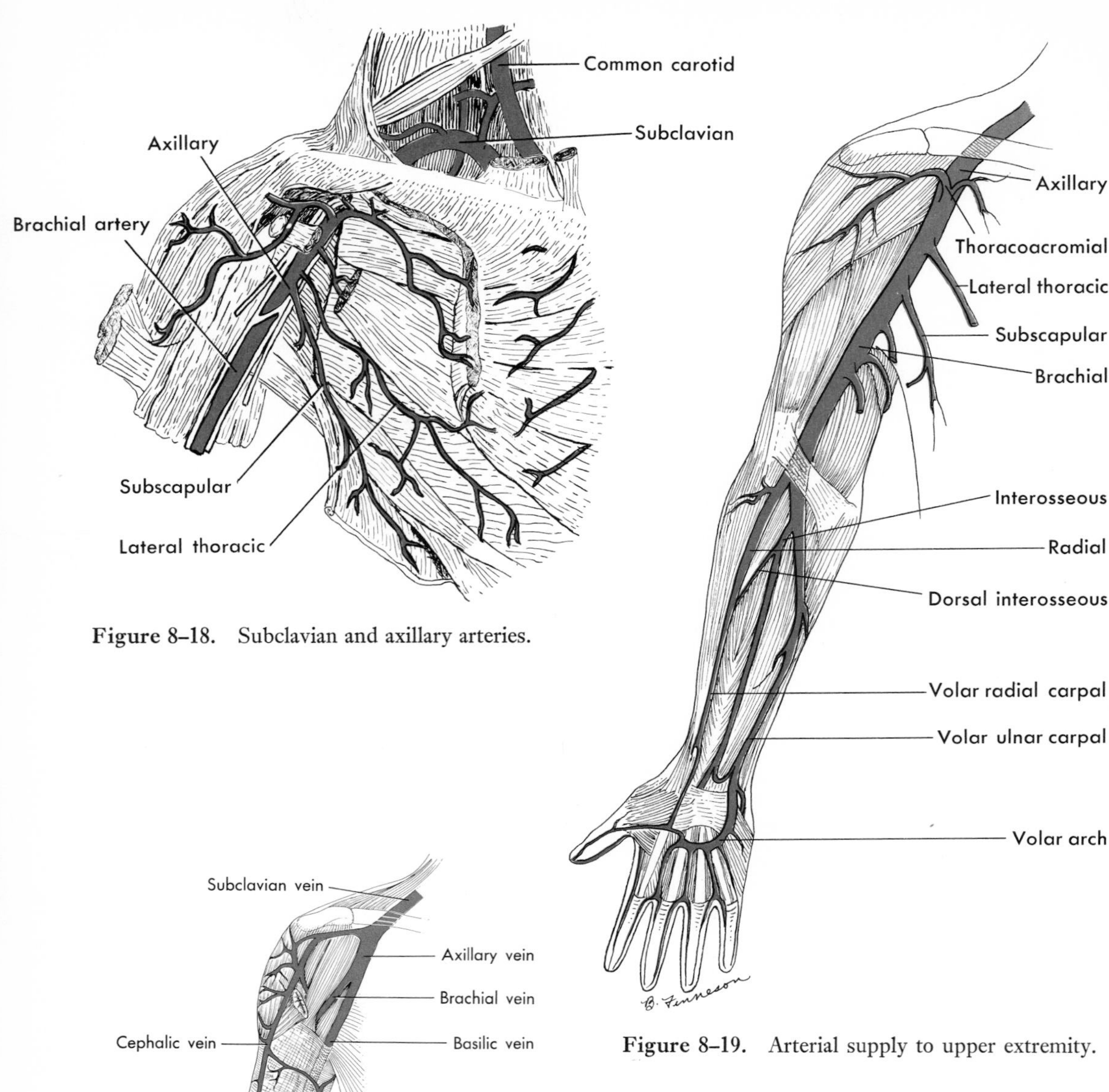

Figure 8–18. Subclavian and axillary arteries.

Figure 8–19. Arterial supply to upper extremity.

Figure 8–20 [Left]. Superficial veins of shoulder, arm, and hand.

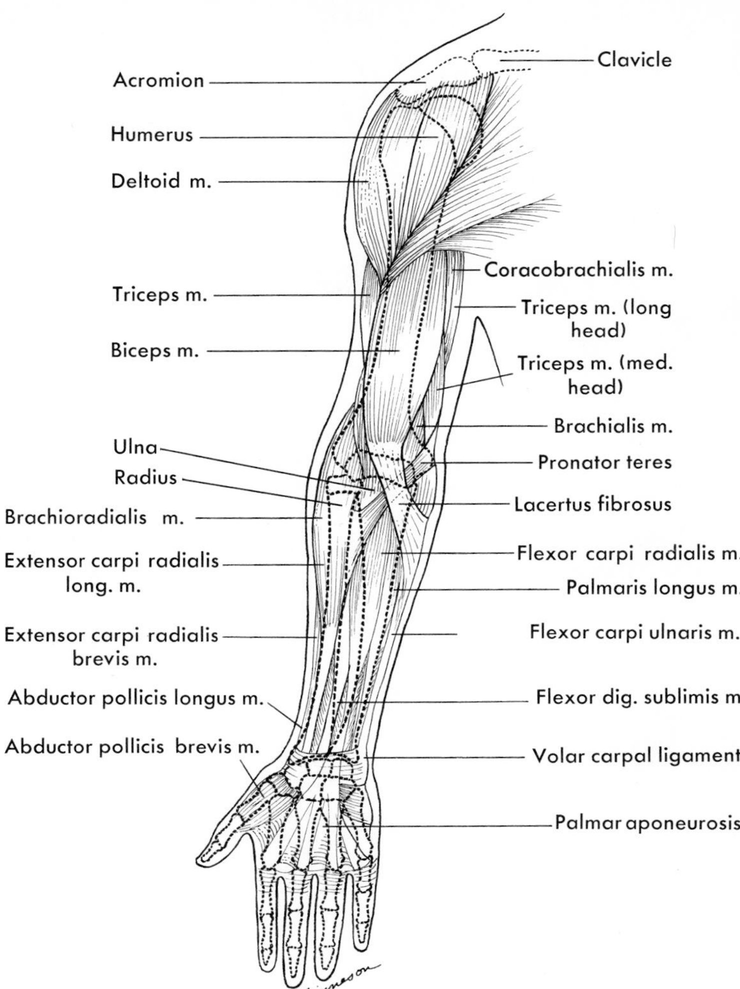

Figure 8–21. Diagram summary. Muscles of upper extremity, showing relationship to bone.

MOVEMENT AT THE HIP JOINT (BALL-AND-SOCKET JOINT)

Name	Origin	Insertion	Nerve Supply	Function
FLEXION				
*Psoas major (Psoas magnus)	Bodies and transverse processes of last thoracic and all lumbar vertebrae	Lesser trochanter of femur and iliac fossa	Lumbar nerves two and three	Flexes thigh on pelvis and helps to rotate thigh medially
Psoas minor (Psoas parvus)	Sides of bodies of T_{12} and L_1	Iliac fascia and body of femur	Branches of femoral nerve (fibers from first, second, and third lumbar nerves)	Acts with psoas major
EXTENSION				
*Gluteus maximus	Iliac crest, sacrum, side of coccyx, and aponeuroses of sacrospinalis	Fascia lata and gluteal ridge of femur	Inferior gluteal (fibers from fifth lumbar and first and second sacral)	Extends femur and rotates it outward

Flexors
Illiopsoas

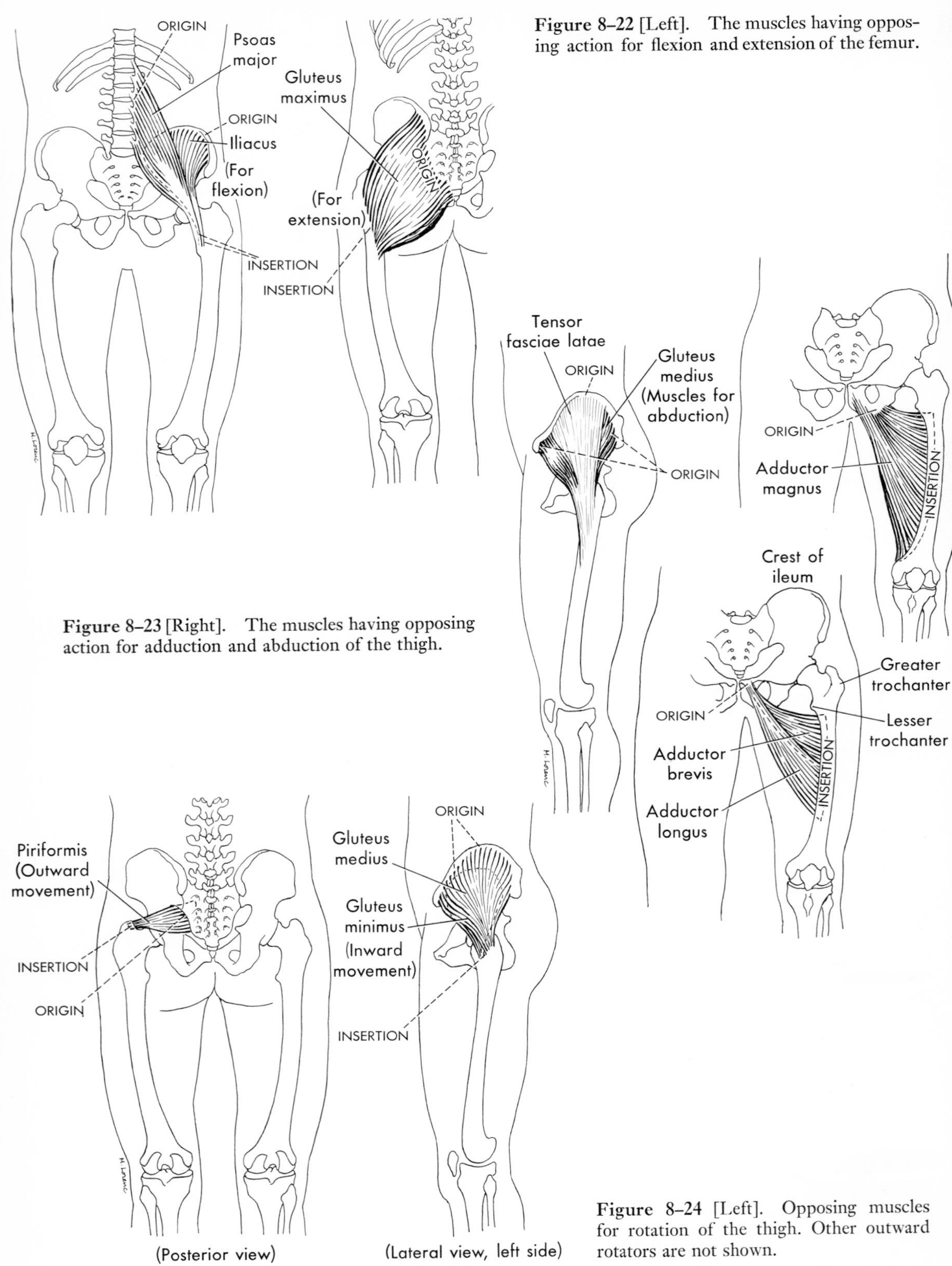

Figure 8–22 [Left]. The muscles having opposing action for flexion and extension of the femur.

Figure 8–23 [Right]. The muscles having opposing action for adduction and abduction of the thigh.

Figure 8–24 [Left]. Opposing muscles for rotation of the thigh. Other outward rotators are not shown.

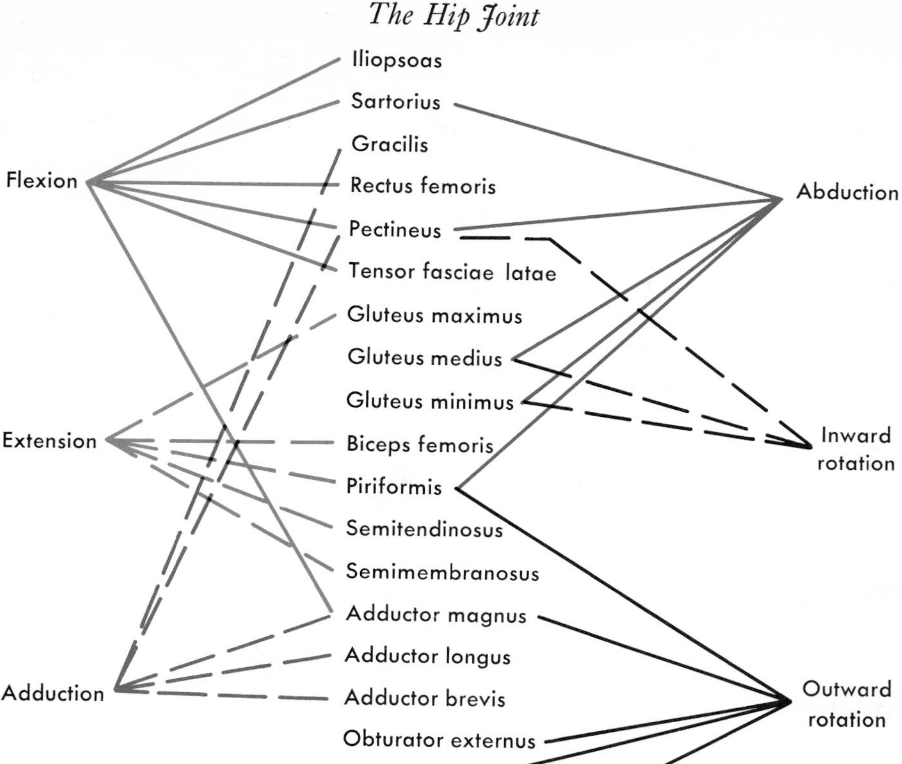

Figure 8–25. Summary of muscle action at the hip.

Name	Origin	Insertion	Nerve Supply	Function
ABDUCTION				
Gluteus medius	Outer surface of ilium and gluteal aponeurosis covering it	Lateral surface of greater trochanter	Superior gluteal nerve (fibers from fourth and fifth lumbar and first sacral nerves)	Abduction of thigh and medial rotation
*Tensor fasciae latae	Anterior crest and spine of ilium	Iliotibial band of fascia lata	Superior gluteal nerve	Tenses fascia lata; flexes and abducts thigh
ADDUCTION				
*Adductor longus	Anterior pubic bone	Linea aspera of femur	Anterior and posterior branches of obturator nerve (fibers from third and fourth lumbar nerves)	Adducts, flexes, and rotates thigh medially; lower portion of magnus is a powerful extensor
Adductor brevis	Outer surface of inferior ramus of pubis			
Adductor magnus	Inferior ramus of pubis and inferior ramus of ischium and ischial tuberosity			
LATERAL ROTATION				
Piriformis	Anterior surface of sacrum	Upper border of great trochanter	Branches from first and second sacral	Rotates thigh laterally abducts it

Name	Origin	Insertion	Nerve Supply	Function
Quadratus femoris	Tuberosity of ischium	Upper part of linea quadrata	Special branch from sacral plexus (fibers from fourth and fifth lumbar and first sacral nerves)	Lateral rotation of thigh
Obturator				
Internus	Internal surface, rami of pubis and ischium	Forepart of great trochanter	Obturator nerve from lumbosacral plexus	Lateral rotation of thigh
Externus	Side obturator membrane and ischio-pubic rami	Trochanteric fossa of femur	Branch of obturator nerve	Lateral rotation of thigh
MEDIAL ROTATION				
Gluteus medius (anterior part)	Outer surface of ilium	Lateral surface of great trochanter	Branches of superior gluteal (fibers from fourth and fifth lumbar and first sacral nerves)	Abducts thigh and rotates it medially
Gluteus minimus	Outer surface of ilium	Anterior border of great trochanter	Branch of superior gluteal (fibers from fourth and fifth lumbar and first sacral nerves)	Medial rotation of thigh and abduction

MOVEMENT AT THE KNEE JOINT (HINGE JOINT)

Name	Origin	Insertion	Nerve Supply	Function
FLEXION				
*Biceps femoris				
Long head	Tuberosity of ischium	Lateral side, head of fibula	Tibial nerve (fibers from first three sacral nerves)	Flexes leg and extends thigh
Short head	Lateral side, linea aspera of femur	Lateral condyle of tibia	Peroneal (fibers from fifth lumbar and first two sacral nerves)	
*Semitendinosus	Tuberosity of ischium	Upper part of body of tibia	Tibial (fibers from fifth lumbar and first and second sacral nerves)	Flexes leg and extends thigh
*Semimembranosus	Tuberosity of ischium	Medial condyle of tibia	Tibial (fibers from fifth lumbar and first and second sacral nerves)	Flexes leg and extends thigh
Popliteus	Lateral condyle of femur	Posterior surface of body of tibia	Tibial (fibers from fifth lumbar and first and second sacral nerves)	Flexes leg
*Gracilis	Symphysis pubis and pubic arch	Medial surface of tibia, below condyle	Obturator	Adducts thigh and flexes leg
*Sartorius	Anterior superior spine of ilium	Medial surface of body of tibia	Femoral nerve	Flexes leg, flexes thigh and rotates it laterally

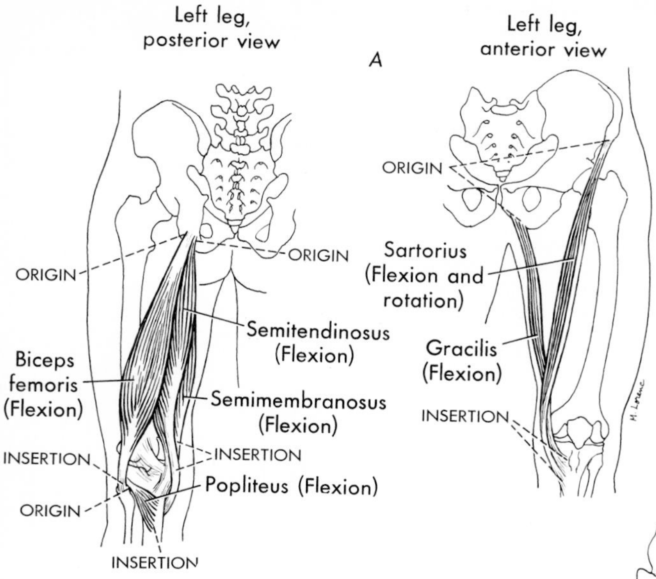

Left leg,
posterior view
A
Left leg,
anterior view
ORIGIN
ORIGIN
ORIGIN
Sartorius
(Flexion and
rotation)
Semitendinosus
(Flexion)
Gracilis
(Flexion)
Biceps
femoris
(Flexion)
Semimembranosus
(Flexion)
INSERTION
INSERTION
INSERTION
Popliteus (Flexion)
ORIGIN
INSERTION

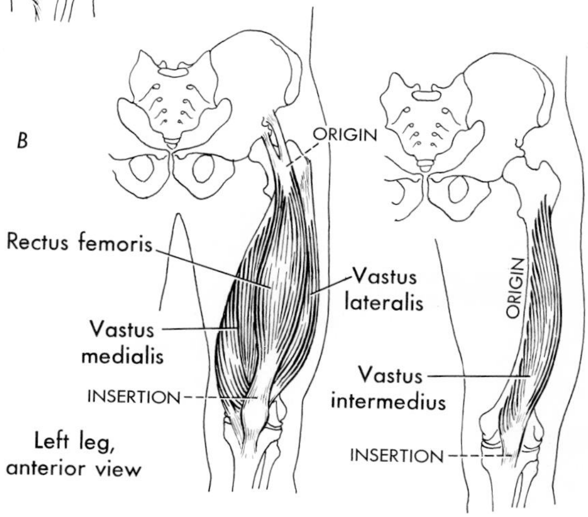

B
ORIGIN
Rectus femoris
Vastus
lateralis
ORIGIN
Vastus
medialis
Vastus
intermedius
INSERTION
INSERTION
Left leg,
anterior view

Figure 8–26. (*A*) The muscles concerned with flexion of the knee. The gracilis also adducts the thigh, and the sartorius assists in flexion and lateral rotation of the thigh. (*B*) The quadriceps femoris muscle for extension of the knee.

Flexion
Extension
Sartorius
Gracilis
Semimembranosus
Semitendinosus
Popliteus
Biceps
femoris
Quadriceps
femoris
Medial rotation
Lateral rotation

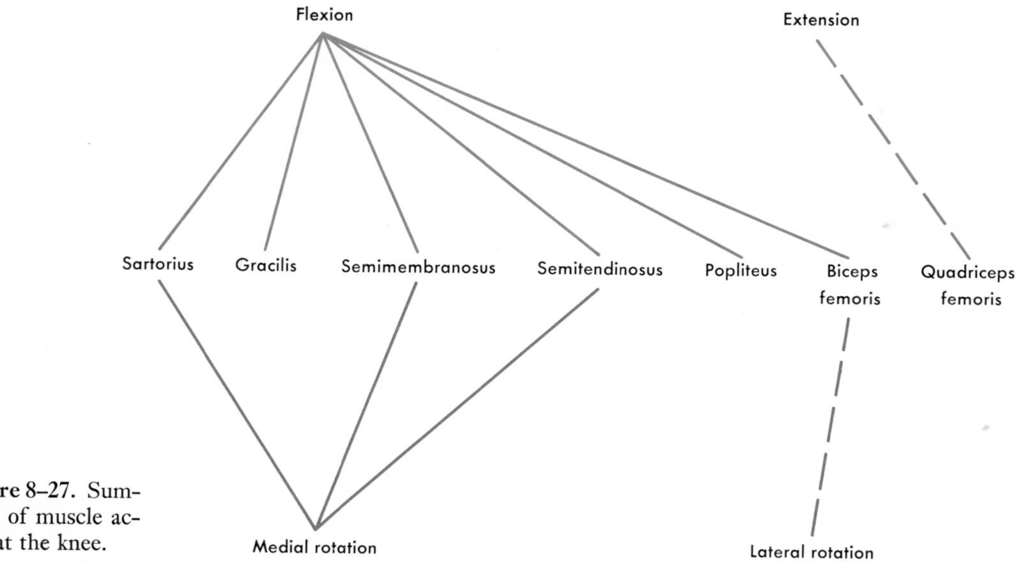

Figure 8–27. Summary of muscle action at the knee.

Name	Origin	Insertion	Nerve Supply	Function
EXTENSION				
*Quadriceps femoris (four heads)				
1. Rectus femoris	Two tendons; one, anterior inferior iliac spine; the other, brim of acetabulum	The four tendons unite at distal part of thigh to form a strong tendon which is inserted into base of patella and tuberosity of tibia	Branches of femoral nerve (fibers from second, third, and fourth lumbar nerves)	Entire quadriceps extends leg; rectus division also flexes thigh
2. Vastus lateralis	Great trochanter and linea aspera of femur			
3. Vastus medialis	Medial lip of linea aspera			
4. Vastus intermedius	Ventral and lateral surfaces of body of femur			

MOVEMENT AT THE ANKLE JOINT

Name	Origin	Insertion	Nerve Supply	Function
PLANTAR FLEXION				
*Gastrocnemius	Two heads from medial and lateral condyles of femur and adjacent part of capsule of knee	Through tendo-calcaneus to calcaneus	Tibial (fibers from first and second sacral nerves)	Plantar flexes foot (points toes downward)
*Soleus	Posterior surface, head of fibula and medial border of tibia	Through tendocalcaneus to calcaneus	Tibial (fibers from first and second sacral nerves)	Plantar flexes foot
Plantaris	Linea aspera of femur and oblique popliteal ligament of knee	Posterior part of calcaneus via tendocalcaneus	Tibial (fibers from fourth and fifth lumbar and first sacral nerve)	Plantar flexes foot
Peroneus longus	Head and lateral surface of body of fibula and lateral condyle of tibia	Lateral side, base of first metatarsal bone, and lateral side of first cuneiform bone	Branches of peroneal nerve (fibers from fourth and fifth lumbar and first sacral nerves)	Plantar flexes and everts foot
Peroneus brevis	Lateral surface, distal two thirds of body of fibula	Tuberosity at base of fifth metatarsal bone, lateral side	Branch of superficial peroneal nerve (fibers as above)	Plantar flexes and pronates (everts and abducts) foot
DORSIFLEXION				
*Tibialis anterior	Lateral condyle and upper portion of body of tibia and interosseous membrane	Undersurface of first cuneiform and base of first metatarsal	Branches of deep peroneal (fibers from fourth and fifth lumbar and first sacral)	Dorsally flexes and supinates foot (adducts and inverts)
Peroneus tertius	Lower, medial surface of fibula and interosseous membrane	Medial and plantar surface of first cuneiform and base of first metatarsal bone	Branches of deep peroneal (fibers as above)	Dorsally flexes and pronates foot

Figure 8–28. The muscles having opposing action for flexion and extension of the ankle.

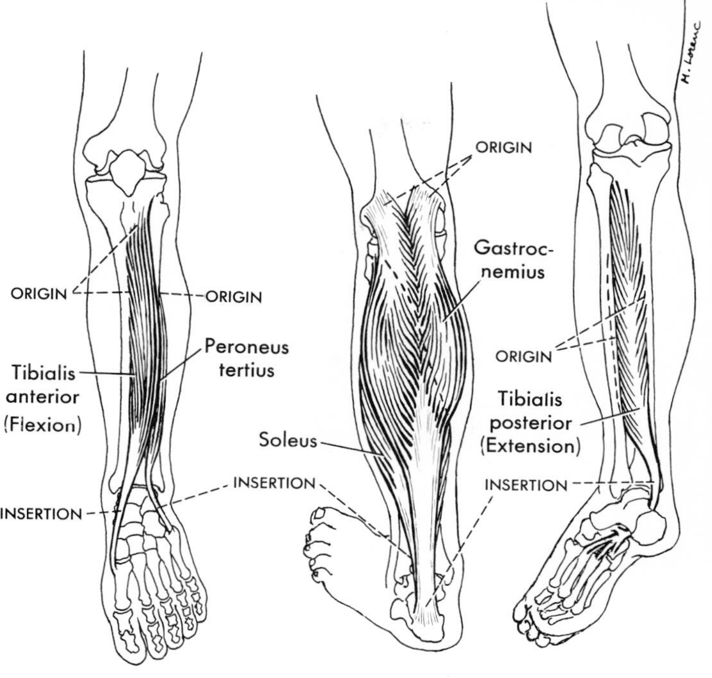

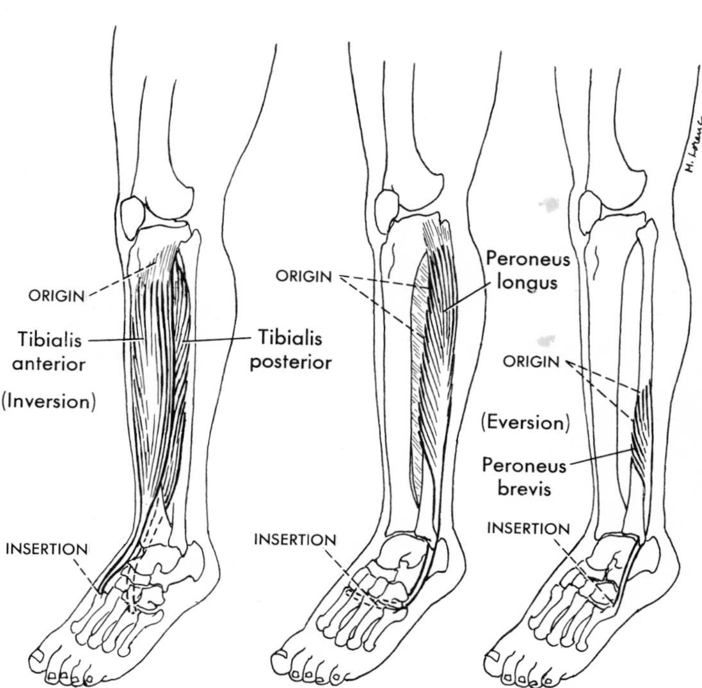

Figure 8–29. Opposing muscles for inversion (supination) and eversion (pronation) of the foot.

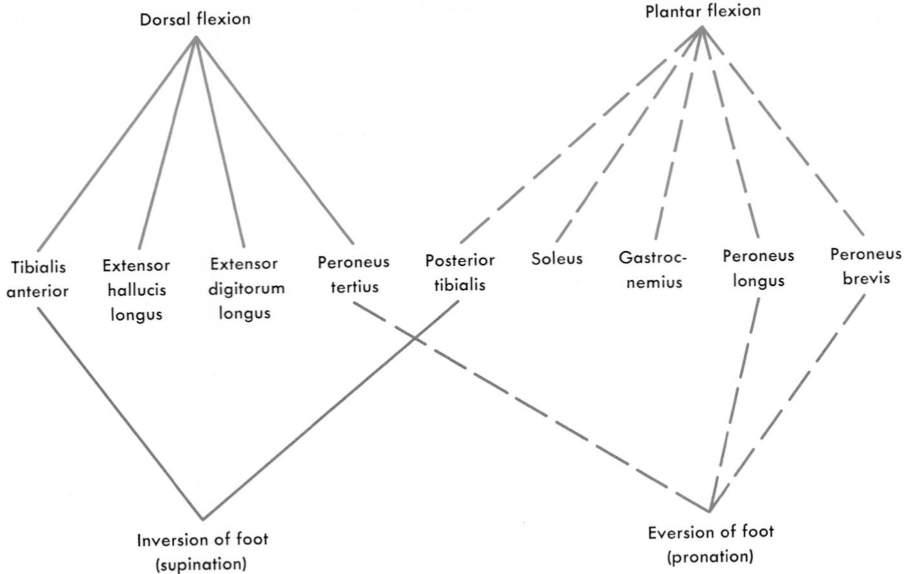

Figure 8–30. Summary of muscle action at the ankle and foot.

Name	Origin	Insertion	Nerve Supply	Function
*Posterior tibial (tibialis posterior)	Whole posterior surface of interosseous membrane, lateral side of posterior surface of body of tibia	Tuberosity of navicular bone, gives extension to third, cuneiform, cuboid, and base of second, third, and fourth metatarsal bones	Branch of tibial nerve (derived from fifth lumbar and first sacral nerves)	Supinates (adducts and inverts foot) and plantar flexes foot

DEEP MUSCLES OF THE TOES

Name	Origin	Insertion	Nerve Supply	Function
Flexor digitorum brevis	Medial process, tuberosity of calcaneus	Sides of second phalanx of lateral four toes	Branches of medial plantar nerve (fibers of fourth and fifth lumbar nerves)	Flexes second phalanges of the four small toes
Abductor hallucis	Medial process, tuberosity of calcaneus	Tibial side of base of first phalanx of great toe	Medial plantar nerve (fibers of fourth and fifth lumbar nerves)	Abducts great toe
Abductor digiti minimi	Lateral process, tuberosity of calcaneus	Fibular side of base of first phalanx of little toe	Branches of lateral plantar nerve (fibers of first and second sacral)	Abducts small toe
Quadratus plantae	Two heads on either side of calcaneus	Tendons of flexor digitorum longus	Branches of lateral plantar nerve	Flexes terminal phalanges of the four small toes

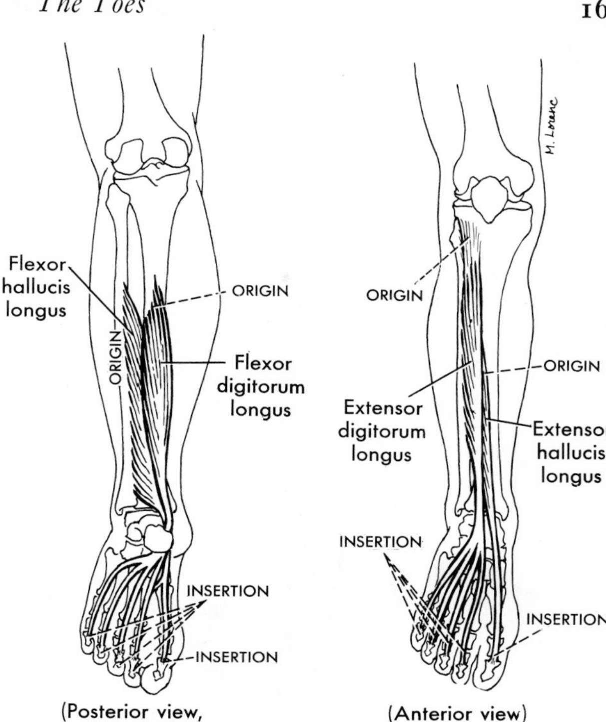

Figure 8–31. The muscles having opposing action for flexion and extension of the toes.

MOVEMENT OF THE TOES

Name	Origin	Insertion	Nerve Supply	Function
FLEXION				
Flexor hallucis longus	Inferior two thirds of posterior surface of fibula	Base of terminal phalanx of great toe	Tibial nerve (fibers of fifth lumbar and first and second sacral nerves)	Flexes great toe, plantar flexes and inverts foot
Flexor digitorum longus	Posterior surface of body of tibia	By four tendons into last phalanges of four outer toes	Tibial nerve	Flexes terminal phalanges of the four toes; plantar flexes and inverts foot
EXTENSION				
Extensor hallucis longus	Inferior two thirds of posterior surface of body of fibula	Base of terminal phalanx of great toe	Branch of deep peroneal nerve (fibers of fourth and fifth lumbar and first sacral nerves)	Extends second phalanx of great toe; dorsally flexes and everts foot
Extensor digitorum longus	Lateral condyle of tibia and anterior surface of body of fibula	Second and third phalanges of the four lesser toes	Branches of deep peroneal (fibers of fourth and fifth lumbar and first sacral nerves)	Extends proximal phalanges of the four lesser toes; dorsally flexes and everts foot
Extensor digitorum brevis	Distal and superior lateral surfaces of calcaneus	Lateral sides of tendons of extensor digitorum longus of medial four toes	Branches of deep peroneal (fibers of fifth lumbar and first sacral nerve)	Extends proximal phalanges of the great and the adjacent three small toes

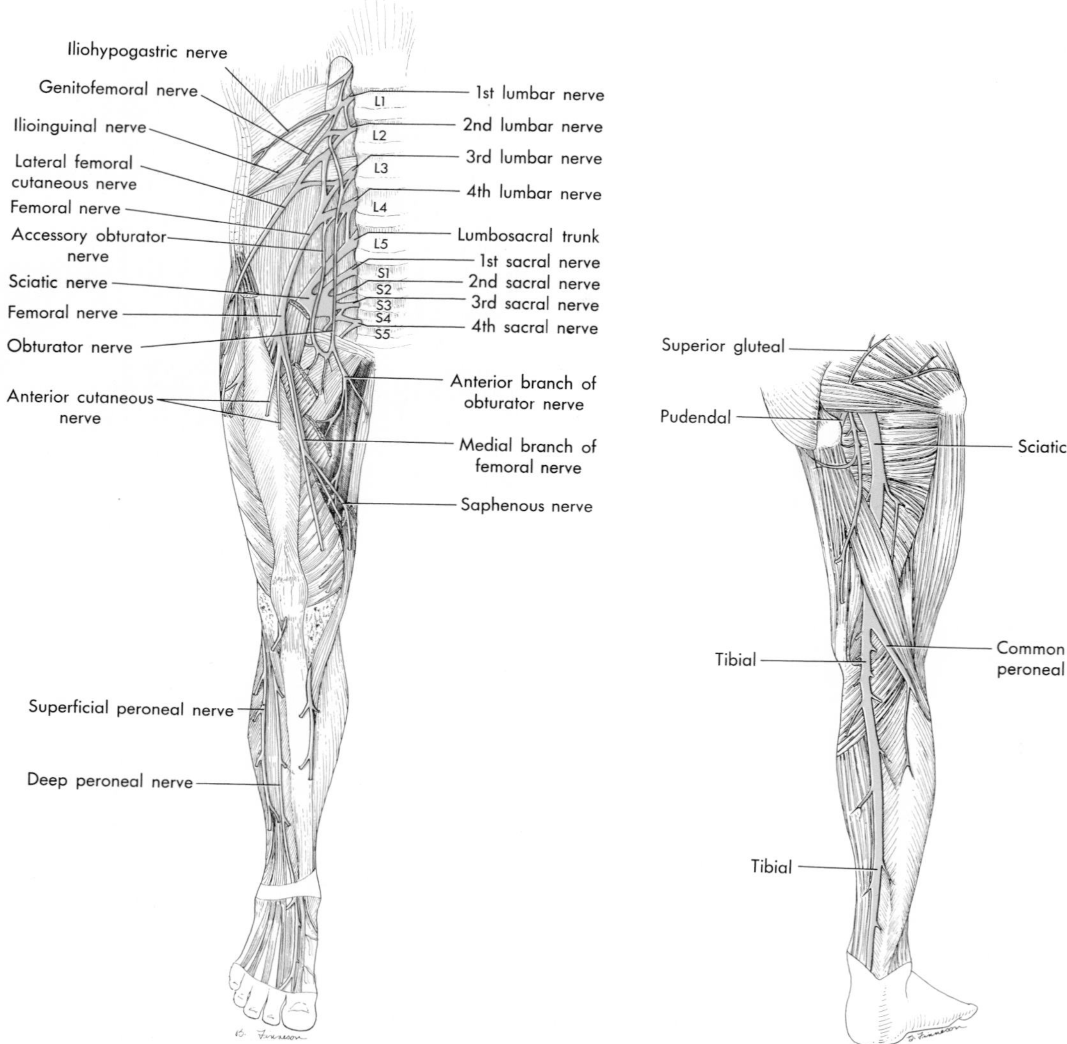

Figure 8–32. Diagram illustrating the lumbosacral plexus and distribution of nerves. Note their relation to muscles of the leg (right).

Figure 8–33. Nerve supply to right lower extremity, posterior view.

Blood Circulation to the Lower Extremity

NAME OF ARTERY — LOCATION AND DISTRIBUTION

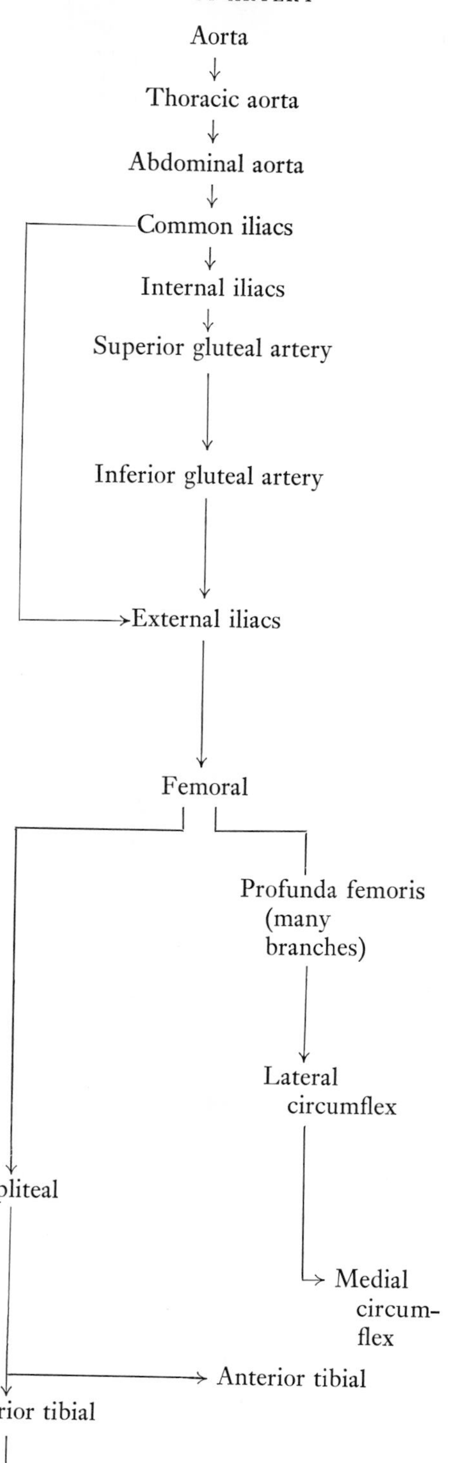

Parietal and visceral branches.

Superior branch anastomoses with the inferior gluteal and lateral sacral arteries. *Deep branch* anastomoses with the deep iliac and lateral femoral arteries.

Many branches—anastomose with branches of the perforating arteries (so named because they perforate the adductor muscle). These arteries surround the gluteal region and posterior thigh. See Figure 8–34.

Passes obliquely, distally, and laterally along the medial border of the psoas major muscle—passes under the inguinal ligament, midway between the anterior superior spine of the ilium and the symphysis pubis, where it enters the thigh and becomes the femoral.

The femoral artery extends from the inguinal (Poupart's) ligament to an opening in the adductor magnus muscle, where it becomes the popliteal. In the first part of its course the artery lies along the middle of the depression on the inner aspect of the thigh, known as the femoral (Scarpa's) triangle. Here pulsation may be felt. The femoral artery supplies blood to the muscles and fascia of the thigh. Branches also extend to the abdominal walls.

The *lateral femoral circumflex artery* anastomoses with branches of the popliteal to form the *circumpatellar* anastomosis, which surrounds the knee joints. The popliteal sends branches to the knee joint and all the posterior femoral muscles, the gastrocnemius and soleus muscles, and skin on back of the leg.

The medial branch supplies the adductors, gracilis, and external obturator muscles.

Distributes blood to the front of the leg.

Posterior tibial lies at the back of the leg and distributes blood to muscles of the back of the leg and nutrient vessels to tibia and fibula.

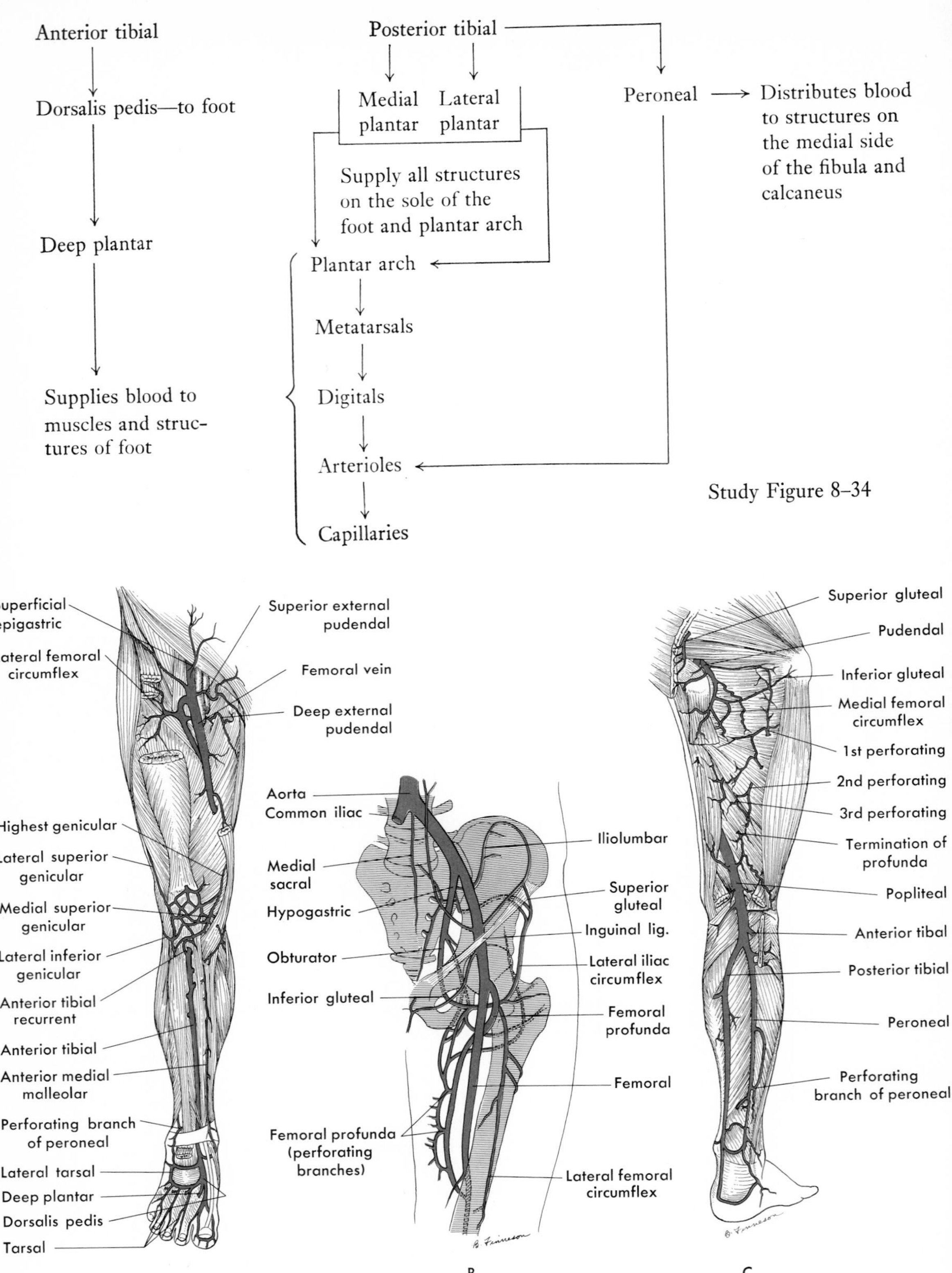

Figure 8–34. Arterial blood supply to the lower extremity.

Blood from the lower extremity is returned by a superficial and deep set of veins. The deep veins accompany the arteries and the superficial veins are beneath the skin between the layers of superficial fascia. All veins from the lower extremity possess numerous valves.

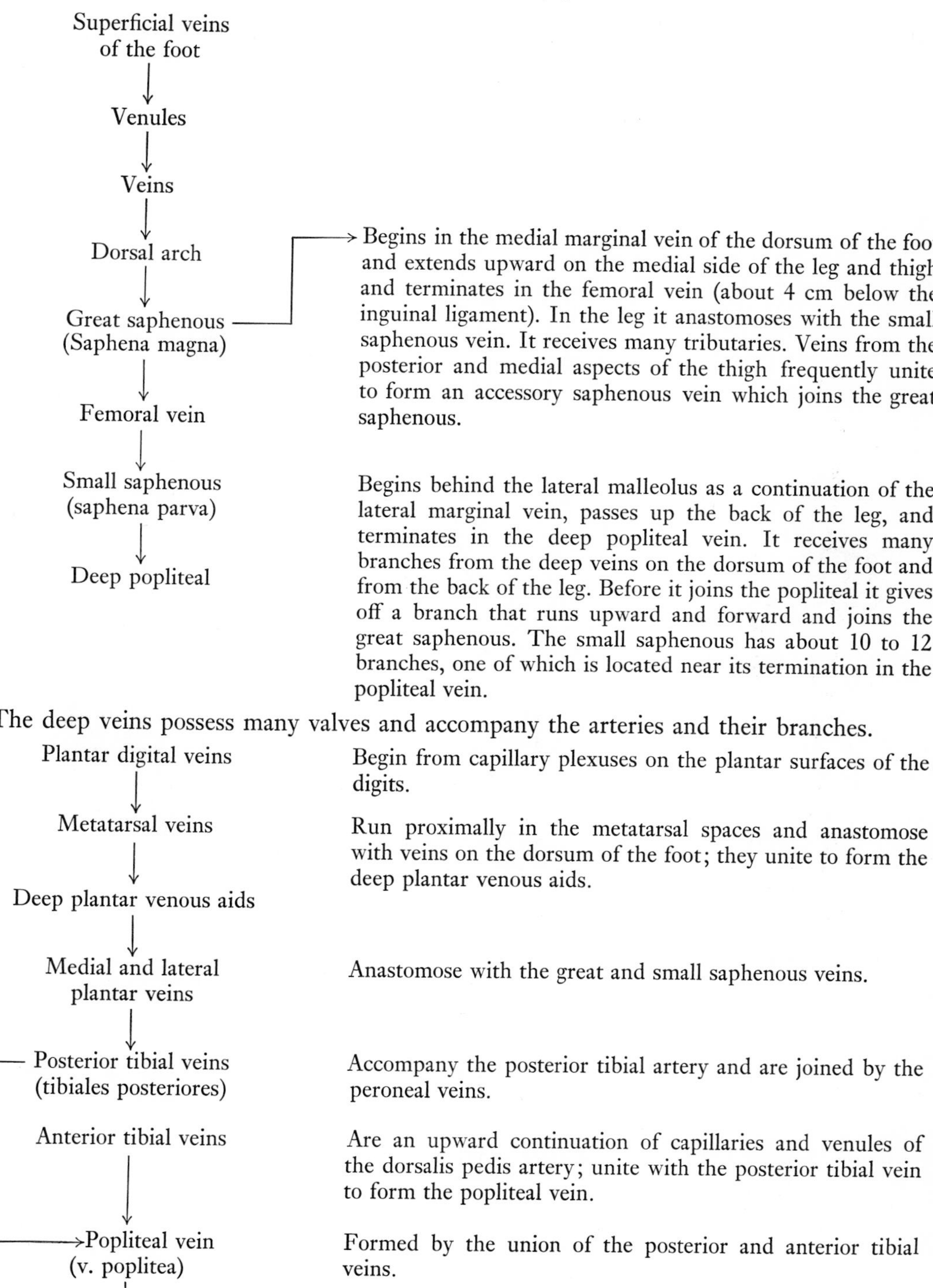

Superficial veins of the foot
↓
Venules
↓
Veins
↓
Dorsal arch
↓
Great saphenous (Saphena magna) — Begins in the medial marginal vein of the dorsum of the foot and extends upward on the medial side of the leg and thigh and terminates in the femoral vein (about 4 cm below the inguinal ligament). In the leg it anastomoses with the small saphenous vein. It receives many tributaries. Veins from the posterior and medial aspects of the thigh frequently unite to form an accessory saphenous vein which joins the great saphenous.
↓
Femoral vein
↓
Small saphenous (saphena parva) — Begins behind the lateral malleolus as a continuation of the lateral marginal vein, passes up the back of the leg, and terminates in the deep popliteal vein. It receives many branches from the deep veins on the dorsum of the foot and from the back of the leg. Before it joins the popliteal it gives off a branch that runs upward and forward and joins the great saphenous. The small saphenous has about 10 to 12 branches, one of which is located near its termination in the popliteal vein.
↓
Deep popliteal

The deep veins possess many valves and accompany the arteries and their branches.

Plantar digital veins — Begin from capillary plexuses on the plantar surfaces of the digits.
↓
Metatarsal veins — Run proximally in the metatarsal spaces and anastomose with veins on the dorsum of the foot; they unite to form the deep plantar venous aids.
↓
Deep plantar venous aids
↓
Medial and lateral plantar veins — Anastomose with the great and small saphenous veins.
↓
Posterior tibial veins (tibiales posteriores) — Accompany the posterior tibial artery and are joined by the peroneal veins.

Anterior tibial veins — Are an upward continuation of capillaries and venules of the dorsalis pedis artery; unite with the posterior tibial vein to form the popliteal vein.
↓
Popliteal vein (v. poplitea) — Formed by the union of the posterior and anterior tibial veins.
↓

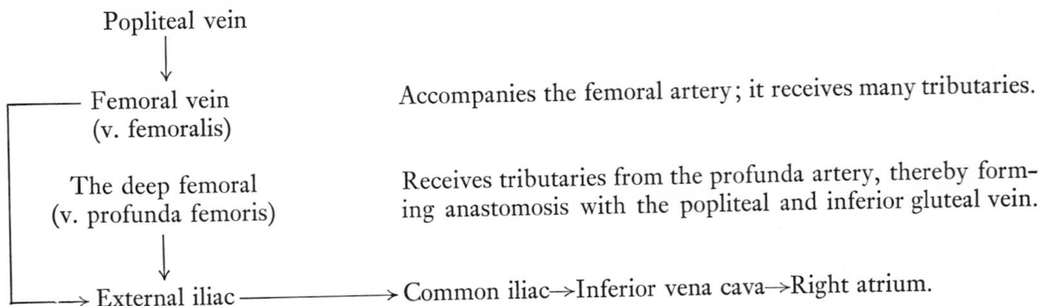

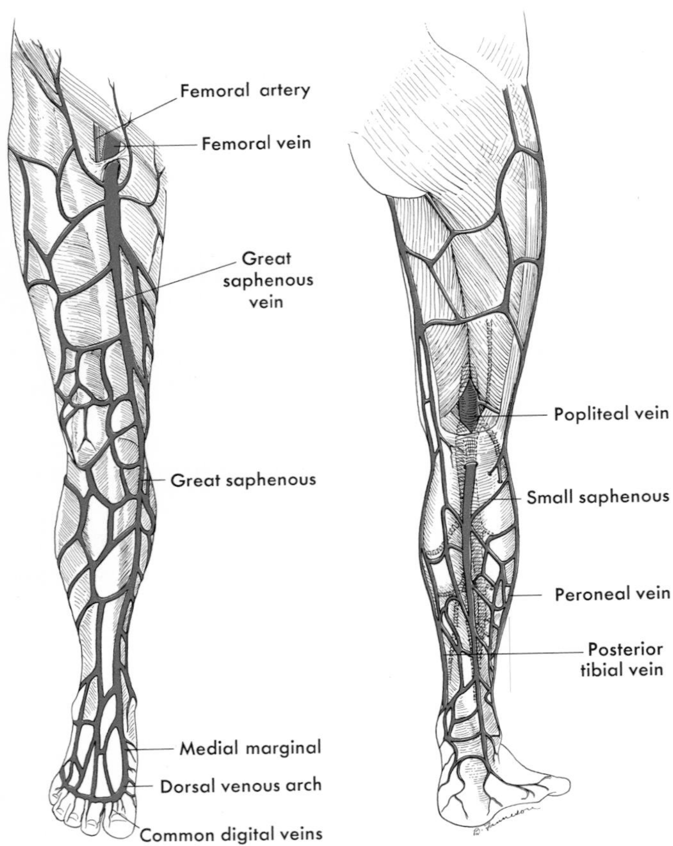

Figure 8–35. Venous return from the lower extremity.

TABLE OF SPINAL NERVES

Spinal Nerves		Plexuses Formed	Some Main Nerves	Distribution to a Few Muscles
Cervical	1			To muscles of occipital triangle
	2	Cervical plexus C2–C4	Branches from plexus	Skin and muscles of cervical region and neck; trapezius, etc.
			Phrenic nerve (chiefly C4)	Motor to diaphragm

Spinal Nerves	Plexuses Formed	Some Main Nerves	Distribution to a Few Muscles
3		Branches from plexus	Deltoid, Pectoralis, Rhomboides; Supraspinatus, Infraspinatus, Biceps
4		Median and ulnar nerve	Flexor carpi radialis, Flexor digitorum sublimis, Flexor pollicis longus, Pronators; Flexor carpi ulnaris, Flexor digitorum profondus, Flexor pollicis brevis
5	Brachial plexus C5–T1		
6			
7		Radial nerve	Triceps, Brachialis, Brachioradialis, Supinator, Extensor digitorum; Extensor carpi radialis, Extensor carpi ulnaris, Extensor policis, Extensor indicis proprius
8			
Thoracic 1			
Thoracic 1–12		Intercostal nerves	Levators costarum, Intercostal muscles, Abdominal muscles; Back muscles
Lumbar 1		Femoral nerve	Iliopsoas, Sartorius; Quadriceps femoris, Knee
2			
3	Lumbosacral T12–S3	Ventral branches of L5–S2	External rotators of thigh
4		Obturator nerve	Gracilis, adductor muscles
5		Gluteal nerves	Gluteal muscles
Sacral 1		Sciatic nerve	Biceps femoris (long head), Semitendinosus, Semimembranosus
2			
3	Lumbosacral T12–S3	Tibial	Posterior tibial, Gastrocnemius, Soleus, Plantaris; Flexor digitorum, Flexor hallucis longus, Small muscles of foot
4			
5		Tibial, superficial, and deep peroneal nerves	Biceps femoris (short head), Anterior tibialis, Extensor digitorum longus and brevis, Extensor hallucis longus, Peroneus longus, brevis, tertius
Coccygeal 1			Muscles over coccyx

QUESTIONS FOR DISCUSSION

1. What groups of muscles are used in the following activities?
   a. Combing the hair
   b. Climbing stairs
   c. Turning to look over the right shoulder
   d. Standing on tiptoe
2. Why is it important for you to know the location and function of the larger muscles and the relationship of nerves and blood vessels to them?
3. What would be the result of injury to the following nerves?
   a. The radial
   b. The median
   c. The ulnar
   d. The femoral
   e. The tibial
   f. The peroneal
4. Discuss in detail the blood supply to:
   a. The arms
   b. The lower extremities
   c. What is the venous return from these structures?
5. Review the main functions and nerve supply of the following muscles:
   a. Biceps brachii
   b. Deltoid
   c. Iliopsoas
   d. Gluteus maximus
   e. Gastrocnemius
   f. Quadriceps
6. Which muscle or muscle groups oppose the muscles in 5, a, e, f?

UNIT III
Awareness and Response to Environment

Interpretation of sensations, reason and understanding, and initiation of thought are readily apparent activities of the nervous system. Yet it is also the controller of unconscious activity, making adjustments to changing functional needs. The quality of our communication with others, and ultimately life itself, are the responsibility of the nervous system.

CHAPTER

9

PARTS OF THE NERVOUS SYSTEM

The Neuron, Receptors, Effectors
The Nerve Impulse
The Reflex Arc and Response

The nervous system, in conjunction with the endocrine system, controls the functioning of the human body, internally and externally. Generally speaking, the nervous system controls rapid activities, such as smooth and skeletal muscle contractions, so that response to the environment is immediate. In addition, the central nervous system receives and processes sensations, storing the information for future use.

The parts of the nervous system are:

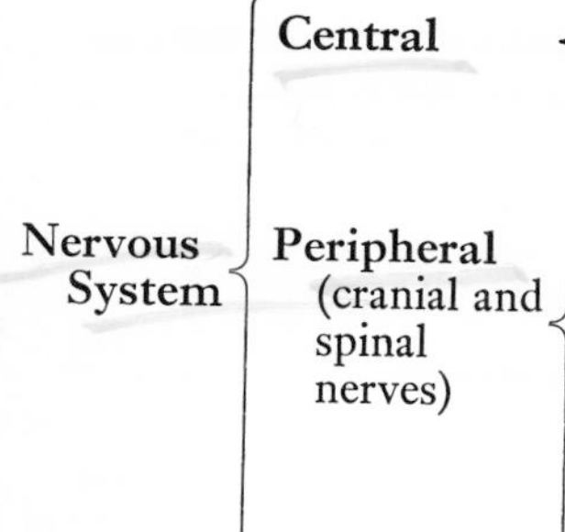

- **Nervous System**
  - **Central**
    - Brain
    - Spinal cord
  - **Peripheral** (cranial and spinal nerves)
    1. Connections of "centers" in the central nervous system with the body wall by cranial and spinal nerve fibers. *The somatic* (pertaining to body wall), *or* **cerebrospinal**, *system*
    2. Connections of "centers" in the central nervous system with the viscera by **visceral fibers** of the autonomic system
       a. Nerve fibers from the brain and sacral spinal cord. *The cranio-sacral, or parasympathetic, system*
       b. Nerve fibers from the thoracolumbar region of the spinal cord and autonomic ganglia. *The thoracolumbar* (*thoracicolumbar*), *or sympathetic, system*

The cerebrospinal system includes (1) those parts of the brain which are concerned with consciousness and mental activities; (2) the parts of the brain, spinal cord, and the nerve fibers, both sensory and motor, that control the skeletal muscles; and (3) the end organs, receptors and effectors, of the body wall.

The autonomic system is known as the visceral or involuntary system because, unlike the cerebrospinal system, it is not under voluntary control. It includes all parts of the nervous system that innervate the smooth muscles of the blood vessels and the viscera, including heart, digestive tract, kidney, and glands.

The efferent (motor) autonomic system is subdivided into (1) the craniosacral, or parasympathetic, and (2) the thoracolumbar, or sympathetic, divisions. Throughout the body the efferent visceral fibers are found with the somatic fibers in all the spinal nerves and in most of the cranial nerves. The afferent (sensory) fibers of both the somatic and autonomic systems have their cell bodies in the spinal ganglia and enter the cord through the dorsal root.

Although the autonomic and somatic

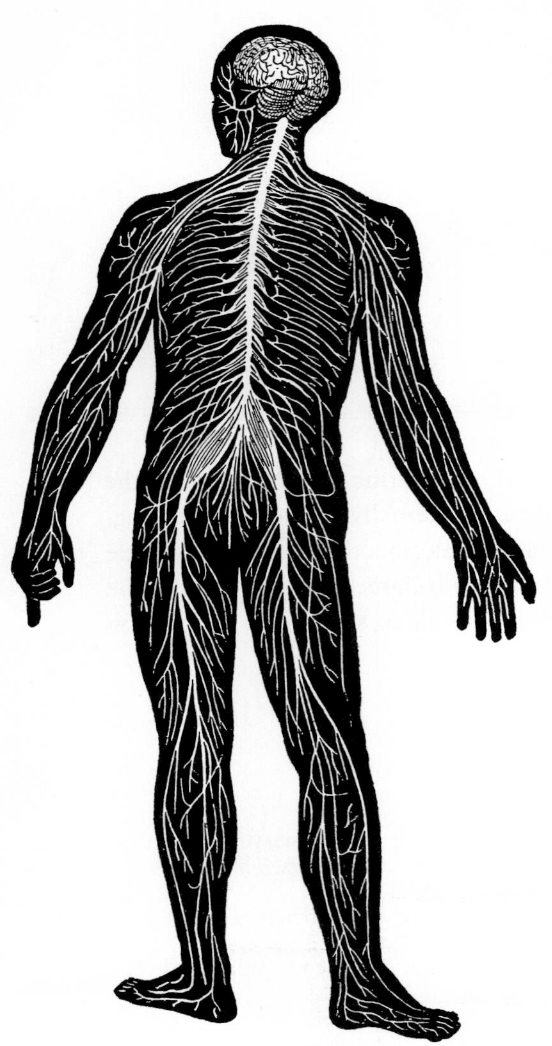

Figure 9–1. Diagram illustrating the brain, spinal cord, and spinal nerves.

nervous systems are anatomically and functionally independent, their activities are closely integrated both centrally and peripherally. Visceral receptors are capable of initiating somatic activity, and somatic receptors can elicit visceral activity. (See Chapter 13.)

Nerve Tissue. Nerve tissue is composed of the functional cell of the nervous system, the neuron; supporting cells, the neuroglia; and phagocytic cells, the microglia; all of which have been described in Chapter 3 (page 51). Figure 9–2 reviews the structure of the neuron.

Gray and White Matter. The cell bodies of neurons and many of their processes are grouped together into gray matter. *Gray matter* is found in the outer layers of the cortex and other parts of the brain and in the core of the spinal cord. It also composes the nuclei and ganglia and the unmyelinated nerve fibers. *White* matter, found in the brain, spinal cord, and nerves, is made up of the long axons of the neurons. It contains nonmyelinated as well as myelinated fibers, though the preponderance of myelinated fibers gives it a creamy color—hence the name. Both gray and white matter contain capillaries as well.

Ganglion. A *ganglion* is an aggregate of neural cell bodies outside of the brain and cord. The cell bodies of the visceral and somatic sensory nerves lie in the dorsal root ganglia. The (postganglionic) cell bodies of the visceral efferent nerves lie in the sympathetic and parasympathetic ganglia of the autonomic nervous system. (See Chapter 13.)

Nucleus. An aggregate of nerve cell bodies within the central nervous system, the fibers of which go to form one anatomical nerve or a tract within the brain or spinal cord, is called a *nucleus*, e.g., the facial nucleus or nucleus of the facial nerve, basal nuclei, cochlear nuclei, vestibular nuclei.

Center. A group of neurons and synapses regulating a certain function is called a *center*. It may be either a nucleus or a ganglion, as these terms refer to an anatomical entity and the term *center* refers to a functional entity. For instance, the rate of respiration is regulated by a *center* in the medulla oblongata, and odor is interpreted by a *center* in the cerebrum. A center may receive information over sensory fibers from a wide variety of receptors. The center then acts like a computer in analyzing and weighing the incoming signals. The response of the center may be a "sensation" or a motor response adjusted appropriately to the coordinated sensory information.

Nerves. A nerve fiber consists of an axis cylinder with its coverings. A bundle of these fibers enclosed in a tubular sheath is called a

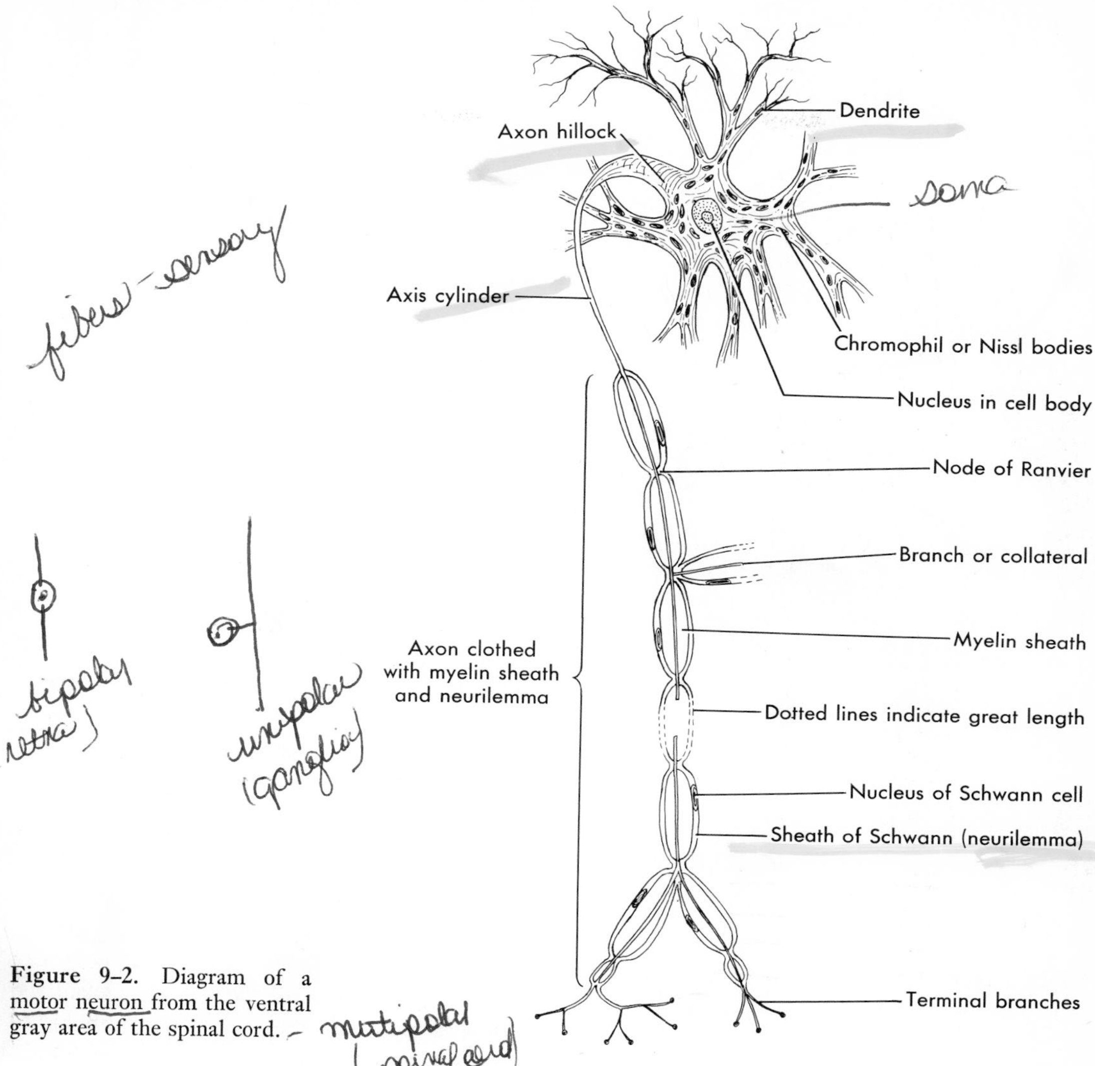

Figure 9–2. Diagram of a motor neuron from the ventral gray area of the spinal cord.

funiculus. A nerve may consist of a single funiculus or of many funiculi collected into larger bundles. Between the individual fibers is connective tissue called *endoneurium*, which serves to bind the fibers together into funiculi. Connective tissue called *perineurium* surrounds each funiculus in the form of a tubular sheath, and all the funiculi are held in a connective-tissue covering called the *epineurium*. The capillaries of the blood vessels supplying a nerve penetrate the perineurium and either run parallel with the fibers or form short transverse connecting vessels. Fine autonomic nerve fibers (vasomotor) accompany these capillaries. Considerably more than 75 per cent of a nerve is composed of nonnervous substance—more than 50 per cent of it is loose connective tissue and blood vessels and more than 25 per cent is myelin.

The nerves branch frequently throughout their course, and these branches often meet and fuse with one another or with the branches of other nerves; yet each axon always remains distinct. The nerve is thus merely an association of individual fibers functioning independently of one another. Most nerves are mixed nerves containing

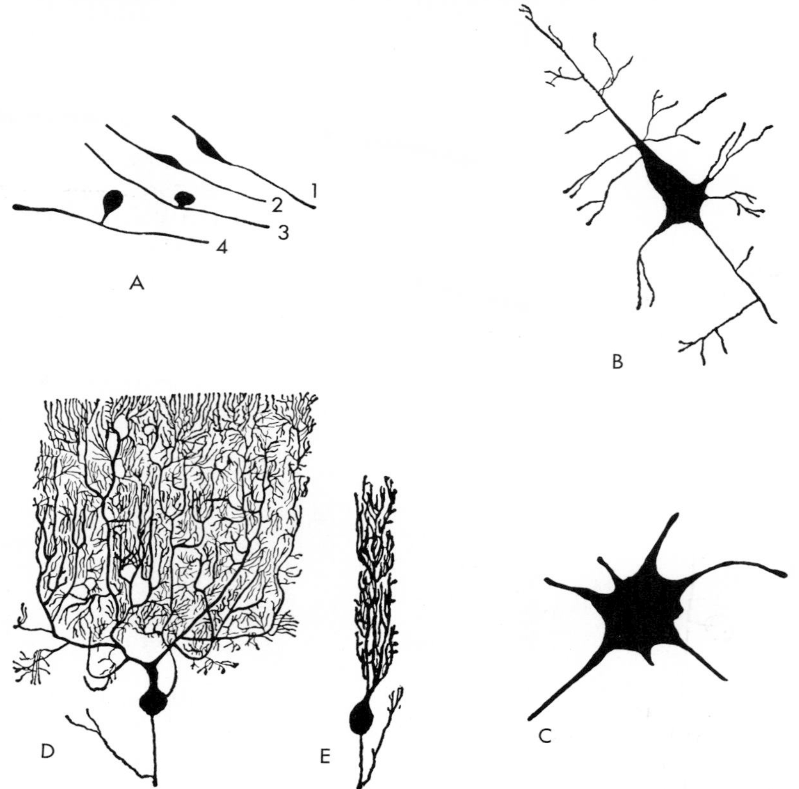

Figure 9–3. Types of neurons. (*A*) Cell of dorsal root ganglion; *1*, *2*, *3*, *4* show how it gradually develops into a unipolar cell. (*B*) Pyramidal cell of cerebral cortex. (*C*) Motor cell of spinal cord. (*D* and *E*) Purkinje cells of cerebellum. (*E*) Profile view.

both sensory and motor fibers. The arrangement of nerve fibers in a nerve trunk can be seen in a cross section of a nerve (Figure 9–5).

The nerve fibers in a nerve have various diameters. In general, it has been found that large fibers are heavily myelinated, originate from large cells, and extend to specialized somatic structures, e.g., motor fibers to striated muscle cells. Nerves as a rule contain all sizes of fibers.

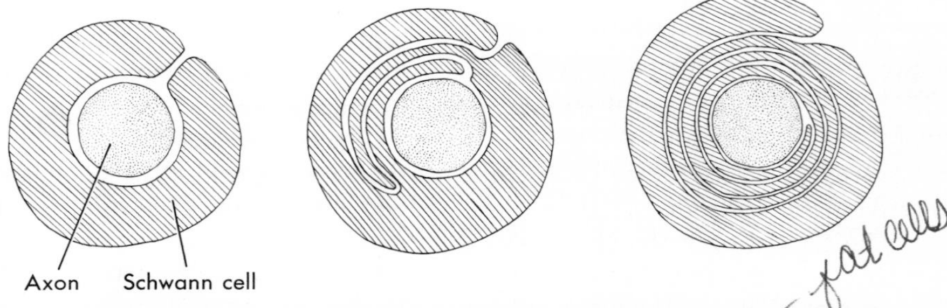

fat cells

Figure 9–4. Diagram to show coiling of a Schwann cell around an axon. Myelin will form in the clear areas between the layers of Schwann cell cytoplasm. (Modified from Crosby, Humphrey, and Lauer.)

Fibers have been classified into A, B, and C groups according to their size and the speed with which the nerve impulse is transmitted. Those in group A are heavily myelinated and therefore of large diameter; they transmit the impulse with a velocity of about 100 m per second. To this group belong large motor fibers (8 to 18μ diameter), fibers to skeletal muscle, and fibers from muscle receptors. The fibers of the B group are preganglionic autonomic fibers with conduction velocities of about 10 to 20 m per second, and those of the C group are pre- and postganglionic nonmyelinated and afferent amyelinated fibers with conduction rates of 0.3 to 1.6 m per second. The relation of size to activity is not as clear in the B and C groups as in the larger fibers of the A group. The ventral roots of spinal nerves are composed largely of A fibers, whereas the dorsal roots contain fibers of all groups. Group A fibers have been further classified into four groups: alpha, beta, gamma, and delta. The gamma fibers supply the muscle spindle, causing it to stretch, and function in maintaining posture against gravity.

Nerve Endings. The fibers of a nerve are axons whose cell body lies in the central nervous system, or, in the case of the autonomic nerves, in autonomic ganglia. The peripheral ending of the axon generally branches into many fine nonmyelinated terminals. The *end organs* have been classified as (1) *receptors*, initiating the sensory impulses to be transmitted over afferent axons, and (2) *effectors*, transmitting the impulse from an efferent, or motor, fiber to muscle or secreting gland. The skeletal muscle motor end-plate has been identified as a distinctive nerve ending. Those in other tissue have not, and it is common to use the term *effector* to refer to the cell which responds, in which is seen the effect of stimulation.

Receptors. Receptors may be free nerve endings, encapsulated endings, or very specialized sense organs such as the rods and cone cells of the eye. A convenient classification of receptors is according to function.

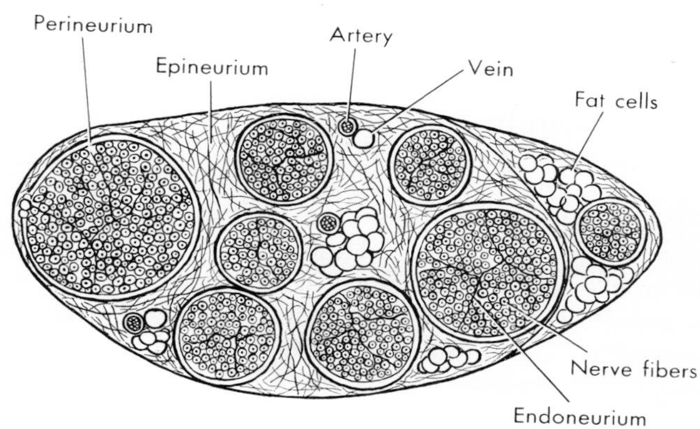

Figure 9–5. Transverse section of the sciatic nerve of a cat. This nerve consists of eight bundles (funiculi) of nerve fibers. Each bundle has its own wrappings (perineurium); and all the bundles are embedded in connective tissue (epineurium) in which arteries, veins, and fat cells can be seen. See Figure 9–2 for the structure of a nerve fiber.

Mechanoreceptors respond to displacement of tissue. These give rise to sensations of:

1. Pressure and touch: free nerve endings in all tissues, pacinian and Meissner's corpuscles in the skin (page 232).
2. Position of joints and of extremities (kinesthesia): free nerve endings and specialized endings in the ligaments around the joints (page 232).
3. Hearing: hair cells in the basilar membrane of the inner ear which respond to sound wave vibrations (page 244).
4. Acceleration and equilibrium: receptors in the vestibular apparatus of the inner ear (page 244).
5. Muscle and tendon stretch: muscle spindles and Golgi tendon apparatus (page 232).
6. Pressure and stretch of heart muscle (page 332) and of lung tissue (page 387).

The latter two categories are not conscious sensations.

Thermoreceptors respond to variations in temperature. They are free nerve endings, Ruffini and Krause end organs. Some respond to cooling, others to warming.

Chemoreceptors include the taste buds of the tongue and pharynx, responding to different chemicals in food; olfactory cells of the nose, responding to chemicals in the air; and receptors of cells in the carotid and aortic bodies, responding to pH and to oxygen and carbon dioxide levels of the blood (nonconscious sensations).

Baroreceptors are spray-type nerve endings which respond to increasing blood pressure. They are found in the arch of the aorta and the wall of the internal carotid arteries, in the carotid sinus.

Photosensitive receptors are found in the retina of the eye, responding to light.

Effectors. Effectors are the muscle or gland cells receiving nerve endings. Somatic effectors are skeletal muscle; their innervation is by way of axons from neurons in the brain and cord. Autonomic effectors are smooth muscle, cardiac muscle, and glands; their innervation is from the sympathetic and parasympathetic systems.

THE NERVE IMPULSE

Membrane Theory of Excitation

Nerve and muscle cells "are excitable"; that is, they are capable of transmitting an electrochemical impulse along the cell membrane. The nerve impulse results from a change in the membrane potential. The axoplasm within the nerve cell differs in ionic concentrations as compared with the fluid outside the cell. In particular, the concentration of potassium ions is higher and the concentration of sodium ions is lower inside than outside the cell. These differences in ionic concentrations are basic to the establishment of a potential difference across the cell membrane, a "membrane potential." In the resting cell the outside is positively charged as compared with the inside. Thus the membrane is said to be polarized and to have a resting membrane potential. It requires a continuous expenditure of metabolic energy to maintain the resting membrane potential by pumping sodium out of the cell. When adequate stimulation occurs, normal permeability is abruptly but only temporarily lost and sodium ions enter the cell rapidly. This inward movement of sodium causes a reversal of the membrane potential, and the outside of the membrane is now negative as

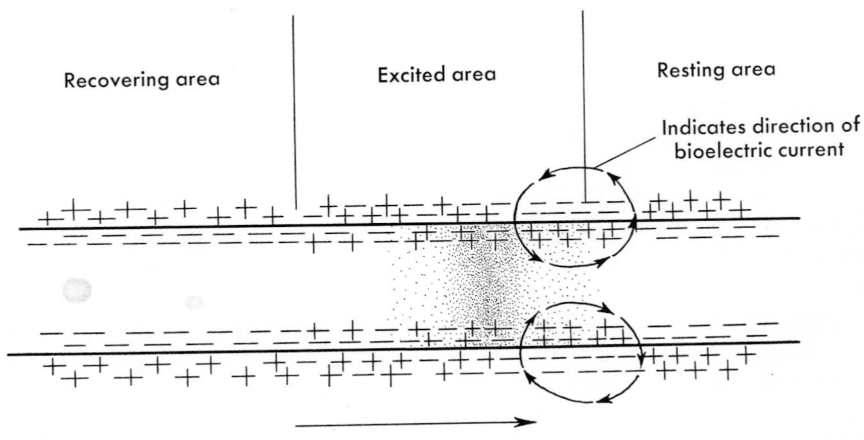

Figure 9–6. Schematic representation of changes in the potential of the nerve fiber membrane as the nerve impulse is transmitted. The predominance of + or − charges is related to movement of sodium and potassium ions across the membrane.

compared with the inside and with other points along the membrane. The increase in sodium permeability is followed by an increase in potassium permeability. Therefore, the sodium influx is followed by rapid outward movement of potassium ions which returns the membrane potential to its resting level. Repolarization of the membrane is accompanied by pumping of sodium ions outward and movement of potassium ions inward until normal cell concentrations are achieved.

The action potential initially generated by movement of sodium ions into the cell is self-propagating. When one part of the membrane is undergoing the action potential, a small electric current flows from the excited region to the resting region next to it, which in turn undergoes the action potential. Thus the impulse is conducted, or propagated, along the nerve fiber. The generation of the nerve impulse and its transmission occur within fractions of a second, and the action potential is an electrical change measured in millivolts.

Energy Production. Energy must be provided within the nerve cells not only for maintaining the action potential by extrusion of sodium ions, but also for synthesis of highly specific compounds which contribute to the structure of these cells. It is well established that the primary source of energy for the cells of the nervous system is through the oxidation of glucose (with simultaneous formation of ATP). Dependence of brain cells on carbohydrate metabolism is illustrated by the fact that the first symptoms of hypoglycemia are reflected in the nervous system; in insulin shock unconsciousness may result. Of all living cells the brain cells are the most sensitive to oxygen shortage, and prolonged deprivation of oxygen results in their permanent damage.

Excitability Periods. The excitability of the nerve fiber shows three periods: the *absolute refractory*, the *relative refractory*, and the *normal periods*.

The *absolute refractory* period is the short period during the action potential when the nerve fiber is inexcitable. The action potential is an all-or-none response which makes it impossible for a fiber continuously to respond to stimuli from a receptor. Small nerve fibers have longer refractory periods than large fibers.

The *relative refractory* period follows the absolute refractory period. During this time the nerve fiber gradually resumes its excitability and finally returns to the *normal* period of resting membrane potential. During the relative refractory period the stimulus must be stronger than during the normal phase in order to generate the action potential.

Amplitude of the action potential is related to the diameter of the nerve fiber, but not to the strength of the stimulus. In general, nerve fibers with large axons have higher "spikes" (action potentials) than small axons. Any stimulus strong enough to excite provokes a spike whose amplitude is independent of the strength of the stimulus since the action potential is an all-or-none response, and a fiber gives either a maximum response to a stimulus or none at all. An increase in the strength of stimulus does not alter the amplitude of the action potential but it may increase the number of action potentials (the frequency of discharge).

Fatigue of nerve fibers is practically impossible if oxygen and glucose supply is adequate, which is usually the case in normal physiology.

Specificity of Receptors. In order for nerve impulses to be initiated by receptors, the stimulus must be *adequate* and at least *minimal*. By an adequate stimulus is meant one whose physical energy is appropriate for the receptor, e.g., light for the eye or sound for the ear. A minimal, or threshold, stimulus refers to the least change in stimulus strength which can excite the receptor.

Intensity of stimulus determines the degree of change imposed on the receptor and is "coded" in the frequency (number per second) of the impulses initiated. With increase in intensity of stimulus, the frequency of discharge by the receptor increases. Furthermore, most receptor systems in their frequency of discharge code information related not only to the absolute strength of the stimulus, but also to the *rate of change* of stimulus strength. The more rapid the increase in intensity of a stimulus, the more rapidly the receptor discharges impulses to the nerve fiber.

Adaptation. When an adequate and minimal stimulus is applied to a receptor, the receptor is excited, and nerve impulses are generated and conducted to the central nervous system by the afferent nerve fiber. The number of impulses resulting from a given stimulus depends on two things: (1) the strength, rate of change of strength, and duration of the stimulus and (2) the inherent properties of the receptors. Some receptors continue to elicit action potentials for as long as the stimulus endures. Other receptors discharge only at the time the stimulus is applied and soon cease discharging, even though the stimulus continues. The former are classed as *slowly adapting* receptors; the latter are *rapidly adapting.* Slowly adapting receptors provide neural information to the central nervous system about steady-state conditions. Rapidly adapting receptors report to the nervous system primarily about changes in conditions. For example, receptors at the base of hairs discharge at the moment the hair is bent but promptly cease discharging even though the hair remains in the bent position. Only movement of the hair is signaled to the central nervous system. In contrast, muscle spindles are slowly adapting. If a muscle is stretched, its muscle spindles discharge at the increased rate for the entire duration of the stretch. Hence, the muscle spindle is said to be slowly adapting. It reports to the nervous system on the static length of a muscle as well as change in length.

The Nerve Fiber and Nerve Impulse. Nerve fibers possess the properties of *irritability* and *conductivity*. Once the nerve impulses are started from the receptor along the fiber, each impulse is like every other impulse; they vary only in frequency and number. The impulses carried by sensory nerve fibers, such as the optic fibers, are similar to those carried by motor nerve fibers. In one instance there is a visual sensation and in the other, contraction of muscle. The difference in result is due to the action of optic nerve impulses on the visual center in the cerebrum and the action of nerve impulses on the muscle. Regardless of how an optic fiber is stimulated, the subjective sensation will be visual. The nature of the sensation resulting from a given type of stimulus depends on *what* nerve fibers are excited, not on *how* they are excited. Normally, impulses start at the receiving end organ of a nerve fiber, but it is possible to induce them at any part of the nerve fiber. When this happens, the brain projects the resulting sensation to the part containing the receptors of the fibers stimulated. This may explain why patients who have suffered an amputation refer the pain to the part that has been removed; the pressure of the surgical dressings or of scar tissue on the nerve fibers excites nerve impulses that are interpreted as having been initiated at the original receptors.

Synapse. Each neuron is a separate and distinct unit. The fine branches of the axon of one neuron seem to interlace with the dendrites of, or lie on the surface of, another neuron, forming a synapse. At the synapse the two neurons involved come into functional contact. There is no protoplasmic continuity of the neurons across the synapse, but there is contact of the terminals, or synaptic knobs, of the axon of one neuron and the cell bodies

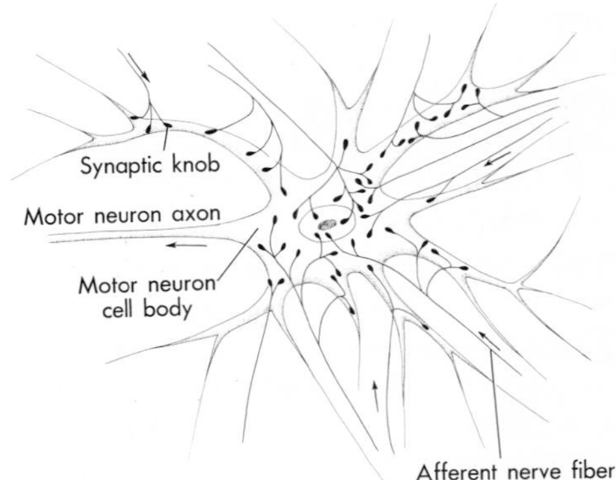

Figure 9–7. Diagram of a motor neuron cell body with dendrite connections from other neurons.

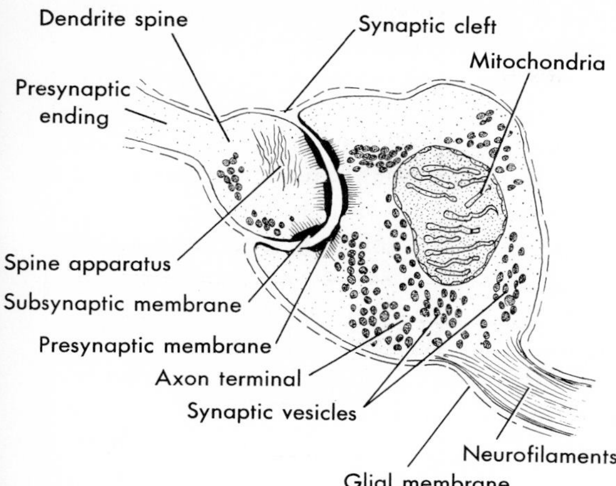

Figure 9–8. Diagram of an electron micrograph of an axodendritic synapse in the cerebral cortex. (Modified from Strong and Elwyn.)

or dendrites of other neurons. Synapses are found in gray matter of brain, spinal cord, and ganglia. Conduction at synapses differs from that along nerve fibers. The chief differences are:

1. Conduction at the synapse is slower than conduction along a nerve fiber. This suggests that there are some time-consuming chemical events occurring at the synapse.
2. There is greater variability in the ease of transmission.
3. There are excitatory and inhibitory synapses.
4. The synapses are more readily susceptible to fatigue and are more easily affected by anesthetics and drugs.
5. In regions containing many synapses, the blood supply is very rich, which suggests more active metabolism.
6. Synaptic transmission is always one way.

Transmission of Impulses at the Synapse. A nerve impulse is not electrically transmitted across synapses. Details of transmission at the myoneural synapse are better understood than for the synapses within the central nervous system. The action potential in the nerve fiber causes the release of acetylcholine, which diffuses across the synapse and depolarizes the muscle cell membrane sufficiently to produce a muscle action potential. The muscle action potential in turn excites contraction. The acetylcholine is rapidly hydrolyzed by the enzyme cholinesterase, and the muscle membrane once again repolarizes. Acetylcholine is also known to be the chemical transmitter at some of the synapses in the autonomic nervous system, but the transmitter at synapses within the central nervous system has not yet been identified.

Facilitation. In actuality a single impulse reaching a central excitatory synapse is almost never enough to cause a second, or postsynaptic, neuron to discharge; several impulses are required to "fire" it. A single presynaptic impulse, however, makes the second neuron more excitable and therefore more responsive to excitatory impulses from other neurons. This excited neuron which does not discharge an impulse is said to be *facilitated.*

Inhibition. One tends to think of activation of a neuron and production of the impulse as resulting in action, e.g., stimulation of a second neuron, stimulating muscle to contract or glands to secrete. This is not always the case; some neurons are inhibitory and their activity decreases the likelihood of the second neuron discharging. Inhibition, like excitation, is related to changes in ionic membrane permeability. When an inhibitory impulse reaches the synapse, the membrane permeability to potassium of the second neuron is increased, and the cell, instead of being depolarized, is hyperpolarized; the inside becomes more negatively charged with respect to the outside and is therefore less excitable (or inhibited). Inhibitory neurons of the somatic nervous system are located in the central nervous system; those of the autonomic nervous system are in the periphery. The spinal cord has many fibers which descend from inhibitory cells of the brain. When a motor neuron affecting skeletal muscle action receives an impulse from these fibers, the result is inhibition, or decreased excitability of the motor neuron, and a decrease or stopping of its discharge. A good example is relaxation of flexor muscles of the arm when extensor muscles are contracted—one set of motor neurons is inhibited when the other set is stimulated.

Spread of Impulses. Incoming impulses have many potential pathways in the central nervous system open to them. Usually the varying resistance offered at different available synapses prevents too wide diffusion of their effects. However, a strong stimulus may produce a great spreading of impulses through the gray matter, and in extreme instances efferent impulses may be sent to all muscles, causing mass contraction or convulsion. In early life spreading of impulses occurs much more readily than in later years, which accounts for the fact that children are more prone to convulsions than adults. This is most probably due to immaturity of inhibitory pathways. Certain drugs, such as strychnine, block transmission at inhibitory synapses, thereby releasing excitatory synapses from restraint.

Convergence. A single neuron receives impulses from many other neurons, which are said to *converge* on that neuron, and thus the neuron is stimulated. Convergence is found in all areas of the central nervous system, in sensory and motor pathways, and in association pathways of the brain.

Fatigue. Fatigue does not readily occur in the axon; however, synaptic transmission may fail, or fatigue, when excessively stimulated. In response to high-level activity in the presynaptic neurons, the postsynaptic neuron at first responds readily, then at progressively slower rates; thus a self-limiting restraint on prolonged hyperactivity is protective in nature. For example, an epileptic seizure, involving mass discharge from many areas of the brain, will eventually cease owing to fatigue of the synapses. This is presumably due to exhaustion of the synaptic transmitter substance, or to desensitization to the action of the transmitter.

THE REFLEX ARC AND RESPONSE

The unit pattern, or functional unit, of the nervous system is the reflex arc. The response it initiates is the reflex response. A short reflex consists of a sensory neuron, an internuncial or connecting neuron, and a motor neuron with its effector. Figure 9–9 shows some possible types of linkage of reflex arcs.

The Reflex Response. When an appropriate stimulus is applied to the receptor ending of the sensory neuron, an impulse is

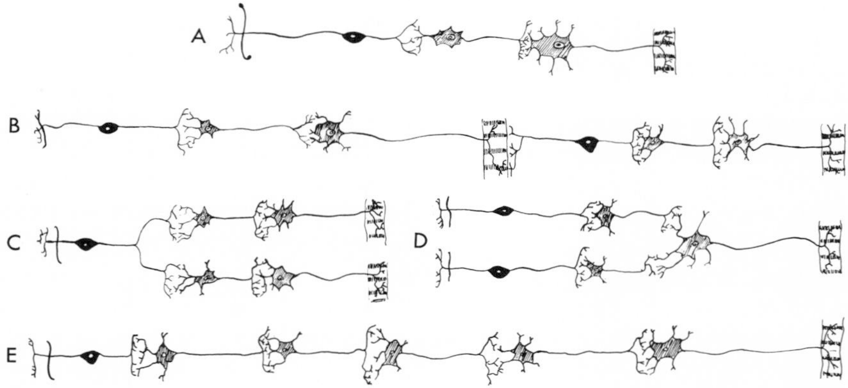

Figure 9–9. Reflex arcs or circuits. (*A*) Reflex arc of three cells—sensory cell body, *black*; connecting cell body, *striped*; motor cell body, *dotted*. (*B*) A short-chain reflex of two simple reflex arcs in sequence. (*C*) One sensory cell connected with two motor cells. (*D*) Two sensory cells connected with one motor cell. (*E*) A long simple reflex arc in which there are four connecting cells between the sensory cell and the motor cell.

initiated which passes along the afferent process to the spinal cord where it synapses with a connecting neuron, which when excited transmits the impulse to the next synapse. Finally a motor neuron is excited, and the nerve impulse is conducted down the efferent fiber, across the peripheral synapse to the muscle or gland cell. Between the simplest form of involuntary activity and the higher activities that involve consciousness, memory, or control are many types of reactions.

Stereotyped Reflexes. These depend on a sensory neuron, a central neuron, and a motor neuron. Stimulation of the sensory neuron results in response by a muscle. Examples of such simple reflexes are the winking reflex caused by an object striking or appearing as if it would strike the cornea, the swallowing reaction due to food on the back of the tongue, avoiding reactions due to tickling, and pricking. The presence, absence, and strength of these reflexes are of value in diagnosis of diseases of the nervous system, because in general they are direct, rapid, stereotyped, and persistent and are modified or inhibited only with difficulty.

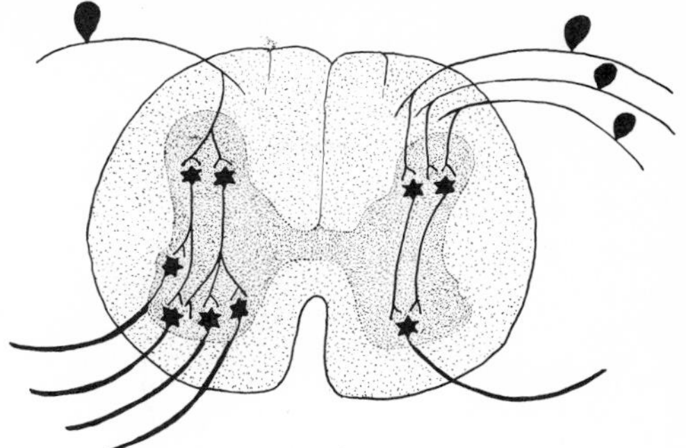

Figure 9–10. A cross section of the spinal cord, showing on the right a converging reflex, on the left a spreading reflex. (See also Figure 9–9.)

Neurologists have developed special tests for such reflexes as the *wink*, *pupillary*, and *patellar* reflex. Patellar reflex is the name given to the jerk of the leg caused by tapping upon the patellar ligament while the leg is crossed, or suspended across the edge of a table or chair. The impulses generated in muscle spindles are conveyed to the spinal cord and via the sciatic nerve to the quadriceps femoris muscle, which contracts and extends the leg. The intensity of this reflex is indicative of the irritability of the nervous system. Injuries to the spinal cord may abolish this reflex entirely. Lesions of the higher centers increase its intensity.

All reflexes can be inhibited as well as stimulated. Spreading and convergence of impulses, facilitation, and inhibition make a greater variety of reactions possible.

QUESTIONS FOR DISCUSSION

1. Name and discuss the structure and function of each part of the neuron.
2. Where are myelinated and nonmyelinated fibers located? Differentiate between nerve fibers of the brain and cord and those in peripheral nerves.
3. What is an appropriate stimulus for receptors that are:
   a. In the skin?
   b. In muscles and tendons?
   c. Chemoreceptors?
4. How does impulse transmission differ in the axon and at the synapse?

SUMMARY

Classification of parts of the nervous system (page 173)

- **Nerve Tissue**
  - **Cells**
    - Neurons, functional cells of nerve tissue
    - Neuroglia, supporting cells
    - Microglia, phagocytic cells
  - **Gray matter**—composed of cell bodies, dendrites
  - **White matter**—composed of nerve fibers, myelinated
  - **Ganglion**—aggregate of cell bodies outside central nervous system
  - **Nucleus**—aggregate of cell bodies within central nervous system, often a specific function
  - **Nerves**
    1. **Funiculus,** a bundle of fibers enclosed in a tubular sheath
    2. **Endoneurium,** connective tissue between the individual fibers
    3. **Perineurium,** connective tissue surrounding each funiculus
    4. **Epineurium,** connective tissue covering several funiculi
- **Neurons**
  - **Consist of**
    - **Cell body,** source of energy, affords nutrients to processes
    - **Cell processes**
      - *Dendrites,* short, rough outline, branch freely
      - *Axons,* long, smooth, branches
  - **Function,** to receive impulses and convey them to other cells
  - **Classification based on number of processes**
    - **Bipolar** cells
    - **Multipolar** cells
  - **Classification based on functions**
    - **Afferent** (receptor, sensory) carry impulses from periphery to center
    - **Efferent** (effector, motor) carry impulses from center to periphery
  - **Nerve fibers**
    - **Myelinated,** white
      - Consist of
        - Axis cylinder
        - Medulla, or myelin sheath
        - Neurilemma, or sheath of Schwann
      - Function of myelin sheath is insulation, and it possibly plays part in chemical processes involved in the production of nerve impulses
      - Nodes of Ranvier, constriction, myelin sheath absent, branching of fiber, permit rapid conduction velocity
    - **Nonmyelinated,** gray or yellow
      - Myelin sheath reduced or absent
  - **Synapse,** interlacing of branches of axon of one neuron with dendrites and cell body of another neuron; no protoplasmic continuity
- **Nerve Endings**
  - 1. **Receptors**
    - May be simple fiber ends, or these ends may be surrounded by accessory structures
  - **Mechanoreceptors**
    - Pressure, touch: free endings, pacinian and Meissner's corpuscles
    - Kinesthesia: free endings and pacinian corpuscles on tendons, joints
    - Hearing: receptors in inner ear
    - Equilibrium: vestibular apparatus in inner ear
    - Muscle and tendon stretch: muscle spindles, Golgi tendon apparatus
  - **Thermoreceptors:** free nerve endings, Ruffini, Krause endings
  - **Chemoreceptors:** taste buds, olfactory cells, receptors of carotid and aortic bodies
  - **Photosensitive receptors:** retina of eye
  - **Baroreceptors:** in aortic arch and carotid sinus
  - 2. **Effectors**
    - Motor end-plate on skeletal muscle
    - Others not known
  - Somatic effector is skeletal muscle
  - Autonomic effectors are smooth and cardiac muscle, glands

- **Nerve Impulse**
  - **Receptor stimuli**
    1. *Stimuli* are physical or chemical changes in the immediate environment
    2. Changes in environment are converted into a rhythmical succession of nervous impulses
    3. *Adequate* stimulus, the *kind* of physical or chemical change to which the receptor is sensitive
    4. *Minimal* stimulus, the *least* change that can excite a receptor
    5. *Subminimal* stimulus, a stimulus below the threshold level which fails to excite
    6. *Intensity* of stimulus, probably related to the degree of change at the receptor and reflected in the frequency of impulses initiated
  - **Adaptation**
    - Adaptation of end organs varies in relation to the speed with which they reach approximate equilibrium with their environment
      1. *Slow* adaptation, long trains (sequences) of nerve impulses issue from end organs in response to prolonged stimulation
      2. *Rapid* adaptation, short trains of impulses issue from end organs even though stimulus is prolonged
  - **Nature of nerve impulse**
    1. All impulses of similar nature whether carried by sensory or motor nerves
    2. Self-propagated disturbance
    3. Excitability of nerve fiber shows three periods
       - *a.* Normal period or phase,
       - *b.* Absolute refractory period, a short period during which the nerve fiber is inexcitable to any stimulus regardless of strength
       - *c.* Relative refractory period, period of less excitability than normal phase—stronger than normal stimulus required to excite
    4. Frequency of nerve impulse varies with the strength of the stimulus
    5. Velocity of conduction of nerve impulse varies with diameter of fiber
    6. Amplitude of nerve impulse is inherent property of cell
    7. Spreading of impulses greater in early life
- **Fatigue**
  - Occurs at synapse
  - Due to depletion of transmittor substance
  - Protective in nature

CHAPTER

10

THE SPINAL CORD AND PRINCIPAL SPINAL PATHWAYS SPINAL NERVES

The pathway for impulses from the periphery and body interior to the brain, and from the brain to these areas, is the spinal cord. It therefore mediates complex responses to sensations as well as an awareness of the external and internal environments. In addition, it serves as a center for immediate responses to receptor stimulation through reflexes within the cord.

The spinal cord, consisting of gray and white matter, lies protected within the spinal canal of the vertebral column. It originates at the level of the foramen magnum, where it is continuous with the medulla and extends downward to the level of the second lumbar vertebra.

The spinal cord diminishes slightly in size from above downward and presents two enlargements—the cervical enlargement (level of fourth cervical to second thoracic vertebrae) and the lumbar enlargement (level of tenth thoracic, widest at twelfth thoracic), which dwindles as the *conus medullaris*, where it gives rise to the nonnervous threadlike *filum terminale*. The filum terminale punctures the dura mater at the level of the second sacral vertebra and terminates on the first coccygeal vertebra (Figure 10–1). At the enlargements the nerves supply the arms and legs, respectively. Since the spinal cord ends opposite the first and second lumbar vertebrae, the roots of the lumbar, sacral, and coccygeal nerves must have a means of reaching their proper intervertebral foramina. Hence these nerves descend in the dural sac along with the filum terminale. This bundle of fibers is known as the cauda equina, as it resembles a horse's tail. The average length of the cord is about 45 cm. It is incompletely divided into lateral halves by a ventral fissure and a dorsal sulcus; because of these fissures only a narrow bridge of the substance of the cord connects its two halves. This bridge, the *transverse commissure*, is traversed throughout its entire length by a minute *central canal*, which opens into the fourth ventricle at its upper end and, at its lower, terminates blindly in the filum terminale.

The spinal cord does not fit as closely into the spinal canal as the brain does into the cranial cavity but is suspended within the canal. It is protected by three membranes and nourished not only by the arterial supply to the spinal cord, but also by the cerebrospinal fluid which circulates between the membranes, especially in the subarachnoid space. These membranes are continuous with the membranes covering the brain and are called by the same names, the *pia mater* closely investing the cord, the *arachnoid mater*, and the *dura mater* outside. The spinal fluid serves to moisten and lubricate the cord and protect it against changing pressures and mechanical damage.

Blood Supply. The blood supply to the

cord is from the anterior spinal artery and from a succession of small arteries which enter the spinal canal through the intervertebral foramina; these branches are derived from the vertebrals, the intercostals, and the arteries in the abdomen and pelvis.

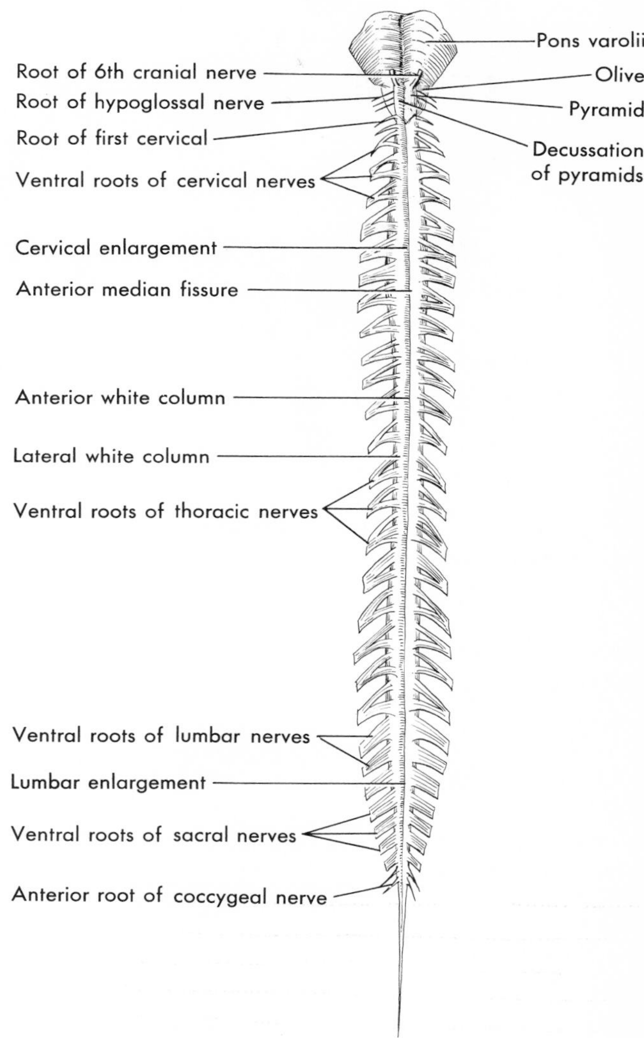

Figure 10–1. Ventral view of the spinal cord. (Modified from Toldt.)

The *gray matter* is in the interior surrounding the central canal and on cross section appears to be arranged in the form of the letter H. The transverse bar on the H is called the *gray commissure* and connects the two lateral masses of gray matter. On each side the gray matter presents a ventral, or anterior, and a dorsal, or posterior, column.[1] The former is short and bulky, whereas the latter is long and slender. The ventral column contains the cell bodies from which the efferent (motor) fibers of the spinal nerves arise. These nerves pass out through openings in the meninges and the intervertebral

[1] This text uses *ventral* and *anterior* for the front aspect, *dorsal* and *posterior* for the back, and *columns* for what were formerly described as *horns* of the gray matter. For each of the three major divisions of the white matter of each half of the cord, *funiculus* instead of *column* is used.

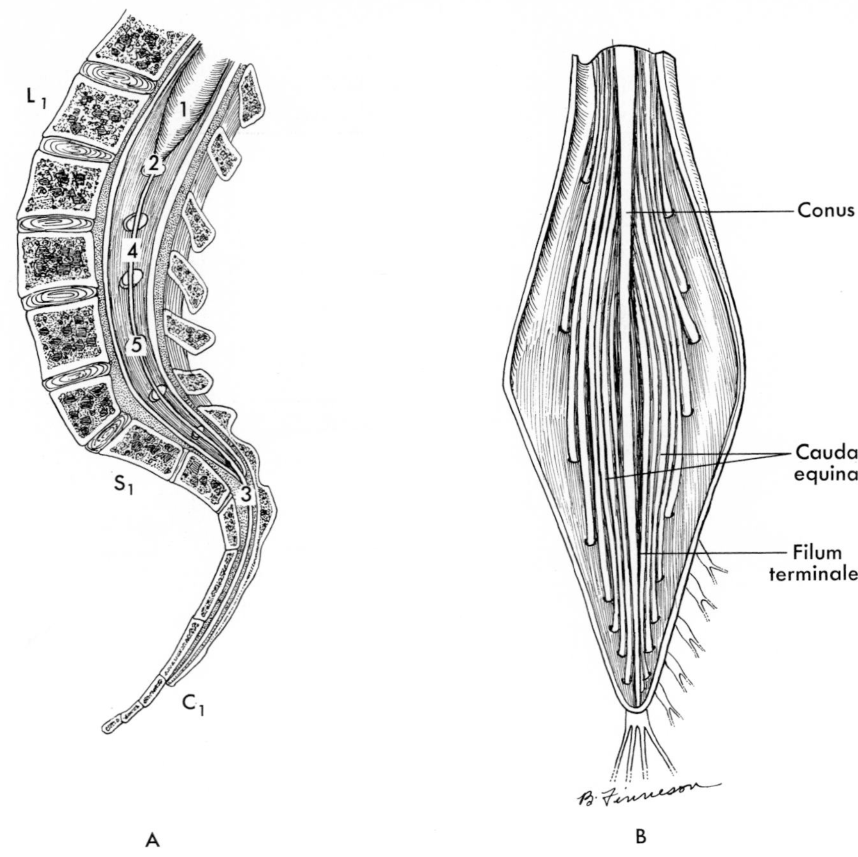

Figure 10–2. (*A*) Longitudinal section of the vertebral column showing the end of the spinal cord. (*1*) Beginning of conus, (*2*) end of conus, (*3*) filum punctures dura, (*4*) spinal canal, (*5*) foramen for exit of spinal nerve, (C_1) first coccygeal vertebra, (L_1) first lumbar vertebra, (S_1) first sacral vertebra. (*B*) The conus filum terminal and cauda equina. (Modified from Toldt.)

foramina. The lateral aspect of the ventral column contains cell bodies which give rise to the efferent fibers of the white *rami communicantes*, or preganglionic fibers of the autonomic system, which travel outside the vertebral column. Preganglionic fibers are efferent, myelinated fibers (*white rami*) which pass from the spinal cord by the way of the ventral column and end around the cells of the sympathetic ganglia. From the cells of the ganglia, nonmyelinated postganglionic fibers go to the various visceral effector organs, i.e., smooth muscle, cardiac muscle, and glands. Some pass back to the spinal nerves and form the *gray rami*. (See Figure 10–13.)

The dorsal column contains cell bodies from which afferent, ascending fibers go up to higher levels of the spinal cord (usually on the opposite side), and to the brain. The fibers of the spinal nerves entering the cord form synapses with the neurons in these columns. The gray matter also contains a great number of connecting (or internuncial) neurons which serve for the passage of impulses (1) from the dorsal to the ventral roots of the spinal nerves, (2) from one side of the cord to the other, and (3) from one segment of the cord to another.

The *white matter*, composed of variably myelinated fibers, is arranged around and between the columns of gray matter; the proportion of gray and white varies in differ-

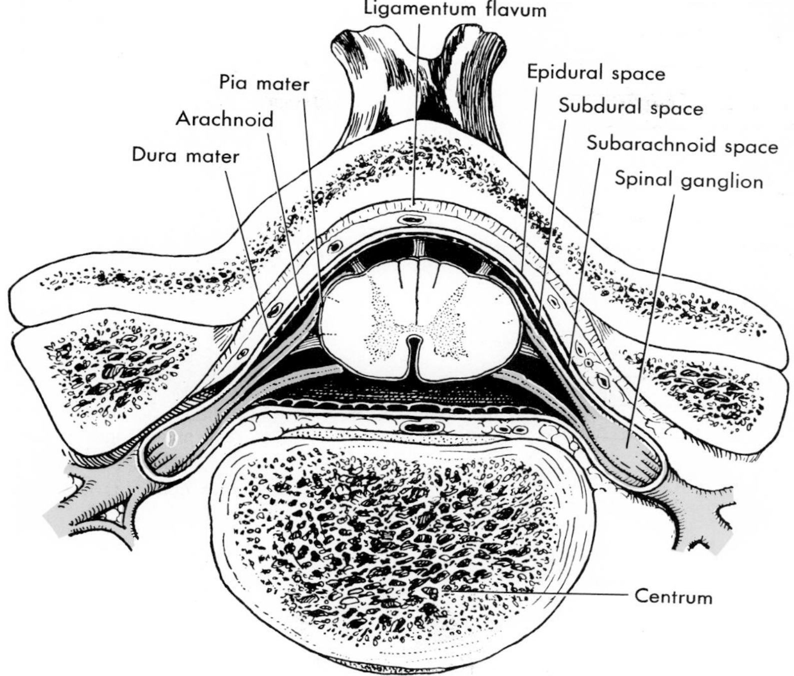

Figure 10–3. Transverse section of spinal cord and vertebra to show their relative positions. Note dorsal root ganglia lying in the intervertebral foramina and dorsal and ventral roots in the spinal canal. The spinal nerve is shown outside the vertebra, with branches to the dorsal body wall, ventral body wall, and viscera.

ent regions of the cord. On each side the white matter may be said to consist of three portions, or funiculi, namely, a ventral, a lateral, and a dorsal funiculus. Each funiculus is in turn divided into smaller segments, or fasciculi.

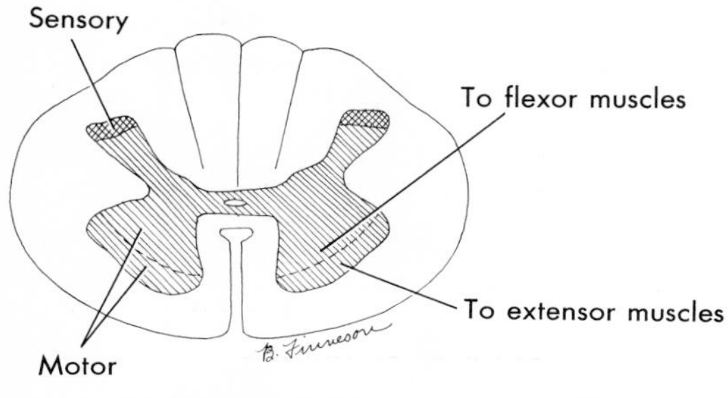

Figure 10–4. Diagram showing location of cell bodies of motor neurons to flexor and extensor muscles.

Some of these funiculi consist of fasciculi made up of fibers which are *ascending*, or sensory (ascending tracts). They serve as pathways to the brain for impulses entering the cord over afferent fibers of spinal nerves. Other funiculi consist of fasciculi which are *descending*, or motor (descending tracts). They transfer impulses from the brain to the motor neurons of the spinal nerves. They begin in the gray matter of the brain, descend, and terminate in the gray matter of the cord, e.g., Figures 10–5 and 10–6. Other funiculi (white in Figure 10–6) are made up chiefly of short ascending and descending fibers beginning in one region of the spinal cord and ending in another.

The funiculi in the dorsal portion are chiefly ascending. Injury to these funiculi will interfere with the passage of sensory impulses and possibly (depending on location and extent of injury) result in loss of sensation

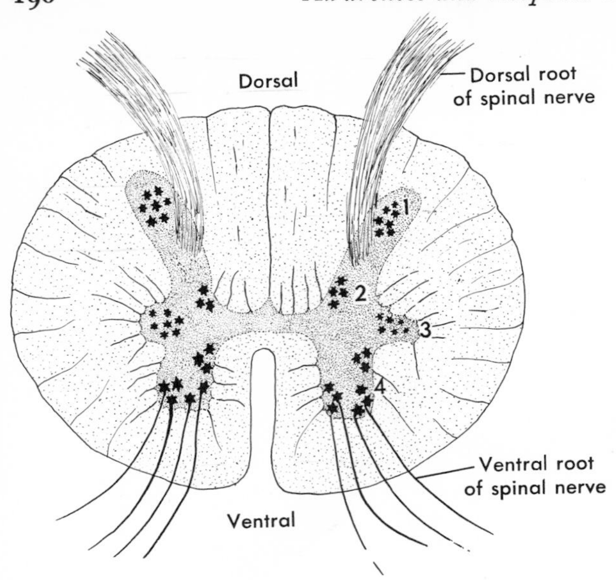

Figure 10–5. Cross section of the spinal cord to show some of the groups of nerve cells. (*1*) Dorsal column cells, (*2*) Clarke's column cells, (*3*) lateral column cells, (*4*) ventral column cells.

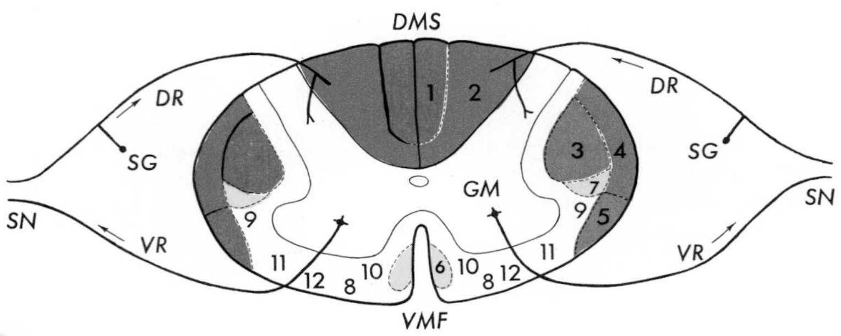

Figure 10–6. Diagram to show general location of some of the conduction paths as seen in a transverse section of the spinal cord. (*DMS*) Dorsal median sulcus, (*DR*) dorsal root, (*GM*) gray matter, (*SG*) spinal ganglion, (*SN*) spinal nerve, (*VMF*) ventral median fissure, (*VR*) ventral root. (*1*) Fasciculus gracilis (tract of Goll), (*2*) fasciculus cuneatus (tract of Burdach), (*3*) lateral cerebrospinal fasciculus (crossed pyramidal tract), (*4*) dorsal spinocerebellar fasciculus, (*5*) ventrolateral spinocerebellar fasciculus (Gowers' tract), (*6*) ventral cerebrospinal fasciculus (direct pyramidal tract), (*7*) rubrospinal tract, (*8*) ventral spinothalamic tracts, (*9*) lateral spinothalamic tracts, (*10*) vestibulospinal tracts, (*11*) tectospinal tracts, (*12*) olivospinal tracts.

in the parts from which the passage of impulses is blocked.

Locomotor ataxia, or *tabes dorsalis*, is a degeneration of the posterior fasciculi and posterior columns of the cord, resulting in disturbances of muscle and joint sensation, interference with reflexes, and consequently with movements such as walking. *Anterior poliomyelitis*, or infantile paralysis, is a viral inflammation of the anterior areas of gray matter and results in paralysis of the muscles supplied with motor nerves from the diseased portion of the cord.

The Pathways of the Cord

Ascending Pathways of the Cord

1. Of the Dorsal Portion of the Spinal Cord (Fasciculus Gracilis and Cuneatus)

A. FASCICULUS GRACILIS. The fibers of fasciculus gracilis are medially placed in the dorsal part of the cord and are made up of long ascending fibers from the sacral, lumbar, and lower thoracic dorsal root ganglia. These fibers terminate around cells in the nucleus gracilis in the low medulla. The fibers from the cells in the nucleus gracilis cross to the opposite side (sensory decussation), ascend, and terminate in the thalamus. The cells in the thalamus send fibers to the postcentral gyrus of the cortex (sensory area).

The peripheral fibers of these dorsal root ganglia form the general sensory kinesthetic fibers of the peripheral nerves from the lower extremity and lower part of the trunk.

B. FASCICULUS CUNEATUS. The fibers of fasciculus cuneatus are more laterally placed in the dorsal part of the cord and are made up of long ascending fibers from the upper thoracic and cervical ganglia. These fibers terminate around cells in the nucleus cuneatus in the medulla. The fibers from the cells of the nucleus cuneatus cross to the opposite side, ascend, and terminate in the thalamus. *Both* these pathways conduct impulses from kinesthetic receptors (on muscles, tendons, and joints) that give rise to sensations of movement and position. Other impulses conducted are for spatial discrimination, for more exact tactile localization, for vibratory sensations, and for two-point discrimination.

The peripheral fibers of these dorsal ganglia form the sensory fibers of the peripheral nerves from the upper extremity, trunk, and neck.

2. The Spinothalamic Pathways. These arise from large cells in the dorsal column of the gray matter of the cord. Most of the fibers cross in the cord and ascend in the white matter of the opposite side as the lateral and ventral spinothalamic pathways (Figure 10–6, areas *8* and *9*). These fibers eventually terminate in the thalamus. The lateral spinothalamic pathway conveys impulses of pain and temperature; the ventral fibers convey impulses of touch and pressure. The cells in the cord receive impulses from sensory fibers of the peripheral nerves.

3. The Dorsal Spinocerebellar Pathways. These arise from cells in the medial gray of the cord (Clarke's column) and pass to the white of the cord of the same side (Figure 10–6, area *4*) and ascend to the medulla. Here they form the inferior cerebellar peduncle and terminate in the cortex of the cerebellum. This pathway conveys impulses from muscles and tendons in all parts of the body, especially from the trunk and lower extremity.

4. The Ventral Spinocerebellar Pathway. This arises from cells in the intermediate gray of the cord. Most of the fibers cross in the cord. They all ascend in the cord (Figure 10–6, area *5*) and reach the cerebellum via the superior cerebellar peduncle. These fibers convey proprioceptive impulses from all parts of the body.

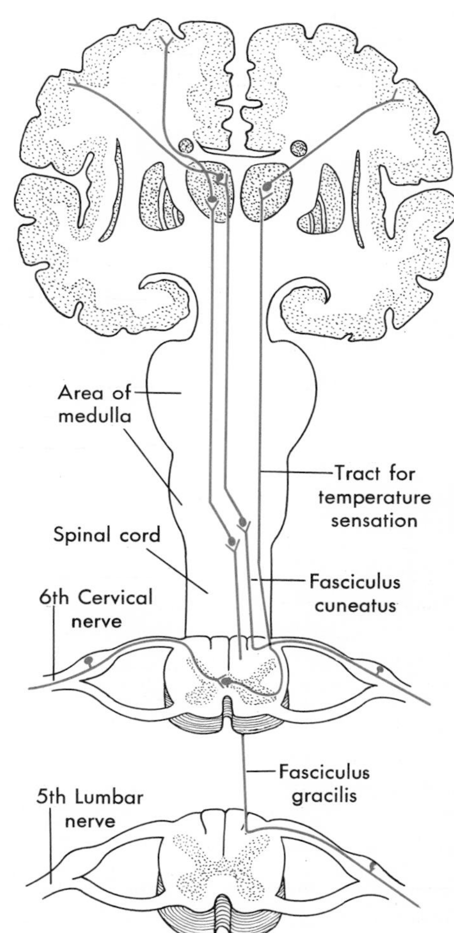

Figure 10–7. Ascending tracts, three shown. Fasciculus (tract) gracilis, concerned with proprioceptor impulses from lower part of body; fasciculus cuneatus, concerned with proprioceptor impulses from upper part of body; and spinothalamic fasciculus, concerned with pain and temperature sensations.

Both the spinocerebellar pathways convey impulses from receptors in muscles, tendons, and joints to the cerebellum. This enables the cerebellum to exert its synergizing and regulative tonic influence on all voluntary muscles. Both these pathways are composed of two neurons, the dorsal root ganglion cells and the cell bodies in the spinal cord gray matter, at the level of entry of the first neuron.

There is a distinct spatial arrangement of fibers in the ascending tracts, most noticeable in the dorsal columns, where fibers from the lower part of the body lie most medially; those entering at progressively higher levels are found progressively more laterally. This spatial arrangement is maintained in the thalamus and in the cortex to which the tertiary neuron of the thalamus projects.

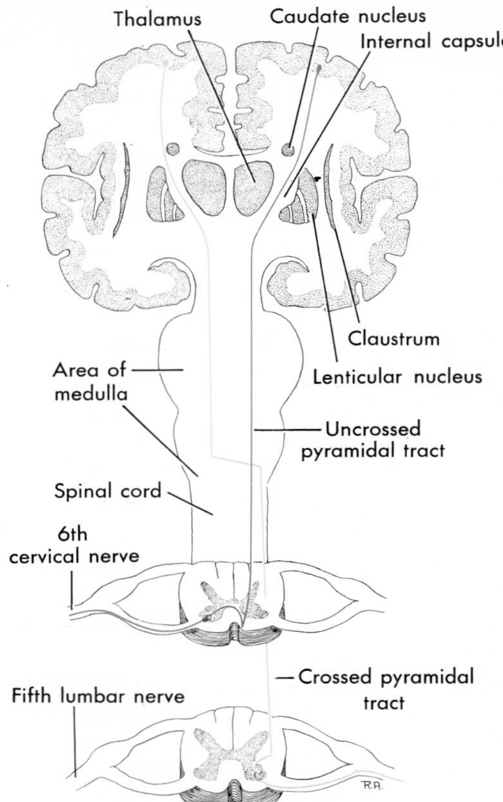

Figure 10–8. Descending tracts, two shown. The lateral corticospinal tract (crossed pyramidal) and the ventral corticospinal tract (direct pyramidal). These tracts contain motor fibers to skeletal muscles.

Descending Pathways of the Cord

1. The Crossed Pyramidal Pathways—(Corticospinal). The nerve fibers arise from the large pyramidal cells in the precentral gyrus of the cerebral cortex and other adjacent areas. They converge and descend through the internal capsule, midbrain, pons, and medulla. As they descend collateral fibers are given off to the motor nuclei of the cranial nerves. In the medulla the majority of the fibers cross to the opposite side (pyramidal decussation) and descend as the crossed pyramidal pathway (Figure 10–6, area *3*).

2. The Uncrossed Pyramidal Pathways. The remaining fibers do not cross but descend on the same side as the direct pyramidal pathway (Figure 10–6, area *6*); most fibers cross to the opposite side just before terminating. All pyramidal fibers terminate around the large motor cells in the ventral gray of the cord and convey impulses which bring about volitional movements, especially fine individual movements that are essential for developing motor skills. The fibers are large and heavily myelinated. Myelinization begins before birth and is not complete until about the third year.

3. Extrapyramidal Pathways

A. THE VESTIBULOSPINAL PATHWAY. This originates from cells in the vestibular nucleus of the medulla and descends uncrossed in the cord and terminates around the large motor cells in the ventral gray of the cord (Figure 10–6, area *10*). Since the vestibular nucleus receives fibers from the vestibular portion of the eighth nerve and from the cerebellum, the tract conveys impulses from the middle ear and cerebellum which exert a tonic influence on the muscles of the extremities and trunk, thus helping to maintain equilibrium and posture.

B. THE RUBROSPINAL PATHWAY. This originates from cells in the red nucleus of the midbrain. The fibers cross and descend in the cord and terminate around cells in the dorsal part of the ventral gray of the cord of the thoracic region. The red nucleus relays impulses from the cerebellum and vestibular apparatus to the motor nuclei of the brain stem and spinal cord, and in this way participates in the coordination of reflex postural adjustments.

C. THE TECTOSPINAL PATHWAYS. These originate from cells in the colliculi of the midbrain. The fibers cross and descend in the cord to terminate around cells in the ventral gray. The fibers convey impulses which mediate reflex activity of the muscles of the head and neck in response to optic stimuli and perhaps auditory stimuli. (Figure 10–6, area *11.*)

D. THE OLIVOSPINAL PATHWAY. This originates from cells in the olivary nucleus of the medulla and perhaps other higher centers and terminates around cells in the ventral gray of the upper part of the cord (Figure 10–6, area *12*). The olivary nucleus receives impulses from and sends impulses to the cerebellum.

All these descending pathways terminate ultimately on the motor neurons of the ventral gray of the cord in either excitatory or inhibitory synapses. The combined effect of these descending impulses determines the frequency of discharge of the motor neurons, and hence the strength of skeletal muscle contraction in reflex or volitional movement.

4. Other Descending Pathways. There are also descending fibers in the cord that terminate on the autonomic preganglionic motor neurons innervating smooth muscle, cardiac muscle, and glandular epithelium. The hypothalamus is the chief coordinating center of the autonomic system. Activities of the hypothalamus are in turn coordinated with those of the thalamus and cortex. The fibers descend from the hypothalamus in a rather diffuse manner and terminate on autonomic cells in the ventrolateral gray of the cord.

In addition to long descending fiber tracts, there are short fiber tracts connecting neighboring segments of the cord, forming part of the intrinsic, or segmental, reflexes of the spinal cord.

Functions of the Spinal Cord. Two major functions are apparent from the foregoing discussion: reflexes and transmission of

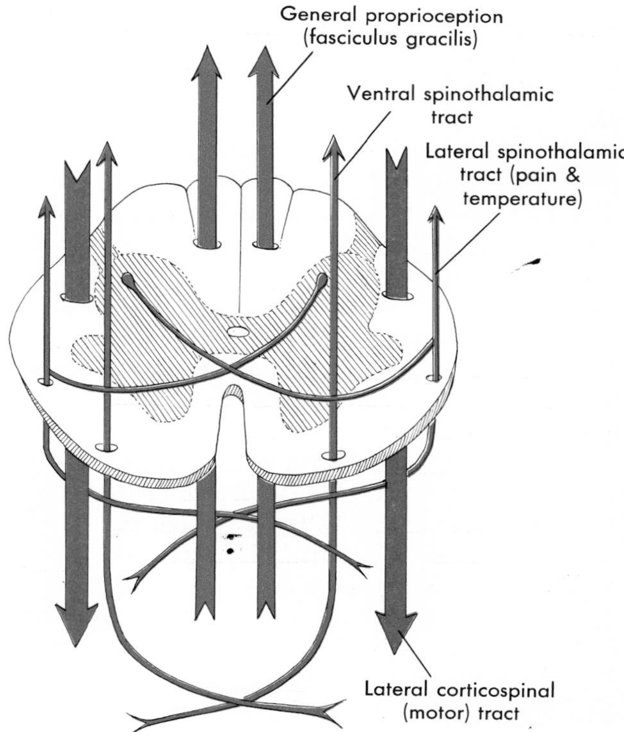

Figure 10–9. Diagram showing location of major afferent and efferent spinal tracts and the direction of impulse. Hemisection of the cord on the right side would cause what symptoms?

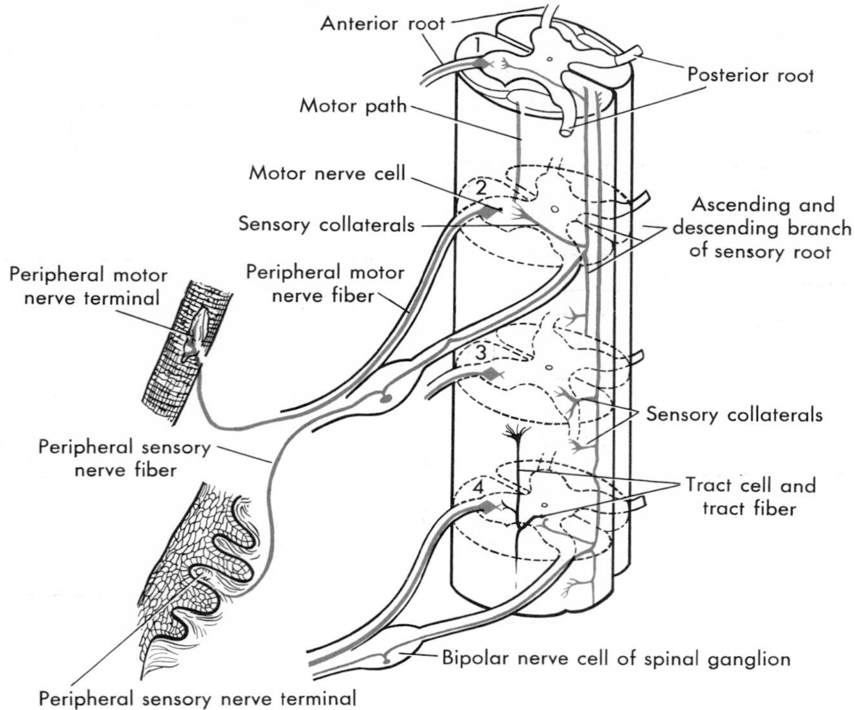

Figure 10–10. Motor (*red*) and sensory (*blue*) conduction paths and reflex arcs of the spinal cord. (Modified from Toldt.)

information. Afferent impulses are forwarded upward; efferent impulses are transmitted downward. The motor neurons in the anterior column at each level of the spinal cord are bombarded with impulses from many pathways. Some are inhibitory, others facilitatory. Thus impulse discharge by this motor neuron is in response to a "summation" of these influences, and for this reason it is called the "final common pathway."

Reflexes Involving the Spinal Cord. Some of the reflexes that involve the spinal cord are (1) those concerned with withdrawal from harmful stimuli, called *flexion reflexes*; walking involves the flexion reflexes; (2) the *extensor* or *stretch reflex*, such as the knee jerk and those concerned with posture and muscle tone maintenance; (3) the *scratch reflex*, or responses to local irritation.

Some spinal cord reflexes are very complex and involve many segments of the spinal cord. In some instances cord reflexes involve the viscera, as in the reflex that empties the bladder. Afferent nerve impulses from receptors in the bladder wall enter the sacral and lumbar regions of the cord, synapse on internuncial neurons, which in turn excite motor neurons which contract and empty the bladder. The same sensory impulses travel to higher brain levels and provide the conscious sensation of a full bladder.

Reflexes whose adjusting mechanism is in the spinal cord may be inhibited by centers in the cerebrum. Micturition is an example. Micturition is initially brought about as a spinal reflex, the stimulus starting from receptors in the bladder itself, so that when the bladder is filled, it automatically empties itself. By training in early infancy, this reflex may be inhibited from the cerebrum, so that micturition takes place only under voluntary control. The same is true of defecation. These are examples of "modulated" primitive reflexes. If the conducting paths to the cerebrum are interrupted, but the spinal reflex path is intact, involuntary micturition and defecation may still be possible.

THE SPINAL NERVES

There are 31 pairs of spinal nerves, arranged in the following groups, and named for the region of the vertebral column from which they emerge:

Cervical	8 pairs
Thoracic	12 pairs
Lumbar	5 pairs
Sacral	5 pairs
Coccygeal	1 pair

The first cervical nerve arises from the medulla oblongata and leaves the spinal canal between the occipital bone and the atlas. The other cervical spinal nerves arise from the spinal cord, and each leaves the spinal canal through an intervertebral foramen *above* the vertebra whose number it bears, e.g., the seventh thoracic nerve emerges through the foramen between the sixth and seventh vertebrae. The eighth spinal nerve emerges from the vertebral column below the seventh cervical vertebra. All the other spinal nerves emerge from the cord below the vertebra whose number it bears. The coccygeal nerve passes from the lower extremity of the canal.

Mixed Nerves. The spinal nerves consist mainly of myelinated nerve fibers and are called mixed nerves because they contain both motor and sensory fibers. Each spinal nerve has two roots, a ventral root and a dorsal root. The fibers of the ventral root *arise from nerve cells comprising the gray matter* in the ventral column and convey motor impulses from the spinal cord to the periphery.

The fibers of the dorsal root arise from the *cells composing the enlargement*, or *ganglion*, of the dorsal root situated in the openings between the arches of the vertebrae. These cell bodies give off a single fiber which divides in a T-shaped manner into two processes. One extends to a sensory end organ of the skin or of a muscle, tendon, or joint. The other extends into the spinal cord, forming the dorsal root of a spinal nerve.

The fibers that enter the cord directly do not pass into the gray matter immediately; some extend upward and some downward in the white matter before doing so. Sooner or later they all enter the gray matter of the spinal cord or brain, where they form synapses with central or motor neurons.

The ventral roots have their origin within the ventral columns of the spinal cord and are motor fibers. The dorsal roots have their

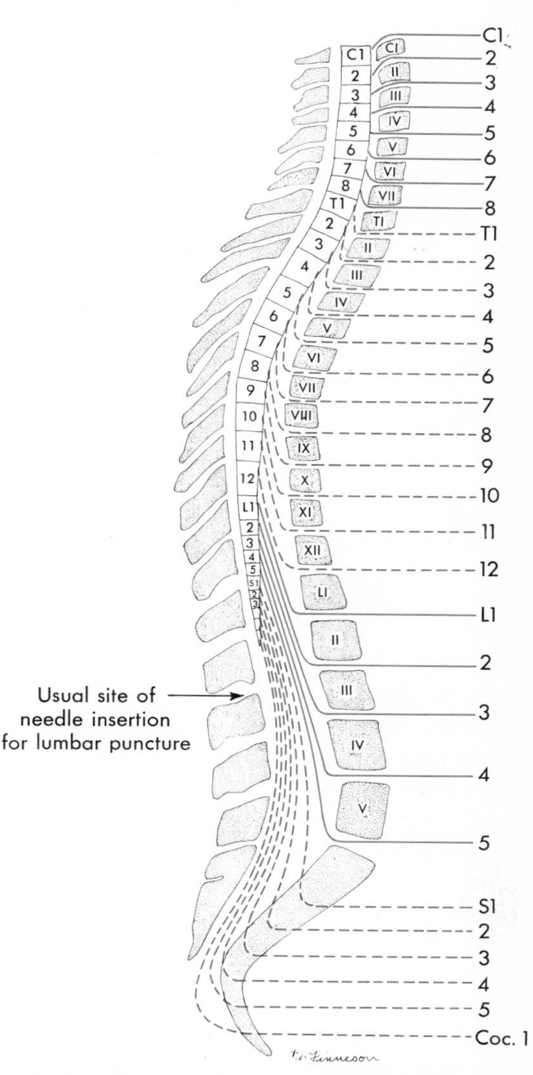

Figure 10–11. Diagram showing segmental relationships of the spinal cord to the vertebral column. Note the site of origin of each spinal nerve in the cord and its point of exit from the vertebral column.

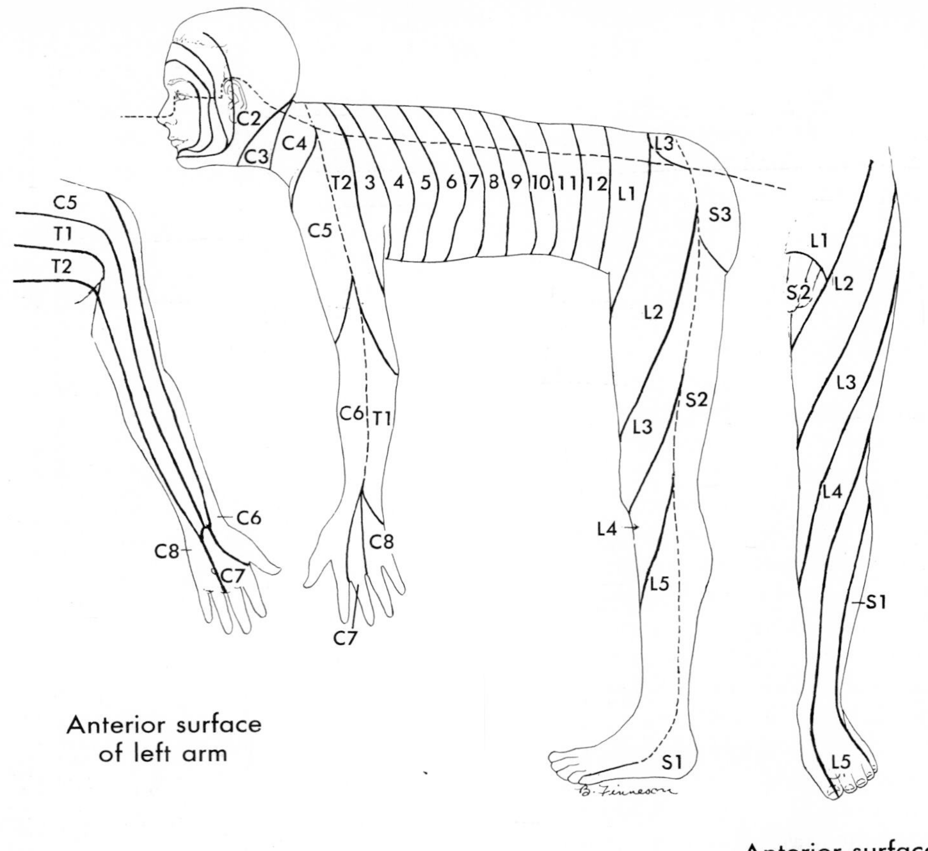

Figure 10–12. Distribution of spinal nerves. (Modified from Pansky and House.)

origin outside the cord, i.e., in the dorsal ganglia, and are sensory fibers. The fibers of these two roots are collected into one bundle and form a spinal nerve just before leaving the canal through the intervertebral openings.

Distribution of Terminal Branches of the Spinal Nerves. Each spinal cord segment is related to the body in a segmental way by its spinal nerves (Figure 10–12). After leaving the spinal column, each spinal nerve divides into three main branches known as the meningeal, or recurrent (distributed to the meninges), the dorsal, and the ventral. The dorsal branches supply the muscles and skin of the back of the head, neck, and trunk. The ventral branches supply the extremities and parts of the body wall in front of the

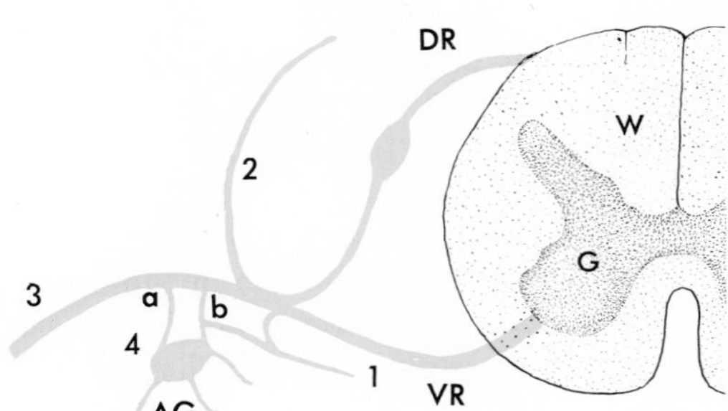

Figure 10–13. The four branches of a typical thoracic spinal nerve. (*1*) Meningeal, or recurrent, branch, (*2*) dorsal branch, (*3*) ventral branch, (*4*) visceral branch, (*a*) gray ramus, (*b*) white ramus, (*AG*) automatic ganglion, (*DR*) dorsal root of spinal nerve, (*G*) gray matter, (*VR*) ventral root of spinal nerve, (*W*) white matter.

spine. There is a fourth, or visceral, branch, *present only in nerves from the first thoracic to the third lumbar*. These connect with the sympathetic ganglia by means of fibers which pass from the nerve to the ganglia (the white and gray rami, see pages 265, 266). Extending from the sympathetic ganglia to their final distribution are the autonomic nerves. These nerves form plexuses called the cardiac, the celiac or solar, the hypogastric, the pelvic, and the enteric. Some nerve fibers from the sympathetic ganglia return to and are distributed with the spinal nerve to supply sweat glands, arrector pili muscles, and the smooth muscle of all blood vessels.

After the nerves emerge from the cord, a plexus is formed in the cervical, brachial, lumbar, and sacral segments from which the peripheral nerves are derived.

The Cervical Plexus. This plexus is formed by the ventral branches of the first four cervical nerves. The second, third, and fourth nerves divide into an upper and a lower branch; these in turn unite to form three loops from which peripheral nerves are distributed. Some fibers of these nerves join the hypoglossal, vagus, and accessory cranial nerves in their course.

The Brachial Plexus. This plexus is formed by the union of the ventral branch of the last four cervical and the first thoracic nerves. See Figure 10–15*A* for fiber composition and nerves formed. Three major cords are formed, the lateral, medial, and posterior. Important nerves formed are the median, ulnar, and radial nerves which supply the upper extremities.

The Lumbar Plexus. This plexus is formed by a few fibers from the twelfth thoracic and the anterior primary divisions of the first four lumbar nerves. Figure 10–15*B* illustrates the peripheral distribution of the fibers to the muscles. The largest nerves formed are the femoral and obturator nerves.

The Sacral Plexus. This plexus is formed by a few fibers from the fourth lumbar nerve, all of the fifth, and the first, second, and third sacral nerves. Figure 10–15*B* illustrates the joining of these fibers and the great nerves formed. The largest is the great sciatic, which supplies the muscles of the lower extremity.

In the thoracic region a plexus is not formed, but the fibers pass as intercostal nerves out into the intercostal spaces to supply the intercostal muscles, the upper abdominal

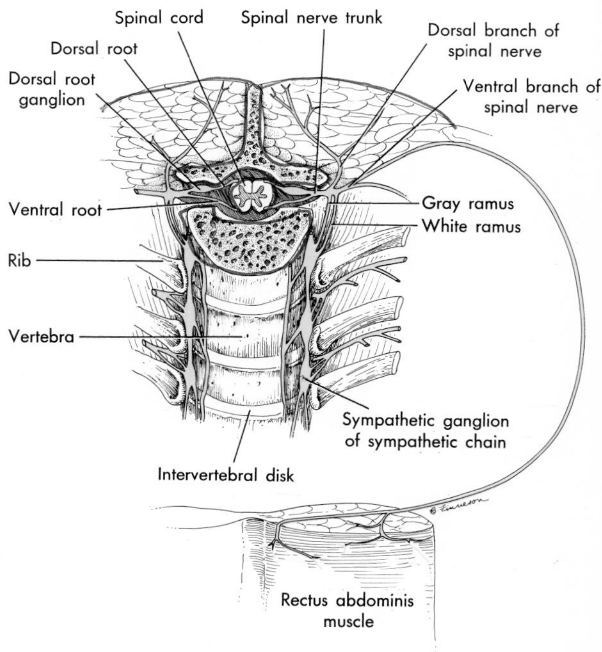

Figure 10–14. Diagram of spinal nerve branching, relationship to spinal cord, sympathetic ganglia, and vertebral column. (Modified from Pansky and House.)

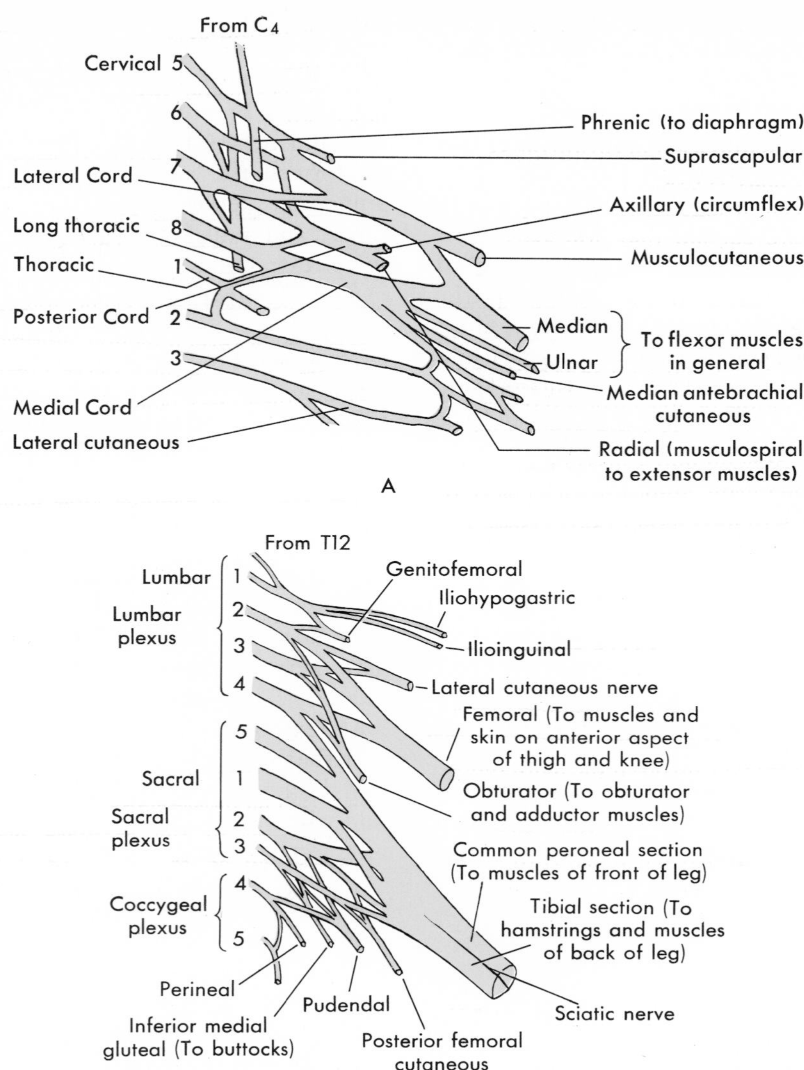

Figure 10–15. *A.* Diagram of brachial plexus, showing distribution of the larger nerves. See page 168 for distribution of the nerves. *B.* Diagram of lumbosacral plexus and distribution of some of the larger nerves. See page 169 for distribution of the nerves.

muscles, and the skin of the abdomen and chest.

Names of Peripheral Nerves. Many of the larger branches given off from the spinal nerves bear the same name as the artery they accompany or the part they supply. Thus, the radial nerve passes down the radial side of the forearm in company with the radial artery; the intercostal nerves pass between the ribs in company with the intercostal arteries. Exceptions to this are the two sciatic nerves, which pass down from the sacral plexus, one on each side of the body near the center of each buttock and the back of each thigh, to the popliteal region, where each divides into two large branches which supply the legs and feet. Motor branches from these nerves pass to the muscles of the legs and feet, and sensory branches are distributed to the skin of the lower extremities. A chart of the spinal nerves and their distribution appears on page 168.

Degeneration and Regeneration of Nerves. Since the cell body is essential for the nutrition of the whole cell, it follows that if the processes of a neuron are cut off, they will suffer from malnutrition and die. If, for instance, a spinal nerve is cut, all the peripheral part will degenerate, because the fibers have been cut off from their cell bodies. The cut connective-tissue framework reunites, but the cut ends of the fibers cannot unite, for the peripheral or severed portion of the nerve fiber begins to degenerate. Its medullary sheath breaks up into a mass of fatty molecules and is gradually absorbed, and finally the central fiber also disappears. In regeneration, many new fibers start to grow out from the central end of the severed axon. If one of these "growth sprouts" makes a successful penetration into the peripheral end of the neurilemma, all other growth sprouts wither and die. The successful sprout continues to grow toward the end organ and is destined to become the new functional fiber. In time it will become surrounded with a myelin sheath. The Schwann cells of peripheral fibers play an important part in both the degeneration and regeneration of the cut fiber. Restoration of function in the nerve may not occur for several months, during which time it is presumed the new nerve fibers are slowly finding their way along the course of those which have been destroyed. Since the nerve fibers of the brain and cord have little or no neurilemma, regeneration after injury does not occur.

QUESTIONS FOR DISCUSSION

1. Differentiate between the symptoms caused by a crush injury to the fourth lumbar vertebra and an injury that involved the tenth thoracic vertebra.
2. Explain the symptoms resulting from an injury that hemisected the spinal cord at the tenth thoracic, left side.
3. Differentiate between the symptoms of an upper and a lower motor neuron lesion.
4. What are the main ascending tracts of the cord? The descending?
5. An injury to the shoulder which pulled excessively on the arm and dislocated the shoulder might injure what nerve fibers?

SUMMARY

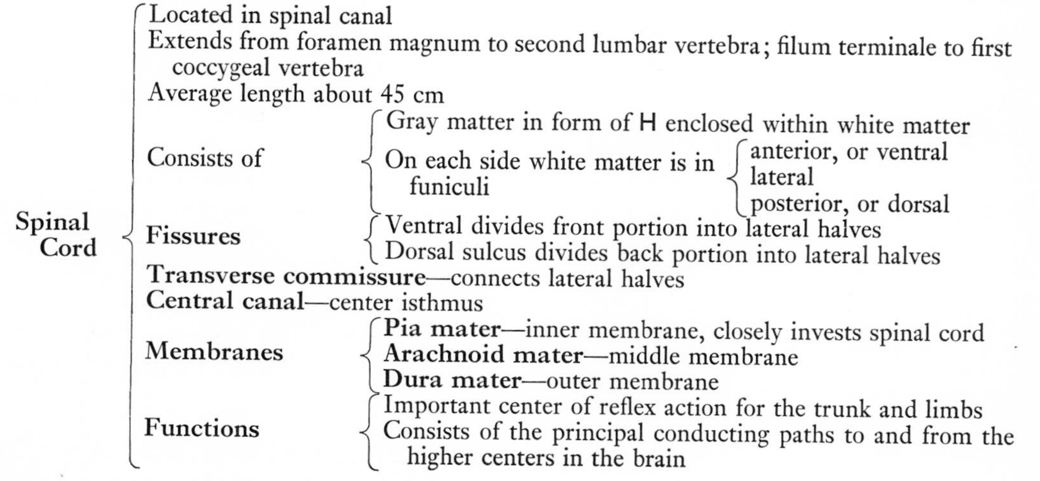

Spinal Cord
- Located in spinal canal
- Extends from foramen magnum to second lumbar vertebra; filum terminale to first coccygeal vertebra
- Average length about 45 cm
- Consists of
  - Gray matter in form of H enclosed within white matter
  - On each side white matter is in funiculi
    - anterior, or ventral
    - lateral
    - posterior, or dorsal
- **Fissures**
  - Ventral divides front portion into lateral halves
  - Dorsal sulcus divides back portion into lateral halves
- **Transverse commissure**—connects lateral halves
- **Central canal**—center isthmus
- Membranes
  - **Pia mater**—inner membrane, closely invests spinal cord
  - **Arachnoid mater**—middle membrane
  - **Dura mater**—outer membrane
- Functions
  - Important center of reflex action for the trunk and limbs
  - Consists of the principal conducting paths to and from the higher centers in the brain

Spinal Nerves

- **Number**
  - Cervical — 8 pairs
  - Thoracic — 12 pairs
  - Lumbar — 5 pairs
  - Sacral — 5 pairs
  - Coccygeal — 1 pair
  - Total: 31 pairs
- **Variety**
  - Myelinated
  - Mixed
    - Sensory
    - Motor
- **Origin**—two roots
  - Ventral, or motor, in gray matter of cord
  - Dorsal, or sensory, in spinal ganglia
- **Distribution**—four main branches
  - Ventral supplies extremities and parts of body in front of spine
  - Dorsal supplies muscles and parts of the body in back of the spine
  - Visceral extends to lateral chain of ganglia and viscera
  - Meningeal, or recurrent, branch returns to meninges

CHAPTER

II

THE BRAIN

Parts of the Brain and Their Function

The Meninges

Cerebrospinal Fluid

Blood Supply

CRANIAL NERVES

The complexity of the brain in structure and the intricate variety of its functioning make it the least understood of all parts of the body. It has been called a "masterful computer"—surely an inadequate description of the organ through which we perceive our world and achieve an understanding based on learning and past experience. One's brain is one's self—unique.

THE BRAIN

The brain is the largest and most complex mass of nervous tissue in the body. It is contained in the cranial cavity and comprises five fairly distinct connected parts: the cerebrum, the midbrain, the cerebellum, the pons, and the medulla oblongata.

In early embryonic life the brain, or encephalon, consists of three hollow vesicles:

1. Cephalic, or prosencephalon (forebrain)
2. Mesencephalon, or midbrain
3. Caudal, or rhombencephalon (hindbrain)

During growth the cerebral hemispheres, their commissures, and the first, second, and third ventricles are developed from the forebrain; the corpora quadrigemina, the cerebral peduncles, and the cerebral aqueduct (a tubular connection between the third and fourth ventricles) are developed from the midbrain; the medulla oblongata, the pons, the cerebellum, and the included fourth ventricle are developed from the hindbrain.

The weight of the brain in the adult male is about 1,380 gm (48.6 oz); in the adult female, about 1,250 gm (44 oz). The weight of the brain is an indication of growth, which in early life depends upon the enlargement of the cells and their processes, the myelinization of the nerve fibers, and an increase in the amount of neuroglia. The brain grows rapidly up to the fifth year and in general ceases to grow much beyond about the twentieth year. In advanced age the brain gradually loses weight owing to dehydration and death of cells.

The development of the brain is not only a matter of growth but also a matter of forming new functional pathways, i.e., new synapses and a permanent modification of the synapses that are functionally active during various forms of activity.

Impulse Transmission. In the brain as in other parts of the nervous system, nerve impulses are transmitted at the synapse from

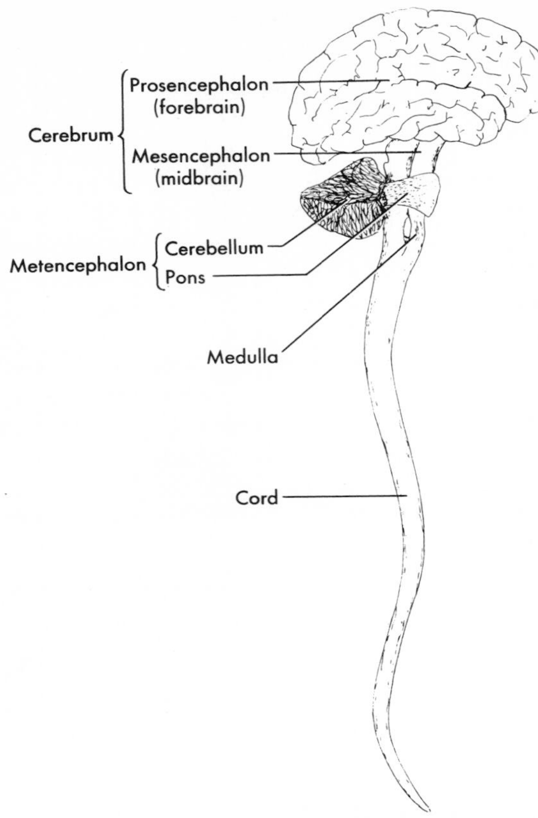

Cerebrum—memory, association, personality. Synthesizes sensory impressions into perceptions. Highest level of somatic motor control. Receives impulses from and sends impulses to all lower levels.

Midbrain—contains many nuclei for control of ocular reflexes, eye movement, higher postural reflex actions. Motor nuclei of cranial nerves III and IV. Nuclei for control of many visceral activities.

Cerebellum—vestibular and postural reflexes, equilibrium and orientation in space. Helps to maintain muscle tone and regulate muscle coordination.

Pons—relay station from lower to the higher centers. Contains nuclei for cerebrocerebellar relay of impulses. Nuclei and pathways for regulation of skeletal muscle tones. Contains nuclei for cranial nerves V, VI, VII, and VIII. Connects both halves of the cerebellum.

Medulla—contains nuclei of many cranial nerves. Location of many vital centers. Contains nuclei for relaying sensory impulses to higher centers. Contains fiber tracts for all ascending and descending impulses.

Cord—only means by which impulses from the periphery can reach higher centers and impulses from higher centers can reach the periphery. Contains neurons which form ascending sensory pathways. Receives incoming sensory fibers and their impulses. Centers for intersegmental and segmental reflexes.

Figure 11–1. Diagram of the central nervous system—cerebrum, midbrain, and medulla pulled apart to show parts.

one neuron to another by chemical transmission. Norepinephrine, serotonin, acetylcholine, and other substances have been demonstrated in various parts of the brain during activity; however, their precise role in synaptic transmission has not yet been established.

Parts of the Brain

The parts of the brain include the forebrain, midbrain, and hindbrain, which are further subdivided:

1. **The Forebrain** (prosencephalon)

a. Cerebral hemispheres (telencephalon), with the lateral ventricles. Each hemisphere includes the cerebral cortex, basal nuclei, rhinencephalon (olfactory portion).

b. The diencephalon (connects cerebral hemispheres with midbrain, and forms the walls of the third ventricle). The diencephalon has four major parts: (1) the epithalamus, (2) the thalamus and the metathalamus, (3) the hypothalamus, and (4) the subthalamus.

2. **The Midbrain** (mesencephalon)—connects the forebrain with the hindbrain.

a. Ventral part—cerebral peduncles, which are the massive bundles of fibers extending from the border of the pons varolii to the optic tract where they disappear into the substance of the forebrain.

b. Dorsal part—includes the corpora quadrigemina (superior and inferior colliculi).

3. **The Hindbrain** (rhombencephalon)

a. Metencephalon—cerebellum, pons.

b. Myelencephalon, or medulla oblongata.

THE FOREBRAIN

The Hemispheres. *The cerebrum* is by far the largest part of the brain. It is egg-shaped and fills the whole of the upper portion of the skull. The entire surface, both upper and lower, is composed of layers of gray matter and is called the cortex. The bulk of the white matter in the interior of the cerebrum consists of small fibers running in three principal directions: (1) from above downward—*projection fibers*, connecting the cerebrum with other parts of the brain and spinal cord; (2) from the front backward—*association fibers*, connecting gyri on the same side of the cerebrum; and (3) from side to side—*commissural fibers*, connecting the right and left sides of the cerebrum. The fibers link the different parts of the brain together and connect the brain with the spinal cord (Figures 11–13 and 11–14). There are also autonomic fibers that link the brain with the spinal cord.

Fissures and Convolutions. In early life the cortex of the cerebrum is comparatively smooth, but as time passes and the brain develops, the surface becomes covered with furrows, which vary in depth. The deeper furrows are called *fissures*, the shallow ones, *sulci*, and the ridges between the sulci are called *gyri* or *convolutions*. The fissures and sulci are infoldings of gray matter; consequently the more numerous and deeper they are, the greater is the amount of gray matter. The length and depth of these fissures and sulci, and the prominence and sizes of the convulsions vary in different parts of the cortex.

The Cerebral Fissures. There are five important fissures which are landmarks.

1. *The longitudinal cerebral fissure*—the cerebral hemispheres are separated by a deep vertical longitudinal fissure. The separation is complete in front and behind, but in the middle portion it extends to the corpus callosum, a wide band of commissural fibers which unite the two hemispheres. In the posterior region the cerebrum overlaps the thalamus, midbrain, and cerebellum. A process of the dura mater extends down into

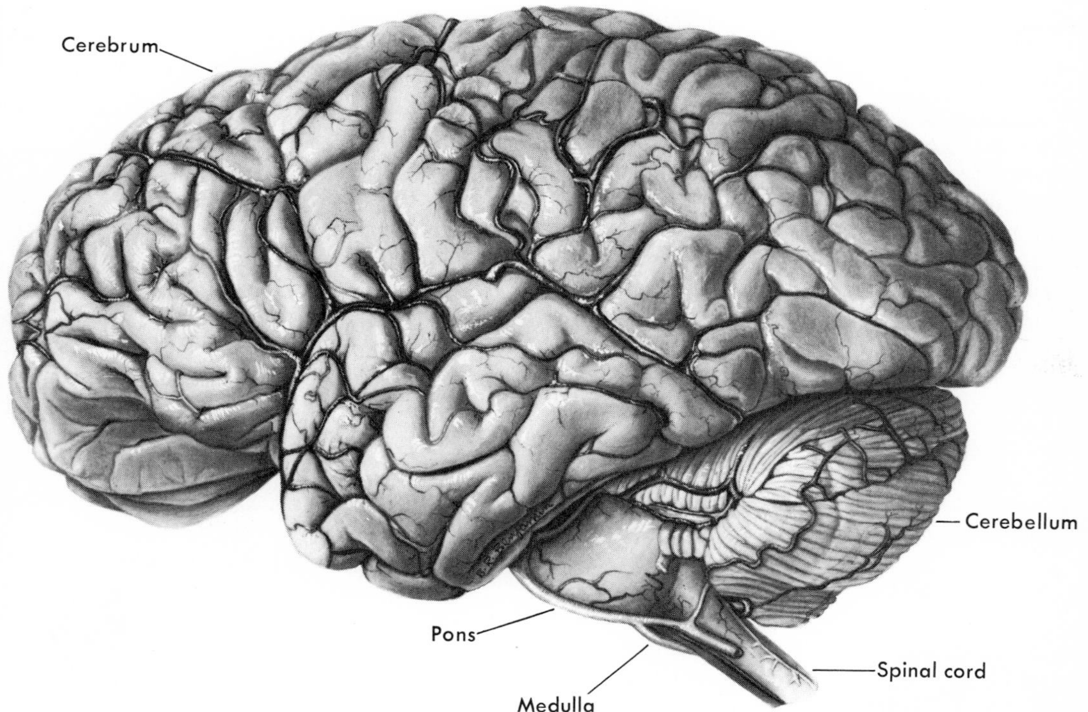

Figure 11–2. Lateral view of the brain, pia in place. Note the blood vessels, cerebrum, cerebellum, pons, medulla, and spinal cord.

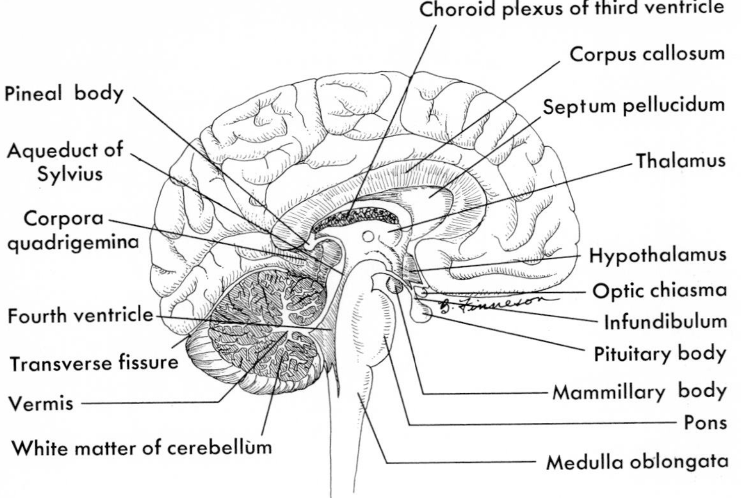

Figure 11–3. Brain stem, cerebellum, and cerebrum seen in midsagittal section of the brain. (Modified from Pansky and House.)

this fissure and separates the two cerebral hemispheres. It is called the *falx cerebri*, because it is narrow in front and broader behind, thus resembling a sickle in shape. It contains important venous sinuses between its two layers.

2. The *transverse fissure* is between the cerebrum and the cerebellum. A process of the dura also extends into this fissure and covers the upper surface of the cerebellum and the undersurface of the cerebrum. It is called the *tentorium cerebelli* and also contains important venous sinuses.

There is one of each of the following in each hemisphere. For location, see Figure 11–4.

3. *Central sulcus*, or *fissure of Rolando*

4. *Lateral cerebral fissure*, or *fissure of Sylvius*

5. *Parieto-occipital fissure*

Lobes of the Cerebrum. The longitudinal fissure divides the cerebrum into two hemispheres, and the transverse fissure divides the cerebrum from the cerebellum. The three remaining fissures, assisted by certain arbitrary lines, divide each hemisphere in five lobes. With one exception these lobes are named from the bones of the cranium under which they lie; hence they are known as: (1) *frontal lobe*, (2) *parietal lobe*, (3) *temporal lobe*, (4) *occipital lobe*, and (5) the *insula* (*island of Reil*[1]).

The frontal lobe is that portion of the cerebrum lying in front of the central sulcus and usually consists of four main convolutions on the convex side.

[1] Johann Christian Reil, Dutch physiologist (1759–1813).

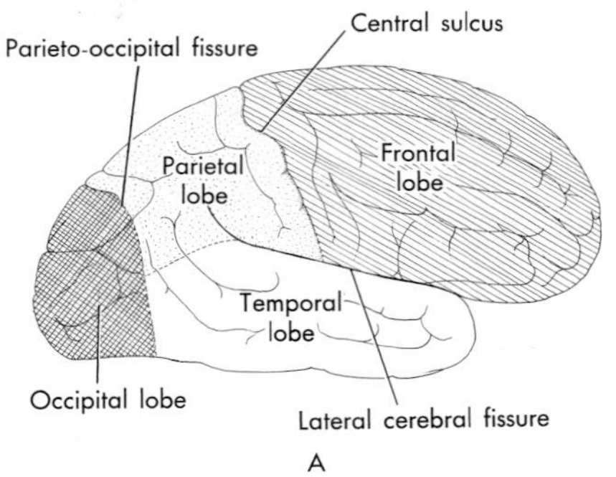

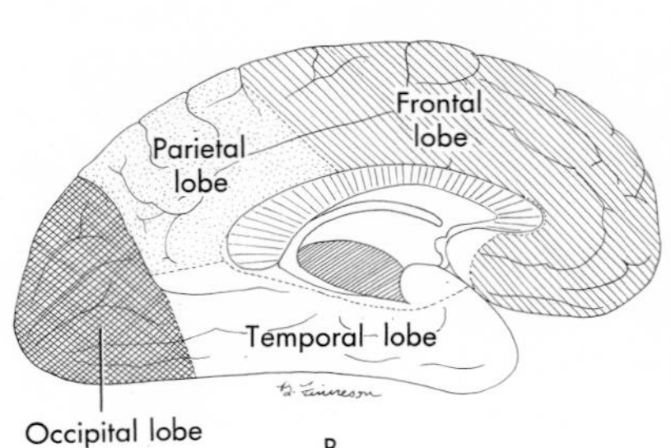

Figure 11–4. Lobes of cerebrum. (*A*) Lateral view. (*B*) Medial view—brain stem removed.

The parietal lobe is bounded in front by the central sulcus and behind by the parieto-occipital fissure.

The temporal lobe lies below the lateral cerebral fissure and in front of the occipital lobe. There are three horizontal convolutions: the superior, middle, and inferior gyri.

The occipital lobe occupies the posterior extremity of the cerebral hemisphere. There is no marked separation of the occipital lobe from the parietal and temporal lobes that lie to the front, but when the surface of the longitudinal cleft is examined, the parieto-occipital fissure serves as a boundary anteriorly for the occipital lobe.

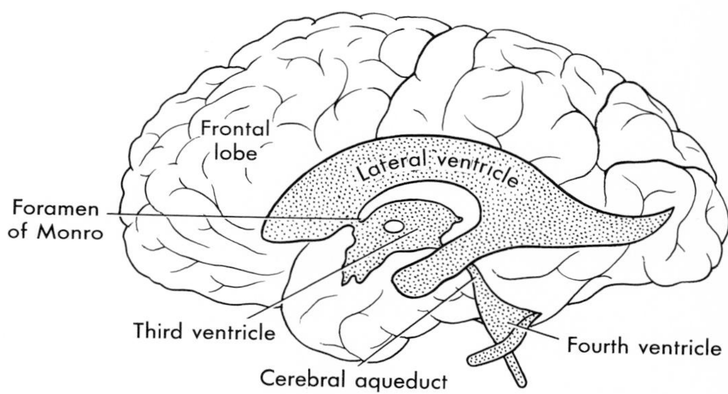

Figure 11–5. Diagram showing ventricles of the brain. Side view.

The insula (island of Reil) is not seen when the surface of the hemisphere is examined, for it lies within the lateral cerebral fissure, and the overlying convolutions of the parietal and frontal lobes must be lifted up before the insula may be seen.

Ventricles of the Brain. The brain contains cavities called *ventricles.* The *two lateral ventricles* are situated one in each of the cerebral hemispheres under the mass of white fibers called the corpus callosum, which connects the two hemispheres. The *basal nuclei* of the brain are in the floor of the lateral ventricles. The cavity of the lateral ventricles is large and may become overdistended with cerebrospinal fluid in certain pathological conditions.

The *third ventricle* is behind the lateral ventricles but connected with each one by means of small openings called the foramina of Monro.[2] The *fourth ventricle* is in front of the cerebellum, behind the pons varolii and the medulla. The third communicates with the fourth by means of a slender canal called the *aqueduct* of the cerebrum (aqueduct of Sylvius[3]). In the roof of the fourth ventricle there is an opening called the foramen of Magendie.[4] In the lateral wall there are two openings called the foramina of Luschka.[5] By means of these three openings, the ventricles communicate with the subarachnoid space, and the cerebrospinal fluid can circulate from one to the other. The so-called fifth ventricle is not a portion of the general cavity—not a true ventricle. It is a narrow space in front of the third, having no connection with the other ventricles.

Meninges. The brain and spinal cord are enclosed within *three* membranes. These are named from without inward: the dura mater, arachnoid mater, and pia mater.

The dura mater is a dense membrane of fibrous connective tissue containing a great many blood vessels. The cranial and spinal portions of the dura mater differ and are described separately, but they form one complete membrane. The *cranial dura mater* is

[2] Alexander Monro (Primus), Scottish anatomist (1697–1767).

[3] François Sylvius, French anatomist (1614–1672).

[4] François Magendie, French physiologist (1783–1855).

[5] Hubert von Luschka, German anatomist (1820–1875).

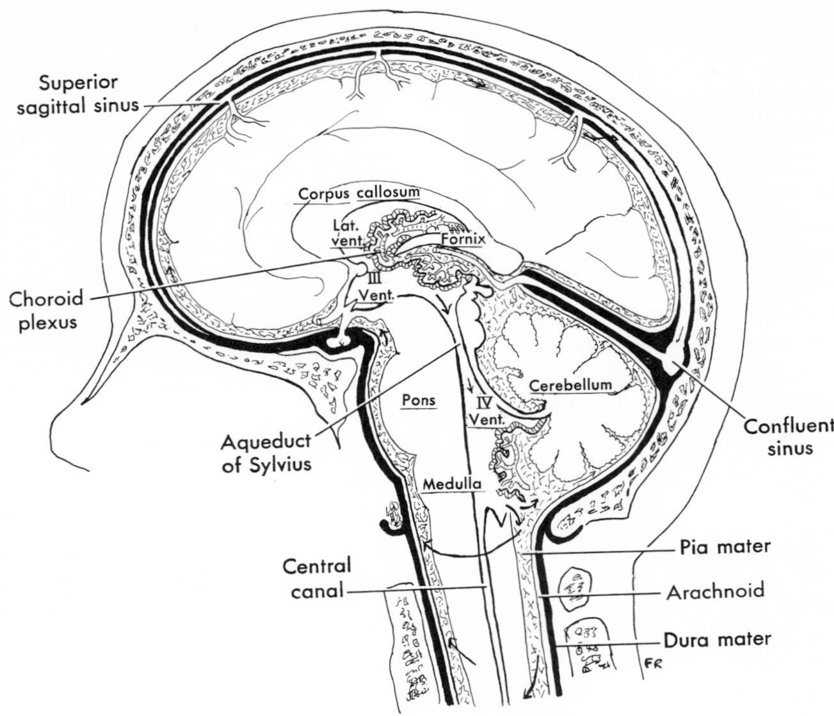

Figure 11–6. Diagram showing relationship of brain and cord to meninges. The choroid plexus forms the cerebrospinal fluid. (Modified from *The Principal Nervous Pathways*, 4th ed., by Andrew T. Rasmussen, The Macmillan Company.)

arranged in *two* layers which are closely connected except where they separate to form sinuses for the passage of venous blood. The outer, or endosteal, layer is adherent to the bones of the skull and forms their internal periosteum. The inner, or meningeal, layer covers the brain and sends numerous prolongations inward for the support and protection of the different lobes of the brain. These projections also form sinuses that return the blood from the brain, and sheaths for the nerves that pass out of the skull. The *spinal dura mater* forms a loose sheath around the spinal cord and consists of only the *inner layer* of the dura mater; the outer layer ceases at the foramen magnum, and its place is taken by the periosteum lining the vertebral canal. Between the spinal dura mater and the arachnoid mater is a potential cavity, the *subdural cavity*, which contains only enough fluid to moisten their contiguous surfaces.

The arachnoid mater is a delicate fibrous membrane placed between the dura mater and the pia mater. The cranial portion invests the brain loosely and, with the exception of the longitudinal fissure, it passes over the various convolutions and sulci and does not dip down into them. The spinal portion is tubular and surrounds the cord loosely. The *subarachnoid space*, between the arachnoid mater and the pia mater, contains a spongy connective tissue forming trabeculae and is filled with cerebrospinal fluid.

The pia mater is a vascular membrane consisting of a plexus of blood vessels held together by fine areolar connective tissue. The cranial portion invests the surface of the brain and dips down between the convolutions. The spinal portion is thicker and less vascular than the cranial. It is closely adherent to the entire surface of the spinal cord and sends a process into the ventral fissure.

The Cerebrospinal Fluid. The meningeal membranes and the spaces filled with fluid form a pad enclosing the brain and cord on all sides. Cerebrospinal fluid is secreted and diffused from the blood by the ependymal cells which cover the *choroid plexuses* of the ventricles. The choroid plexuses are highly vascular folds or processes of the pia mater which are found in the ventricles. The capillary network is intricate and resembles other cerebral capillaries. These differ greatly in their selective permeability from those in other parts of the body. For this reason drugs in the blood stream often do not penetrate brain tissue and infections of the brain are difficult to cure. The term *blood-brain barrier* is sometimes used to refer to this phenomenon. The choroid plexus capillaries are covered by thick, highly differentiated cells that have the structure needed for *active* transport. After filling the lateral ventricles, the cerebrospinal fluid escapes by the foramen of Monro into the third ventricle and thence by the aqueduct into the fourth ventricle. From the fourth ventricle the fluid is poured through the medial foramen of Magendie and the two lateral foramina of Luschka into the subarachnoid spaces and reaches the cisterna magna. From the cisterna magna the cerebrospinal fluid may pass down the spinal canal within the subarachnoid space where it circulates around and upward and finally enters the venous circulation. From the cisterna magna this fluid also bathes all parts of the brain. From the subarachnoid spaces it is absorbed through the villi of the arachnoid mater, which project into the dural venous sinuses; a small amount passes into the perineural lymphatics of the cranial and spinal nerves. Experimentally, it has been

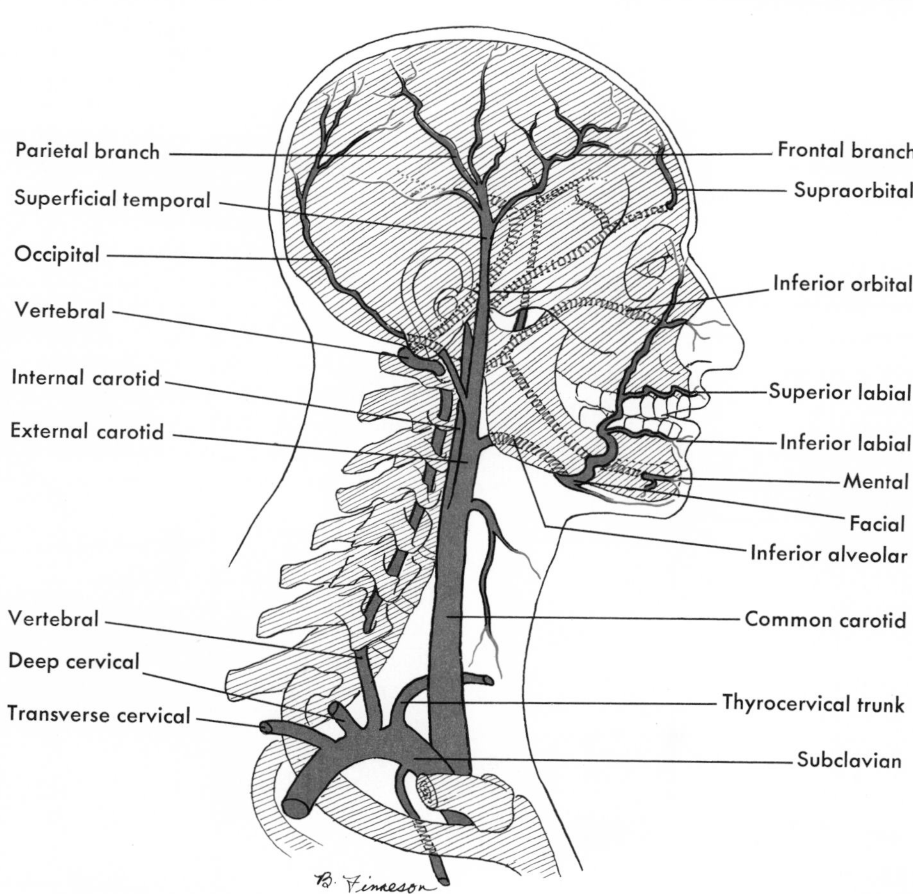

Figure 11–7. Diagram of arterial blood supply to head, face, and brain.

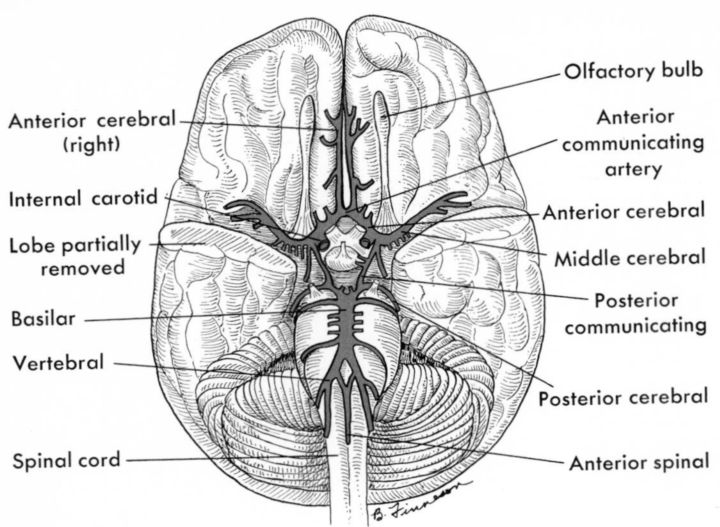

Figure 11–8. The circle of Willis.

found that dyes added to the cerebrospinal fluid travel along the course of certain cranial nerves, especially the olfactory. This loophole affords an opportunity for the entry of infection from the nasal cavities to the cerebral cavity.

The cerebrospinal fluid is highly variable in quantity, which is usually given as from 80 to 200 ml. It is colorless, alkaline, and has a specific gravity of 1.004 to 1.008. It consists of water with traces of protein, some glucose, and electrolytes, as in blood plasma, a few lymphocytes, and some pituitary hormones. Since the cerebrospinal fluid bathes the neural tissue of the cord and brain, its composition sets the composition of the extracellular fluid. It is now known that metabolic energy is continually expended to maintain the constant composition of cerebrospinal fluid in spite of fluctuations in arterial blood. If the membranes of the brain or cord are inflamed, there is usually a change in the normal characteristics of the fluid.

Infection and inflammation of the meninges of the brain will quickly spread to those of the cord. Such inflammation results in increased secretion, which, as it collects in a confined bony cavity, gives rise to symptoms of pressure, such as headache, slow pulse, slow respirations, and partial or complete unconsciousness. Cerebrospinal fluid may be removed by lumbar puncture. The needle by which the fluid is withdrawn is usually inserted between the third and fourth lumbar vertebrae (Figure 10–11, page 195) (thus below the end of the cord) into the subarachnoid space, the patient usually lying on his left side, with knees drawn up in order to arch the back, so as to slightly separate the vertebrae. In this position the pressure of the fluid is normally 70 to 180 mm of water. This pressure is raised when pressure in the brain is elevated, as in cerebral edema or inflammatory swelling. The fluid, or exudate, will contain the products of the inflammatory process and the organisms causing it. Lumbar puncture is used for (1) diagnosis of meningitis, syphilis, increased intracranial pressure, cerebral hemorrhage, and intracranial tumors; and (2) therapeutic effect: (a) to relieve pressure in meningitis and hydrocephalus; and (b) rarely for the introduction of sera, such as antimeningitis serum, or drugs.

Blood Supply. The internal carotid and vertebral arteries are the source of blood to the brain. The vertebral arteries arise from the subclavian arteries and ascend on either side to the level of the sixth cervical vertebra, where they enter the foramina of the transverse processes and continue upward in the foramina of the upper six thoracic vertebrae. They wind behind the atlas, enter the skull through the foramen magnum, and unite to form the basilar artery.

Circle of Willis.[6] This is an arterial

[6] Thomas Willis, English anatomist (1621–1675).

anastomosis at the base of the brain. It is formed by the union of the *anterior cerebral arteries*, which are branches of the internal carotid, and the *posterior cerebral arteries*, which are branches of the basilar. The circle extends from the lower to the upper border of the pons, lying in the median groove. It ends by dividing into the two posterior cerebral arteries. These two arteries are connected on either side with the internal carotid by the posterior communicating arteries. In front, the anterior cerebral arteries are connected by the anterior communicating arteries. These arteries form a complete circle. This arrangement (1) equalizes the circulation of the blood in the brain and (2) in case of destruction of one of the arteries, provides for the blood reaching the brain through other vessels. Venous drainage from the brain is through the large sinuses, shown in Figure 11–9, and into the internal jugular veins at either side of the neck.

Functions of the Cerebrum. In higher vertebrates the cerebrum constitutes a larger proportion of the central nervous system than in the lower forms. It is especially large in animals that are capable of profiting by experience; the areas that govern all our mental activities—reason, intelligence, will, and memory—are located in the cerebrum. It is the discriminating area of consciousness, the interpreter of sensations (correlation), the instigator and coordinator of voluntary acts, and it exerts strong control (both facilitatory and inhibitory) over many reflex acts. Laughing, weeping, micturition, defecation, and many other acts might be cited as examples of the latter.

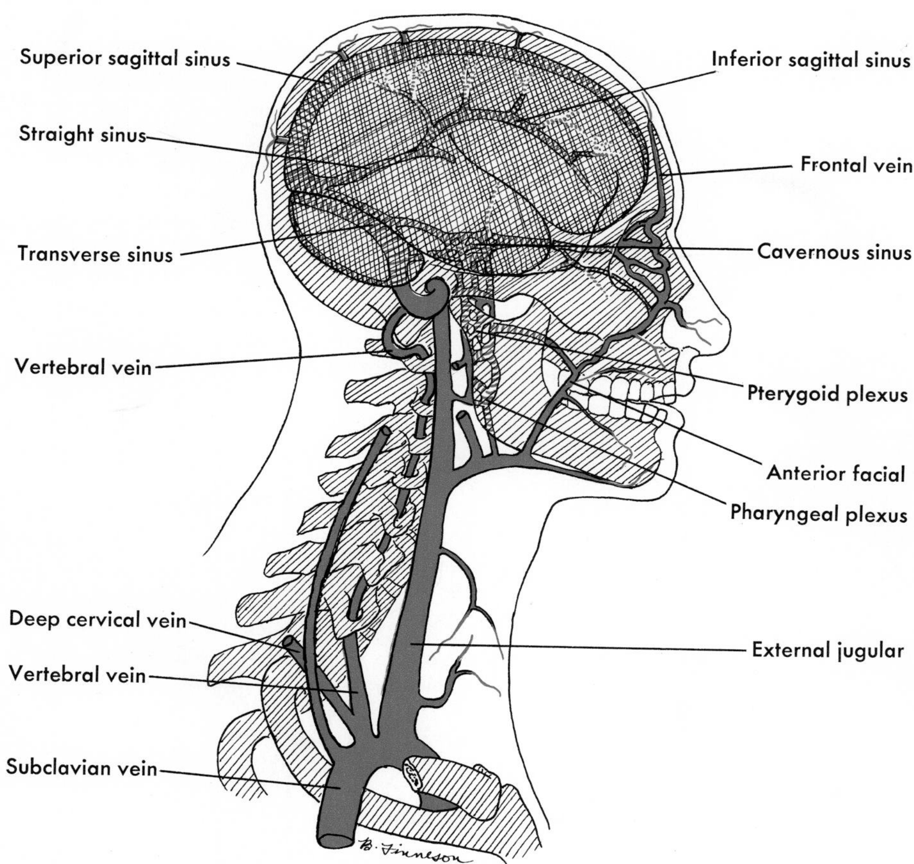

Figure 11–9. Venous return from brain, head, and face.

Consciousness and memory are two areas of cerebral activity which encompass much or all of its other more specific activities. The conscious brain is kept aware of environmental changes by way of afferent nerve impulses and responds appropriately. The unconscious brain fails to respond to these changes; only very basic physiological activities and reflexes persist during unconsciousness. For example, the cardiovascular and respiratory systems continue to function.

There seems to be no specific control center for consciousness, although the hypothalamus and the reticular area of the brain stem are known to play important roles. Sedatives which produce sleep act by interfering with the transmission of impulses to the cortex from those deeper brain areas. Sleep is similar to unconsciousness in that both conditions involve unawareness of surroundings; however, one can be aroused from sleep but not from unconsciousness. Furthermore, the electrical activity which can be recorded as an electroencephalogram (EEG) is different during sleep and coma.

Prolonged lack of sleep results in progressive malfunction of the brain to the point of psychotic manifestations if forced wakefulness is long enough. The inescapable conclusion is that sleep is necessary for normal brain functioning.

At certain stages of sleep (varying from relatively light, easily arousable sleep to very deep sleep) dreaming occurs. It is possible to recognize the occurrence of dreaming by rapid eye movements (REM sleep) and other physiological changes. When sleep is interrupted during REM sleep, the subject reports that he was dreaming. If the subject is awakened every time he starts to dream for a succession of nights, and then is permitted to sleep undisturbed, the amount of sleeping time devoted to dreaming is greatly increased —an indication that dreaming may be a necessary part of sleep, perhaps as a release of psychic energy.

Memory and learning are activities of the cortex, although other cerebral areas are involved. For example, sensory impulses from the eye or ear are transmitted to the appropriate cortical areas, so that at a later date they may be recalled—for pleasure or interpretation and thought. Somehow the initial impulses cause a change in neurons or neural connections so that at a later date activation of some of these neurons causes a

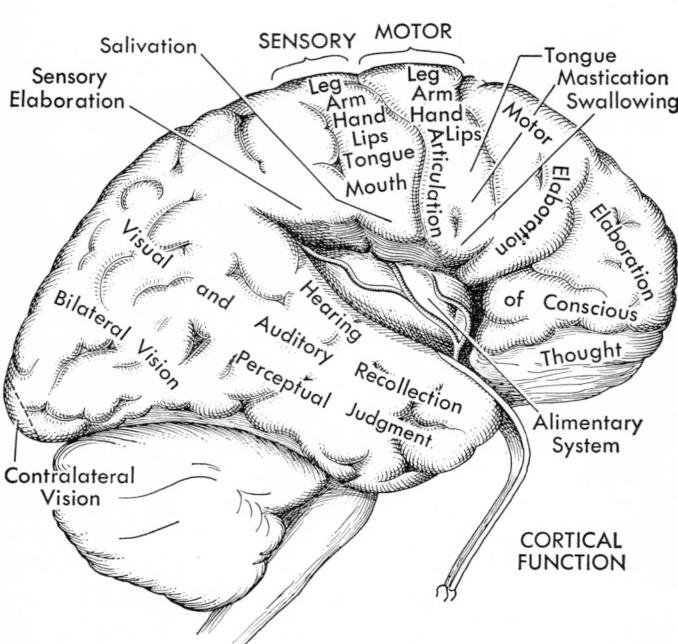

Figure 11–10. Cortical function. This illustration will serve as a summary restatement of conclusions, some hypothetical (e.g., the elaboration zones), others firmly established. The suggestion that the anterior portion of the occipital cortex is related to both fields of vision rather than to one alone is derived from the results of stimulation. (W. Penfield and T. Rasmussen, *The Cerebral Cortex of Man.* Courtesy of The Macmillan Company.)

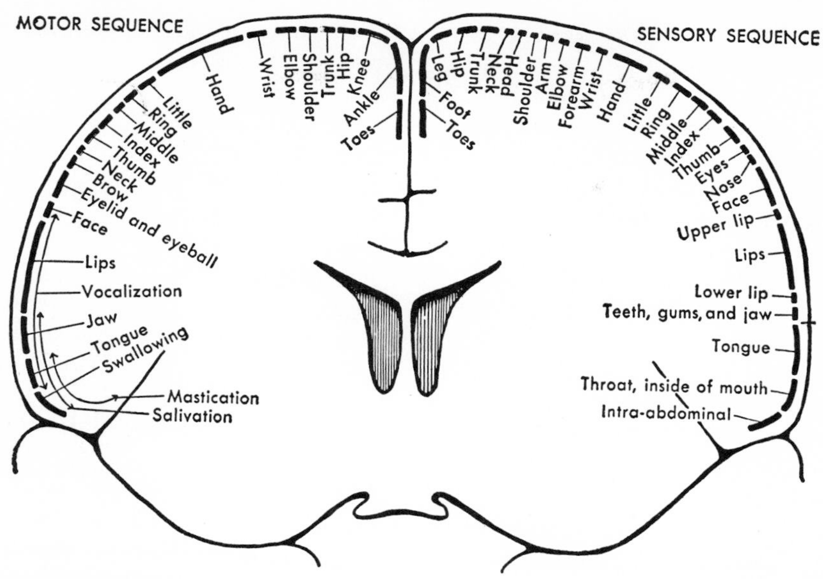

Figure 11–11. Cross section of the cerebrum through the sensorimotor region with the motor and sensory sequences indicated. The lengths of the solid bars represent an estimate of the average relative cortical areas from which the corresponding responses were elicited. (W. Penfield and T. Rasmussen, *The Cerebral Cortex of Man.* Courtesy of The Macmillan Company.)

memory to be presented. What the exact changes may be is an intriguing puzzle involving RNA synthesis.

Localization of Brain Function. As the result of numerous experiments on animals and close observation of the effects of electrical stimulation of the cerebral cortex on human individuals and clinical results of cerebral disease, physiologists have been able to localize certain areas in the brain which control motor, sensory, and other activities. Some knowledge has been gained concerning the areas in the cerebrum which are concerned with the higher mental activities. In no case, however, is the control of a function limited to a single center, for practically all mental processes involve the discharge of nervous energy from one center to another. All parts of the cerebrum interconnect. Change in the nervous activity of any part alters the excitability of the whole. Any activity, therefore, is the result of all the changes throughout the whole of the cortex. No one area acts alone to govern a particular function. As Herrick[7] says, such areas "are merely nodal points in an exceedingly complex system of neurons which must act as a whole in order to perform any function whatsoever."

Names of Areas. The portions of the cerebrum which govern muscular movement are known as *motor areas*, those controlling sensation as the *sensory areas*, and those connected with the higher faculties, such as reason and will, as *association areas.*

Motor Area. The surface of the brain involved in the function of movement is the precentral gyrus of the frontal lobe, i.e., the gray matter immediately in front of the central sulcus. The large pyramidal cells whose fibers form corticospinal pathways are located in the precentral gyrus and arranged so that motor cells for toe movement are located in the lowest area on the medial side of the cortex and motor cells for face movement are located near the lateral cerebral fissure. Figure 11–11 illustrates the spatial arrangement of both motor and sensory areas.

Sensory Area. The somatic sensory area occupies the part of the cortex behind the central sulcus and can be divided into regions like those of the motor area just in front of

[7] C. J. Herrick, *An Introduction to Neurology.*

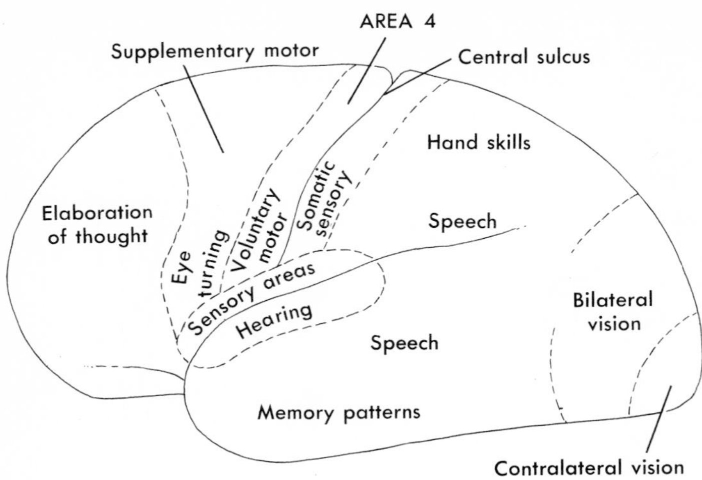

Figure 11–12. Functional areas of cerebral cortex. (Modified from Penfield and Rasmussen.)

the sulcus. The *visual area* is situated in the posterior part of the occipital lobe and the *auditory area*, in the superior part of the temporal lobe.

The area for the sense of *taste* has been located deep in the fissure of Sylvius near the island of Reil. See Figure 11–10 for *alimentary system* areas. The area concerned with interpretation of the sense of smell is located on the medial aspect of the temporal lobe (uncus).

The *motor speech* area is located in the frontal lobe, anterior to the laryngeal area in the premotor region of the motor cortex. It is known as Broca's area. The temporal speech region is believed to be concerned with choice of thoughts to be expressed, and the parietal region, with choice of words used in the expression of thoughts. In right-handed persons the area is more fully developed in the left hemisphere; and in left-handed persons, in the right hemisphere. The basis of language is a series of memory pictures. The mind must know and recall the names of things in order to mention them; it must have seen or heard things in order to describe them and to have learned the words to express these ideas. Even this is not enough. All these factors must work together under the influence of the center for articulate speech, which, as seen in Figure 11–12, is in close connection with those for the larynx, tongue, and the muscles of the face. Injury to these centers results in some form of inability to speak (aphasia), to write (agraphia), or to understand spoken words (word deafness) or written words (word blindness). It is customary, therefore, to distinguish two types of aphasia, i.e., motor and sensory. By *motor aphasia* is meant the condition of those who are unable to speak although there is no paralysis of the muscles of articulation. By *sensory aphasia* is meant the condition of those who are unable to understand written, printed, or spoken symbols of words, although the sense of vision and that of hearing

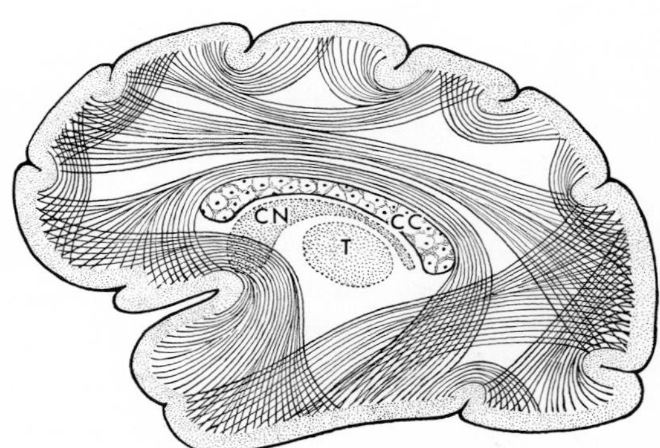

Figure 11–13. Section of brain, showing association fibers connecting the gyri and commissural fibers connecting the two sides of the brain. The commissural fibers are cut across and appear as dots. The myelin sheaths surrounding these fibers appear as white areas. (*CC*) Corpus callosum, (*CN*) caudate nucleus, (*T*) thalamus.

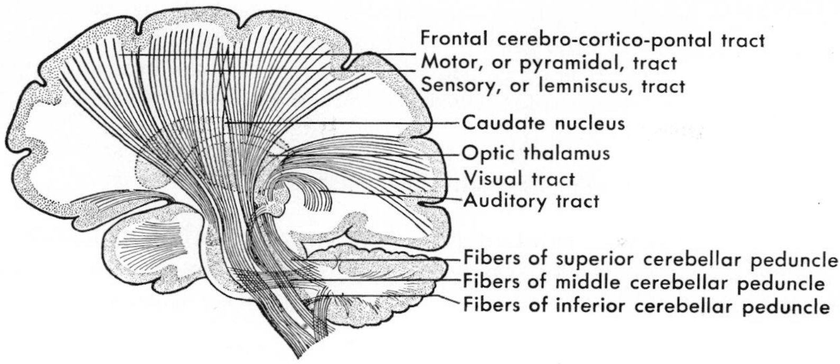

Figure 11–14. Dorsoventral section of brain, showing some of the fiber tracts from the spinal cord to the cerebral cortex. Fiber tracts to cerebellum are also shown.

are unimpaired. These centers are really memory centers, and aphasia is due to loss of memory of words, meaning of words seen or heard, or formation of letters.

Association Areas. The motor and sensory areas form, so to speak, small islands which are surrounded on all sides by cerebral tissue in which as yet no definite functions have been localized. These regions are designated as association areas and are made up of association fibers which connect motor and sensory areas. Animals that are capable of acquiring conditioned reflexes have a greater development of these areas. It is thought that the association areas are plastic and register the effects of individual experience.

After removal of the cerebrum, any animal becomes a simple reflex animal. In other words, all its actions are then removed from volition and consciousness. All responses that depend upon memory of acquired experience are lost.

The Basal Nuclei—Location and Physiology. Located deep within the cerebral hemispheres are masses of gray matter called the basal nuclei, which consist of four nuclei located near the thalamus. These are the caudate, the lentiform (made up of putamen and globus pallidus), the amygdaloid, and the claustrum. The *internal capsule* contains corticospinal, corticobulbar, and sensory fibers. The anterior limb lies between the caudate and lentiform nuclei, and the posterior limb lies between the thalamus and lentiform nuclei. (The lentiform and caudate nuclei plus that portion of the internal capsule are called the corpus striatum.) (See Figures 11–16 and 11–17 for specific locations.) Hemorrhage into the internal capsule (as is the case in cerebrovascular accident, or stroke) causes damage or destruction of fibers, most commonly the corticospinal fibers.

The basal nuclei are all interconnected with many fibers; some are connected as well to the thalamus and hypothalamus. The *functions* are not clear, but there is evidence that the basal nuclei play an important role in extrapyramidal control of motor activities.

The Caudate Nucleus and Putamen	Regulates gross intentional movements of the body that are performed *unconsciously* through pathways into the globus pallidus and thalamus to the cerebral cortex and finally downward into the spinal cord via the corticospinal and extrapyramidal spinal pathways. The motor cortex controls *conscious* specific fine movements
Globus Pallidus	Is concerned with regulation of muscle tone essential for intended, specific movements of the body. It is believed that it can also excite the cerebral cortex
The Subthalamic Nuclei	Are concerned with various rhythmical motions such as walking and running

Review hypothalamus

The Red Nucleus	Receives impulses from the dentate nucleus of the cerebellum and from the caudate nucleus and putamen. It sends fibers down into the spinal cord. It is concerned with movements of the head and upper trunk and is necessary for reflexes concerned with righting oneself in space
The Substantia Nigra	Receives many fibers from other basal nuclei. It is believed to function in controlling associative movements

The thalamus, subthalamus, substantia nigra, and red nucleus function in close association with these nuclei.

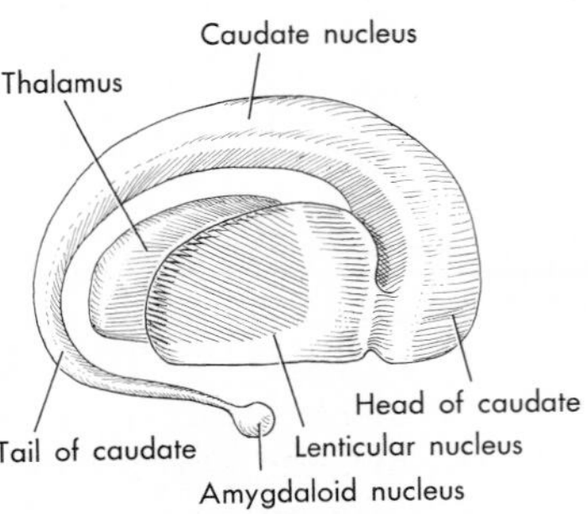

Figure 11–15. The basal nuclei.

Degenerative changes cause disturbances of motor activity, such as tremor, involuntary movement, and muscular rigidity. Rupture of blood vessels in or near the internal capsule is a frequent occurrence. Patients having suffered such a cerebral vascular accident may become hemiplegic (paralyzed on one side).

The Rhinencephalon. This comprises all portions of the cerebral hemispheres concerned with reception and integration of olfactory impulses, and regulation of motor activities in response to olfactory stimuli. The olfactory lobe, or bulb, receives fibers from the olfactory nerve. The olfactory tract distributes the fibers to the cortical olfactory areas. The hippocampus represents the cortical part of the olfactory system of most importance. There are connections with the hypothalamus that are concerned with visceral reflexes.

The Mammillary Bodies. These are two small, round nuclear masses situated below the floor of the third ventricle and behind the optic chiasma. They receive fibers from the olfactory areas of the brain and from ascending pathways, and send fibers to the thalamus and to other brain nuclei. They form relay stations for olfactory fibers and are concerned with olfactory reflexes.

The Diencephalon

The Thalamus. The thalamus is a large bilateral, oval structure located above the midbrain. It receives all sensory impulses either directly or indirectly from all parts of the body with the exception of olfactory sensations. It also receives impulses from the cerebellum, cerebral cortex, and many nuclei. The thalamus contains many nuclei concerned with specific functions. The medial and lateral geniculate bodies known as the metathalamus are parts of the thalamus which relay auditory and visual reflexes.

Some of the impulses received by the thalamus are associated, and some are simply relayed to specific areas of the cerebral cortex. In this way it is evident that the thalamus functions as a sensory integrating center of great physiological importance. Bodily well-being or malaise is believed to be interpreted by the thalamus rather than by the cortex. Appreciation of part of temperature, crude touch, and pain is possible even though the sensory cortex is destroyed. Through connections with the hypothalamus influence is exerted on both visceral and somatic activities.

The Hypothalamus. The hypothalamus lies below the thalamus and forms part of the lateral walls and floor of the third ventricle. It is a control center for visceral activities by means of (1) neural connections with the posterior pituitary gland, the thalamus, and the midbrain, and (2) the blood supply to the pituitary gland, through which various "releasing factors" synthesized in the hypothalamus reach the pituitary and regulate hormonal secretion.

Functions of the hypothalamus will be referred to in detail in appropriate areas of

THE THALAMIC NUCLEI CONNECTIONS

Impulses from	
Touch receptors Pressure receptors Joint receptors Temperature receptors Pain receptors	Are received by cells in the posteroventral nucleus of the thalamus. With the possible exception of the pain impulse, these impulses are relayed to the postcentral gyrus in parietal lobe cortex for interpretation
Olfactory sensations	Are relayed to the thalamus via the mammillary bodies to the cortex
Taste fibers	Are finally projected to the thalamus from the geniculate ganglion and are relayed to the postcentral cortex close to the face area
Auditory fibers	Are projected from the cochlear nuclei and inferior colliculi to the thalamus and from there relayed to the temporal cortex
Visual fibers	Are projected to the lateral geniculate bodies of the thalamus and from there relayed to the calcarine cortex

the text; however, they may be summarized here:

1. AUTONOMIC NERVOUS CONTROL. The main subcortical control center for regulation of parasympathetic and sympathetic activities is the hypothalamus. In general the anterior and medial portions are related to the parasympathetic system; the posterior and lateral portions regulate the sympathetic system.

2. CARDIOVASCULAR REGULATION. Stimulation of the posterior hypothalamus causes a rise in blood pressure and an increase in heart rate. Stimulation of the preoptic area has the opposite effect. These effects are produced via impulses to the cardiovascular centers of the medulla.

3. TEMPERATURE REGULATION. The temperature of the blood flowing through the preoptic and anterior hypothalamic areas causes heat loss through vasodilation in the skin, sweating, and increased respiration if the temperature is above normal (37° C, 98.6° F). If the blood temperature is below normal, there are constriction of skin blood vessels, cessation of sweating, increased activity of the adrenal medulla, and perhaps shivering. Thus the external temperature of air has little effect on the cells and tissue fluid of the body.

4. FOOD INTAKE. Two centers in the hypothalamus regulate the amount of food ingested. The "feeding center" in the lateral hypothalamus is presumably stimulated by hunger sensations and the overall need for food (such as accompanies starvation) since electrical stimulation of this area causes eating of whatever food is available to the animal (appetizing or not). The "satiety center" in the medial hypothalamus is stimulated when the animal has taken in enough food. Electrical stimulation of the satiety center inhibits the feeding center, and the animal abruptly stops eating. Destruction of this nucleus, on the other hand, produces animals who eat until they are too obese to move. They always "feel hungry" because there is no satiety center to inhibit the feeding center.

5. WATER BALANCE. Cells in the supraoptic and paraventricular nuclei respond to the osmotic pressure of the blood—the "osmoreceptors." When there is an increase in the osmotic pressure due to water lack, the antidiuretic hormone (ADH) is secreted, reaching the posterior pituitary by traveling along the nerve fiber from this area to the gland. The action of ADH when secreted in the blood stream is to cause the tubular cells of the kidney to conserve water, thus permitting the blood to become less concentrated. A "thirst" area is found near the

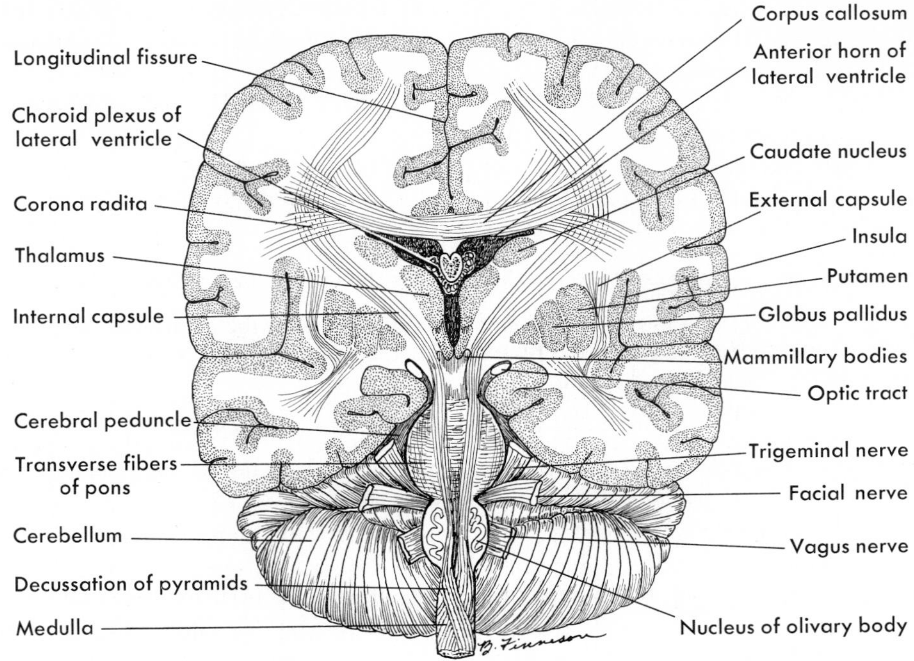

Figure 11–16. Section of brain to show basal nuclei, internal capsule, pons, and medulla.

satiety center which, when stimulated, causes the animal to seek water. In the normal individual the thirst area is stimulated when the osmolality of blood is elevated.

6. Gastrointestinal Activity. The dorsomedial nucleus causes increased peristalsis and secretion from intestinal glands, when stimulated.

7. Sleeping-Waking Activity. The upper portion of the reticular activating system lies in the central lower hypothalamus. This activity will be discussed below.

8. Emotions. Experimental stimulation of inferior lateral portion of the hypothalamus in animals results in extreme excitation with symptoms of rage, such as hissing and arching of the back in cats and elevated blood pressure and cardiac rate. This evidence together with the knowledge that in man many of the "symptoms" of various emotions

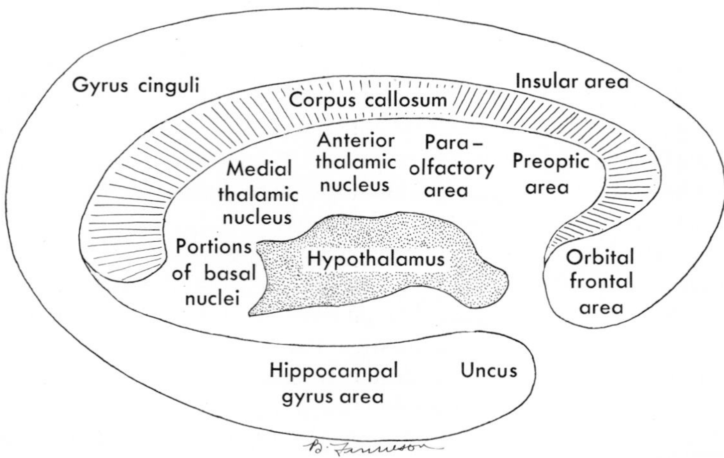

Figure 11–17. Diagrammatic representation of the limbic system.

are those controlled by the autonomic nervous system indicate that the hypothalamus may be a center for emotional responses.

The Limbic System. The hypothalamus is the central structure in this system, which includes the cortex of the preoptic area, that on the medial ventral surfaces of the frontal lobes in front of, and curving up and caudally over, the corpus callosum, and laterally to the hippocampal gyrus on the medial surfaces of the temporal lobes. Subcortical areas beneath this cortex and close to and surrounding the hypothalamus are included. The connections thus afforded, particularly with the thalamus, are thought to control the various behavioral and emotional responses. "Pleasure" centers as well as "punishment" centers have been identified in animals by means of localized electrical stimulation. Continual stimulation of a "pleasure" center, for example, will cause the animal to suffer great pain in order to achieve continual electrical stimulation of such a center.

The Reticular Formation. The reticular formation is composed of large and small nerve cells and an intricate system of interlacing fibers which run in all directions. It begins in the upper part of the spinal cord and extends upward where it terminates in the diencephalon. The reticular cells receive collaterals from all the great ascending pathways and nuclei. Efferent impulses are sent to both higher and lower brain centers. The reticular area is believed to be essential for control of cortical activities such as initiation and maintenance of alert wakefulness, hence has been called the activating system. It exerts some sort of a regulatory action on the brain and cord by either excitation or inhibition of certain activities, such as spinal cord reflexes, or voluntary movements. Muscle tone and smooth, coordinated muscle activity are dependent upon this system. Its function is not to relay a specific impulse or message but simply to arouse the brain for action. Any stimulus reaching the reticular formation alerts the cortex to a state of wakefulness so that, when a specific stimulus reaches a specific cortical center, it may be identified and action may result, as, for example, being wakened by a loud noise or other unusual

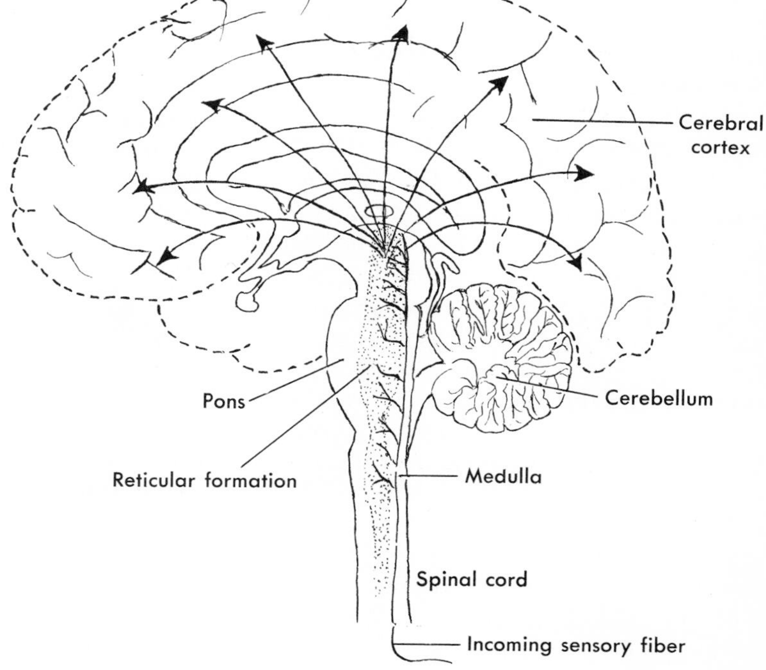

Figure 11–18. Section of brain showing the reticular formation. It is composed of interlacing fibers and nerve cells which form the central core of the brain stem. Incoming fibers from the spinal tracts send collaterals into the reticular formation. *Arrows* indicate the general arousal of higher brain centers which the reticular area controls.

environmental condition. Impulses through the reticular system can be blocked by hypnotic drugs; thus, emotional response to environmental stress is reduced. Injury or disease to the system results in permanent unconsciousness.

THE MIDBRAIN

The midbrain (mesencephalon) is a short, constricted portion which connects the pons and cerebellum with the hemispheres of the cerebrum. It is directed upward and forward and consists of (1) a pair of cylindrical bodies called the cerebral *peduncles*, which are made up largely of the descending and ascending fiber tracts from the cerebrum above, the cerebellum, medulla, and spinal cord below; (2) four rounded eminences, called the *corpora quadrigemina* (Figure 11–3, page 204), which contain important correlation centers and also nuclei concerned with motor coordination (the superior colliculi for optic reflexes, the inferior for auditory reflexes); and (3) an intervening passage or tunnel, the cerebral aqueduct (aqueduct of Sylvius), which serves as a communication between the third and fourth ventricles.

The Brain Stem. The pons, the medulla, and the midbrain containing the cerebral and cerebellar peduncles, corpora quadrigemina, red nucleus, etc., are frequently called the brain stem. (See Figure 11–3, page 204.)

THE HINDBRAIN (RHOMBENCEPHALON)

The Cerebellum and Its Functions. The cerebellum occupies the lower and posterior part of the skull cavity. It is below the posterior portion of the cerebrum, from which it is separated by the *tentorium cerebelli*, a fold of the dura mater, and behind the pons and the upper part of the medulla. It is oval, constricted in the center, and flattened from above downward. The constricted central portion is called the *vermis*, and the lateral expanded portions are called the *hemispheres*.

The surface of the cerebellum consists of gray matter and is not convoluted but is traversed by numerous furrows, or sulci. The gray matter contains cells from which fibers pass to form synapses in other areas of the brain and cells with which fibers entering the cerebellum from other parts of the brain synapse. The cerebellum is connected with the cerebrum by the *superior peduncles*, with the pons by the *middle peduncles*, and with the medulla oblongata by the *inferior peduncles* (Figure 11–14). These peduncles are bundles of fibers. Impulses from the motor centers in the cerebrum, from the semicircular canals of the inner ear, and from the muscles enter the cerebellum by way of these bundles. Outgoing impulses are transmitted to the motor centers in the cerebrum, down the cord, and thence to the muscles.

The cerebellum receives tactile, kinesthetic, auditory, visual, cortical, and pontine impulses. It sends nerve impulses into all the motor centers innervating the body wall and helps to maintain posture and equilibrium and the tone of the voluntary muscles. It modifies the stretch reflexes. Movements elicited by spinal reflexes are also modified. The *dentate nucleus* is large and receives most of the fibers from Purkinje cells and relays the impulses to the thalamus. From there impulses are sent on to the frontal motor cortex.

There are other smaller nuclei that relay impulses to the reticular formation of the midbrain and to the red nucleus. None of the activities of the cerebellum comes into consciousness. In man, injury to the cerebellum results in muscular weakness, loss of tone, and inability to accurately control the movements of the skeletal muscles. There may be difficulty in walking due to poor coordination of the muscles of the legs or difficulty in talking due to lack of coordination of the muscles moving the tongue and jaw. The area of the body affected is determined by the location and extent of the injury to the cerebellum. Only parts of the body on the same side as the injury to the cerebellum are involved; if both sides of the cerebellum are injured, the lack of muscle tone and coordination may be so great that the person is helpless.

The Pons. The pons is situated in the front of the cerebellum between the midbrain and the medulla oblongata. It consists of interlaced transverse and longitudinal white

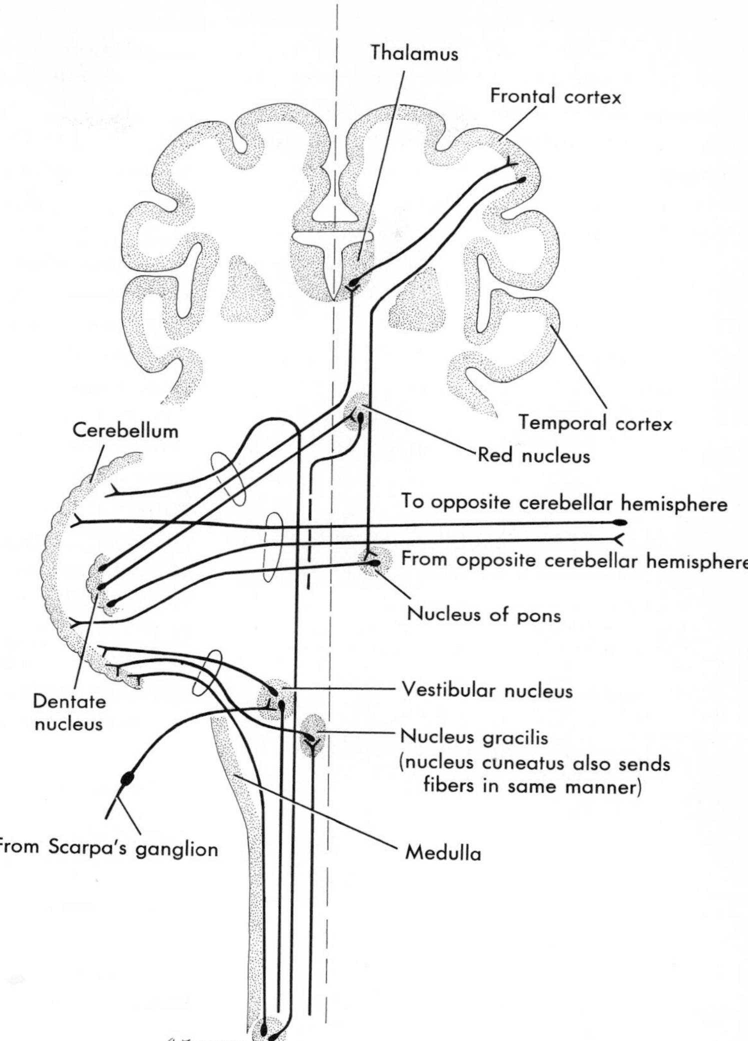

Figure 11–19. Connections of cerebellum with spinal cord and cerebrum.

fibers intermixed with gray matter. The transverse fibers are those derived from the middle peduncles of the cerebellum and serve to join its two halves. The longitudinal fibers connect the medulla with the cerebrum. In it also are the nuclei of all or a part of the fibers of the fifth, sixth, seventh, and eighth cranial nerves.

Function. The pons is a bridge of union between the two halves of the cerebellum and a bridge between the medulla and the midbrain. The fifth (trigeminal) nerve emerges from the side of the pons near its upper border. The sixth (abducens), seventh (facial), and eighth (vestibulocochlear) nerves emerge in the superficial furrow which separates the pons from the medulla (Figure 11–20). (There is a pneumotaxic center in the pons that participates in the regulation of respiration.)

The Medulla Oblongata. The medulla oblongata (spinal bulb) is continuous with the spinal cord, which, on passing into the cranial cavity through the foramen magnum, widens into a pyramid-shaped mass which extends to the lower margin of the pons. Externally, the medulla resembles the upper part of the spinal cord, but the internal structure is different. All the afferent and efferent tracts of the spinal cord are represented in the medulla, and many of them decussate, or cross, from one side to the other, whereas others terminate in the medulla. The nerve cells of the medulla are grouped to form *nuclei*, some of which are centers in which the cranial nerves arise. The motor fibers of the glossopharyngeal and of the vagus nerves, also the cranial portion of the accessory nerves, arise in the *nucleus ambiguus*. The hypoglossal nerve arises in the *hypoglossal nucleus*. Some of the nuclei are relay stations of sensory tracts to the brain, e.g., the *nucleus gracilis* and *nucleus cuneatus*. Some serve as centers for the control of bodily functions, e.g., the *cardiac*, *vasoconstrictor*, and *respiratory centers*.

Function. The medulla serves as an organ of conduction for the passage of impulses between the cord and the brain. It contains (1) the cardiac, (2) the vasoconstrictor, and (3) the respiratory centers and controls many reflex activities.

THE CARDIAC INHIBITORY CENTER. This consists of a bilateral group of cells lying in the medulla at the level of the nucleus of the *vagus nerve*. The vagal fibers from this center go to the heart and unite with the cardiac branches from the thoracolumbar nerves to form the *cardiac plexus* (Figure 16–15, page 332), which envelops the arch and ascending portion of the aorta. From the cardiac plexus the heart receives these *inhibitory fibers*. This center constantly discharges impulses which tend to hold the heart to a slower rate than it would assume if this check did not exist. The activity of the heart is also influenced by impulses from the *cardiac sympathetic nerves*, which increase the rate of the heartbeat and are called accelerator nerves. The inhibitory and accelerator fibers are true antagonists, having opposing effects on the heart.

THE VASOCONSTRICTOR CENTER. This consists of a bilateral group of cells in the medulla. Fibers from these cells descend in the cord and at various levels form synapses with autonomic spinal neurons in the lateral columns of gray matter. These spinal neurons are preganglionic vasoconstrictor fibers which terminate on postganglionic neurons in the sympathetic ganglion. The postganglionic neurons innervate the smooth muscle of the arteriole walls. The center is in a constant state of activity which is increased or decreased reflexly by excitatory or inhibitory impulses from peripheral somatic and visceral receptors. One must conceive of different cells in this center being connected by definite vasoconstrictor paths with different parts of the body, e.g., the intestines or the skin. Cells which, when stimulated, cause peripheral vasoconstriction and a rise of arterial pressure are called the *pressor center*. Cells which cause an opposite effect, i.e., a decrease in peripheral vasoconstriction and a fall in arterial pressure, are called the *depressor center*.

THE RESPIRATORY CENTER. This consists of a bilateral group of cells located in the medulla. The center is automatic, possessing an inherently rhythmical activity. However, it is very responsive to impulses from sensory fibers of most cranial and spinal nerves and from regions of the brain. The effect of sensory nerves on activity of the respiratory center is to alter the rate and depth of respiration. Sensory fibers which alter the activity of the cardiac and vasoconstrictor centers may also affect the respiratory center, as do alterations of oxygen and carbon dioxide tensions of the blood.

In addition to the control of respiration and circulation, many other reflex activities are effected through the medulla by means of the vagus and other cranial nerves, which originate in this region. Such reflex activities are sneezing, coughing, vomiting, winking, and the movements and secretions of the alimentary canal.

THE CRANIAL NERVES—THEIR STRUCTURE, LOCATION, AND FUNCTION

Twelve pairs of cranial nerves emerge from the undersurface of the brain and pass through the foramina in the base of the cranium. They are classified as motor, sensory, and mixed nerves (Figure 11–20).

The origin of the cranial nerves is comparable to that of the spinal nerves. The motor fibers of the spinal nerves arise from cell bodies in the ventral columns of the cord, and the sensory fibers arise from cell bodies in the ganglia outside the cord. The motor cranial nerves arise from cell bodies within the brain, which constitute their *nuclei of origin*. The sensory cranial nerves arise from groups of nerve cells outside the brain. These cells may form ganglia on the trunks of the nerves, or they may be located in peripheral sensory organs, such as the nose and eyes. The central processes of the sensory nerves run into the brain and end by arborizing on nerve cells which form their *nuclei of termination*. The nuclei of origin of the motor nerves and the nuclei of termination of the sensory nerves are connected with the cerebral cortex.

Numbers and Names. The cranial nerves are named according to the order in which they arise from the brain, and also by names which describe their nature, function, or distribution.

I.	Olfactory	Sensory
II.	Optic	Sensory
III.	Oculomotor	Motor
IV.	Trochlear	Motor
V.	Trigeminal	Mixed
VI.	Abducens	Motor
VII.	Facial	Mixed
VIII.	Vestibulocochlear	Sensory
IX.	Glossopharyngeal	Mixed
X.	Vagus	Mixed
XI.	Accessory	Motor
XII.	Hypoglossal	Motor

The following chart indicates the functions and principal connections in the brain. Figure 11–21, *A* and *B*, shows the brainstem nuclei of nerves III through XII. Nerves I and II are in reality tracts, rather than true nerves, since the primary receptor neuron terminates in a ganglion near the specialized receptors, the olfactory bulb in the case of nerve I, and the retina in the case of nerve II.

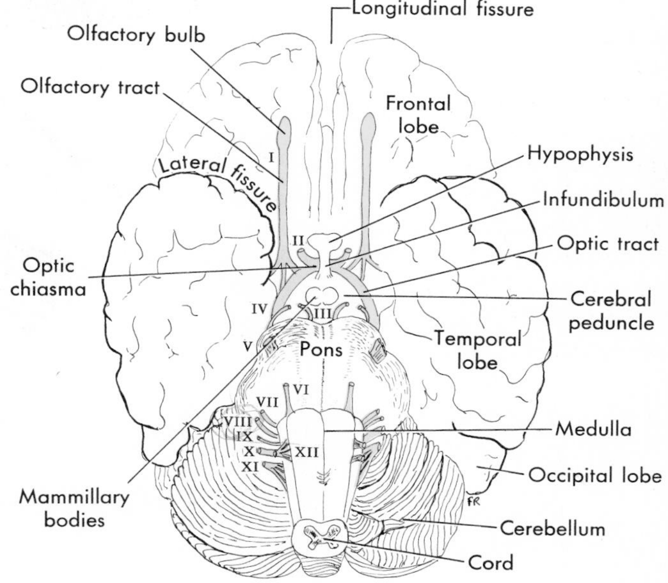

Figure 11–20. Undersurface of brain showing cerebrum, cerebellum, the pons, and medulla; note the infundibulum to which the pituitary, or hypophysis, is attached. The numerals indicate the cranial nerves. Note the olfactory bulb and tract, mammillary bodies, and the optic chiasma.

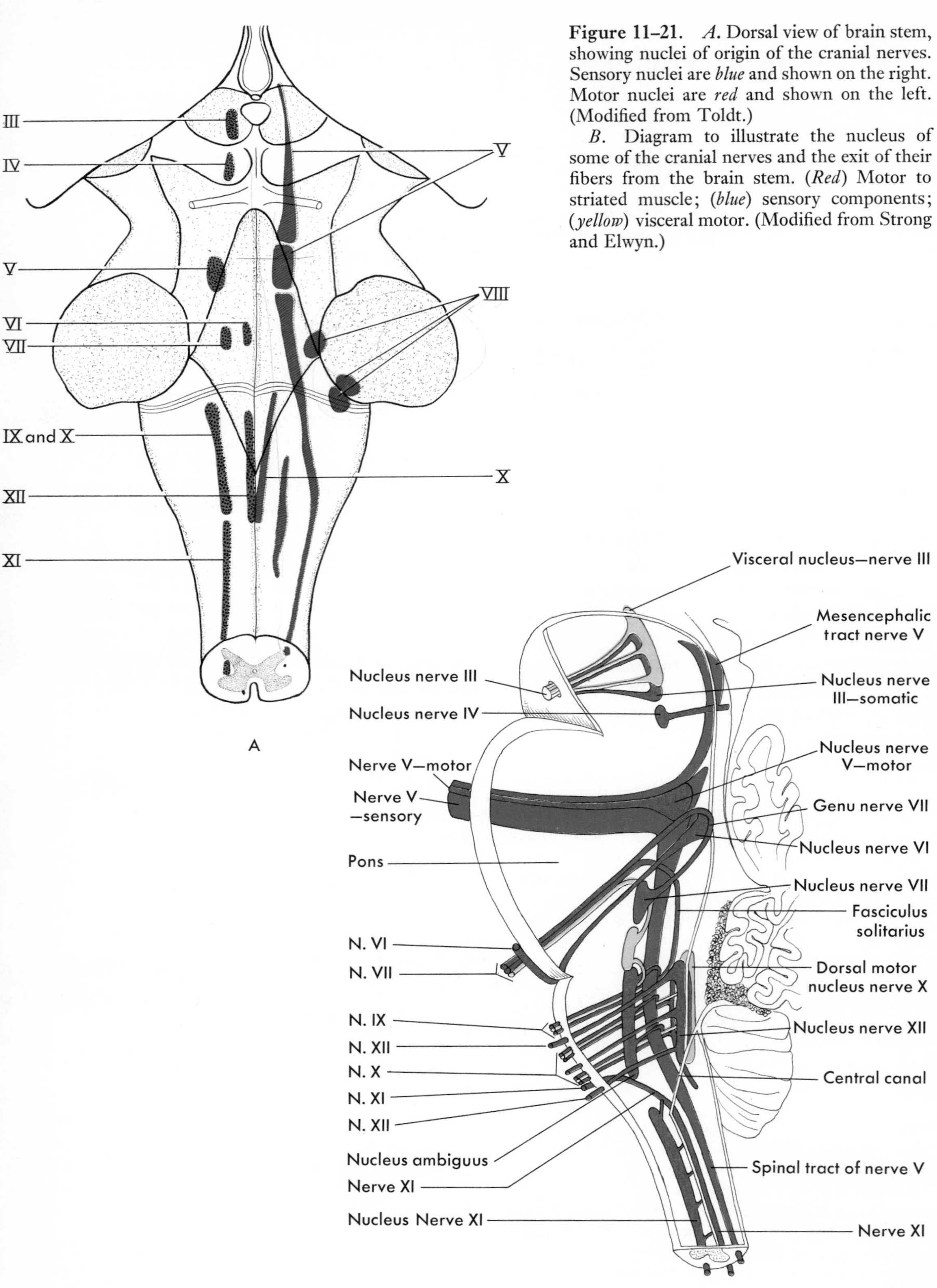

Figure 11–21. *A.* Dorsal view of brain stem, showing nuclei of origin of the cranial nerves. Sensory nuclei are *blue* and shown on the right. Motor nuclei are *red* and shown on the left. (Modified from Toldt.)

B. Diagram to illustrate the nucleus of some of the cranial nerves and the exit of their fibers from the brain stem. (*Red*) Motor to striated muscle; (*blue*) sensory components; (*yellow*) visceral motor. (Modified from Strong and Elwyn.)

CRANIAL NERVES

No.	Name	Sensory (S) Motor (M)	Function	Central Connections
I	Olfactory	S	Smell: from receptors in nasal mucosa, via olfactory bulb to olfactory cortex (hippocampus)	Mammillary bodies, thalamus, nuclei of cranial nerves for reflexes of swallowing, secretion, and motility of digestive tract
II	Optic	S	Vision: from receptors in retina to lateral geniculate body of thalamus	From thalamus to cortex; nuclei of nerves III, IV, VI for visual reflexes and to spinal cord tracts for body reflexes, e.g., turning head from light
III	Oculomotor	M	Movement of eyeball up, down, and inward Raising the lid Constriction of pupil	Nuclei of nerves III, IV, VI have reflex connection with their nuclei of the opposite side of brain stem, with each other for visual reflexes; from the cochlear nuclei for reflexes related to sound; from the vestibular nuclei for correlating sight with balance and equilibrium; from the cortex for voluntary eye movement
		(s)*	Kinesthetic sensation from muscles innervated	
IV	Trochlear	M	Movement of eyeball up and out	Reflex connections as for nerve III
		(s)	Kinesthetic sensation from muscle innervated	
V	Trigeminal 3 branches:		Sensation from all 3 branches enters the semilunar ganglion and nucleus	To thalamus, then postcentral gyrus of cortex Reflex connections of trigeminal sensory and motor nuclei with each other, those of opposite side, and those of nerves VII, IX From cortex for voluntary movement of muscles
	1. Ophthalmic	S	Sensations of pain, touch, temperature from conjunctiva, skin of nose, upper lid, for head, nasal mucosa	
	2. Maxillary	S	Sensations of pain, touch, temperature from cheek, upper lip, nasal mucosa, hard palate, upper jaw and teeth, maxillary sinuses Kinesthetic sensation from muscles of mastication	
		M	Contraction of muscles of mastication	
	3. Mandibular	S	Sensations of pain, temperature, touch from lower jaw, teeth and lips, mouth, anterior tongue, external ear, and meatus Kinesthetic sensation from muscles innervated	
VI	Abducens	M	Movement of eyeball laterally	Reflex connections as with nerve III
		(s)	Kinesthesia of muscle innervated	

* Indicates presence of a few fibers, central connections unknown.

Cranial Nerves

No.	Name	Sensory (S) Motor (M)	Function	Central Connection
VII	Facial	M	Contraction of superficial face and scalp muscles and of stapedius muscle of middle ear Secretion of glands of mucous membrane of nose and mouth; of submaxillary, sublingual, and lacrimal glands	Reflex connections between motor and sensory nuclei of nerve VII, from opposite sides; with extrapyramidal and tectospinal tracts to spinal nerves; with nuclei of nerve V
		S	Taste from anterior two thirds of tongue: from taste buds to nucleus solitarius in medulla Kinesthesia from muscles innervated	From nucleus to thalamus and postcentral gyrus
VIII	Vestibulocochlear (2 *separate* parts)			
	Cochlear	S	Hearing: from receptors in cochlea of inner ear to medial geniculate body of thalamus	From thalamus to auditory cortex in temporal lobe Reflex connections between nuclei of nerves III, IV, VI; with tectospinal tract to spinal nerves, for reflexes to sound
	Vestibular	S	Position sense and equilibrium: from receptors in semicircular canals of inner ear to vestibular nucleus	From vestibular nucleus to cerebellum, then to cortex Reflex connections with opposite side, with vestibulospinal tract for postural reflexes; with nuclei of nerves III, IV, VI for reflex eye movement
IX	Glossopharyngeal	M	Tongue movement, swallowing	Reflex connections between sensory and motor nuclei of nerve IX on both sides, with nuclei of nerve X, with extrapyramidal and tectospinal tracts for gag and swallowing reflexes
		S	General sensation from pharynx, soft palate, posterior tongue, eustachian tube, and tympanic membrane	
			Taste from posterior third of tongue: from taste buds to nucleus solitarius	From nucleus to thalamus and postcentral gyrus of cortex
			Chemoreceptor sensation of blood levels of O_2, CO_2, pH in carotid body; from these receptors to nucleus solitarius	Reflex connections with cardiac center of medulla, with sympathetic centers for blood pressure regulation, with respiratory center for adjusting rate and depth of breathing

No. Name	Sensory (S) Motor (M)	Function	Central Connection
X Vagus	M	Swallowing: contraction of muscles of soft palate, pharynx Speaking: contraction of intrinsic muscles of larynx Constriction of bronchi: contraction of smooth muscle of thorax Increased peristalsis: contraction of smooth muscle of abdominal viscera Decreased rate of cardiac muscle contraction Secretion of glands of stomach and intestines	Reflex connections with extrapyramidal and tectospinal tracts, with thalamus and nuclei of nerves V, VII, IX Reflex connections between motor and sensory nuclei of vagus nerve
	S	Pain, touch, temperature sensation from auditory meatus, meninges; general sensation from pharynx, larynx, trachea, esophagus; sensations of nausea, abdominal distention, lung stretch	From sensory nucleus to thalamus and postcentral gyrus
XI Accessory	M	Speaking: contraction of intrinsic muscles of larynx Shoulder and head movement: contraction of trapezius and sternocleidomastoid muscles	Reflex connections with corticospinal tract for voluntary movement; with tectospinal and vestibulospinal tracts for postural reflexes
XII Hypoglossal	M	Speaking, mastication, swallowing: contraction of tongue muscles	Reflex connections with cortex, extrapyramidal and tectospinal tracts; with sensory nuclei of nerves V, IX, X

The central connections of the optic nerve are shown in Figure 11–22. The optic fibers from each retina pass backward through the optic foramen; and shortly after leaving the orbit, the two nerves come together, and the fibers from the nasal portions of the retinas cross. This is called the *optic chiasma* and is incomplete crossing of fibers because the fibers from the temporal retinas do not cross.

The optic nerve is formed by fibers of the ganglionic layer of the retina. They pass backward, forming the optic nerve, and synapse in the *lateral geniculate body*. Cell bodies in the geniculate body form the optic radiation and terminate in the visual cortex of the occipital lobe. This means that there are two cells in the optic pathway. A branch of the optic nerve fibers passes to the superior colliculi. Cell bodies in the superior colliculi send collateral fibers to the nuclei of the oculomotor, trochlear, and abducens nucleus. The main fiber bundle from the superior colliculus descends into the upper part of the spinal cord (tectospinal tract) and terminates on the large motor cells of the ventral gray column.

The *vestibular center*, at the junction of the medulla and pons, shown in Figure 11–23, is

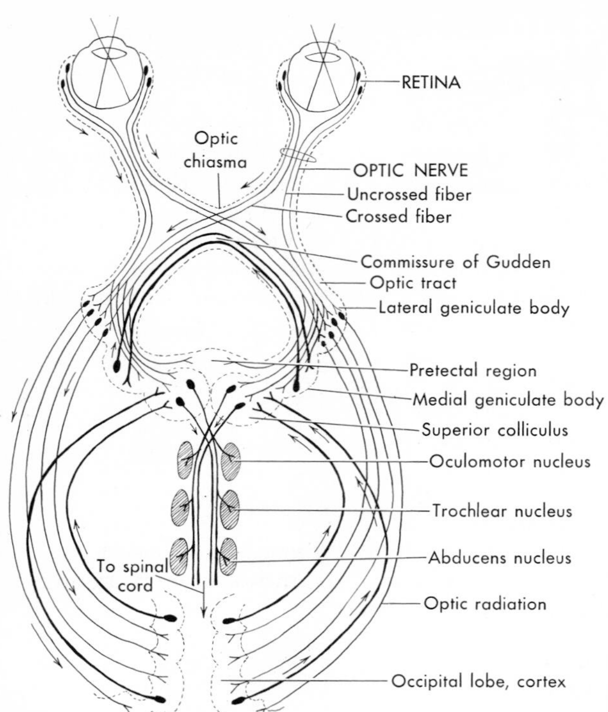

Figure 11–22. Diagram of visual pathway. Note the arrows as they indicate the direction in which impulses travel, and connections between nuclei.

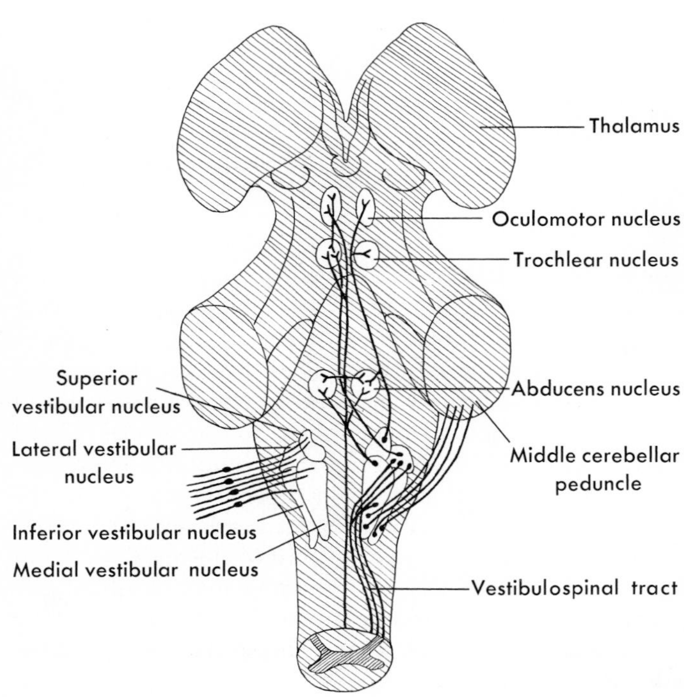

Figure 11–23. Diagram showing interconnections between the vestibular nuclei and extrinsic eye muscle nuclei.

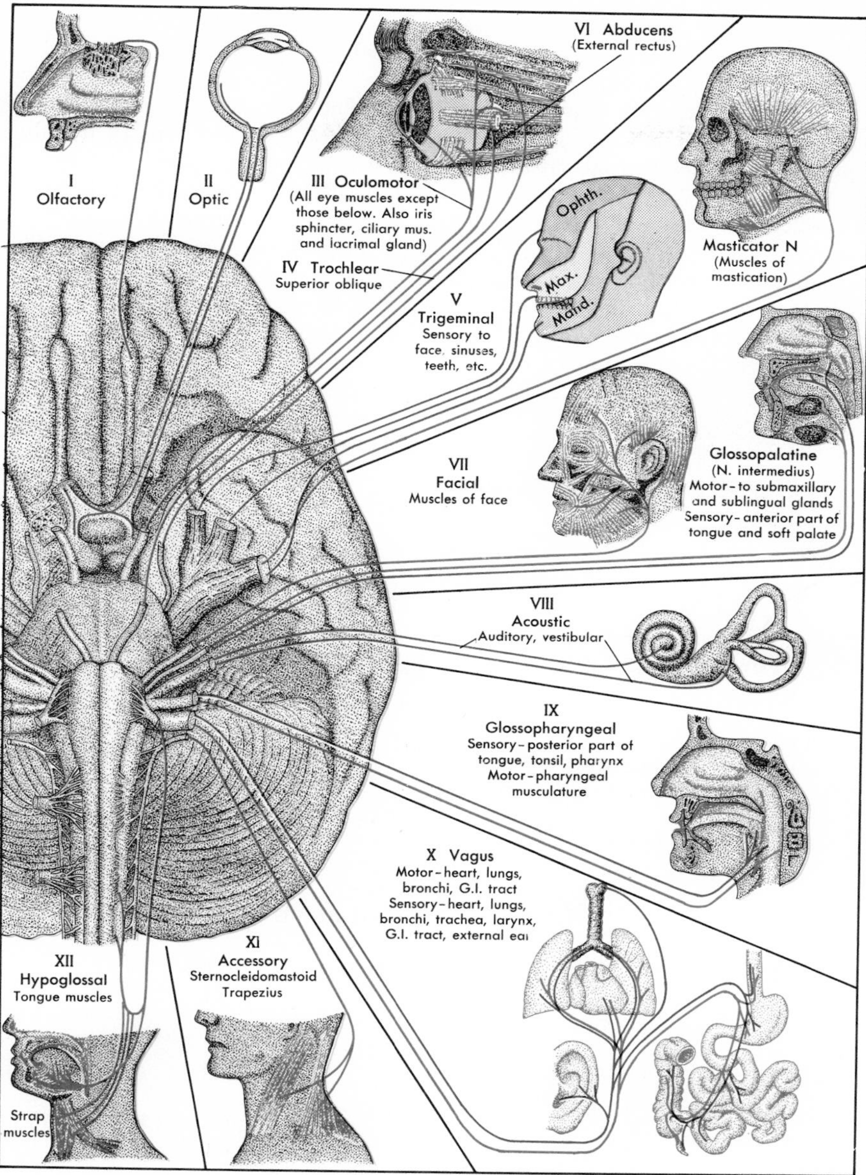

Figure 11–24. Diagram showing base of brain, the emergence of the cranial nerves, their distribution to the structures, and the functions with which they are concerned. (*Blue*) sensory; (*red*) motor. (Reproduced from full-color illustration in *Ciba Collection of Medical Illustrations*, Vol. 1, "Nervous System." Courtesy of Ciba Pharmaceutical Products, Inc., Summit, N.J.)

the site of termination of most of the vestibular fibers in the vestibular nerve. Some pass without synapsing to the portion of the cerebellum lying closest to the medulla. Fibers ending in the vestibular nuclei synapse with second-order neurons which send fibers to the same area of the cerebellum, to other areas of the brain stem, as well as to the vestibulospinal tract and to the centers for control of extraocular eye muscles. Thus eye movement is coordinated reflexly with movement of the body.

QUESTIONS FOR DISCUSSION

1. An individual has had a cerebrovascular accident that involves the lenticular artery and causes pressure on the internal capsule on the right side.
   a. Where will there be loss of motor function? Explain.
   b. What additional problems and/or symptoms would be present if the accident had involved the left side of the brain?
2. Name and discuss five functions of the hypothalamus.
3. Which part of the brain receives practically all the incoming sensory impulses? Explain what happens to these impulses.
4. Explain the arousal mechanism of the brain.
5. What part of the brain contains the nuclei for the following cranial nerves? What are their functions?
   a. Oculomotor
   b. Vagus
   c. Facial

SUMMARY

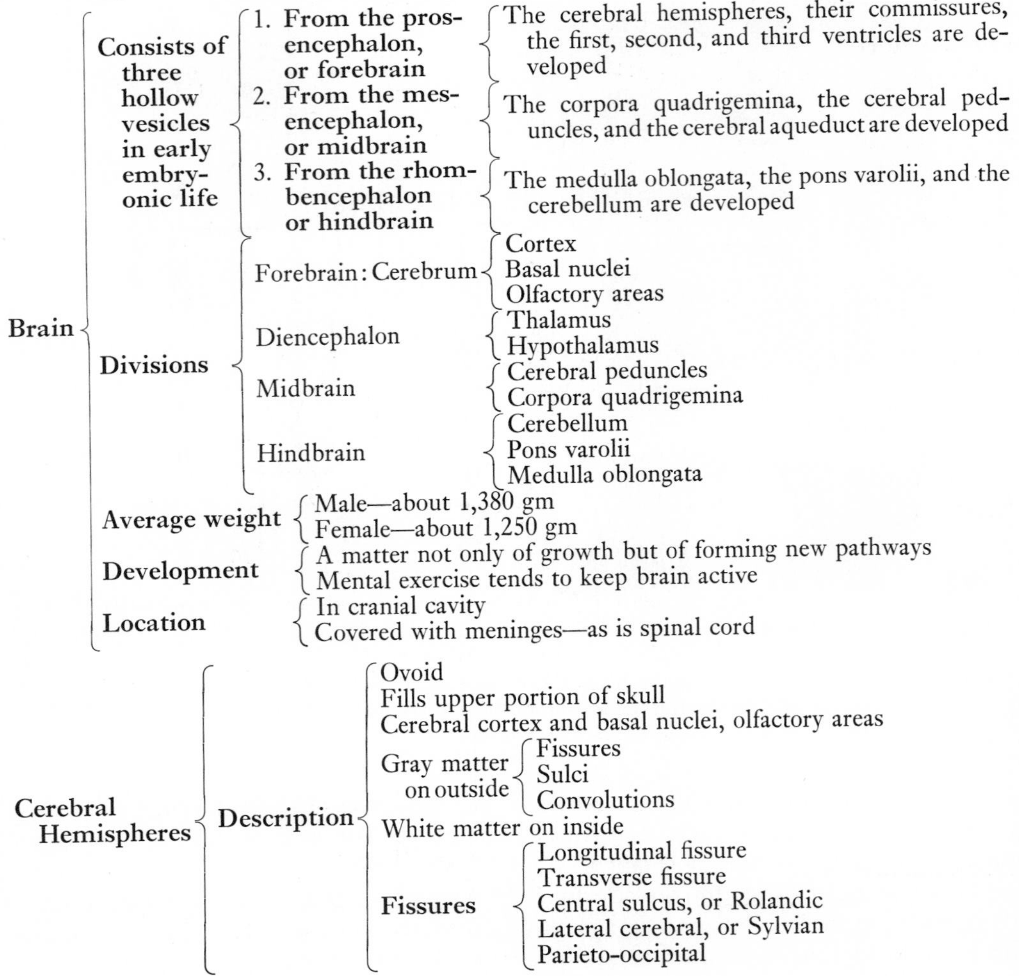

- **Brain**
  - **Consists of three hollow vesicles in early embryonic life**
    1. **From the prosencephalon, or forebrain** — The cerebral hemispheres, their commissures, the first, second, and third ventricles are developed
    2. **From the mesencephalon, or midbrain** — The corpora quadrigemina, the cerebral peduncles, and the cerebral aqueduct are developed
    3. **From the rhombencephalon or hindbrain** — The medulla oblongata, the pons varolii, and the cerebellum are developed
  - **Divisions**
    - Forebrain: Cerebrum — Cortex; Basal nuclei; Olfactory areas
    - Diencephalon — Thalamus; Hypothalamus
    - Midbrain — Cerebral peduncles; Corpora quadrigemina
    - Hindbrain — Cerebellum; Pons varolii; Medulla oblongata
  - **Average weight** — Male—about 1,380 gm; Female—about 1,250 gm
  - **Development** — A matter not only of growth but of forming new pathways; Mental exercise tends to keep brain active
  - **Location** — In cranial cavity; Covered with meninges—as is spinal cord
- **Cerebral Hemispheres**
  - **Description**
    - Ovoid
    - Fills upper portion of skull
    - Cerebral cortex and basal nuclei, olfactory areas
    - Gray matter on outside — Fissures; Sulci; Convolutions
    - White matter on inside
    - **Fissures** — Longitudinal fissure; Transverse fissure; Central sulcus, or Rolandic; Lateral cerebral, or Sylvian; Parieto-occipital

- **Cerebral Hemispheres** (*cont.*)
  - **Description** (*cont.*)
    - **Lobes**
      - Frontal
      - Parietal
      - Occipital
      - Temporal
      - Insula, or island of Reil
    - **Ventricles**
      - Lateral ventricles (two)
      - Third ventricle
      - Fourth ventricle
      - Fifth ventricle—not a true ventricle

- **Meninges, or Membranes, of Brain and Cord**
  - **Cranial dura mater**—arranged in two layers. Outer layer adherent to bones of skull; inner layer covers the brain
  - **Spinal dura mater**—consists of only the inner layer, forms a loose sheath around the cord
  - **Arachnoid mater**—serous membrane placed between the dura mater and pia mater of both brain and cord
  - **Cranial pia mater**—vascular membrane, invests brain and dips down into crevices and depressions, forms choroid plexuses
  - **Spinal pia mater**—is closely adherent to cord and sends a process into the anterior fissure

- **Cerebrospinal Fluid**
  - Found in subarachnoid space and ventricles of the brain
  - Formed by choroid plexuses of the ventricles from blood
  - Clear, limpid fluid, specific gravity 1.004 to 1.008
  - Quantity variable, 80–200 ml
  - Contains traces of protein, glucose, salts, lymphocytes, and pituitary hormones
  - **Function**
    - Nutritive medium for nerve cells
    - Acts as a shock absorber

- **Blood Supply**
  - Arterial—basilar and internal carotid arteries
  - Venous—superior, inferior, transverse sinuses draining into internal jugular veins

- **Cerebrum**
  - **Functions**
    - Governs all mental activities
      - Sleep—necessary for recovery of neurons
      - Organ of associative memory
      - Reason
      - Intelligence
      - Will
      - Seat of consciousness
      - Interpreter of sensations
      - Instigator of voluntary acts
      - Exerts a controlling force on reflex acts
  - **Names of**
    - **Motor area**—in front of central sulcus
    - **Sensory areas**
      - Behind the central sulcus
      - Visual—occipital lobe
      - Auditory—superior part of the temporal lobe
      - Olfactory, Gustatory—anterior part of temporal lobe
    - **Association areas**—cerebral tissue surrounding motor and sensory areas, in which as yet no definite functions have been localized

- **Diencephalon**
  - **Description**
    - Basal nuclei
    - Connects cerebral hemispheres with midbrain, and forms walls of third ventricle
  - **Functions**
    - Auditory and visual reflexes
    - Sensory integration
    - Regulation of autonomic nervous system, water balance, sleep-waking, body temperature, food intake, and cardiovascular activity

- **Diencephalon** (*cont.*)
  - **Areas**
    - Thalamus
    - Hypothalamus
    - Metathalamus
    - Epithalamus
    - Limbic system
- **Reticular Formation**
  - **Description**
    - Network of interlacing cells and fibers
    - Extends from upper spinal cord to diencephalon
  - **Function**
    - Alerts cortex to wakefulness
    - Sends efferent impulses to higher and lower centers
- **Midbrain**
  - **Description**
    - Short, constricted portion connects pons and cerebellum with the hemispheres of the cerebrum
    - Consists of
      - Pair of cerebral peduncles
      - The corpora quadrigemina
      - The cerebral aqueduct
    - Contains nuclei of the III and IV cranial nerves
- **Cerebellum**
  - **Description**
    - Oval, constricted in center
    - Central portion called vermis
    - Lateral portions called hemispheres
    - Gray matter on exterior
    - White matter in interior
    - Connected with cerebrum by superior peduncles
    - Connected with pons by middle peduncles
    - Connected with medulla by inferior peduncles
  - **Function**
    - Participates in the coordination and integration of posture and all voluntary movements
- **Pons**
  - **Description**
    - Situated between the midbrain and the medulla oblongata. Consists of interlaced transverse and longitudinal white fibers mixed with gray matter
  - **Function**
    - Connects two halves of cerebellum and also medulla with cerebrum
    - Contains nuclei of trigeminal, abducens, facial, and vestibulocochlear nerves
    - Participates in the regulation of respiration
- **Medulla Oblongata**
  - **Description**
    - Pyramid-shaped mass, upward continuation of cord. Sensory and motor tracts or spinal cord represented. Many of them cross from one side to the other in the medulla; some end in medulla
    - Gray matter forms nuclei
    - Nuclei serve as
      - Centers in which cranial nerves arise, centers for control of bodily functions
      - Relay stations of sensory tracts to brain
  - **Function**
    - Vital centers
      - Cardiac center
      - Vasoconstrictor center
      - Respiratory center
    - Controls such reflex activities as
      - Sneezing
      - Coughing
      - Vomiting
      - Winking
      - Movement and secretion of digestive tract

CHAPTER

12

SENSATION

Tactile Sense — *Pain* — *Hearing*
Kinesthesia — *Taste* — *Equilibrium*
Temperature — *Smell* — *Vision*

STRUCTURAL COMPONENTS

It is through the sense organs that man derives information about the world in which he lives and his relationship to it. Our receptors are insensitive to many forms of energy and their limitations restrict our knowledge. However, man has devised methods for converting some forms of physical energy into dimensions that fall within the sensitivities of the sense organs. Thus, knowledge of the microscopic forms of life depends upon the extension of sight by means of magnifying lenses.

All sensory impulses, except olfaction, feed into the thalamus. From the thalamus the impulses may go (1) to specific cortical areas to provide primary sensations, (2) to diffuse cortical areas to permit integration of sensory and motor activities, and (3) to hypothalamic regions to provoke appropriate autonomic responses. Hence, sensory impulses not only produce conscious sensation but also evoke visceral responses in the form of altered heart rate, modified digestive processes, blushing, and many other visceral changes.

Sensations are the conscious results of processes which take place within the brain in consequence of nervous impulses derived from receptors. Many sensations are not followed by motor reactions but are stored as memory concepts and may be called into play at any time. Because the distribution of receptors varies from one area of the body to another, the sensitiveness of different regions varies. The distal parts of the arms and legs are better endowed with receptors than are the proximal limbs and the trunk.

Sensations are interpreted in the brain, but recognized as occurring in the periphery. The projection of sensations to the part that is stimulated tends to obscure the role of the brain. In reality individuals see and hear in the brain, and the eye and ear serve only as end organs responding to the stimulus. All sensory impulses except olfactory are relayed through the thalamus before reaching the cortex. Through facilitation and inhibition at this relay in the thalamus, impulses to the cortex tend to be directed, or "focused," and the individual may give attention to some sensory inputs more than to others. For example, when concentrating on studying, one does not hear distracting sounds. Multiple afferent inputs from different sense organs tend to diminish one's awareness of any particular one. This characteristic permits distraction from pain, for example, by conversation or active movement.

Classification. One classification of sensation is based on the part of the body to which the sensation is projected—*external* and *internal* sensations. External sensations are sight, hearing, taste, smell, touch, pressure, and temperature. The internal are pain, position sense, vestibular sensations, hunger, thirst, and other less well-defined sensations from the viscera.

The sensations of taste, smell, hearing, balance, and vision are termed *special senses* since their receptors are structurally more specialized and occur in specific locations, rather than generally throughout the body as are touch and temperature receptors.

Somatic sensations may be classified as *epicritic* and *protopathic*. Epicritic sensations are highly critical and discriminatory ones, such as differentiating between two points placed close together on the skin, vibratory and touch sensation, and differentiating between temperature differences. Protopathic sensations are less specific, poorly localized, and of a marked affective nature. They include crude touch, pain, temperature sensations aroused by extremes of temperature, and visceral sensations.

Another classification is *exteroceptive*: sensations from the body surface; *proprioceptive*: kinesthesia, equilibrium, pressure relating to body position; *deep* sensation: from bone, fasciae, etc.; and *visceral* sensations arising from internal organs.

TACTILE SENSATION

At least four kinds of receptors—free nerve endings, Meissner's corpuscles, pacinian corpuscles, and nerve fibers at the base of each hair—give rise to touch sensations. The hair nerve ending is stimulated by change of position of the hair, producing a brief burst of impulses followed by rapid adaptation. Meissner's and pacinian corpuscles are also rapidly adapting. These can sense a quick touch or deformation of tissue, but not a sustained touch. Free nerve endings slowly adapt to continuous stimulation, as we all know from experience with particles "in the eye," which we continue to feel until they are removed. Although the cornea of the eye has only free nerve endings, it gives rise to all qualities of sensation.

Pressure sensations differ from touch sensations in that they are more enduring. We can discriminate between a light pressure of a finger on the arm and a hard pressure. Free nerve endings in the superficial and deep layers of skin and other tissue are receptors of pressure, as well as the pacinian corpuscles.

KINESTHESIA, OR POSITION SENSE

Kinesthesia is the recognition of location and rate of movement of the parts of the body in relation to other parts. Ruffini's end organ as well as the Golgi endings in joint capsules and ligaments around joints give rise to position sense. Some of these receptors respond to flexion of the joint, others to extension. Thus we are conscious of the degree and direction to which the elbow is flexed or extended. The receptors which are stimulated by joint movement signal rate, as well as direction and extent of movement.

Degree of muscle stretch and tension are detected by special muscle receptors. However, these sensory impulses are transmitted to the cerebellum rather than to the cortex; so they produce no conscious sensation.

TEMPERATURE

Degrees of temperature from 12° to 50° C are perceived and discriminated by humans. Some regions of the body, such as the fingertips and face, have morphologically specific structures which are attuned to particular temperature ranges. Krause end bulbs discharge at all steady-state skin temperatures between 12° and 35° C and paradoxically at 50° C. These receptors also discharge whenever the skin is rapidly cooled from any tem-

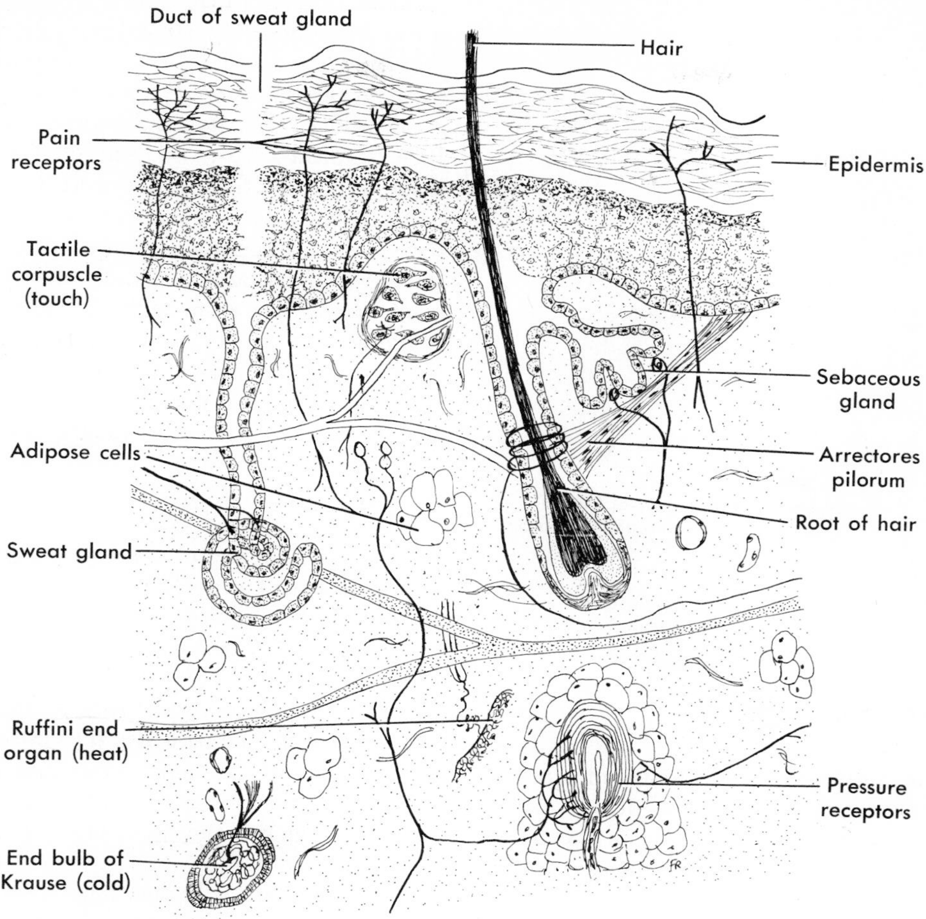

Figure 12–1. Diagram of skin showing receptors for pain, pressure, touch, heat, and cold.

perature. Most receptors are paralyzed or inactivated by cold if maintained for any length of time at 12° C or less. Warm receptors, the Ruffini end organs, are found at greater skin depths, are more sparse, and have lower discharge frequencies than cold receptors. They discharge at skin temperatures between 25° and 45° C and increase their firing rate whenever the skin is warmed. In skin regions lacking morphologically specific receptors, temperature sensation is less acute and is subserved by free nerve endings. Hot and burning sensations result from the combined sensory inputs from cold, warm, and free nerve endings.

These receptors respond strongly to *change* in temperature. Because of this, and owing to adaptation, one feels colder in a cooling environment than one would at the same temperature if it were steady. Total adaptation does not occur so that it is possible to feel cold and warmth, even though the intensity is less than on initial exposure.

PAIN

Pain perception is a protective mechanism which occurs whenever tissue is damaged. Receptors for pain are the free nerve endings which are found in the skin, muscles, joints,

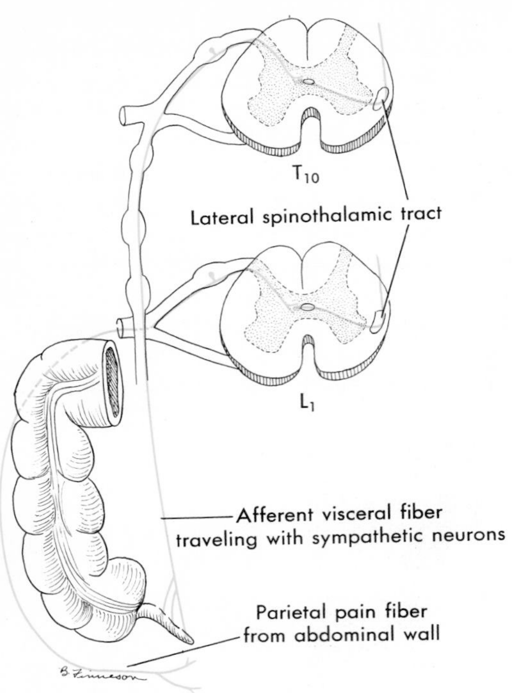

Figure 12–2. Neural pathway for visceral pain.

tendons, dura mater, periosteum, and arterial walls. Other stimuli for pain include excessive heat or cold and blocking of the blood flow to a tissue. Spasm of muscle of the digestive tract, or distention of the intestine, common bile duct, and ureter, all cause pain—probably by interfering with the blood supply as the tissue is stretched or squeezed, and ischemia results.

Impulses for pain are transmitted to the thalamus by way of the lateral spinothalamic tract. Awareness of pain takes place in the thalamus, but localization and recognition of the kind and intensity of pain take place in the postcentral convolution of the cerebral cortex. Pain impulses are also relayed to other thalamic nuclei and to the hypothalamus.

All individuals have about the same threshold for pain, but the reaction to pain varies widely between individuals, depending upon such factors as ethnocultural background, childhood experiences, and emotional status. Because of its emotional overlay, pain is very different from other sensations.

Pain may be described as sharp, dull, boring, piercing, pricking, aching, throbbing, stabbing, burning, constant, and intermittent. Aching pain is usually a deep pain with varying degrees of intensity and may be either diffuse or localized. Burning pain results from diffuse stimulation of all pain receptors in an area, e.g., burns or other types of tissue injury. As the intensity of the pain stimulus increases and more nerve fibers are involved, the intensity of the pain also increases. Deep pain is frequently associated with nausea and a fall in blood pressure, whereas superficial pain will quicken the pulse and raise blood pressure.

Headache is usually due to external causes rather than causes inside the head. Tension of muscles at the back of the head, straining eye muscles to focus for long periods, or inflammation of the sinuses will result in aching of the head in the related areas. Pain from within

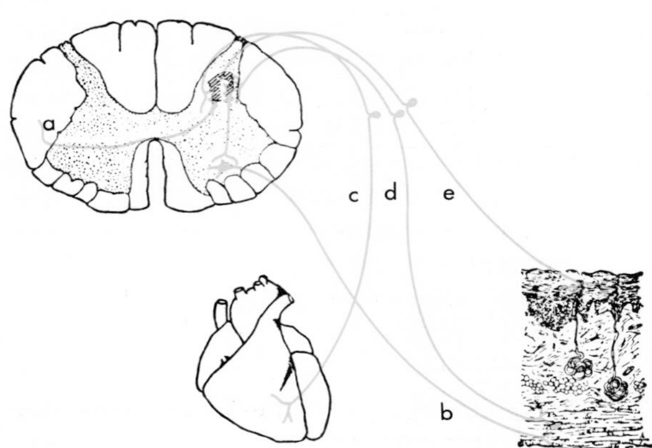

Figure 12–3. Diagram to show a possible neural path for referred pain of cardiac origin. Nerve impulses (*c*) from disturbed heart bring about an "irritable area" in gray matter of cord. Nerve fibers from skin and muscle (*d* and *e*) enter this same region. Nerve fibers from this region carry impulses over path *a* to the spinothalamic tract and the cerebral cortex and over path *b* to the chest muscles, which contract in an exaggerated manner.

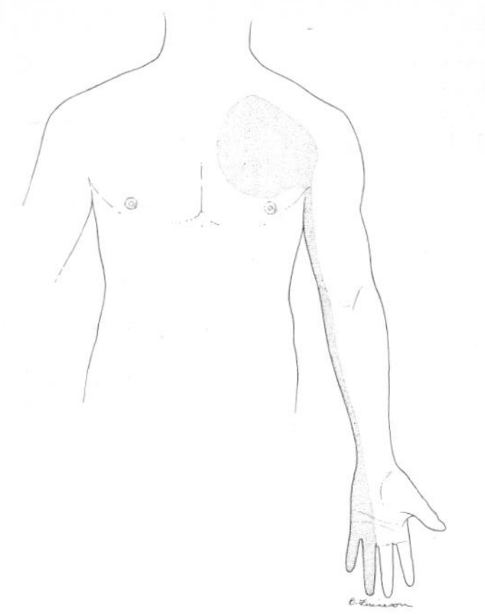

Figure 12–4. Referred pain. Pain from cardiac region is referred to the left side of the chest and down the inside of the left arm.

the head occurs when the meninges are stretched, as with increased spinal fluid pressure, or loss of spinal fluid, and when blood vessels are dilated. The latter is thought to be the cause of migraine headaches.

Referred Pain. In some instances visceral pain is not localized specifically in the organ but is felt on the surface of the body. Pain of this kind is spoken of as *referred pain.* It has been shown that the different visceral organs have a more or less definite relation to certain areas of the skin. Pain arising from stimuli in the intestines is located in the skin of the back, loins, and abdomen, in the area supplied by the ninth, tenth, and eleventh thoracic nerves. Pain from irritation in the stomach is located in the skin over the ensiform cartilage, that from the heart in the scapular region. An explanation for referred pain is that the pain is referred to the skin region that is supplied from the spinal segment from which the organ in question receives its sensory fibers. The misreference results from excitation of a secondary neuron in the spinal cord which also normally is excited by neurons that supply that particular skin area. Examples of referred pain are: in appendicitis, the abdominal pains are often remote from the usual position of the appendix; in some pneumonia cases, abdominal pain is the prominent symptom; in angina pectoris, the pain radiates to the left shoulder and down the left arm (Figures 12–3 and 12–4). In this instance pain fibers from the heart are carried in the first, second, and third thoracic roots along with afferent fibers from the chest wall and arm.

HUNGER

The feeling that is commonly designated as hunger occurs normally at a certain time before meals and is usually projected to the region of the stomach. It is presumably due to contractions of the empty stomach, which stimulate the receptors distributed to the mucous membrane. If food is not taken, hunger increases in intensity for a time and is likely to cause fatigue and headache. Professional fasters state that after a few days the pangs of hunger diminish and sometimes disappear. In illness hunger contractions may not occur at all, even when the food taken is not sufficient. Probably this results from a lack of muscular tone in the stomach. On the other hand, hunger contractions may be frequent and severe even if an abundance of food is taken regularly, as in diabetes, or following a period of starvation.

Appetite. Appetite is similar to hunger but is less related to physiological activity, such as stomach contractions. The desire for a specific food is related to appetite, whereas when one is hungry, any one of a variety of foods may satisfy. Cultural and social factors influence one's appetite so that certain foods satisfying and desirable to natives of the United States may be repulsive to natives of Africa.

Food intake is regulated by the hypothalamus (see page 215), and many centers in the brain stem and spinal cord are involved in the actual process of eating, e.g., salivation, chewing, swallowing.

THIRST

This sensation may be defined as a conscious desire for water, which is to be distinguished from the desire to moisten the mouth and tongue. Thirst, as mentioned in the previous chapter, arises from the body's need for water, when tissues are dehydrated, and when the blood osmolality is increased. The "thirst" center in the hypothalamus, in conjunction with the osmoreceptors in the nearby area which secrete a hormone to cause kidney conservation of water, thus aids in the maintenance of total body water.

NAUSEA

This sensation may be due to stimulation of receptors in the stomach or to impulses coming from other receptors of the body, e.g., the organs of sight, taste, and smell.

TASTE

The adequate stimulus for taste receptors is a substance in solution. In the case of dry substances saliva serves as the solvent. It is also necessary that the surface of the organs of taste be moist. The substances that excite the special sensation of *taste* act by producing a permeability change in the taste buds, and this change initiates the nerve impulses.

Taste Buds. Taste buds are ovoid bodies with an external layer of supporting cells, and contain in the interior a number of elongated cells, which end in hairlike processes that project through the central taste pore. These cells are the sense cells, and the hairlike processes probably are the parts stimulated by the dissolved substances. The taste buds are found chiefly in the surface of the tongue, though some are scattered over the soft palate, fauces, and epiglottis.

The Tongue. The tongue is a freely movable muscular organ consisting of two distinct halves united in the center. The root of the tongue is directed backward and is attached to the hyoid bone by several muscles. It is connected with the epiglottis by three folds of mucous membrane, and with the soft palate by means of the glossopalatine arches.

Papillae of the Tongue. The tongue is covered with mucous membrane, and the upper surface is studded with papillae. The papillae are projections of connective tissue covered with stratified squamous epithelium and contain loops of capillaries, among which nerve fibers are distributed. The papillae give the tongue its characteristic rough appearance. There are four varieties of these papillae:

Vallate (circumvallate) papillae are the

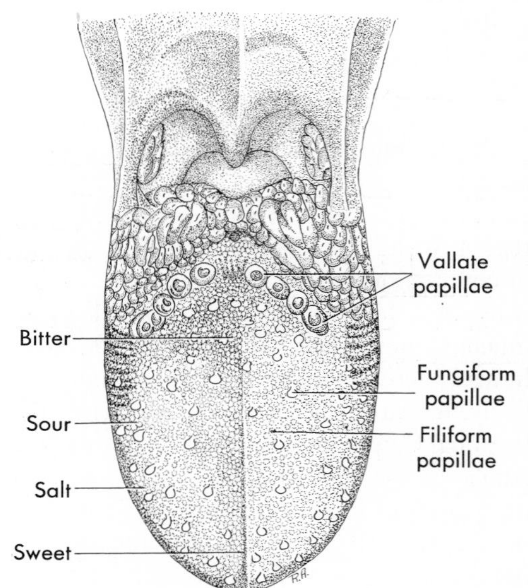

Figure 12–5. The upper surface of the tongue, showing kinds of papillae and areas for taste.

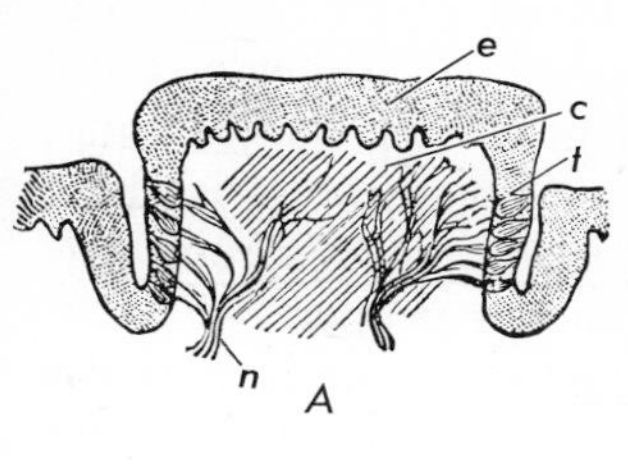

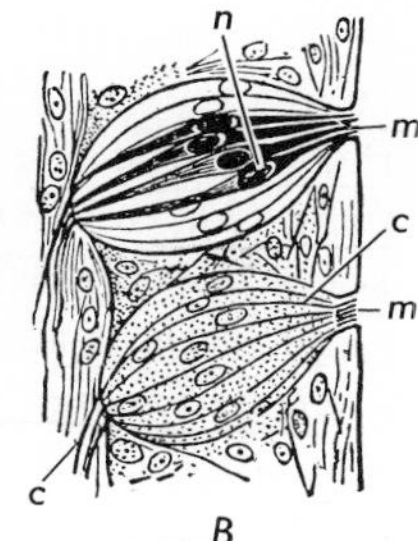

Figure 12–6. (*A*) A vallate papilla cut lengthwise, (*c*) corium, (*e*) epidermis, (*n*) nerve fibers, (*t*) taste buds. (*B*) The two taste buds at *t* more highly magnified, the lower as seen from the outside showing (*c*) the outer or supporting cells; the upper as seen in section showing (*n*) four inner cells with processes (*m*) projecting at the mouth of the bud.

largest, are circular, and form a V-shaped row near the root of the tongue. They contain *taste buds*.

Fungiform papillae, so named because they resemble fungi in shape, are found principally on the tip and sides of the tongue.

Filiform papillae cover the anterior two thirds of the tongue and bear delicate brushlike processes which seem to be specially connected with the sense of touch.

Simple papillae similar to those of the skin cover the larger papillae and the whole of the mucous membrane of the dorsum of the tongue. All papillae contain taste buds.

The sense of touch is very highly developed in the tongue, as are the senses of temperature and pain. Tactile and muscular feedback depends on these to a great extent, i.e., the accuracy of the tongue in many of its important uses—speech, mastication, deglutition, sucking.

Classes of Taste. Taste sensations are very numerous, but four fundamental, or primary, sensations are recognized, namely, salty, bitter, acid, and sweet. Quantitative appreciation of taste is not great. All other taste sensations are combinations of these or combinations of one or more of them with sensations of odor or with sensations derived from stimulation of other receptors in the tongue. The seemingly great variety of taste sensations is due to the fact that they are confused or combined with simultaneous odor sensations. Thus the flavors in fruits are designated as tastes because they are experienced at the time these objects are eaten. If the nasal cavities are closed, as by holding the nose, the so-called taste often disappears in large measure. Very disagreeable tastes are usually due to unpleasant odor sensations, hence the practice of holding the nose when swallowing a nauseous dose. On the other hand, some volatile substances which enter the mouth through the nostrils and stimulate the taste buds are interpreted as odors. The odor of chloroform is largely due to stimulation of the sweet taste buds of the tongue.

Taste on the posterior third of the tongue is mediated by the glossopharyngeal nerve. Taste on the anterior two thirds of the tongue is mediated by the facial nerve. The vagus nerve mediates taste sensations from around the epiglottis. These fibers convey taste impulses to the medulla and pons where they terminate on cell bodies of the secondary fibers. These secondary fibers cross in the medulla and then ascend to the thalamus. Tertiary neurons project to the primary receiving area of the sensory cortex, on the parietal lobe near the sylvian fissure.

SMELL

The sensory endings for the sense of smell are located in the olfactory membrane over the surface of the superior nasal conchae and the upper part of the septum. These sensory nerve endings are the least specialized of the special senses.

The Olfactory Nerves. The olfactory sensory endings are modified epithelial cells scattered freely among the columnar epithelium of the mucous membrane. These sensory cells are called *olfactory cells*, and the other epithelial cells, supporting cells.

Olfactory cells are bipolar, and slender, peripheral, hairlike processes known as olfactory hairs extend beyond the surface of the epithelial membrane. The central or deep

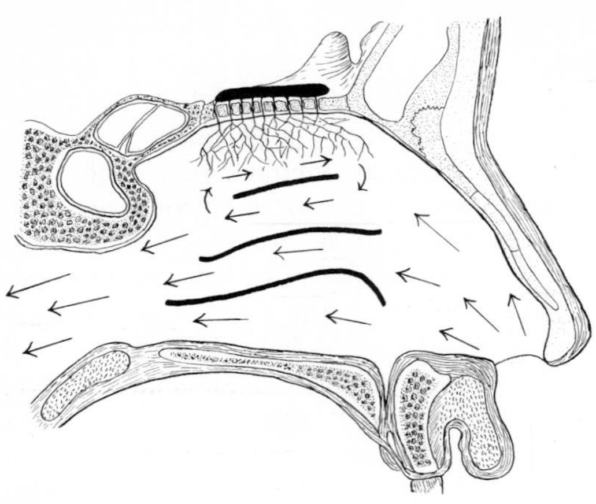

Figure 12–7. Diagram of lateral wall of left nasal cavity. The three black lines represent the region of the inferior, middle, and superior conchae. *Arrows* indicate the direction of air flow. The olfactory lobe is shown with nerve fibers extending through orifices in the cribriform plate of the ethmoid bone. Olfactory nerve fibers are distributed in the mucosa above the superior conchae, the cell bodies lying in the nasal mucosa.

process passes through the basement membrane and joins adjacent processes to form bundles of unmyelinated fibers of the *olfactory nerve.* These bundles of nerves form a plexus in the submucosa and eventually form about 20 or more nerves which pierce the cribriform plate of the ethmoid bone and end in a mass of gray matter called the olfactory bulb. In the olfactory bulb these fibers form synapses with the dendrites of the mitral cells. Impulses from the mitral cells are conducted to their various terminations in the olfactory lobe, of either the same or the opposite side.

The cells of the bulb lie in synaptic relation to cells whose processes form the olfactory tract and finally terminate in the gray of the cortex in the parolfactory area and hippocampal gyrus of the temporal lobe. Some of the fibers terminate in other nuclei of the brain, and through various synaptic connections reach the thalamus.

The nerve fibers which ramify over the lower part of the lining membrane of the nasal cavity are branches of the fifth, or trigeminal, nerve. These fibers furnish the tactile sense and enable one to perceive, by the nose, the sensations of cold, heat, tickling, pain, and tension, or pressure. It is these nerve fibers which are excited by strong irritants, such as ammonia or pepper.

Odoriferous substances emit particles which usually are in gaseous form. In order to stimulate, these particles must penetrate into the upper part of the nasal chamber. In the olfactory area the cells are always bathed in fluid from *special glands*, so that the diffusing particles dissolve. The fluid acts chemically upon the sensitive hairs of the olfactory cells, initiating impulses which travel to the olfactory lobe and give rise to the sensation of smell. Few odors are detected in the dry, hot desert.

To smell anything particularly well, air is sniffed into the higher nasal chambers, thus bringing the odoriferous particles in greater numbers into contact with the olfactory hairs. Odors can also reach the nose by way of the mouth.

Each substance smelled causes its own particular sensation, and one is able not only to recognize a multitude of distinct odors but also to distinguish individual odors in a mixed odor. These odors are difficult to classify, i.e., it is not possible to pick out what might be called the fundamental odor sensations.

The sensation of smell develops quickly after the contact of the odoriferous stimulus and may last a long time. When the stimulus is repeated, the sensation very soon dies out, and the end organs of the sensory cells quickly become adapted. This accounts for the fact that one may easily become accustomed to unpleasant odors, an advantage when these odors have to be endured. On the other hand, it emphasizes the importance of acting on the first sensation of a disagreeable odor, so as not to become accustomed to it.

The olfactory center in the uncus and the hippocampus of the brain is widely connected with other areas of the cerebrum. Olfactory memories may be vivid. The sense of smell is widely and closely connected with the other senses and with many psychical activities.

HEARING

The auditory apparatus consists of the external ear; the middle ear, or tympanic cavity; the internal ear, or labyrinth; and the acoustic nerve and acoustic center.

The External Ear. This consists of an expanded portion, named the pinna or auricula, and the external acoustic meatus, or auditory canal.

The Pinna. The pinna projects from the side of the head. It consists of a framework of cartilage, containing some adipose tissue and muscles; in the lobe, the cartilage is replaced by soft connective tissues. The pinna is covered with skin and joined to the surrounding parts by ligaments and muscles. It is very irregular in shape. The pinna serves to some extent to collect sound waves and direct them toward the external acoustic meatus.

The External Acoustic Meatus (External Auditory Canal). This is a tubular passage, about 2.5 cm in length, which leads from the concha to the tympanic membrane. It forms an S-shaped curve and is directed inward, forward, and upward, then inward and backward. Lifting the pinna upward and backward tends to straighten the canal, but in children it is best straightened by drawing the pinna downward and backward. The external portion of this canal consists of cartilage, which is continuous with that of the pinna; the internal portion is hollowed out of the temporal bone. It is lined by a prolongation of the skin, which in the outer half of the canal is very thick and not at all sensitive, and in the inner half is thin and highly sensitive. Near the orifice the skin is furnished with a few hairs and farther inward with modified sweat glands, and the ceruminous glands, which secrete the yellow, pasty cerumen, or earwax. The hairs and the cerumen protect the ear from the entrance of foreign substances.

The *tympanic membrane* (membrana tympani) separates the auditory canal from the tympanic cavity. It consists of a thin layer of fibrous tissue covered externally with skin and internally with mucous membrane. It is ovoid and extends obliquely downward and inward and forms an angle with the floor of the meatus. It is chiefly innervated by a branch of the mandibular nerve (branch of fifth, the trigeminal, nerve).

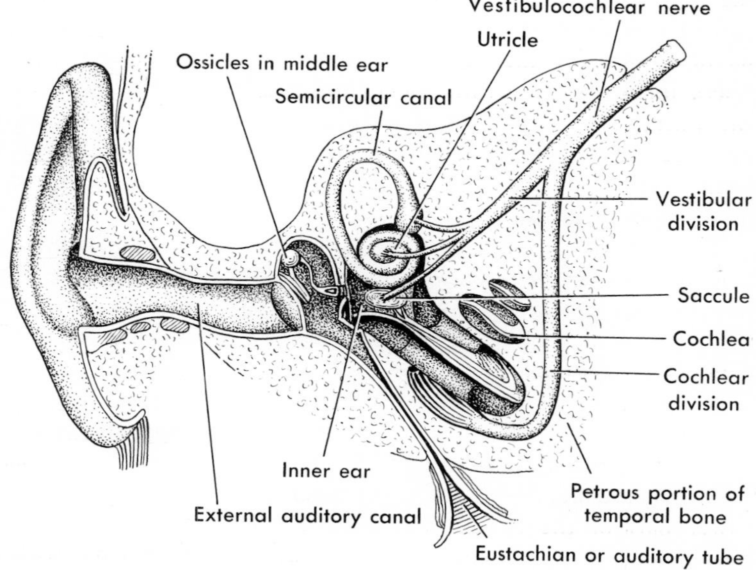

Figure 12–8. Section of the right ear showing middle and inner ear structures.

The Tympanic Cavity, or the Middle Ear. This is a small, irregular bony cavity, situated in the petrous portion of the temporal bone. This air cavity is so small that probably five or six drops of water would fill it. It is separated from the external auditory canal by the tympanic membrane, and from the internal ear by a very thin bony wall ($^1/_{24}$ in.) in which there are two small openings: the *fenestra vestibuli* (*oval*) and the *fenestra cochleae* (*round*). In the posterior, or mastoid, wall there is an opening into the mastoid antrum and mastoid cells; and because of this, infection of the middle ear may extend into the mastoid cells and cause mastoiditis. The temporal bone at this point is very porous, and any suppurative process is exceedingly dangerous, for the infection may travel inward and invade the brain. In the anterior, or carotid, wall is an opening into the eustachian tube, a small canal which leads to the nasopharynx. Thus, there are five openings in the middle ear; namely, the opening between it and the auditory canal; the fenestra vestibuli and the fenestra cochleae, which connect with the internal ear; the opening into the mastoid cells; and the opening into the eustachian tube. The walls of the tympanic cavity are lined with mucous membrane, which is continuous anteriorly with the mucous membrane of the auditory tube and posteriorly with that of the mastoid antrum and mastoid cells.

Ossicles. Stretching across the cavity of the middle ear from the tympanic membrane to the fenestra vestibuli are three tiny, movable bones, named, because of their shapes, the *malleus*, or hammer, the *incus*, or anvil, and the *stapes*, or stirrup. The handle of the malleus is attached to the tympanic membrane, and the head is attached to the base of the incus. The long process of the incus is attached to the stapes, and the footpiece of the stapes occupies the fenestra vestibuli. These little bones are held in position, attached to each other, to the tympanic membrane, and to the edge of the fenestra vestibuli, by minute ligaments and muscles. They are set in motion with every movement of the tympanic membrane. Vibrations of the membrane are communicated to the malleus, received by the incus, and transmitted to the stapes, which rocks in the fenestra vestibuli and is therefore capable of transmitting to the fluid in the cavity of the labyrinth the impulses which it receives. These bones form a series of levers, the effect of which is to magnify the force of the vibrations received at the tympanum about 10 times that at the oval window.

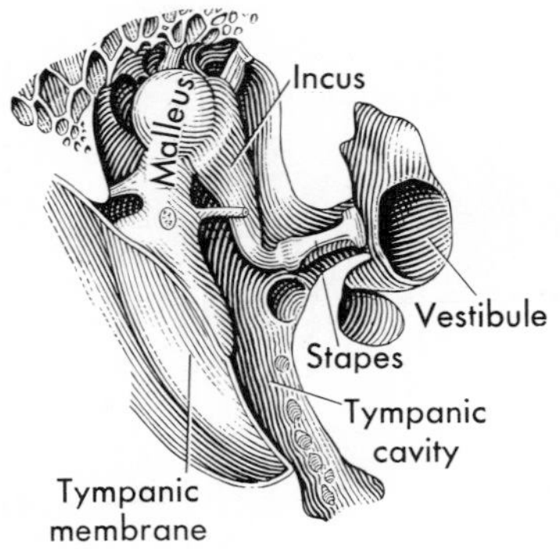

Figure 12–9. Chain of ossicles and their ligaments, seen from the front.

The auditory, or *eustachian*, *tube* connects the cavity of the middle ear with the pharynx. It is about 36 mm long and about 3 mm ($^1/_8$ in.) in diameter at its narrowest part and lined with mucous membrane. By means of this tube the pressure of the air on both sides of the tympanic membrane is equalized. In inflammatory conditions, the auditory tube may become occluded, and may prevent this equalization. Under such conditions, hearing is much impaired until the tube is opened. The pharyngeal opening of the tube is closed except when swallowing, yawning, and sneezing.

The Internal Ear, or Labyrinth. This receives the ultimate terminations of the vestibulocochlear nerve. It consists of an *osseous labyrinth*, which is composed of a series of peculiarly shaped cavities, hollowed out of the petrous portion of the temporal bone and named from their shape:

Osseous labyrinth
1. The vestibule
2. The cochlea (snail shell)
3. The semicircular canals

Within the osseous labyrinth is a *membranous labyrinth*, having the same general

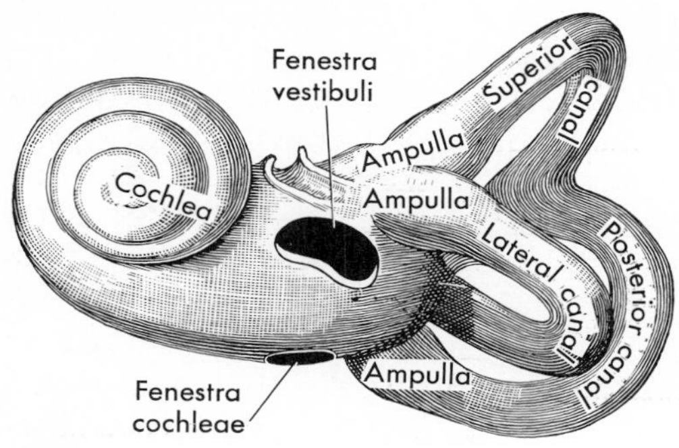

Figure 12–10. Left osseous labyrinth, viewed from lateral side. (Modified from Cunningham.)

form as the cavities in which it is contained, though considerably smaller, being separated from the bony walls by a quantity of fluid called the *perilymph.* It does not float loosely in this liquid but is attached to the bone by fibrous bands. The cavity of the membranous labyrinth contains fluid—the *endolymph*—and on its walls the ramifications of the acoustic nerve are distributed.

The *vestibule* is the central cavity of the osseous labyrinth; it is situated behind the cochlea and in front of the semicircular canals. It communicates with the middle ear by means of the fenestra vestibuli in its lateral or tympanic wall. The membranous labyrinth of the vestibule does not conform to the shape of the bony cavity but consists of two small sacs, called respectively the *saccule* and the *utricle*. The saccule is the smaller of the two and is situated near the opening of the scala vestibuli of the cochlea; the utricle is larger and occupies the upper and back part of the vestibule. These sacs are not directly connected with each other. From the posterior wall of the saccule, a canal, the *ductus endolymphaticus*, is given off. This duct is joined by a duct from the utricle and ends in a blind pouch on the posterior surface of the petrous portion of the temporal bone. The utricle, saccule, and ducts contain endolymph and are surrounded by perilymph. The inner wall of the saccule and utricle consists of two kinds of modified columnar cells on a basement membrane. One is a specialized nerve cell provided with stiff hairs, which project into the endolymph. Between the nerve cells are supporting cells, which are not ciliated and are not connected with nerve endings. The hair cells serve as end organs for fibers of the vestibular branch of the vestibulocochlear nerve, which arborize around the base of each hair cell. Small crystals of calcium carbonate, called *otoliths*, are located on the hair cells of the utricle. The otoliths give weight to the hair cells and make them more sensitive to change in position. Impulses are set up when the otoliths pull or push on the hairs.

The *cochlea* forms the anterior part of the bony labyrinth and is placed almost horizontally in front of the vestibule. It resembles

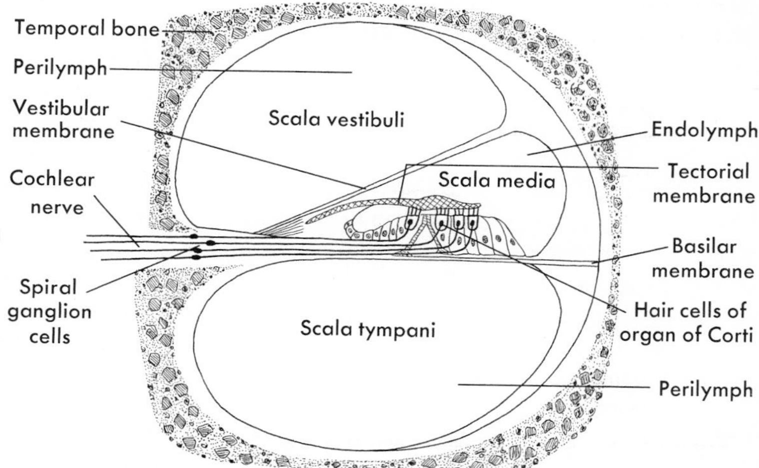

Figure 12–11. Diagram showing cross section of cochlea.

a snail shell and consists of a spiral canal of $2\frac{3}{4}$ turns around a hollow, conical central pillar called the *modiolus*, from which a thin *lamina* of bone projects like a spiral shelf about halfway toward the outer wall of the canal. Within the bony cochlea is a *membranous cochlea*, which begins at the fenestra ovalis and duplicates the bony structure.

The *basilar membrane* stretches from the free border of the lamina to the outer wall of the bony cochlea and completely divides its cavities into two passages, or *scalae*, which, however, communicate with each other at the apex of the modiolus by a small opening. The upper passage is the scala vestibuli, which terminates at the fenestra vestibuli; and the lower is the scala tympani, which terminates at the fenestra cochleae.

From the free border of the lamina, a second membrane, called the *vestibular membrane* (Reissner[1]), extends to the outer wall of the cochlea and is attached some distance above the basilar membrane. A triangular canal, called the *ductus cochlearis* or *scala media*, is thus formed between the scala vestibuli above and the scala tympani below.

On the basilar membrane the sound-sensitive epithelium of the *organ of Corti*[2] is located. This consists of a large number of *rod-shaped cells* and *hair cells*, extending into the endolymph of the scala media. The *tectorial membrane* projects from the spiral lamina over these cells of the organs of Corti. The hairs of the hair cells are attached to the tectorial membrane so that as the basilar membrane vibrates, the hair cells are alternately stretched and relaxed. The fibers of the cochlear branch of the vestibulocochlear nerve arise in the nerve cells of the *spiral ganglion*, which is situated in the modiolus. These cells are bipolar and send fibers toward the brain in the vestibulocochlear nerve and the other fibers to end in terminal arborizations around the hair cells of the organ and the other fibers to end in terminal arborizations around the hair cells of the organ of Corti.

[1] Ernst Reissner, German anatomist (1824–1878).
[2] Alfonso Corti, Italian anatomist (1822–1888).

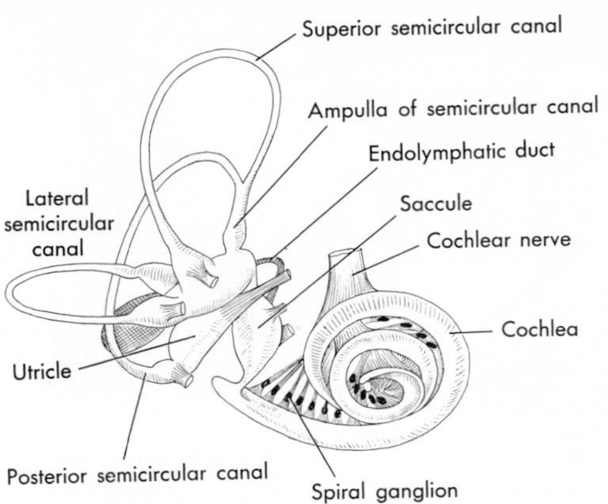

Figure 12–12. The bony labyrinth has been removed to show the membranous labyrinth that is filled with endolymph and from which all the nerves of the internal ear arise.

The *semicircular canals* are three bony canals lying above and behind the vestibule and communicating with it by five openings, in one of which two tubes join. They are known as the *superior*, *posterior*, and *lateral* canals, and their position is such that each one is at right angles to the other two. One end of each tube is enlarged and forms what is known as the *ampulla*.

The *semicircular ducts* (membranous semicircular canals) are similar to the bony canals in number, shape, and general form, but their diameter is less. They open by five orifices into the utricle, one opening being common to the medial end of the superior and the upper end of the posterior duct. In the ampullae the membranous canal is attached to the bony canal, and the epithelium is thrown into a ridge (the *crista ampullaris*) of cells with hairlike processes, which project into the endolymph. The hair cells are covered with a gelatinous substance which contains the otoliths. These are minute particles of calcium carbonate which pull and push on the hairs when the position of the head is changed. Hair movement initiates reflexes that maintain balance against gravity. Some of the peripheral terminations of the vestibular branch of the vestibulocochlear nerve are distributed to these cells. Between the hair cells are supporting cells.

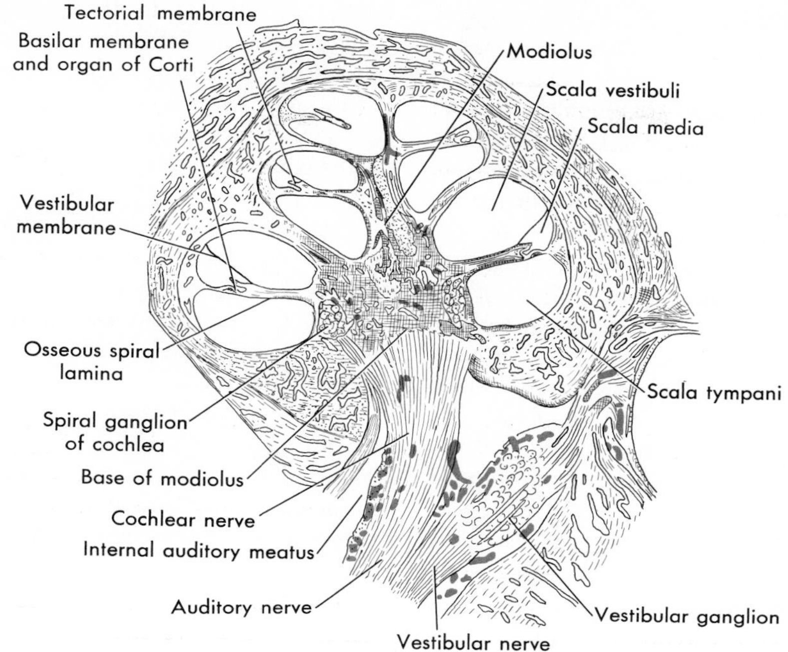

Figure 12–13. Section of the cochlea, showing the scalae. *Red* indicates blood supply. (Modified from Toldt.)

The Acoustic Center. The primary acoustic center is in the *temporal lobe* of the cerebrum. Removal of both temporal lobes produces complete deafness. Removal of one temporal lobe impairs hearing. This suggests that some fibers from each ear cross at some point in their afferent pathways and terminate in the opposite cortex. This is similar to the partial decussation of visual fibers occurring in the optic chiasma.

The vestibulocochlear nerve (VIII) is sensory and contains at least two sets of fibers, which differ in their origin, destination, and function. One set of fibers is known as the cochlear division and the other as the vestibular.

The cochlear nerve arises from bipolar cells in the spiral ganglion of the cochlea. The

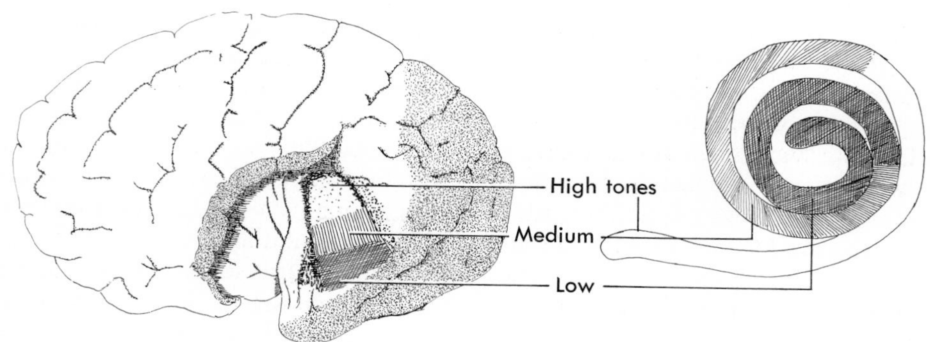

Figure 12–14. Diagram showing relationship between cochlea and acoustic area of cortex and interpretations of sound in the brain. For more details, see Penfield and Rasmussen, *The Cerebral Cortex of Man*, The Macmillan Company, 1950.

peripheral fibers pass to the cells of the organ of Corti, at which point the sound waves initiate the nerve impulses. The central fibers, forming part of the cochlear branch of VIII, pass into the lateral border of the medulla, terminating in the dorsal and ventral cochlear nuclei. From these nuclei the path is continued by secondary neurons to the auditory centers in the medial geniculate bodies of the thalamus. Some of the fibers cross and some do not. The cell bodies of the thalamus form the third cell in the primary auditory pathway, the processes of which terminate in the temporal lobe of the cortex.

The vestibular nerve arises from bipolar cells in the *vestibular ganglion* (ganglion of Scarpa), situated in the internal acoustic meatus. The peripheral fibers divide into three branches, which are distributed to the hair cells of the saccule, the utricle, and the ampullae of the semicircular canals. The central fibers, forming part of the vestibular branch, terminate in the vestibular nuclei in the medulla (Figure 11–23, page 226). From these nuclei some fibers project to the cerebellum, and others pass down the spinal cord as the vestibular spinal tract to form connections with motor centers of the spinal nerves. Connections between vestibular and ocular nuclei provide the neural circuitry for reflex eye movements which accompany changes in the position of the body in space.

Process of Hearing. All bodies that produce sound are in a state of vibration and communicate their vibrations to the air with which they are in contact. The range of air vibrations for sound is from 40 to 20,000 vibrations per second.

When these air waves, set in motion by sonorous bodies, enter the external auditory canal, they set the tympanic membrane vibrating. The vibrations of the tympanic membrane are then communicated by means of the auditory ossicles stretched across the middle ear to the perilymph and then to the endolymph of the inner ear. The movements of the fluids, in rhythm with the air, stimulate the nerve endings in the organ of Corti; and from these, impulses are conveyed to the center of hearing in the temporal cortex. Characteristics of the sensation of sound are *loudness*, which varies with the *amplitude* of vibrations; *pitch*, which varies with the frequency of vibrations; and *timbre*, which is due to the pattern which the complex of vibrations makes.

A unit for measuring the loudness of sound is the *bel* (which measures air pressure changes); for convenience a tenth of a bel, or a decibel, is used. Zero decibels is the threshold of hearing, and normal conversation is about 65 decibels.

The *resonance* theory of Helmholtz, postulates that the cochlea is the analyzer of sound. The theory makes use of the structure of the basilar membrane, which is said to have some 24,000 fibers running across it. These fibers vary gradually in length from around 130 μ at the base to about 275 μ at the apex of the cochlea. The short fibers vibrate in response to vibrations of the tympanic membrane brought about by high notes; the long fibers at the apex vibrate in response to low tone vibrations. Man is thought to be able to distinguish more than 10,000 pitches of tone. There are also more than 15,000 hair cells on the basilar membrane and more than 15,000 fibers in the cochlear nerve. This almost constitutes an adequate physical mechanism for discrimination in auditory sensation. Abnormal conditions in any part of the auditory mechanism may excite the auditory nerve and give rise to noises that are described as rushing, roaring, humming, and ringing.

Since the cochlea is embedded in a bony cavity, vibrations from any or all skull bones can cause fluid vibrations of the cochlea itself. Thus, in deafness due to calcification and immobility of ossicles, it is possible to hear by bone conduction. Some hearing-aid devices amplify air waves into vibrations that will be readily transmitted through the mastoid bone. If disease has destroyed the receptor hair cells or the afferent nerve fibers, hearing aids will be of no use. Prolonged and excessive noise causes deafness, presumably through damage to the fibers in the organ of Corti.

EQUILIBRIUM

Among the various means (such as sight, touch, and muscular sense) whereby one is enabled to maintain equilibrium, coordinate movements, and become aware of position in space, one of the most important is the *action of the vestibule and semicircular canals*. Movements of the head set up movements in the endolymph of the canals and bend the receptor hair cells, which in turn initiate nerve impulses that are then transmitted to the cerebellum.

The canals are so arranged that any movement of the head causes an increase in the pressure of the endolymph in one ampulla and a corresponding diminution in the ampulla of the parallel canal on the opposite side. With movement of the endolymph, the hair cells are stimulated, transmitting impulses by fibers of the vestibular nerve, through the cell bodies of the vestibular ganglion and the axons of the vestibulocochlear nerve, to the cerebellum. Impulses from receptors in the semicircular canals and from the otoliths, due to change in position of the head, initiate the righting reflex. Balance against gravity is thus maintained by the coordinated or effective response of the antigravity muscles. The cerebellum links the impulses that arise from stimulation of the sensory nerves of the semicircular canals, joints, etc., and sends the nerve impulses on to the motor centers of the cerebrum and spinal cord.

VISION

The visual apparatus consists of the eyeball, the optic nerve, and the visual center in the brain. In addition to these essential organs, there are accessory organs which are necessary for the protection and functioning of the eyeball.

Accessory Organs of the Eye. Under this heading are grouped eyebrows, eyelids, conjunctiva, lacrimal apparatus, muscles of the eyeball, and the fascia bulbi.

The eyebrow is a thickened ridge of skin, covered with short hairs. It is situated on the upper border of the orbit and protects the eye from too vivid light, perspiration, etc.

The eyelids (palpebrae) are two movable folds placed in front of the eye. They are covered externally with skin and internally with a mucous membrane, the conjunctiva, which is reflected from them over the bulb of the eye. They are composed of muscle fibers and dense fibrous tissue known as the *tarsal plates.* The upper lid is attached to a small muscle which is called the elevator of the upper lid (*levator palpebrae superioris*). Arranged as a sphincter around both lids is the *orbicularis oculi* muscle, which closes the eyelids.

The slit between the edges of the lids is called the palpebral fissure. It is the size of this fissure which causes the appearance of large and small eyes, as the size of the eyeball itself varies but little. The eyelids provide protection for the eye—movable shades which cover the eye during sleep, protect the eye from bright light and foreign objects, and spread the lubricating secretions of the eye over the surface of the eyeball.

Eyelashes and Sebaceous Glands. From the margin of each eyelid, a row of short, thick hairs—the eyelashes—project. The follicles of the eyelashes receive a lubricating fluid from the sebaceous glands which open into them. If these glands become infected, a sty results. A *sty,* therefore, is comparable to a pimple or furuncle resulting from the infection of retained sebaceous fluid in other regions of the skin.

Lying between the conjunctiva and the tarsal cartilage of each eyelid is a row of elongated sebaceous glands—the tarsal, or meibomian, glands—the ducts of which open on the edge of the eyelid. The secretion of these glands lubricates their edges and prevents adhesion of the eyelids. Distention of the gland is termed a *chalazion.*

The Conjunctiva. The mucous membrane which lines the eyelids and is reflected over the forepart of the eyeball is called the conjunctiva. It is continuous with the lining membrane of the ducts of the tarsal glands, the lacrimal ducts, lacrimal sac, nasolacrimal duct, and nose.

Lacrimal Apparatus. This apparatus consists of the lacrimal gland, the lacrimal ducts, the lacrimal sac, and the nasolacrimal duct.

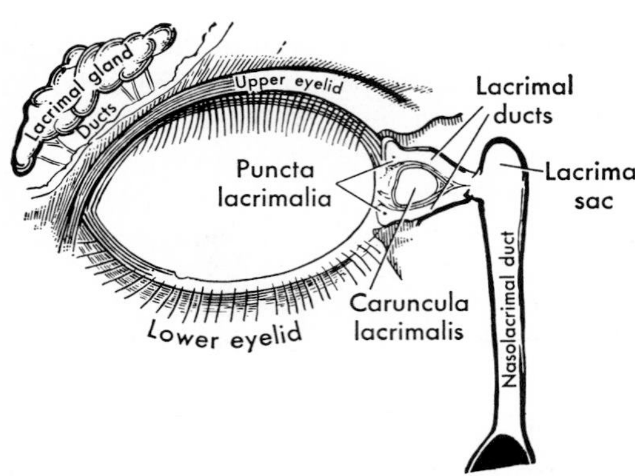

Figure 12–15. The lacrimal apparatus. (After Gray's *Anatomy*.)

The *lacrimal gland* is a compound gland and is lodged in a depression of the frontal bone at the upper and outer angle of the orbit. It is about the size and shape of an almond and consists of two portions, a superior and inferior, which are partially separated by a fibrous septum.

Six to twelve minute *ducts* lead from the gland to the surface of the conjunctiva of the upper lid. The secretion (tears) is usually just enough to keep the eye moist and, after passing over the surface of the eyeball, flows through the *puncta* into two tiny *lacrimal ducts* and is conveyed into the *lacrimal sac* at the inner angle of the eye. The *lacrimal sac* is the expanded upper end of the *nasolacrimal* duct, a small canal that opens into the nose. It is oval and measures from 12 to 15 mm in length. The *caruncula lacrimalis* (caruncle) is a small reddish body situated at the medial commissure. It contains sebaceous and sudoriferous glands and forms the whitish secretion which collects in this region.

The lacrimal gland secretes tears. This secretion is a dilute solution of various salts in water, which also contains small quantities of mucin. The ducts leading from the lacrimal gland carry tears to the eyeball, and the lids spread it over the surface. Ordinarily this secretion is evaporated, or carried away by the nasolacrimal duct, as fast as formed; but under certain circumstances, as when the conjunctiva is irritated or when painful emotions arise, the secretion of the lacrimal gland exceeds the drainage power of the nasolacrimal duct, and the fluid, accumulating between the lids, at length overflows and runs down the cheeks. The purpose of the lacrimal secretion is to keep the surface of the eyes moist and to help remove microorganisms and dust.

Inflammation from the nose may spread to the nasolacrimal ducts, blocking them and thus cause a slow dropping of tears from the inner angle of the eye. The lacrimal glands do not develop sufficiently to secrete tears until about the fourth month of life, hence, the need for protecting a baby's eyes from bright light and dust.

Fascia Bulbi. Between the pad of fat and the eyeball is a thin membrane—the fascia bulbi—which envelops the eyeball from the optic nerve to the ciliary region and forms a socket in which the eyeball rotates.

Muscles. Muscles of the eye are listed in the following chart.

The Orbits. The orbits are the bony cavities in which the eyeballs are contained. Each orbit is shaped like a funnel; the large end, directed outward and forward, forms a strong bony edge which protects the eyeball. The small end is directed backward and inward and is pierced by a large opening—the optic foramen—through which the optic nerve and the ophthalmic artery pass from the cranial cavity to the eye. A larger opening to the outer side of the foramen—the superior orbital fissure—provides a passage for the orbital branches of the middle meningeal artery and the nerves which carry impulses to and from the muscles, i.e., the oculomotor,

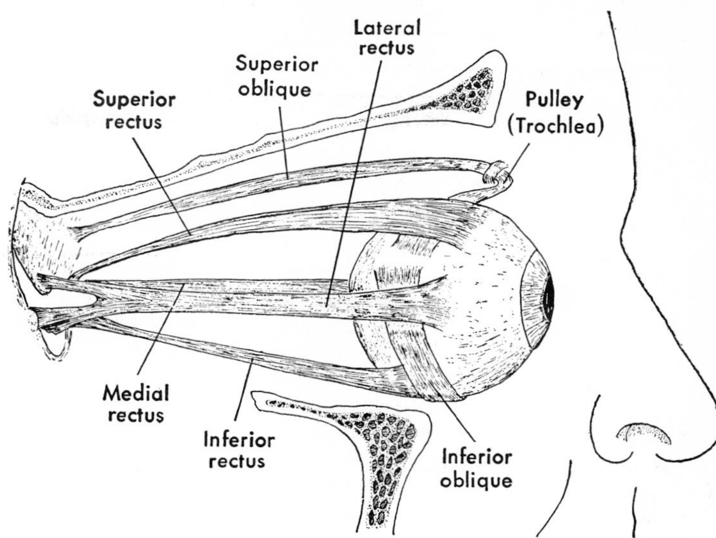

Figure 12–16. The extrinsic muscles of the eyeball in the right orbit. Note tendinous insertions of superior and inferior oblique muscles between the superior and lateral recti.

the trochlear, the abducens, and the ophthalmic. The inner portion of the eyeball contains a pad of fat which serves to cushion the eyeball, and which diminishes when starvation occurs. Then the eyeballs sink into the orbit.

Muscles of the Eye and Lids

Muscle	Origin	Insertion	Nerve Supply	Function
I. Extrinsic				
Superior rectus	Apex of orbital cavity	Upper and central portion of eyeball	Oculomotor	Rolls eyeball upward
Inferior rectus	Apex of orbital cavity	Lower and central portion of eyeball	Oculomotor	Rolls eyeball downward
Lateral rectus	Apex of orbital cavity	Midway on outer side of eyeball	Abducens	Rolls eyeball laterally
Medial rectus	Apex of orbital cavity	Midway on inner side of eyeball	Oculomotor	Rolls eyeball medially
Superior oblique	Apex of orbital cavity	Eyeball between superior and lateral recti	Trochlear	Rolls eyeball on its axis, directs cornea downward and laterally
Inferior oblique	Orbital plate of maxilla	Eyeball between superior and lateral recti	Oculomotor	Rolls eyeball on its axis, directs cornea upward and laterally
II. Intrinsic				
Sphincter pupillae		Circular muscle attached at circumference to sclera, cornea, and ciliary processes	Parasympathetic fibers, oculomotor	Constriction of pupil

Muscle	Origin	Insertion	Nerve Supply	Function
Dilator pupillae		Radiating fibers from pupil outward, attached at circumference to sclera, cornea, and ciliary processes	Sympathetic fibers, from ciliary ganglion and trigeminal nerve	Dilation of pupil
III. MUSCLES OF LID				
Orbicularis oculi	Nasal part of frontal bone; frontal process of maxilla; medial palpebral ligament	Palpebral portion is inserted into lateral palpebral raphe; orbital portion surrounds orbit; upper fibers blend with frontalis and corrugator muscle	Temporal and zygomatic branches of facial nerve	Palpebral portion closes lids gently; orbital portion, stronger closing
Levator palpebrae superioris	Inferior surface of small wing of sphenoid	Tarsus and orbicularis oculi and skin of eyelid	Fibers from oculomotor nerve	Raises upper eyelid, antagonist to orbicularis oculi

The muscles of the eye and eyelids receive their blood supply from both the internal and external carotid arteries (Fig. 11–7, page 207). See Figure 11–9, page 209, for venous return.

The Bulb of the Eye, or Eyeball. The bulb of the eye is spherical, but its transverse diameter is less than the anteroposterior so that it projects anteriorly and looks as if a section of a smaller sphere had been engrafted on the front of it.

The bulb of the eye is composed of three coats, or tunics. From the outside of the eyeball inward toward its center these are:

Fibrous: (1) sclera, (2) cornea
Vascular: (1) choroid, (2) ciliary body, (3) iris
Nervous: retina

The eye contains four refracting media. These are cornea, aqueous humor, crystalline lens and capsule, and vitreous body.

The Fibrous Tunic. This is formed by the sclera and cornea.

1. *The sclera*, or *white of the eye*, covers the posterior five sixths of the eyeball. It is composed of a firm, unyielding, fibrous membrane, thicker behind than in front, and serves to maintain the shape of the eyeball and to protect the delicate structures contained within it. It is opaque, white, and smooth externally; behind, it is pierced by the optic nerve. Internally it is brown in color and is separated from the choroid by a fluid space. It is supplied with few blood vessels. A *venous sinus*—the canal of Schlemm[3]—encircles the cornea at the corneoscleral junction. Its nerves are derived from the ciliary.

2. *The cornea* covers the anterior sixth of the eyeball. It is directly continuous with the sclera, which, however, overlaps it slightly above and below. The cornea, like the sclera, is composed of fibrous tissue, which is firm and unyielding, but, unlike the sclera, it has no color and is perfectly transparent; it has been aptly termed the "window of the eye." The cornea is well supplied with nerves (derived from the ciliary) and lymph spaces which surround the nerves but is destitute of blood vessels, so that it is dependent on the lymph for nutriment. Injury to the cornea causes scarring and impairs vision.

[3] Friedrich Schlemm, German anatomist (1795–1858).

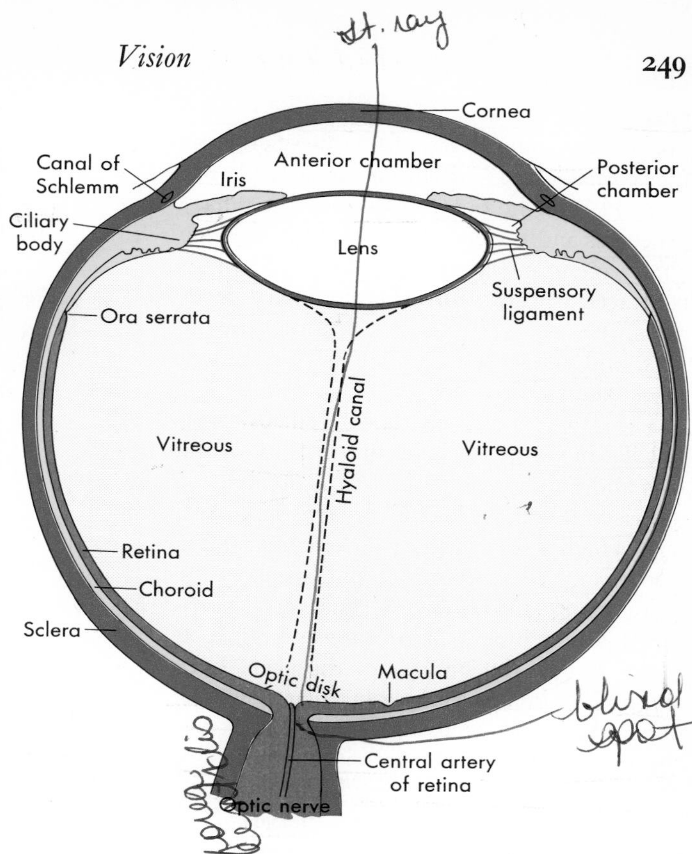

Figure 12–17. Horizontal section of the eyeball. Retina, *red;* choroid, *yellow* (between red and blue) sclera, *blue.*

The Vascular Tunic (Uvea, or Uveal Tract). This consists, from behind forward, of the choroid, the ciliary body, and the iris.

1. *The choroid* is a thin, dark-brown membrane lining the inner surface of the posterior five sixths of the sclera. It is pierced behind by the optic nerve. The inner surface is attached to the pigmented layer of the retina and extends anteriorly to the ora serrata. It consists of a dense capillary plexus and small arteries and veins carrying blood to and from the plexus. Between these vessels are pigment cells which with other cells form a network, or stroma. The blood vessels and pigment cells render this membrane dark and opaque, so that it darkens the chamber of the eye by preventing the reflection of light. It extends to the ciliary body.

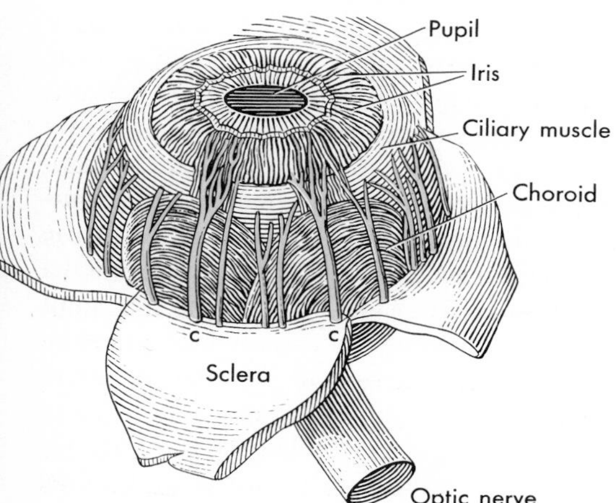

Figure 12–18. Diagram of the eyeball, sclera cut and turned back. Note pupil, iris, ciliary muscle, choroid; (*c*) ciliary nerves and optic nerve.

2. *The ciliary body* includes the orbicularis ciliaris, the ciliary processes, and the ciliaris muscle. The orbicularis ciliaris is a zone about 4 mm in width, which is directly continuous with the anterior part of the choroid.

Just behind the edge of the cornea, the choroid is folded inward and arranged in radiating folds, like a plaited ruffle, around the margin of the lens. There are from 60 to 80 of these folds, and they constitute the ciliary processes. They are well supplied with nerves and blood vessels and also support a muscle, the ciliaris (ciliary) muscle. The fibers of this muscle arise from the sclera near the cornea, and, extending backward, are inserted into the outer surface of the ciliary processes and the choroid. This muscle is the chief agent in accommodation. When it contracts, it draws forward the ciliary processes, relaxes the suspensory ligament of the lens, and allows the elastic lens to resume a more convex form.

3. *The iris* is a circular, colored disk suspended in the aqueous humor in front of the lens and behind the cornea. It is attached at its circumference to the ciliary processes, with which it is practically continuous, and is also connected to the sclera and cornea at the point where they join one another. Except for this attachment at its circumference, it hangs free in the interior of the eyeball. In the middle of the iris is a circular hole, the *pupil*, through which light is admitted into the eye chamber. The iris is composed of connective tissue containing branched cells, numerous blood vessels, and nerves. The color of the eye is related to the number and size of pigment-bearing cells in the iris. If there is no pigment or very little, the eye is blue; with increasing amounts of pigment the eye is gray, brown, or black. It also contains two sets of antagonistic muscles described in the chart on page 247.

The posterior surface of the iris is covered by layers of pigmented epithelium designed to prevent the entrance of light.

FUNCTION OF THE IRIS. The function of the iris is to regulate the amount of light entering the eye and thus assist in obtaining clear images. This regulation is accomplished by the action of the muscles described above, as their contraction or relaxation determines the size of the pupil. When the eye is accommodated for a near object or stimulated by a bright light, the sphincter muscle contracts and diminishes the size of the pupil. When, on the other hand, the eye is accommodated for a distant object or the light is dim, the dilator muscle contracts and increases the size of the pupil.

The Retina, or Nervous Tunic. The retina, the innermost coat of the eyeball, is a delicate membrane of tissue which receives the images of external objects and transfers the impressions evoked by them to the center of sight in the cortex of the cerebrum. It occupies the space between the choroid coat and the hyaloid membrane of the vitreous body and extends forward almost to the posterior margin of the ciliary body, where it terminates in a jagged margin known as the *ora serrata*. It consists of three sets of neurons so arranged that the cell bodies and processes form seven layers. In addition there are two limiting membranes, one membrane (membrana limitans interna) in contact with the vitreous layer, and the second (membrana limitans externa) marking the internal limit of the rod-and-cone layer, and one pigmented layer between the layer of rods and cones and the choroid coat.

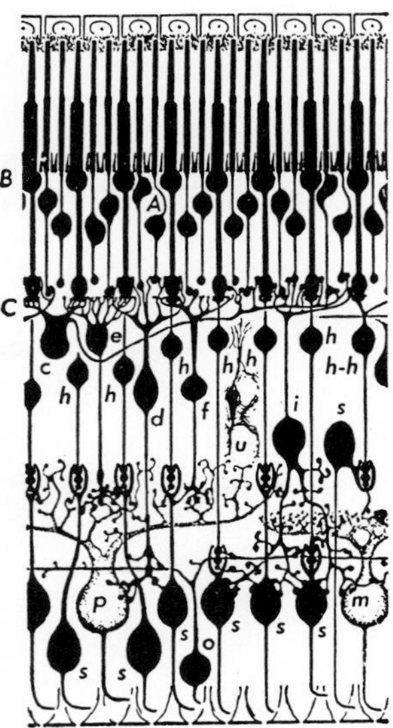

Figure 12–19. Scheme of the structure of the primate retina, as shown by Polyak, 1941. (*A*) Rod, (*B*) cone, (*C*) horizontal cell, (*d*) diffuse ganglionic cell. This diagram illustrates the very complex arrangement of retinal cells. (Courtesy of University of Chicago Press.)

The seventh layer, called the layer of rods and cones, is the light-sensitive layer where light energy is converted to nerve impulses which are transmitted to the brain by the optic nerve. To reach the light-sensitive receptors lying in this seventh retinal layer, light must pass through the cornea, aqueous humor, lens, vitreous humor, and each of the retinal layers before striking the rods and cones.

In the center of the receptor layer of the retina, there is a small special region, the fovea, in which there are only cones. Moving from the fovea to the periphery of the retina the concentration of cones diminishes and the concentration of rods increases until at the most peripheral edges of the retina one finds only rods.

The rods and cones are two different types of visual receptors. They differ both structurally and functionally, each subserving very important roles in vision.

The rods are particularly important for vision in dim illumination because it takes very little light to stimulate them. Although the rods are stimulated by most of the wave lengths in the visible spectrum, they cannot produce a color sensation. They permit light and dark discrimination and form and movement perception but provide poor visual acuity. Rhodopsin is the photosensitive pigment within the rods. This material is bleached by light, and it is slowly regenerated in the dark. It takes almost an hour in total darkness for complete resynthesis of rhodopsin. As the rhodopsin is regenerated, the sensitivity of the rods progressively increases. This gradual increase in retinal sensitivity is called dark adaptation. Vitamin A and nicotinamide are essential for resynthesis of rhodopsin and any vitamin A deficiency will delay or reduce rhodopsin regeneration. The resulting condition is known as night blindness (nyctalopia); the rods are less capable of increasing their sensitivity in dim illumination.

In contrast the cones are particularly important for color vision in bright illumination. The cones need more intense light to be excited than do the rods, and the cones maximally alter their sensitivity to decreased illumination within 10 to 15 minutes. Their range of sensitivity is small compared to the 100 million sensitivity range over which the rods can function. The cones are responsible for visual acuity. In the fovea, where only cones exist, there is only one cone per nerve fiber. It is as if each receptor has its own "private line" to the brain. The cones also contain a photosensitive pigment which has not been isolated in man, but is thought to be similar to rhodopsin. Three types of cones exist, containing different types of pigment which make them sensitive to red, green, or blue color selectively.

Blind Spot. The optic nerve pierces the eyeball not exactly at its most posterior point but a little to the inner side, called the blind spot. Because it contains no receptor cells, this point is insensitive to light. The central artery of the retina, a branch of the ophthalmic artery, and its vein pass into the retina along with the optic nerve.

Macula Lutea. One point of the retina is of great importance—the macula lutea, or yellow spot. It is situated about 2.08 mm (1/12 in.) to the outer side of the exit of the optic nerve and is the exact center of the retina. In its center is a tiny pit—*fovea centralis*—which is the center of direct vision. At this point there is an absence of rods but a great increase in the number of cones. This is the region of greatest visual acuity. In reading, the eyes move so as to bring the rays of light from word after word into the center of the fovea.

Refracting Media. The cornea and the aqueous humor form the first refracting media. The *aqueous humor* fills the forward chamber; the latter is the space bounded by the cornea in front and by the lens, suspensory ligament, and ciliary body behind. This space is partially divided by the iris into an anterior and a posterior chamber. The aqueous humor is a clear, watery solution containing minute amounts of salts, mainly sodium chloride. It is derived mainly from the capillaries by diffusion and it drains away through the veins and through the spaces of Fontana[4] into the venous canal of Schlemm and then on into the larger veins of the eyeball.

The *crystalline lens* enclosed in its capsule is a transparent, refractive body, with convex anterior and posterior surfaces. It is placed directly behind the pupil, where it is retained in position by the counterbalancing pressure

[4] Felice Fontana, Italian physiologist (1720–1805).

of the aqueous humor in front and the vitreous body behind, and by its own suspensory ligament, formed in part by the hyaloid membrane and in part by fibers derived from the ciliary processes. The posterior surface is considerably more curved than the anterior, and the curvature of each varies with the period of life. In infancy, the lens is almost spherical; in the adult, of medium convexity; and in the aged, considerably flattened. The capsule surrounding the lens is elastic, and with age it loses its original elasticity. Its refractive power is much greater than that of the aqueous or vitreous body. In cataract the lens or its capsule becomes less transparent and blurs causing loss of vision. Cataracts are treated by removing the opaque lens and compensating with an artificial lens, i.e., eyeglasses.

The *vitreous body*, a semifluid albuminous tissue enclosed in a thin membrane, the hyaloid membrane, fills the posterior four fifths of the bulb of the eye. The vitreous body distends the greater part of the sclera, supports the retina, which lies upon its surface, and preserves the spheroidal shape of the eyeball. Its refractive power, though slightly greater than that of the aqueous humor, does not differ much from that of water.

In glaucoma, intraocular pressure increases, cupping the optic disk and interfering with the proper distribution of blood to all the inner tissues of the eye. This increased pressure may be due to increased blood pressure in the larger blood vessels of the eye, to altered osmotic conditions of blood and eye fluids, to rigidity of the eyeball, or to improper functioning of intrinsic muscles of the eye. It may or may not cause pain. If the increased pressure persists, it can lead to irreversible damage to the visual cells.

Perception of Light and Color. Electromagnetic vibrations from the sun or other light source occur in waves of varying length. Vibrations from 400 mμ to 800 mμ long are called the visible spectrum (light and color waves). Those shorter than this are known as ultraviolet rays; those much longer are electrical waves.

WAVE LENGTHS AND COLOR

Wave length	Color
723 mμ–647 mμ	= red
647 mμ–585 mμ	= orange
585 mμ–575 mμ	= yellow
575 mμ–492 mμ	= green
492 mμ–455 mμ	= blue
455 mμ–424 mμ	= indigo
424 mμ–397 mμ	= violet

When light waves enter the eye, they give rise to impulses which are carried by the optic nerve to the occipital cortex, where the visual sensation results.

Color blindness refers to the inability to discriminate colors properly. About 9 per cent of normal healthy males are color blind to some degree.

Color-blind individuals are classifiable in relation to normal subjects who are called *trichromats*. Individuals lacking one type of cone pigment are called *dichromats*. The most usual type of dichromat is the *protanope* who lacks sensitivity to wave lengths in the red end of the spectrum. Another type of dichromat is the *deuteranope*, whose sensitivity is weak or lacking in the green region of the spectrum. Though the deuteranopes do not have a red deficiency, they confuse red and green. The *tritanope* is a rare type of dichromat who lacks blue-type cones. These individuals confuse blue and green. Some individuals have all three types of cone pigments, but one type may be deficient rather than absent, and they are called *anomalous trichromats*. These individuals rarely misname colors, but they confuse colors. These confusions provide the basis for some of the standard "hidden-figure" type of color tests.

Refraction. The central components of a light wave enter the eyes perpendicularly, and the sides obliquely. For clear vision the oblique rays must converge and come to a focus with the central rays on the retina. The cornea, aqueous humor, crystalline lens, and vitreous humor form a system of refractory devices. Rays of light are bent, or undergo refraction, chiefly on entering the cornea from the air, on entering the lens from the aqueous humor, and on leaving the lens and entering the vitreous fluid.

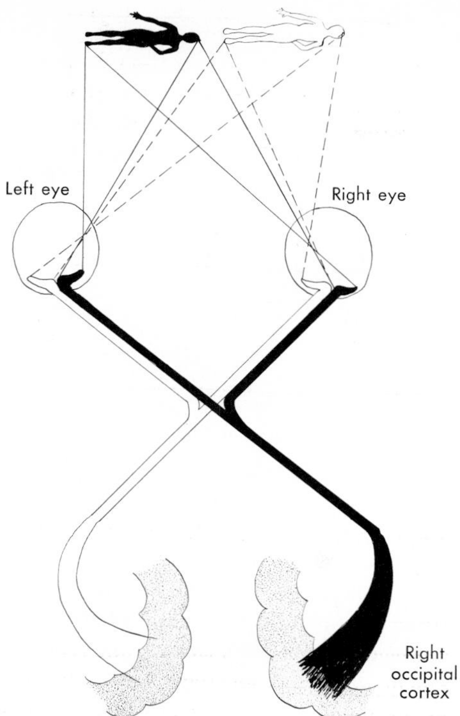

Figure 12–20. Diagram showing crossing of optic fibers. The fibers from the *nasal* half of the left retina and the fibers from the lateral half of the right retina are projected to the right occipital cortex and vice versa for the opposite side. See Figure 11–24, page 226, for optic pathway and synapsing of fibers.

Physiology of Vision. Visible objects reflect light rays which fall upon them. These reflected rays are brought to a focus on the rods and cones of the retina, and the resulting nerve impulses are transmitted to the optic nerve and thence through various relay stations to the centers of vision in the occipital lobes of the cerebrum. From here it is believed the impulses are transmitted to the association areas, where they awaken memories that enable one to interpret their meaning. The cones of the fovea centralis are the place of most acute vision and the part on which the light rays are focused when the eyes are accommodated for near objects. In a bright light the object is focused directly on the fovea, and the reflexes controlling accommodation help to bring this about. In a dim light the tendency is to diverge the eyes and thus bring the image into the peripheral and sensitive part of the retina. The visual field includes the entire expanse of space seen in a given instant without moving the eyes.

The temporal portion of the retina receives light waves from the nasal field of vision. The nasal portion of the retina receives light waves from the temporal field of vision. These fields may be tested to determine the specific areas of retinal (or optic tract) damage (Figure 12–21).

Binocular Vision. The value of two eyes instead of one is that true binocular vision is possible. This is distinctive in that it is stereoscopic. A stereoscopic picture consists of two views taken from slightly different angles. In stereoscopic vision, two optical images are made from slightly different angles. This gives the impression of distance and depth and is equivalent to adding a third dimension to the visual field. The processes necessary for binocular vision are convergence, or turning the eyes inward; change in the size of the pupil; accommodation; and refraction. In binocular vision it is necessary to turn the eyes inward, in order that the two images of a given object may lie upon what are called corresponding points of the two retinas. Excitation of two corresponding points causes only one sensation, which is the reason why binocular vision is not ordinarily double vision. Convergence of the eyes is brought about by innervation of the medial rectus muscles. The correspondence of the two retinas and of the movements of the eyeballs is produced by a close connection of the nerve centers controlling the contraction of eye muscles.

Change in the Size of the Pupil. When one looks at a near object in a bright light, the pupil contracts, so that the entering rays are directed to the central part of the lens, i.e., the part where the convexity and the consequent refractive power are greatest, and to the fovea centralis. In a dim light the pupil is dilated, causing a diffusion of the rays to the peripheral parts of the retina where the concentration of rhodopsin is high. The constriction of the pupil is brought about by the reflex contraction of the circular muscle of the iris by the oculomotor nerve in response to strong light stimulating the retina; in dim light the stimulation of the retina is lessened and the pupil dilates. In excitement, fear, etc., its dilation is due to stimulation of autonomic nerve fibers that are distributed by the ophthalmic branch of the trigeminal nerve.

Accommodation. Accommodation is the adjustment of the eye to focus on objects at different distances, because for an image to be sharply focused it must fall on the retina. Accommodation involves three coordinated responses: (1) the convergence of the eyes, (2) pupillary constriction, and (3) alteration in the refractiveness of the lens. The first two reflexes were discussed in the preceding paragraphs. Alteration in lens refractiveness is also a reflex response. A blurred image on the retina initiates afferent impulses in the optic nerve which signal the motor center of the ciliary muscle, the chief effector in accommodation. When the eye is at rest or fixed upon distant objects, the suspensory ligament, which extends from the ciliary processes to the capsule of the lens, exerts a tension upon the capsule of the lens which keeps the lens flattened, particularly the anterior surface to which it is attached. When the eye fixates on near objects, as in reading or sewing, the ciliary muscle contracts and draws forward the choroid coat, which in turn releases the tension of the suspensory ligament upon the capsule of the elastic lens and allows the anterior surface to become more convex. The accommodation for near objects is an active process and is always more or less fatiguing. On the contrary, the accommodation for distant objects is a passive process; consequently the eye rests for an indefinite time upon remote objects without fatigue.

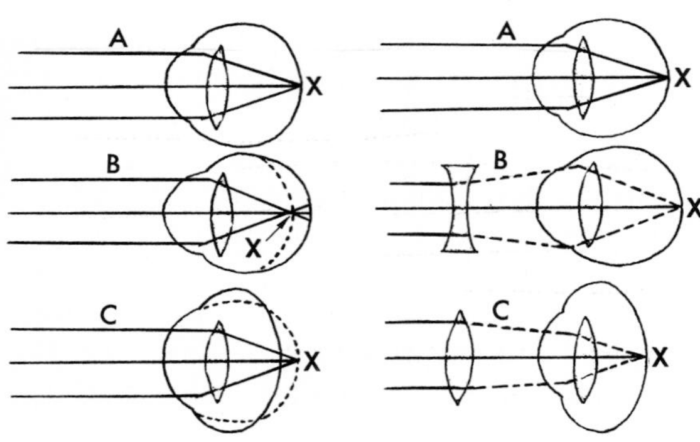

Figure 12–21. (Left) Diagrams illustrating rays of light converging in (*A*) normal eye, (*B*) myopic eye, and (*C*) hypermetropic eye. The parallel lines indicate light rays entering the eye; *X* is the point of convergence, or focus. In *A* the rays are brought to a focus (*X*) on the retina. In *B* they come to a focus in front of the retina. In *C* they would come to a focus behind the retina.
(Right) Diagrams illustrating the convergence of light rays in a normal eye (*A*) and the effects of concave lens (*B*) and convex lens (*C*) on rays of light.

Inversion of Images. Owing to refraction, light rays as they enter the eye cause the image of external objects on the retina to be *inverted*. The question then arises, "Why is it that objects do not appear to be upside down?" This question is answered if it is remembered that actual visual sensations take place in the brain and that the projection of these sensations to the exterior is a secondary act that has been learned from experience.

Abnormal Conditions That Interfere with Refraction. The normal eye is one in which at a distance of about 20 ft parallel rays of light focus on the retina when the eye is at rest. Such an eye is designated as emmetropic, or normal. Any abnormality in the refractive surfaces or the shape of the eyeball prevents this focusing of parallel rays and makes the eye ametropic, or abnormal.

The most common refractive conditions are myopia, hypermetropia, presbyopia, and astigmatism.

Myopia. Myopia, or nearsightedness, is a condition in which rays of light converge too soon and are brought to a focus before reaching the retina. This is the opposite of hypermetropia and is caused by a cornea or lens that is too convex or an eyeball of too great depth. This condition is remedied by wearing concave lenses, which cause parallel rays of light to diverge before they converge and focus on the retina.

Hypermetropia. Hypermetropia, or farsightedness, is a condition in which rays of light from near objects do not converge soon enough and are brought to a focus behind the retina.

A hypermetropic eye must accommodate slightly for distant objects and overaccommodate for near objects. Hypermetropia is usually caused by a flattened condition of the lens or cornea, or an eyeball that is too shallow; and convex lenses are used to concentrate and focus the rays in a shorter distance.

Presbyopia. Presbyopia is a defective condition of accommodation in which distant objects are seen distinctly but near objects are indistinct. It occurs as an aging process and is caused by a loss of the elasticity of the lens and lack of tone of the ciliary muscle.

Astigmatism. Astigmatism means that the curvature of the refracting surfaces is unequal; e.g., the cornea is more curved vertically than it is in a horizontal direction or vice versa.

The commonest form is that in which the vertical curvature is greater than the horizontal, and is described as regular astigmatism.

QUESTIONS FOR DISCUSSION

1. An individual receives a third-degree burn of both lower extremities. The deep structures of the skin are destroyed.
   a. Which sensations are lost? Explain.
   b. Which receptors are involved?
   c. Where in the brain are these sensations interpreted?
2. Explain how receptors function as a protective mechanism.
3. Explain why injury to the right occipital lobe (visual area) causes partial loss of vision in both eyes.
4. When an individual has a severe "cold in the head," sense of taste for most foods is lost. Explain.
5. How does receptor adaptation affect sensation?
6. Explain the phenomenon of referred pain.
7. Trace the pathway for hearing from the external ear to the cerebral cortex.
8. Trace the nerve fibers forming the optic pathway from the retina to the visual area of the occipital lobe.
9. Explain how an individual perceives color.
10. Explain how the eye accommodates to near and to far vision.

SUMMARY

Sensation—Interpreted in brain, may be modified or ignored

Tactile Sense
- Touch receptors—free nerve endings, hair nerve endings, Meissner's, pacinian corpuscles; all rapidly adapting except possibly free end organs
- Pressure different from touch; wide range of degree of pressure sensed

Kinesthesia
- Identifies location of parts of body, movement of parts
- Receptors located in joints, ligaments, joint capsules, pacinian, Ruffini end organs, Golgi end organs
- Receptors are warm and cold receptors

Temperature
- Range of temperature: 12° through 50° C; above this or below, pain results
- Adaptation occurs but incompletely

Pain
- Receptor is free nerve ending
- Stimulus is tissue damage, excessive heat or cold, inadequate blood supply, spasm of muscle, stretch of tubes
- Headache due to external head muscle spasm, stretching of meninges, dilation of brain blood vessels
- Referred pain is visceral pain which is referred to skin area supplied with nerve fibers from same spinal segment
- Function of pain is protective

Hunger
- Normal gastric hunger due to contractions of empty stomach, acting on nerves distributed to mucous membrane, and to hypothalamic centers
- Hunger contractions may be frequent and severe, even when food is taken regularly, as in diabetes

Appetite
- Aroused in part through sensory nerves of taste and smell, associated with previous experiences
- Thought of food associated with appetite induces flow of saliva and gastric fluid

Thirst
- Center in hypothalamus responds to dehydration and concentration of blood
- Aids in maintaining body water balance

Nausea
- May be due to stimulation from the stomach, to substances in the blood, to impulses from organs of sight, taste, and smell

Taste
- Sensory apparatus
  1. Taste buds are end organs
  2. Nerve fibers of trigeminal, facial, and glossopharyngeal, vagus nerves
  3. Center in sensory cortex of parietal lobe
- Solution of savory substances must come in contact with taste buds
- Taste buds are distributed over
  - Surface of tongue
  - Soft palate and fauces
  - Tonsils and pharynx

Tongue
- Freely movable muscular organ
- Attached to hyoid bone, epiglottis, and the glossopalatine arches
- Surface covered by papillae containing capillaries and nerves
  - Vallate
  - Fungiform
  - Filiform
  - Simple
- **Nerves**
  - Sensory
    - Lingual branch of trigeminal
    - Chorda tympani, branch of the facial
    - Glossopharyngeal
  - Motor—hypoglossal
- **Sense of**
  1. Taste
  2. Temperature
  3. Pressure
  4. Pain

  are all well developed

Classification of Taste Sensations
- **Four primary sensations**
  - Salty, bitter, acid, sweet
- **All others are**
  - Combinations of primary sensations
  - Combinations of one or more plus odor

Smell
- Sensory apparatus
  - Olfactory nerve endings
  - Olfactory nerve fibers spread out in fine network over surface of superior nasal conchae and upper third of septum
  - Olfactory bulb and center in hippocampus and paraolfactory area
- Odors
  - Minute particles usually in gaseous form
    - Must be capable of solution in mucus
- Olfactory center in the brain is widely connected with other areas of the cerebrum
- Branches of trigeminal nerve found in lining of lower part of nose (pressure)

Hearing
- Auditory apparatus
  - External ear
  - Middle ear, or tympanic cavity
  - Internal ear, or labyrinth
  - Vestibulocochlear nerve
  - Acoustic center in temporal lobe

Ear
- **External ear**
  - Pinna, or auricle
    - **Structure**—cartilaginous framework, some fatty and muscular tissue, covered with skin
    - **Function**—collects sound waves
  - External acoustic meatus
    - 2.5 cm long, partly cartilage, partly bone
    - Leads from the concha to the tympanic membrane
    - Near orifice skin is furnished with hairs and ceruminous glands
    - Ceruminous glands secrete a yellow, pasty substance (wax)

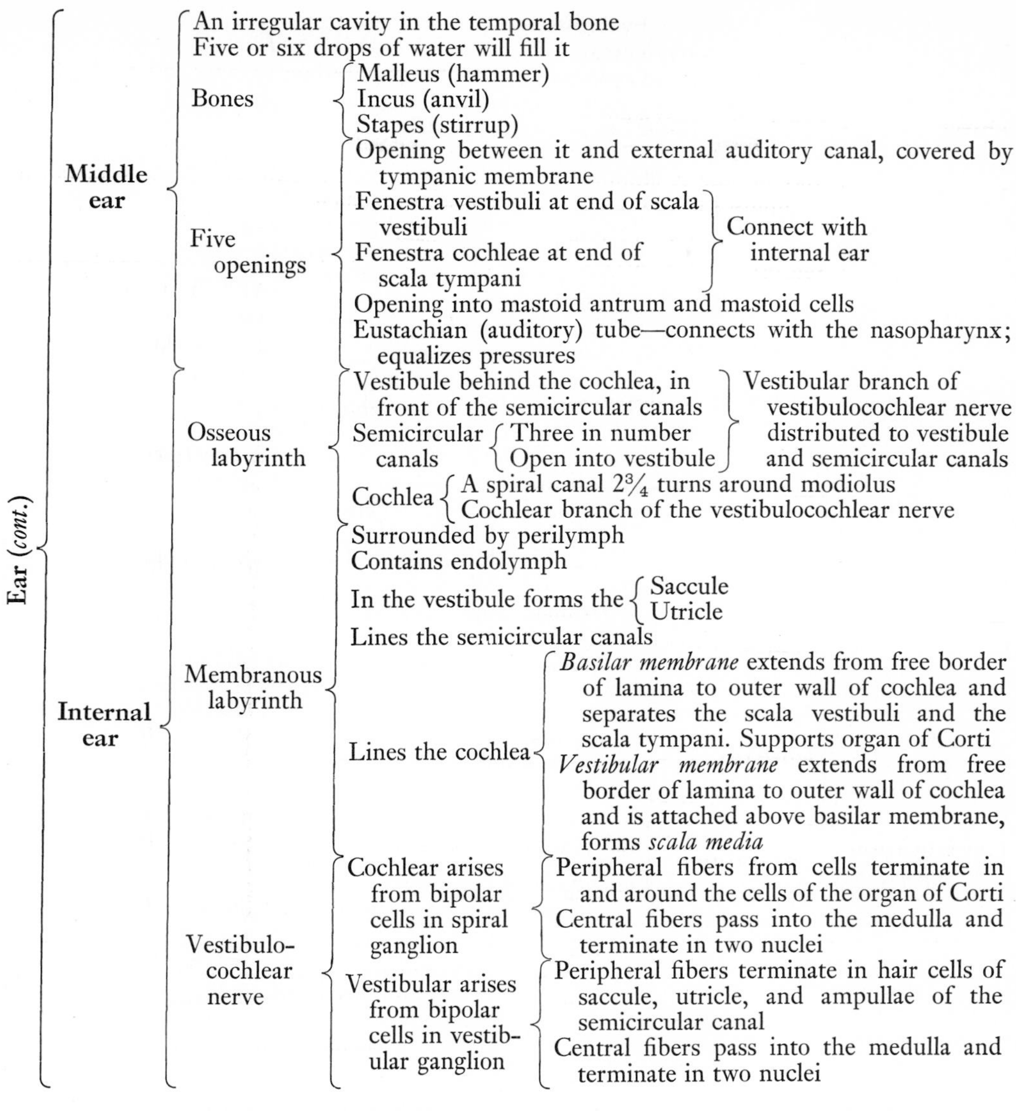

- **Ear** (*cont.*)
  - **Middle ear**
    - An irregular cavity in the temporal bone
    - Five or six drops of water will fill it
    - Bones
      - Malleus (hammer)
      - Incus (anvil)
      - Stapes (stirrup)
    - Five openings
      - Opening between it and external auditory canal, covered by tympanic membrane
      - Fenestra vestibuli at end of scala vestibuli; Fenestra cochleae at end of scala tympani — Connect with internal ear
      - Opening into mastoid antrum and mastoid cells
      - Eustachian (auditory) tube—connects with the nasopharynx; equalizes pressures
  - **Internal ear**
    - Osseous labyrinth
      - Vestibule behind the cochlea, in front of the semicircular canals; Semicircular canals (Three in number; Open into vestibule) — Vestibular branch of vestibulocochlear nerve distributed to vestibule and semicircular canals
      - Cochlea
        - A spiral canal $2\frac{3}{4}$ turns around modiolus
        - Cochlear branch of the vestibulocochlear nerve
    - Membranous labyrinth
      - Surrounded by perilymph
      - Contains endolymph
      - In the vestibule forms the
        - Saccule
        - Utricle
      - Lines the semicircular canals
      - Lines the cochlea
        - *Basilar membrane* extends from free border of lamina to outer wall of cochlea and separates the scala vestibuli and the scala tympani. Supports organ of Corti
        - *Vestibular membrane* extends from free border of lamina to outer wall of cochlea and is attached above basilar membrane, forms *scala media*
    - Vestibulo-cochlear nerve
      - Cochlear arises from bipolar cells in spiral ganglion
        - Peripheral fibers from cells terminate in and around the cells of the organ of Corti
        - Central fibers pass into the medulla and terminate in two nuclei
      - Vestibular arises from bipolar cells in vestibular ganglion
        - Peripheral fibers terminate in hair cells of saccule, utricle, and ampullae of the semicircular canal
        - Central fibers pass into the medulla and terminate in two nuclei

Process of Hearing
- Air waves enter external auditory canal, set tympanic membrane vibrating, vibrations communicated to ossicles, transmitted through fenestra vestibuli to perilymph, stimulate nerve endings in organ of Corti, impulses carried to center of hearing in brain

Unit of measure of sound intensity is the *bel*. A tenth of a bel, or decibel, is used for measurement. Zero decibels is the threshold of hearing. Sixty-five decibels—normal conversation

Sense of Equilibrium
- Function of the vestibule and semicircular canals
- Lining membrane supplied with sensory hairs and otoliths which connect with vestibular nerve
- Flowing of the endolymph stimulates the sensory hairs; this is transmitted to the vestibular branch of the VIIIth nerve, thence to cerebellum

Visual Apparatus
- Bulb of the eye
- Optic nerve
- Center in brain

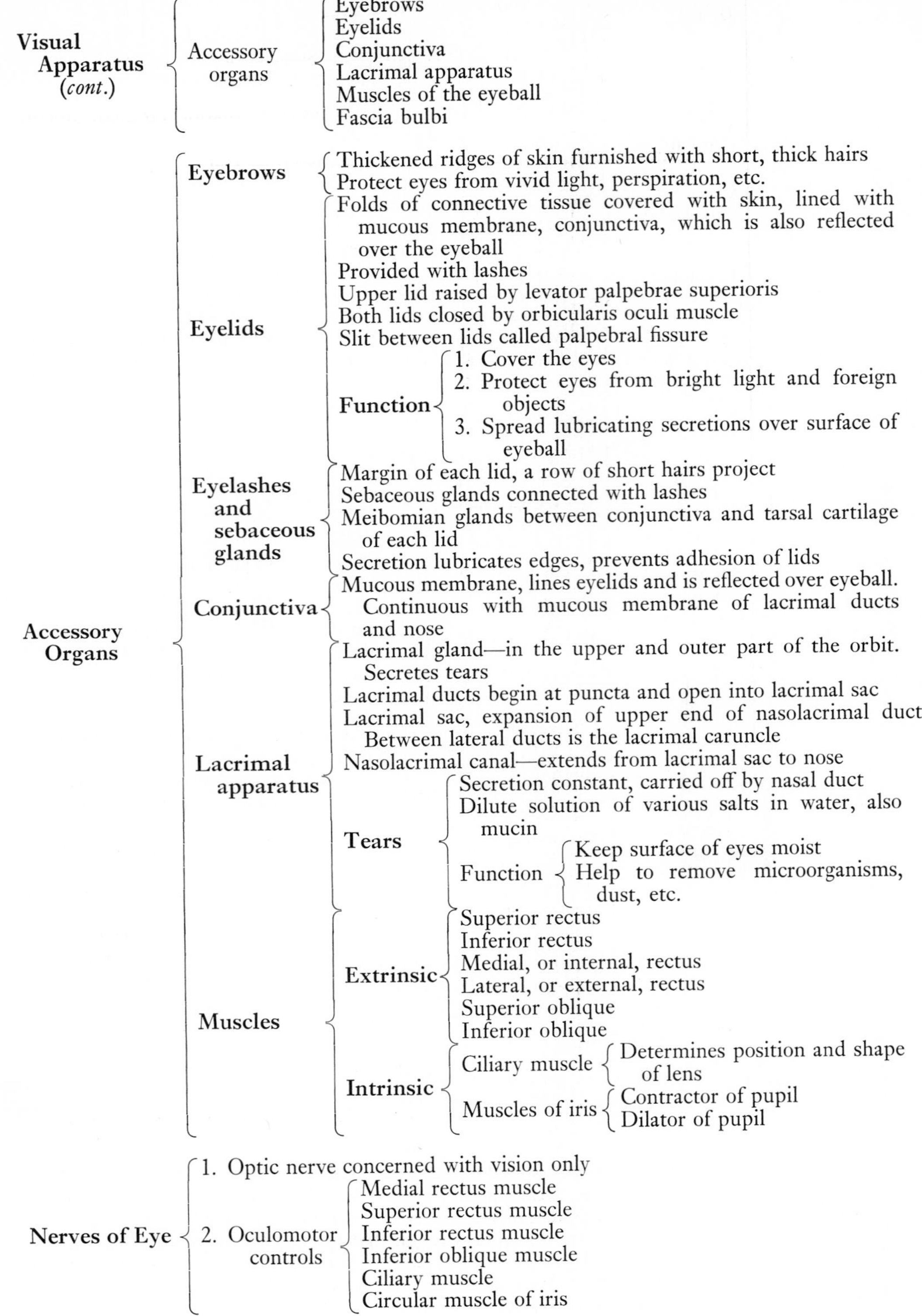

- **Visual Apparatus** (*cont.*)
  - Accessory organs
    - Eyebrows
    - Eyelids
    - Conjunctiva
    - Lacrimal apparatus
    - Muscles of the eyeball
    - Fascia bulbi

- Accessory **Organs**
  - **Eyebrows**
    - Thickened ridges of skin furnished with short, thick hairs
    - Protect eyes from vivid light, perspiration, etc.
  - **Eyelids**
    - Folds of connective tissue covered with skin, lined with mucous membrane, conjunctiva, which is also reflected over the eyeball
    - Provided with lashes
    - Upper lid raised by levator palpebrae superioris
    - Both lids closed by orbicularis oculi muscle
    - Slit between lids called palpebral fissure
    - **Function**
      1. Cover the eyes
      2. Protect eyes from bright light and foreign objects
      3. Spread lubricating secretions over surface of eyeball
  - **Eyelashes and sebaceous glands**
    - Margin of each lid, a row of short hairs project
    - Sebaceous glands connected with lashes
    - Meibomian glands between conjunctiva and tarsal cartilage of each lid
    - Secretion lubricates edges, prevents adhesion of lids
  - **Conjunctiva**
    - Mucous membrane, lines eyelids and is reflected over eyeball. Continuous with mucous membrane of lacrimal ducts and nose
  - **Lacrimal apparatus**
    - Lacrimal gland—in the upper and outer part of the orbit. Secretes tears
    - Lacrimal ducts begin at puncta and open into lacrimal sac
    - Lacrimal sac, expansion of upper end of nasolacrimal duct. Between lateral ducts is the lacrimal caruncle
    - Nasolacrimal canal—extends from lacrimal sac to nose
    - **Tears**
      - Secretion constant, carried off by nasal duct
      - Dilute solution of various salts in water, also mucin
      - Function
        - Keep surface of eyes moist
        - Help to remove microorganisms, dust, etc.
  - **Muscles**
    - **Extrinsic**
      - Superior rectus
      - Inferior rectus
      - Medial, or internal, rectus
      - Lateral, or external, rectus
      - Superior oblique
      - Inferior oblique
    - **Intrinsic**
      - Ciliary muscle
        - Determines position and shape of lens
      - Muscles of iris
        - Contractor of pupil
        - Dilator of pupil

- **Nerves of Eye**
  1. Optic nerve concerned with vision only
  2. Oculomotor controls
     - Medial rectus muscle
     - Superior rectus muscle
     - Inferior rectus muscle
     - Inferior oblique muscle
     - Ciliary muscle
     - Circular muscle of iris

Nerves of Eye (*cont.*)
- 3. Trochlear controls superior oblique muscle
- 4. Abducens controls lateral rectus muscle
- 5. Ophthalmic supplies general sensation, such as pressure, muscle sense, and pain and sympathetic fibers to dilator pupillae

Orbit
- A bony cavity formed by seven bones — Frontal, malar, maxilla, palatine, ethmoid, sphenoid, lacrimal
- Contains eyeball, muscles, nerves, vessels, lacrimal glands, fat, fascia bulbi, and fascia holding structures in place
- Lined by fibrous tissue
- Pad of fat—supports eyeball
- Fascia bulbi is a serous sac which envelops eyeball from optic nerve to ciliary region
- Shaped like funnel
  - Large end directed outward and forward
  - Small end directed backward and inward
- **Optic foramen**—opening for passage of optic nerve and ophthalmic artery
- **Superior orbital fissure**—opening for passage of orbital branches of middle meningeal artery and oculomotor, trochlear, abducens, and ophthalmic nerves

Bulb of the Eye
- Spherical, but it projects anteriorly
- **Coats**
  - 1. Fibrous—sclera and cornea
  - 2. Vascular—choroid, ciliary body, and iris
  - 3. Nervous—retina
- **Refracting media**
  - 1. Cornea and aqueous humor
  - 2. Crystalline lens and capsule
  - 3. Vitreous body

Fibrous Tunics
- **Sclera**
  - Tough, fibrous, sclera
  - Covers posterior five sixths of eyeball
  - Opaque, white and smooth externally, brown internally
- **Cornea**
  - Fibrous, transparent—covers one sixth of eyeball
  - Well supplied with nerve fibers

Vascular Tunic
- **Choroid**
  - Composed of dense capillary network and stroma of cells, some of which are pigmented, lines the sclera
- **Ciliary body**
  - Includes the orbicularis ciliaris, the ciliary processes, and the ciliaris muscle. The orbicularis ciliaris is a zone about 4 mm in width which is continuous with anterior part of choroid
  - Ciliary processes 60–80 radiating folds, arranged like a plaited ruffle around margin of lens
  - Support ciliaris muscle—action of this muscle determines shape or refractiveness of lens
- **Iris**
  - A circular colored disk suspended in front of lens and behind cornea. Hangs free except for attachment at circumference to the ciliary processes and choroid. Central perforation—pupil
  - Pupil contracted by circular, or sphincter, muscle
  - Pupil dilated by radial, or dilator, muscle
  - Composed of connective tissue, containing numerous blood vessels and nerves. Contains pigment cells
  - **Function**—regulates size of pupil and thereby amount of light entering eye

Nervous Tunic, or Retina
- Nervous layer—contains elements essential for reception of rays of light. Situated between the choroid coat and hyaloid membrane of the vitreous humor, extends forward and terminates in the *ora serrata*
- Has three sets of neurons so arranged that seven layers are formed. These are held in place by neuroglia and two membranes. Counting from the hyaloid membrane (membrana limitans interna) outward
- 1. Nerve fibers, or stratum opticum

Nervous Tunic, or Retina (*cont.*)
- 2. Cell bodies of third-order neurons, or ganglionic layer
- 3. Area of synapses of second and third neurons, or inner plexiform layer
- 4. Cell bodies of second neurons, or inner nuclear layer
- 5. Areas of synapses between first and second neurons, or outer plexiform layer
- 6. Cell bodies of first neurons, or outer nuclear layer
- Membrana limitans externa, marking internal limit of rods and cones
- 7. Rods and cones of first neurons are end organs, or receptors, for the optic nerve
- Pigmented layer between rods and cones and choroid
- **Blind spot**
  - Entrance of optic nerve and central artery and vein of the retina
  - There are no rods and cones
  - Totally insensitive to light
- **Macula lutea**
  - 2 mm outer side of blind spot
  - Central pit—fovea centralis—is the center of direct vision

Refracting Media
- **Cornea**
  - Transparent, refractive structure covering the anterior one sixth of the eye bulb
- **Aqueous humor**
  - Aqueous chamber is between cornea in front and lens, suspensory ligament, and ciliary body behind. Aqueous humor is a watery solution containing minute amounts of salts
  - Dialyzed from capillaries, drains away through canal of Schlemm
- **Crystalline lens**
  - Transparent, refractive body enclosed in an elastic capsule
  - Double convex in shape. Situated behind the pupil
  - Held in position by counterbalancing of aqueous humor, vitreous body, and suspensory ligament
- **Vitreous body**
  - Semifluid, albuminous tissue enclosed in hyaloid membrane
  - Fills posterior four fifths of bulb of the eye, distends sclera, and supports retina

Perception of Light and Color
- Waves vary in length
  - Waves between 400 and 800 mμ in length are called light and color waves—the visual spectrum

Refraction—bending or deviation in the course of rays of light, in passing obliquely from one transparent medium into another of different density

Vision
- Visible objects reflect light waves which fall upon them
- These reflected rays are brought to focus on receptors (rods and cones) of retina, where a chemical change in rhodopsin initiates nerve impulses, which are transmitted to optic nerve, and thence to centers of vision in occipital lobe of cerebrum, from here to association areas
- Color blindness due to abnormal cones

Processes Necessary for Binocular Vision
1. Convergence, or turning the eyes inward, in order to place the image on corresponding points of the two retinae
2. Change in size of pupil—contracts in a bright light—dilates in a dim light
3. Accommodation—capacity of the eyes and lenses to adjust so that objects at varying distances can be seen clearly
4. Refraction—bending of light rays entering the pupil so they come to a focus on the retina

Abnormal Conditions
- **Myopia**
  - Nearsightedness
  - **Cause**—rays of light converge too soon
- **Hypermetropia**
  - Farsightedness
  - **Cause**—rays of light do not converge soon enough
- **Presbyopia**
  - Defective condition of accommodation in which distant objects are seen distinctly but near objects are indistinct
- **Astigmatism**
  - Condition in which the curvature of the refracting surfaces is defective

CHAPTER

13

THE AUTONOMIC NERVOUS SYSTEM

Structure and Function

Interdependence of the Craniosacral and Thoracolumbar Systems

The central nervous system is concerned with control and response to environmental changes. There is purposeful, planned response to environmental needs; action is controlled.

The autonomic nervous system controls internal environment, such as, for example, heart action, adjustment of circulation to meet body needs, secretion of digestive juices, and peristaltic activity. There is also a personal nonintellectual response to environment, such as emotional reaction to a given situation, which in turn may affect physiological functioning.

The division of the nervous system into the cerebrospinal system and the visceral system is based more on a difference in function than on an actual anatomical separation. The *visceral* system is both afferent and efferent in function. This system possesses a certain independence of the cerebrospinal system. It regulates and controls vital activities. There is no consciousness of these activities, except as they contribute in a general way to a sense of well-being.

Most of the centers controlling these processes are located within the central nervous system; but there is coordination of cellular activities even within the walls of the viscera, and this intraorgan integration helps to control such activities as gastrointestinal motility and secretion, cardiac output, sweating, urinary output, arterial blood pressure, and many other physiological processes. Some autonomic functions are almost completely controlled by the central nervous system; others are only partly controlled by the central nervous system. Some visceral functions can be performed quite independently of any nervous control. The heart muscle contracts automatically; some of the glands are excited to secrete by chemical substances in the blood such as the secretion of pancreatic fluid in response to the hormone *secretin*. Even though such activities are not directly dependent on the nervous system, they may be regulated or modulated by the nervous system, because in all visceral functions the nonnervous and the nervous cooperate in a most intimate way.

Efferent Visceral. In the autonomic system two neurons connect the central nervous system and the end organ. The fiber of a neuron lying in the *central nervous system* extends to an *autonomic ganglion* and synapses on the dendrites or cell body of an autonomic neuron. The fiber of the second neuron passes from the ganglion to the effector to be innervated. The fiber of the first neuron is called

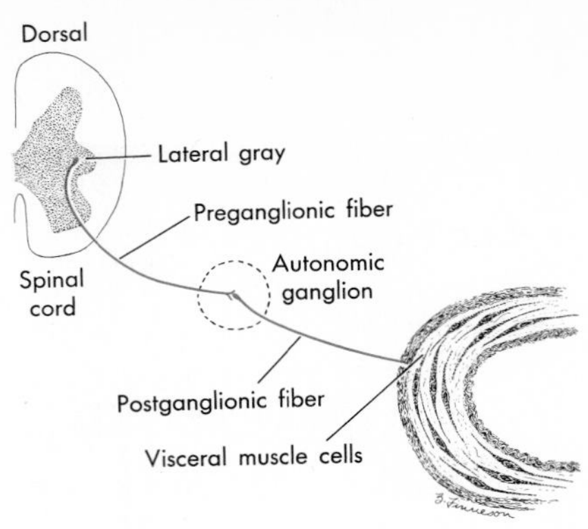

Figure 13–1. Diagram showing the relationship of the preganglionic and postganglionic neurons of the autonomic nervous system.

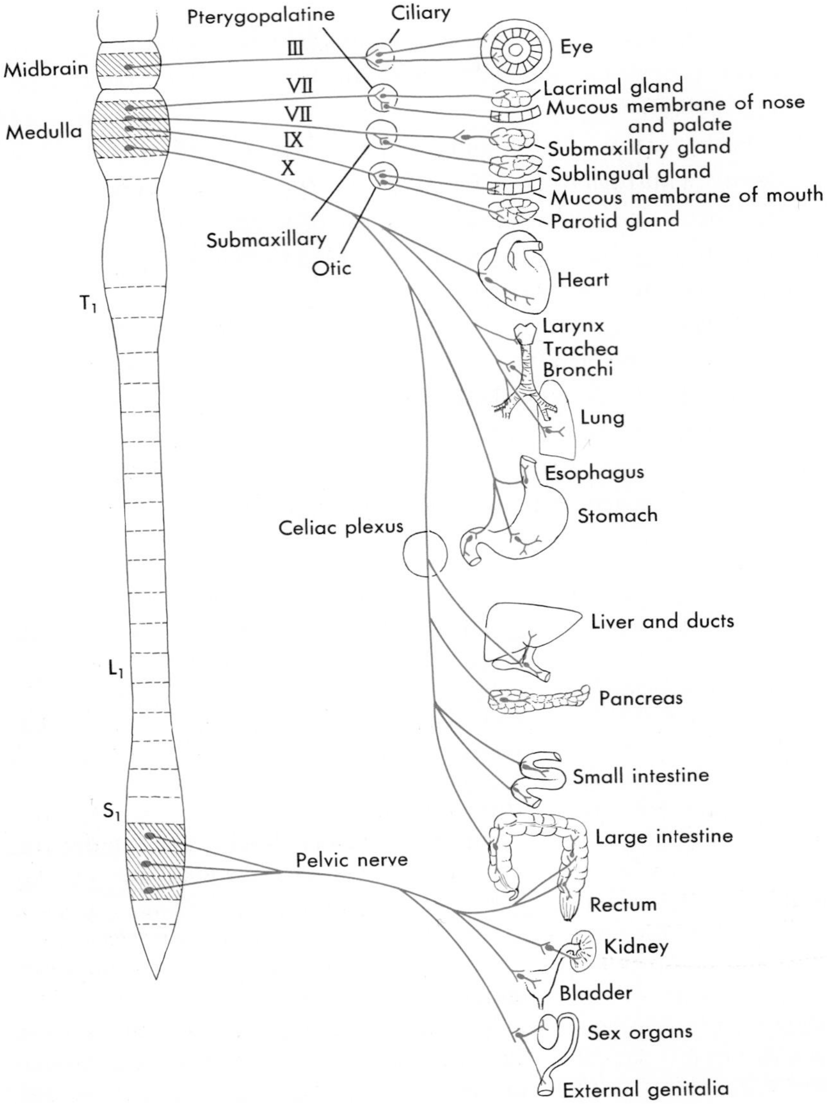

Figure 13–2. Craniosacral autonomic system.

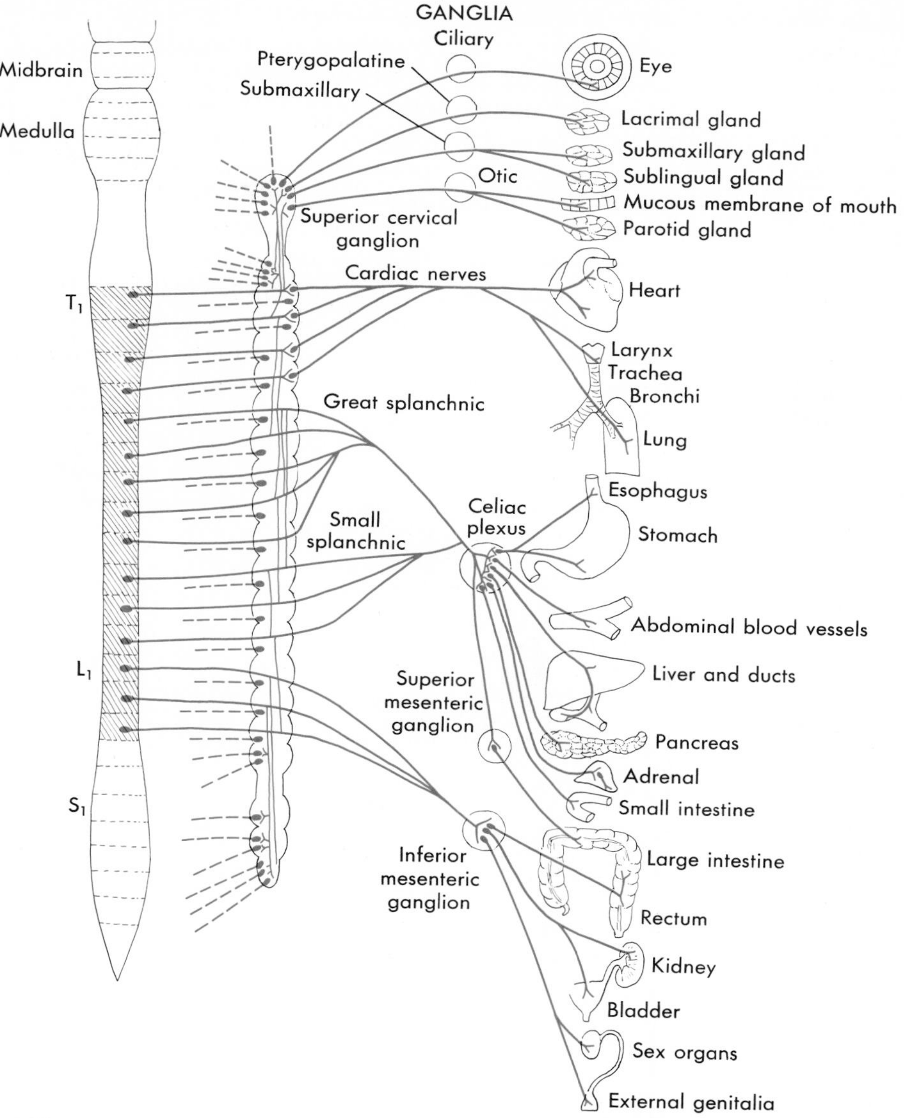

Figure 13–3. Diagram of the thoracolumbar nervous system. *Dashed red lines* represent fibers to blood vessels (vasomotor), arrector pili muscles (pilomotor), and sweat glands (secretory).

the *preganglionic fiber*; the fiber of the second neuron is called the *postganglionic fiber*.

The Craniosacral, or Parasympathetic, System. This system includes all the fibers that arise from the midbrain (tectal autonomics), from the medulla and pons (bulbar autonomics), and from the sacral region of the cord (sacral autonomics).

The *tectal autonomics* arise from nuclei in the midbrain, send preganglionic fibers with the oculomotor nerve into the orbit, and pass to the ciliary ganglion, where they terminate by forming synapses with motor neurons whose axons (postganglionic fibers) proceed as the short ciliary nerves to the ciliary muscle of the eye and to the pupillary sphincters.

The *bulbar autonomics* arise from nuclei in the medulla and pons and emerge in the seventh, ninth, and tenth cranial nerves.

Fibers from the seventh nerve are distributed to lacrimal, nasal, submaxillary, and sublingual glands. Fibers from the ninth nerve are distributed to the parotid gland. Fibers from the tenth nerve are distributed to the heart, lungs, esophagus, stomach, the small intestine, proximal half of the colon, gallbladder, liver, and pancreas.

Some of the fibers of the vagus nerve are distributed to the skeletal muscles of the larynx and pharynx from the nucleus ambiguus. The vagus also carries important afferent nerve fibers from pressor receptors in arteries and stretch receptors of the lungs to the medulla.

The sacral autonomics include autonomic fibers which emerge from the spinal cord. Neurons of the second, third, and fourth, and sometimes the first sacral spinal nerves send fibers to the pelvis, where they form the pelvic nerve, which sends fibers to the pelvic plexus, from which postganglionic fibers are distributed to the pelvic viscera. Motor fibers pass to the smooth muscle of the descending colon, rectum, anus, bladder, and reproductive organs. Vasodilator fibers are distributed to the organs and to the external genitals.

Thoracolumbar, or Sympathetic, System. This includes (1) small neurons in the gray lateral columns of the thoracic and lumbar regions of the cord giving rise to preganglionic fibers; (2) the sympathetic ganglia and their postganglionic fibers—the

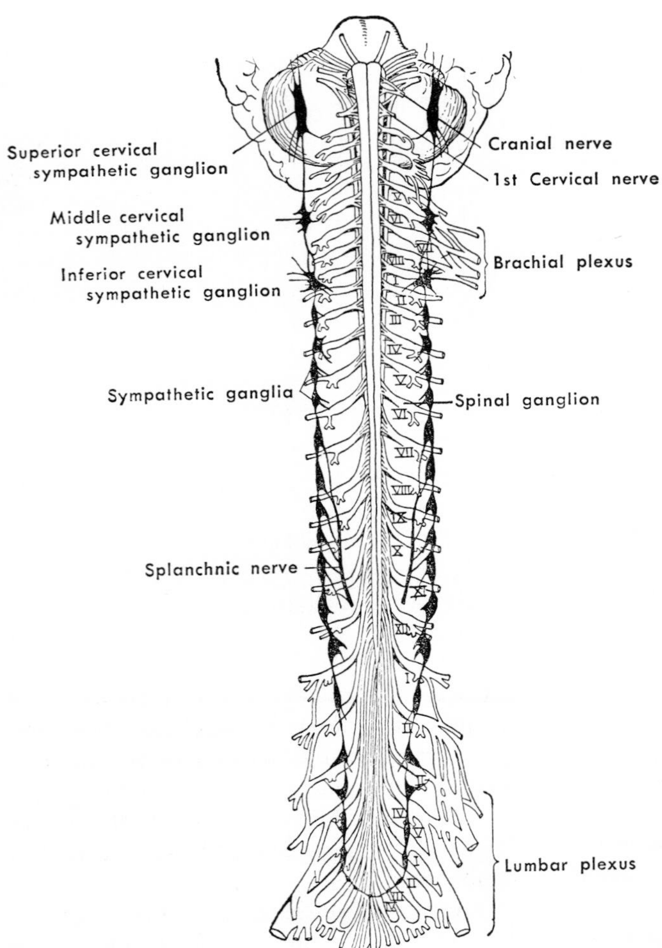

Figure 13–4. Diagram of spinal cord, spinal nerves, and the right and left chains of autonomic ganglia. At the top the medulla is seen, with some of the cranial nerves. The cerebellum is seen behind the medulla at the sides, and behind the cerebellum the cerebrum is shown at the sides. (From Huxley, after Allen Thomson.)

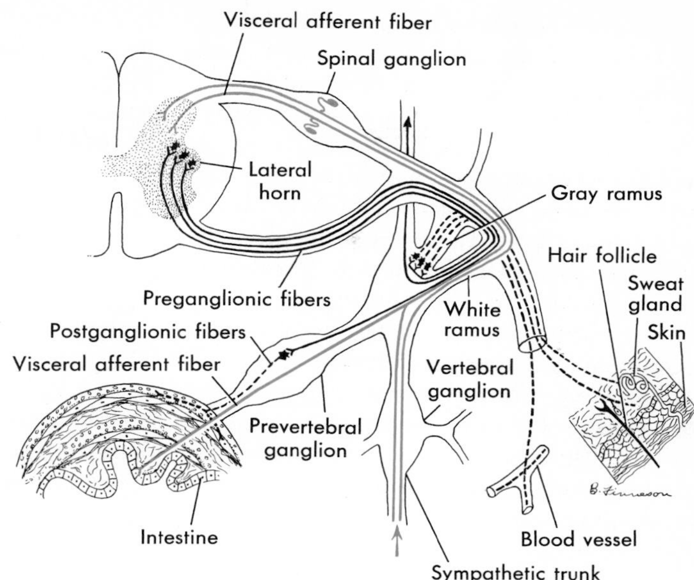

Figure 13–5. Diagram showing origin of sympathetic preganglionic and postganglionic fibers and their distribution.

lateral chain of the sympathetic trunk; and (3) the great prevertebral plexuses. Postganglionic fibers may arise either from a ganglion in the lateral chain or from a ganglion in one of the great plexuses.

The sympathetic centers of the spinal cord are composed of groups of cells lying in the lateral columns of the gray matter of the cord from the first thoracic to lumbar two or three. They give rise to preganglionic fibers which terminate in one of the sympathetic ganglia.

The sympathetic ganglia (Figure 13–4) consist of paired chains of ganglia which lie along the ventrolateral aspects of the vertebral column, extending from the base of the skull to the coccyx. They are grouped as cervical, thoracic, lumbar, and sacral, and, except in the neck, they correspond in number to the vertebrae against which they lie:

Cervical	Thoracic	Lumbar	Sacral
3 pairs	10–12 pairs	4 pairs	4–5 pairs

The sympathetic ganglia are connected with each other by nerve fibers called gangliated cords, and with the spinal nerves by branches called *rami communicantes.* In the thoracic and lumbar regions these communications consist of two rami, a white ramus and a gray ramus (Figure 13–5).

The white rami fibers are *myelinated fibers* passing from the central nervous system to the sympathetic ganglia. The gray rami fibers are *nonmyelinated postganglionic* fibers that are the axons of cells in the sympathetic ganglia and are distributed chiefly with the peripheral branches of all the spinal nerves to the periphery.

The White Rami Fibers. The cell of origin of these fibers lies in the lateral gray of the spinal cord from the first thoracic (T_1) to the second or third lumbar segments. The fibers leave by way of the anterior root with the somatic efferent axons. They leave the spinal nerve by way of the white rami and enter the sympathetic ganglia, where they may terminate on a sympathetic postganglionic neuron or may pass up or down in the sympathetic chain for some distance before ending on a sympathetic neuron. These are the fibers that form the gangliated cord of the sympathetic chain.

The fibers from T_1 to T_5 (preganglionic) emerge from the cord and synapse in the sympathetic ganglia. The fibers of the sympathetic cells in the ganglia (postganglionic fibers) are distributed to the heart, lungs, and blood vessels.

The fibers from T_6 to T_{12} form the splanchnic nerves. These preganglionic fibers pass through the sympathetic ganglia and terminate in the celiac ganglia (solar plexus). The postganglionic fibers are distributed to the esophagus, stomach, and intestine as far as the proximal colon, liver, and gallbladder.

The fibers from L_1 to L_3 form the *preganglionic* fibers that terminate in the inferior mesenteric ganglia. The *postganglionic* fibers are distributed to the distal part of the colon, rectum, and genitourinary organs.

The Gray Rami Fibers. These have their cells of origin in the sympathetic ganglia and are distributed via the spinal nerves to arteries, arterioles (vasoconstrictors), veins, venules, sweat glands, and pilomotor muscles (Figure 13–5).

The fibers to the blood vessels, glands, and walls of the viscera are distributed by various sympathetic ganglia. For the head region the fibers, after entering the sympathetic chain, pass upward and end in the *superior cervical ganglion*; from this ganglion postganglionic fibers emerge from the various plexuses that arise from this ganglion. (See Figure 13–3.)

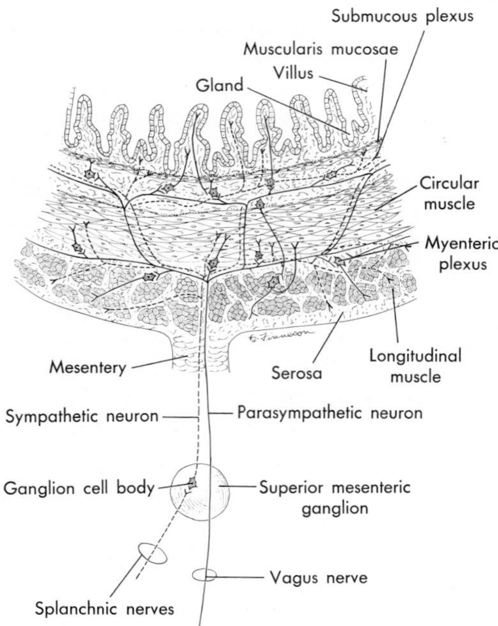

Figure 13–6. Distribution of autonomic neurons to the enteric system.

The Great Plexuses of the Thoracolumbar System. These consist of ganglia and fibers derived from the lateral chain ganglia and the spinal cord. They are situated in the thoracic, abdominal, and pelvic cavities and are named the cardiac, celiac, mesenteric, lumbar, and sacral plexuses.

1. THE CARDIAC PLEXUS. This is situated at the base of the heart, lying on the arch and the ascending portion of the aorta.

2. THE CELIAC PLEXUS (SOLAR PLEXUS). This is situated behind the stomach, between the suprarenal glands. It surrounds the celiac artery and the root of the superior mesenteric artery. It consists of two large ganglia and a dense network of nerve fibers uniting them. It receives the greater and lesser splanchnic nerves of both sides and some fibers from the vagi and gives off numerous secondary plexuses along the neighboring arteries. The names of the secondary plexuses indicate the arteries they accompany and the organs to which they distribute branches.

Phrenic	Superior gastric	Spermatic
Hepatic	Suprarenal	Superior mesenteric
Splenic	Renal	Inferior mesenteric
		Aortic

These nerves form intricate networks, and any one organ may receive branches from several nerves. This increases the number of pathways and connections between the organs.

3. THE MESENTERIC PLEXUS. This is situated in front of the last lumbar vertebra and the promontory of the sacrum. It is formed by the union of numerous filaments which descend on either side from the aortic plexus and from the lumbar ganglia; below, it divides into the lumbar and sacral plexuses.

The Enteric System. This system includes the myenteric (Auerbach's[1]) plexus and the submucous (Meissner's[2]) plexus in the wall of the digestive canal. They extend

[1] Leopold Auerbach, German anatomist (1828–1897).

[2] Georg Meissner, German anatomist and physiologist (1829–1905).

from the upper level of the esophagus to the anal canal. The myenteric plexus is situated between the longitudinal and circular muscular coats in the wall of the gastrointestinal tract. This plexus is responsible for coordinating the timing and strength of contractions and secretions of the intestinal wall. The submucous plexus lies in the submucosa. These plexuses are intimately connected with each other (Figure 13–6).

Function of the Autonomic System. The autonomic system innervates (1) all plain muscular tissue in the body, (2) the heart, and (3) the glands. The ganglia serve as relay stations for many of the impulses passing from the midbrain, pons, and medulla, or spinal cord, or they may act independently of these influences.

In general, most organs have a double autonomic innervation, one from the thoracolumbar system and one from either the cranial or the sacral autonomic system. The functions of these two systems are usually antagonistic. With the exception of nicotine, which paralyzes all autonomic ganglia, most drugs which act on the autonomic system affect principally either the craniosacral system, as do atropine, pilocarpine, and physostigmine, or the thoracolumbar system, as do epinephrine and ergotoxine. There are new drugs that block the transmission of impulses from the preganglionic neurons to the postganglionic neurons. All of these interfere with the transmission of impulses in both the parasympathetic and sympathetic systems to varying degrees. These drugs are useful in the treatment of high blood pressure and intestinal hyperactivity.

Neural Transmission. As in the somatic nervous system the action of the autonomic impulses causes release of a chemical transmitter substance. Autonomic fibers are classed as cholinergic and adrenergic fibers on the basis of the transmitter substance. All preganglionic fibers release from the vesicles in their nerve endings acetylcholine, which diffuses across the synaptic cleft and produces permeability changes in the membrane of the postganglionic neuron. The transmitter is rapidly hydrolyzed by the enzyme acetylcholinesterase. Since all preganglionic fibers of both parasympathetic and sympathetic systems release acetylcholine they are called "cholinergic." All parasympathetic postganglionic fibers are also cholinergic. Most sympathetic postganglionic fibers release norepinephrine and are called "adrenergic." Monoamine oxidase is the enzyme that rapidly destroys norepinephrine.

Cells stimulated by adrenergic fibers have been subdivided into two groups (α and β), based on their response to certain drugs. Stimulation of β fibers results in increased rate and strength of cardiac contraction, vasodilation, and bronchial relaxation.

Afferent Visceral Fibers. The afferent fibers of many receptors in the viscera carry impulses from receptors in the organs to the spinal cord and brain. The afferent fibers of the vagus, with cell bodies located in the nodosal ganglion, innervate sensory endings in the heart, lungs, and other viscera of the thoracic and abdominal cavity. The pelvic nerve carries afferent fibers from receptors in the mesentery and in the colon wall. Visceral reflexes are mediated through the spinal cord and brain stem. Visceral pain is carried by fibers in the sympathetic nerves. Motor, vasomotor, and secretory reflexes are mediated over autonomic neural arcs and do not reach consciousness. Sensations of bladder and colon distention are mediated over the afferent fibers of the pelvic nerve.

Interdependence of the Craniosacral and Thoracolumbar Systems. Marked stimulation of one system, or even part of one system, is likely to stimulate some part of the other system, thus checking excessive stimulation with the untoward results that might follow. Stimulation of the part of the vagus that supplies the bronchial tubes may cause such marked constriction of the tubes that interference with breathing, pain, and distress may result; this in turn stimulates the thoracolumbar system to lessen the contraction of the tubes. For another example, the afferent branch of the vagus connected with the aorta is stimulated when the blood pressure within the vessel rises. These afferent impulses initiate efferent impulses which

Analysis of Figure 13–7

Fibers from the various ganglia are distributed to organ listed in center column

Parasympathetic—Blue Fibers			Thoracolumbar—Red Fibers	
Nucleus of Origin of Preganglionic Cell	Postganglionic Cell Bodies, Peripheral Ganglia	Name of Part	Postganglionic Cell Bodies, Peripheral Ganglia	Nucleus of Origin of Preganglionic Cell Body
Edinger-Westphal nucleus, midbrain	Ciliary ganglion	Eye, iris, ciliary muscle	Superior cervical sympathetic, no fibers to ciliary muscle	Lateral gray of cord, T_1–T_2 or T_3
Superior salivatory nucleus in pons	Pterygopalatine ganglia	Lacrimal glands	Superior and middle cervical sympathetic ganglia	Lateral gray of cord, T_1–T_2
Superior salivatory nucleus in pons	Submandibular ganglion	Submaxillary, submandibulary glands	Superior and middle cervical sympathetic ganglia	Lateral gray of cord, T_1–T_3 or T_4
Inferior salivatory nucleus in medulla	Otic ganglia	Parotid glands	Superior and middle cervical sympathetic ganglia	Lateral gray of cord T_1–T_3 or T_4
Dorsal motor nucleus of vagus	Ganglia of pulmonary plexus	Lungs and bronchi	Inferior cervical and T_1–T_5 sympathetic ganglia	Lateral gray of cord, T_1–T_5
Dorsal motor nucleus of vagus	Intracardiac ganglia of the atria	Heart	Superior, middle, and inferior cervical sympathetic ganglia and T_1–T_6 sympathetic ganglia	Lateral gray of cord, T_1–T_6
Dorsal motor nucleus of vagus	Myenteric and submucous plexuses	Esophagus	Sympathetic ganglia T_1–T_3	Lateral gray of cord, T_1–T_6
Dorsal motor nucleus of vagus	Myenteric and submucous plexuses	Stomach, small intestine, and transverse colon	Celiac and superior mesenteric ganglia	Lateral gray of cord, T_5–L_{11}
Autonomic nucleus of the lateral gray of cord, S_2–S_4	Ganglia of myenteric, submucous, and hemorrhoidal plexuses	Descending colon, rectum, and internal sphincter	Lumbar and inferior mesenteric sympathetic ganglia	Lateral gray of cord, T_{12}–L_3
Autonomic nucleus of the lateral gray in cord, S_2–S_4	Ganglia of vesical branches of internal iliac artery	Urinary bladder and internal urethral sphincter	Lumbar and inferior mesenteric sympathetic ganglia	Intermediolateral gray of cord, T_{12}–L_2
Autonomic nucleus of the lateral gray in cord, S_2–S_4	Ganglia along branches of aorta and internal iliac arteries	Reproductive organs	Lumbar, sacral, and inferior sympathetic ganglia	Intermediolateral gray of cord, T_{10}–L_2

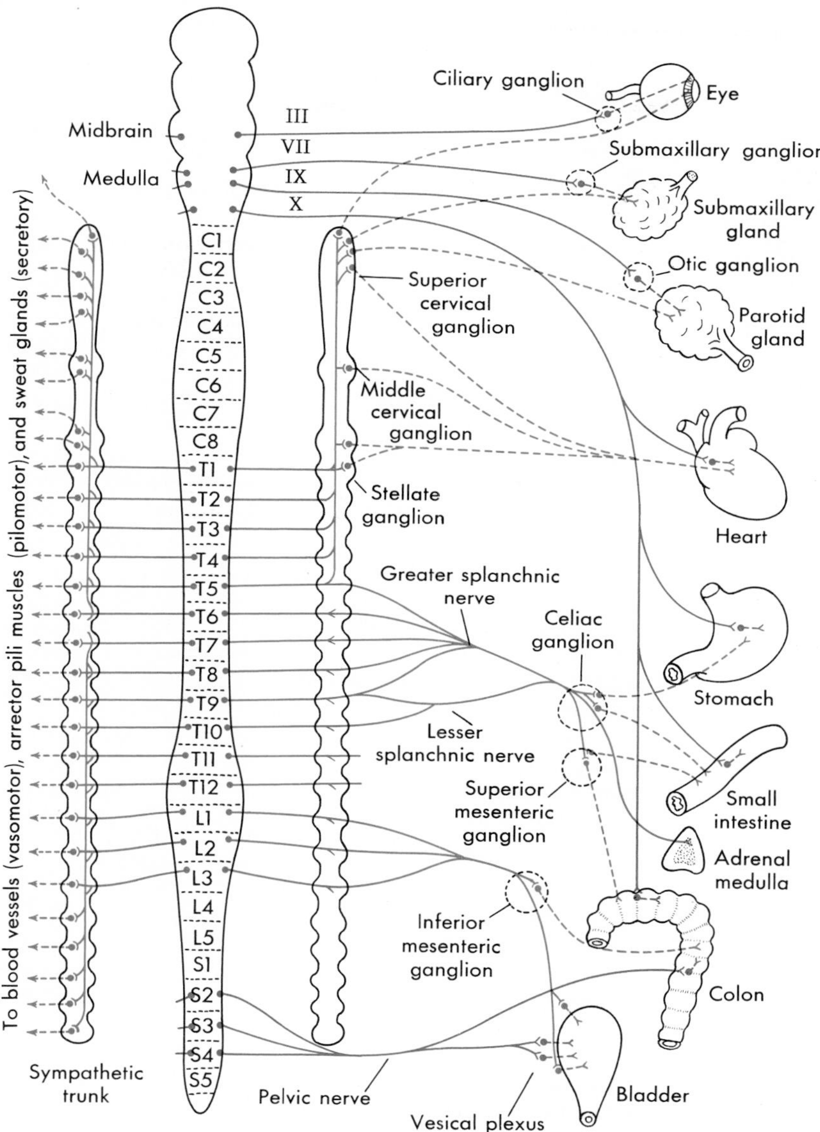

Figure 13–7. Diagrammatic representation of some of the chief conduction pathways of the autonomic nervous system. For clarity, the nerves to blood vessels, arrector pili muscles, and sweat glands are shown on the left side of the figure and the pathways to other visceral structures only on the right side. The sympathetic division is shown in red, the parasympathetic in blue. *Solid lines* represent preganglionic fibers; *broken lines* represent postganglionic fibers. (Modified from *Bailey's Textbook of Histology*, 13th ed., revised by P. E. Smith and W. M. Copenhaver. Courtesy of the Williams and Wilkins Company.)

are (1) inhibitory to the heart, thus slowing its action, and (2) inhibitory to the vasoconstrictor center, thus lessening vasoconstriction.

Antagonistic action of the craniosacral and thoracolumbar systems are listed so that the results following stimulation of these two systems may be compared (page 271).

The chief subcortical center for regulation of both parasympathetic and sympathetic activities lies in the hypothalamus. The

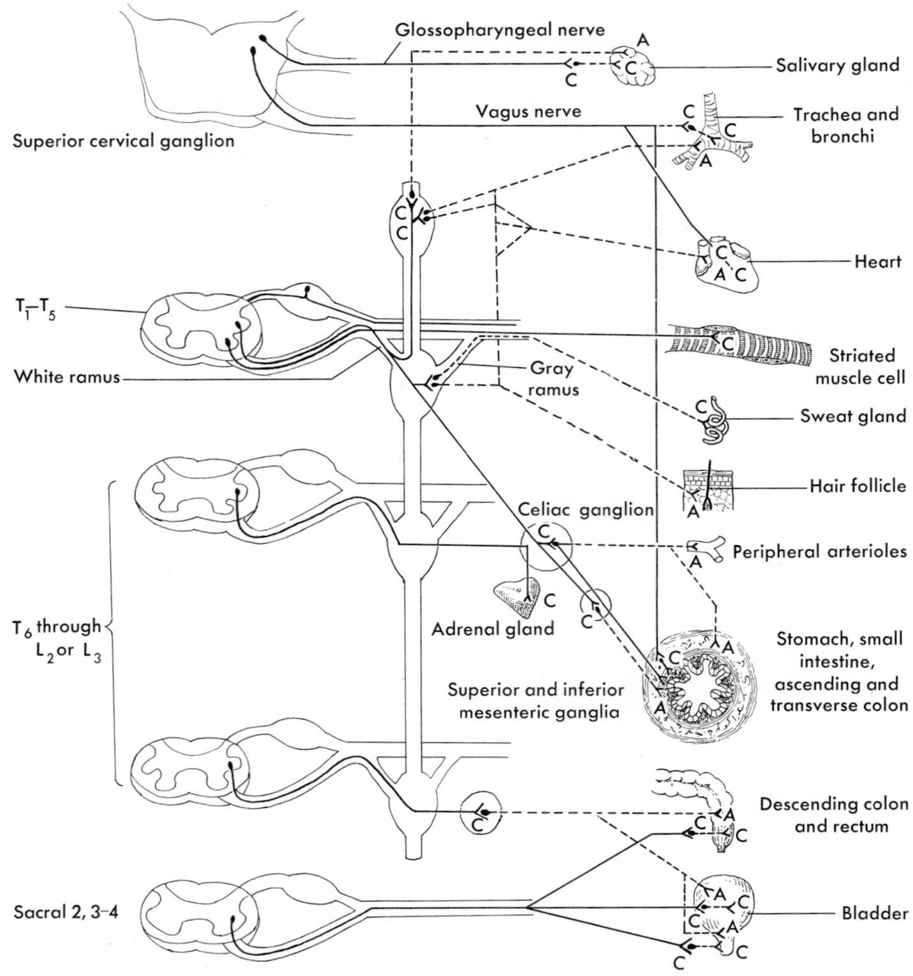

Figure 13–8. Diagram of autonomic nervous system showing cholinergic (*C*) and adrenergic (*A*) nerve endings.

anterior and medial areas of the hypothalamus control parasympathetic activities. When this region is stimulated, there are slowing of the heart rate, increased motility and tone of the alimentary musculature, and vasodilation of peripheral blood vessels. This area is also concerned with maintaining water balance. Diabetes insipidus results if this area is destroyed.

The posterior and lateral hypothalamic regions are concerned with control of sympathetic activities. When these areas are stimulated, the prompt sympathetic responses are dilation of the pupil, increased heart rate, vasoconstriction causing an elevation of blood pressure, and inhibition of the digestive organs and bladder. These centers complement each other in regulation of body processes. For instance, if the body temperature falls, the "heat conservation" center in the caudal hypothalamus initiates (1) shivering, which promptly increases heat production, and (2) marked vasoconstriction of cutaneous blood vessels, which reduces heat loss through the skin. If body temperature increases, a "heat loss" center in the anterior hypothalamus responds by initiating (1) sweating, (2) dilatation of cutaneous blood

Name of Part	Effect of Craniosacral (Parasympathetic) Stimulation	Effect of Thoracolumbar (Sympathetic) Stimulation
Eye—Iris	Constricts the pupil (miosis)	Dilates the pupil (mydriasis)
Ciliary muscle	Contracts ciliary muscle; accommodation of the lens for near vision	No effect
Lacrimal glands	Stimulates secretion	Little or no effect
Lungs—Bronchi	Constricts bronchial tubes	Dilates bronchial tubes
Heart—Muscle	Slows heart rate	Accelerates heart rate and strengthens ventricular contraction
Arteries in viscera		
Lungs	No innervation	Very mildly constricts vessels
Coronary arteries	Constricts arteries	Vasodilation
Abdominal	No innervation	Vasoconstriction
Arteries in somatic tissue		
Muscle	No innervation	Vasoconstriction
Skin	No innervation	Vasoconstriction
Glands—Sweat	No innervation	Marked sweating
Salivary	Increased secretion; thin, watery, containing many enzymes	Vasoconstriction; decrease in amount of saliva; becomes viscid in character
Gastric	Increased secretion	Secretion inhibited
Intestinal	Increased tension in walls	Walls of gut relaxed
Liver	No effect	Glucose released
Gallbladder and ducts	Stimulates bile flow	Inhibits bile flow
Kidney	No effect	Vasoconstriction, which leads to decreased urine flow
Bladder	Muscle wall contracted; internal sphincter relaxed	Muscle wall relaxed; internal sphincter constricted
Intestinal organs—		
Motility	Increased peristalsis and tone of wall increased	Decreased peristalsis and muscle tone; wall relaxed
Sphincters	Internal sphincter relaxed	Sphincter constricted
Adrenal gland		
Cortex	No effect	Increased secretion
Medulla	Little or no effect	Increased secretion
Basal metabolism	No effect	Metabolism markedly increased
Blood sugar	No effect	Increased; liver releases glycogen
Blood coagulation	No effect	Increased coagulation
Mental activity	No effect	Increased activity
Sex organs	Vasodilation and erection	Contraction of uterine musculature, ductus deferens, seminal vesicle, vasoconstriction
Piloerector muscles	No effect	Excited; hair stands on end

vessels, and (3) constriction of splanchnic blood vessels, which shunts blood to the skin's surface where heat is removed from the body by radiation and conduction. Sweating cools the skin if the external environmental conditions are conducive to rapid evaporation. If the posterior hypothalamus is destroyed, a state of almost total lethargy results. The hypothalamus sends fibers down to the preganglionic autonomic centers of the brain stem and to the lateral gray of the spinal cord. By these connections there are pathways through which impulses from receptors, responding to changes in the environment, are transmitted to the thalamus, to the cortex, to the hypothalamus, and finally to the viscera. It is through these and other pathways that "fleeting thoughts" or other emotional crises affect the heart rate, vascular beds, and other autonomic physiological processes.

Cortical centers that regulate autonomic activity are located in prefrontal lobes and temporal regions. Stimulation of these areas during emotional states arouses autonomic areas of the hypothalamic centers. There are also regulating centers in the thalamus. Both conscious and unconscious areas of the cortex can cause autonomic response. The action of the sympathetic nervous system is augmented by the hormones of the adrenal medulla. See Chapter 23 for discussion.

The thoracolumbar system is strongly stimulated by pain and unpleasant excitement such as anger, fear, or insecurity. The animal responses to anger and fear are fight and flight, and the conditions brought about by stimulating the thoracolumbar system are such as to favor these responses; i.e., the bronchial tubes are relaxed and rapid breathing is rendered easier; the constriction of the blood vessels in the stomach and intestines and the increased heart action deliver more blood to the skeletal muscles and thus provide them with the extra oxygen and nutrients needed for increased muscular activity; the supply of glucose from the liver is also increased, thus providing for greater production of energy. Increased activity of sweat glands produces perspiration. If the environmental conditions permit the evaporation of this excess perspiration, body temperature will be maintained more nearly constant. All these responses are closely connected with the suprarenal glands, which secrete epinephrine and norepinephrine. The amount of secretion is increased when the thoracolumbar system is stimulated.

In acute stress situations the physiological response is to prepare the body for fight and flight. However, it must be remembered that in certain stressful situations physiological response may be mainly either sympathetic or parasympathetic or a combination of both. Excessive response to environmental conditions of portions of either of these divisions of the autonomic nervous system may predispose the individual to physiological disorders classified as psychosomatic or psychovisceral diseases. Such changes may include a great variety of physiological disorders, a few of which are hypertension, peptic ulcers colitis, and headache.

QUESTIONS FOR DISCUSSION

1. Discuss the physiological means by which stress raises blood pressure.
2. An individual has been under stress and complains of increased peristalsis with severe cramps. The doctor orders an anticholinergic drug. Explain the reasons for the symptoms and why the drug was ordered.
3. Analyze and explain the physiological response to stress.
4. Compare the physiological responses of the sympathetic and parasympathetic systems on the heart and on the gastrointestinal wall.
5. What is the connection between the spinal cord and the sympathetic ganglia?
6. What is the enteric system?
7. What part of the brain is concerned with sympathetic activities?
8. Discuss neural transmission at the preganglionic and the postganglionic synapses.

SUMMARY

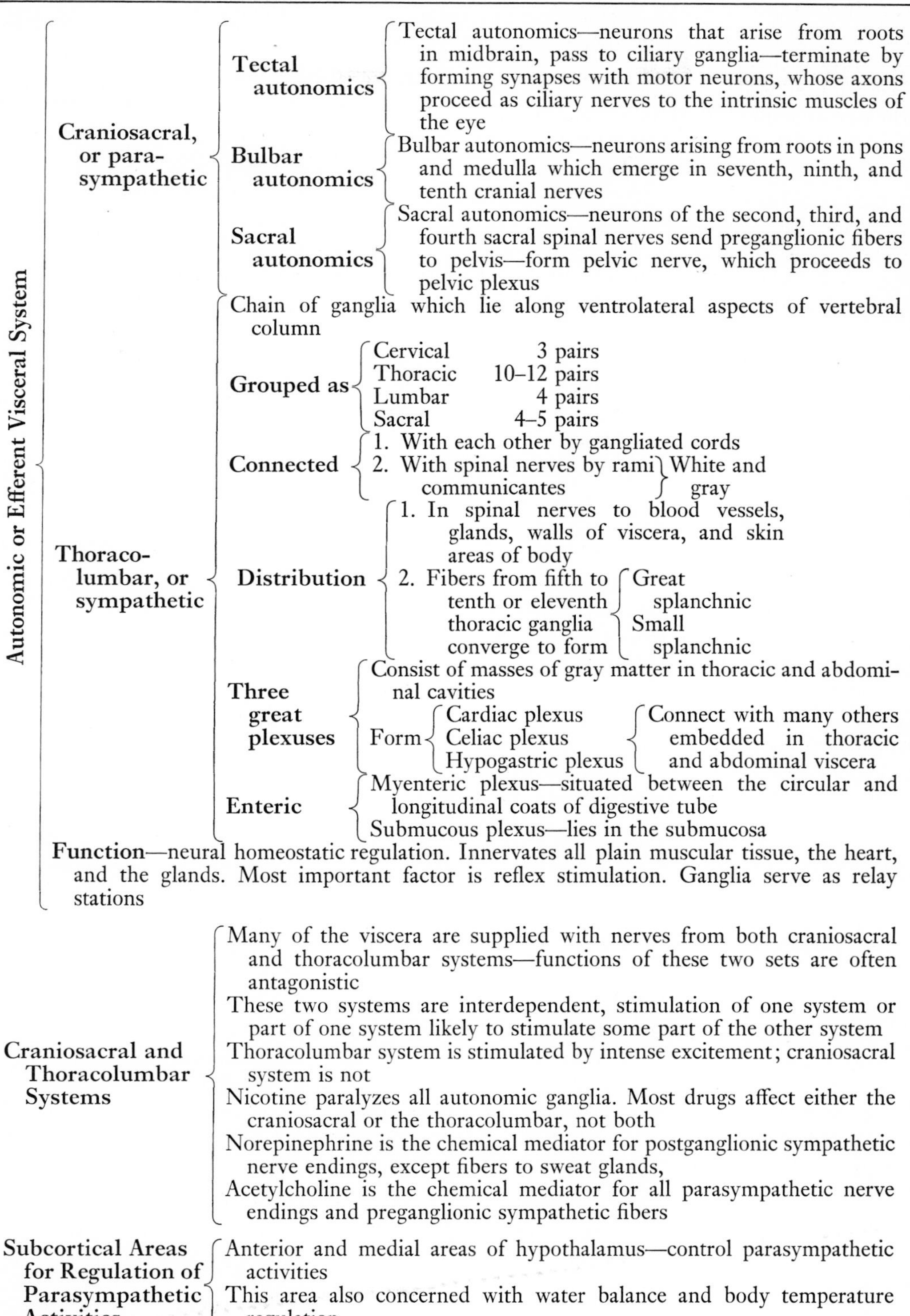

- **Autonomic or Efferent Visceral System**
  - **Craniosacral, or parasympathetic**
    - **Tectal autonomics**
      - Tectal autonomics—neurons that arise from roots in midbrain, pass to ciliary ganglia—terminate by forming synapses with motor neurons, whose axons proceed as ciliary nerves to the intrinsic muscles of the eye
    - **Bulbar autonomics**
      - Bulbar autonomics—neurons arising from roots in pons and medulla which emerge in seventh, ninth, and tenth cranial nerves
    - **Sacral autonomics**
      - Sacral autonomics—neurons of the second, third, and fourth sacral spinal nerves send preganglionic fibers to pelvis—form pelvic nerve, which proceeds to pelvic plexus
  - **Thoraco-lumbar, or sympathetic**
    - Chain of ganglia which lie along ventrolateral aspects of vertebral column
    - **Grouped as**
      - Cervical 3 pairs
      - Thoracic 10–12 pairs
      - Lumbar 4 pairs
      - Sacral 4–5 pairs
    - **Connected**
      - 1. With each other by gangliated cords
      - 2. With spinal nerves by rami communicantes — White and gray
    - **Distribution**
      - 1. In spinal nerves to blood vessels, glands, walls of viscera, and skin areas of body
      - 2. Fibers from fifth to tenth or eleventh thoracic ganglia converge to form
        - Great splanchnic
        - Small splanchnic
    - **Three great plexuses**
      - Consist of masses of gray matter in thoracic and abdominal cavities
      - Form
        - Cardiac plexus
        - Celiac plexus
        - Hypogastric plexus
        - — Connect with many others embedded in thoracic and abdominal viscera
    - **Enteric**
      - Myenteric plexus—situated between the circular and longitudinal coats of digestive tube
      - Submucous plexus—lies in the submucosa
  - **Function**—neural homeostatic regulation. Innervates all plain muscular tissue, the heart, and the glands. Most important factor is reflex stimulation. Ganglia serve as relay stations

- **Craniosacral and Thoracolumbar Systems**
  - Many of the viscera are supplied with nerves from both craniosacral and thoracolumbar systems—functions of these two sets are often antagonistic
  - These two systems are interdependent, stimulation of one system or part of one system likely to stimulate some part of the other system
  - Thoracolumbar system is stimulated by intense excitement; craniosacral system is not
  - Nicotine paralyzes all autonomic ganglia. Most drugs affect either the craniosacral or the thoracolumbar, not both
  - Norepinephrine is the chemical mediator for postganglionic sympathetic nerve endings, except fibers to sweat glands,
  - Acetylcholine is the chemical mediator for all parasympathetic nerve endings and preganglionic sympathetic fibers

- **Subcortical Areas for Regulation of Parasympathetic Activities**
  - Anterior and medial areas of hypothalamus—control parasympathetic activities
  - This area also concerned with water balance and body temperature regulation

Regulation of Sympathetic Activities
- Posterior and lateral hypothalamic areas—control sympathetic activities
- The parasympathetic and sympathetic nervous systems complement each other in regulation of body processes
- Augmented by hormones of adrenal medulla

Cortical Control—Located in prefrontal lobes and temporal regions

UNIT IV

Means of Distributing Materials to and from Cells

The blood circulates continuously throughout the body in a network of blood vessels. It is driven along these blood vessels by the action of the heart, which is placed in the center of the vascular system. The arteries conduct the blood out from the heart and distribute it to the different parts of the body; the veins bring it back to the heart again. From the arteries the blood flows through a network of minute vessels, the capillaries, into the veins. The whole forms a closed system of tubes.

CHAPTER

14

THE BLOOD

Characteristics

Volume

Composition

Physiology

BLOOD GROUPS

Each of the enormous number of living cells which make up the body is supplied with materials to enable it to carry on its activities, and at the same time materials resulting from its activities are removed. Most cells are far from the source of supplies and the organs of elimination, hence the need of a medium to distribute supplies and collect materials not needed by cells. This need is met primarily by the blood, which consists of cells and an intercellular liquid, and by tissue fluid.

CHARACTERISTICS OF BLOOD

Blood is bright red, approaching scarlet in the arteries, but a dark red or crimson in the veins. It is a viscous or sticky liquid. Its viscosity is about $4\frac{1}{2}$ to $5\frac{1}{2}$ times that of water, or it flows approximately $4\frac{1}{2}$ to $5\frac{1}{2}$ times more slowly than water under the same conditions. It is a little heavier than water; its specific gravity varies between 1.041 and 1.067. In general, 1.058 is taken as a fair average. Blood has a characteristic odor, a salty taste, a temperature of about 38° C (100.4° F), and a pH value of from approximately 7.35 to 7.45. These ranges cover the values for both arterial and venous blood.

Blood Volume. In the adult, blood volume is about one thirteenth of body weight and plasma volume about one twentieth of body weight. Normally there is little variation in quantity of blood. The ratio between blood quantity and tissue fluid quantity, however, is not constant. Probably many factors cause this ratio to change. An example is body response to changes in environmental temperature. It is thought that as environmental temperature rises the quantity of blood increases in relation to the tissue fluid, whereas with decrease in environmental temperature there is increase in tissue fluid with a decrease in blood quantity.

The quantity of blood varies with age, sex, muscularity, adiposity, activity, state of hydration, condition of the heart and blood vessels, and many other factors. There are also wide and unpredictable individual variations. Studies reveal that prolonged bed rest results in a reduction in plasma volume. Peripheral venous pressure and central venous pressure are also reduced, and fluid is lost from the blood to interstitial spaces.

Appearance of Blood. Seen with the naked eye, the blood appears opaque and homogeneous; but on microscopic examination, it is seen to consist of cells, or *corpuscles*, in an intercellular liquid, the *plasma*. The

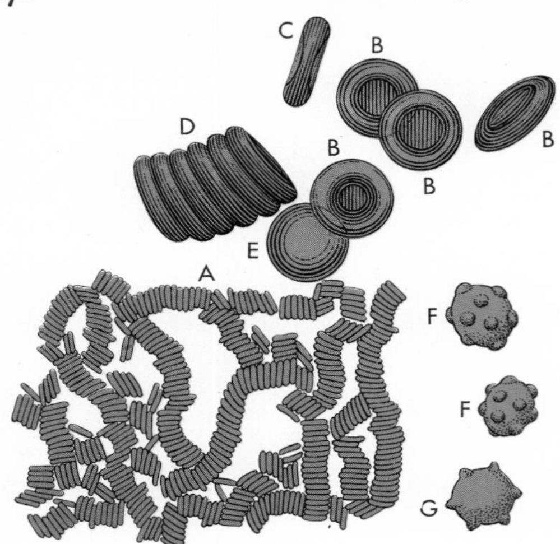

Figure 14–1. Erythrocytes of the blood, magnified. (*A*) Moderately magnified. The erythrocytes are seen lying in rouleaux. (*B*) Erythrocytes much more highly magnified, face view. (*C*) In profile. (*D*) In rouleau, more highly magnified. (*E*) An erythrocyte swollen into a sphere by imbibition of water. (*F*) Erythrocytes puckered or crenated all over. (*G*) Same at edge only.

volume of cells and plasma is approximately equal. The percentage of the blood made up of *red blood* cells is called the hematocrit; the normal figure is ±47 per cent. The ratio varies in relation to hydration and other clinical conditions. Averages for men are ±7; for women, ±5.

Erythrocytes. Under the microscope erythrocytes are seen to be homogeneous circular disks, without nuclei, and biconcave in profile. The average size is about 7.7 μ in diameter.[1] On microscopic examination, when viewed singly by transmitted light, they have a yellowish-red tinge. It is only when great numbers of them are gathered together that a distinctly red color is produced. Erythrocytes consist of a colorless, filmy, elastic framework, or stroma, in which hemoglobin is deposited, surrounded by a delicate membrane. The stroma is composed of protein and lipid substances including cholesterol. The blood group substances A and B and the Rh antigen are located in the stroma. Erythrocytes are soft, flexible, and elastic, so that they readily squeeze through apertures and passages narrower than their own diameters and immediately resume their normal shape.

Origin of Erythrocytes—Hematopoiesis. In the embryo the first blood cells arise from mesenchymal cells in the yolk sac. The next phase of development is chiefly in the liver and to some extent the spleen. Hematopoiesis takes place in bone marrow at about the fifth month and decreases in the liver as it increases in red bone marrow. After birth red bone marrow is the only tissue concerned with red cell formation. Red cells arise from *endothelial cells* of the capillaries of the *red marrow* of bone called hemocytoblasts. The hemocytoblast loses its nucleus and cytoplasmic granules, becomes smaller, assumes the shape of the erythrocytes, and gradually develops hemoglobin before reaching the blood stream. Immature erythrocytes, reticulocytes, and normoblasts (nucleated) are sometimes found in blood.

The life-span of these cells is thought to be about 120 days. Sections of bone marrow show many stages of blood cell formation. When and how the erythrocytes disintegrate are not known. One supposition is that as they age, they undergo hemolysis and fragmentation in the blood. Another is that they are destroyed in the spleen, lymph nodes, and liver. Most of the iron freed by the disintegration of erythrocytes is reused.

For complete maturation of the red cells vitamin B_{12} is necessary. The mucosa of the fundus of the stomach elaborates a substance called the *intrinsic factor*. The function of the intrinsic factor is to promote absorption of vitamin B_{12}, which is present in food. Absorbed vitamin B_{12} is the main antianemic principle in the liver. It is stored in the liver and liberated as needed, taken by circulation to the bone marrow where it functions enzymatically to complete the maturation of the red blood cell. Proteins, several vitamins, folic acid, copper, cobalt, and iron are essential for red cell formation.

Primary anemia, a pernicious anemia, results if the stomach fails to elaborate the intrinsic fac-

[1] The micron (symbol μ) equals 1/1000 of a millimeter (0.001 mm).

tor. Such anemias have been treated successfully by introducing purified vitamin B_{12} directly into the body by hypodermic injection.

Number of Erythrocytes. The average number of erythrocytes in a cubic millimeter of normal blood is given as 5,500,000 to 7,000,000 for men and 4,500,000 to 6,000,000 for women. Pathological conditions may cause a marked diminution in number, and differences have been observed in health. The number varies with altitude, temperature, nutrition, mode of life, and age, being greatest in the fetus and newborn child, and with the time of day, showing a diminution after meals.

Hemoglobin is comprised of a complex protein molecule named *globin* and a non-protein portion named *heme* (hematin), which contains iron. One red cell contains several million molecules of hemoglobin. Under normal conditions the adult body produces about 6.25 gm of hemoglobin per day. The destruction of hemoglobin occurs coincidentally with that of the erythrocyte. The entire function of hemoglobin depends upon its capacity to combine with oxygen in the lungs and then release it readily in the capillaries of the tissues. In the tissues it picks up carbon dioxide.

Amount of Hemoglobin. In adults 100 ml of normal blood contains on the average between 11.5 and 19 gm of hemoglobin—in males the average is 14 to 18 gm; in females, 11.5 to 16 gm. It has been suggested that 16.6 gm be taken as 100 per cent. In children (4 to 13 years old) the average is 12 gm; at birth it is about 17.2 gm of hemoglobin per 100 ml of blood.

Hemolysis, or Laking. Disruption of the erythrocyte membrane leads to the cell's hemoglobin content going into solution in the plasma. This process is hemolysis, or laking. The resulting colorless erythrocytes are referred to as "ghosts." Substances that cause this action are called hemolytic agents. Hemolysis may be brought about (1) by hypotonic solutions, which diminish the concentration of substances in the plasma, (2) by the action of foreign blood serums, (3) by such agents as snake venom, the products of defective metabolism, the products of bacterial activity, or immunizing substances produced within the body, (4) by the addition of ether or chloroform, (5) by the addition of salts or fatty acids, (6) by the addition of bile salts, (7) by alternate freezing and thawing, (8) by amyl alcohol or saponin, (9) by ammonia and other alkalis, (10) by incompatible blood transfusions, and (11) by certain types of allergic reactions called autoimmune responses. Erythrocytes which have lost their hemoglobin are incapable of serving as oxygen carriers.

Color index is an expression which indicates the amount of hemoglobin in each erythrocyte compared with the amount considered normal for the cell. Color index is significant in the anemias, especially in pernicious anemia.

Functions of Erythrocytes. The functions of the erythrocytes include carrying oxygen to the tissues, carrying carbon dioxide from the tissues, and maintaining normal acid-base balance (pH value), viscosity, and specific gravity.

In the capillaries of the lungs hemoglobin becomes fully saturated with oxygen, forming oxyhemoglobin. The erythrocytes carry the oxyhemoglobin to the capillaries of the tissues, where they give up the oxygen. Here part of the oxyhemoglobin becomes reduced hemoglobin and is ready to be carried to the lungs for a fresh supply of oxygen. The color of the blood is dependent upon the combination of the hemoglobin with oxygen; when the hemoglobin has its full complement of oxygen, the blood has a bright-red hue, and when the amount is decreased, it changes to a dark-crimson hue. The scarlet blood is usually found in the arteries and is called arterial; the dark crimson is in the veins and is called venous blood.

Polycythemia. The condition in which there is an increase of erythrocytes above the normal is called polycythemia. Conditions associated with cyanosis and residence in high altitudes are usually followed by polycythemia. It is thought that low atmospheric pressure existing in high altitudes decreases the ability of hemoglobin to combine with oxygen, and this reduction of oxygen tends to stimulate the formation of new

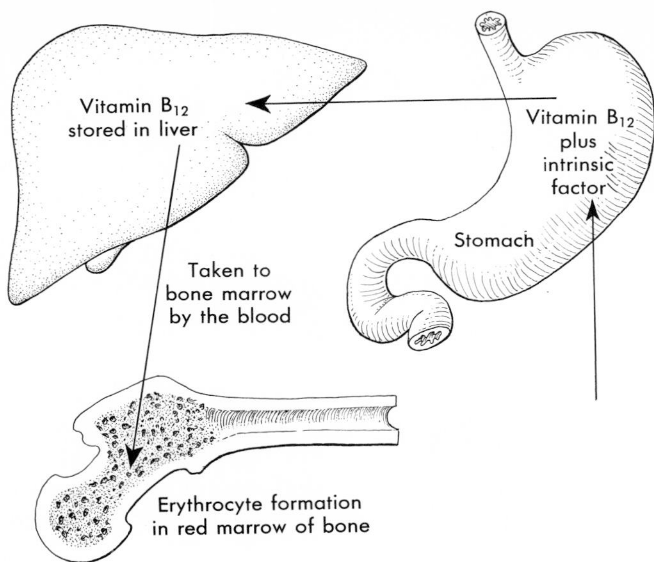

Figure 14–2. Factors necessary for maturation of red blood cells.

cells. This result represents the chief benefit anemic people derive from residence in high altitudes.

In shock due to diffusion of plasma to tissues, after profuse perspiration, diarrhea, and loss of body fluids from other causes, there is an apparent (not real) increase in erythrocytes, due to a decreased amount of plasma.

Anemia. This term is applied to conditions associated with a deficiency of erythrocytes or a deficiency of hemoglobin in the cells. A deficiency of erythrocytes results from (1) hemorrhage, (2) hemolysis, or (3) inability to produce new erythrocytes due to lack of nutritious food, diseases of the bone marrow, and various infections.

Insufficient iron in the diet may be one cause of anemia. Foods rich in iron include brain and visceral meats such as beef liver, heart, and gastric mucosa. Certain vegetables, such as kale, spinach, lentils, peas, and beans, and cereals, such as oatmeal and whole-grain wheat, contain a high percentage of utilizable iron.

White Blood Cells, or **Leukocytes.** White cells are minute ameboid cells, variable in size. They have been called the mobile units of the reticuloendothelial system. Some of them are formed in the red bone marrow and others are formed in lymphatic tissue.

The number of white cells in a cubic millimeter of blood is from 5,000 to 9,000 (about 1 white to 700 red). An increase in number is designated as *leukocytosis* and occurs in such infections as pneumonia, appendicitis, or other acute infection. A decrease in the number of leukocytes is designated as *leukopenia.*[2] Physiological leukocytosis up to 10,000 occurs under normal conditions, such as digestion, exercise, pregnancy, and cold baths. More than 10,000 per cubic millimeter usually indicates pathological leukocytosis.

Varieties of White Cells. White cells may be classified in many ways, depending upon structure, cytoplasmic granules, and their reaction to dyes.

WHITE CELLS

Number	Kind	Size
Granulocytes, 60–70%	Neutrophils	9–12 μ
	Eosinophils	10–14 μ
	Basophils	8–10 μ
Agranulocytes Lymphocytes, 20–30%	Small	7–10 μ
	Large	Up to 20 μ
Monocytes 5–8%	Mononuclear	9–12 μ
	Transitional	

[2] This should not be confused with *leukemia*, a disease characterized by an increase in the white cells of the blood. *Temporary* increases to 20,000 or more after exercise, etc., are thought to be due to changes in circulation.

GRANULOCYTES, OR GRANULAR LEUKOCYTES. In the adult granulocytes are formed in red marrow. They show marked pseudopodial movement. They are formed in red marrow from the myeloblast.

1. *Neutrophils*, or polymorphonuclear leukocytes, have a nucleus that is lobulated, and the granules of the cytoplasm stain with neutral dyes. They form from 55 to 65 per cent of the total number of leukocytes. Their phagocytic properties are extreme for many bacteria (phagocytosis).

2. *Eosinophils* are similar in size and structure to the neutrophils, but the granules of the cytoplasm are larger and stain with acid dyes such as eosin. Normally they are present in small numbers (2 to 4 per cent), but under certain pathological conditions they show a marked increase. It is thought they arise in the bone marrow, as do the

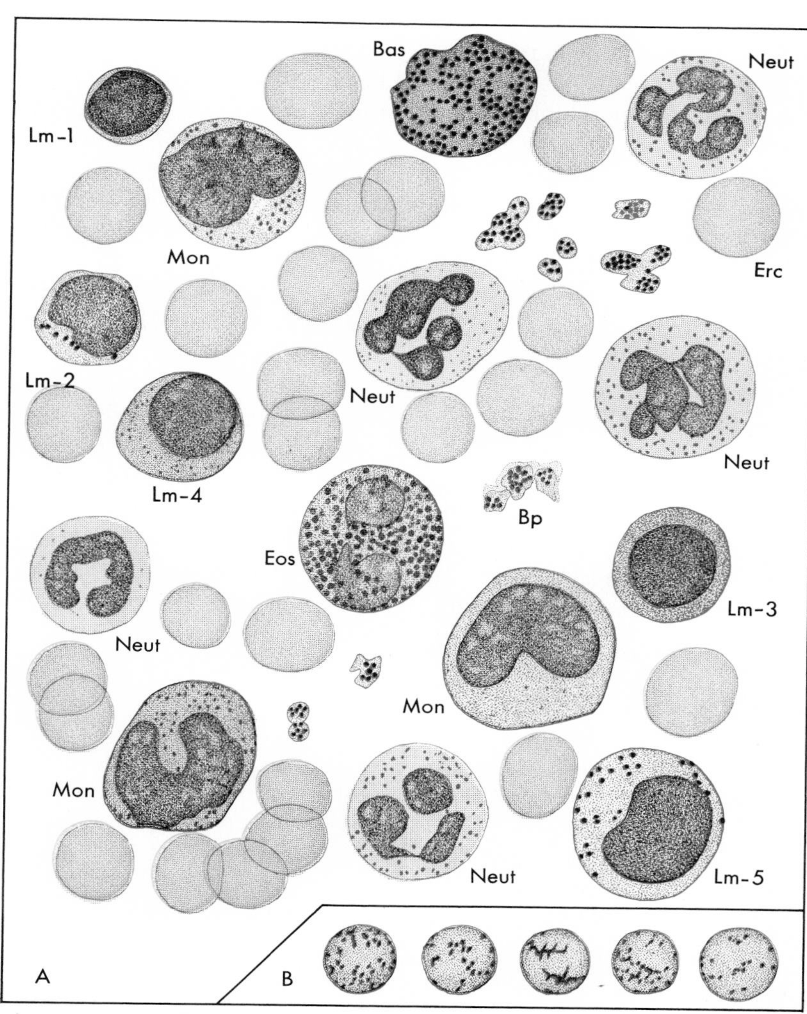

Figure 14–3. (*A*) Cells from normal human blood (Wright's stain). (*Bas*) Basophil leukocyte, (*Bp*) aggregations of blood platelets, (*Eos*) eosinophil leukocyte, (*Erc*) erythrocytes, (*LM 1–5*) lymphocytes (*1–3* are small and medium sizes and *4–5* are the less numerous larger forms), (*Mon*) monocytes, (*Neut*) neutrophil leukocytes. (*B*) Reticulocytes from normal human blood stained with dilute cresyl blue. (Modified from *Bailey's Textbook of Histology*, 13th ed., revised by P. E. Smith and W. M. Copenhaver. Courtesy of The Williams and Wilkins Company.)

neutrophils. After the administration of ACTH there is a decrease in the number of circulating eosinophils. Therefore, eosinophil counts are important, as they give evidence of adrenal function. Eosinophils are increased in certain allergic conditions.

3. *Basophils* are formed in bone marrow, have a polymorphic nucleus, and the granules of the cytoplasm stain with basic dyes. They are found in small numbers ($\frac{1}{2}$ per cent). Their function is unknown. However, their number increases during the healing process of inflammation and during chronic inflammatory processes. Basophils contain relatively large amounts of histamine (about one half of the histamine content of normal blood).

LYMPHOCYTES. Lymphocytes are formed in reticular tissue of lymph nodes and spleen and enter the blood stream from capillaries or via the thoracic duct. Their cytoplasm is nongranular, and the nucleus is large. Small lymphocytes are more numerous than large ones. The number of lymphocytes is high in early life, decreasing from about 50 per cent to about 35 per cent of the leukocytes at 10 years. The role of the lymphocytes in body defense is probably related to their ability to be transformed into macrophages at the site of tissue inflammation. Lymphocytes can also change into tissue histiocytes and into fibroblasts. The lymphocytes are also concerned with the formation of antibodies. The administration of the glucocorticoids causes atrophy of lymph nodes and depresses production of lymphocytes. In certain infectious diseases and local infections lymph node activity and resultant increase in circulating lymphocytes form a protective mechanism.

MONOCYTES. Monocytes include the large mononuclear and transitional types. They are large cells, each with an indented eccentric nucleus, and they can function effectively as phagocytes. Recent studies show that they have potentialities for tissue growth, development of enzyme systems, and ability to synthesize protein. The monocyte is formed chiefly in bone marrow.

Ameboid Movement. The neutrophils and monocytes possess the power of making ameboid movements, hence the name of "wandering" cells. White blood cells can squeeze through the walls of capillaries into surrounding tissues by the process called *diapedesis*; it occurs normally but is greatly stimulated and increased by pathological conditions. Diapedesis also refers to the migration of red blood cells through the walls of capillaries.

Functions of the White Cells. The functions of the white blood cells are many and are incompletely understood. Important functions include: (1) They help to protect the body from pathogenic organisms. It is believed that they either ingest bacteria and thus destroy them directly, or that they form certain substances, called *bacteriolysins*, antibodies which cause bacterial dissolution. Leukocytes which ingest bacteria are called *phagocytes*, and the process is *phagocytosis*. The neutrophils are thought to be most active in attacking bacteria; Metchnikoff[3] called them *microphages*, According to some authorities phagocytosis depends on certain substances in the blood known as opsonins which prepare bacteria for the ingestion by the leukocytes. (2) They cooperate in promoting tissue repair and regeneration. It is thought that the cells of connective and epithelial tissue cannot obtain material for growth directly from the blood. The leukocytes, however, can synthesize growth-promoting substances directly from the blood. It is proposed to call these substances *trephones*.

The proportion of the different classes of leukocytes in the blood varies during disease conditions, especially during infections. Differential counts have a great practical value in diagnosis.

The leukocytes do not swim, but "crawl"; hence they need surfaces such as capillary walls and connective tissue fibers to crawl on for their motion. In observation of blood flow through vessels in the frog they are seen to hug the vessel wall, whereas the red cells remain in the center of the stream.

[3] Elie Metchnikoff, Russian biologist (1845–1916).

Life Cycle of White Cells. Little is known of the life period of white cells, which is probably very short, but they are thought to be destroyed in the spleen, liver, and bone marrow. In the absence of infection neutrophils are believed to have a life-span of less than a day. The neutrophils may remain in the marrow reserve four or five days after development. It may take about four or five days to progress from a myeloblast to a segmented cell. It is possible that monocytes have a longer life-span and persist in areas of local infection considerably longer than neutrophils. Lymphocytes are believed to have a life-span of several months.

Characteristics and Functions of the White Blood Cells. Little is known of the functions of leukocytes while in the blood stream. However their function becomes apparent outside the vascular system. The movement of all leukocytes is identical with that of the ameba.

CHARACTERISTICS AND FUNCTIONS OF THE WHITE BLOOD CELLS

Name	Number	Where Formed	Nucleus	Cytoplasm	Motility	Function
Lymphocytes 3 mo to 3 yr 3 yr to 5 yr 5 yr to 15 yr Adults	 52–64% 34–48% 28–42% 20–30%	Reticular tissue of lymph glands and nodes; spleen; bone marrow and other lymph tissue	Very large, single, generally spherical, may be indented. Sharply defined. Stains blue Paler nuclei	Stains pale blue. Occasional scattered reddish-violet granules. Cytoplasm abundant	Movement active in connective tissue. Leave blood stream in large numbers, especially in fasting	Form serum globulin, both beta and gamma. Form antibodies at site of inflammation. Can change into a macrophage or plasma cell
Monocytes	6–8%	Lymph glands, spleen	Single, lobulated or deeply indented, or horseshoe-shaped. Stains blue	Abundant—cytoplasm—stains a gray blue	Marked. Migrate readily through capillary walls into the connective tissues	Phagocytic for the bacilli of tuberculosis Phagocytic properties for cell debris and foreign material excellent Young cells most active
Granular leukocytes, neutrophils Filamented types have 2 or more lobes in nucleus; nonfilamented types, 1 lobe	55–65%	In bone marrow from neutrophilic myelocytes	Lobulated—1 to 5 or more lobes. Stains deep blue. Number of lobes is significant in relation to the relative degree of maturity of cells	Fine neutrophilic granules in cytoplasm—pink cast	Marked. Migrate from blood stream. Believed to be removed from blood stream by reticuloendothelial system	Phagocytic properties extreme for many bacteria. Increased in infections and inflammatory conditions. Represents degree of toxic absorption. They make powerful proteolytic ferments. By disintegration and rupture of the cell itself become pus corpuscles. Lost in saliva, uterine secretions, where they destroy spermatozoa

Name	Number	Where Formed	Nucleus	Cytoplasm	Motility	Function
Eosinophils	1–3%	In bone marrow from eosinophilic myelocytes	Shape irregular. Stains blue, but less deeply than neutrophils. Usually 2 lobes in nucleus	Sky-blue tinge with many coarse, uniform, round or oval bright-red granules	Less marked. Often extravascular, especially in fluids under the linings of respiratory and digestive tracts	No phagocytic action. Increased in infection by animal parasites, especially worms. Number decreased by glucocorticoids
Basophils	0.25–0.7%	In bone marrow from basophilic myelocytes	Light purple, indented or slightly lobulated, centrally located. Quite hidden by granules	Mauve color with many large deep-purple granules	Least motile. Contain relatively large amounts of histamine	Function unknown

Inflammation. When tissues become inflamed either from injury or from infection, there is irritation, followed by an increased supply of blood to the part. If the irritation continues or is severe, the flow of blood slackens, and a condition of stasis, or engorgement, results. The leukocytes become active and migrate in large numbers through the walls of the blood vessels (diapedesis) into the infected tissues. Some of the blood plasma exudes, and a few erythrocytes are forced through the capillary walls. This constitutes inflammation; and the symptoms of redness, heat, swelling, pain, and loss of function are due to irritation caused by the toxins of the bacteria, to the increased supply of blood, to the engorgement of the blood vessels, and to the collection of fluid in the tissues (edema), which is spoken of as inflammatory exudate. Under these conditions a death struggle between the leukocytes and bacteria takes place. If the leukocytes win, they kill the bacteria, remove every vestige of the struggle, and find their way back to the blood. This process of recovery is described as *resolution* and is dependent upon the individual's resistance, i.e., the rapid formation of phagocytes, opsonins, etc. If the bacteria are victorious, large numbers of phagocytes and tissue cells will be destroyed, and *suppuration*, i.e., the formation of pus, ensues. *Pus* consists of dead and living bacteria, phagocytes, necrotic tissue, and material that has exuded from the blood vessels.

Also, in the case of a wound, the leukocytes accumulate in the region of the wound and act as barriers against infection. When inflammation is deep and the local symptoms cannot be observed, knowledge of the increase of the white cells is of assistance in determining the severity of the infection and the degree of resistance being offered by the body. This requires not only an absolute count, i.e., the total number of white cells in 1 cu mm of blood, but also the differential count i.e., the relative number of each type of leukocytes, particularly the number of neutrophils. In making a *differential count*, the number of each kind of white cells in 100 is counted. A high absolute count with a high neutrophil percentage indicates severe infection and good body resistance. A high absolute count with a moderate neutrophil percentage indicates a moderate acute infection and good resistance. A low absolute count with a high neutrophil percentage indicates severe infection and weak resistance.

Blood Platelets, or Thrombocytes. These are fragments of the cytoplasm of large megakaryocytes, a type of cell formed in red marrow. Thrombocytes are disk-shaped bodies about 2 to 4 μ in diameter. In edge view they appear as short rods; in face view, as round plates. The average number is about 400,000 per cubic millimeter of blood. They are formed from megakaryocytes in the bone marrow by fragmentation of the cytoplasm. The sticking together of platelets seals small leaks in injured blood vessels and hence prevents further loss of blood.

Function. When exposed to air or rough surfaces (conditions accompanying a wound and hemorrhage), large numbers of blood platelets disintegrate and granules are released. These particles together with many other factors rapidly convert prothrombin to thrombin. When platelets disintegrate, histamine, norepinephrine, and serotonin are liberated. These substances have vasoconstrictor activity and hence play a role in control of bleeding.

Blood Plasma. Blood plasma is a complex fluid of a clear amber color. It contains a great variety of substances, as might be inferred from its double relation to the cells, serving as it does as a source of nutrition and as a means of removing products of metabolism.

Water. About nine tenths of the plasma is water. This proportion is kept fairly constant by water intake and water output by the kidneys. There are also the continual exchanges of fluid which take place between the blood, intercellular tissue fluid, and the cells. Plasma has a specific gravity of 1.026, viscosity about five to six times greater than water, and pH of 7.4 with an average range of 7.32 to 7.41.

Blood Proteins. The hemoglobin of erythrocytes represents about two thirds of the blood proteins, and plasma proteins, about one third.

The Plasma Proteins. There are three major types of proteins in the plasma of circulating blood: serum albumin, serum globulin, and fibrinogen. Albumin is concerned with maintaining oncotic pressure; antibodies are globulins; fibrinogen aids in blood clotting.

Formation of Plasma Proteins. Practically all of the serum albumin and fibrinogen are formed in the liver. Plasma cells are the main (if not the sole) source of immune globulins.

The normal range of concentration of the plasma proteins is from 6.8 to 8.5 gm per 100 ml of plasma. These figures vary with age; in premature infants the concentration is low. There is a gradual increase with age. Normal levels are established at about 18 to 20 months.

Serum albumin forms about 53 per cent of the total plasma proteins. Globulins form about 43 per cent and fibrinogen about 4 per cent of the total plasma proteins. The liver forms plasma proteins rapidly, as much as 100 gm in 24 hours. However, the synthesis of plasma proteins by the liver depends on the concentration of amino acids in the blood.

Function. The blood proteins serve to maintain colloidal (oncotic) characteristics of blood and give it viscosity. All of the plasma proteins, but especially serum albumin, are concerned with the regulation of blood volume. They are responsible for the colloidal osmotic pressure (oncotic) which provides the "pull pressure" of the plasma essential for holding and pulling water from the tissue fluid into the blood vessels. Plasma proteins serve as a source of nutrition for the tissues of the body and contribute to the solution and transport of lipids, fat-soluble vitamins, bile salts, and hormones in the blood through the formation of complexes.

Immune substances are associated with serum globulin. Fibrinogen is essential for blood clotting. The plasma proteins aid in the regulation of acid-base balance.

Prothrombin is a plasma globulin, found in the blood in a concentration of about 15 mg per 100 ml. It is formed continually in the liver and is used by the body for the coagulation of blood. Vitamin K is essential for its synthesis.

Heparin is a conjugated polysaccharide that is secreted into the blood continuously by the *mast cells* found in the connective tissue surrounding capillary networks. It is a powerful anticoagulant. It prevents the change of prothrombin to thrombin and destroys thrombin.

Nutrients. These are the end products resulting from the digestion of food —amino acids, glucose, and neutral fats. Under normal conditions amino acids are present in a small proportion; glucose concentration is from 80 to 120 mg per 100 ml of blood. Temporary increases in these amounts may follow the ingestion of a large quantity of food.

Cholesterol is found in all tissues and body fluids. Its source in the body is (1) from absorption in the intestinal tract from saturated fats (exogenous cholesterol) and (2) from formation in large quantities by the cells, especially liver cells (endogenous cholesterol). It is an essential component of all cells, especially nerve tissue and steroid hormones.

Cholesterol is used by the liver to form cholic acid, which in turn helps to form bile salts; in the adrenal gland to form cortical hormones; by the ovaries to form progesterone and perhaps estrogen; and by the testes to form testosterone. Large quantities of cholesterol are precipitated in the corneum of the skin. Cholesterol and other lipids in the skin help prevent water evaporation.

The *electrolytes* found in the blood are derived from food and from the chemical reactions going on in the body. The most abundant is sodium chloride. (See Chapter 25.)

Gases. Dissolved gases—oxygen, nitrogen, and carbon dioxide—are found in the blood. Carbonic acid is continually entering the blood from the tissues. However, the blood contains certain buffer substances, i.e., sodium bicarbonate, sodium phosphate, protein, hemoglobin, and others, which enter into combination with the carbon dioxide so that only a small percentage is present in simple solution.

Antibodies. This term is applied to substances that are antagonistic to invading organisms. Antibodies are formed in all parts of the reticuloendothelial system, especially in the lymph nodes, the lymphoid tissue of the gastrointestinal tract, the liver, the spleen, and the bone marrow. The site of formation is related to the portal of entry of the invading organism (antigens). Lymphocytes can change into plasma cells and become active in antibody formation.

Recovery from many infections is due to an accumulation of these substances in the blood and to the effectiveness of the phagocytes in destroying the invading organisms. When bacteria enter the body, they stimulate the production of antibodies. Antibodies may be classified as (1) lysins, which act by dissolving organisms, (2) opsonins, which aid the white cells by sensitizing or preparing the organisms for ingestion, and (3) agglutinins, which clump the organisms in masses. Antitoxins are also classed as antibodies, because they neutralize the toxins formed by pathogenic organisms. The antibodies existing in the blood at any given time depend upon the condition of health, recovery from infection, etc.

Summary—Composition of Blood Plasma

Electrolytes	
Cations	mEq/L
Sodium	138–142
Potassium	4–5
Calcium	4.5–5
Magnesium	2
Anions	
Chloride	103
Phosphates	2
Sulfates	1
Bicarbonates	27
Organic acid	6
Protein	16
Other Minerals	
Iron, Copper, Iodine	Traces
Enzymes, Vitamins, Hormones	Variable concentrations
Proteins, gm per cent	
Serum albumin	5–6
Serum globulin	3
Fibrinogen	0.4
Nonprotein Nitrogen, mg per cent	
Urea	26
Uric acid	3
Creatinine	1.0
Creatine	0.4
Ammonium salts	0.2
Nutrients, gm per cent	
Glucose	80–120
Lactic acid	7–8
Amino acids	5–6
Fatty acids	368–370
Cholesterol	150–182
Phospholipids	200
Cerebrosidin	15
Lecithin	10–15
Water	90% by volume
Gases	
Nitrogen	
Oxygen 2% (not very soluble)	
Carbon dioxide 60–64% (soluble)	

Functions of the Blood. Blood is the transporting medium of the body. The functions as commonly listed are:

It carries oxygen from the lungs to the tissues and carbon dioxide from the tissues to the lungs.

It carries to the tissues nutritive materials absorbed from the intestine and transports them to the tissues for utilization.

It carries products formed in one tissue to other tissues where they are used. In other words, it transports hormones to the tissues requiring them.

It carries the products of metabolism to the organs of excretion—the lungs, kidneys, intestine, and skin.

It aids in maintaining the temperature of the body at the normal level.

It aids in maintaining the normal acid-base balance of the tissues.

It constitutes a defense mechanism against the invasion of harmful organisms.

It aids in maintaining fluid balance between blood and tissues.

It clots, preventing loss of blood after trauma (hemostasis).

The Clotting of Blood

Blood drawn from a living body is fluid. It soon becomes viscid and, if left undisturbed, forms a soft jelly, As the cells settle out of the plasma, a pale, straw-colored liquid begins to form on the surface, and finally the entire jelly separates into a firm mass, or *clot*, and a liquid called *blood serum*. If a portion of the clot is examined under the microscope, it is seen to consist of a network of fine needlelike fibers, in the meshes of which are entangled the red and some of the white cells. As the clot shrinks, the red cells are held more firmly by this network; but some of the white cells, owing to their power of ameboid movement, escape into the serum. The needlelike fibers are composed of fibrin. Many theories have been advanced to account for the formation of the insoluble fibrin from soluble fibrinogen. The exact process is not known, but it is thought to be comparable to the clotting of milk under the influence of rennin.

The Coagulation of Blood. The basic steps in the coagulation process include:

1. Thromboplastin and serotonin are released from injured tissues.
2. Thromboplastin initiates a series of chemical reactions which convert prothrombin into thrombin.
3. Thrombin functions as an enzyme to convert fibrinogen into fibrin threads that enmesh platelets, red cells, and plasma to form the clot.

Blood contains the substances antithromboplastin (antithrombin) and antiprothrombin (heparin) concerned with *preventing* the clotting of blood in the blood vessels, and three substances concerned with the clotting of blood. These include (1) fibrinogen, (2) calcium ions, and (3) prothrombin (thrombogen). When blood clots, prothrombin and calcium ions form thrombin, and thrombin changes fibrinogen to fibrin, which is insoluble. The fibrin and the blood cells form the clot.

For the blood to clot, the two substances concerned with the prevention of clotting must be neutralized. These substances are neutralized by thromboplastin which is set free by the crushed tissue cells, the platelets, or thrombocytes, and the blood corpuscles. This accounts for the fact that blood clots only when tissues are wounded.

The following tables present the *factors* concerned with the clotting process and where they function.

The genetic disorders related to blood coagulation include:

1. Antihemophilic factor VIII (AHF) deficiency causes 80 to 82 per cent of hemorrhagic disorders of the hemophilia type.
2. Plasma thromboplastin component IX (PTC) deficiency causes 11 to 15 per cent of hemorrhagic diseases.
3. Plasma thromboplastin antecedent (PTA), factor XI, deficiency causes 5 to 7 per cent of hemorrhagic disorders.

Value of Clotting. This property is of importance in arresting hemorrhage, the clot closing the openings of wounded vessels. The procedures used to check hemorrhage

THE FACTORS CONCERNED WITH BLOOD CLOTTING

Probable Source	Factors	Synonyms and Description
Liver	I	Fibrinogen; a globulin
Liver	II	Prothrombin; an albumin; vitamin K essential for synthesis
Injured tissues and blood during coagulation process	III	Thromboplastin (tissue); extrinsic prothrombin activator
Food	IV	Calcium
Liver	V	Proaccelerin; a labile factor in plasma accelerator globulin (AcG)
	VI	(No six)
Liver	VII	Proconvertin; a stable factor; a globulin Serum prothrombin conversion accelerator (SPCA)
Source unknown; gene controlling production of VIII is on the X chromosome	VIII	Antihemophilic factor (AHF); a globulin, thromboplastinogen; plasma thromboplastic factor (PTF); platelet cofactor I
Liver	IX	Plasma thromboplastic component (PTC); a globulin; Christmas factor (CF); platelet cofactor II
Liver	X	Stuart-Prower factor found in serum and plasma, not consumed during coagulation, is a globulin
Liver	XI	Plasma *thromboplastin* antecedent (PTA)
Liver	XII	Hageman factor; when substance is absent, blood does not coagulate in a normal period of time on contact with a glass surface
	XIII	Fibrin-stabilizing factor

are directed toward hastening the formation of a clot and stimulating the blood vessels to contract so that a smaller-sized clot will be sufficient.

The time it takes for the blood of human beings to clot is usually about four to six minutes. Estimation of coagulation time is important as a preliminary to operation when there is any reason to expect dangerous capillary oozing, as in tonsillectomies or operations upon jaundiced persons. The normal time depends on type of test used. This time is known as *clotting time* and is used as a clinical index of the individual's blood-clotting properties. In rare individuals the blood does not clot readily or at all, so that any injury or operation involving hemorrhage is dangerous. This condition is called *hemophilia*. Only males suffer from this condition. Adult females are exempt from hemophilia, but they may transmit it to their offspring.

Anticoagulants such as Heparin and Bishydroxycoumarin (Dicumarol). These are frequently given to retard the clotting process. Heparin is believed to prevent conversion of fibrinogen to fibrin. It does not affect bleeding time. Bishydroxycoumarin inhibits prothrombin synthesis in the liver.

Why Blood Does Not Clot Within the Blood Vessels. In accordance with the theory of clotting which has been considered, blood does not clot within the blood vessels because of the absence of thromboplastin and the presence of antiprothrombin and antithrombin.

Bleeding Time. If the ear lobe is punctured, blood will drip from the wound.

In normal individuals the bleeding will stop spontaneously in a very few minutes. The time required for cessation of bleeding is called *bleeding time*. This process is controlled by vascular constriction and perhaps a platelet factor rather than by coagulation alone. Normal bleeding time is about one to four minutes.

Intravascular Clotting. It is well known that clots occasionally form within the blood vessels. The most frequent causes are:

1. Any foreign material, even air, that is introduced into the blood and not absorbed may stimulate the formation of thrombin and a clot.
2. When the internal coat of a blood vessel is injured, as for instance by a ligature or the bruising incidental to operations, the endothelial cells are altered and may act as foreign substances. If in addition there is a stasis of blood at this point, disintegration of the blood platelets and white cells may result in the formation of thrombin and a clot. The products of bacteria and other toxic substances may injure the lining of a blood vessel and produce the same result. Inflammation of the lining of a vein is called *phlebitis*.

Thrombus and Embolus. A clot which forms inside a blood vessel is called a thrombus, and the condition is called *thrombosis*. A thrombus may be broken up and disappear, but the danger is that it may lodge in the lung or certain parts of the brain, where it blocks circulation and causes instant death. A thrombus that becomes dislodged from its place of formation is called an embolus. Such a condition is called *embolism*.

Hemorrhage. During hemorrhage blood pressure falls and the heart rate is accelerated in

Summary—Steps in the Coagulation of Blood

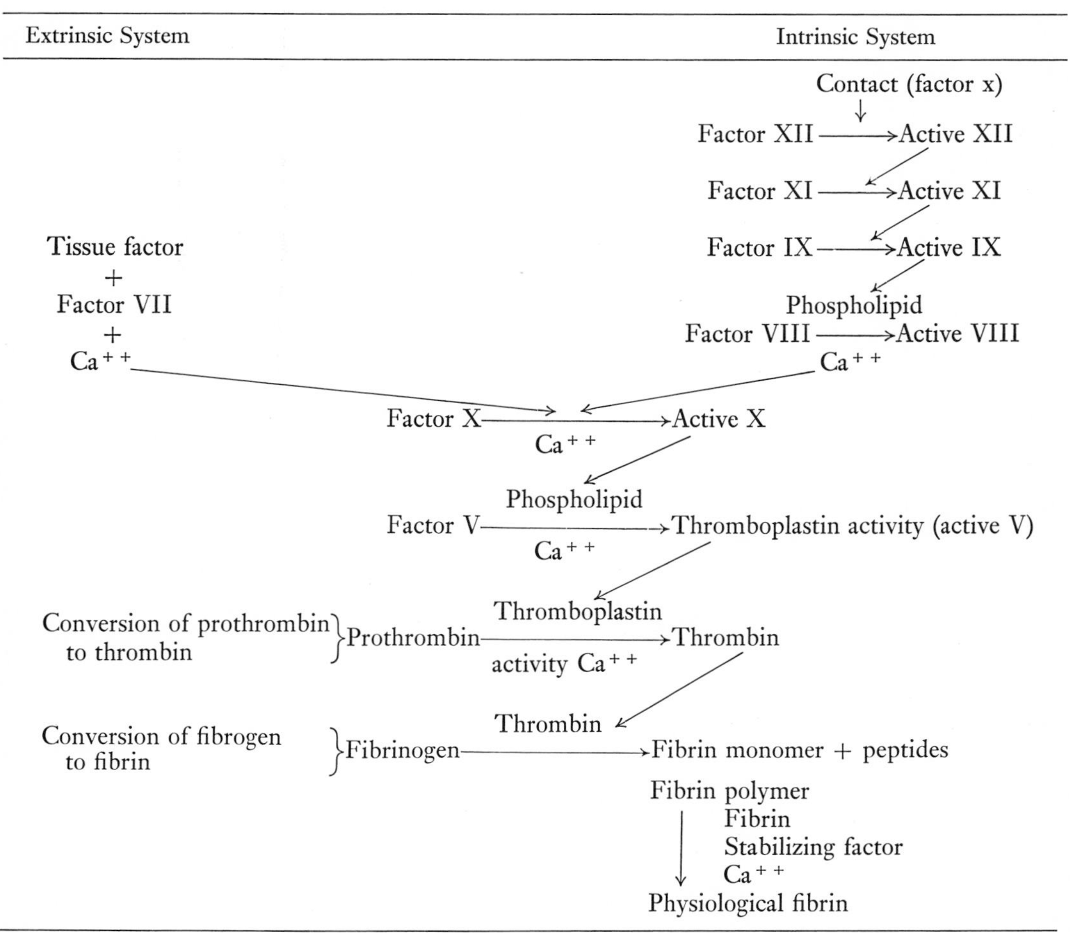

an effort to maintain cardiac output. The liver and spleen give up all possible blood to increase venous return. If hemorrhage is not controlled, there is further reduction in arterial blood pressure. Vasoconstriction is marked, the pulse is thready and rapid, the skin clammy and cold, the individual is restless, anxious, and air hungry. Blood flow to the tissues is decreased and the cell needs in relation to oxygen are not met.

The ischemic kidney from any cause initiates the secretion of renin, a vasoexcitatory material (VEM). Renin in the presence of enzymes converts angiotensin I to angiotensin II which constricts arterioles and raises blood pressure. In this way blood supply to the kidney is increased. If hemorrhage has not been controlled and pressure continues to fall, the arterioles and precapillary sphincters relax and open and more blood moves into the capillaries. When this occurs, there is danger of irreversible shock due to hemorrhage.

Regeneration of the Blood after Hemorrhage. During hemorrhage it is probable that a healthy individual may recover from the loss of blood amounting to 3 per cent of the body weight. Experiments on animals show that the plasma of blood regains its normal volume within a few hours after a slight hemorrhage and within 24 to 48 hours if much blood has been lost. The number of red cells and hemoglobin is restored slowly returning to normal after a number of days or even weeks.

Blood Typing

Blood typing, or classification into groups, is dependent upon agglutination of blood cells. The following tables tabulate laboratory findings when blood of various types is added to serum of a known type. They also show all combinations of agglutinogens and agglutinins possible in blood. To explain this phenomenon, blood cells are said to contain two substances called antigens or agglutinogens, designated by the capital letters A and B. Serum is said to have two antibodies called agglutinins, designated by a and b. Clumping occurs when an agglutinogen and an agglutinin of the same letter come into contact. These groups, or types, have been variously designated. Systems of nomenclature in current use are shown below with their relationship to the agglutinogens and agglutinins in each type. The descriptive names O, A, B, AB are terms of the agglutinogens in the red cells.

Blood types are determined by adding whole blood to serum of a known type. If the cells are agglutinated by serum a, agglutinogen A must be present; similarly, agglutination with serum b indicates blood of type B. As indicated in the table below, in practice it is necessary only to use serum a and serum b to test for the four blood groups. These are the major blood groups; there are many subgroups. The most important are A_1 and A_2. The recognized subgroups are A_1, A_2, A_1B, and A_2B. About 80 per cent of individuals in group A belong to subgroup A_1; 20 per cent belong to subgroup A_2; about 60 per cent of individuals in group AB belong to subgroup A_1B; and 40 per cent belong to A_2B.

Cross Matching. Before a blood transfusion is given, as a safety measure, cross matching is done to determine compatibilities. This means that a suspension of red cells from the donor and a small amount of defibrinated serum from the recipient are mixed

ABO Blood Groups

Name of Blood Group	Antigens in Red Cells	Antibodies in Serum	Incidence in Caucasians per cent
O	—	Anti-A and anti-B	45
A	A	Anti-B (b)	41
B	B	Anti-A (a)	10
AB	A and B	—	4

BLOOD AGGLUTINATION

Agglutinogens (Antigens)	Agglutinins in Serum (Antibodies)			
Cells	ab	b	a	o
O	–	–	–	–
A	+	–	+	–
B	+	+	–	–
AB	+	+	+	–

+ Denotes agglutination.
– Denotes absence of agglutination.
When antigen A meets antibody a, or when antigen B meets antibody b, agglutination takes place.

together to determine whether or not agglutination occurs. A second test is done to cross-match the cells of the recipient to the serum of the donor. If no agglutination occurs, it can be assumed that the blood of the donor and the blood of the recipient are of the same type.

The Rh Factor. If the Rh antigen is present on the red blood cell, the individual will be Rh positive. If the antigen is absent, the individual will be Rh negative. About 83 per cent of American Caucasians and 93 per cent of American Negros are Rh positive. There are several subgroups of Rh-positive blood.

In giving a blood transfusion, if an Rh-negative person receives Rh-positive blood, the recipient will develop an anti-Rh agglutinin which may cause hemolytic reaction. Anti-Rh agglutinins are similar to the a and b agglutinins in their action, as they attach to Rh-positive red blood cells and cause them to agglutinate.

The major Rh types in blood include Rh_0, Rh′, and Rh″ factors. The Rh_0 antigen is the one that is strongly antigenic. A person is considered to be Rh negative when his blood does *not* contain Rh factors.

According to the Fischer-Race concept, there are three sets of allelic genes: C and c, D and d, E and e; every person inherits a total of three genes from each parent, one gene from each pair. The resultant possible codes of genes gives cde, Cde, cdE, CdE, cDe, CDe, cDE, and CDE. Using all possible combinations, there are 36 different genotypes possible. Persons who have the D

INHERITANCE OF RH FACTORS

Mother Rh– Offspring Father Rh+

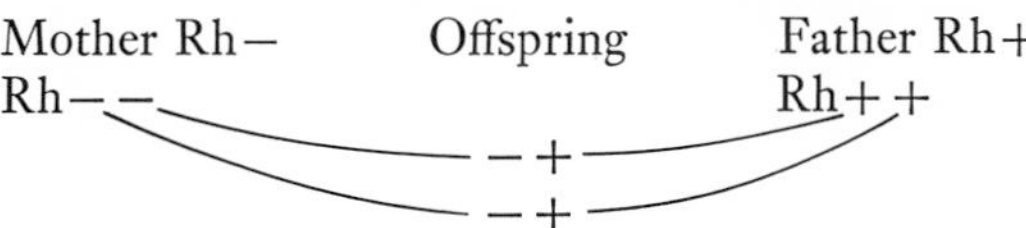

Possibilities—all children will type Rh positive but carry a recessive gene.

Mother Rh– Offspring Father Rh+, but carries a recessive gene

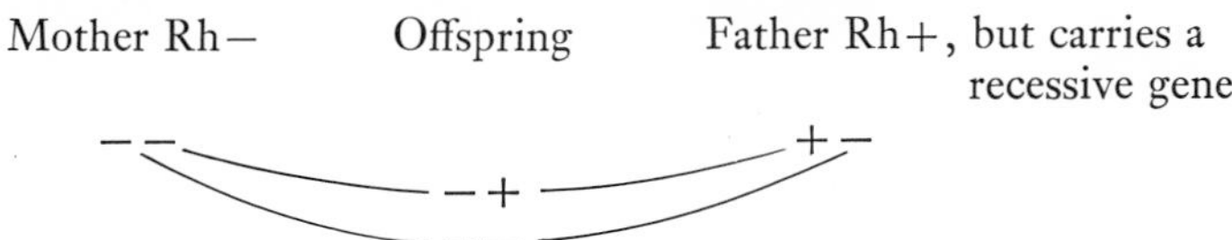

Possibilities—there is a 50–50 chance that children will carry recessive genes and a 50–50 chance that the children will carry a dominant gene for Rh+.

Mother Rh+ with recessive gene Offspring Father Rh+ with recessive gene

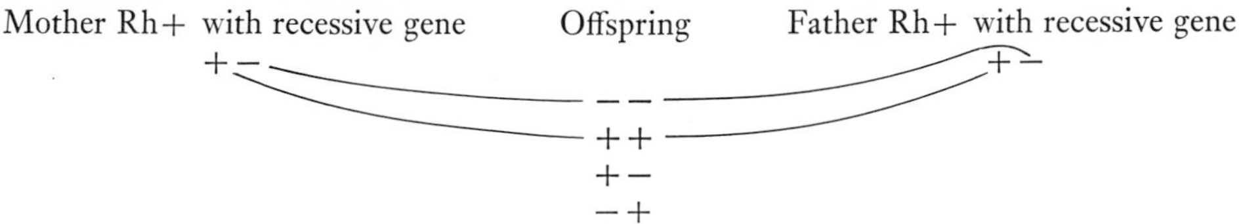

Possibilities—three children will type for Rh positive, but *two* will carry a recessive gene. One child will be Rh negative.

(Rh_0) antigen are considered Rh positive and those who do not have the D (Rh_0) antigen are considered Rh negative.

It is also believed that most cases (about 90 per cent) of *erythroblastosis fetalis* are caused by the production of anti-Rh agglutinins in the mother's blood (if the mother is Rh negative and the father is Rh positive, the child may be Rh positive). Leakage of agglutinogens through fetal circulation into mother's circulation causes formation of anti-Rh agglutinins which in turn destroy the red cells of the fetus. However, not all children born of such parents develop hemolytic reactions. The remaining 10 per cent is due to ABO incompatibilities.

Blood groups are inherited, as mendelian dominants; therefore, group O is recessive to groups A, B, and AB.

In the embryo agglutinogens are found in the red blood cells about the sixth week. At birth the concentration is about one fifth of the adult level. Normal concentrations are reached during adolescence. Agglutinins as a rule are not present in the blood of the newborn. Specific agglutinins are formed in blood plasma within two weeks and reach the highest concentration at about 10 years of age. Agglutinin concentration is variable in all individuals at all ages. Once established, blood groups do not change—that is, once a group B always a group B.

Inheritance of Blood Groups

Mother ♀ Offspring Father ♂

Ib Ib (group A) (no recessive gene) Ia Ia (group B) (no recessive gene)

Ib Ia

Ib Ia

Possibilities are that all children will be group AB

Ia Ib (group AB) Offspring ii (group O) (recessive genes)

Ib i

Ia i

Possibilities are that children will be group A with recessive genes and group B with recessive genes

Ia i (group B) Offspring ii

ii

Ia i

Possibilities are that children will be group B with recessive gene and group O

Ib i (group A) Offspring ii

ii

Ib i

Possibilities are that children will be group A with recessive gene and group O

Symbols:

Ib Ib = group A
Ia Ia = group B
Ia Ib = group AB
ii = group O (recessive)

QUESTIONS FOR DISCUSSION

1. Discuss the life cycle of the red blood cells.
2. What are the functions of:

   a. Red blood corpuscles?
   b. White blood cells?
   c. Platelets?

3. What are the functions of plasma proteins?
4. What is the advantage of transfusing whole blood rather than plasma?
5. Under what circumstances may plasma or a plasma expander be given?
6. How much blood may a donor give and what physiological responses occur in the donor to replace the blood lost?
7. Why is it necessary to have a laboratory report on cross matching, blood groups, and Rh factors before a transfusion can be done?
8. What is cross matching?

SUMMARY

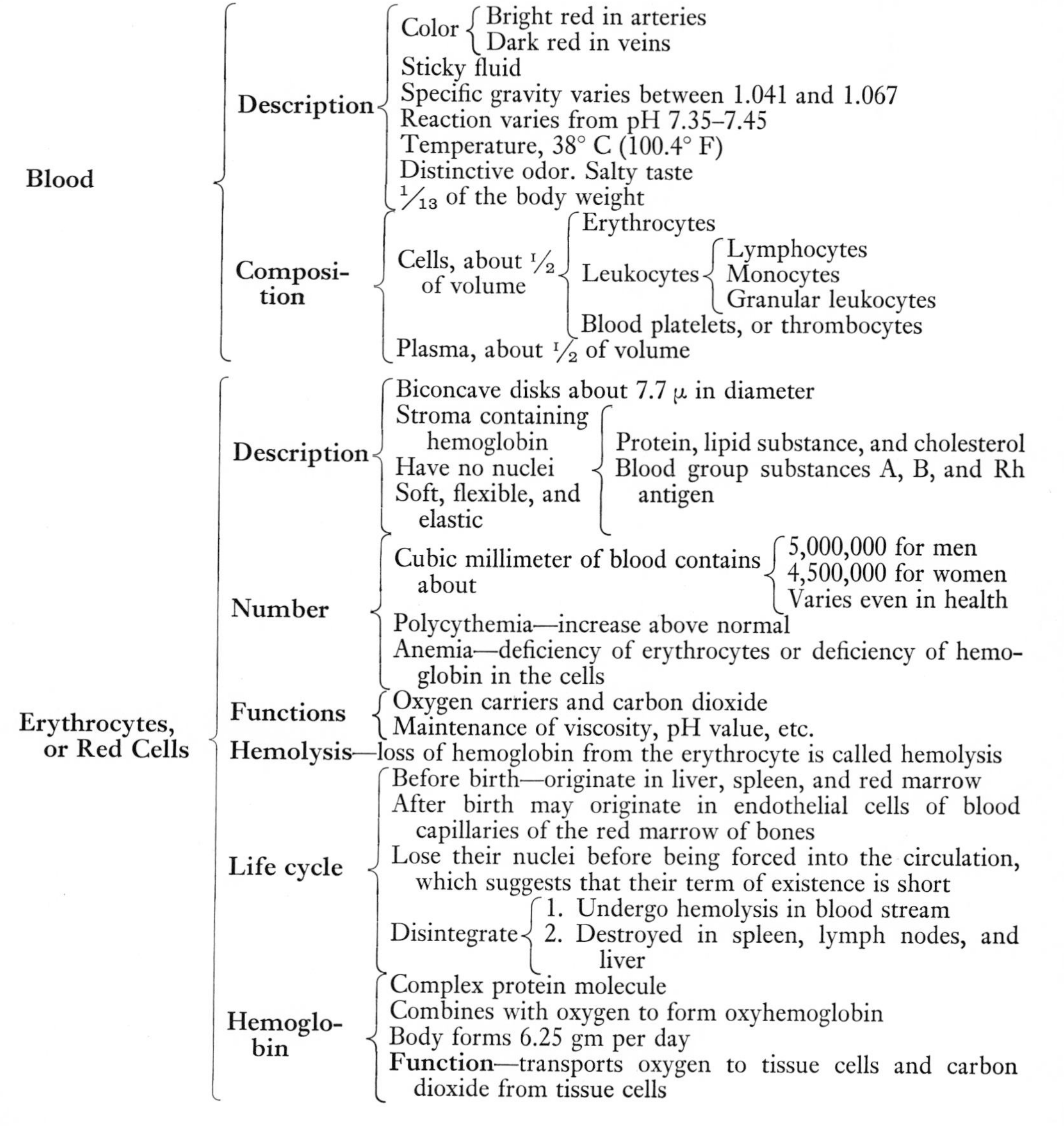

- **Blood**
  - **Description**
    - Color
      - Bright red in arteries
      - Dark red in veins
    - Sticky fluid
    - Specific gravity varies between 1.041 and 1.067
    - Reaction varies from pH 7.35–7.45
    - Temperature, 38° C (100.4° F)
    - Distinctive odor. Salty taste
    - $^1/_{13}$ of the body weight
  - **Composition**
    - Cells, about $^1/_2$ of volume
      - Erythrocytes
      - Leukocytes
        - Lymphocytes
        - Monocytes
        - Granular leukocytes
      - Blood platelets, or thrombocytes
    - Plasma, about $^1/_2$ of volume
- **Erythrocytes, or Red Cells**
  - **Description**
    - Biconcave disks about 7.7 μ in diameter
    - Stroma containing hemoglobin
      - Protein, lipid substance, and cholesterol
      - Blood group substances A, B, and Rh antigen
    - Have no nuclei
    - Soft, flexible, and elastic
  - **Number**
    - Cubic millimeter of blood contains about
      - 5,000,000 for men
      - 4,500,000 for women
      - Varies even in health
    - Polycythemia—increase above normal
    - Anemia—deficiency of erythrocytes or deficiency of hemoglobin in the cells
  - **Functions**
    - Oxygen carriers and carbon dioxide
    - Maintenance of viscosity, pH value, etc.
  - **Hemolysis**—loss of hemoglobin from the erythrocyte is called hemolysis
  - **Life cycle**
    - Before birth—originate in liver, spleen, and red marrow
    - After birth may originate in endothelial cells of blood capillaries of the red marrow of bones
    - Lose their nuclei before being forced into the circulation, which suggests that their term of existence is short
    - Disintegrate
      1. Undergo hemolysis in blood stream
      2. Destroyed in spleen, lymph nodes, and liver
  - **Hemoglobin**
    - Complex protein molecule
    - Combines with oxygen to form oxyhemoglobin
    - Body forms 6.25 gm per day
    - **Function**—transports oxygen to tissue cells and carbon dioxide from tissue cells

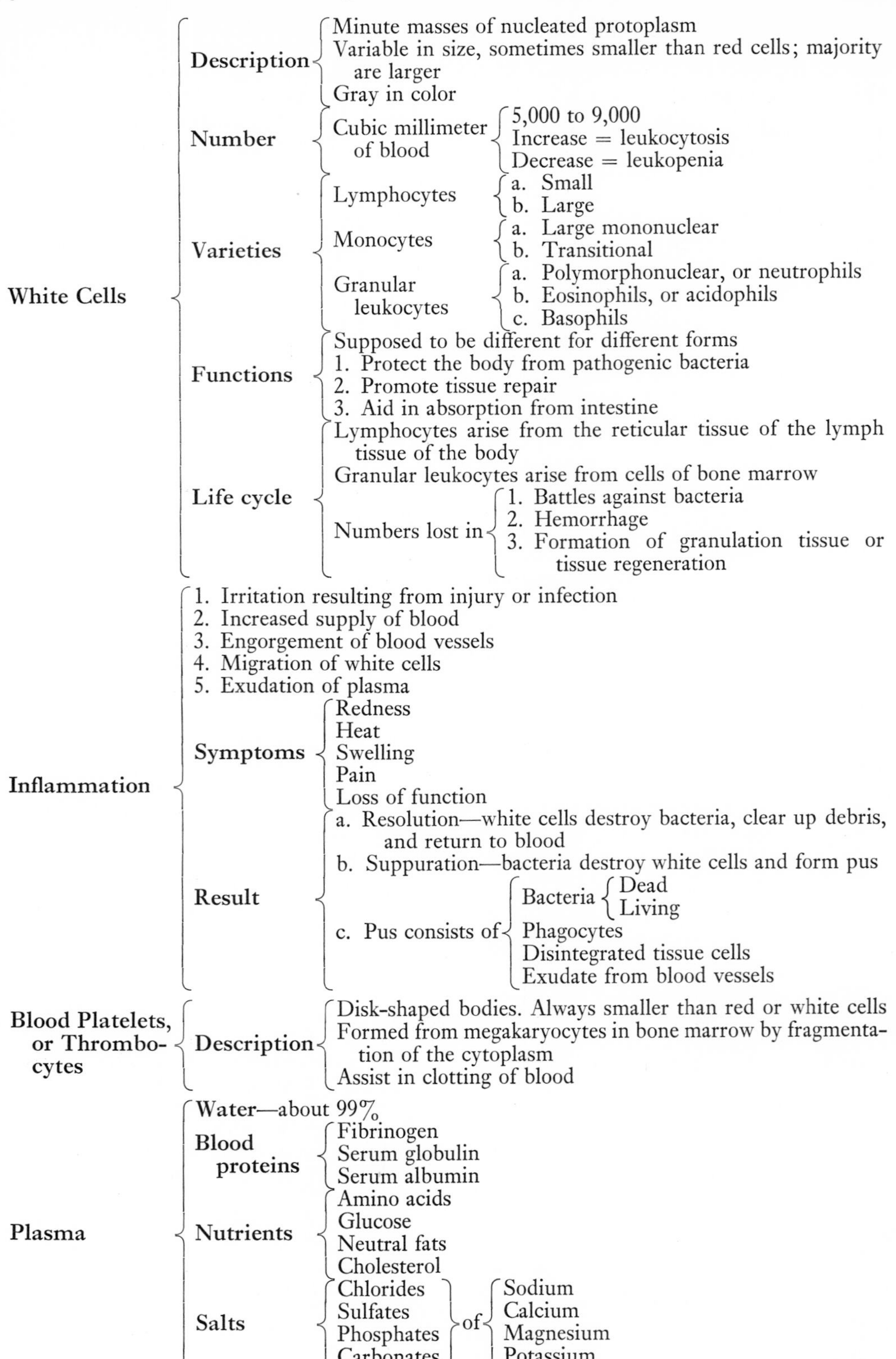

- **White Cells**
  - **Description**
    - Minute masses of nucleated protoplasm
    - Variable in size, sometimes smaller than red cells; majority are larger
    - Gray in color
  - **Number**
    - Cubic millimeter of blood
      - 5,000 to 9,000
      - Increase = leukocytosis
      - Decrease = leukopenia
  - **Varieties**
    - Lymphocytes
      - a. Small
      - b. Large
    - Monocytes
      - a. Large mononuclear
      - b. Transitional
    - Granular leukocytes
      - a. Polymorphonuclear, or neutrophils
      - b. Eosinophils, or acidophils
      - c. Basophils
  - **Functions**
    - Supposed to be different for different forms
    - 1. Protect the body from pathogenic bacteria
    - 2. Promote tissue repair
    - 3. Aid in absorption from intestine
  - **Life cycle**
    - Lymphocytes arise from the reticular tissue of the lymph tissue of the body
    - Granular leukocytes arise from cells of bone marrow
    - Numbers lost in
      - 1. Battles against bacteria
      - 2. Hemorrhage
      - 3. Formation of granulation tissue or tissue regeneration
- **Inflammation**
  - 1. Irritation resulting from injury or infection
  - 2. Increased supply of blood
  - 3. Engorgement of blood vessels
  - 4. Migration of white cells
  - 5. Exudation of plasma
  - **Symptoms**
    - Redness
    - Heat
    - Swelling
    - Pain
    - Loss of function
  - **Result**
    - a. Resolution—white cells destroy bacteria, clear up debris, and return to blood
    - b. Suppuration—bacteria destroy white cells and form pus
    - c. Pus consists of
      - Bacteria
        - Dead
        - Living
      - Phagocytes
      - Disintegrated tissue cells
      - Exudate from blood vessels
- **Blood Platelets, or Thrombocytes**
  - **Description**
    - Disk-shaped bodies. Always smaller than red or white cells
    - Formed from megakaryocytes in bone marrow by fragmentation of the cytoplasm
    - Assist in clotting of blood
- **Plasma**
  - Water—about 99%
  - **Blood proteins**
    - Fibrinogen
    - Serum globulin
    - Serum albumin
  - **Nutrients**
    - Amino acids
    - Glucose
    - Neutral fats
    - Cholesterol
  - **Salts**
    - Chlorides, Sulfates, Phosphates, Carbonates
    - of
    - Sodium, Calcium, Magnesium, Potassium

- **Plasma** (*cont.*)
  - **Iron**
    - In the form of transferrin
  - **Other organic substances**
    - Purine bases
    - Urea
    - Uric acid
    - Creatine
    - Creatinine
  - **Gases**
    - Oxygen
    - Carbon dioxide
    - Nitrogen
  - **Special substances**
    - Internal secretions—hormones—antithrombin—antiprothrombin—prothrombin—heparin
    - Enzymes
  - **Antibodies**
    - Lysins—dissolve bacteria
    - Opsonins—prepare bacteria for ingestion
    - Agglutinins—clump bacteria in masses
    - Antitoxins—neutralize toxins
- **Functions of Blood**
  - Carries oxygen from lungs to tissues
  - Carries carbon dioxide from tissues to lungs
  - Carries food material to tissues
  - Carries hormones and internal secretions
  - Carries waste products to organs of excretion
  - Aids in maintaining normal temperature
  - Aids in maintaining acid-base balance of tissues
  - White cells and globulins constitute defense mechanism against infection
  - Aids in maintaining internal fluid pressure
  - Clots, preventing loss of blood after trauma
- **Clotting**
  - **Serum**—blood minus fibrin and cells
  - **Factors**
    - Contains 13 factors concerned with the clotting of blood
    - Thromboplastin activated
    - Prothrombin converted to thrombin
    - Active thrombin converts fibrinogen to fibrin
  - **Process**
    - Cellular elements of blood and tissues → tissue extract
    - Thromboplastin neutralizes antithrombin and antiprothrombin
    - Prothrombin + calcium ions + thromboplastic substance + platelet accelerator → thrombin
    - Thrombin + serum activator → active thrombin
    - Active thrombin + fibrinogen + platelet factor → insoluble fibrin
    - Fibrin + cells of blood → clot
  - **Value**—checks hemorrhage
- **Bleeding Time**
  - **Definition**—Time required for cessation of bleeding after an injury (1 to 4 min)
  - **Process**—Vasoconstriction and a platelet factor
- **Intravascular Clotting**
  - **Theory to account for absence of clotting**
    - Absence of tissue extracts
    - Presence of antithrombin and antiprothrombin
  - **Causes**
    - Any foreign material introduced into blood and not absorbed will stimulate clotting
    - Injury to internal coat of blood vessels
  - **Thrombus**—name given to clot which forms inside vessel
  - **Embolus**
    - A thrombus that has become dislodged from place of formation
- **Regeneration of Blood After Hemorrhage**
  - Plasma is regenerated rapidly, red cells within a few days or weeks
- **Treatments to Increase Volume of Blood**
  - **Hypodermoclysis**—injection of fluids into subcutaneous tissue
  - **Intravenous infusion**—injection of solution into vein
  - **Transfusion**—transfer of blood of one person to another

Blood Typing
- *Unknown blood* to be typed, after dilution, with citrated saline, is added to *known b* (anti B) *serum* and *a* (anti A) *serum*
- **Unknown belongs to**
  - Group O—no agglutination
  - Group A—agglutination in a serum only
  - Group B—agglutination in b serum only
  - Group AB—agglutination in b serum and a serum

Cross Matching
- Suspension of cells from donor cross-matched with defibrinated serum of recipient and serum of donor cross-matched with cells of recipient

Rh Factor
- Population
  - 85% positive
  - 15% negative

CHAPTER

15

DIVISIONS OF THE VASCULAR SYSTEM

Arteries, Capillaries, and Veins—Their Structure, Function, Location, and Nerve Supply

The architectural arrangement and structure of arteries and veins are important in the distribution of blood to and from the capillary beds where the real work of the vascular system is accomplished. The arteries deliver blood to the capillaries and the veins return it to the heart.

The arteries are distributed throughout the body in a systematic manner. The vessels leaving the heart are large but soon divide into branches. This division continues until minute branches are distributed to all parts of the body.

At each division the branches are smaller, but since they are numerous, the total of their diameters is much greater than that of the artery from which they sprang. This means that as the blood flows from the heart toward the capillaries it flows in an ever-widening bed. The diameter of the aorta at the heart is about 1 in. The branches of the large arteries leave them at abrupt angles; the branches of the smaller arteries take progressively less abrupt changes of direction.

ARTERIES—STRUCTURE AND FUNCTION

The arteries carry blood from the heart to the capillaries. Arteries are composed of three coats:

1. An inner coat (*tunica intima*) consists of three layers—a layer of endothelial cells, a layer of delicate connective tissue which is found only in vessels of considerable size, and an elastic layer consisting of a membrane or network of elastic fibers (Figure 15–1).

2. A middle coat (*tunica media*) consists mainly of smooth-muscle fibers with various amounts of elastic and collagenous tissue. In the larger arteries elastic fibers form layers which alternate with the layers of muscle fibers. In the largest arteries white connective-tissue fibers have been found in this coat.

3. The external coat (*tunica externa*, or *adventitia*) is composed of loose connective tissue in which there are scattered smooth-muscle cells or bundles of cells arranged longitudinally. In all but the smallest arteries this coat contains some elastic tissue. The structure and relative thickness vary with the size of the artery.

The great extensibility of the arteries enables them to receive the additional amount of blood forced into them at each contraction of the heart. Elasticity of arteries serves as a buffer to the large volume of blood forced into the system by the heartbeat. If these vessels were rigid (as is true in arteriosclerosis), the systolic blood pressure would be markedly increased.

The strength of an artery depends largely upon the outer coat; it is far less easily cut or

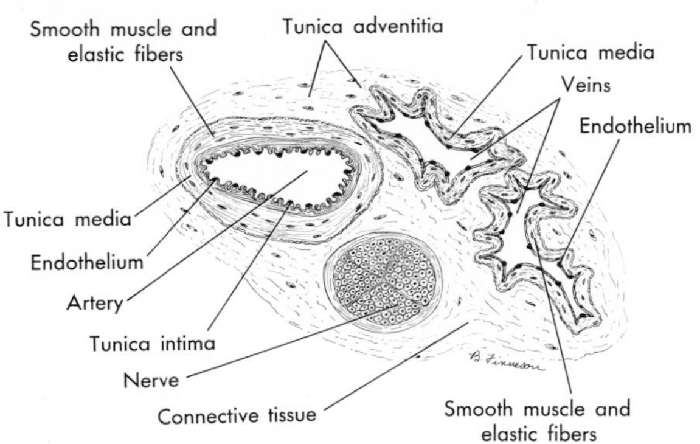

Figure 15–1. Cross section through artery, veins, and nerve. Note differences in the structure of the walls of an artery and of a vein.

torn than the other coats and serves to resist undue expansion of the vessel.

The arteries do not *collapse* when empty, and when an artery is severed, the orifice remains open. The muscular coat, however, contracts somewhat in the region of the opening, and the elastic fibers cause the artery to retract a little within its sheath, so as to diminish its caliber and permit a blood clot to plug the orifice. This property of a severed artery is an important factor in the arrest of hemorrhage.

Most of the arteries are accompanied by a *nerve* and *one or two veins*, all surrounded by a sheath of connective tissue, which helps to support and hold these structures in position.

Size of the Arteries. The largest arteries in the body, the aorta and pulmonary artery, measure more than 3 cm in diameter at their connection with the heart. These arteries give off branches which divide and subdivide into smaller branches. The smallest arteries are called *arterioles*, and at their distal ends, where only the internal coat remains, the capillaries begin. The arteriolar walls contain a great proportion of smooth muscle in relation to elastic tissue, and they are to be thought of as muscular rather than elastic.

The Elastic Arteries. These include the large arteries and are called *conducting arteries* because they conduct blood from the heart to the *medium-sized arteries*. The middle coat contains a large amount of elastic tissue, and the wall is comparatively thin for the size of the vessel.

The Muscular Arteries. These include the arteries of medium size, and their middle coat is chiefly muscular. Muscular arteries are also called *distributing* arteries because they distribute the blood to the various organs and by contraction or relaxation they aid in regulating the volume of blood passing to structures to meet varying functional demands.

Division of Arteries. The way in which the arteries divide varies. (1) An artery may give off several branches in succession and still continue as a main trunk, e.g., the thoracic or abdominal portion of the aorta. (2) A short trunk may subdivide into several branches at the same point, e.g., the celiac artery. (3) An artery may divide into two branches of nearly equal size, e.g., the division of the aorta into the two common iliacs.

Blood Supply of the Arteries. The blood which flows through the arteries nourishes only the inner coat. The external and middle coats are supplied with arteries, capillaries, and veins, called *vasa vasorum*, or blood vessels of the blood vessels.

Vasomotor Nerves. The muscular tissue in the walls of the blood vessels is well supplied with nerve fibers, chiefly from the sympathetic portion of the autonomic system. These nerve fibers are called *vasomotor* and are divided into two sets: (1) vasoconstrictor and (2) vasodilator. A center in the medulla oblongata (vasoconstrictor center) is constantly sending impulses to the vessels, thus keeping them in a state of tone. The vasoconstrictor center is a *reflex center* and is connected with afferent fibers coming from all parts of the body. Vasoconstrictor fibers are *sympathetic* and are widely distributed to arteries and arterioles. They mediate constriction of vessels, and by tonic action speed of blood flow is controlled. Vasodilator nerve fibers have several origins and are found on the sympathetic, parasympathetic, and somatic sensory nerves. There is no direct evidence that they are tonically active, but they appear to "discharge selectively" when a local increase in blood flow is needed.

There is a diffuse network of sympathetic nerve fibers in the adventitia of all arteries, called the *periarterial plexus*. Nerve fibers are also present in the muscular coat. Arterioles are directly and completely under *nervous* control. Pressure from increased volume, exerted on the blood stream in the muscular arteries, causes relaxation of the arterioles and more blood can move through to the capillary bed. The exact function of vasodilator nerve fibers is not well understood. Sudden, widespread relaxation of arterioles lowers blood pressure by decreasing peripheral resistance and shock may result.

As the arteries decrease in size and approach the capillary network, they are called arterioles. Proximal to the capillary channel there are modified arterioles called metarterioles. They have a wall which contains widely separated smooth-muscle cells. A precapillary sphincter is located around the arteriole before it enters the capillary net. Arterioles are well supplied with vasoconstrictor fibers.

CAPILLARIES

The capillaries are exceedingly minute vessels which average about 7 to 9 μ in diameter. They connect the arterioles (smallest arteries) with the venules (smallest veins).

Structure. The walls of the capillaries consist of one layer of endothelial cells continuous with the layer which lines the arteries, the veins, and the heart. These cells are held together by cell "cement." There is a substance called hyaluronic acid that forms a gelatinous material in the cell membrane and tissue spaces. It holds cells together and binds water in the tissues.

Distribution. The capillaries communicate freely with one another and form interlacing networks of variable form and size in the different tissues. All the tissues, with the exception of the cartilages, hair, nails, cuticle,

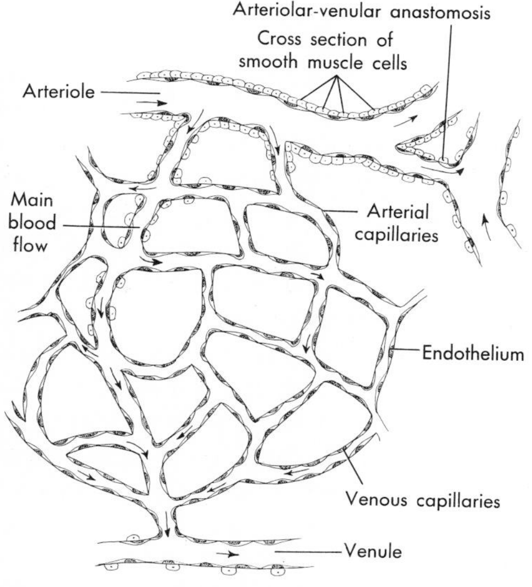

Figure 15–2. Diagram of capillary bed showing arteriole and venule. *Arrows* indicate direction of blood flow.

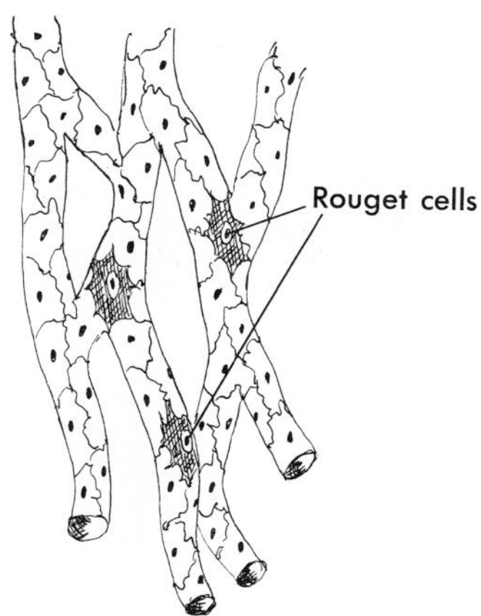

Figure 15–3. Capillary networks form the means by which cells receive oxygen and nutrient materials. There are about 7000 sq meters of capillaries in the adult.

and cornea of the eye, are traversed by networks of capillary vessels. The capillary diameter is so small that the blood cells often must pass through them in single file, and very frequently the cell is larger than the caliber of the vessel and becomes distorted as it passes through. In many parts the capillaries lie so close together that a pin's point cannot be inserted between them. They are most abundant and form the finest networks in those organs where the blood is needed for purposes other than local nutrition, such as, for example, *secretion or absorption.*

Function. It is in the capillaries that the chief work of the blood is done, and the object of the vascular mechanism is to cause the blood to flow through these vessels in a steady stream. It has been estimated that there are about 7,000 sq meters of blood capillaries in the adult body. This gives a large area for exchange of substances between the blood and tissue fluid. In the glandular organs the capillaries supply the substances requisite for secretion; in the ductless glands they also take up the products of secretion; in the alimentary canal they take up some of the digested food; in the lungs they absorb oxygen and give up carbon dioxide; in the kidneys they discharge the waste products collected from other parts; all of the time, everywhere in the body, through their walls an interchange is going on which is essential to the life of the body. The greater the metabolic activity of the tissue, the denser the capillary nets.

VEINS—STRUCTURE AND FUNCTION

The veins return blood to the heart and are formed by the confluence of the capillaries. The structure of the veins is similar to that of the arteries. They have three coats: (1) an inner endothelial lining, (2) a middle muscular layer, and (3) an external layer of areolar connective tissue. The main differences between the veins and arteries are: (1) the middle coat is not as well developed and not as elastic in the veins; (2) many of the veins are provided with valves; (3) the walls of veins are much thinner than those of arteries and hence tend to collapse when not filled with blood.

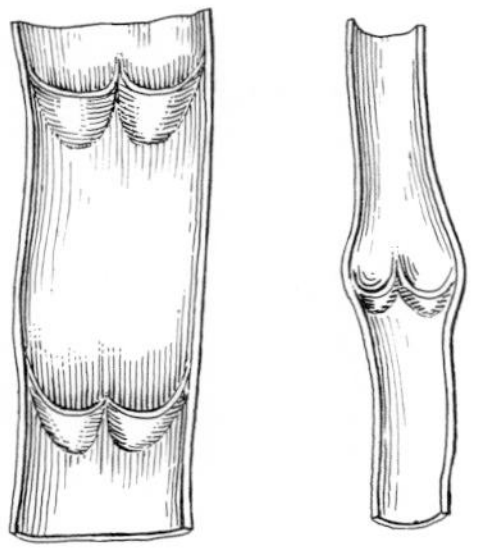

Figure 15–4. Diagram showing valves of veins. (*A*) Part of a vein, laid open, with two pairs of valves. (*B*) Longitudinal section of vein showing valves closed.

Valves. The valves are semilunar folds of the internal coat of the veins and usually consist of two flaps, rarely one or three.

The convex border is attached to the side of the vein, and the free edge points toward the heart. Their function is to prevent reflux of the blood and keep it flowing in the right direction, i.e., toward the heart.

If for any reason the blood on its onward course toward the heart is driven backward, the refluent blood, getting between the wall of the vein and the flaps of the valve, will press them inward until their edges meet in the middle of the channel and close it. The valves are most numerous in the veins where reflux is most likely to occur, i.e., the veins of the extremities. For the same reason a greater number are found in the lower than in the upper limbs. They are absent in many of the small veins, in the large veins of the trunk, and in veins not subjected to muscular pressure. The veins, like the arteries, are supplied with blood vessels and sympathetic nerves.

It must be remembered that, although the arteries, capillaries, and veins each have the distinctive structure described, it is difficult to draw the line between the arteriole and the large capillary and between the large capillary and the venule. The veins, on leaving the capillary networks, only gradually assume their several coats, and the arteries dispense with their coats in the same imperceptible way as they approach the capillaries.

Anastomosis of Vessels. The distal ends of arteries unite at frequent intervals, when they are said to anastomose. Such anastomoses permit free communication between the currents of the blood, tend to obviate the effects of local interruption, and promote equality of distribution and of pressure. Anastomoses occur between the larger as well as the smaller arteries. Where great activity of the circulation is necessary, as in the brain, two branches of equal size unite; e.g., the two vertebral arteries unite to form the basilar (Figure 11–8, page 208). In the abdomen, the intestinal arteries have frequent anastomoses between their larger branches. In the limbs, anastomoses are most numerous around the joints, the branches of the arteries above uniting with branches from the arteries below.

Anastomoses are of importance to the surgeon. By their enlargement, a collateral circulation is established after an artery is ligated. This means that subsidiary vascular channels, which are present in the circulatory network, form a secondary circulation through a part. The effectiveness with which these new channels transport blood varies.

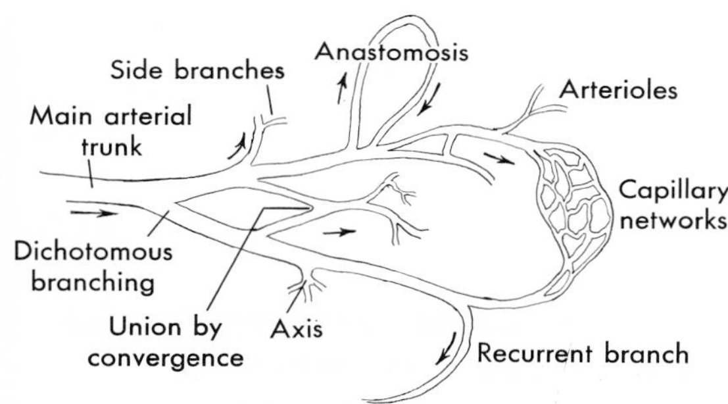

Figure 15–5. Diagram showing anastomosis, branching, and confluence of arteries. This arrangement permits free movement of blood.

A *plexus*, or network, is formed by the anastomosis of a number of arteries in a limited area. Arteries usually occupy situations protected against accidental injury or the effects of local pressure. Arteries usually pursue a fairly straight course, but in some parts of the body they are *tortuous*. The external maxillary (facial) artery, both in the neck and on the face, and the arteries of the lips (inferior and superior labial) are extremely tortuous and thereby accommodate themselves to the varied movements in speaking, laughing, and turning the head.

DIVISION OF THE VASCULAR SYSTEM

The blood vessels of the body are arranged in three main systems: (1) The *pulmonary*, which is the shorter system, provides for the circulation of the blood from the right ventricle to the lungs and back to the left atrium. (2) The *systemic*, which is the longer system, provides for the circulation of the blood from the left ventricle to all parts of the body by means of the aorta and its branches and the return to the right atrium by means of the venae cavae. (3) *Coronary* vessels and circulation include arteries, capillaries, and veins.

ARTERIES

The Aorta. The aorta is the main trunk of the arterial system. Arising from the left ventricle of the heart, it passes toward the right over the pulmonary artery, then arches toward the back over the root of the left lung, descends along the vertebral

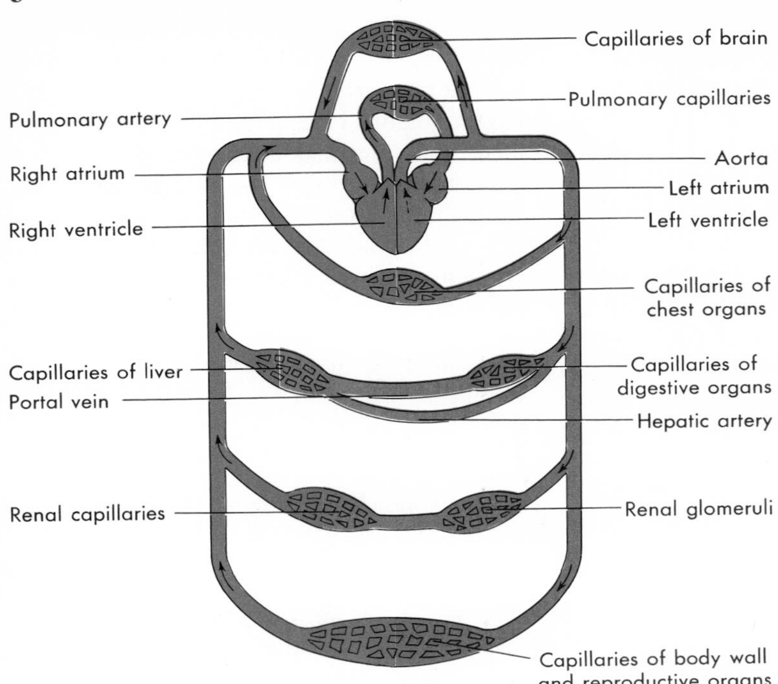

Figure 15–6. Diagram of circulation. In the portal circulation the two sets of capillaries are in different organs, the digestive organs and the liver, while in the renal circulation the two sets are in the same organ, the kidney.

The two sets of capillaries in the kidney are visible only on microscopic examination. The blood vessels connecting the renal glomeruli and renal capillaries are called efferent arterioles. What work is accomplished in these capillaries?

column, and, after passing through the diaphragm into the abdominal region, ends opposite the fourth lumbar vertebra by dividing into the right and left common iliac arteries. In this course the aorta forms a continuous trunk, which gradually diminishes in size from its commencement to its termination. It gives off large and small branches along its course.

The aorta is called by different names throughout its length: (1) the ascending aorta, (2) the arch of the aorta, and (3) the descending aorta, which (a) above the diaphragm is referred to as the thoracic aorta and (b) below the diaphragm is called the abdominal aorta.

1. The Ascending Aorta. This is short, about 5 cm (2 in.) in length, and is contained within the pericardium. The only branches of the ascending aorta are the right and left *coronary arteries*, which are described in the next chapter.

2. The Arch. This extends from the ascending aorta upward, backward, and to the left in front of the trachea, then backward and downward on the left side of the body of the fourth thoracic vertebra, where it becomes continuous with the descending aorta. Three branches are given off from the arch of the aorta—the *brachiocephalic*, the *left common carotid*, and the *left subclavian* arteries. Branches of these arteries supply the head and the upper extremities.

The *brachiocephalic* artery arises from the right upper surface of the arch, and ascends obliquely toward the right until, reaching a level with the upper margin of the clavicle, it divides into the right common carotid and right subclavian arteries.

3. The Descending Aorta. This extends from the body of the fourth thoracic vertebra to the body of the fourth lumbar vertebra.

a. *The thoracic aorta* is comparatively straight and extends from the fourth thoracic vertebra on the left side to the aortic opening in the diaphragm in front of the last thoracic vertebra. Branches from the thoracic aorta supply the body wall of the chest cavity and the viscera which it contains.

b. *The abdominal aorta* commences at the aortic opening of the diaphragm in front of the lower border of the last thoracic vertebra

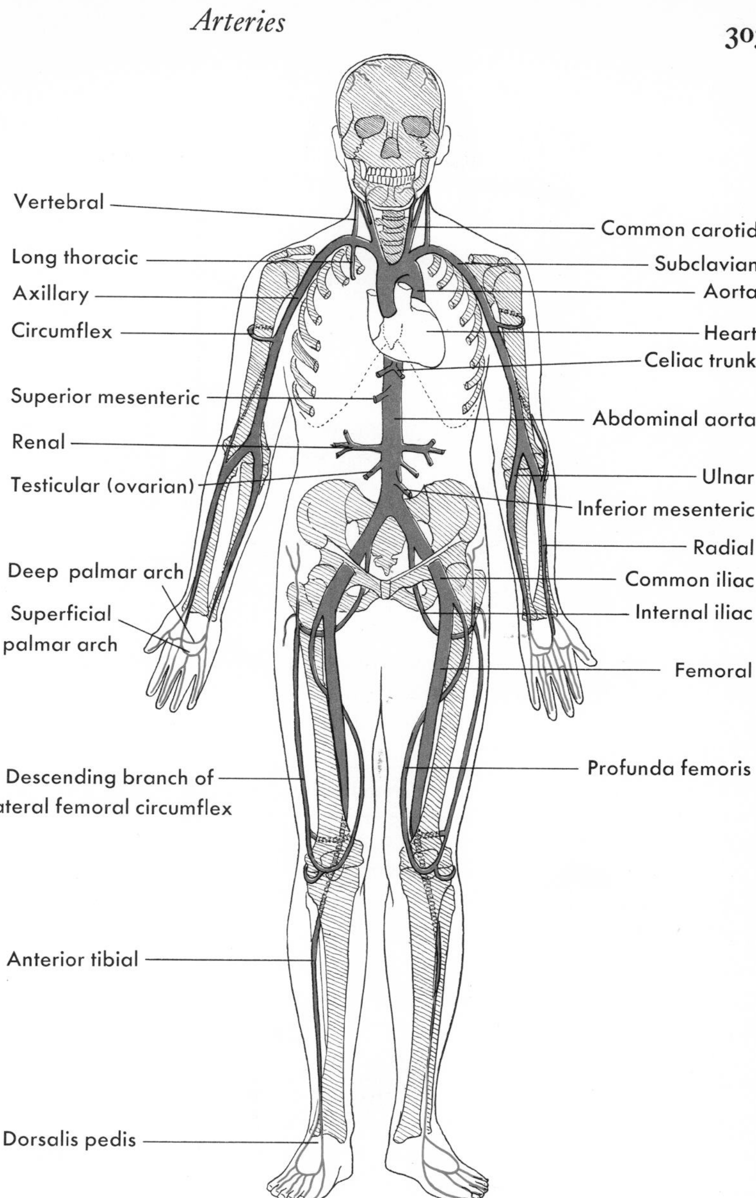

Figure 15–7. Diagram of arterial circulation. Many arteries named.

and terminates below by dividing into the two common iliac arteries. The bifurcation usually occurs opposite the body of the fourth lumbar vertebra, which corresponds to a spot on the front of the abdomen slightly below and to the left of the umbilicus. Branches from the abdominal aorta supply the body wall of the abdominal cavity and the viscera it contains.

Arteries of the Head and Neck. The principal arteries are the two common carotids and the vertebral (Figure 11–7, page 207).

The Circle of Willis.[1] This is an arterial anastomosis at the base of the brain (Figure 11–8, page 208).

Arteries of the Chest. The branches derived from the thoracic aorta are numerous but small, and the consequent decrease in size in the diameter of the aorta is not marked.

These branches may be divided into two

[1] Thomas Willis, English anatomist (1622–1675).

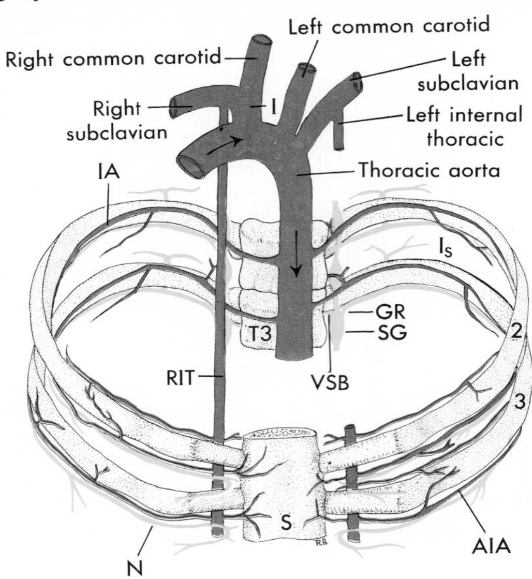

Figure 15–8. Internal thoracic artery and its branches to the intercostal muscles. (*2* and *3*) Second and third ribs, (*AIA*) anterior intercostal artery, (*GR*) gray ramus, (*I*) brachiocephalic artery, (*IA*) intercostal artery, (*IS*) intercostal space, (*N*) nerve, (*RIT*) right internal thoracic artery, (*S*) sternum, (*SG*) sympathetic ganglion, (*T3*) third thoracic vertebra, (*VSB*) ventral somatic branch of spinal nerve.

sets: (a) the visceral, or those which supply the viscera, and (b) the parietal, or those which supply the walls of the chest cavity.

Visceral Group	Parietal Group
Pericardial arteries	Intercostal arteries
Bronchial arteries	Subcostal arteries
Esophageal arteries	Superior phrenic arteries
Mediastinal arteries	

The pericardial arteries are small and are distributed to the pericardium.

The bronchial arteries extend to the lungs. They vary in number, size, and origin. There are two left bronchial arteries, which arise from the thoracic aorta, and one right bronchial artery, which arises from the first aortic intercostal or from the upper left bronchial. Each vessel runs along the back part of the corresponding bronchus, dividing and subdividing along the bronchial tubes, supplying them and the cellular tissue of the lungs.

The esophageal arteries are four or five in number; they arise from the front of the aorta and form a chain of anastomoses along the esophagus. They anastomose with the esophageal branches of the thyroid arteries above and with ascending branches from the left gastric and the left inferior phrenic arteries below.

The mediastinal arteries are numerous small arteries which supply the nodes and areolar tissue in the posterior mediastinum.

The intercostal arteries are usually nine in number on each side; they arise from the back of the aorta and are distributed to the lower nine intercostal spaces. Each intercostal artery is accompanied by a vein and a nerve, and each one gives off numerous branches to the muscles and skin (Figure 7–8, page 136) and to the vertebral column and its contents.

The subcostal arteries lie below the last ribs and are the lowest pair of branches derived from the thoracic aorta.

The superior phrenic arteries are small. They arise from the lower part of the thoracic aorta and are distributed to the posterior part of the upper surface of the diaphragm.

Arteries of the Pulmonary System. The blood vessels of the pulmonary system include (1) the *pulmonary artery* and all its branches, (2) the *capillaries* which connect these branches with the veins, and (3) the *pulmonary veins*. (See Chapter 19.)

Blood Vessels of the Systemic System. These consist of (1) the *aorta* and all the arteries that originate from it, including the terminal branches called arterioles; (2) the capillaries which connect the arterioles and venules, and (3) all the venules and veins of the body which empty into the superior and inferior venae cavae and then into the heart, as well as those which empty directly into the heart (coronary veins).

Arteries of the Abdomen. The branches derived from the abdominal aorta may be divided into two groups:

Visceral Branches	Parietal Branches
Celiac (celiac axis)	Inferior phrenics
Superior mesenteric (page 412)	Lumbars
Middle suprarenals (page 495)	Middle sacral
Renals (page 513)	
Internal spermatics (male) Ovarian (female) (page 556)	
Inferior mesenteric (page 414)	

The visceral branches are discussed with the organs supplied by them.

The inferior phrenics (two) arise from the aorta or celiac artery. They are distributed to the undersurface of the diaphragm.

The lumbar arteries, usually four on each side, are analogous to the intercostals. They arise from the back of the aorta opposite the bodies of the upper four lumbar vertebrae. These arteries distribute branches to the muscles and skin of the back. A spinal branch enters the spinal canal and is distributed to the spinal cord and its membranes.

The middle sacral artery arises from the posterior part of the abdominal aorta and descends in front of the fourth and fifth lumbar vertebrae and the sacrum and ends on the pelvic surface of the coccyx. It supplies the sacrum, sacral canal, coccyx, gluteus maximus, and the rectum.

Arteries of the Pelvis. At about the fourth lumbar vertebra the aorta divides into two *common iliac arteries.* These arteries divide into the hypogastric, or internal, which sends branches to the pelvic walls, pelvic

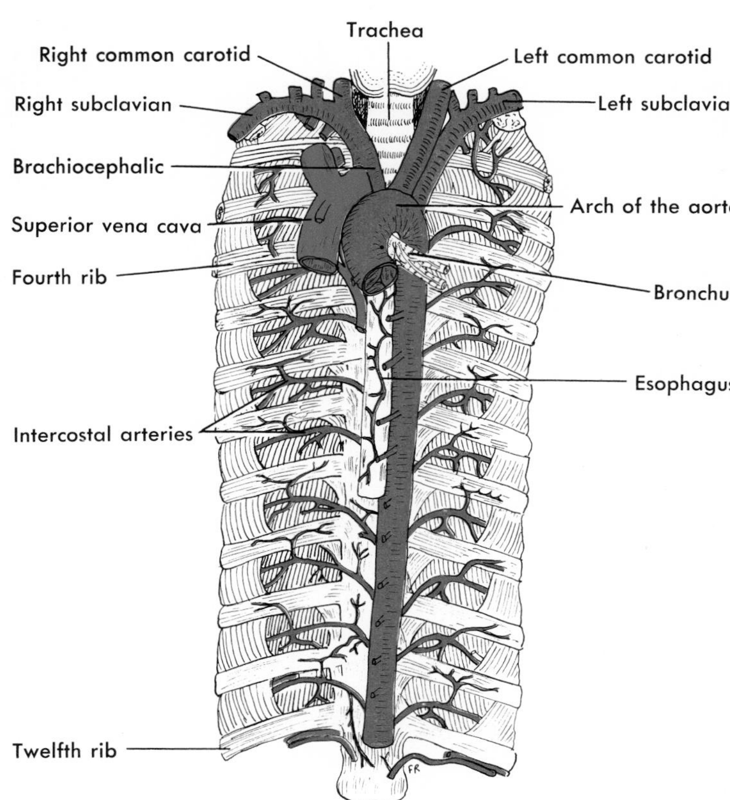

Figure 15–9. Thoracic aorta. The thoracic aorta extends from the fourth to the twelfth thoracic vertebrae.

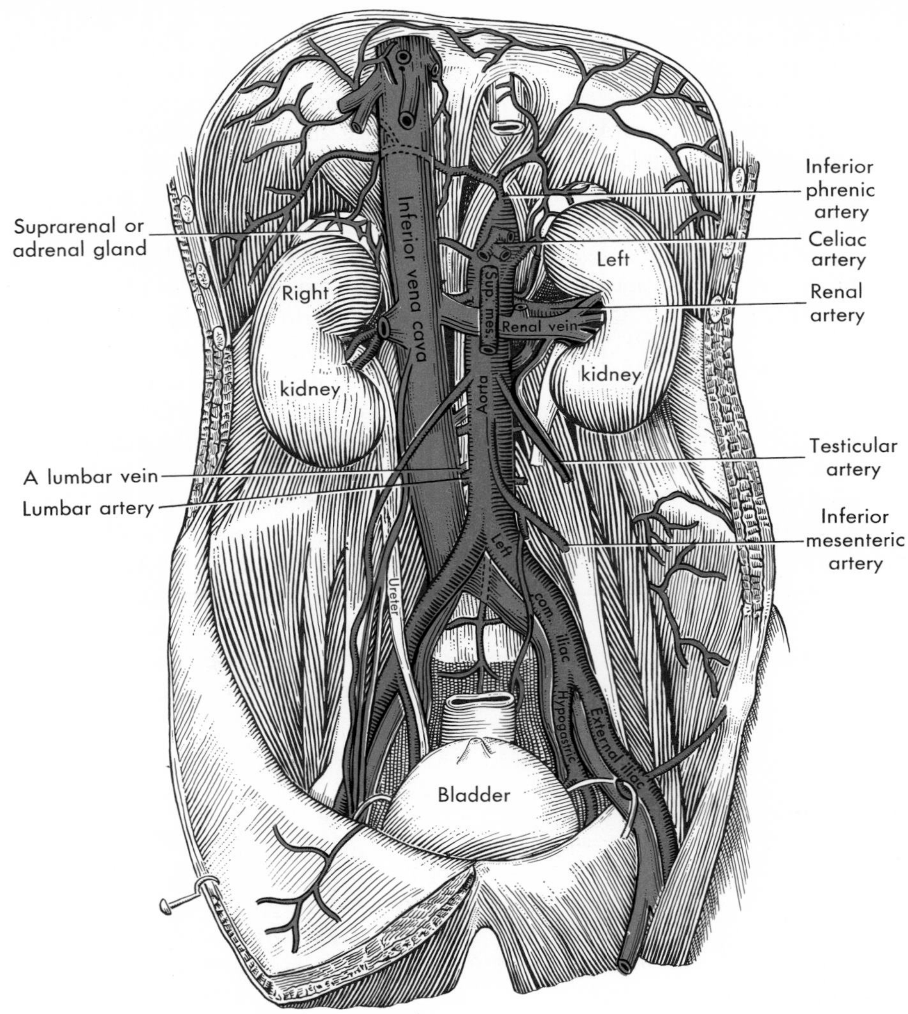

Figure 15–10. The abdominal aorta and inferior vena cava. The abdominal aorta bifurcates into the right and left common iliac arteries opposite the fourth lumbar vertebra.

viscera, external genitalia, the buttocks, and the medial side of each thigh. The external iliacs descend and supply the muscles of the thigh, and its branches supply the leg and foot. (See page 166.)

Arteries of the Upper Extremity. The subclavian artery is the first portion of a long trunk which forms the main artery of each upper limb. Different portions are named in terms of the regions through which they pass, viz., *subclavian*, *axillary*, and *brachial*, which divides into the *radial* and *ulnar* arteries. The right *subclavian* arises at the division of the *brachiocephalic* and the left *subclavian* from the arch of the aorta,

The *thyrocervical* sends branches to the thyroid, trachea, esophagus, and muscles of the neck and scapula.

The *internal thoracic* artery extends downward under the costal cartilages to the level of the sixth intercostal space, where it branches into the musculophrenic and superior epigastric arteries. It sends branches to the mammary glands, the diaphragm, areolar tissue and lymph nodes of the mediastinum, the intercostal muscles, pericardium, and abdominal muscles.

The *costocervical* sends branches to the upper part of the back, the neck, and the spinal cord and its membranes.

Arteries of the Lower Extremities. The external iliac arteries form a large continuous trunk which extends downward in the lower limb and is named, in successive parts of its course, the *femoral*, the *popliteal*, and the *posterior tibial*. The *femoral artery* lies in the upper three fourths of the thigh, its limits being marked above by the *inguinal* (Poupart's) *ligament* and below by the opening in the adductor magnus muscle. It then becomes the popliteal artery. In the first part of its course the artery lies along the depression on the inner aspect of the thigh, known as the femoral triangle (Scarpa's triangle).[2] Here the pulsation of the artery may be felt and circulation through the vessel may be easily controlled by pressure (Figure 15–7, page 303). Branches from the femoral artery supply the abdominal walls and external genitalia, and a descending branch, the *lateral circumflex*, anastomoses with branches of the popliteal to form the *circumpatellar anastomosis*, which surrounds the knee joint. As it descends it becomes the *popliteal artery*, then the *posterior tibial artery*, and gives off other branches. At the ankle it divides into the *medial* and *lateral plantar* arteries, which supply the structures of the foot.

The *peroneal artery* is a large branch of the posterior tibial and supplies the structures of the medial side of the *fibula* and *calcaneus*. The *anterior tibial* is a small branch of the popliteal artery and extends along the front of the leg and at the ankle becomes the *dorsalis pedis* artery. The dorsalis pedis anastomoses with branches from the posterior tibial and supplies blood to the foot (Figure 15–7, page 303).

VEINS

Arteries begin as *large vessels* which gradually become *smaller* until they end in arterioles, which merge into capillaries. The *veins* begin as small branches, the *venules*; at first they are scarcely distinguishable from *capillaries* which unite to form larger and larger vessels. They differ from arteries in their large size, greater number, thinner walls, and the presence of valves in many of them. These valves prevent backward circulation. In general, the total diameter of the veins returning blood from any organ is at least twice the diameter of the arteries carrying blood to the organ. The veins consist of three sets of vessels: the *pulmonary*, *coronary*, and *systemic*. The *pulmonary veins* convey oxygenated blood from the lungs to the left atrium. These veins begin as capillary networks upon the air cells (alveolae) and unite to form one vein for each lobule, two from the left lung and three from the right. The vein from the middle lobe of the right lung unites with that of the upper lobe, and finally two trunks from each lung are formed which open into the left atrium. They have no valves (see Chapter 19). The *coronary veins*, which return blood from the myocardium, unite to form the coronary sinus, which opens into the right atrium and directly into the heart (see Chapter 16).

Veins of the Neck and Head. The *external jugulars*, one on each side, which return blood from the parotid glands, facial muscles, exterior cranium, and other superficial structures, terminate in the subclavian veins.

The *internal jugular veins* are continuous with the lateral sinuses and begin in the jugular foramen at the base of the skull. They descend on either side of the neck and unite first with the external carotid, then with the

[2] The femoral triangle (Scarpa's triangle) corresponds to the depression just below the fold of the groin. Its apex is directed downward. It is bounded above by the inguinal ligament, and the sides are formed laterally by the sartorius muscle and medially by the adductor longus. Antonio Scarpa, Italian anatomist (1752–1832).

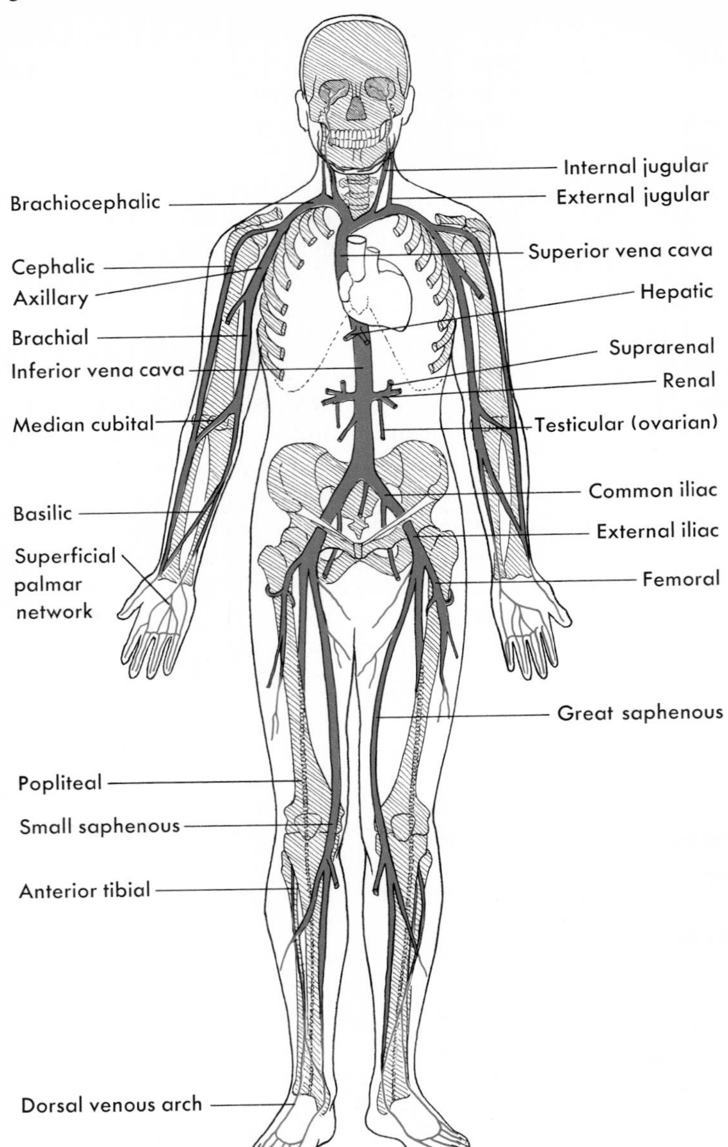

Figure 15–11. Diagram of venous circulation. Many veins named.

common carotid, and join the subclavian at a right angle to form the brachiocephalic vein. They *receive* blood from the veins and sinuses of the cranial cavity, the superior part of the face, and the neck. See Figure 15–11.

Veins of the Thorax. The *brachiocephalic vein* is formed by the union of the *subclavian* and *internal jugular* veins. It receives blood from the head, neck, mammary glands, and upper part of the thorax. It empties into the superior vena cava.

The *internal thoracic veins* receive tributaries corresponding to the branches of the artery. They unite to form a single trunk and end in the *brachiocephalic* vein.

The *superior vena cava* is formed by the union of the right and left brachiocephalic veins and opens into the *right atrium*, opposite the third right costal cartilage.

A *supplementary channel* between the inferior and superior venae cavae is formed by the *azygos veins*. There are three, and they lie along the front of the vertebral column. In case of obstruction these veins form a channel by which blood can be returned from the lower part of the body to the *superior* vena cava.

The azygos vein (right, or major, azygos) begins opposite the first or second lumbar vertebra as the *right ascending lumbar vein* or by a branch of the *right renal vein* or from the *inferior vena cava.* (The lumbar veins empty into the inferior vena cava. They correspond to the lumbar arteries given off by the abdominal aorta and return the blood from the muscles and skin of the loins and walls of the abdomen.)

The azygos vein ascends on the right side of the vertebral column to the level of the fourth thoracic vertebra, where it arches over the root of the right lung and empties into the superior vena cava.

The hemiazygos vein (left lower, or minor, azygos) begins in the left lumbar or renal vein. It ascends on the left side of the vertebral column, and at about the level of the ninth thoracic vertebra it connects with the right azygos vein. It receives the lower four or five intercostal veins of the left side and some esophageal and mediastinal veins.

The *accessory hemiazygos vein* (left upper azygos) connects above with the highest left intercostal vein and opens below into either the azygos or the hemiazygos. It receives veins from the three or four intercostal spaces between the highest left intercostal vein and highest tributary of the hemiazygos; the left bronchial vein sometimes opens into it.

The azygos veins return blood from the intercostal muscles to the superior vena cava. The internal thoracic veins are venae comitantes for the internal thoracic arteries and are tributaries of the right and left brachiocephalic veins.

The Bronchial Veins. A bronchial vein is formed at the root of each lung and returns the blood from the larger bronchi and from the structures at the root of the lung; that of the right side opens into the azygos vein near its termination. (See Chapter 19.)

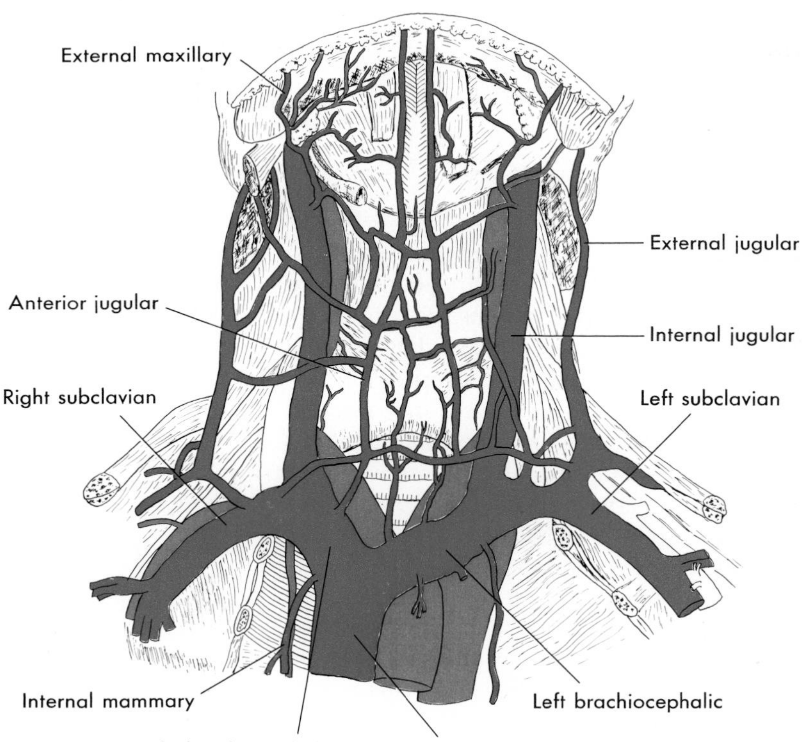

Figure 15–12. Veins of the neck and upper part of thorax, front view. Which hormones enter the circulation through these veins?

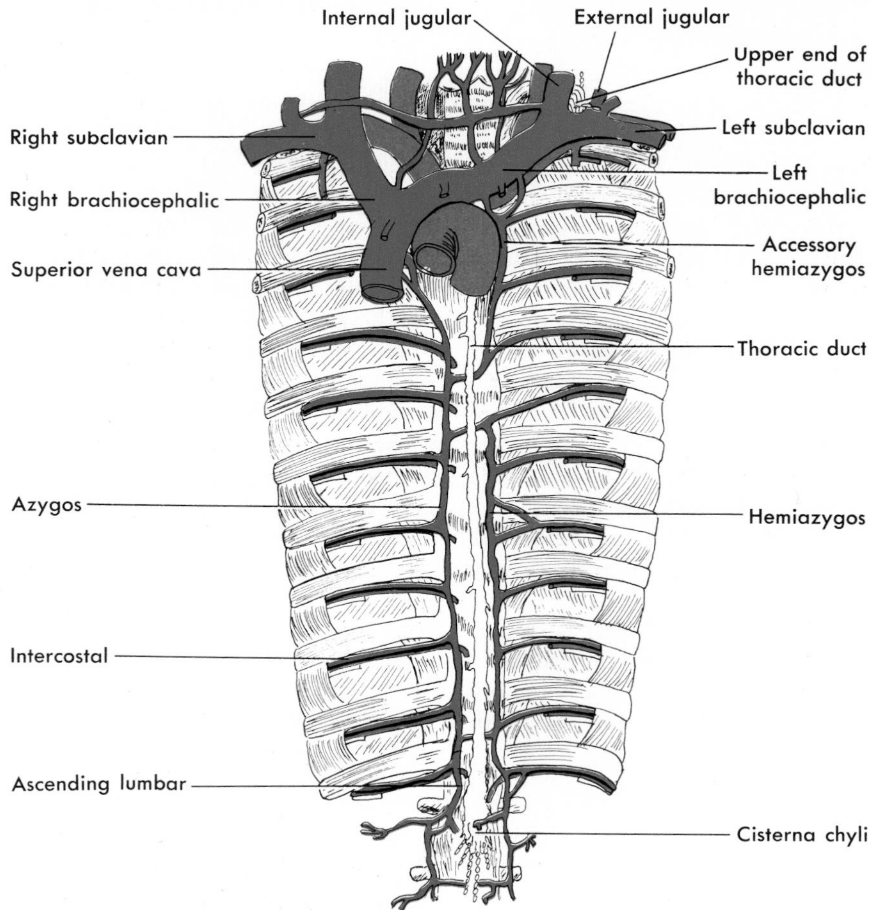

Figure 15–13. Azygos and intercostal veins, also thoracic duct.

Veins of the Abdomen and Pelvis. *External iliac veins* are continuations of the femoral veins. The iliac veins are formed by the union of veins corresponding to the branches of the hypogastric arteries.

The *internal* (hypogastric) and *external iliac* veins unite to form the *common iliacs.* The *common iliacs* extend from the base of the sacrum to the fifth lumbar vertebra and then unite to form the *inferior vena cava*. The *inferior vena cava* begins at the junction of the two common iliacs and ascends along the right side of the aorta, perforates the diaphragm, and terminates by entering the right atrium of the heart. It receives veins having the names of the parietal and visceral branches of the abdominal aorta. These veins are the lumbar, renal, suprarenal, inferior phrenic, hepatic, and right spermatic or ovarian.

There are a few exceptions:

1. The right suprarenal vein empties into the inferior vena cava; the left empties into the left renal or left inferior phrenic.

2. The right inferior phrenic empties into the inferior vena cava; the left often consists of two branches, one of which empties into the left renal or suprarenal vein and the other into the inferior vena cava.

3. The hepatic veins empty into the inferior vena cava, but they commence in the sinusoids of the liver.

4. The right spermatic vein empties into the inferior vena cava, but the left empties into the left renal vein. The ovarian veins end in the same way as the spermatic veins in the male.

The portal and accessory portal system includes blood returning from the spleen and digestive organs, through the liver, and on into the hepatic vein. These systems are discussed in detail with the digestive organs (Chapter 20).

The systemic veins return blood from all parts of the body to the right atrium of the heart. The systemic veins consist of three sets: *superficial*, *deep*, and *venous* sinuses. The *superficial veins* are found just beneath the skin in the superficial fascia. The superficial and deep veins frequently unite. The *deep veins* accompany the arteries and are usually enclosed in the same sheath. The deep veins accompany the smaller arteries and are called *venae comitantes*, or companion veins. The larger arteries have only one accompanying vein, called *vena comes*. The deep veins do not accompany the arteries in certain parts of the body, such as the skull and liver and the larger veins from the bones. *The venous sinuses* are canals found only in the interior of the skull. (See Chapter 11.)

The *systemic veins* are divided into three groups: (1) veins that empty into the heart, (2) veins that empty into the superior vena cava, and (3) veins that empty into the inferior vena cava. Veins emptying into the superior vena cava are the veins of the head, neck, upper extremities, and thorax, and the azygos. Veins emptying into the inferior vena cava include those from the lower extremities, abdomen, and pelvis, and the azygos vein.

Veins of the Upper Extremity. Blood from the upper extremity is returned by a *deep* and *superficial* set of veins. The *deep veins* are the venae comitantes of the hand, forearm, and arm and are called by the same name as the arteries. There are frequent anastomoses with one another and with the superficial veins. *The superficial veins* are larger than the deep veins and return more blood, especially from the distal part of the limb. They include the following:

The *cephalic vein* begins in the dorsal network of the hand and winds upward around the radial border of the forearm to below the bend of the elbow, where it joins the *accessory cephalic* vein to form the *cephalic* of the upper arm.

The *basilic vein* begins in the ulnar part of the dorsal network and extends along the posterior surface of the ulnar to below the elbow, where it is joined by the *median cubital*.

The *axillary vein* is a continuation of the basilic. It ends at the outer border of the first rib in the subclavian vein. It receives blood from the *brachial cephalic vein* and other veins.

The *subclavian vein* is a continuation of the axillary vein and unites with the internal jugular to form the brachiocephalic vein. At the junction with the *internal jugular* and *left subclavian* vein, it receives the thoracic duct and the *right subclavian* vein receives the right lymphatic duct.

Veins of the Lower Extremity. Blood from the lower extremity is returned by a *superficial* and a *deep* set of veins. The *superficial* veins are beneath the skin between the layers of fascia. The *deep veins* accompany the arteries. Both sets are provided with valves, which are more numerous in the deep veins. The superficial veins include the *great saphenous*, which begins in the marginal vein of the dorsum of the foot, extends up the medial side of the leg and thigh, and ends in the *femoral vein* just below the inguinal ligament. It receives many branches from the sole of the foot; in the leg it anastomoses with the small *saphenous vein* and receives many *cutaneous veins*. Branches from the posterior and medial aspects of the thigh frequently unite to form an *accessory saphenous* vein. The *small saphenous vein* (see Figure 15–11) begins behind the lateral malleolus as a continuation of the *lateral marginal vein* and extends up the back of the leg to end in the *deep popliteal* vein. It receives many branches from the deep veins on the dorsum of the foot and from the back of the leg. The *deep veins* accompany the arteries below the knee. They are in pairs and are called by the same names as the arteries. Veins from the foot empty into the *anterior* and *posterior* tibial veins, which unite to form the *popliteal vein*, which is continued as the *femoral* and becomes the *external iliac vein*. (See Figure 15–11.)

Blood Circulation in Upper Extremity

Blood leaves the left ventricle, traverses arteries, arterioles, capillaries, venules, and veins and is returned to the right atrium via the superior vena cava

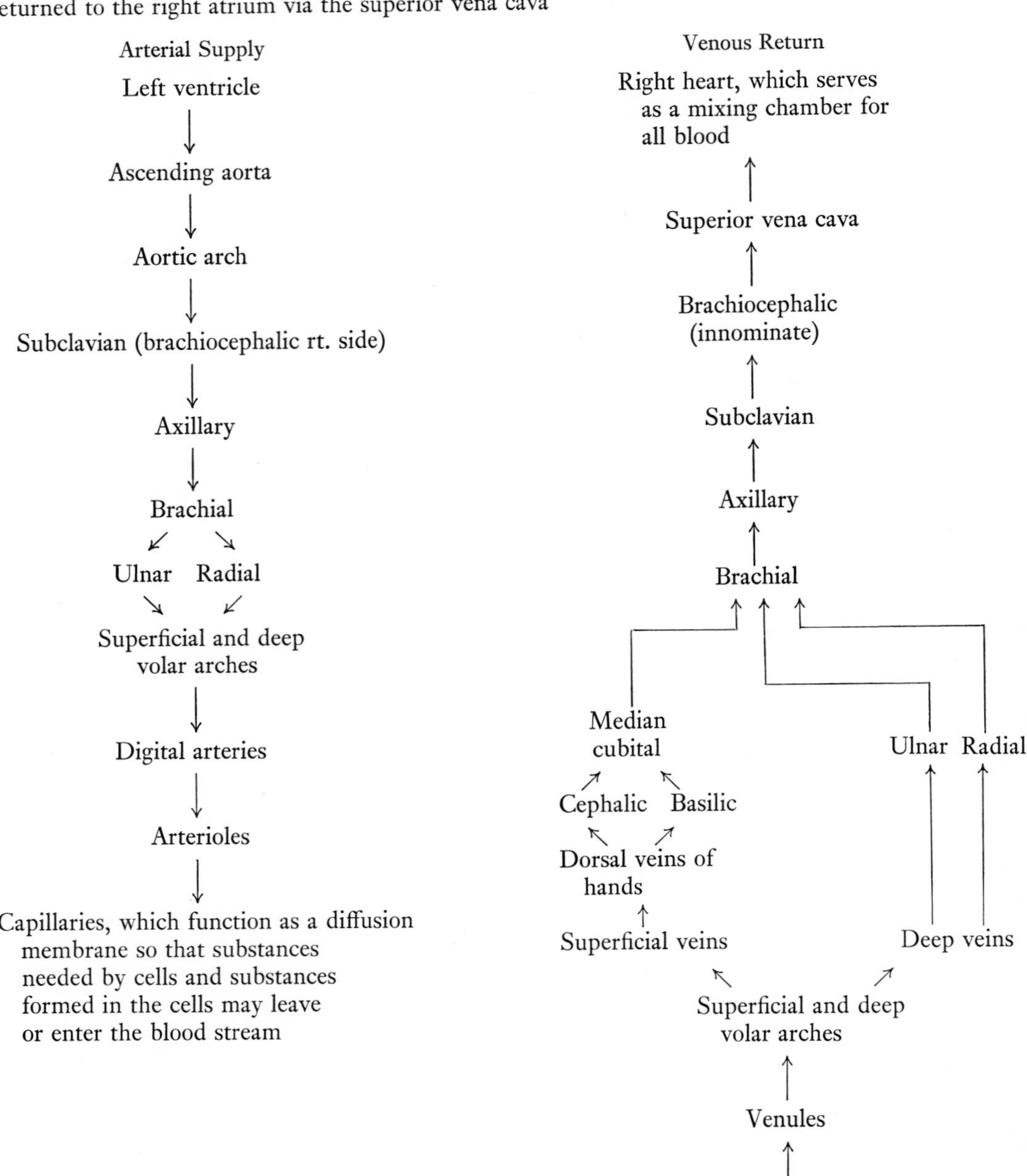

BLOOD CIRCULATION IN LOWER EXTREMITY

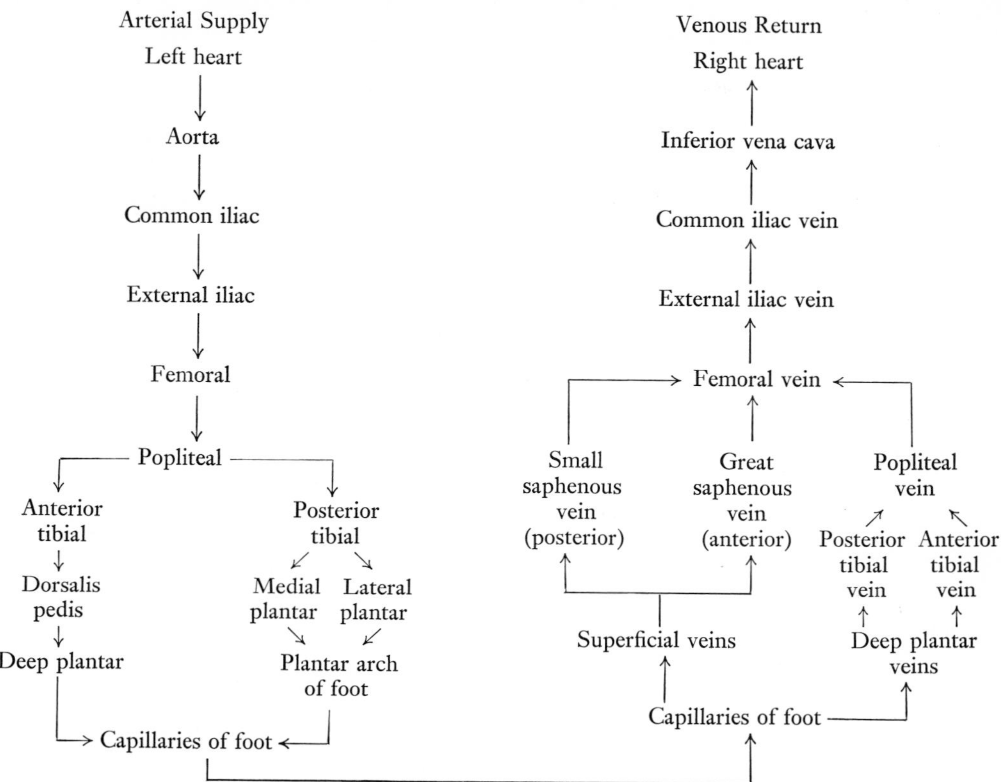

QUESTIONS FOR DISCUSSION

1. Where and how would you place pressure to stop bleeding from an artery?
2. How would you know whether it was a vein or artery bleeding?
3. Which veins are usually used for venipuncture? Why?
4. Where are the most accessible places to take the pulse? Name the arteries in each instance.
5. What are the differences in blood flow in arteries, veins, and capillaries?
6. Where would you place pressure to stop bleeding from a vein?
7. How do the cells of the body receive their nutrients from the arteries?
8. Discuss the structural differences between arteries, capillaries, and veins.

SUMMARY

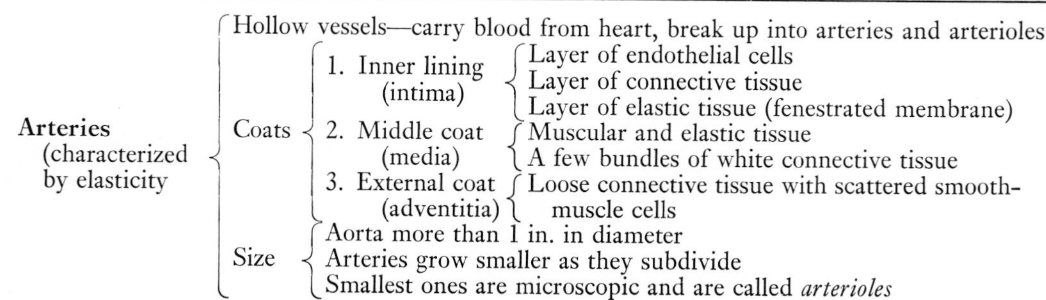

Arteries (characterized by elasticity)
- Hollow vessels—carry blood from heart, break up into arteries and arterioles
- Coats
  - 1. Inner lining (intima)
    - Layer of endothelial cells
    - Layer of connective tissue
    - Layer of elastic tissue (fenestrated membrane)
  - 2. Middle coat (media)
    - Muscular and elastic tissue
    - A few bundles of white connective tissue
  - 3. External coat (adventitia)
    - Loose connective tissue with scattered smooth-muscle cells
- Size
  - Aorta more than 1 in. in diameter
  - Arteries grow smaller as they subdivide
  - Smallest ones are microscopic and are called *arterioles*

Capillaries (characterized by multiplicity)
- Tiny vessels about 8 μ in diameter. Connect arterioles to venules
- One layer of endothelial cells
- Communicate freely in networks

Veins (characterized by valves)
- Collapsible vessels, smallest ones called *venules*
- Begin where capillaries end
- Carry blood to the heart
- Three coats, same as arteries, but thinner
- Valves—semilunar pockets

Vasa vasorum—term applied to blood vessels that are supplied to coats of other blood vessels

Vasomotor—term applied to *nerve fibers* supplied to blood vessels
- Vasoconstrictor, well understood
- Vasodilator, not as well understood

Arteries
- Begin as large trunks, grow smaller
- Usually deep-seated for protection
- Division
  - Trunk gives off several branches
  - One branch that divides into several or two branches of nearly equal size
- Anastomosis—distal ends unite
- Plexus—many anastomoses within limited area

Division of the Vascular System
- **Pulmonary system**
  1. Pulmonary artery conveys venous blood from right ventricle to lungs
     - Right pulmonary artery—right lung
     - Left pulmonary artery—left lung
  2. Capillaries connect arterioles to venules
  3. Four pulmonary veins—two from each lung—convey oxygenated blood to left atrium
- **Systemic system**
  - Provides for systemic circulation
  1. Aorta and all its branches
  2. Capillaries connect arterioles to venules
  3. Veins empty into heart either directly or by means of inferior and superior venae cavae

Aorta
- **Ascending aorta**
  - About 5 cm long
  - Branches
    - Right coronary
    - Left coronary
- **Arch of aorta**
  - Extends from ascending aorta to body of fourth thoracic vertebra
  - Branches
    - Brachiocephalic
      - Right common carotid
      - Right subclavian
    - Left common carotid
    - Left subclavian
- **Descending aorta**
  - Thoracic aorta
    - Extends from lower border of fourth thoracic vertebra to aortic opening in diaphragm
    - Branches supply body wall and viscera of thorax
  - Abdominal aorta
    - Extends from aortic opening in diaphragm to body of fourth lumbar vertebra. Branches supply body wall and viscera of abdominal cavity

Arteries of the Head and Face
- **Left common carotid** arises from arch of aorta
  - **External carotid**
    - Branches supply thyroid gland, tongue, throat, face, ear, and dura mater
  - **Internal carotid**
    - Branches supply brain, eye and its appendages, forehead, and nose
- **Right common carotid** arises at division of brachiocephalic
  - **External carotid**
    - Branches same as on left side
  - **Internal carotid**
    - Branches same as on left side

- **Arteries of the Chest**
  - **Visceral group**
    - **Pericardials**—to pericardium
    - **Bronchials**—nutrient vessels of lungs
    - **Esophageals**—to esophagus
    - **Mediastinals**—to nodes and areolar tissue in mediastinum
  - **Parietal group**
    - **Intercostals**—to lower nine intercostal spaces
    - **Subcostals**—anastomose with superior epigastrics, lower intercostals, and lumbar arteries
    - **Superior phrenics**—upper surface of diaphragm
- **Arteries of the Abdomen, Visceral Branches**
  - **Celiac artery**
    - **Left gastric**—lesser curvature of stomach left to right
    - **Hepatic artery** divides into right and left branches before entering liver
      - **Right gastric**—lesser curvature of stomach right to left
      - **Gastroduodenal**
        - *Superior pancreaticoduodenal* to duodenum and head of pancreas
        - *Right gastroepiploic*—greater curvature of stomach right to left
      - **Cystic**—gallbladder
    - **Lienal, or splenic**
      - Branches to pancreas
      - **Left gastroepiploic**—greater curvature of stomach left to right
  - **Superior mesenteric** — Supplies small intestine except duodenum, cecum, ascending colon, half of transverse colon
  - **Inferior mesenteric** — Supplies left half transverse colon, whole of descending and sigmoid colon, continued as *superior hemorrhoidal artery* to rectum
  - **Middle suprarenals** — To suprarenal glands—anastomose with branches of phrenic and renal arteries
  - **Renal arteries** — Each divides into four or five branches before entering kidney
  - **Internal spermatics** — Supply the testes
  - **Ovarian arteries** — Supply ovaries, send small branches to the ureters and uterine tubes; one branch unites with uterine artery and assists in supplying uterus
- **Arteries of the Abdomen, Parietal Branches**
  - **Inferior phrenics**—distributed to undersurface of diaphragm
  - **Lumbar arteries** — Distribute branches to muscles and skin of back, to the spinal cord and its membranes, and to the lumbar vertebrae
  - **Middle sacral**—passes down to coccygeal gland
- **Arteries of the Pelvis**
  - **Common iliacs** about 5 cm
    - **Internal iliacs** — Branches to pelvic walls, viscera, genitals, buttocks, medial side of thighs
    - **External iliacs**
      - Branches to psoas major
      - Inferior epigastric
      - Deep iliac circumflex
- **Arteries of the Upper Extremities**
  - **Subclavian**—forms main artery of each upper limb. Different portions named according to regions through which they pass
  - **Right subclavian**
    - Extends from the brachiocephalic to the first rib
    - Branches are
      - Vertebral, thyrocervical
      - Internal thoracic
      - Costocervical
  - **Left subclavian**
    - Extends from arch of aorta to first rib
    - Same branches as right subclavian
  - **Axillary arteries**
    - In axillary regions
    - Branches to shoulders, chest, and arms
  - **Brachial arteries** — Extend from axillary arteries to below bend of elbows, where they divide into ulnar and radial arteries

Arteries of the Upper Extremities (*cont.*)
- **Ulnar arteries** — Extend along ulnar border of forearms to palms of hands
- **Radial arteries** — Extend along radial side of forearms to palms of hands
- (Ulnar and radial arteries together) Form the superficial and deep *volar arches*

Arteries of the Lower Extremities
- **External iliacs** form main arteries of lower limbs. Different portions named according to regions through which they pass
- **Femoral arteries** — Extend along inguinal ligaments to openings in adductor magnus muscles. Send branches to abdominal walls, external genitalia, muscles and fasciae of the thighs
- **Popliteal arteries** — Back of knees, send branches to knee joints, posterior femoral muscles, gastrocnemius, soleus, skin of back of legs. Below knee joints divide into posterior tibials and anterior tibials
- **Posterior tibials** — Back of legs, from bifurcation of popliteal to ankle. Send branches to back of legs and to tibiae and fibulae. Give off peroneal arteries about 1 in. below bifurcation of popliteals. *Peroneals* distribute blood to fibulae and calcaneus bones
- **Anterior tibials** — Front of legs from bifurcation of popliteal to ankle—then become the *dorsalis pedis arteries*
- **Dorsalis pedis arteries** — Dorsum of each foot, anastomose with branches from posterior tibials and supply blood to feet

Veins
- Begin small, grow larger
- **Differ from arteries**
  - Larger size
  - Greater number
  - Thinner walls
  - Valves
  - More frequent anastomoses
- **Sets**
  - Superficial, or cutaneous, beneath the skin
  - Deep
    - Usually accompany the arteries
    - Exceptions are
      - Veins in skull and vertebral canal
      - Hepatic veins
      - Large coronary veins
  - Venous sinuses—canals formed by separation of layers of dura mater
- **Venae comitantes** — Deep veins accompanying smaller arteries, such as brachial, radial, ulnar, peroneal, tibial, are in pairs. A single deep vein accompanying a larger artery, such as femoral, popliteal, axillary, and subclavian artery, is called a *vena comes*
- **Veins to heart**
  - **Coronary veins** from heart
  - **Superior vena cava** — Veins of head, neck, thorax, and upper extremities empty into this vein
  - **Inferior vena cava** — Veins of abdomen, pelvis, and lower extremities empty into this vein

Veins of the Head and Neck
- **External jugulars** — Formed in parotid glands, terminate in the subclavians. Receive blood from deep parts of the face and the exterior of the cranium
- **Internal jugulars** — Continuous with the lateral sinuses, unite with subclavians to form the innominates. Receive blood from the veins and sinuses of the cranial cavity, superficial parts of face and neck

- **Veins of the Thorax**
  - **Brachiocephalics**
    - Formed by union of internal jugular and subclavians. Receive internal thoracic veins
    - One on each side of body
  - **Superior vena cava**
    - Formed by union of right and left brachiocephalic veins. 7.5 cm (3 in.) long
    - Opens into right atrium
  - **Supplementary channel**
    - 1. **Azygos vein**
    - 2. **Hemiazygos vein**
    - 3. **Accessory hemiazygos vein**
    - Connect inferior vena cava below with superior vena cava above
  - **Bronchial veins**
    - Formed at the root of each lung
    - Return blood from larger bronchi and structures at root of lungs
    - Right bronchial vein empties into azygos
    - Left bronchial vein empties into highest left intercostal or the accessory hemiazygos

- **Veins of the Abdomen and Pelvis**
  - **Hypogastrics (internal iliacs)**
    - Formed by union of veins corresponding to branches of hypogastric arteries
  - **Common iliacs**
    - Formed by union of external iliacs and hypogastrics. Extend from base of sacrum to the fifth lumbar vertebra
  - **Inferior vena cava**
    - Formed by union of the common iliacs
    - Extends from fifth lumbar vertebra to the right atrium of the heart
    - Receives many tributaries corresponding to arteries given off from the aorta

- **Veins of the Upper Extremities**
  - **Superficial veins**
    - Are larger, take a greater share in returning blood
    - **Cephalics**: Begin in dorsal venous network, join accessory cephalics of arms below elbows, empty into axillaries
    - **Basilics**: Begin in dorsal venous network, are joined by median basilics below elbows, are continued as axillaries
  - **Deep veins**
    - Accompany arteries, are called by same names, i.e., metacarpals, radials, ulnars, brachials, axillaries, and subclavians
    - **Axillaries**: Are continuations of the basilics, end at outer border of first ribs, receive brachials, cephalics, and deep veins
    - **Subclavians**: Are continuations of the axillaries, unite with internal jugulars to form brachiocephalics

- **Veins of the Lower Extremities**
  - **Superficial veins**
    - Are between the layers of superficial fasciae
    - Provided with valves
    - **Great saphenous veins**: Begin in medial marginal veins, extend upward, and end in femoral veins. Receive branches from soles of feet. Anastomose with small saphenous veins, receive cutaneous veins and accessory saphenous veins
    - **Small saphenous**
      - Continuation of lateral marginal veins, end in deep popliteal veins
      - Receive branches on dorsum of each foot and back of each leg

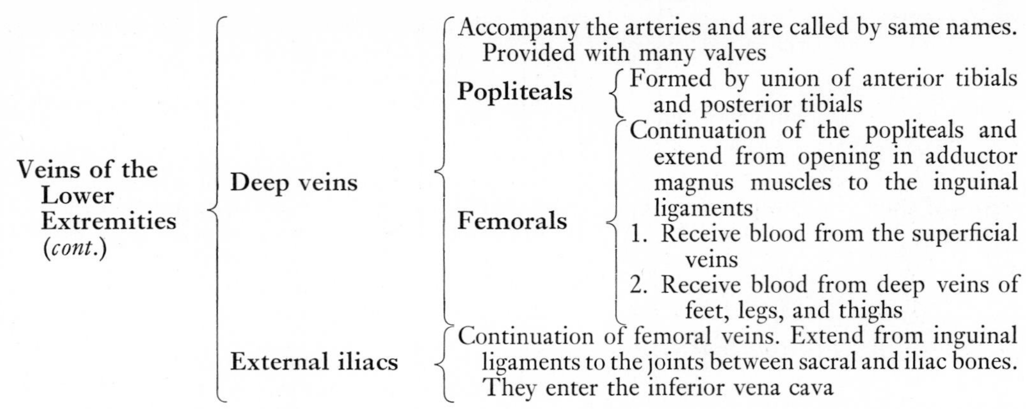

- **Veins of the Lower Extremities** (*cont.*)
  - **Deep veins**
    - Accompany the arteries and are called by same names. Provided with many valves
    - **Popliteals**
      - Formed by union of anterior tibials and posterior tibials
    - **Femorals**
      - Continuation of the popliteals and extend from opening in adductor magnus muscles to the inguinal ligaments
      - 1. Receive blood from the superficial veins
      - 2. Receive blood from deep veins of feet, legs, and thighs
  - **External iliacs**
    - Continuation of femoral veins. Extend from inguinal ligaments to the joints between sacral and iliac bones. They enter the inferior vena cava

CHAPTER

16

THE HEART

Structure and Function
Coronary Circulation
Cardiac Cycle
Nervous Control

The pumping action of the heart is fundamental to adequate nutrition of cells and maintenance of internal environment. Without this pumping action cells would starve, waste products would build up, and life of the cell and of the individual would cease.

THE HEART

The heart is a hollow, muscular organ, situated in the thorax between the lungs and above the central depression of the diaphragm. It is about the size of the closed fist, shaped like a blunt cone, and so suspended by the great vessels that the broader end, or base, is directed upward, backward, and to the right. The pointed end, or apex, points downward, forward, and to the left. As placed in the body, it has an oblique position, and the right side is almost in front of the left. The impact of the heart during contraction is felt against the chest wall in the space between the fifth and sixth ribs, a little below the left nipple, and about 8 cm (3 in.) to the left of the median line.

The Heart Wall. The heart wall is composed of (1) an outer layer, the *epicardium*, (2) a middle layer, the *myocardium*, and (3) an inner layer, the *endocardium*. The epicardium is the serous membrane, or visceral pericardium.

Pericardium. The heart is covered by a serous membrane called the pericardium. It consists of two parts: (1) an external fibrous portion and (2) an internal serous portion.

1. The External Fibrous Pericardium. This is composed of fibrous tissue and is attached by its upper surface to the large blood vessels which emerge from the heart. It covers these vessels for about 3.8 cm (1½ in.) and blends with their sheaths. The lower border is adherent to the diaphragm, and the front surface is attached to the sternum.

2. The Internal, or Serous, Portion of the Pericardium. This is a completely closed sac; it envelops the heart and lines the *fibrous* pericardium. The heart, however, is not within the cavity of the closed sac (Figure 16–2). The portion of the serous pericardium which lines it and is closely adherent to the heart is called the *visceral* portion (*viscus*, an organ); the remaining part of the serous pericardium, namely, that which lines the fibrous pericardium, is known as the *parietal* portion (*paries*, a wall). The visceral and parietal portions of this serous membrane are everywhere in contact. Between them is a small quantity of pericardial fluid preventing friction as their surfaces continually slide over

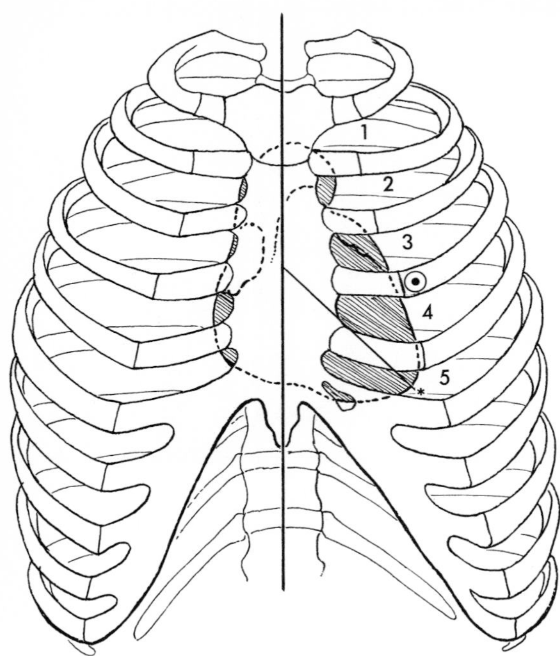

Figure 16–1. Heart in situ. (*1, 2, 3, 4, 5*) Intercostal spaces, vertical line represents median line. Space outlined by the triangle indicates the superficial cardiac region. ⊙ shows the location of the nipple, on the fourth rib. * indicates the area for placing the stethoscope to take the apex beat of the heart.

each other with the constant beating of the heart. The pericardial fluid may aid in cushioning the heart, which is especially important with rapid bodily movements. Inflammation of the pericardium is called pericarditis.

Endocardium. The inner surface of the cavities of the heart is lined by a thin membrane called endocardium. It is composed of endothelial cells and covers the valves, surrounds the chordae tendineae, and is continuous with the lining membrane of the large blood vessels. The endocardium contains many blood vessels, a few bundles of smooth muscle, and parts of the conducting system. Inflammation of the endocardium is called endocarditis

Myocardium. The main substance of the heart is cardiac muscle, called myocardium. This tissue includes the muscle bundles of (1) the atria, (2) the ventricles, and (3) the atrioventricular bundle (of His).[1] Inflammation of the myocardium is known as myocarditis. Obstruction of the coronary circulation (page 325) to the myocardium may cause myocardial infarction.

1. The principal muscle bundles of the atria radiate from the area which surrounds the orifice of the superior vena cava. One, the interatrial bundle, connects the anterior surfaces of the two atria. The other atrial muscle bundles are confined to their respective atria, though they merge to some extent.

2. The muscle bundles of the ventricles begin in the atrioventricular fibrous rings. They form U-shaped bundles with the apex of the U toward the apex of the heart. There are many of these bundles, but for general description they may be divided into four

[1] Wilhelm His, Jr., German physiologist (1863–1934).

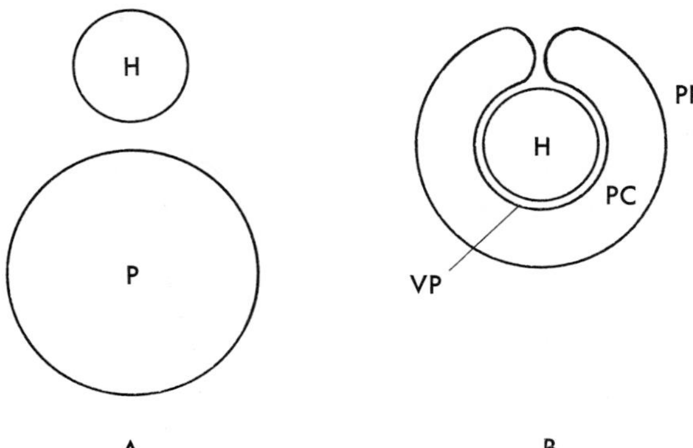

Figure 16–2. Diagram of the heart and serous pericardium. *A* shows heart (*H*) and pericardium (*P*) lying separately; *B* shows the pericardium invaginated by the heart; *PC*, pericardial cavity, which actually is a very narrow space filled with pericardial fluid; *PP*, parietal layer that lines the fibrous pericardium; *VP*, visceral layer that clings close to the heart muscle.

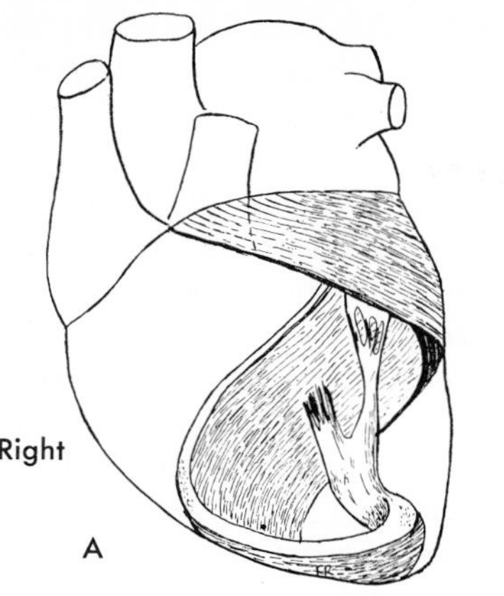

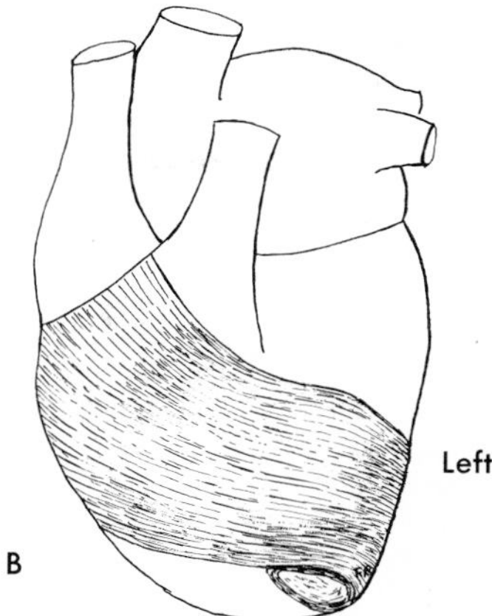

A, *B*. Note how the two groups of muscle fibers wind around both the right and the left ventricles on the outside.

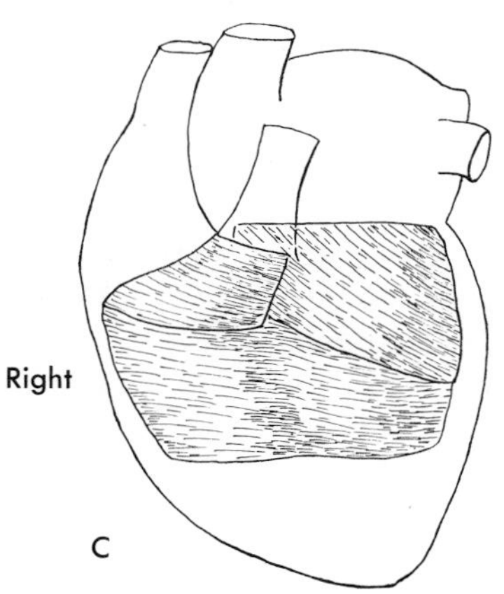

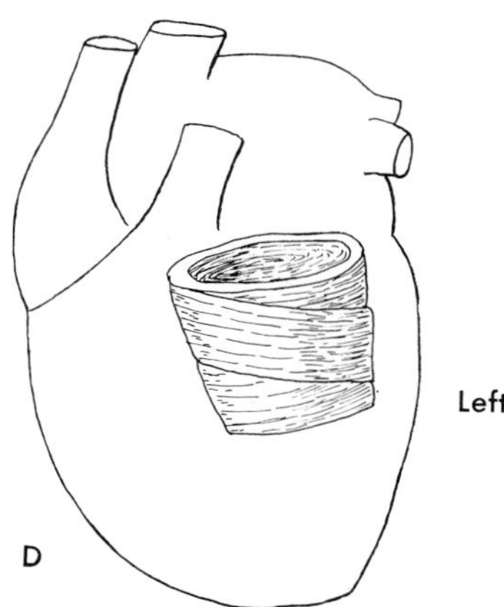

C. Note how the second layer of muscle fibers winds around both the right and left ventricles.
D. Note that the innermost layer winds around the left ventricle only.

Figure 16–3. Diagram showing arrangement of muscle fibers of the heart. When these muscles contract, what happens to the blood vessels? Position of heart more upright than normal. (Modified from Wiggers and Schaeffer.)

groups. One group begins at the *left* atrioventricular ring, passes toward the right and the apex, where it forms whorls, and then ends either in the left ventricular wall, the papillary muscles, or the septum and the right ventricular wall (Figure 16–3).

A second bundle repeats this path except that it starts at the *right* ventricular ring, passes to the left in the anterior wall of the heart, and ends in the same structures as above.

These two groups form an outer layer which winds around both ventricles. Under these is a third group of muscle bundles which again wind around both ventricles. There is a fourth group of muscle bundles which wind around the left ventricle. Thus the left ventricle has a much thicker wall than the right. During contraction the squeeze of the spirally arranged muscle bundles forces blood out of the ventricles.

3. The muscular tissue of the atria is not continuous with that of the ventricles. The walls are connected by fibrous tissue and the atrioventricular bundle of modified muscle

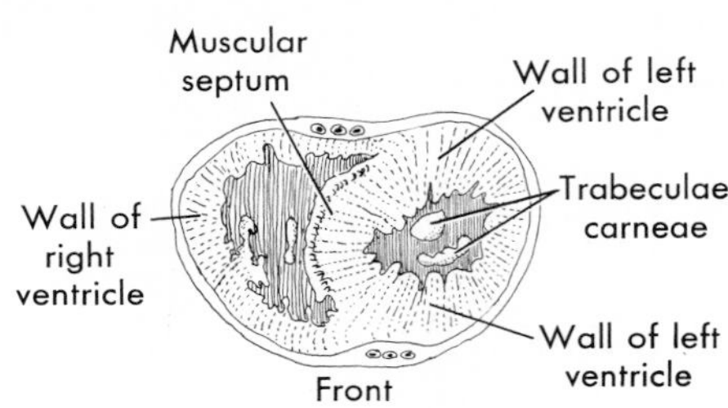

Figure 16–4. Cross section through ventricles, showing relative thickness of their walls and shape of cavities.

cells. This bundle arises in connection with the atrioventricular (AV) node, which lies near the orifice of the coronary sinus in the right atrium. From this node the atrioventricular bundle passes forward to the membranous septum between the ventricles, where it divides into right and left bundles, one for each ventricle. In the muscular septum between the ventricles each bundle divides into numerous strands, which spread over the internal surface just under the endocardium. The greater part of the atrioventricular bundle consists of spindle-shaped muscle cells. The significance of the atrioventricular bundle is discussed on page 327.

The Cavities of the Heart. The heart is divided into right and left halves, frequently called the right heart and the left heart, by a muscular partition, the ventricular septum, which extends from the base of the ventricles to the apex of the heart. The atrial septum is inconspicuous. The two sides of the heart have no communication with each other after birth. The right side contains *venous* and the left side *arterial* blood. Each half is subdivided into two cavities: the upper, called the *atrium*, and the lower, the *ventricle*. The left ventricle ejects blood into the extensive systemic circulatory system under much higher pressure than is required of the right ventricle for ejecting blood into the relatively short pulmonary circulation. The structural arrangement of cardiac muscle fibers provides for the thicker muscle required in this pumping action. (See Figure 16–3.) Both the right and left sides of the heart contract and relax almost simultaneously.

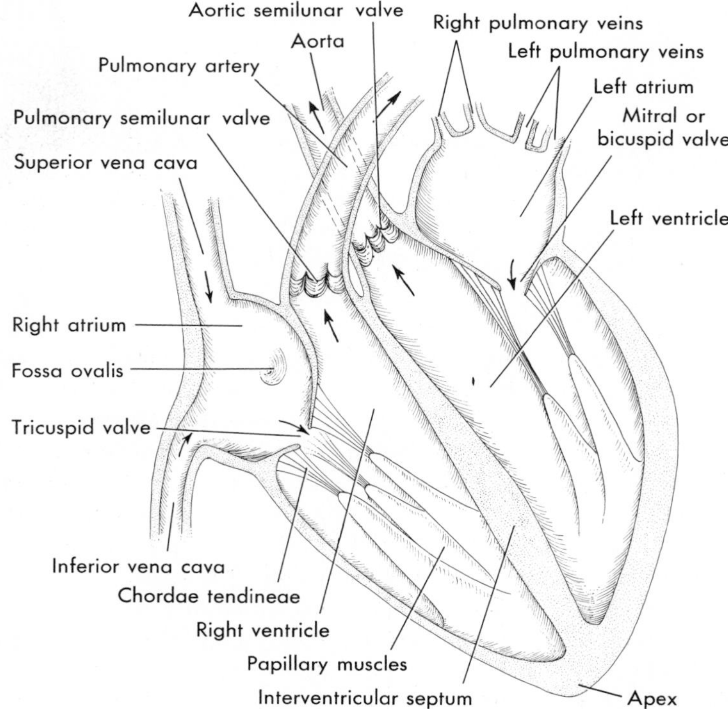

Figure 16–5. Longitudinal section of heart showing chambers and valves. *Arrows* indicate direction of blood flow.

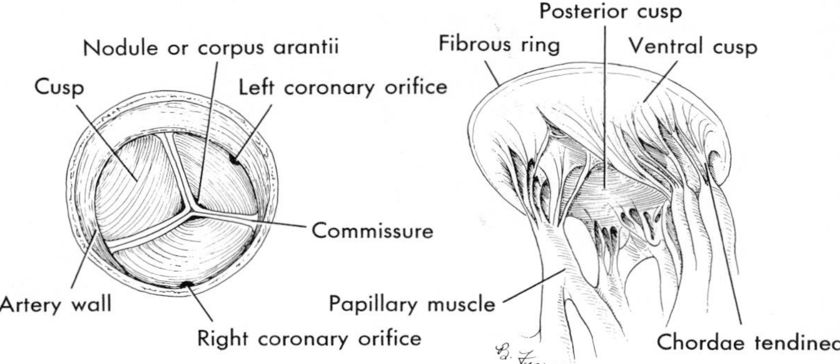

Figure 16–6. Valves of the left side of the heart. (*A*) Aortic valve closed, seen from above. (*B*) Mitral valve seen from below.

Muscular columns, called the *trabeculae carneae* (*columnae carneae*), project from the inner surface of the ventricles. They are of three kinds: The first are attached along their entire length and form ridges, or columns. The second is a rounded bundle; the moderator band (*trabecula septomarginalis*) projects from the base of the anterior papillary muscle to the ventricular septum. It is formed largely of specialized fibers concerned with the conducting mechanisms of the heart. Third are the *papillary muscles*, which are continuous with the wall of each ventricle at its base. The apexes of the papillary muscles give rise to fibrous cords, called the *chordae tendineae*, which are attached to the cusps of the atrioventricular valves. These muscles contract when the ventricular walls contract.

Orifices of the Heart. The orifices comprise the left and right atrioventricular orifices and the orifices of eight large blood vessels connected with the heart.

On the right side of the heart, the superior and inferior venae cavae and coronary sinus empty into the atrium, and the pulmonary artery leaves the ventricle.

On the left side of the heart, four pulmonary veins empty into the atrium, and the aorta leaves the ventricle. There are some smaller openings to receive blood directly from the heart substance, and before birth there is an opening between the right and left atria called the *foramen ovale*. Normally this closes soon after birth. Its location is visible in Figure 27–14, page 582.

Valves of the Heart. Between each atrium and ventricle there is a somewhat constricted opening, the atrioventricular orifice, which is strengthened by fibrous rings and protected by valves. The openings into the aorta and pulmonary artery are also guarded by valves.

The Tricuspid Valve. The right atrioventricular valve is composed of three irregular-shaped flaps, or cusps, and hence is named *tricuspid.* The flaps are formed mainly of fibrous tissue covered by endocardium. At their bases they are continuous with one another and form a ring-shaped membrane around the margin of the atrial openings; their pointed ends project into the ventricle and are attached by the chordae tendineae to small muscular pillars, the papillary muscles, in the interior of the ventricles.

The Bicuspid Valve. The left atrioventricular valve consists of two flaps, or cusps, and is named the *bicuspid*, or *mitral*, valve. It is attached in the same manner as the tricuspid valve, which it closely resembles in structure except that it is much stronger and thicker in all its parts. Chordae tendineae are attached to the cusps and papillary muscles in the same way as on the right side; they are less numerous but thicker and stronger.

PHYSIOLOGY. The tricuspid and bicuspid valves freely permit the flow of blood from the atria into the ventricles because the free edges of the flaps are pointed in the direction of the blood current; but any flow forced backward gets between the flaps and the walls of the ventricles and drives the flaps upward until, meeting at their edges, they unite and form a complete transverse partition

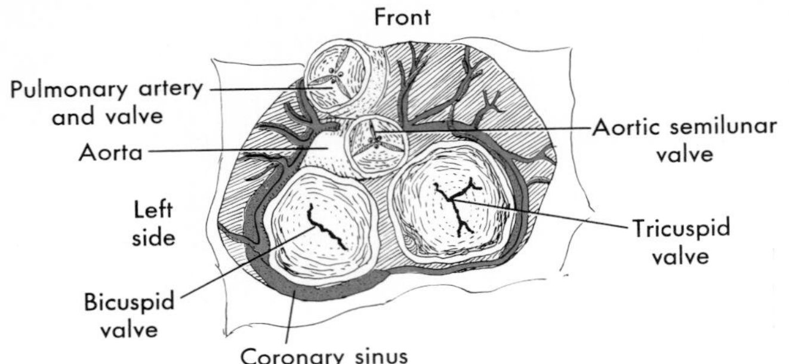

Figure 16–7. Valves of the heart as seen from above, atria removed.

between the atria and ventricles. The valves remain open as long as the pressure of the blood is higher in the atria than in the ventricles. When the muscles of the ventricles begin to contract, the pressure in the ventricular chambers rises and the valves close. The valves are kept from everting into the atrial chambers by the chordae tendineae, which are kept taut by the papillary muscles.

Semilunar Valves. The orifice between the right ventricle and the pulmonary artery is guarded by the *pulmonary valve*, and the orifice between the left ventricle and the aorta is guarded by the *aortic valve*. These two valves are called *semilunar valves* and consist of three semilunar cusps, each cusp being attached by its convex margin to the inside of the artery where it joins the ventricle, while its free border projects into the lumen of the vessel. Small nodular bodies, called the *corpora Arantii*,[2] are attached to the center of the free edge of each pocket.

The aortic valve is larger and stronger, and the corpora Arantii are thicker and more evident. Between the cusps of the valve and the aortic wall are slight dilatations called the aortic sinuses or sinuses of Valsalva.[3] The coronary arteries have their origin from two of these sinuses.

PHYSIOLOGY. The semilunar valves offer no resistance to the passage of blood from the heart into the arteries, as the free borders project into the arteries, but they form a complete barrier to the passage of blood in the opposite direction. In this case each pocket becomes filled with blood, and the free borders are floated out and distended so that they meet in the center of the vessel. The corpora Arantii assist in the closure of the valves and help to make the barrier complete.

The orifices between the two caval veins and the right atrium and the orifices between the left atrium and the four pulmonary veins are not guarded by valves. The opening from the inferior vena cava is partly covered by a membrane known as the caval (eustachian) valve.

Lymph Vessels. The heart is richly supplied with lymph capillaries, which form a continuous network from the endocardium, through the muscle layers to the epicardium. These capillaries form larger vessels which accompany the coronary blood vessels and finally enter the thoracic duct.

Coronary Vessels. The blood vessels of the heart include the coronary arteries and coronary veins.

Coronary Arteries. The *left coronary* artery has its origin in the left aortic sinus, runs under the left atrium, and divides into the anterior descending and circumflex branches. The anterior branch descends in the anterior interventricular sulcus to the apex, supplying branches to both ventricles. Occlusion of this artery is common. The circumflex runs in the left part of the coronary sulcus and curves around and nearly reaches the posterior sulcus. It supplies branches to the left atrium and ventricle.

The right coronary artery has its origin in the right aortic sinus and turns to the right under the right atrium to the coronary sulcus.

[2] Aranzio Arantius, Italian anatomist (1530–1589).

[3] Antonio Maria Valsalva, Italian anatomist (1666–1723).

There are two branches, the *posterior descending* and the *marginal branch*. Branches of the left and right coronaries anastomose and encircle the heart forming a crown, hence their name. They supply the heart muscle with blood. Blood within the cavities of the heart nourishes only the endocardium.

Coronary Veins. The coronary sinus receives most veins of the heart and terminates in the right atrium.

The great cardiac veins begin at the apex and ascend to empty into the coronary sinus.

There are smaller veins: the small cardiac, middle cardiac, and posterior veins, which begin at the apex and ascend to enter the coronary sinus.

The mouths of the great and small cardiac veins have single cuspid valves, but are rarely efficient. Very small veins begin in the wall of the heart and open directly into the chambers of the heart (thebesian veins).

The Coronary Circulation. The purpose of the coronary circulation is to distribute blood, containing oxygen, nutrients, and other substances, to the cardiac muscle cells and return to general circulation the products of metabolism.

The coronary arteries leave the aorta close to the heart. These arteries fill during myocardial relaxation and empty during contraction. Normally the rate of blood flow through these vessels is from 50 to 75 ml of blood per 100 gm of heart muscle per minute, depending upon the heart rate and heart volume. In other words, if the heart weighs 300 gm, from 150 to 225 ml of blood will flow through coronary vessels per minute. Since the output of the heart has been estimated to be about 3 to 4 liters per minute, this means that about 10 per cent of the heart output flows through the coronary arteries. This blood is returned to the heart via the coronary sinus, which opens directly into the right atrium. The coronary vessels carry supplies to, and products of metabolism from, the tissues of the heart. If this circulation is interfered with (by occlusion of vessels),

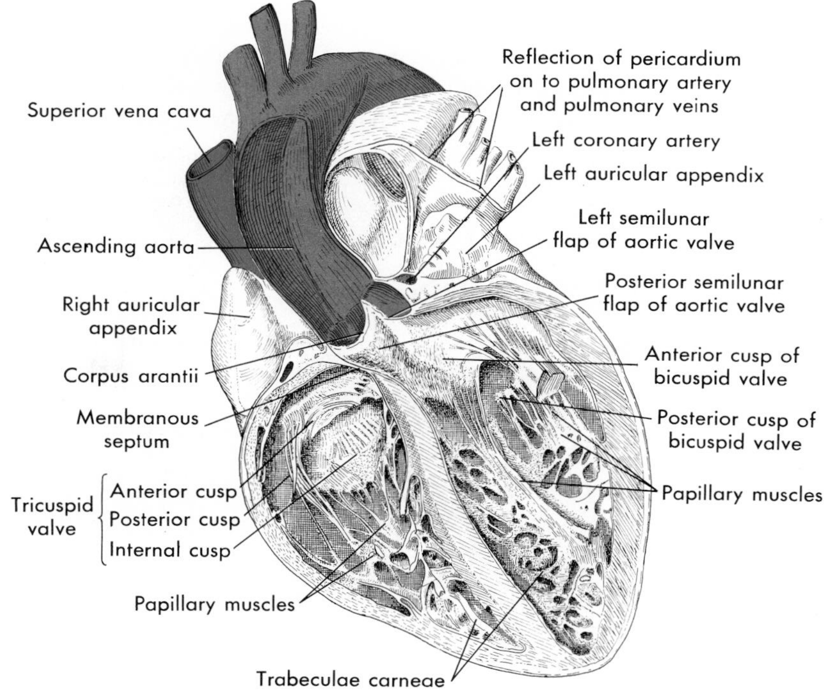

Figure 16–8. The heart, seen from the front. (Modified from Toldt.) What is the function of the right heart? The left heart? Why are valves needed?

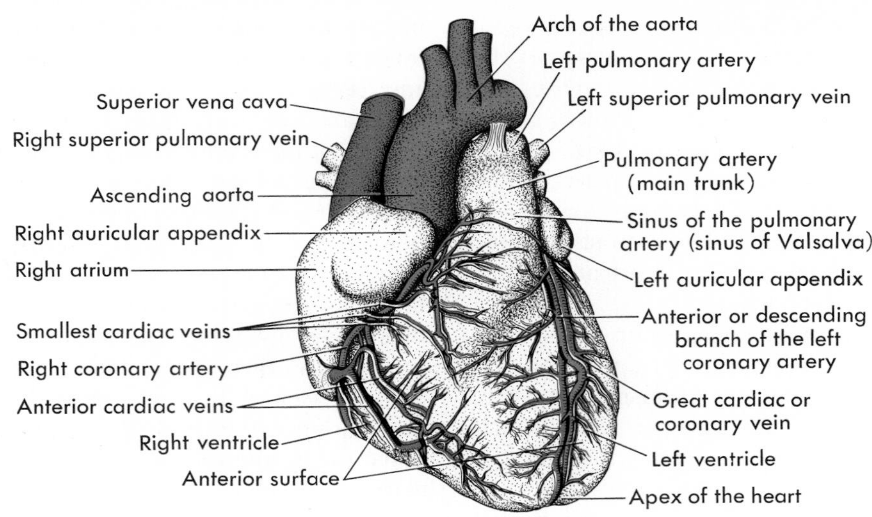

Figure 16–9. Diagram of the heart showing coronary arteries and veins. Anterior view. The great cardiac vein and artery indicate location of the septa. (Modified from Toldt.)

normal contractions of the heart are impossible.

In man it takes about 23 seconds to complete a circuit of medium length from the left ventricle to the right atrium (systemic circulation). The blood which enters the right atrium goes through the lungs (pulmonary circulation) before it gets back to the left atrium. This double circulation, pulmonary and systemic, is constantly going on, as each half of the heart is in a literal sense a force pump.

The Collateral Circulation. The channels of communication between the artery-capillary-vein system of the heart are complex and numerous. There are direct channels between the coronary arteries and the chambers of the heart. At the apex of the heart the descending branches of both coronaries form an important anastomosis. In the myocardium

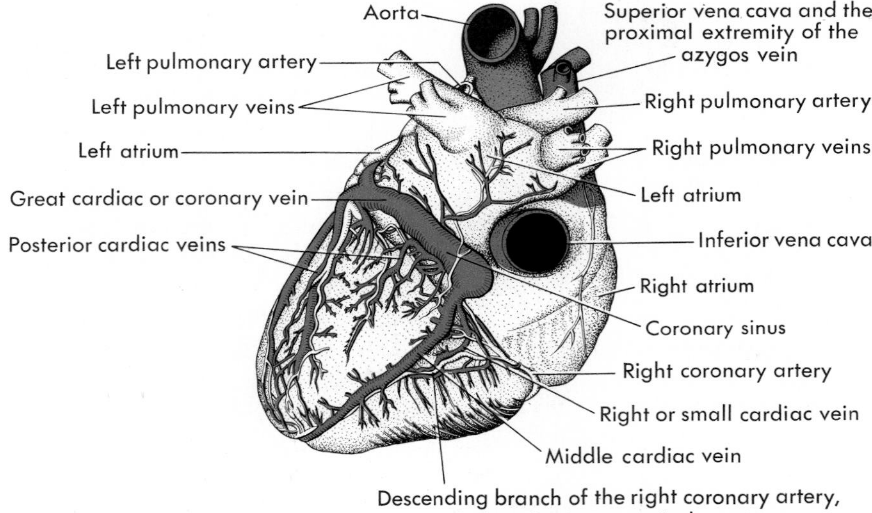

Figure 16–10. Diagram of the heart showing the coronary sinus and large veins on the dorsal wall of the heart. Which ventricle is to the left in the diagram? (Modified from Toldt.)

of the posterior wall of the heart, branches of the circumflex artery anastomose with branches of the right coronary. Thus two crowns are formed around the heart. Since adequate valves are not found in the coronary vessels, it is possible that blood may backflow into the myocardium and enter the chambers of the heart.

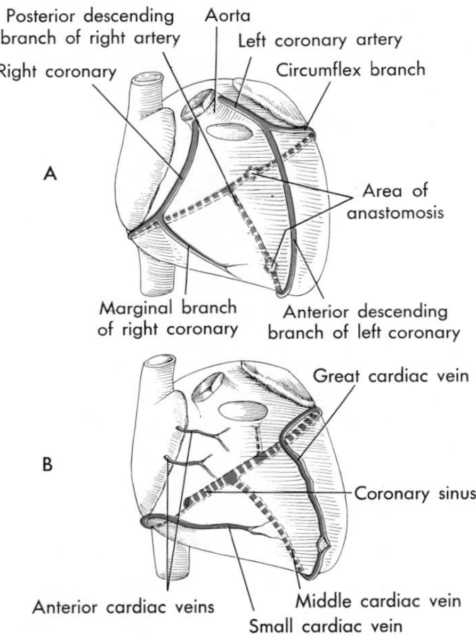

Figure 16–11. Diagram showing coronary arteries (*A*) and veins (*B*) and their connections. *Dotted lines* indicate vessels on posterior heart.

The Heart, the Cause of Circulation. The heart has four chambers, two thin-walled atria above and two thick-walled ventricles. It is divided by a septum into the right and left halves, commonly called the right and left heart. The right atrium has four main orifices, the superior and inferior venae cavae, the coronary sinus, and the atrioventricular orifice. This orifice is guarded by the right atrioventricular valve. The pulmonary artery leaves the right ventricle. It is guarded by the pulmonary semilunar valve. The left atrium has five orifices, the four pulmonary veins and the atrioventricular orifice. This orifice is guarded by the left atrioventricular valve. The aorta leaves the left ventricle. It is guarded by the aortic semilunar valve.

The Heart as a Pump. The muscles of the atria and ventricles are so arranged that when they contract they lessen the capacity of the chambers which they enclose. The contracting chambers drive the blood through the heart to the arteries.

The Sinoatrial Node (SA) and the Atrioventricular Node (AV). The SA and AV nodes are specialized cells found in the right atrial wall. The SA node is located beneath the opening of the superior vena cava. The specialized fibers are continuous over the atria.

The SA node is the causal factor of contraction. It initiates the electrical impulse which spreads out over both the atria (causing them to contract) to the AV node. From here the impulse spreads down the entire bundle and finally reaches each cardiac muscle fiber of the ventricles, causing them to contract (Figure 16–12). The SA node has been called the pacemaker of the heart.

The AV node is located near the coronary sinus at the AV junction. The Purkinje system begins at the AV node and forms the AV bundle, which passes to the ventricular septum, where it divides into two large bundle branches which supply both ventricles. Each branch spreads along the endocardial surface of the septum to the apex of the heart and then turns upward over the lateral wall of each ventricle. Purkinje fibers enter the ventricular walls and finally fuse with heart muscle fibers. In this way each muscle fiber receives the impulse.

The Wave of Contraction. If a stimulus is applied to one end of a muscle, a wave of contraction sweeps over the entire tissue. It is therefore easy to conceive how a wave of contraction can sweep over the muscular tissue of the atria, which is practically continuous. The question is—how is this wave transmitted to the muscular tissue of the ventricles, which, in man, is *not* continuous with that of the atria? The connecting pathway is furnished by the atrioventricular node (AV node), which transmits the nerve

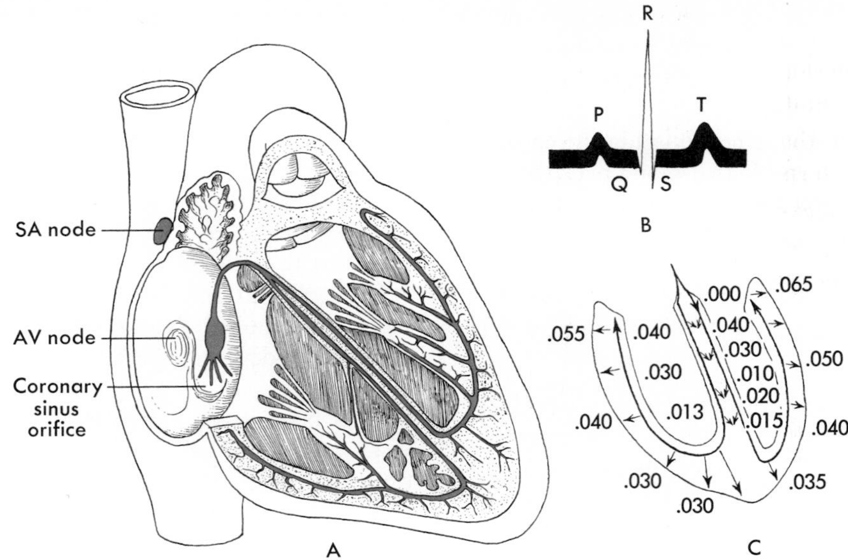

Figure 16–12. (*A*) Diagram of the atrioventricular bundle of His. The atrioventricular (*AV*) node can be seen near the opening of the coronary sinus in the right atrium. At the upper end of the ventricular septum the bundle divides. The two branches run down in the ventricular septum and give off many smaller branches to the papillary muscles and to the muscular walls of the ventricles. Bundle indicated in *red*. Part of the sinoatrial node is seen in *red* between the base of the superior vena cava and the right auricular appendix. The tip of the left ventricular chamber is not shown. The figures in *C* indicate the time in seconds taken for the nerve impulses to reach the areas indicated.

(*B*) Electrocardiogram. *Lead II*, showing contraction of different parts of the heart to show excitation during one cycle. *Wave P* occurs during atrial excitation or systole; *wave QRS* occurs during ventricular systole; *wave T* occurs as ventricular excitation subsides.

impulses by means of the AV bundle and causes the wave of contraction to spread from the atrioventricular openings over the ventricles to the mouths of the pulmonary artery and the aorta.

The Electrocardiogram. During contraction, electrical changes constantly take place in heart muscle. Active cardiac muscle fibers are electrically negative to resting fibers. The electrical differences in various parts of the heart, which occur constantly, can be led off from the surface of the body by electrodes placed on the extremities, or on the chest and abdomen, and connected to a galvanometer. The standard leads used are: (1) from right and left arms; (2) from right arm and left leg; and (3) from left arm and left leg. Leads from the chest directly over the heart called V leads are routinely used.

Each lead shows the difference of electrical potentials in the heart as recorded at the body surface. The record made is called the electrocardiogram and shows the events of the cardiac cycle. Each electrical heart cycle begins with a peaked elevation, called the P wave, which is caused by the spread of excitation from the SA node out over the atria and to the AV node. The QRS deflections are recorded as the electrical impulse spreads down the AV bundle and out over the ventricles (ventricular systole). The T wave is recorded as ventricular excitation subsides.

The electrocardiogram is of value in diagnosis of many types of heart disease.

Heart Block. Through disease, the AV node and bundle may be damaged, with the result that they lose their power to conduct nerve impulses from the atria to the ventricles. The atria will continue to contract at the rate established by the nerve impulses, but the ventricles adopt a slower rate, usually about 30 to 40 a minute. Since the pulse is caused by ventricular contractions, the pulse drops to 30 or 40 per minute. This condition is known as heart block and may be caused by various diseases such as arteriosclerosis, chronic myocarditis, coronary thrombosis involving the septum, or by the accumulative effects of digitalis.

Atrial Fibrillation. In the normal heartbeat, all groups of muscle fibers of the atria and the ventricles contract in almost simultaneous phase. This forces blood out of the atria and into the ventricles, followed by ventricular contraction, which forces blood into the pulmonary artery and the aorta. In atrial fibrillation the muscle fibers of the atria contract almost continuously and asynchronously. In consequence the muscles of the atria undergo irregular twitchy movements. More important, this means that the AV node is stimulated in an irregular fashion so that the ventricles contract normally but with a completely irregular rhythm. This results in an irregular and rapid pulse. The cause of atrial fibrillation is not known, but it is thought to be the abnormal initiation of numerous irregular impulses in many areas of the atrial muscle tissue. Ventricular contractions are so irregular that when a contraction occurs almost immediately after the preceding contractions, little blood is present in the ventricle, and therefore, the pulse is very feeble. This results in the peculiar finding that the pulse rate taken at the wrist may be 60 to 70, yet on listening to the heart, the rate may be 120 to 140. Thus, one can hear all the heartbeats, but some of the contractions may pump too little blood to be felt as a pulse in the wrist. The difference between the heart rate heard on listening to the heart and the pulse rate is called a *pulse deficit.* Normal people, of course, do not have a pulse deficit. Digitalis reduces the rate of ventricular contraction because of its effect upon the AV node in reducing the rate at which it can respond to the large number of impulses coming from the atria. This drug produces a slower, stronger, and more regular pulse, as well as reducing pulse deficit.

Ventricular Fibrillation. This is a separate disorder. In this case the ventricles are involved with the continuously asynchronous contraction of muscle fibers. Unless this disorder is interrupted within several seconds after its onset, the patient will not survive because virtually no blood is pumped into the lungs or into the systemic circulation by ventricles that are fibrillating.

The Cardiac Cycle. The cardiac cycle consists of three phases: (1) a period of contraction called the *systole*, (2) a period of relaxation called the *diastole*, and (3) a period of rest. The average heart rate of man at rest is 70 to 72 beats per minute. If we assume a pulse rate of 70 to 72, the time required for a cardiac cycle is 0.8^{+} second, and half of this, or 0.4 second, represents the quiescent phase.

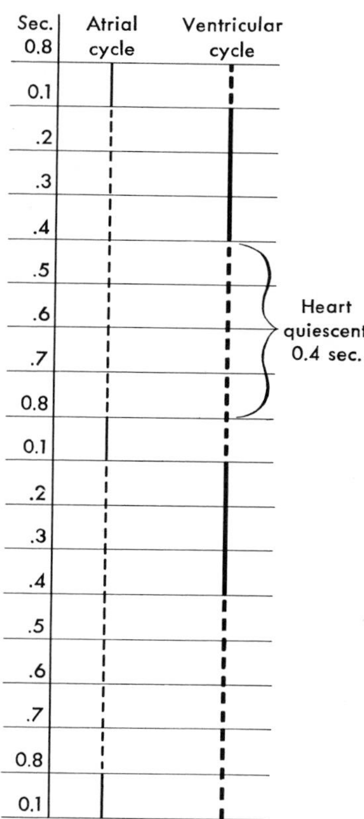

Figure 16–13. Atrial cycle and ventricular cycle, showing overlapping of diastole giving 0.4-second quiescent period of whole heart. (*Solid lines*) Systole, (*dotted lines*) diastole.

When the heart beats more rapidly, it is the rest period that is shortened. See Figure 16–13.

Systole, starting at the venoatrial junction, moves over the atria and then, after a very brief pause at the fibrous rings surrounding the atrioventricular openings, continues over the ventricles in such a way as to force the blood up into the great arteries.

Cardiac Output. At each systole a

volume of blood variously estimated at around 80 ml (man at rest) is forced from the left ventricle into the aorta. This is known as the *stroke volume.* A similar amount is forced from the right ventricle into the pulmonary artery. The total cardiac output per beat is, therefore, 160 ml.

Taking a pulse rate of 70, 5.6 liters (70 × 80 ml) of blood leave the left ventricle per minute. This is known as the *minute volume.* A similar amount leaves the right ventricle. With an increase or decrease in stroke volume, in pulse rate, or in both, the total output per minute would be increased or decreased. During exercise the total cardiac output may be doubled.

The heart muscle receives 10 per cent of cardiac output; the brain, 15 per cent; the liver, stomach, and intestines, 25 per cent; the kidneys, 20 per cent; and the soma,

MOVEMENT OF BLOOD THROUGH THE RIGHT HEART AND LUNGS

Venae cavae ↓	During diastole of the atria, via the superior and the inferior venae cavae, coronary sinus, and other small vessels, blood enters and fills the right atrium and ventricle, which for the time may be thought of as a single chamber with the tricuspid valve open
Right atrium $\frac{5*}{0\text{–}2}$	The atrium contracts (atrial systole) and forces the blood over the open valve into the ventricle, which has been passively filled and now becomes well distended by the extra supply
Tricuspid valve ↓	After a brief pause (0.1 second), rising muscle tension causes rapid rise in the pressure of the ventricle; when this pressure exceeds that of the atrium, the cusps approximate each other to close the valve. Chordae tendineae become taut and prevent the cusps from everting
Right ventricle — Semilunar valve $\frac{16}{3}$ ↓	As soon as the rapidly rising pressure in the ventricle exceeds the pressure in the pulmonary artery, the pulmonary semilunar valve is forced open and blood moves on into the pulmonary artery. The valve closes rapidly
Pulmonary artery $\frac{20}{10}$ mean 15 ↓	The pulmonary artery divides into the right and left branches and transmits blood to the lungs
Divides into two branches ↓	
Lungs — Capillaries 6 ↓	Here blood passes through innumerable capillaries that surround the alveoli of the lungs. Blood gives up carbon dioxide and the red cells are recharged with oxygen
Capillaries unite to form veins ↓	The venules unite to form larger veins until finally two pulmonary veins from each lung are formed. These return the oxygenated blood to the heart and complete the pulmonary circulation
Pulmonary veins ↓ 4	
Left atrium $\frac{4\text{–}6}{1\text{–}2}$	

* Numbers indicate pressure, mm Hg.

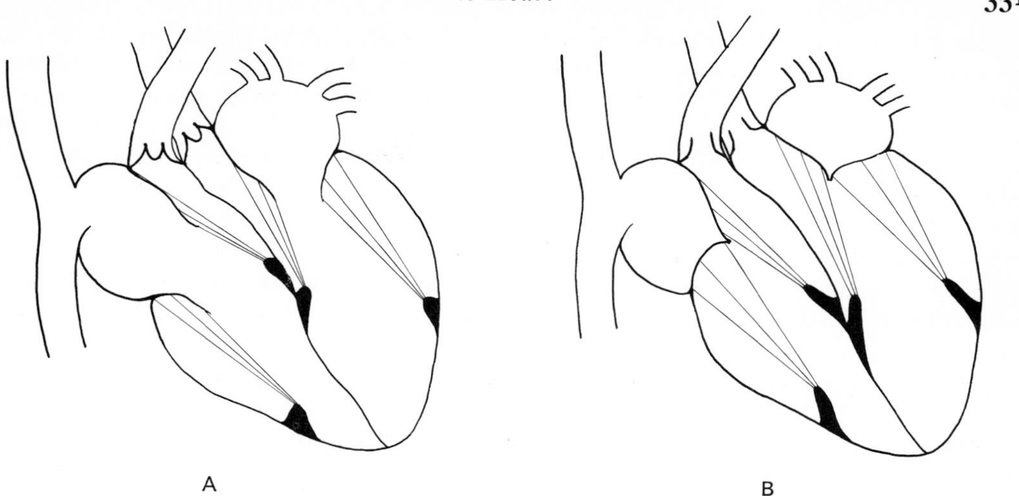

Figure 16–14. Diagrams to show position of heart valves in the cardiac cycle. No attempt has been made to show contraction. In *A*, the atrioventricular valves are open, and aortic and pulmonary valves are closed. In *B*, the atrioventricular valves are closed, and the aortic and pulmonary valves are open.

30 per cent of the cardiac output. Blood supply to the brain is the most constantly maintained. In other organs the supply varies directly with activity. During digestion the stomach and intestine receive far more blood than when at secretory rest.

Heart Sounds and Murmurs. If the ear is applied over the heart or one listens with the stethoscope, certain sounds are heard, which recur with great regularity. Two chief sounds can be heard during each cardiac cycle. The first sound is a comparatively long, booming sound; the second, a short, sharp one. The sounds resemble the syllables *lubb* ($\overline{oo}$) *dup* (*ŭ*). Heart sounds are caused by *acceleration* or *deceleration* of blood and *turbulence* developing during rapid blood flow. The first sound occurs at the onset of ventricular contraction; blood is accelerating and surging toward the AV valves. The acceleration occurs just before the valves are completely closed and taut. At this time, vibrations of the *first* heart sound are heard. The *second* sound is heard toward the end of systole when blood is decelerated, and ventricular and arterial pressures fall. Blood in the pulmonary artery and root of the aorta rushes back toward the ventricular chambers, but the flow is abruptly arrested by the closing of the semilunar valves. This causes much turbulence of the blood, and the second sound is heard. In certain diseases of the heart these sounds become changed and are called *murmurs*. These are often due to failure of the valves to close properly, thus allowing regurgitation.

Cause of the Heartbeat. The cause of the heartbeat is still unknown. General belief favors the *myogenic theory*, that is, the theory that the function of the nerve tissue in the heart is regulatory, that the contractions are due to the inherent power of contraction possessed by the muscle cells of the heart themselves. It is believed that inorganic ions, neurohumoral substances, and other factors still *unknown* are responsible for the innate myogenic rhythmicity, but the exact role of each remains to be determined. Three ions are especially important, namely, calcium, potassium, and sodium, which are always present in blood. There is a well-marked antagonism between the effects of calcium and the effects of potassium and sodium. Calcium has a direct stimulating effect and promotes contraction; potassium and sodium promote relaxation. Heart muscle becomes flaccid and heart rate slows in the presence of excess potassium ions in extracellular fluids.

The heart is not in a state of continuous contraction because of the *long refractory phase* of the cardiac muscle. From the time just before the contraction process begins, in response to a stimulus, until some time after relaxation begins, the heart muscle is refractory to further stimulation. Once the heart muscle begins to contract, it must relax (partially or completely) before it will contract again.

Automaticity. The most remarkable power of cardiac muscle is its automaticity. By this is meant that the stimuli which excite it to activity arise within the tissue itself. The degree of automatic power possessed by different regions of the heart varies. Some parts beat faster than others. The most rapidly contracting part is the SA node.

Nerve Supply. The heart is supplied with two sets of motor nerve fibers. One set reaches the heart through the vagus nerves of the craniosacral system. Nerve impulses over these fibers have a tendency to slow or stop the heartbeat and are called *inhibitory*. The other set is sympathetic. The visceral branches of the first five thoracic nerves have their cells of origin in the lateral column of gray of the spinal cord. These fibers terminate in the sympathetic ganglia, forming the superior, middle, and inferior cardiac nerves. The postganglionic fibers pass to the heart where they quicken and augment the heartbeat and are called *accelerators*. The vagus nerve has its origin in a nucleus in the medulla. The accelerator nerves also have connections in the medulla and through these centers either set may be stimulated.

In addition, the heart is supplied with afferent nerve fibers: one set from the aortic arch, called *depressor* fibers; the other set from the right side of the heart, called *pressor* fibers. Both sets of afferent fibers run within the sheath of the vagi to the cardiac center in the medulla. Impulses over the depressor fibers bring about reflex inhibition of the heart—aortic reflex. Impulses over the pressor (sympathetic) fibers bring about reflex acceleration of the heart—right heart reflex.

Nervous Control of the Heart (see Figure 16–15). Although the heart contracts automatically and rhythmically, the continuously changing frequency and volume of the heart are controlled by the two sets of nerve fibers which enter the cardiac plexus. The sympathetic fibers follow along the coronary vessels and innervate all areas of both atria and ventricles. In general, stimulation of the sympathetic system increases the activity of the heart by *increasing* both force and rate of heartbeat, thereby increasing the effectiveness of the heart as a pump.

The vagus nerves chiefly innervate the atria and *decrease* the activity of the heart. At the SA node acetylcholine is secreted at the vagal endings, which decreases the rate and rhythm of the node. It also decreases excitability of the AV junctional fibers between the muscles of the atria and the Purkinje system, thereby slowing transmission of impulses.

This means that the heartbeat is controlled by two antagonistic influences, one tending to slow the heart action and the other to quicken it. If the inhibitory center is stimulated to greater activity, the heart is slowed still further, If the activity of this center is depressed, the heart rate is increased, because the inhibitory action is removed. Stimulation of the accelerator nerves results in a quickened heartbeat.

Reflexes adjusting heart rate may be classified as those initiated by pressure receptors and those initiated by chemoreceptors.

Pressoreceptors. Right Heart Reflex. There are receptors in the large veins entering the right heart and right atrium that are sensitive to changes in venous pressure. Increased pressure will accelerate heart action. Venous return and cardiac output are increased, which prevents pooling of blood in the venous system. Impulses are conveyed over afferent vagal fibers to the cardiac center in the medulla.

Pressoreceptors or stretch receptors have been demonstrated on the pulmonary veins

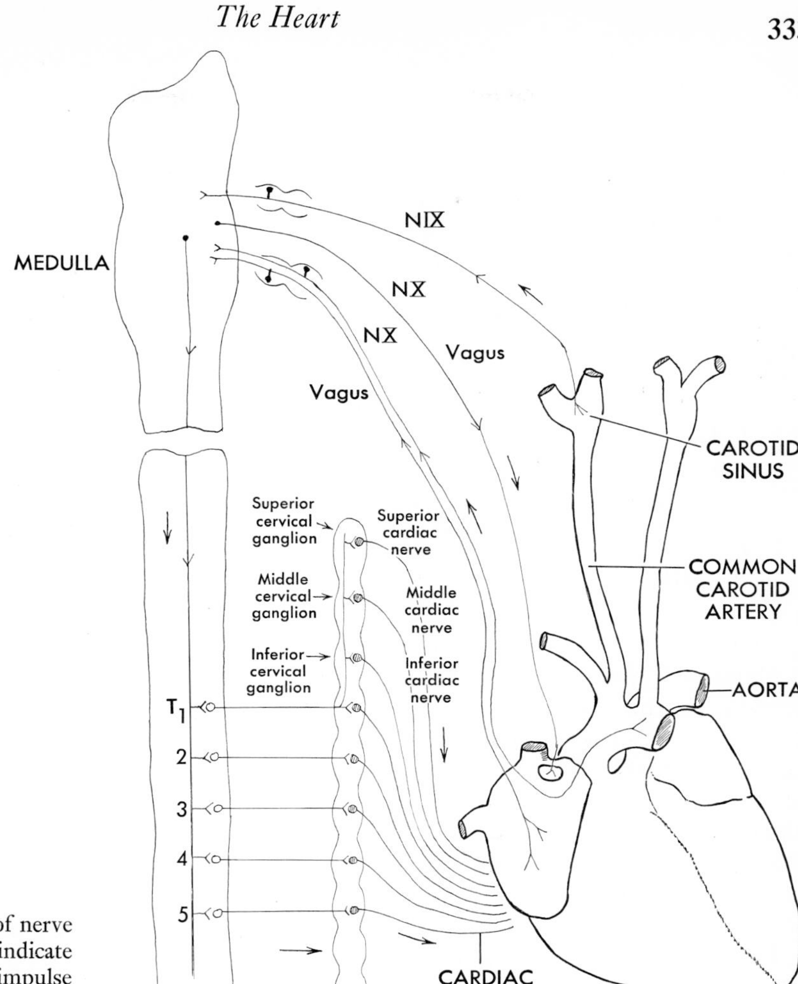

Figure 16–15. Diagram of nerve supply to heart. *Arrows* indicate the direction of nerve impulse travel.

and in the wall of the left atrium. If pulmonary venous pressure increases, a reflex inhibition of the vasomotor center occurs which causes dilation of the vessels and reduction of pressure in the lungs. This reflex is important because it protects against pulmonary edema resulting from excessive pulmonary pressure.

Pressoreceptors are also located in the arteries of the neck and thorax above the heart level. When pressure in these arteries falls, sympathetic response helps to maintain normal pressure.

The Aortic Reflex. There are pressoreceptors in the arch of the aorta (aortic sinus) that are sensitive to changes in blood pressure. Fluctuation in arterial pressure activates these receptors, and impulses are conveyed over afferent nerve fibers of cranial nerves IX and X to the cardiac centers and the heart is adjusted to meet body needs. A *rise* in pressure slows the heart rate.

The Carotid Sinus Reflex. The carotid sinus is a slightly dilated area of the internal carotid artery at the bifurcation of the carotid into the internal and external carotid arteries. Afferent nerve fibers in the cardiac branch of the glossopharyngeal nerve carry nerve impulses from pressure receptors in the carotid sinus to the cardiac center influencing heart action. These receptors respond to arterial pressure changes that initiate sympathetic reflexes which readjust or lower arterial pressure. Conversely, if pressure falls, these receptors respond and blood pressure is raised.

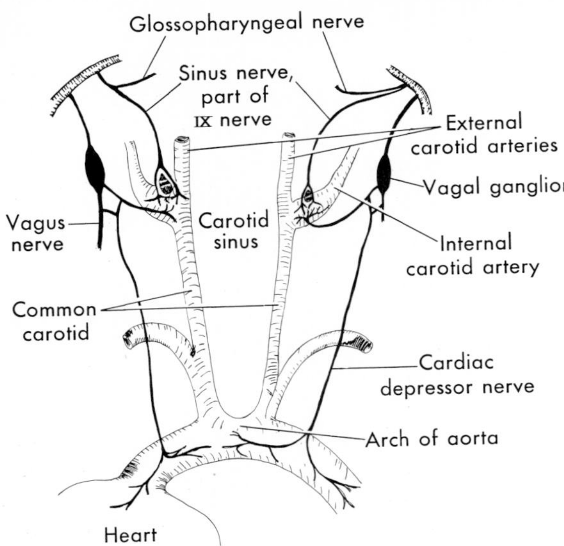

Figure 16–16. Diagram showing receptors on the arch of the aorta, cardiac depressor nerves, carotid sinus, and connections with nerve IX and nerve X.

Chemoreceptors. There are chemoreceptors in the carotid bodies and aortic body that are sensitive to lack of oxygen. Impulses from these receptors are conveyed to the cardiac center and the heart rate is accelerated, thereby increasing cardiac output, and more blood is moved on to the tissue cells. Chemoreceptors are also stimulated by an increase in carbon dioxide.

Factors Affecting the Frequency and Strength of the Heart's Action. The frequency and strength of the heartbeat are affected by blood pressure; emotional excitement or keen interest; reflex influences which are of an unconscious character; the temperature of the blood; such characteristics of heart muscle as tone, irritability, contractility, and conductivity; physical factors such as size, sex, age, posture, and muscular exercise; changes in the condition of the blood vessels; and certain internal secretions.

Under normal conditions the pulse rate is inversely related to the arterial blood pressure; that is, a rise in the arterial blood pressure causes a decrease in pulse rate, and a decrease in arterial blood pressure causes an increase in pulse rate.

The pulse rate is very susceptible to changing sensations. Especially is this true in emotional excitement. The heart also responds to reflex influences which are of an unconscious character, such as activity of the visceral organs. After meals the heart increases in rate and strength of beat.

Experimentally it has been demonstrated that abnormally high or low temperatures of the blood affect the frequency of the beat. If the heart is perfused with hot liquid, the rate is increased in proportion to the temperature until the maximum point, about 44° C (111.2° F), is reached. If the temperature is raised above this, the heart soon ceases to beat. In fever the increased rate of the heart action is thought to be due partly to the effect of the higher temperature of the blood on the heart muscle. On the other hand, if cold liquid is perfused through an animal heart, the rate is decreased, and the heart ceases to beat at about 17° C (62.6° F). Slowing of the heart by carefully inducing a fall in body temperature (hypothermia) permits cardiac surgery which would not be possible with a rapidly moving heart at normal body temperature. At the same time this hypothermia slows cellular metabolism, thus decreasing the need for oxygen.

Conditions that affect the irritability, contractility, and conductivity of the heart muscle or reduce its normal *tone* are likely to change the frequency of the heartbeat, either accelerating or slowing the action. If the tone is decreased, the strength of the contractions is diminished.

In almost all warm-blooded animals the frequency of the heartbeat is in inverse proportion to the size of the body. An elephant's heart beats about 25 times per minute, a mouse's heart about 700 times per minute. Generally speaking, the smaller the animal, the more rapid is the consumption of oxygen in its tissues. The increased need for oxygen is met partly by a faster heart rate.

The heartbeat is somewhat more rapid in women than in men. The heart rate of a female fetus is generally 140 to 145 per minute, that of the male, 130 to 135.

Age has a marked influence. At birth the rate is about 140 per minute, at three years about 100, in youth about 90, in adult life about 75, in old age about 70, and in extreme old age 75 to 80.

The *posture* of the body influences the rate of the heartbeat. Typical figures are: standing, 80; sitting, 70; and recumbent, 66. If an individual remains in a recumbent position and keeps quiet, the work of the heart may be decreased considerably. This is the reason why patients with certain types of heart disease are kept in a recumbent position. On other occasions the physician may suggest the sitting position for his heart patient, if the patient is emotionally more relaxed in that position.

Muscular exercise increases the heart rate. This is due to (1) the activity of the cardioinhibitory center in the medulla being *depressed* by the motor impulses from the more anterior portions of the brain to the muscles, probably by means of collateral fibers to the cardiac center; (2) a stimulation of the cardioaccelerator center; (3) an increased secretion of epinephrine and other hormones which accelerate heart action; (4) increased temperature of the blood; and (5) the pressure of the contracting muscles (including respiratory movement) on the veins sending more blood to the heart, so that the right side is filled more rapidly. This increase of venous pressure reflexly accelerates the heartbeat.

In order to function effectively, the heart requires a certain amount of resistance, and normally this is offered by the blood vessels. The heart will beat more slowly and strongly in response to increased resistance, provided the resistance is not too great. In the latter case the heart is likely to dilate, and its action becomes frequent and weak. The most common cause of abnormally high resistance is abnormal constriction of the arterioles, and this in turn results in high systolic and diastolic pressure (hypertension). In the presence of arteriosclerosis the vessels do not stretch during contraction of the heart which causes systolic blood pressure to rise (systolic hypertension). When the resistance is below normal, the heartbeats are frequent and weak. Lessened resistance is due either to a relaxed condition of the blood vessels or to the loss of much blood or of much fluid from the blood.

Certain internal secretions affect the frequency and strength of the heartbeat. *Thyroxin* produces a faster pulse. The partial removal of excessively active thyroid glands results in a slower heart rate. *Epinephrine* from the adrenal glands increases the frequency and force of the heartbeat.

QUESTIONS FOR DISCUSSION

1. Discuss the valves of the heart and explain why edema occurs when the individual has a constricted tricuspid valve.
2. Discuss the function of the right heart reflex in relation to exercise.
3. Discuss coronary circulation, and explain what is meant by collateral circulation.
4. Explain the value of an electrocardiogram.
5. What factors modify blood pressure?
6. What is believed to be the cause of the heartbeat?
7. Discuss the location and function of the pressoreceptors.
8. Where are the chemoreceptors located? What substances are they sensitive to?
9. Which hormones affect the heart rate? Explain.

SUMMARY

- **Cardiovascular System**
  - Heart
  - Arteries—small arteries are named arterioles
  - Capillaries
  - Veins—small veins are named venules
- **Heart**
  - **Location**
    - Between lungs
    - Above diaphragm
  - **Structure**
    - Outside covering—*pericardium*
      - Fibrous portion
      - Serous
        - Visceral
        - Parietal
    - Muscle substance—*myocardium*
      - Muscle bundles of the atria
      - Muscle bundles of the ventricles
      - Atrioventricular bundle—bundle of muscular and nervous tissue located in septum between right and left heart, which connects the musculature of atria and ventricles
    - Smooth lining on inside—*endocardium*
  - **Cavities**
    - **Right heart**
      - **Right atrium**
        - Receives blood
        - Thin walls
      - **Right ventricle**
        - Expels blood into pulmonary artery
        - Thick walls
    - **Left heart**
      - **Left atrium**
        - Receives blood
        - Thin walls
      - **Left ventricle**
        - Expels blood into aorta
        - Very thick walls
  - **Orifices**
    - **Right heart**
      - **Right atrium**
        - Superior vena cava—returns blood from upper portion of body
        - Inferior vena cava—returns blood from lower portion of body
        - Coronary sinus—returns blood from heart muscle
      - Atrioventricular orifice between atrium and ventricle
      - **Right ventricle**
        - Pulmonary artery—carries blood from heart to lungs
    - **Left heart**
      - **Left atrium**
        - Two right pulmonary veins } Return blood from lungs
        - Two left pulmonary veins } Return blood from lungs
      - Atrioventricular orifice between atrium and ventricle
      - **Left ventricle**
        - Aorta—distributes blood to all parts of the body
  - **Valves**
    - **Right atrioventricular or tricuspid valve**—composed of three cusps, situated in the right ventricle
    - **Left atrioventricular or bicuspid, or mitral, valve**—composed of two strong, thick cusps, situated in the left ventricle
    - **Function**—prevent flow of blood from ventricles into atria
    - **Semilunar valves**
      - **Aortic**—composed of three half-moon-shaped pockets between aorta and left ventricle
      - **Pulmonary**—composed of three half-moon-shaped pockets between pulmonary artery and right ventricle
      - **Function**—prevent flow of blood from arteries into ventricles
  - **Lymph vessels**
    - Heart well supplied with lymph capillaries
  - **Coronary circulation**
    - Arteries
      - Right coronary } branches from aorta
      - Left coronary } branches from aorta

Heart (*cont.*)

- **Coronary circulation** (*cont.*)
  - Veins
    1. Cardiac veins empty into coronary sinus
    2. Three or four small veins empty into right atrium
    3. Veins of Thebesius empty into atrium and ventricles
  - Function—distribute blood to cardiac muscle
- **Collateral circulation**
  - Channels of communication—complex and numerous at apex of heart—descending branches of both coronaries anastomose
- **Pumping action**
  - By rhythmical contractions blood is moved from veins through heart into arteries
- **Wave of contraction**
  - Starts at sinoatrial node, transmitted through the atrial muscle to the AV node, which in turn transmits it via the AV bundle to the ventricles
  - *Heart block*—condition resulting from damage to atrioventricular bundle and consequent failure to transmit impulses from atria to ventricles. Rate of contraction of ventricles slower than that of atria
  - *Fibrillation*—rhythmical contractions interfered with. Atria undergo irregular twitching movements. Contractions of ventricles irregular and rapid. Difference between heart rate and pulse called *pulse deficit*
- **Cardiac cycle**
  - Coordinated contraction of cardiac muscle
  - 1. **Systole**—contraction
  - 2. **Diastole**—dilatation
  - 3. **Rest**—quiescent
    - Cardiac cycle, 70–72 per minute
    - Occupies about 0.8 second
    - Systolic and rest period each about 0.4 second
- **Heartbeat**
  - **Cause**
    1. Unknown. Myogenic theory makes automatic contractility of muscle cells responsible
       Stimulated by epinephrine and norepinephrine
       Inhibited by acetylcholine
    2. SA and AV nodes control frequency of electrical impulses over the heart from veins through heart to arteries
    3. Rate and strength of beat meet needs of body; under chemical and nervous control
- **Heart sounds**
  - **First**—turbulence of blood caused by closure of atrioventricular valves and contractions of the ventricles
  - **Second**—turbulence of blood caused by closure of the semilunar valves
  - Other sounds may be identified
- **Nerve supply**
  - Craniosacral—vagus—inhibitory to heart
  - Thoracolumbar—visceral branches from first five thoracic nerves. Accelerators to heart
- **Cardiac nerves**
  - Fibers from superior, middle, inferior ganglion
    - Form the superior, middle, and inferior cardiac nerves accelerators to heart
- **Right heart reflex**
  - Receptors in large veins of right heart
  - Increases heart rate and cardiac output
- **Aortic reflex**
  - Receptors on arch of aorta
  - Sensitive to fluctuations in arterial pressure
  - A rise in pressure slows heartbeat
- **Carotid sinus reflex**
  - Receptors respond to arterial pressure rise
  - Slows heart rate
- **Chemoreceptors**
  - Located in carotid bodies and aortic bodies
  - Sensitive to lack of oxygen

Factors affecting blood pressure

- Frequency of and strength of heartbeat
- Influenced by
  - Emotional excitement
  - Unconscious reflex influences
  - Sex, posture, physical influences
  - Many other causes
- Pulse rate influenced by
  - Changing sensations
  - Emotional excitement
  - Unconscious reflex influences
  - Posture, muscular exercise, temperature of blood
  - Epinephrine and other hormones

CHAPTER

17

PHYSIOLOGY OF CIRCULATION

Factors Modifying and Maintaining Circulation

Velocity and Pressure

Each cell of the body is dependent on the blood for its very existence, and it is the work of the heart, arteries, capillaries, and veins that makes possible the transporting of all substances to and from cells.

The function of the heart is to adjust circulation in relation to the metabolic rate of body cells. By chemical and nervous control, the needs of these cells are met promptly through adjustments of pulse rate and pulse volume, which increase and decrease the volume of blood reaching the tissue capillaries per minute. Variable cellular needs are thus met by changes in the number, size, and area of the open capillaries and in the temperature and the minute volume of the blood in these open capillaries.

The blood is contained in a closed set of vessels, which it completely fills. Interposed in this set of vessels is the heart, which fills with blood from the veins and then contracts, thereby forcing this blood into the capillaries of all parts of the body.

This is a description of the general circulation, but the student must understand that both sides of the heart contract almost simultaneously; i.e., the blood fills the atria and ventricles on both sides of the heart at the same time; both atria contract practically together,[1] forcing the blood over the open valves into the ventricles. After a brief pause both ventricles contract, and the blood is forced into the pulmonary artery and into the aorta. The ventricles pump out equal quantities of blood, but the blood from the left ventricle is sent on a longer circuit than the blood from the right.

The Pulmonary Circulation. The shorter circulation, from the right ventricle to the left atrium, is called the *pulmonary circulation.* The purpose of the pulmonary circulation is to carry the blood which has been through the body, giving up oxygen and collecting carbon dioxide, to the air sacs of the lungs, where the red cells are recharged with oxygen and the carbon dioxide is reduced to the normal amount.

The Systemic Circulation. The more extensive circulation, from the left ventricle to all parts of the body and the return to the right atrium, is known as the *systemic circulation.* The purpose of the systemic circulation

[1] Careful measurements have shown that the contraction of the left atrium lags behind that of the right atrium from 0.01 to 0.03 second.

MOVEMENT OF BLOOD THROUGH THE LEFT HEART AND TO THE SOMATIC CAPILLARIES AND BACK TO THE LEFT HEART

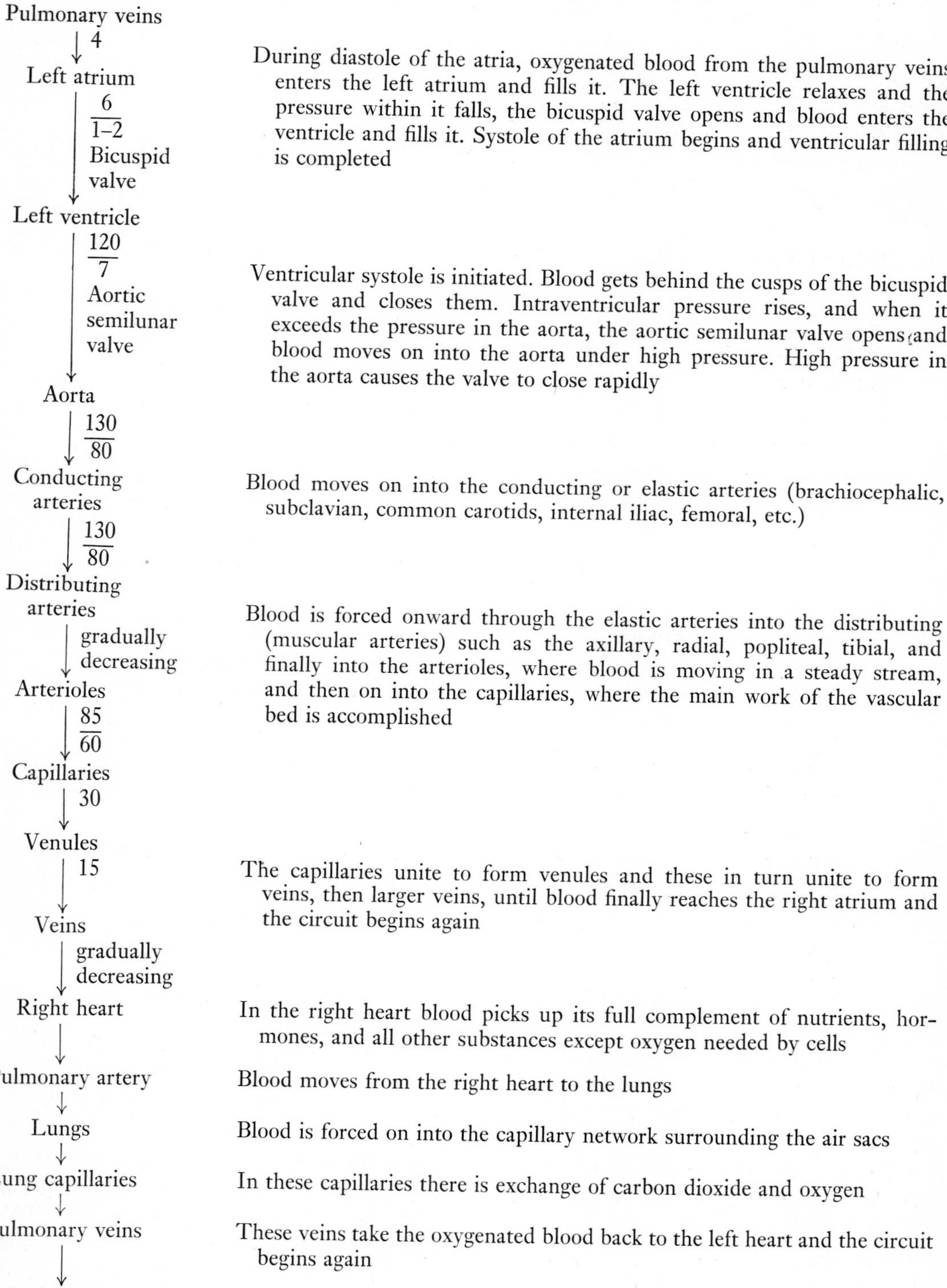

Pulmonary veins	
↓ 4	
Left atrium	During diastole of the atria, oxygenated blood from the pulmonary veins enters the left atrium and fills it. The left ventricle relaxes and the pressure within it falls, the bicuspid valve opens and blood enters the ventricle and fills it. Systole of the atrium begins and ventricular filling is completed
↓ 6/1–2 Bicuspid valve	
Left ventricle	
↓ 120/7 Aortic semilunar valve	Ventricular systole is initiated. Blood gets behind the cusps of the bicuspid valve and closes them. Intraventricular pressure rises, and when it exceeds the pressure in the aorta, the aortic semilunar valve opens and blood moves on into the aorta under high pressure. High pressure in the aorta causes the valve to close rapidly
Aorta	
↓ 130/80	
Conducting arteries	Blood moves on into the conducting or elastic arteries (brachiocephalic, subclavian, common carotids, internal iliac, femoral, etc.)
↓ 130/80	
Distributing arteries	Blood is forced onward through the elastic arteries into the distributing (muscular arteries) such as the axillary, radial, popliteal, tibial, and finally into the arterioles, where blood is moving in a steady stream, and then on into the capillaries, where the main work of the vascular bed is accomplished
↓ gradually decreasing	
Arterioles	
↓ 85/60	
Capillaries	
↓ 30	
Venules	
↓ 15	The capillaries unite to form venules and these in turn unite to form veins, then larger veins, until blood finally reaches the right atrium and the circuit begins again
Veins	
↓ gradually decreasing	
Right heart	In the right heart blood picks up its full complement of nutrients, hormones, and all other substances except oxygen needed by cells
↓	
Pulmonary artery	Blood moves from the right heart to the lungs
↓	
Lungs	Blood is forced on into the capillary network surrounding the air sacs
↓	
Lung capillaries	In these capillaries there is exchange of carbon dioxide and oxygen
↓	
Pulmonary veins	These veins take the oxygenated blood back to the left heart and the circuit begins again
↓	
Left heart	

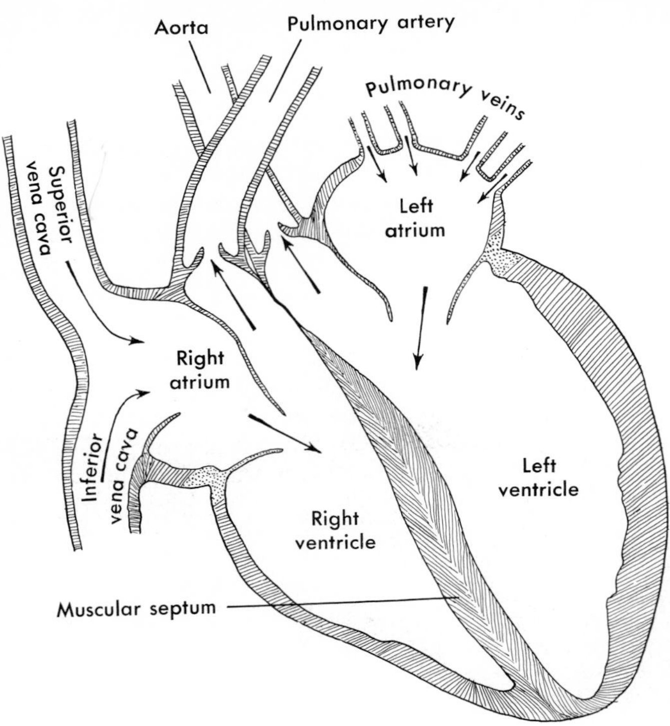

Figure 17–1. A diagram to show the four chambers of the heart and the valves which guard their openings, seen from the front. *Arrows* indicate direction of blood flow.

is to carry oxygen and nutritive material to the tissues and remove products of metabolism from the tissues. After leaving the left ventricle, portions of the blood pursue different courses; some portions enter the coronary arteries, some go to the head, some to the upper and lower extremities, and some to the different internal organs. Some portions go on shorter circuits and arrive back at the heart sooner than other portions that travel farther away from the center.

An example of a long circuit in the systemic circulation is the circulation from the left heart to the toes and back to the right heart, then to the lungs and to the left heart.

The table on page 339 summarizes circulation of blood from the left heart through the somatic capillaries and back to the left heart.

An example of a short circuit is the circulation of blood through the walls of the heart itself.

MODIFYING FACTORS OF CIRCULATION

Distribution of Blood to Different Parts of the Body. In health the distribution of blood varies, as determined by the needs of the different parts. When the digestive organs are active, they need an extra supply of blood, which may be supplied by redistribution of blood from less active organs. Other causes may result in an increased supply of blood to an organ. If the skin is exposed to high temperatures, the arterioles which bring blood to it are dilated, and the blood flow near the surface is increased. This aids in the radiation of heat and in the control of body temperature. On the other hand, slight chilling causes contraction of the skin arterioles and resulting paleness. The blood supply to the brain is relatively constant. According to recent studies, blood supply to the brain is not reduced during sleep and not increased by mental activity.

MOVEMENT OF BLOOD THROUGH ORGANS

Name of Part	Resting Tissue (amount of blood per 100 gm of tissue per unit of time)	Needs in General
Skeletal muscle	5 ml per minute	During exercise the amount of blood needed is proportional to metabolic activity; strenuous exertion, about 35 ml per 100 gm of tissue per minute
Bone	Receives a rich blood supply	During physical activity, there is increased blood flow
Heart and coronary arteries	Receive 10 per cent of cardiac output	The amount then varies directly with heart rate. Flow is slowest during systole
Lungs	Blood passing through the lungs per minute is directly related to heart rate and stroke volume; i.e., if stroke volume is 70 ml and pulse rate is 72, about 5,040 ml of blood pass through the lungs in one minute	
Liver	200–300 ml per minute	Through the sluice mechanism located on the hepatic veins, the liver has the ability to either hold back or give blood to circulation as need arises
Stomach	25 ml per minute	When actively secreting digestive fluids and absorbing end products of digestion and fluids, the amount of blood through organs is tremendously increased
Intestines	65–70 ml per minute	
Kidneys	Receive about 1,300 ml of the total resting output of the heart	Normally, each minute, the glomeruli filter about 120 ml of protein-free fluid, and at the tubule, about 119 ml are returned to the blood stream
Thyroid gland	560 ml per minute	Metabolic activity is mediated through thyroxin; it is essential that blood flow and gland activity keep pace with metabolic needs
Spleen	40 ml per minute	The spleen serves as a reservoir for blood, and during excessive demands for blood by the body, the spleen releases blood
Human brain	Receives 15 per cent of cardiac output, or about 200 ml per minute	Not affected by physical or mental activity

The table above summarizes and gives a general concept of the body's need for blood and the effect of activity on the needs in general.

During physical activity, the amount of blood passing through bones, skeletal muscles, heart, and lungs is increased proportionately to the activity. This means that other organs will receive less blood per unit of time.

Circulation Time. Circulation time is the term used to denote the time needed for a substance injected into the antecubital vein to reach an artery or part (for example, the

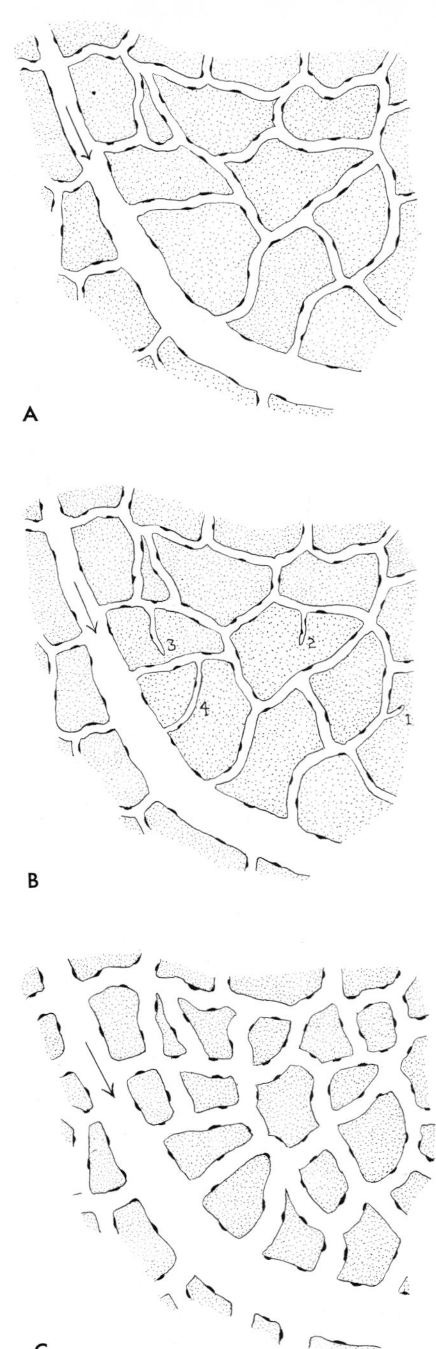

Figure 17–2. Diagrams showing opening of extra capillaries with increasing arterial pressure. *A* shows capillaries; *B* and *C* show progressive opening of an increasing number of capillaries. *1*, *2*, *3*, and *4* in *B* show the different degrees of the opening of capillaries. The *arrows* indicate the direction of blood flow.

tongue) where it may be detected. This is a subjective means of testing and varies with the individual's ability to specify the instant the substance is tasted or recognized. Substances usually used in these instances are calcium gluconate, Decholin, saccharin, histamine, and others. Ether has been used; a small amount of ether is introduced into an antecubital vein and the time taken for the ether to be identified on the breath of the subject is measured. It has been found that circulation time from the antecubital vein to the tongue (using saccharin) is about 8 to 15 seconds. From arm to face (using histamine) it is from 14 to 25 seconds before the flush is noted.

Tonus of Blood Vessels. Normally the blood vessels maintain a state of tonus about halfway between contraction and dilatation. It is thought that adjustments in the blood supply to various parts are brought about by increasing or decreasing the tone of the local blood vessels. Two factors are important, (1) vasomotor nerve fibers and (2) chemical stimuli.

1. The vasomotor nerve fibers consist of two antagonistic sets. The vasoconstrictors cause the muscular coats of the blood vessels to contract, lessen the diameter of the vessels, and thereby increase resistance to blood flow. The vasodilator fibers increase the diameter of the blood vessels, probably by allowing the muscular coats to relax, and thereby decrease resistance to blood flow.

2. Chemical substances, such as the lactic acid and carbon dioxide produced during muscular activity, may lessen the tonus of the blood vessels in the part affected, resulting in local dilatation and an increased supply of blood to the part needing it. At the same time, chemoreceptors convey impulses to the vasoconstrictor center, stimulate it, and thereby increase the tonus of blood vessels in other parts of the body. On the other hand, angiotensin and hormones, such as epinephrine and vasopresssin, cause constriction of the blood vessels.

Epinephrine and many other drugs are used medicinally to cause vasoconstriction, and amyl nitrite is inhaled to bring about vasodilatation, particularly when a condition like angina pectoris[2] makes quick relief necessary. Both the arteries and the veins are capable of dilatation or constriction under the influence of nerve fibers or chemical stimuli.

In surgical shock there is marked interference with the circulation of the blood owing to dilatation of the arteriolar bed and consequent decrease in arterial pressure, which may fall below the level essential to the welfare of the tissues. The pulse becomes rapid and weak, and respiration increases. It is thought that dilatation of the arterioles may be brought about by substances such as histamine formed in injured tissues.

Factors Maintaining Arterial Circulation. The most important factors maintaining *arterial* circulation are the pumping action of the heart, the extensibility and elasticity of the arterial walls, the peripheral resistance in the region of the small arteries, especially arterioles in the splanchnic areas, and the quantity of blood in the body.

The Extensibility and Elasticity of the Arterial Walls. During each systole the ventricles force blood into arteries that are already full (about 30 to 60 ml each). The extensibility of the arteries enables them to distend and receive this extra supply of blood. The period of distention corresponds to the systole of the heart. Just as soon as the force is removed, the elasticity of the arteries causes them to contract to their former diameter, and this exerts such a pressure on the contained blood that the blood is forced into the capillaries just rapidly enough to allow the arteries time to reach their usual size during diastole of the heart. The arteries thus not only serve as conducting vessels but exert a force that assists the heart in driving the blood into the capillaries.

The extensibility and elasticity of the arteries change with the health and age of the individual. Sometimes as the result of disease, and usually with age, the arterial walls become less elastic and less well adapted for the unceasing work they are called upon to perform.

Peripheral Resistance. Blood flow is opposed by frictional forces within the vessels. Friction results from the relationships between the *layers of fluid wetting* the vessel walls and the *more central layers of the moving stream.* Frictional *resistance* to flow varies therefore with the character of the fluid, that is, with its *viscosity.* This means that there is *direct relationship* between *viscosity* of the blood and *peripheral resistance.* The greater the viscosity, the greater the resistance to blood flow.

It is the function of the vasomotor fibers to "set" the diameters of the muscular arterioles in relation to constantly varying local needs for blood. The *elastic* arteries compensate for heart systole and diastole, thus maintaining a *steady flow* of blood in the capillaries, the arteries accommodating the extra blood forced into them during heart systole and by their contraction forcing the blood toward the capillaries during heart diastole. Inasmuch as local needs for blood vary constantly and through constantly varying limits, it is the function of the autonomic nervous system (and locally produced chemical substances such as carbon dioxide), reflecting these needs, to set the diameters of the arterioles so that the peripheral resistance meets these local needs (much blood needed, wide arterioles; less blood needed, narrower arterioles). *On the basis of peripheral resistance thus established*, it is the function of the arterioles, to expand and contract, changing an intermittent flow in the arteries to a *steady* flow in capillaries. It is easily seen that this is a *fine* adjustment, the elastic arteries giving a *steady* flow in capillaries on *many bases of diameter* of arterioles set by local needs. This fine adjustment (associated with optimum activity of the heart) is the mechanism by means of which homeostasis, or state of constancy, of body fluids is maintained.

The kidneys play an important role in the

[2] Angina pectoris is a disease characterized by attacks of severe constricting pains in the chest, which radiate into the left arm. It is accompanied by a great sense of cardiac oppression and usually is caused by spasm of a coronary artery due to various pathological states.

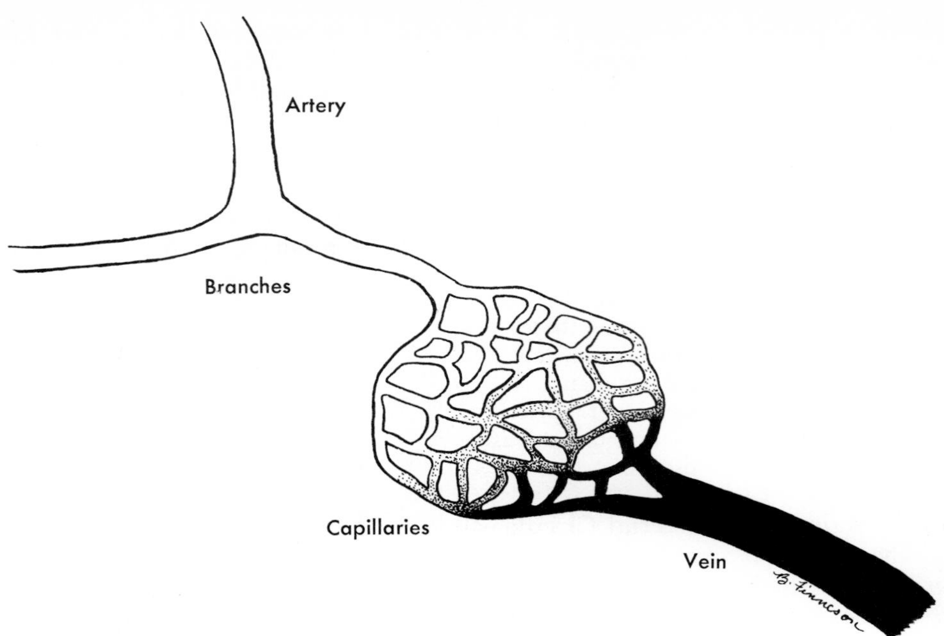

Figure 17–3. Diagram to illustrate variations in blood flow. A vessel divided into two branches. These are individually of smaller cross section than the main trunk, but united they exceed it. Linear velocity will be lower in the branches than in the parent artery. The sum of the cross-sectional areas of the capillaries is greater than that of the artery or vein.

regulation of arterial pressure. It is known that the kidneys can regulate arterial pressure by *increasing* urine output, which decreases volume and lowers pressure, or by *decreasing* urine output, thereby increasing blood volume, which raises arterial pressure. If the kidney is deprived of part of its blood supply from any cause, blood pressure rises. When the kidney is deprived of part of its blood supply, it secretes renin. Renin activates a globulin of a plasma protein which eventually becomes a substance called angiotensin II. This is the most active vasopressor substance known. It also acts on the adrenal cortex to increase aldosterone secretion, which stimulates the kidney to retain sodium and water. The net effect is an increase in blood pressure.

Quantity of Blood. It is evident that, other things being equal, the quantity of blood to be moved is an important factor. Except in cases of severe hemorrhage, loss of blood is compensated for by a transfer of liquid from the tissues into the blood vessels.

Factors Maintaining Venous Circulation. The effect of the pumping action of the heart is not entirely spent in forcing the blood through the arteries and capillaries. A little force still remains to propel the blood back to the heart again, and the presence of valves keeps it flowing in the right direction, i.e., toward the heart. The return flow is also favored by (1) the suction action of the heart caused by the negative pressure of the relaxing ventricle, (2) the heart and respiratory movements, which cause continual changes of pressure against the thin-walled veins in the thorax and abdomen, and (3) the contractions of the skeletal and visceral muscles, which exercise a massaging action upon the veins and, aided by the valves, propel the blood toward the heart.

Veins are capable of dilating, constricting, and storing large amounts of blood and giving blood to circulation when needed. The pressure in peripheral veins depends on the pressure maintained in the right atrium, so that if right atrial pressure is affected, all venous pressure is affected. Right atrial pressure is regulated by the ability of the heart to pump blood and the tendency of blood from the periphery to flow toward the heart. Measurement of this pressure is commonly done by threading a long fine catheter into one of the large veins of the arm and thence into the right atrium. This pressure is referred to as *central venous pressure.*

A strong heartbeat is capable of pumping large quantities of blood with ease; this tends to *decrease* right atrial pressure; a weak heartbeat tends to *elevate* right atrial pressure. Factors that tend to *raise pressure* in the right atrium include increased blood volume, increase in venous tone, increased venous pressure, and dilatation of the small systemic blood vessels. Factors that tend to *reduce* right atrial pressure include reduced blood volume, decreased venous tone, and vasoconstriction of small systemic blood vessels.

These same factors also help to regulate cardiac output, as the amount of blood leaving the left heart depends on the flow of blood into the right heart. In a *standing* position venous pressure is lowest—10 mm Hg to 0 mm Hg above the level of the heart and about 90 mm Hg in the lower legs owing to the effect of gravity. This gravitational effect on the cardiovascular system may be markedly accentuated when the body undergoes angular acceleration, as when a plane rapidly accelerates upward. The centrifugal force pushes the pilot against the seat with many times the normal pull of gravity.

The physiological effect of *positive* gravity causes blood in the vascular system to be forced into vessels of the lower part of the body. Veins of the legs and abdominal cavity become distended with blood. The heart receives very little because blood does not return uphill to the heart. Cardiac output falls very low or may reach zero. Arterial pressure falls and unconsciousness results. A *small* positive acceleration can cause some dizziness, but on the whole, circulation is maintained so that cardiac output is sufficient to prevent blackouts. Pressure suits that cover the legs and place pressure over the abdomen prevent pooling of blood during positive acceleration. Tightening of the abdominal muscles also helps to prevent symptoms.

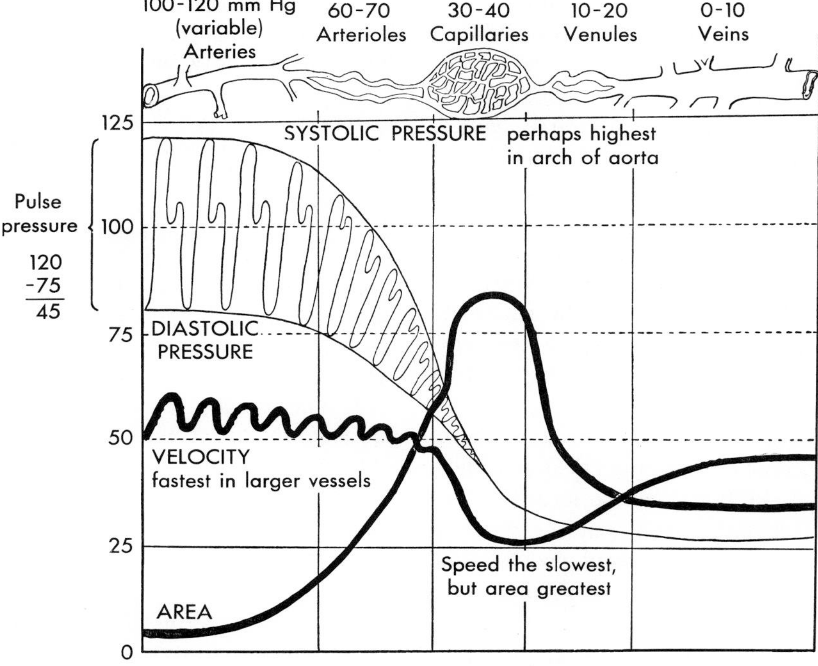

Figure 17–4. Diagram showing relationships between arterial, capillary, and venous blood pressures, relationship of area in various blood vessels, and speed with which blood moves through them.

In negative acceleration, as when a plane dives, the reverse is true. Cardiac output increases and arterial pressure is increased. High pressure causes vessels in the head and brain to be overfilled with blood, and edema of the brain may occur.

The Velocity of the Blood Flow. In all the large arteries the blood moves rapidly; in the capillaries, very slowly; in the veins the velocity is augmented as they increase in size, but it never equals that in the aorta. The underlying principle is that in any stream the velocity is greatest where the cross section of the channel is least, and lowest where the cross section is greatest. When a vessel divides, the sum of the cross sections of the two branches is greater than that of the main trunk. Consequently the velocity will be reduced when arteries divide and increased when veins unite. One reason why the velocity in the veins never equals that in the aorta is that the cross section of the venae cavae is greater than the cross section of the aorta. The actual interchange of materials between the blood and the tissues takes place in the capillaries (since the walls of the arteries and veins are too thick to permit diffusion), hence the value of the slow, constant flow of blood in the capillaries.

THE PULSE

The alternate expansion and contraction of an artery constitute the pulse. When the finger is placed on an artery which approaches the surface of the body and is located over a bone, a sense of resistance is felt, which seems to be increased at intervals corresponding to the heartbeat. In certain arteries the pulse may be seen with the eye. When the finger is placed on a vein, very little resistance is felt; and under ordinary circumstances no pulse can be perceived by the touch or by the eye. The pulse *does not mark* the arrival of the ejected blood at the point felt, but represents the *pressure change* brought about by the ejection of blood from the heart into the already full aorta and propagated as a wave through the blood column and the arterial wall to the periphery.

As each expansion of an artery is produced by a contraction of the heart, the pulse as felt in any superficial artery is a convenient guide for ascertaining the character of the heart's action.

All arteries have a pulse, but it is more readily counted wherever an artery approaches the surface of the body. These locations are as follows: the *radial* artery, at the wrist—the radial artery is usually employed for this purpose on account of its accessible situation; the *temporal* artery, above and to the outer side of the eye; the *external maxillary* (*facial*) artery, where it passes over the lower jawbone, which is about on a line with the corners of the mouth; the *carotid* artery, on the side of the neck; the *brachial* artery, along the inner side of the biceps; the *femoral* artery, where it passes over the pelvic bone; the *popliteal* artery, behind the knee; the *dorsalis pedis*, over the instep of the foot.

Points to Note in Feeling a Pulse. In feeling a pulse, the following points should be noted:

1. The *frequency*, or *number of beats per minute*, should be normal for the individual concerned. The intervals between the beats should be of equal length. A pulse may be irregular in frequency and rhythm. When a pulsation is missed at regular or irregular intervals, the pulse is described as *intermittent*.
2. The *force*, or *strength*, of the heartbeat. Each beat should be of equal strength. Irregularity of strength is due to lack of tone of the cardiac muscle or of the arteries. Occasionally the heartbeat appears to be divided, and two pulsations are felt, the second being weaker than the first. This is known as a *dicrotic* pulse.
3. The *tension*, or *resistance* offered by the artery to the finger, is an indication of the pressure of the blood within the vessels and the elasticity or inelasticity of the arterial walls. A pulse is described as *soft* when the tension is low and the wall of the artery is elastic. A pulse is described as *hard* when the tension is high and the wall of the artery is stiff, thick, and unyielding.

Average Frequency of the Pulse. The average frequency of the pulse in men is 65 to 70; in women, 70 to 80. A person in perfect health may have a much higher or a much lower rate. The relative frequency of the pulse and respirations is about four heartbeats to one respiration.

As a rule, the rapidity of the heart's actions is in inverse ratio to its force. An infrequent pulse, within physiological limits, is usually a strong one, and a frequent pulse comparatively feeble, the pulse in fever or debilitating affections becoming weaker as it grows more rapid. As the pulse is an indication of the frequency of the heartbeat, it follows that the factors which influence the heartbeat will also influence the pulse.

BLOOD PRESSURE

Blood pressure is defined as the pressure the blood exerts against the walls of the vessels in which it is contained. The term includes arterial, capillary, and venous pressure; but it is commonly applied to pressure existing in the large arteries, usually the left brachial artery just above the elbow. A vein is easily flattened under the finger; an artery offers a stronger resistance. This is an indication of a great difference between arterial and venous pressure. This difference is also shown when an artery and a vein are cut; the blood springs from the artery in a pulsating spurt, indicating a high pressure, whereas the flow from the vein is continuous, and even when copious "wells up" rather than "spurts out," indicating a low pressure.

Blood pressure is highest in the arteries during the period of ventricular systole. This is systolic pressure. During ventricular diastole blood pressure tends to fall and reaches a minimum just before the beginning of the next systole. The minimum is called diastolic pressure. Diastolic pressure represents the pressure in the arteries when the heart is in diastole. Pressure in the arteries is high and fluctuating, slightly higher in the large trunks than in their branches. When the blood reaches the capillaries, the surface is multiplied and the friction increased. This offers resistance to the flow, and the result is a *decided drop in the pressure.* Pressure in the veins is low and relatively constant. It must be higher in the small veins than in the large ones they unite to form, as the direction of the blood flow is from the smaller to the larger veins. Their chief effect on blood flow is their great relative ability to hold large volumes of blood under low pressure. When one rises from a recumbent or sitting position to standing, systolic pressure as well as diastolic pressure rises.

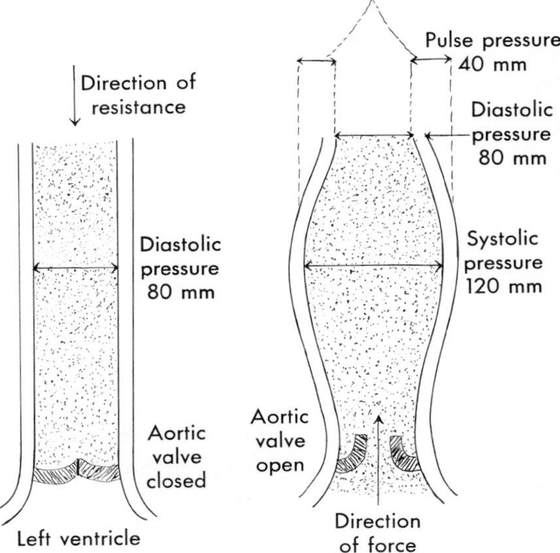

Figure 17–5. Diagram showing relationship between direction of resistance and direction of force in measuring arterial blood pressure.

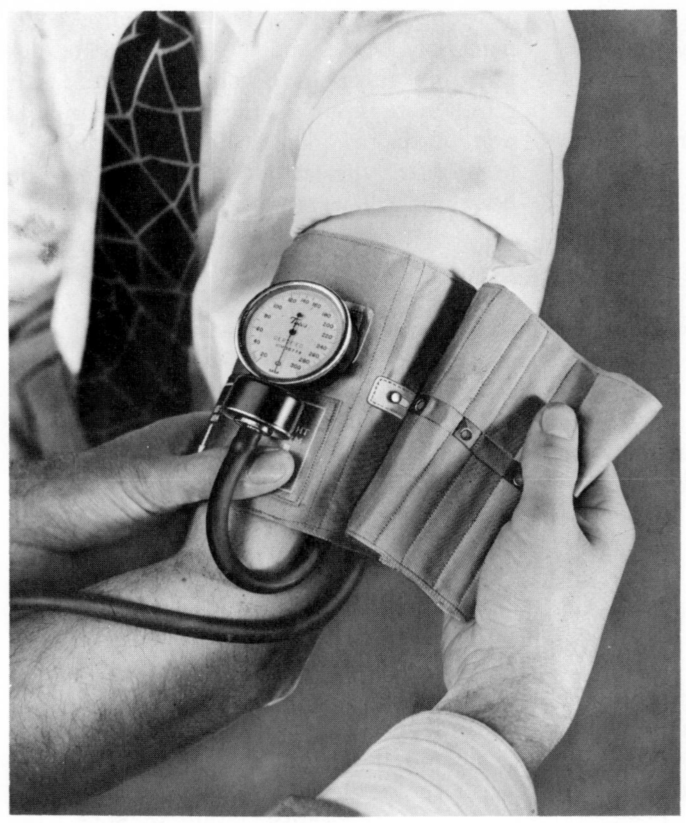

Figure 17–6. Method of using aneroid sphygmomanometer for measuring arterial blood pressure. (Courtesy of Taylor Instrument Company.)

Method of Determining Blood Pressure. A rough estimate of systolic blood pressure may be determined at the radial artery. If the radial artery is hard and incompressible, it may indicate either that some change has occurred in the vessel or that the pressure is high. If, however, the pulse is easy to obliterate with the fingers, it is usual to find a low pressure.

Many forms of apparatus have been devised by which a more accurate knowledge of this phenomenon can be obtained. The apparatus is called a sphygmomanometer and consists of a scaled column of mercury (mercury manometer) marked in millimeters, which is connected by rubber tubing with an elastic air bag contained in a fabric cuff. The air bag is in turn connected with a small hand pump. Some instruments are constructed with a spring scale (aneroid manometer), but the principle is the same. The air bag contained in the sleeve is wrapped snugly about the arm just above the elbow with the air bag centered over the brachial artery. A finger is placed upon the pulse at the wrist (as the bag is inflated), and a point is finally reached where the pulse disappears; then the bag is very slowly deflated until the pulse can just be felt. The pressure in the bag, therefore, against the artery from the outside, as indicated by the reading on the instrument, is approximately equal to the pressure which the blood exerts against the wall of the artery from the inside. This is known as the *systolic pressure* and is the greatest pressure which cardiac systole causes in the brachial artery. In the auscultation method of reading blood pressure, a stethoscope is placed over the brachial artery in the bend of the elbow. Blood pressure is then indicated by sounds heard through the stethoscope. The bag is inflated as before until all sounds cease. It is then slowly deflated until the pulse can just be heard. The reading on the manometer at this time indicates systolic pressure. The deflation of the bag is then continued, and the reading on the manometer just before the last sound of the disappearing pulse indicates *diastolic pressure*, which is the lowest pressure which cardiac diastole causes in the brachial artery.

As pressure falls in the sphygmomanometer, the sounds heard change. First a clear, sharp, tapping sound is heard that corresponds to systolic pressure. The next sounds become softer, and as pressure continues to fall the sound gets louder again, then becomes muffled—this corresponds to diastolic pressure. The sound lasts during the next 4 or 6 mm of Hg fall, and then all sounds cease to be heard. Diastolic pressure is usually recorded when the muffled sound is heard and when the sound is completely lost

$$\frac{120 \text{ (systolic)}}{80\text{–}75 \text{ (diastolic)}}.$$

Pulse Pressure. In the normal adult, the height of a pulse, the systolic pressure, is about 120 mm Hg; its lowest point, the diastolic pressure, about 80 mm Hg. The difference between these two pressures is 40 mm Hg. This is called the *pulse pressure*. Factors that affect pulse pressure include stroke volume, output of the heart, and total distensibility of the arterial tree.

The greater the stroke volume, the greater the output and the greater the pressure rise during systole and the *greater* will it *fall* during diastole. This causes a greater pulse pressure. It is evident that pulse pressure varies and is dependent upon (1) the energy of the heart, (2) the elasticity of the blood vessels, (3) the peripheral resistance, and (4) the quantity of circulating blood.

Capillary pressure is the pressure of the blood within the capillaries. Capillary pressure in man when in a sitting position is on the average about 12 to 32 mm Hg. It is somewhat higher when standing and lower when lying down.

Venous pressure is the pressure blood exerts within the veins. Normal venous pressure is on the average 60 to 120 mm of water in a recumbent position. A needle is inserted into the antecubital vein with the needle connected to a water manometer. Venous pressure is expressed in relation to the level of the tricuspid valve. Increasing attention is being given to venous pressure, as it is a valuable index in determining the efficiency of heart muscle.

Normal Degree of Blood Pressure. The average blood pressure of an adult male as recorded by the sphygmomanometer over the brachial artery is about 110 to 120 mm systolic and 65 to 80 mm diastolic. Some observers report that the systolic pressure is higher in men than in women. Individual variations are not uncommon, but 140 mm for men and 130 mm for women are considered the normal upper limits. A systolic pressure of 150 mm suggests hypertension. It varies during mental and muscular work and shows a tendency to fall during fatigue. Cold, drugs, etc., which constrict the arterial pulse may raise the blood pressure. Heat and the drugs of the vasodilator group, like nitroglycerin, may lower it. There is a normal range of blood pressure in all parts of the vascular system. (See Figure 17–4.)

Blood pressure is dependent upon the force of the contraction of the ventricles, the elasticity of the arteries, and the tone of the muscular tissue in their walls, and the resistance offered to the flow of blood through the vessels. Minor factors are respiration and the accompanying pressure changes in the chest cavity, the amount of blood in the body, and gravity. Gravity tends to increase pressure in arteries below the level of the heart and to decrease pressure in arteries at levels above the heart.

Venous pressure is low; but when one is standing, the pressure in the veins of the legs and feet is high, owing to gravity—hence the frequency of varicose veins in the lower limbs. Walking relieves this pressure because the contraction of the muscles forces the blood upward in the veins and the valves of the veins favor this movement.

Variations in Blood Pressure Under Normal Conditions. Variation in arterial blood pressure is compatible with health and is affected by age, sex, muscular activity, digestion, emotions, position, and sleep.

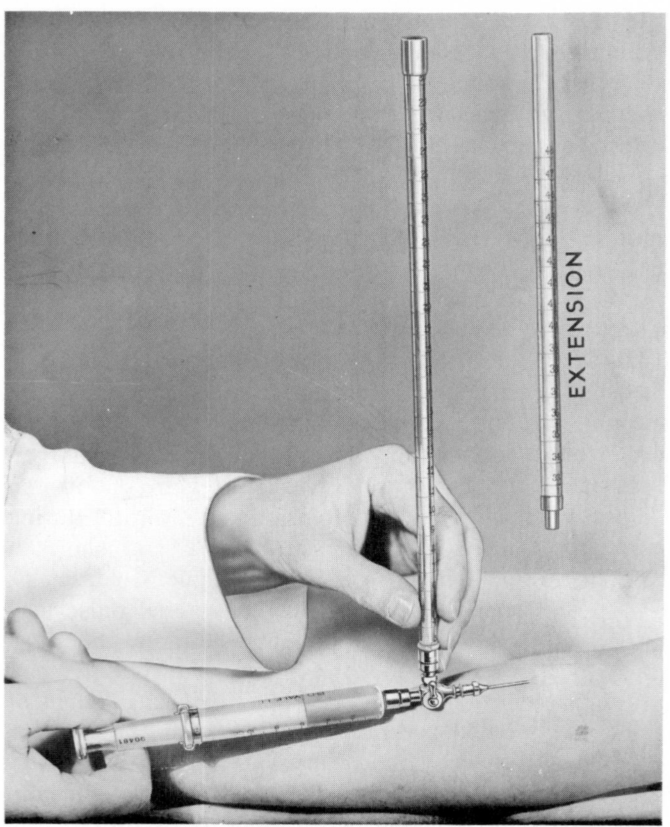

Figure 17–7. Use of water manometer for measuring venous blood pressure. (Courtesy of Taylor Instrument Company.)

At birth the average systolic pressure is 40 mm Hg. It increases rapidly during the first month to 80 mm. Then it increases slowly, and at the age of 12 years the average reaches 105 mm. At puberty a somewhat sudden increase occurs; the average is 120 mm. A steady, slow, but not marked increase in blood pressure occurs normally from adolescence to adulthood.

Blood pressure is increased by muscular activity. The amount of increase depends upon the amount of energy required for the activity and upon individual differences. Systolic pressure is raised slightly after meals. Pain and emotional factors, such as fear or worry, raise systolic pressure considerably. Increased intracranial pressure also raises systolic blood pressure and slows the heart rate. During quiet, restful sleep systolic pressure falls; the lowest point is reached during the first few hours. It rises slowly until the time of waking. Excess weight causes an increase in the number of blood capillaries, raises blood pressure, and thereby places more work on the heart.

Systolic pressure is about 8 to 10 mm lower in women than in men. After menopause there is an increase, and the pressure remains a little above the male average.

Blood pressure is raised above normal when the distensibility of the arteries is reduced, as in arteriosclerosis; by various diseases of the heart, liver, and kidneys which interfere with the venous circulation; by stimulation from the vasoconstrictor center in the medulla; usually by fever and increased intracranial pressure, as in fracture of the skull. Blood pressure may also be abnormally high in persons who have increased peripheral resistance due to heredity.

Blood pressure is decreased below normal when the heartbeat is weak, when the blood vessels are relaxed, and when the total quantity of blood in the vessels is reduced. When blood volume is diminished, the mean circulatory filling pressure of the entire circulatory system falls. Venous pressure falls, venous return to the heart diminishes, and cardiac output and pressure in the capillaries fall. Since hydrostatic pressure is decreased, little fluid and oxygen move across the membrane at the arterial end of the capillary into the tissue spaces. However, fluid will move from the tissue spaces into the venous ends of the capillary, and absorption continues from all tissue spaces and the alimentary tract until volume is restored or until fluid in tissue spaces is exhausted. Blood loss causes thirst, and fluids given by mouth will aid in restoration of volume.

QUESTIONS FOR DISCUSSION

1. Discuss the heart in relation to the adjustment of circulation.
2. What changes take place in blood as it circulates through the following organs: right heart, lungs, liver, kidneys, adrenal glands?
3. Discuss the factors that modify the circulation of blood.
4. Discuss the factors that maintain and modify arterial and venous circulation.
5. In taking a pulse what points are important to note and record?
6. Discuss the differences between arterial and venous pressures.
7. Assume that each time the heart beats, 80 ml of blood moves into the lungs and the heart rate is 72 beats per minute. How much blood moves through the heart to the lungs in one minute, one hour, one day, one week, one year, 10 years, 80 years?
8. How would exercise, rest, and sleep each affect the above findings?

SUMMARY

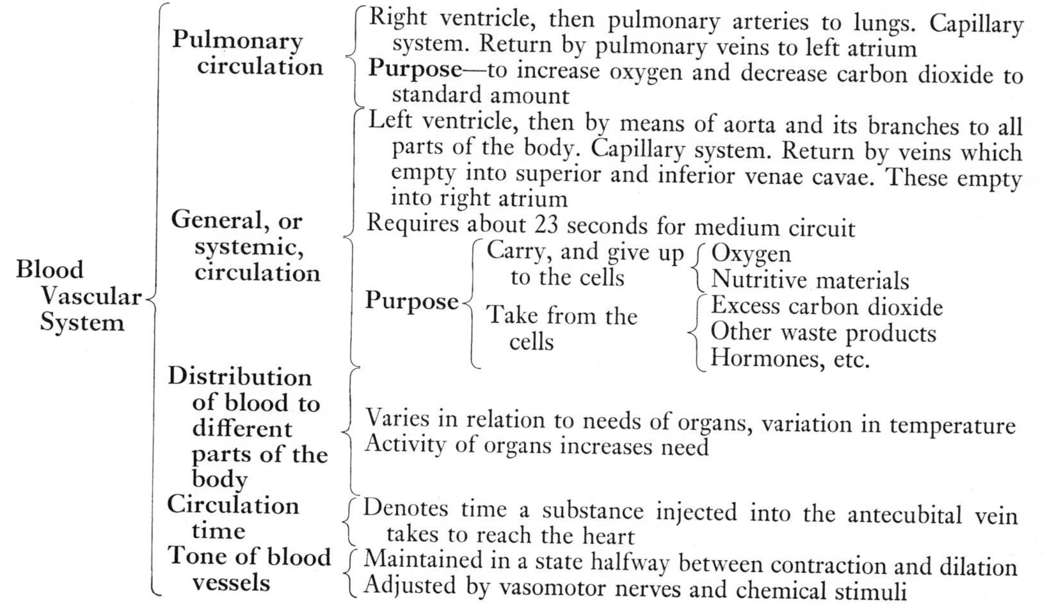

Blood Vascular System	**Pulmonary circulation**	Right ventricle, then pulmonary arteries to lungs. Capillary system. Return by pulmonary veins to left atrium		
		Purpose—to increase oxygen and decrease carbon dioxide to standard amount		
	General, or systemic, circulation	Left ventricle, then by means of aorta and its branches to all parts of the body. Capillary system. Return by veins which empty into superior and inferior venae cavae. These empty into right atrium		
		Requires about 23 seconds for medium circuit		
		Purpose	Carry, and give up to the cells	Oxygen Nutritive materials
			Take from the cells	Excess carbon dioxide Other waste products Hormones, etc.
	Distribution of blood to different parts of the body	Varies in relation to needs of organs, variation in temperature Activity of organs increases need		
	Circulation time	Denotes time a substance injected into the antecubital vein takes to reach the heart		
	Tone of blood vessels	Maintained in a state halfway between contraction and dilation Adjusted by vasomotor nerves and chemical stimuli		

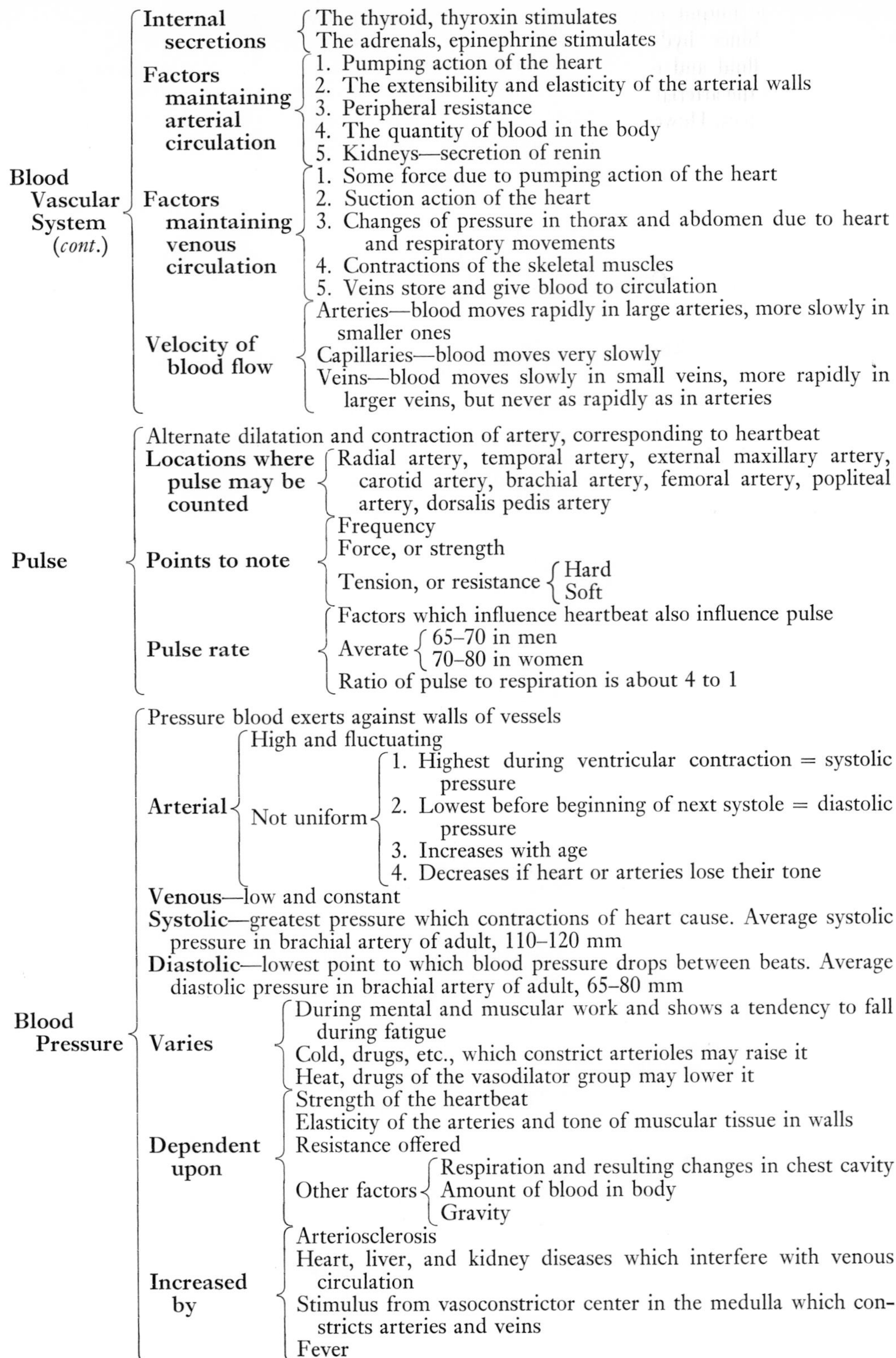

- **Blood Vascular System** (*cont.*)
  - **Internal secretions**
    - The thyroid, thyroxin stimulates
    - The adrenals, epinephrine stimulates
  - **Factors maintaining arterial circulation**
    1. Pumping action of the heart
    2. The extensibility and elasticity of the arterial walls
    3. Peripheral resistance
    4. The quantity of blood in the body
    5. Kidneys—secretion of renin
  - **Factors maintaining venous circulation**
    1. Some force due to pumping action of the heart
    2. Suction action of the heart
    3. Changes of pressure in thorax and abdomen due to heart and respiratory movements
    4. Contractions of the skeletal muscles
    5. Veins store and give blood to circulation
  - **Velocity of blood flow**
    - Arteries—blood moves rapidly in large arteries, more slowly in smaller ones
    - Capillaries—blood moves very slowly
    - Veins—blood moves slowly in small veins, more rapidly in larger veins, but never as rapidly as in arteries
- **Pulse**
  - Alternate dilatation and contraction of artery, corresponding to heartbeat
  - **Locations where pulse may be counted**
    - Radial artery, temporal artery, external maxillary artery, carotid artery, brachial artery, femoral artery, popliteal artery, dorsalis pedis artery
  - **Points to note**
    - Frequency
    - Force, or strength
    - Tension, or resistance
      - Hard
      - Soft
  - **Pulse rate**
    - Factors which influence heartbeat also influence pulse
    - Averate
      - 65–70 in men
      - 70–80 in women
    - Ratio of pulse to respiration is about 4 to 1
- **Blood Pressure**
  - Pressure blood exerts against walls of vessels
  - **Arterial**
    - High and fluctuating
    - Not uniform
      1. Highest during ventricular contraction = systolic pressure
      2. Lowest before beginning of next systole = diastolic pressure
      3. Increases with age
      4. Decreases if heart or arteries lose their tone
  - **Venous**—low and constant
  - **Systolic**—greatest pressure which contractions of heart cause. Average systolic pressure in brachial artery of adult, 110–120 mm
  - **Diastolic**—lowest point to which blood pressure drops between beats. Average diastolic pressure in brachial artery of adult, 65–80 mm
  - **Varies**
    - During mental and muscular work and shows a tendency to fall during fatigue
    - Cold, drugs, etc., which constrict arterioles may raise it
    - Heat, drugs of the vasodilator group may lower it
  - **Dependent upon**
    - Strength of the heartbeat
    - Elasticity of the arteries and tone of muscular tissue in walls
    - Resistance offered
    - Other factors
      - Respiration and resulting changes in chest cavity
      - Amount of blood in body
      - Gravity
  - **Increased by**
    - Arteriosclerosis
    - Heart, liver, and kidney diseases which interfere with venous circulation
    - Stimulus from vasoconstrictor center in the medulla which constricts arteries and veins
    - Fever

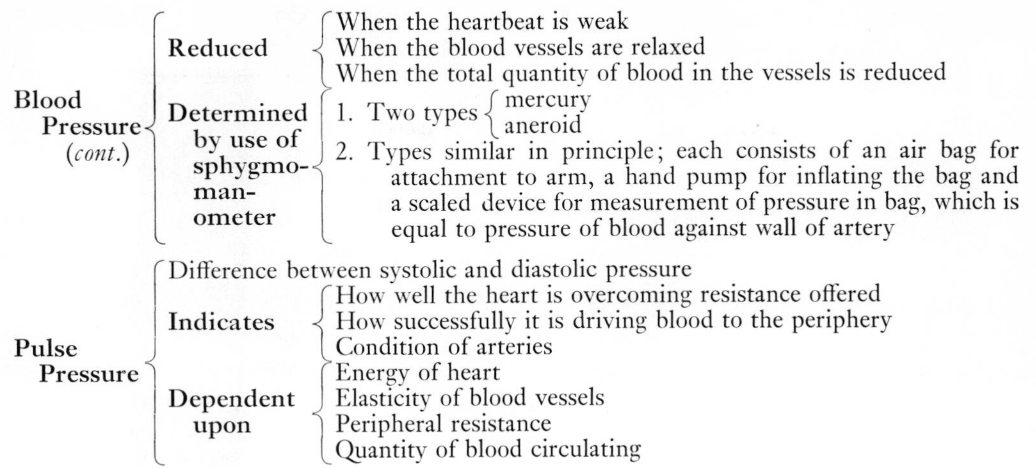

- **Blood Pressure** (*cont.*)
  - **Reduced**
    - When the heartbeat is weak
    - When the blood vessels are relaxed
    - When the total quantity of blood in the vessels is reduced
  - **Determined by use of sphygmomanometer**
    1. Two types
       - mercury
       - aneroid
    2. Types similar in principle; each consists of an air bag for attachment to arm, a hand pump for inflating the bag and a scaled device for measurement of pressure in bag, which is equal to pressure of blood against wall of artery

- **Pulse Pressure**
  - Difference between systolic and diastolic pressure
  - **Indicates**
    - How well the heart is overcoming resistance offered
    - How successfully it is driving blood to the periphery
    - Condition of arteries
  - **Dependent upon**
    - Energy of heart
    - Elasticity of blood vessels
    - Peripheral resistance
    - Quantity of blood circulating

CHAPTER

18

THE LYMPH VASCULAR SYSTEM

Source and Function of Lymph

THE RETICULOENDOTHELIAL SYSTEM

The lymphatic system has been called the "middle man" between blood and tissue fluid. Colloidal material cannot re-enter the blood capillaries; hence, the lymph capillaries are ever present to receive colloids as well as electrolytes, water, and other substances and return them to the blood stream. Lymph nodes function in the protective mechanism of the body.

LYMPH

Sources of Lymph. Lymph is interstitial fluid that flows into the lymphatic capillaries. It is formed by the physical process of filtration. Colloidal substances from tissue fluid are returned to lymph capillaries rather than to the blood. Water, crystalloids, and other substances also enter the lymph capillaries. Since the process of tissue fluid formation is continuous, lymph formation is also continuous. The lymph system supplements the capillaries and veins in the return of the tissue fluid to the blood. This drainage system is called the lymph vascular system. Even with this system, fluid may accumulate in the tissue spaces, although it does not do so normally. See Chapter 2.

Filtration pressure normally is highest in blood capillaries (as compared with tissue fluid pressure and lymph pressure) because of the beating heart and elastic arteries. Substances like the colloids, therefore, which are filtered out of the blood capillaries cannot enter them again but can enter the lymphatic capillaries. Hence, it is frequently said that one function of the lymph capillaries is to return blood proteins from tissue fluids to the blood stream.

Another function of the lymph capillaries is to maintain volume and pressure conditions in the spaces occupied by the tissue fluids. Hydrostatic pressure maintained by the heart and elastic arteries is sufficient to supply fluids via the tissue spaces to the cells, but lacking this hydrostatic pressure to remove the fluids, the extra lymph capillaries are needed.

The lymphatic vessels of the extremities have valves similar to those of the veins. Likewise these valves function by causing lymph to be conducted centrally when voluntary muscles of the extremity contract. This is the major force causing flow of lymph.

Composition of Lymph. Lymph, tissue fluid, and plasma are similar in composition. Lymph consists of a fluid plasma containing a variable number of lymphocytes, a few granulocytes, no blood platelets (hence clots slowly), carbon dioxide, and *very* small quantities of oxygen. Other contained substances vary in kinds and amounts in relation to the location of lymphatic vessels. In the lymphatics of the intestine, fat content is high during digestion. Water, glucose, and salts are in about the same concentration as in blood plasma. Protein concentration is lower. Enzymes and antibodies are also present.

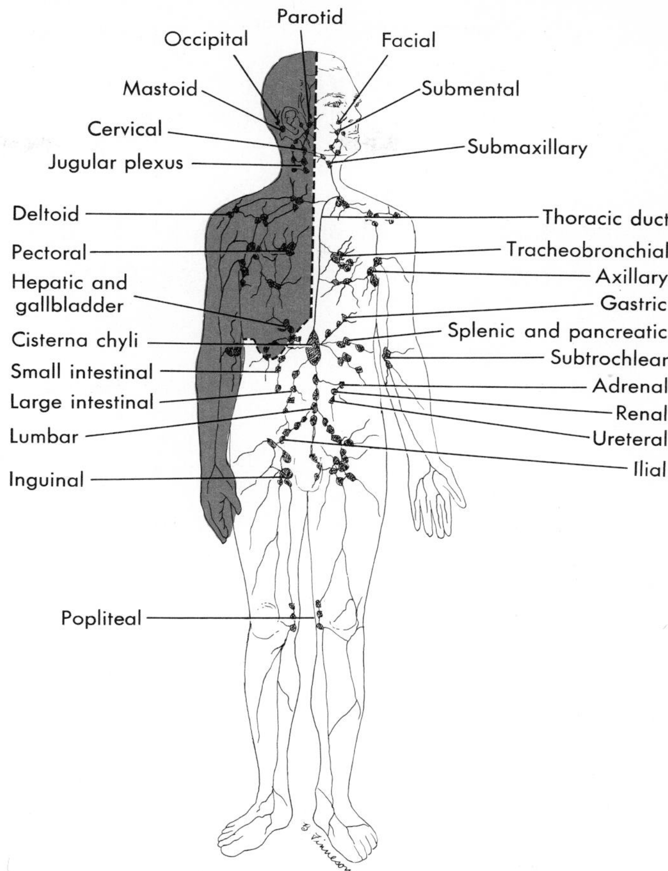

Figure 18–1. The regions from which lymph flows into the right lymphatic duct are suggested by the *red* area, and those which are tributary to the thoracic duct are suggested by the *clear* area. The locations of lymph nodes of the body are also shown.

Lymph has a specific gravity between 1.015 and 1.023.

Lymph Vascular System

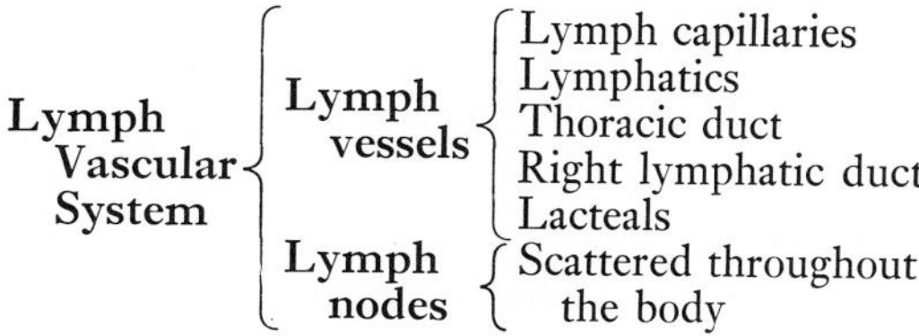

- **Lymph Vascular System**
  - **Lymph vessels**
    - Lymph capillaries
    - Lymphatics
    - Thoracic duct
    - Right lymphatic duct
    - Lacteals
  - **Lymph nodes**
    - Scattered throughout the body

Lymph Vessels. The plan upon which the lymphatic system is constructed is similar to that of the blood vascular system, if the heart and the arteries are omitted. In the tissues are located the closed *ends of minute microscopic vessels, called lymph capillaries*, which are comparable to, and often larger and more permeable than, the blood capillaries. The lymph capillaries are distributed in the same manner as the blood capillaries. Just as the blood capillaries unite to form veins, the lymph capillaries unite to form larger vessels called *lymphatics.* The lymphatics continue to unite and form larger and larger vessels until finally they converge into two main channels, (1) the thoracic duct, and (2) the right lymphatic duct.

The thoracic duct, or *left lymphatic*, begins in the dilatation called the *cisterna chyli* (chyle cistern), located on the front of the body of the second lumbar vertebra. It ascends upward in front of the bodies of the vertebrae and enters the brachiocephalic vein at the angle of junction of the left internal jugular and left subclavian veins. It is from 38 to 45 cm long, about 4 to 6 mm in diameter, and has several valves. At its termination a pair of valves prevent the passage of venous

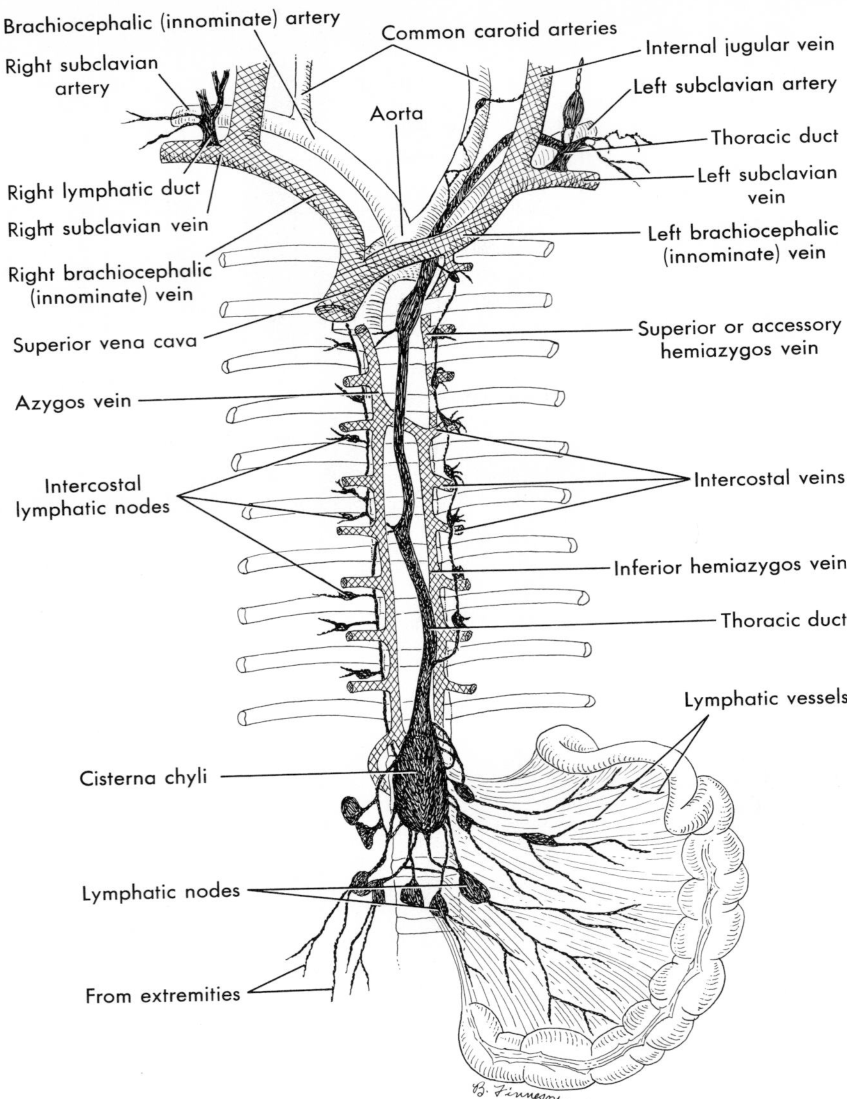

Figure 18–2. Lymphatic drainage to cisterna chyli and thoracic duct.

blood into the duct. It receives the lymph from the left side of the head, neck, and chest, all of the abdomen, and both lower limbs, and also the chyle from the lacteals. Its dilatation, the cisterna chyli, receives the lymph from the lower extremities and from the walls and viscera of the pelvis and abdomen.

The right lymphatic duct is a short vessel, usually about 1.25 cm in length. It pours its contents into the brachiocephalic vein at the junction of the right internal jugular and subclavian veins. Its orifice is guarded by two semilunar valves.

The lymphatics from the right side of the head, the right arm, and the upper part of the trunk enter the right lymphatic duct.

Structure of the Lymph Vessels. The lymphatics resemble the veins in their structure as well as in their arrangement. The smallest consists of a single layer of endothelial cells which have a dentated outline. The larger vessels have three coats similar to those of the veins, except that they are thinner and more transparent. Their valves are like those of the veins but are so close together that when distended they give the vessel a beaded or jointed appearance. They are usually absent in the smaller networks. The valves allow the passage of material from the smaller to the larger lymphatics and from these into the veins.

Distribution and Classification of Lymph Vessels. In general the lymph vessels accompany and are closely parallel to the veins. Lymph vessels have been found in nearly every tissue and organ which contain blood vessels. The nails, cuticle, and hair are without them, but they permeate most other organs. No lymphatic *capillaries* have been found in the central nervous system, the *internal* ear, cartilage, epidermis, spleen, or eyeball. Lymphatic vessels have not yet been demonstrated in the cornea, but lymph spaces are represented by the channels in which nerve fibers run. These channels are lined by an endothelium. The lymph, like the blood in the veins, is returned from the limbs and viscera by a superficial and a deep set of vessels. The superficial lymph vessels are placed immediately beneath the skin and accompany the superficial veins. In certain regions they join the deep lymphatics by penetrating the deep fasciae. In the interior of the body they lie in the submucous tissue throughout the whole length of the gastropulmonary and genitourinary tracts and in the subserous tissue of the thoracic and abdominal walls. The *deep lymphatics* accompany the *deep veins*. They are few in number and are larger than the superficial lymphatics.

The Lacteals. The lymphatics that have their origin in the villi of the small intestine are called *lacteals*. During the process of

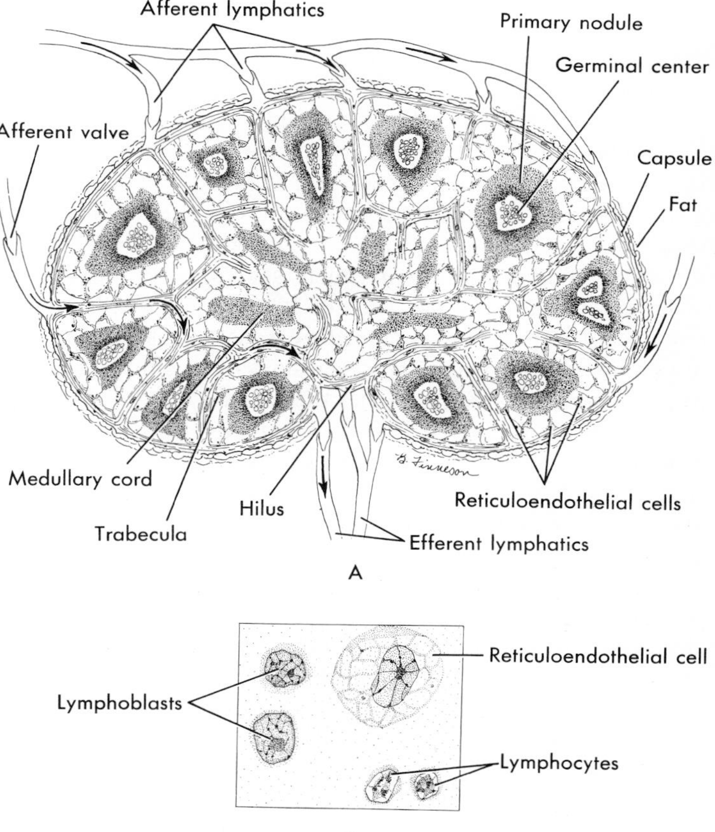

Figure 18–3. (*A*) Diagram of a lymph node, highly magnified. (*B*) Cells found in the lymph nodes.

digestion they are filled with chyle, white in color from the fat particles suspended in it. The lacteals enter the lymphatic vessels that run between the layers of the mesentery, pass through the mesenteric nodes, and finally terminate in the cisterna chyli.

Physiology. The function of the lymphatics is to convey tissue fluid from the tissues to the veins. Functionally, they may be considered supplementary to the capillaries and the veins, as they gather up a part of the fluid which exudes through the thin capillary walls and return it to the brachiocephalic veins. Removal of protein from tissue fluid is a most important additional function. In the brachiocephalic veins lymph becomes mixed with the blood and enters the superior vena cava and then the right atrium of the heart. The function of the lacteals is to help in the absorption of digested food, especially fats.

Lymph Nodes. Lymph nodes are small, oval or bean-shaped bodies, varying in size from that of a pinhead to that of an almond, and are located in the course of the lymphatics. They generally present a slight depression, called the *hilus*, on one side. The blood vessels enter and leave through the hilus. The outer covering is a capsule of connective tissue containing a few smooth-muscle fibers. The capsule sends fibrous bands called *trabeculae* into the substance of the node, dividing it into irregular spaces, which communicate freely with each other. The irregular spaces are occupied by a mass of lymphoid tissue, which, however, does not quite fill them as it never touches the capsule or trabeculae but leaves a narrow interval between itself and them. The spaces thus left form channels for the passage of the lymph, which enters by several afferent vessels. After circulating through the node, the lymph is carried out by efferent vessels which emerge from the hilus. The trabeculae support a free supply of blood vessels. It is said that no lymph on its way from the lymph capillaries ever reaches the blood stream without passing through at least one node.

Location of Nodes. There are a superficial and a deep set of nodes just as there are a superficial and a deep set of lymphatics and veins. Occasionally, a node exists alone, but they are usually in groups or chains at the sides of the great blood vessels. Lymph nodes are found on the back of the head and neck, draining the scalp; around the sternomastoid muscle, draining the back of the tongue, the pharynx, nasal cavities, roof of the mouth, and face; and under the rami of the mandible, draining the floor of the mouth.

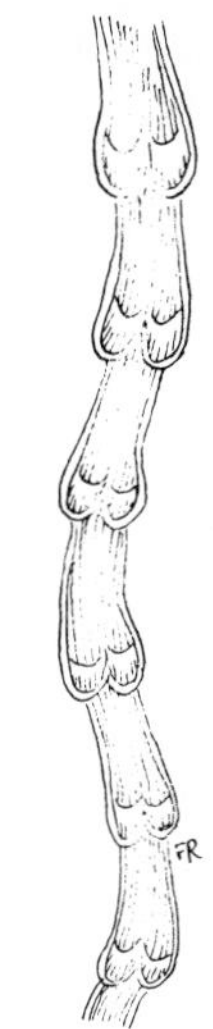

Figure 18–4. Diagram illustrating valves of lymphatics.

In the upper extremities there are three groups—a small one at the bend of the elbow, which drains the hand and forearm; a larger group in the axillary space, into which the first group drains; and a still larger group under the pectoral muscles. The last-named drains the mammary gland and the skin and muscles of the chest.

In the lower extremities there is usually a small node at the upper part of the anterior tibial vessels, and in the popliteal space back of the knee there are several; but the greater number are massed in the groin. These nodes drain the lower extremities and the lower part of the abdominal wall. The lymph nodes of the abdomen and pelvis are divided into a parietal and a visceral group. The parietal nodes are behind the peritoneum and in close association with the larger blood vessels. The visceral nodes are associated with the visceral arteries. The lymph nodes of the thorax are similarly divided into a parietal set, situated in the thoracic wall, and a visceral set associated with the heart, pericardium, trachea, lungs, pleura, thymus, and esophagus.

Function of the Lymph Nodes. The lymph nodes are credited with two important functions.

1. They produce lymphocytes and antibodies. As lymph passes through the nodes, fresh lymphocytes are added to the fluid. The lymphocytes are formed in the nodes by cell division. Serum globulin and antibodies are also added to lymph in the nodes.

2. The nodes are located in the course of the lymph vessels, and the lymph takes a tortuous course among the cells of the node. This suggests that they serve as filters and are a defense against the spread of infection. The lymph draining from an infected area carries the products of suppuration, and perhaps the infecting organisms themselves, to the first nodes in its pathway. Unless the infection is severe, the odds are against the organisms, and the lymph is more or less "disinfected" before it passes on. Nodes engaged in such a struggle are usually enlarged and tender, and if they are overpowered, they themselves may become the foci of infection.

Factors Controlling the Flow of Lymph. The flow of tissue fluid from the tissue spaces to the lymph capillaries and on to the veins is maintained chiefly by three factors.

1. Difference in Pressure. The tissue fluid is under greater pressure than the lymph in the lymph capillaries, and the pressure in the larger lymphatics near the ducts is much less than in the smaller vessels. Con-

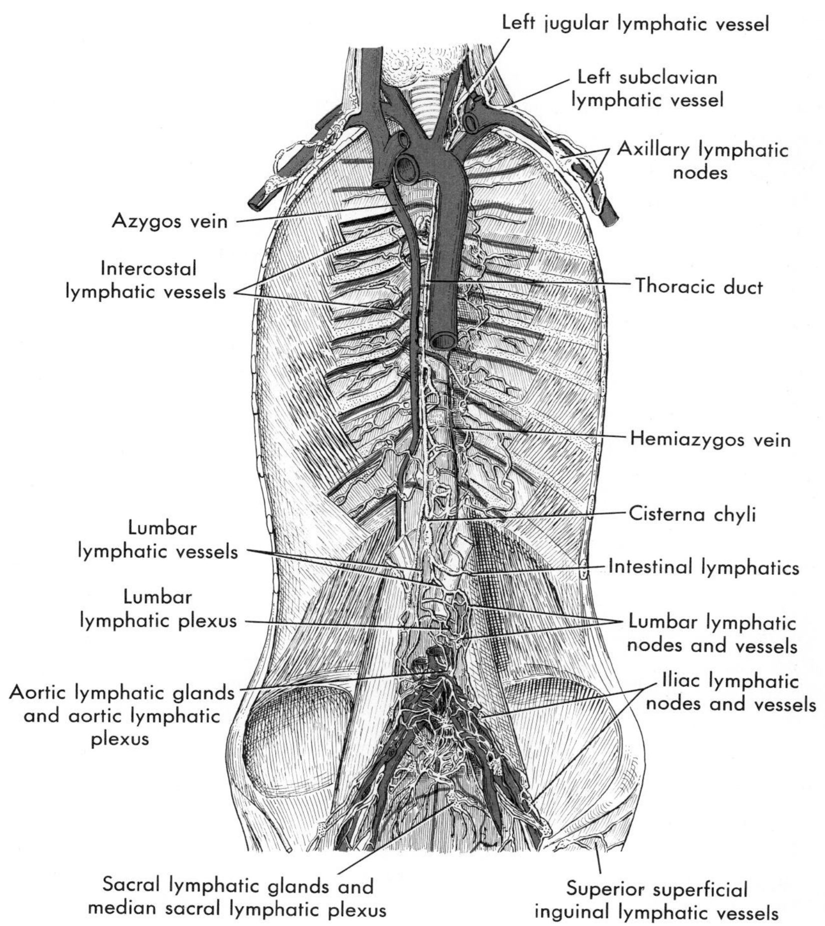

Figure 18–5. The lymph nodes and vessels of the dorsal body wall. (Modified from Toldt.)

sequently the lymphatics form a system of vessels leading from a region of high pressure, the tissues, to a region of low pressure, the interior of the large veins of the neck.

2. Muscular Movements and Valves. Contractions of the skeletal muscles compress the lymph vessels and force the lymph on toward the larger ducts. The numerous valves prevent a return flow in the backward direction. The flow of lymph from resting muscles is small in quantity, but during muscular exercise and massage it is increased. The flow of chyle is greatly assisted by the peristaltic and rhythmical contractions of the muscular coats of the intestines. Pulsation waves moving over the enormous number of minute arteries existing everywhere act to "push ahead" the lymph from valve to valve, on to the larger lymphatics.

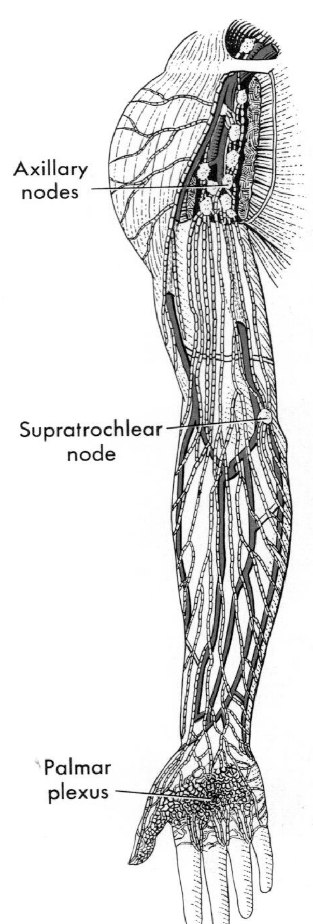

Figure 18–6. The lymph nodes and vessels of the upper limb.

3. Respiratory Movements. During each inspiration the pressure on the thoracic duct is less than on the lymphatics outside the thorax, and lymph is accordingly sucked into the duct. During the succeeding expiration the pressure on the thoracic duct is increased, and some of its contents, prevented by the valve from escaping below, are pressed out into the brachiocephalic veins.

Edema. The fluid in the various tissues of the body varies in amount from time to time, but under normal circumstances remains fairly constant. Under abnormal conditions, these limits may be exceeded, and the result is known as edema. Similar excessive accumulations may also occur in the larger fluid spaces, the serous cavities.

Among the possible causes of edema are:

Any obstruction to the flow of lymph from the tissues, such as an infection in the lymph nodes.

An excessive formation, the fluid gathering in the tissues faster than it can be carried away by a normal flow.

General or local rises in capillary blood pressure (often resulting from increases in venous pressure).

Increased permeability of capillary membrane.

Edema may also be a symptom of some other primary conditions, such as certain types of cardiac, liver, and renal diseases, or mechanical obstruction of veins.

The Spleen (Lien). The spleen is a highly vascular, bean-shaped organ situated directly beneath the diaphragm, behind and to the left of the stomach. It is covered by peritoneum and held in position by folds of this membrane. Beneath the serous coat is a connective-tissue capsule from which trabeculae run inward, forming a framework, in the interstices of which is found the *splenic pulp*, made up of a network of fibrillae and blood cells—red corpuscles, the various forms of white cells, and large, rounded phagocytic cells (the macrophages of the reticuloendothelial system), which engulf fragmentary red corpuscles and invading organisms such as

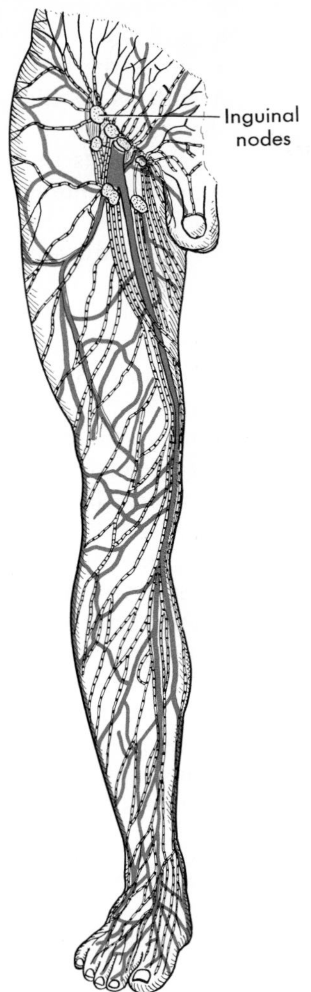

Figure 18–7. The lymph nodes and vessels of the lower extremity.

the *Salmonella typhosa*. Scattered throughout the pulp are masses of lymphoid tissue called malpighian follicles.[1] Smooth-muscle fibers are found in both the outer capsule and the trabeculae.

The blood supply is brought by the splenic artery, a branch of the celiac artery; the splenic artery divides into six or more branches, which enter the concave side of the spleen at a depression called the hilum. The arrangement of the blood vessels is peculiar to this organ. After entering, the arteries divide into many branches and terminate in tufts of arterioles, which open freely into the splenic pulp. Each follicle lies in close relation to a small artery. The blood is collected by thin-walled veins, which unite to form the splenic vein. The splenic vein unites with the superior mesenteric to form the portal vein, which carries the blood to the liver.

Function. 1. The spleen can store large quantities of blood and release it on physiological demand.

2. The spleen forms red blood cells in the embryo.

3. The spleen destroys and removes fragile or aged red blood cells.

4. The malpighian follicles of the spleen are a place of origin for lymphocytes.

5. Phagocytic—the reticuloendothelial cells (RE) in the spleen pulp and venous sinuses function as a secondary line of defense for removing bacteria, debris, or other infectious agents that have entered the blood stream.

Enlargement of the spleen occurs in certain pathological conditions (Banti's disease, Gaucher's disease, certain anemias), and splenectomy gives favorable results. Enlargement also accompanies malaria, leukemia, Hodgkin's disease, but removal in these cases is medically contraindicated.

The Thymus. The thymus, as part of the lymphatic system, usually consists of two lobes, but they may unite to form a single lobe or may have an intermediate lobe between them. It is situated in the upper chest cavity along the trachea, overlapping the great blood vessels as they leave the heart. Each lobe has several lobules, each of which is composed of an outer *cortex* and *medulla*. The cortex is composed of closely arranged lymphocytes which obscure the fewer number of reticular cells. In the medulla the reticulum is coarser and the lymphoid cells are fewer in number. There are many reticular cells. In the medulla are rounded nests of cells, 30 to 100 μ in diameter, called the corpuscles of Hassall.[2] The arteries are derived from the

[1] Marcello Malpighi (1628–1694), a physician and professor of comparative anatomy at Bologna.

[2] Arthur Hill Hassall, English physician (1817–1894).

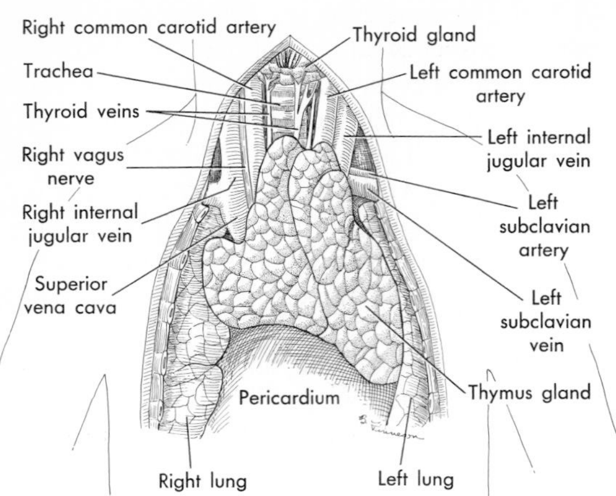

Figure 18–8. Thymus gland of newborn infant.

internal thoracic and the superior and inferior thyroids. The nerves are derived from the vagi of the craniosacral system and from the thoracolumbar system. At birth the thymus is large, and it gradually decreases in size after puberty, the corpuscles of Hassall disappearing more slowly than other portions.

Experiments with animals have shown that stress situations reduce the size of the thymus markedly. Recent research clearly demonstrates that the thymus is essential for the normal development of immunological functioning. In the mouse, if the thymus is removed at birth, it fails to produce circulating antibodies against foreign substances. For example, a thymectomized mouse will accept a skin graft from another animal. Normally the skin graft is rejected due to antibody formation.

Antibodies are produced primarily by the plasma cells of the spleen, lymph nodes, and other lymphoid tissues. Smaller amounts of antibody are formed also by lymphocytes and by reticular cells directly. Current theory regarding antibody formation proposes that lymphoid tissue reticular cells are of hundreds of different types, each capable of producing a specific type of antibody. When an antigen enters the blood stream it comes in contact with its specific reticulum cell, which is then stimulated to produce antibody—which counteracts that particular antigen. Since there are hundreds of different types of reticular cells, hundreds of different types of antibody are potentially possible.

The relation of the thymus to antibody formation is significant. As mentioned above, removal of the thymus from the fetus suppresses the individual's ability to form antibody and permits skin grafts from another animal. During fetal life the thymus produces the precursor cell which locates in all lymphoid tissue and becomes the reticulum cell. It is the reticulum cell which is capable of conversion to the plasma cell and forms antibodies under stimulation of the appropriate antigen. During fetal life also the thymus "learns" to recognize the protein of its body cells and fails to produce antibody against this protein. Proteins from another of the same or different species are thus "foreign" antigens and stimulate antibody production.

Current efforts to transplant tissue such as the kidney from one individual to another are hampered by the normal immune mechanism. Only grafts from a genetically closely related individual will be tolerated by the recipient. However recent research indicates that it is possible to "type" individuals on the basis of antigens located on the leukocyte, thus making possible the matching of a recipient with a suitable donor.

Tonsillar tissue is composed of a mass of lymphoid tissue embedded in mucous membrane. The epithelial lining dips between the lymphoid tissue forming crypts or glandlike pits. Many reticuloendothelial cells are found in the tonsils.

THE RETICULOENDOTHELIAL SYSTEM

The reticuloendothelial system (RES) is composed of cells and tissue that function in phagocytizing microorganisms or foreign particles or are capable of forming antibodies (immune bodies) against them. The RE cells also have the ability (1) to develop into

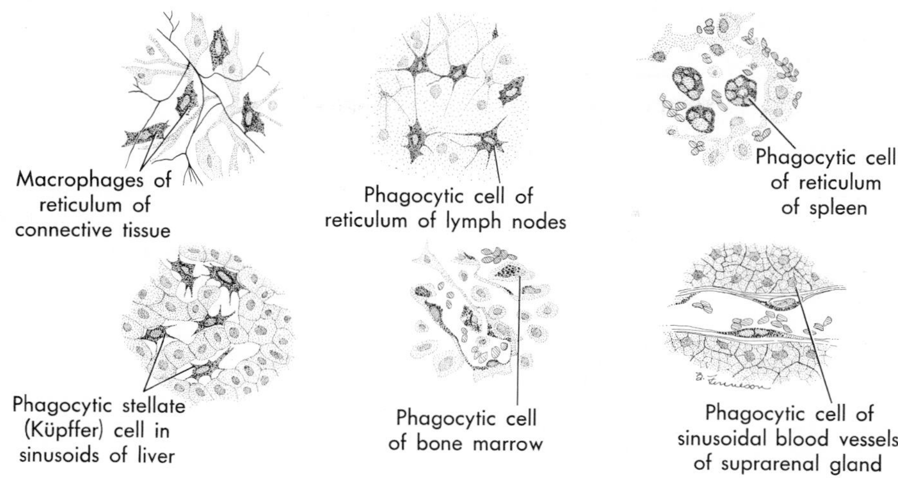

Figure 18–9. Cells of the reticuloendothelial system.

lymphocytes in the lymph nodes, (2) to develop into tissue histiocytes which wander through tissues and function as phagocytes, and (3) to form plasma cells which are the primary producers of immune bodies.

Reticular connective tissue is characterized by fibers which form an interlacing network or reticulum, in which are formed reticular cells. The cells are usually stellate in shape with many processes and centrally placed nuclei.

RE cells are mainly aggregated in the spleen, bone marrow, lymph nodes, tonsils, and thymus. Large numbers of stellate RE cells (Kupffer cells) are located along the liver sinusoids. RE cells also lie along the sinusoids of the pituitary and adrenals and along all blood vessels. The microglia cells of the nervous system and macrophages and plasma cells of loose connective tissue are components of the RE system.

It is believed that RE cells are probably derived from primitive mesenchymal cells which form the hematopoietic cells.

The functions of this system *cannot be overemphasized* in the normal individual, and in pathological conditions it is the active agent in the removal of broken-down tissue cells and microorganisms and in the formation of antibodies.

QUESTIONS FOR DISCUSSION

Mr. Green was admitted to the hospital with an infected toe. There was a red streak up the leg, associated with large painful masses in the groin. His foot and leg were edematous. He was taken to surgery for drainage of the toe infection and given antibiotics, and the leg was placed at rest.

1. What was the cause of the red streak in the leg?
2. The masses in the groin were enlarged lymph nodes. Explain why they were so large and painful.
3. Where else in the body are lymph nodes found and what is their function?
4. What were some of the probable causes of the edema in Mr. Green's leg and why was it placed at rest?
5. Explain why lymph capillaries, vessels, and nodes are important in everyday living.
6. What is believed to be the function of the thymus gland?
7. What are antibodies? Are they helpful or harmful? In what ways?

SUMMARY

- **Lymph**
  - **Source**
    - Formed from tissue fluid by the physical process of diffusion
  - **Description**
    - Colorless or yellowish liquid
    - Slightly alkaline reaction
    - Salty taste. No odor
    - Consists of blood plasma plus lymphocytes
    - Specific gravity varies between 1.015 and 1.023
    - Contains a relatively low content of blood proteins
    - Contains a relatively low content of nutrients
    - Contains a relatively high content of products of metabolism
  - **Function**
    - Carries nutrients from blood to tissues
    - Carries products of metabolism from tissues to blood
    - Dependent upon diffusion
- **Lymph Vascular System**
  - **Lymph vessels**
    - Lymph capillaries
    - Lymphatics
    - Thoracic duct
    - Right lymphatic duct
    - Lacteals
  - **Lymph nodes**
- **Lymph Vessels**
  - **Lymph capillaries**
    - Origin in tissues
    - One coat of endothelium
    - Start as blind ends of microscopic lymph capillaries, unite to form lymphatics
    - Distribution comparable to that of blood capillaries
  - **Lymphatics**—three coats—numerous valves
  - **Thoracic duct**
    - Begins in cisterna chyli, located on front of body of second lumbar vertebra
    - 38–45 cm long. 4–6 mm in diameter
    - Has three coats—numerous valves
    - Receives lymph from side of head, neck, and chest, left arm, all of abdomen, and both lower limbs. Receives chyle from lacteals
    - Pours lymph and chyle into left brachiocephalic vein
  - **Right lymphatic duct**
    - About 1.25 cm long
    - Receives lymph from right side of hand, neck, and chest, also right arm
    - Pours lymph into right brachiocephalic vein
  - **Classification**
    - **Superficial**—beneath skin, accompany superficial veins
    - **Deep**—accompany deep blood vessels
  - **Lacteals**
    - Lymphatics of the intestines
    - Many originate in villi of small intestine
    - Contain
      - During digestion—chyle—lymph carrying emulsified fat
      - During period of fasting—lymph
    - Absorb fatty substances
  - **Functions**—drain off lymph from all parts of the body and return it to the brachiocephalic veins
- **Lymph Nodes**
  - **Description**
    - Shape
      - Oval
      - Bean-shaped
    - Size varies from that of pinhead to that of almond
    - Outer capsule—connective tissue with some muscle fibers
    - Interior divided into irregular spaces like sponge
    - Spaces partially filled with lymphoid tissue. Communicating channels for lymph, which enters by afferent, leaves by efferent vessels
    - Are well supplied with blood

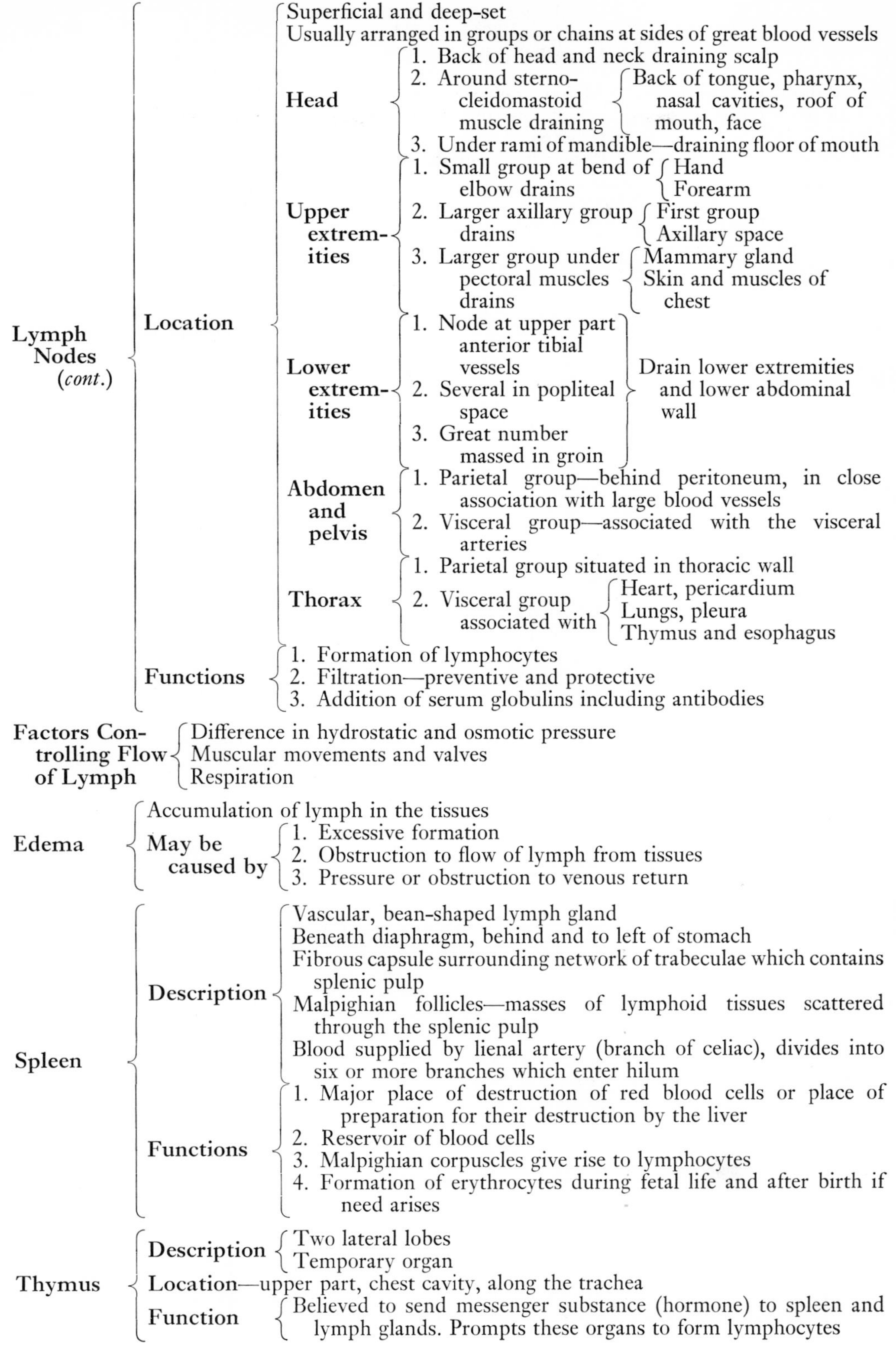

- **Lymph Nodes** (*cont.*)
  - **Location**
    - Superficial and deep-set
    - Usually arranged in groups or chains at sides of great blood vessels
    - **Head**
      1. Back of head and neck draining scalp
      2. Around sternocleidomastoid muscle draining
         - Back of tongue, pharynx, nasal cavities, roof of mouth, face
      3. Under rami of mandible—draining floor of mouth
    - **Upper extremities**
      1. Small group at bend of elbow drains
         - Hand
         - Forearm
      2. Larger axillary group drains
         - First group
         - Axillary space
      3. Larger group under pectoral muscles drains
         - Mammary gland
         - Skin and muscles of chest
    - **Lower extremities**
      1. Node at upper part anterior tibial vessels
      2. Several in popliteal space
      3. Great number massed in groin
      - Drain lower extremities and lower abdominal wall
    - **Abdomen and pelvis**
      1. Parietal group—behind peritoneum, in close association with large blood vessels
      2. Visceral group—associated with the visceral arteries
    - **Thorax**
      1. Parietal group situated in thoracic wall
      2. Visceral group associated with
         - Heart, pericardium
         - Lungs, pleura
         - Thymus and esophagus
  - **Functions**
    1. Formation of lymphocytes
    2. Filtration—preventive and protective
    3. Addition of serum globulins including antibodies
- **Factors Controlling Flow of Lymph**
  - Difference in hydrostatic and osmotic pressure
  - Muscular movements and valves
  - Respiration
- **Edema**
  - Accumulation of lymph in the tissues
  - **May be caused by**
    1. Excessive formation
    2. Obstruction to flow of lymph from tissues
    3. Pressure or obstruction to venous return
- **Spleen**
  - **Description**
    - Vascular, bean-shaped lymph gland
    - Beneath diaphragm, behind and to left of stomach
    - Fibrous capsule surrounding network of trabeculae which contains splenic pulp
    - Malpighian follicles—masses of lymphoid tissues scattered through the splenic pulp
    - Blood supplied by lienal artery (branch of celiac), divides into six or more branches which enter hilum
  - **Functions**
    1. Major place of destruction of red blood cells or place of preparation for their destruction by the liver
    2. Reservoir of blood cells
    3. Malpighian corpuscles give rise to lymphocytes
    4. Formation of erythrocytes during fetal life and after birth if need arises
- **Thymus**
  - **Description**
    - Two lateral lobes
    - Temporary organ
  - **Location**—upper part, chest cavity, along the trachea
  - **Function**
    - Believed to send messenger substance (hormone) to spleen and lymph glands. Prompts these organs to form lymphocytes

Tonsillar Tissue	**Description**	Interlacing network with phagocytic cells Composed of lymphoid tissue Many RE cells
Reticular Connective Tissue	**Location**	All loose connective tissue, lymph nodes, spleen, liver, sinusoids, bone marrow, adrenal glands, anterior lobe of pituitary, nervous system
	Function	Phagocytic properties paramount

UNIT V

Materials to Be Distributed to and from Cells

The life of the cell requires the supply of essential materials for growth and for other structural activities, as well as a source of energy for these activities. Unit V is devoted to the kinds of materials needed by cells, how they enter the body, how they are used, and how the use is regulated.

CHAPTER

19

THE RESPIRATORY ORGANS

Physiology of Respiration in the Alveolus and the Tissue Capillary
Nervous and Chemical Controls of Respiration
Oxygen Therapy

The normal sequence of chemical changes in tissue cells depends on oxygen, hence the need for a continuous supply. One of the chief end products of these chemical changes is carbon dioxide, hence the need for continuous elimination of carbon dioxide. In unicellular animals the intake of oxygen and the output of carbon dioxide occur at the surface by diffusion. As organisms increase in size and complexity, specialized structure is developed which functions to bring oxygen to the cells of the organism.

In man the circulating blood in the alveolar capillaries takes up oxygen and gives up carbon dioxide, and later in the capillaries of the tissues it gives up oxygen and takes up carbon dioxide.

This exchange of gases is known as respiration and is dependent upon the proper functioning of certain organs, the *respiratory system.*

NOSE

The nose is the special organ of the sense of smell, but it also serves as a passageway for air going to and from the lungs. It filters, warms, and moistens the entering air and also helps in phonation. It consists of two parts—the external feature, the nose, and the internal cavities, the nasal fossae.

The Nose. This is composed of a triangular framework of bone and cartilage, covered by skin and lined by mucous membrane. On its undersurface are two oval openings, the nostrils (*anterior nares*), which are the external openings of the nasal cavities.

The Nasal Cavities. These are two wedge-shaped cavities, separated from each other by a partition, or septum. The septum is formed in front by the crest of the nasal bones and the frontal spine and in the middle by the perpendicular plate of the ethmoid. The septum is usually bent more to one side than the other, a condition to be remembered when a tube must be inserted.

The conchae (Figure 19–1) and processes of the ethmoid, which are exceedingly light and spongy, project into the nasal cavities and divide them into three incomplete passages from before backward—the superior, middle, and inferior meatus. The palate and maxillae separate the nasal cavities from the mouth, and the horizontal plate of the ethmoid forms the partition between the cranial and nasal cavities.

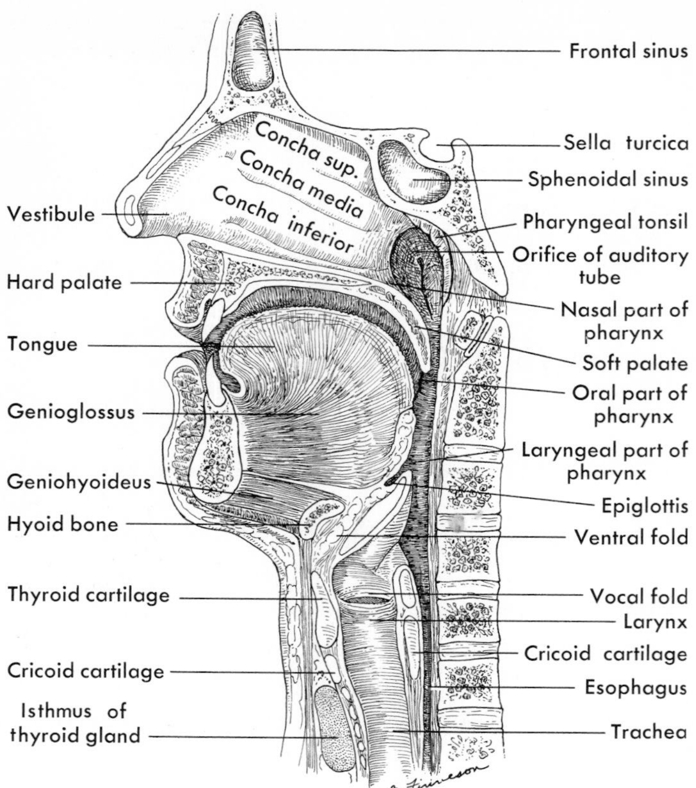

Figure 19–1. Sagittal section of nose, mouth, pharynx. (Modified from *Gray's Anatomy*.)

The nasal cavities[1] communicate with the air in front by the anterior nares, and behind they open into the nasopharynx by the two *posterior nares*. The cavities are lined with mucous membrane. At the entrance each cavity or vestibule is lined with thick, stratified, squamous epithelium containing sebaceous glands and numerous coarse hairs. The middle, or respiratory, portion of the cavity is lined with pseudostratified epithelium with many ciliated and goblet cells. The upper, or olfactory, portion is lined with neuroepithelium which contains olfactory cells which are the receptors for smell. This membrane, which is highly vascular, is continuous externally with the skin and internally with the mucous membrane lining the sinuses and other structures connected with the nasal passages. Inflammatory conditions of the nasal mucous membrane may extend into the sinuses.

[1] Eleven bones enter into the formation of the nasal cavities: the floor is formed by the palatine (2) and part of the maxillae bones (2); the roof is formed chiefly by the horizontal plate of the ethmoid bone (1), the sphenoid (1), and the small nasal bones (2); in the outer walls we find, in addition to processes from other bones, the two conchae (2). The vomer (1) forms part of the septum.

Advantage of Nasal Breathing. Under normal conditions breathing should take place through the nose. The arrangement of the conchae makes the upper part of the nasal passages very narrow; these passages are thickly lined and freely supplied with blood, which keeps the temperature relatively high and makes it possible to moisten and warm the air before it reaches the lungs. The hairs at the entrance to the nostrils and the cilia of the epithelium serve as filters to remove particles which may be carried in with the inspired air.

Nerves and Blood Vessels. The mucous membrane of the superior conchae and upper third of the septum contains the endings of the olfactory nerve fibers. The nerve fibers for the muscles of the nose are fibers of the facial (seventh cranial), and the skin receives fibers from the ophthalmic and maxillary nerves, which are branches of the trigeminal (fifth cranial). Blood is supplied to the external nose by branches from the external and internal maxillary arteries, which are derived from the external carotid. The lateral walls and the septum of the nasal cavities are supplied with nasal branches of the ethmoidal arteries, which are derived from the internal carotid.

The mouth serves as a passageway for the entrance of air, and the pharynx transmits the air from the nose or mouth to the larynx, but both are closely associated with digestion and will be described with the digestive organs.

RESPIRATORY TRACT

The respiratory tract is composed of the following organs in addition to the nose and nasopharynx already described: (1) larynx, (2) trachea, (3) bronchi, and (4) lungs.

The Larynx. The larynx, or organ of voice, is placed in the upper and front part of the neck between the root of the tongue and the trachea. Above and behind it lies the pharynx, which opens into the esophagus, and on either side of it lie the great vessels of the neck. The larynx is broad above and shaped somewhat like a triangular box, with flat sides and prominent ridge in front (the "Adam's apple"). Below it is narrow and rounded where it blends with the trachea. It is made up of nine fibrocartilages, united by extrinsic and intrinsic ligaments and moved by numerous muscles.

CARTILAGES OF THE LARYNX

SINGLE CARTILAGES
- Thyroid, resembles a shield, rests on cricoid. Consists of two plates joined at acute angle in midline forming laryngeal prominence.
- Cricoid, shaped like seal ring with signet part in back.
- Epiglottis, shaped like leaf with stem inserted in union of two thyroid plates.

PAIRED CARTILAGES
- Arytenoid, pyramid-shaped, rest on upper border of cricoid cartilages on either side.
- Corniculate, conical nodules of elastic cartilage, articulate with upper inner surface of arytenoid cartilages. They prolong the arytenoids backward and medially.
- Cuneiform, elongated pieces of elastic cartilage on either side in the aryepiglottic fold.

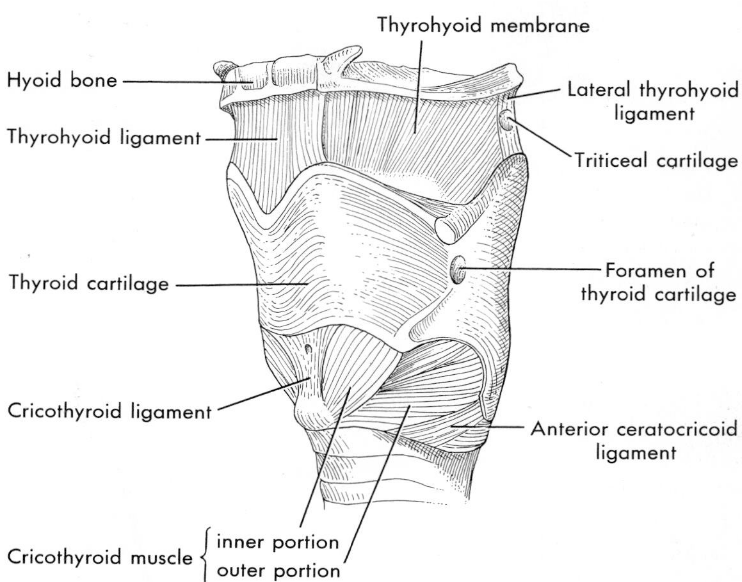

Figure 19–2. The larynx seen from the left side and front.

The larynx is lined throughout with mucous membrane, which is continuous above with that lining the pharynx and below with that lining the trachea.

The cavity of the larynx is divided into two parts by two folds of mucous membrane stretching from front to back but not quite meeting in the middle line. They thus leave an elongated fissure called the *glottis*, which is the narrowest segment of the air passages. The glottis is protected by a lid of fibro-cartilage called the *epiglottis*.

The Vocal Folds. Embedded in the mucous membrane at the edges of the slit are fibrous and elastic ligaments, which strengthen the edges of the glottis and give them elasticity. These ligaments, covered with mucous membrane, are firmly attached at both ends to the cartilages of the larynx and are called the inferior or *true vocal folds*, because they function in the production of the voice. Above the vocal folds are two ventricular folds, which do not function in the production of the voice but serve to keep the true vocal folds moist, in holding the breath, and in protecting the larynx during the swallowing of food.

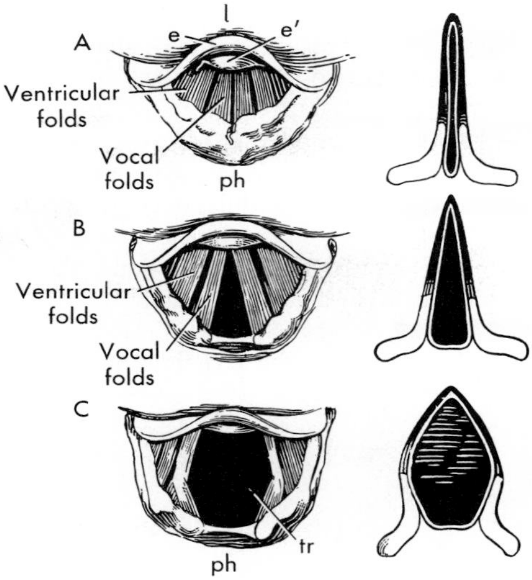

Figure 19–3. The larynx as seen by means of the laryngoscope in different conditions of the glottis. (*A*) While singing a high note. (*B*) In quiet breathing. (*C*) During a deep inspiration. (*l*) Base of tongue, (*e*) upper free edge of epiglottis, (*e′*) cushion of epiglottis, (*ph*) part of anterior wall of pharynx, (*tr*) trachea.

The glottis varies in shape and size according to the action of muscles upon the laryngeal walls. When the larynx is at rest during quiet breathing, the glottis is V-shaped; during a deep inspiration it becomes almost round, while during the production of a high note the edges of the folds approximate so closely as to leave scarcely any opening at all.

Muscles of the Larynx. Many of the muscles of the neck, face, lips, tongue, and diaphragm are concerned with speech. The muscles of the larynx are extrinsic and intrinsic.

The extrinsic muscles include the:

1. Infrahyoid Muscles	2. Suprahyoid Muscles (some of)
Omohyoid	Stylopharyngeus
Sternohyoid	Palatopharyngeus
Thyrohyoid	Inferior and middle constrictors of the pharynx
Sternothyroid	

In prolonged inspiratory efforts, such as in singing, these muscles produce tension on the lower part of the cervical fascia and hence prevent the apices of the lungs and the large blood vessels from being compressed. In the act of swallowing, the larynx and hyoid bone are drawn up with the pharynx—these muscles depress them. In addition, they elevate and depress the thyroid cartilage.

The intrinsic muscles are confined entirely to the larynx and are shown in Figure 19–2. The posterior cricoarytenoid muscles rotate the arytenoid cartilages outward, thereby separating the vocal folds. The lateral cricoarytenoid muscles rotate the arytenoid cartilages inward, thereby approximating the vocal folds. The arytenoid muscles approximate the arytenoid cartilages, especially in the back. These muscles also open and close the glottis.

The cricothyroid muscles elevate the arch of the cricoid cartilage in front, causing the lamina to be depressed and thereby increasing the distance between the vocal processes and thyroid cartilages.

The thyroarytenoid muscles draw the arytenoid cartilages forward toward the thyroid, and in this way they shorten and relax the vocal folds. Working together, these muscles regulate the degree of tension on the vocal folds.

Nerves and Blood Vessels. The laryngeal nerves are derived from the internal and external branches of the superior laryngeal, branches of the vagi. Blood is supplied to the larynx by branches of the superior thyroid artery which arises from the external carotid, and from the inferior thyroid, a branch of the thyroid axis, which arises from the subclavian artery.

Phonation. This term is applied to the production of vocal sounds. All the respiratory organs function in the production of vocal sounds, but the vocal folds, the larynx, and the parts above are specially concerned. The speech centers and parts of the brain which control all the movements of the tongue and jaw are of special importance. The organs of phonation in man are similar to those of many animals much lower in the scale of life; the association areas of the brain account for the greater variety of sounds that man can produce.

Voice. The vocal folds produce the voice. Air driven by an expiratory movement out of the lungs throws the two elastic folds into vibrations. These impart their vibrations to the column of air above them and so give rise to the sound which we call the voice. The pharynx, mouth, and nasal cavities above the glottis act as resonating cavities. The volume and force of the expired air and the amplitude of the vibrations of the vocal folds determine the loudness or intensity of the voice. The pitch of the voice depends upon the number of vibrations occurring in a given unit of time. This in turn is dependent on the length, thickness, and degree of elasticity of the vocal folds and the tension by which they are held. When the folds are tightly stretched and the glottis almost closed, the highest sounds are emitted.

Differences Between the Male and Female Voice. The size of the larynx varies in different individuals, and this is one reason for differences in pitch. At the time of puberty, the growth of the larynx and the vocal folds is much more rapid and accentuated in the male than in the female. In the male the increase in the size of the larynx causes an increase in the length of the vocal folds and also gives rise to the laryngeal prominence. These changes in structure are accompanied by changes in the voice, which becomes deeper and lower. Before the characteristic adult voice is attained, there occurs what is described as a break in the voice, due to the inability of the individual to control the longer vocal folds.

The Trachea, or Windpipe. This is a membranous and cartilaginous tube, cylindrical, about 11.2 cm in length and about 2 to 2.5 cm from side to side. It lies in front of the esophagus and extends from the larynx on the level of the sixth cervical vertebra to the upper border of the fifth thoracic vertebra, where it divides into the two bronchi, one for each lung. The placement of the trachea in the chest cavity is such that the upper portion is more anterior than the lower. Thus, when one is lying prone, secretions in the bronchi and trachea tend to flow upward—facilitating drainage of fluid in lung infections.

The walls of the trachea are strengthened by C-shaped rings of hyaline cartilage placed so that the "open" portion is toward the esophagus. Like the larynx it is lined with mucous membrane and has a ciliated epithelium on its inner surface; goblet cells are numerous. The mucous membrane, which extends into the bronchial tubes, keeps the internal surface of the air passages free from dust particles, the mucus entangles particles inhaled, and the movements of the cilia continually sweep this dust-laden mucus upward into the pharynx. The submucosa consists of loose connective tissue and contains mixed glands and fat.

The Bronchi. The two bronchi into which the trachea divides differ slightly, the right bronchus being shorter, wider, and more vertical in direction than the left. They enter the right and left lung, respectively, and

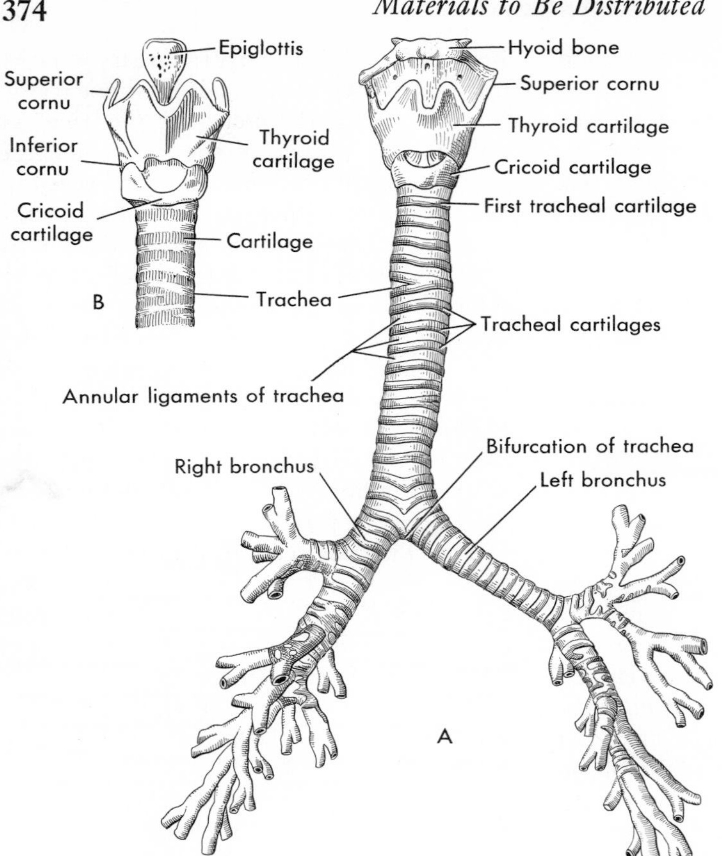

Figure 19–4. The trachea and bronchial ramification, front view. (*A*) Showing ramifications. (*B*) Showing details of glottis and epiglottis. (Modified from Toldt.)

then break up into a great number of smaller branches, which are called the bronchial tubes and bronchioles. The two bronchi resemble the trachea in structure, but as the bronchial tubes divide and subdivide into the smaller bronchi, the incomplete rings of cartilage are replaced by cartilaginous plates, and as they further divide their walls become thinner, the small plates of cartilage cease, the fibrous tissue disappears, and the smallest tubes are composed of only a thin layer of muscular and elastic tissue lined by ciliated epithelium. Each bronchiole terminates in an elongated saccule called the atrium. Each atrium bears, on all parts of its surface, small, irregular projections known as *alveoli*, or air cells. The lining of the walls of the alveoli consists of very thin epithelial cells. Underlying it is a thin, homogeneous basement membrane, which closely approximates the epithelial cells and the capillary wall.

Nerves and Blood Supply to Trachea and Bronchi. The nerves are composed of fibers from the vagi, the recurrent nerves (which decrease the diameter of the bronchi), and the thoracolumbar system (which increase the diameter). Blood is supplied to the trachea by the inferior thyroid arteries.

LUNGS

Anatomy. The lungs (pulmones) are cone-shaped organs which fill the two lateral chambers of the thoracic cavity and are separated from each other by the heart and other contents of the mediastinum. Each lung presents an outer surface which is convex, a base which is concave to fit over the convex portion of the diaphragm, and an apex which extends about 2.5 to 4 cm (1 to 1½ in.) above the level of the sternal end of the first rib. Each lung is connected to the heart and trachea by the pulmonary artery, pulmonary vein, bronchial arteries and veins, the bronchus, plexuses of nerves, lymphatics, lymph nodes, and areolar tissue, which are covered by the pleura and constitute the *root* of the lung. On the inner surface is a vertical notch called the *hilum*, which gives passage to the structures which form the root of the lung. Below and in front of the hilum is a deep concavity, called the cardiac impression, where the heart lies; it is larger and deeper on the left than on the right lung, because the heart projects farther to the left side.

The right lung is larger and broader than the left, due to the inclination of the heart to the left side; it is also shorter by 2.5 cm, as a result of the diaphragm's rising higher on the right side to accommodate the liver. It is divided by fissures into three lobes—superior, middle, and inferior.

The left lung is smaller, narrower, and longer than the right and is divided into two lobes—superior and inferior.

The substance of the lungs is porous and spongy; owing to the presence of air it crepitates when handled and floats in water. It consists of bronchial tubes and their terminal dilatations, numerous blood vessels, lymphatics, and nerves, and an abundance of elastic connective tissue. Each *lobe* of the lung is composed of many *lobules*, and into each lobule a *bronchiole* enters and terminates in an *atrium*. Each atrium presents a series of air cells, or *alveoli*, 700,000,000 or more in number. Each alveolus is somewhat globular in form with a diameter of about 100 μ. The amount of surface exposed to the air and covered by the capillaries is enormous. It is estimated that the entire inner surface of the lungs amounts to about 90 sq m, more than 100 times the skin surface of the adult body. Of this lung area about 70 sq m are respiratory.

Nerves of the Lungs. The craniosacral nerve supply is made up of fibers in the vagus nerves. The thoracolumbar nerve supply is made up of fibers in the visceral branches of the first four thoracic spinal nerves.

Blood Vessels of the Lungs. Two sets of vessels are distributed to the lungs: (1) the pulmonary artery and its branches, the lung capillaries, and the four pulmonary veins

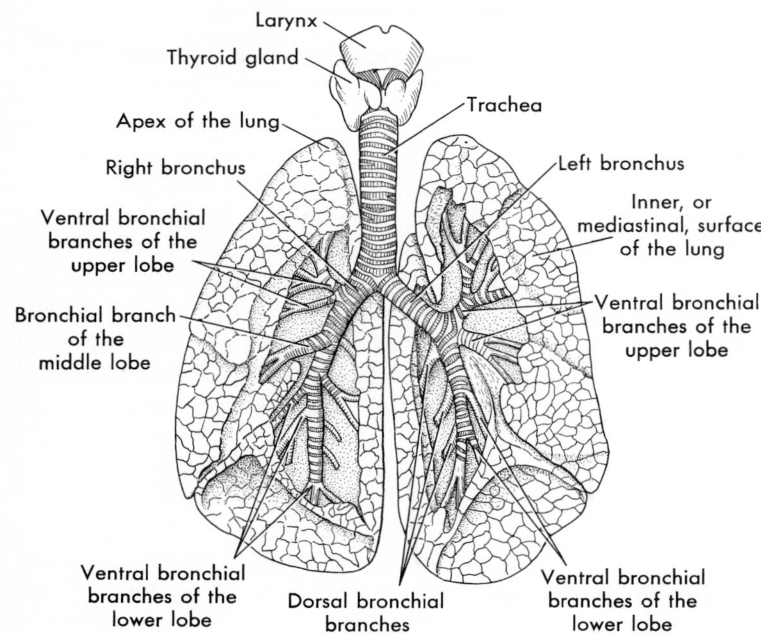

Figure 19–5. The trachea, bronchi, and bronchial tubes. The tissues have been removed to show the air tubes.

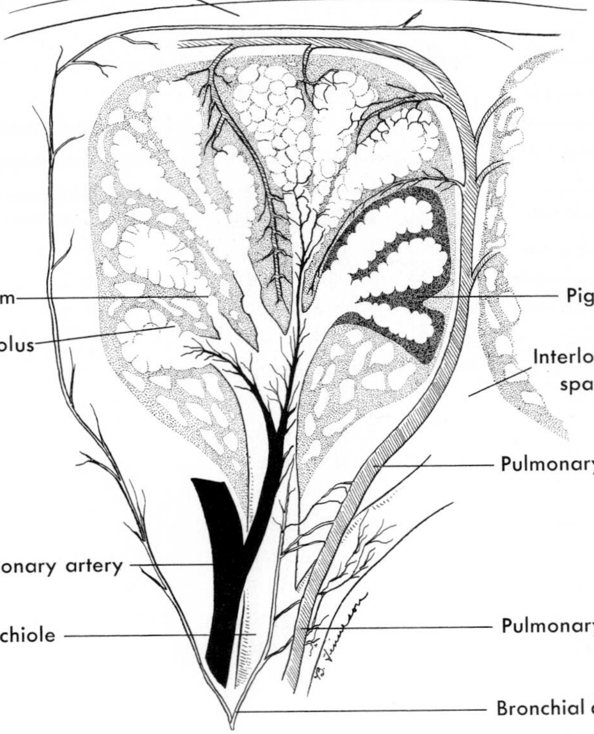

Figure 19–6. Diagram of a lobule of the lung showing a bronchiole dividing into two branches. Note the three atria, in vertical section, the alveoli of each opening into the common passageway. In the next group the first atrium shows a pulmonary arteriole surrounding the opening of each alveolus and pulmonary venules draining blood from around the alveoli. Around the fourth group is a deep deposit of pigment, such as occurs in old age and in persons who inhale coal dust, etc.

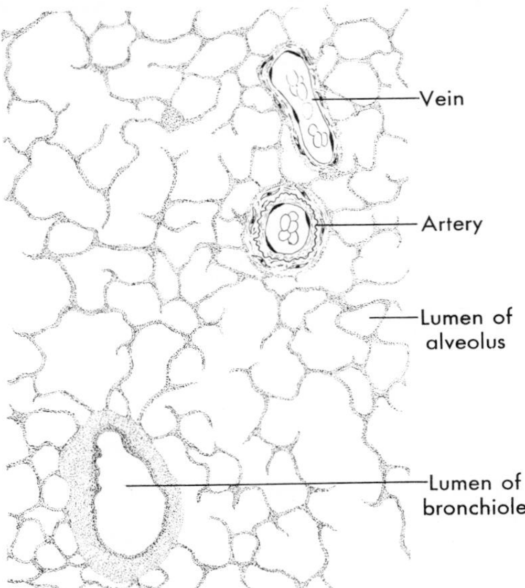

Figure 19–7. Diagram of lung section. There are about 700 to 800 million alveoli in the lungs. These are surrounded by a network of capillaries for the exchange of oxygen and carbon dioxide.

and their branches; and (2) the bronchial arteries, capillaries, and veins.

The pulmonary artery conveys *venous* blood from the right ventricle to the lungs. The main trunk is a short, wide vessel about 5 cm in length and a little more than 3 cm in width. It arises from the right ventricle and passes upward, backward, and to the left. About the level of the intervertebral disk between the fifth and sixth thoracic vertebrae, it divides into two branches, the right and left pulmonary arteries, which pass to the right and left lungs. Before entering the lungs, each artery divides into two branches. The *right* pulmonary is longer and larger than the left. It runs horizontally to the right, *behind* the ascending aorta and superior vena cava to the root of the right lung, where it divides into two branches. The larger lower branch goes to the middle and lower lobes; the smaller upper branch goes to the upper lobe.

The *left* branch of the pulmonary artery is

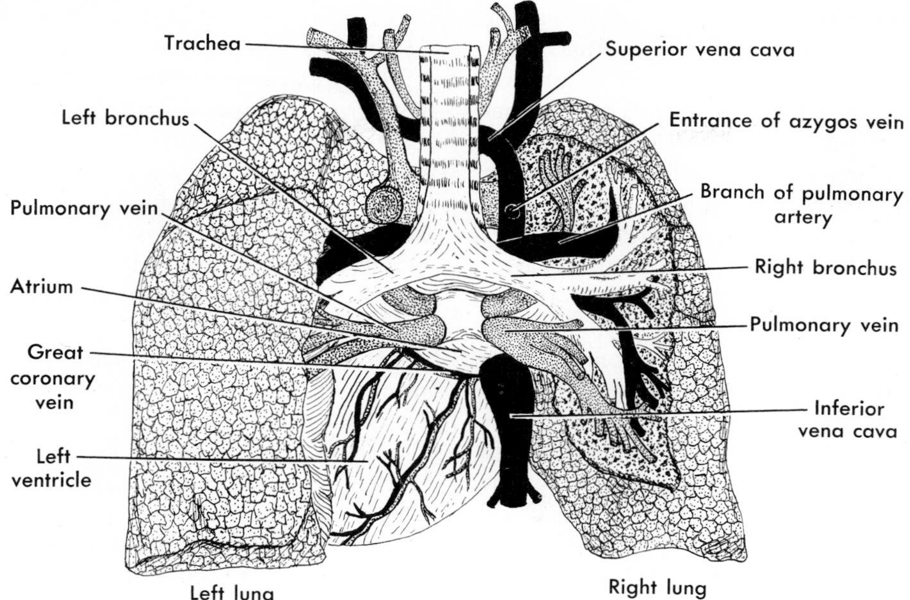

Figure 19–8. The pulmonary artery and aorta. The dorsal part of the right lung has been removed, and the pulmonary vessels and the bronchial tubes are thus exposed.

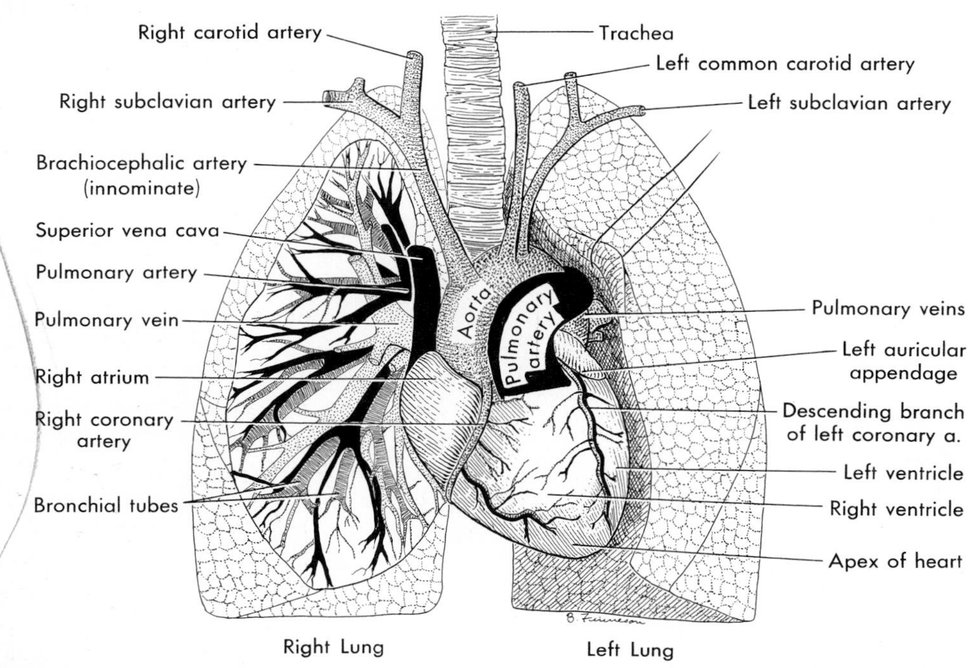

Figure 19–9. The pulmonary artery and aorta. The front part of the right lung has been removed, and the pulmonary vessels and the bronchial tubes are thus exposed.

smaller and passes horizontally in *front* of the descending aorta and left bronchus to the root of the left lung, where it divides into two branches, one to each lobe. These branches divide and subdivide, grow smaller in size, and finally merge into capillaries which form a network upon the walls of the air cells (alveoli). These capillaries unite, grow larger in size, and gradually assume the characteristics of veins. The veins unite to form the pulmonary veins.

The air in the alveoli is separated from the blood in the capillaries only by the thin membranes forming their respective walls. The air sacs are surrounded by capillaries which form a surface area of about 150 sq m for the exchange of oxygen and carbon dioxide. Blood pressure in the pulmonary arteries is 20/10, and in the capillaries about 4 to 6 mm Hg. In the soma the capillaries are surrounded by tissue fluid, which exerts pressure against the capillaries, but the capillaries in the lungs are not opposed by such pressures. This means that pressures must be lower to prevent disturbances of hydrostatic and osmotic forces of the blood in the lungs.

The pulmonary veins convey *oxygenated* blood from the lungs to the left atrium. These veins commence in the capillary network upon the air cells and unite to form one vein for each lobule. These further unite to form one vein for each lobe, two for the left lung and three for the right. The vein from the middle lobe of the right lung usually unites with that from the upper lobe, and finally two trunks from each lung are formed. They have no valves and open separately into the left atrium. (See Figures 19–8 and 19–9 for the relationship of these blood vessels to the heart.)

The branches of the *bronchial arteries* supply blood to the lung substance—the bronchioles, coats of the blood vessels, the lymph nodes, and the pleura. The bronchial veins formed at the root of each lung receive veins which correspond to the branches of the bronchial arteries. Some of the blood supplied by the bronchial arteries passes into

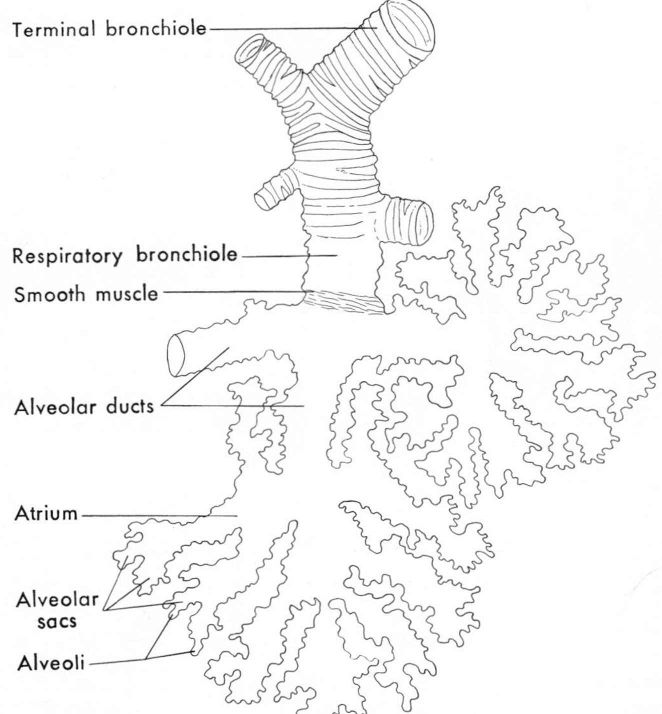

Figure 19–10. A pulmonary, or lung, unit. There is cartilage in the wall of the terminal bronchiole, and the lining is ciliated epithelium. There is no cartilage in the wall of the respiratory bronchiole, and the lining changes from ciliated epithelium to simple squamous epithelium.

the pulmonary veins, but the greater amount is returned to the bronchial veins. The right bronchial vein ends in the azygos vein, the left in the highest intercostal or hemiazygos vein.

Pleura. Each lung is enclosed in a serous sac, one layer of which is closely adherent to the inner chest wall and superior surface of the diaphragm—the parietal pleura; the other closely covers the lung—visceral or pulmonary pleura. The cavity thus formed is a potential space since the layers are in intimate contact. The pleura is a thin, transparent, moist membrane which forms serous fluid. The two layers move easily upon each other with respiratory movements of the chest wall. If the surface of the pleura becomes inflamed (pleurisy), friction results, and the sounds produced by this rubbing can be heard through the stethoscope. Any collection of fluid, as with inflammation, in the pleural cavities will cause compression and possibly collapse of portions of the lung.

If a puncture occurs through the chest walls so that air enters between the two layers of the pleura (pneumothorax), the lung will collapse. If the puncture is closed, the air will be gradually absorbed, and the lung will resume its normal position. Certain types of tuberculosis are treated by artificial pneumothorax. This is accomplished by surgical removal of part of the chest wall or by injections of air into the chest cavity.

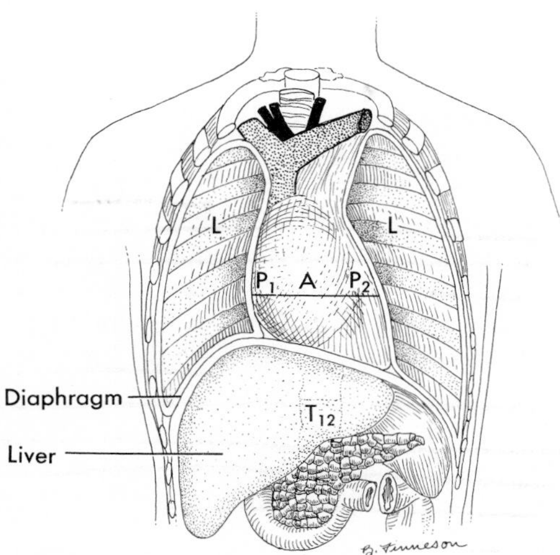

Figure 19–11. Diagram showing thoracic cavity. Line *A* indicates the mediastinum. P_1 and P_2 indicate the mediastinal pleura. *L* indicates lung spaces surrounded by pleura.

The mediastinum, or interpleural space, lies between the right and left pleurae in the median plane of the chest. It extends from the sternum to the spinal column and is entirely filled with the thoracic viscera, namely, the thymus, heart, aorta and its branches, pulmonary artery and veins, venae cavae, azygos vein, various veins, trachea, esophagus, thoracic duct, lymph nodes, and lymph vessels, all lying in connective tissue.

Physiology of Respiration

The main purposes of respiration are to supply the cells of the body with oxygen and eliminate the excess carbon dioxide which results from oxidation. Respiration also helps to maintain the normal pH of body fluids and normal temperature of the body and eliminates about 350 ml of water each 24 hours.

It is common to discuss respiration under three headings:

1. The process of *ventilation* (*breathing*) may be subdivided into inspiration, or breathing in, and expiration, or breathing out.
2. *External respiration* includes external oxygen supply, or the passage of oxygen from the alveoli of the lungs to the blood, and external carbon dioxide elimination, or the passage of carbon dioxide from the blood to the alveoli.
3. *Internal respiration* includes internal oxygen supply, or the passage of oxygen from the blood to the tissue cells, and internal carbon dioxide elimination, or the passage of carbon dioxide from the tissue cells to the blood.

It is evident that external respiration is a process which takes place in the lungs and internal respiration is a process which takes place in the cells that make up the tissues.

Ventilation (Breathing). The thorax is a closed cavity which contains the lungs. The lungs may be thought of as elastic sacs,

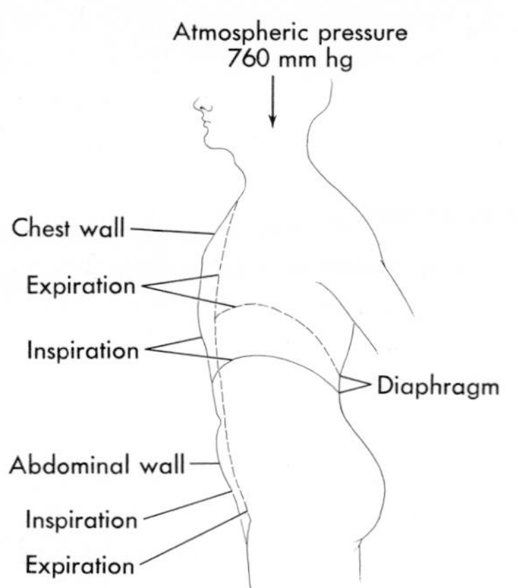

Figure 19–12. Changes in position of diaphragm and abdominal wall, and in size of thoracic cavity during respiration.

the interiors of which remain permanently open to the outside air by way of the bronchi, trachea, glottis, and nasopharynx; alveolar pressure, or the pressure against the lungs from inside, is therefore atmospheric pressure and is usually given as 760 mm Hg at sea level. The lungs are protected externally from atmospheric pressure by the walls of the chest.

The primary muscle of respiration is the diaphragm—without which adequate respiration is impossible. Other muscles involved (see table, page 137) may be classed as accessory, even though some such as the external intercostals are involved in normal quiet breathing. The accessory muscles and those of the abdomen are noticeably involved during forced expiration and inspiration, as when there is oxygen lack.

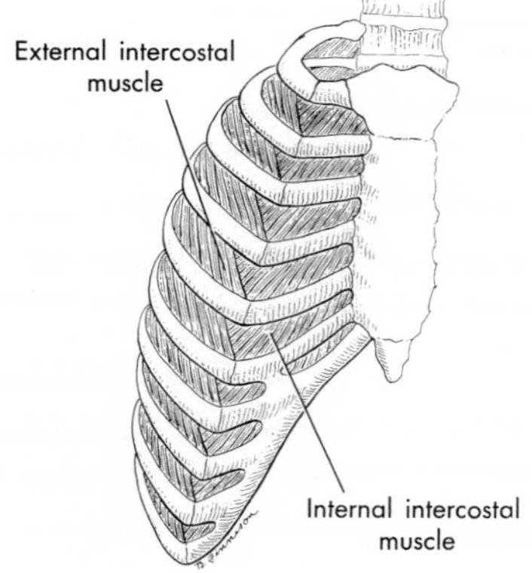

Figure 19–13. The intercostal muscles of the right thorax.

During *inspiration* the upward-curving diaphragm contracts, pulling downward, and increasing the vertical length of the thoracic cage. The intercostal muscles pull the ribs upward and outward. Thus the thoracic cage is increased in size laterally, dorsoventrally, and vertically. It is this *active* increase in size of the cage which causes lung expansion and the "pulling" in of air.

Expiration is passive; all the contracted muscles relax. Surface tension of fluid lining the alveoli causes a continual tendency of the alveoli to collapse, as does the elasticity of lung tissue. Therefore, with relaxation of respiratory muscles, the lung recoils and air is pushed out of the lungs. Forced expiration is made possible by action of accessory muscles to actively decrease the size of the thorax in all its dimensions. The diaphragm is *not* involved actively, but is pushed upward beyond its normal position by contraction of abdominal muscles against the abdominal organs.

Deep ventilation aerates the lung more adequately than shallow ventilation because there is greater lung expansion, air is moved in and out in larger amounts, and more alveoli are involved.

Pressures

INTRAPLEURAL PRESSURE. The intrapleural space is a potential space between the lung and the chest wall. The lungs fill the chest cavity, because the moist membranes constantly absorb any gas or fluids that may enter the space. However, the lungs have a continual tendency to collapse and to pull away from the chest wall. After the lungs have been *stretched on inspiration*, the tendency to collapse is increased to about −5 or −6, and on *expiration*, the collapse tendency is about −4 mm Hg in relation to atmospheric pressure of 760 mm.

INTRA-ALVEOLAR PRESSURE. The respiratory muscles cause respiration by compressing or distending the lungs, which, in turn, will cause pressures in the alveoli to rise or fall. On *inspiration* pressures become slightly negative in relation to atmospheric pressure, about −3 mm Hg. Air is pulled inward through the respiratory airways. On *expiration* intra-alveolar pressure rises to about +3 mm Hg, which causes air to move *outward* through the respiratory airway. During expiratory effort intra-alveolar pressure can increase markedly. Inspiratory effort can reduce the pressure markedly.

Gas Laws. Two gas laws can be applied to respiration.

1. Boyle's Law. This law states that "volume varies inversely with the pressure at constant temperature." If pressure is applied to a gas, the molecules are forced closer together and volume decreases.

On inspiration as the diaphragm descends, the thoracic cavity enlarges and pressure in the pleural space decreases to about 751 mm Hg. Since the atmospheric pressure is 760 mm Hg, air rushes into the expanded lungs against the lower pressure.

On *expiration* the diaphragm relaxes and rises. As a result the volume of the thoracic cavity *decreases*. This *decrease* in volume is associated with an *increase* in pressure in the lung tissue of about 7 mm Hg due to lung elasticity. Thus the slight pressure rise above 760 mm Hg forces air out of the lung.

2. Charles's (Gay-Lussac's) Law. If pressure of a given quantity of gas remains constant, but the temperature *varies*, the volume of gas *increases* directly in proportion to the increase in temperature. Therefore, there are more molecules of oxygen, for example, in cold air than in warm air of equal volume.

Capacity of the Lungs. After the lungs are once filled with air they are never completely emptied. In other words, no expiration ever completely empties the alveoli; neither are they completely filled. The quantity of air which a person can expel by a forcible expiration, after the deepest inspiration possible, is called the *vital capacity* and averages about 4,000 to 4,800 ml for an adult man. It is the sum of tidal, complemental, and supplemental air. Figure 19–15 illustrates lung capacity.

Tidal air designates the amount of air that flows in and out of the lungs with each quiet respiratory movement. The average figure for an adult male is 500 ml.

Inspiratory reserve volume designates the amount of air that can be breathed in over

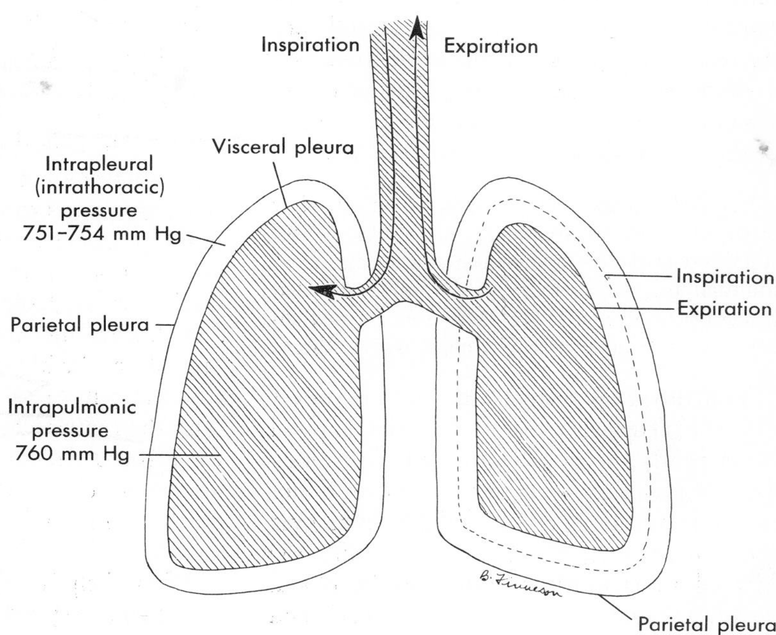

Figure 19–14. Diagram showing parietal and visceral pleura and pressure changes during respiration.

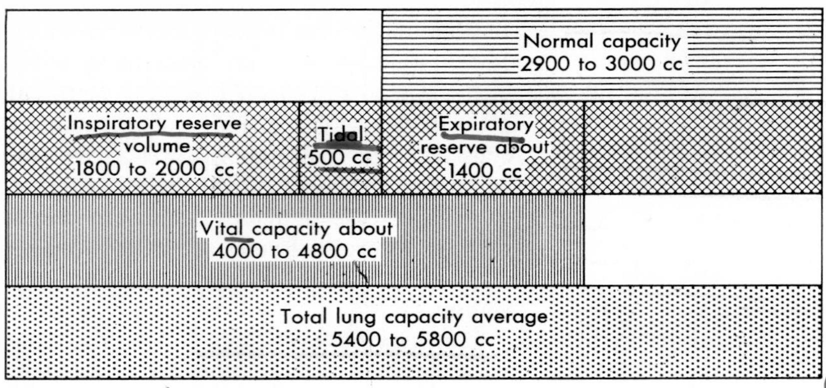

Figure 19–15

and above the tidal air by the deepest possible inspiration. It is estimated at about 1,800 to 2,000 ml.

Expiratory reserve volume is the amount of air that can be breathed out after a quiet expiration by the most forcible expiration. It is equal to about 1,400 ml.

Residual air is the amount of air remaining in the lungs after the most powerful expiration. This has been estimated to be about 1,200 to 1,500 ml.

Reserve air is the residual air plus the supplemental air in the lungs under conditions of normal breathing, that is, about 3,000 ml.

When the thorax is opened, the lungs collapse, driving out the supplemental and residual air; but before the alveoli are entirely emptied, the small bronchi leading to them collapse and entrap a little air in the alveoli. The small amount of air caught in this way is designated as *minimal air.*

Before birth the lungs contain no air. If, after birth, respirations are made, the lungs do not collapse completely on account of the capture of minimal air. Whether or not the lungs will float has constituted one of the facts used in medicolegal cases to determine if a child was stillborn.

Ventilatory Changes in Air. However dry the external air may be, the expired air is nearly, or quite, saturated with moisture. An average of about 500 ml of water is eliminated daily in the breath. Whatever the temperature of the external air, the expired air is nearly as warm as the blood, having a temperature between 36.7° and 37.8° C (98° and 100° F). In man, breathing is one of the subsidiary means by which the temperature and the water content of the body are regulated. The heat required to warm the expired air and vaporize the moisture is taken from the body and represents a daily loss of heat. It requires about 0.5 Cal to vaporize 1 gm of water.

Taking the respiratory rate as 18 per minute and respiratory depth at 500 cc, one breathes in and out 12,000 liters of air per day. Since inspired air contains about 20 per cent oxygen and expired air about 16 per cent, this difference of 4 per cent represents the oxygen retained by the body—some 480 liters per day—and used by the tissues. This amount is often stated as about 350 cc per minute.

External Respiration. This term is applied to the interchange of gases that takes place in the lungs. There is a continuous flow of blood through the capillaries, so that at least once or twice each minute all the blood in the body passes through the capillaries of the lungs. This means that the time during which any portion of blood is in a position for respiratory exchange is only a second or two. Yet during this time, the following changes take place: the blood loses carbon dioxide and moisture; it gains oxygen, which combines with the reduced hemoglobin of the red cells, or erythrocytes, forming oxyhemoglobin, and as a result of this the crimson color shifts to scarlet; and its temperature is slightly reduced.

It is helpful to compare the average amounts of oxygen and carbon dioxide found in venous and in arterial blood. The actual amounts of oxygen and carbon dioxide in venous blood vary with the metabolic activity of the tissues and differ, therefore, in the various organs according to the state of activity of each organ and the volume of its blood supply per unit of time. The main result of the respiratory exchange is to keep the gas content of the arterial blood nearly constant at the figures given. Under normal conditions it is not possible to increase appreciably the amount of oxygen absorbed by the blood flowing through the lungs.

OXYGEN AND CARBON DIOXIDE VOLUMES PER CENT IN BLOOD

	Arterial Blood		Venous Blood	
Gas	Total	In Solution	Total	In Solution
Oxygen	19–21	0.24	12–14	0.1
Carbon dioxide	48–50	2–2.5	56–58	3.0

From the pulmonary artery blood moves into the lung capillary networks, where the exchange of oxygen and carbon dioxide takes place. This is called *gas exchange* in the lungs. The blood contains a carbon dioxide concentration of about 56 to 58 per cent by volume and an oxygen concentration of about 12 to 14 per cent by volume, with some of each gas in solution. The rates of gaseous exchange are influenced by the following factors: (1) area of contact for the exchange, (2) length of time blood and air are in contact, (3) volume of blood passing through the alveolar network, (4) permeability of cells forming the capillary and alveolar membranes, (5) differences in concentrations of gases in alveolar air and the blood, and (6) rate at which chemical reaction takes place between the gases and the blood. Respiratory efficiency is also related to the number of red cells, hemoglobin content of the red cells, and area of the red cell.

In the alveoli the total area for exchange of gases has been estimated to be 25 to 50 times the total surface area of the body. The respiratory mechanism is delicately balanced, so that alveolar air remains constant at about 14 to 15 per cent by volume of oxygen and 5.5 per cent by volume of carbon dioxide. It is with this air that the blood is in contact for gaseous exchange. Blood in the alveolar capillaries is proportionate to the amount of physical activity. At rest, the amount of blood in alveolar capillaries is about half the amount present during hard work.

Translating the concepts of concentrations of oxygen and carbon dioxide expressed in volumes per cent into terms of partial pressures, they may be stated simply as follows:

Atmospheric pressure at sea level exerts about 1 ton pressure per square foot, usually expressed in millimeters or inches. The total pressure of gases in the atmosphere is 760 mm Hg. Because oxygen forms 20.96 or about 21 per cent by volume of the atmosphere, its partial pressure is 21 per cent of 760, or 160 mm Hg (159.6). Carbon dioxide forms about 0.04 per cent by volume of the atmosphere, and its partial pressure is 0.04 per cent of 760, or 0.30 mm Hg. The other gases exert partial pressures in direct proportion to their volumes. Nitrogen exerts the highest partial pressure since its volume per cent is 79.

The tension of a gas in solution equals the partial pressure of that particular gas in the gas mixture with which the solution has established equilibrium. For example, in atmospheric air the partial pressure and tension of oxygen remain constant at 160 mm Hg and will change only if the relative concentration of oxygen in the total mixture is changed. The absolute amount or quantity of a gas in solution may vary, even if the partial pressure and tension remain constant. In applying the law of partial pressures, if the temperature remains constant the quantity of gas which goes into solution in any given liquid, e.g., plasma, is proportional to the partial pressure of the gas.

The following table illustrates the partial pressure of gas in inspired, expired, and alveolar air.

Analyzing the figures for oxygen in this table, it will be seen that oxygen pressure from

Gas	Inspired Air (mm Hg)	Expired Air (mm Hg)	Alveolar Air (mm Hg)
Oxygen	160	116	103
Carbon dioxide	0.30	28	40
Nitrogen	594.70	569	570
Water vapor	5.00	47	47
	760.00	760	760

inspired air (atmospheric air) to alveolar air falls and for carbon dioxide the decrease in pressure is in the reverse direction. That is, carbon dioxide pressure in the alveolar air is high, and in the inspired or atmospheric air the pressure is low. These inverse relationships between the pressures for oxygen and carbon dioxide in alveolar air promote the interchange of these gases in the lungs. The tensions of oxygen and carbon dioxide in alveolar air vary with depth and frequency of respiration. For example, in voluntary hyperventilation carbon dioxide tension falls and oxygen tension rises. If respiration is suspended for any reason, carbon dioxide tension rises and oxygen tension falls.

Nitrogen is an inert gas in relation to respiration; however, about 0.83 per cent by volume of the gas is dissolved in the plasma. This is neither used nor produced in the body.

Partial pressure or tension of oxygen in blood varies in relation to venous and arterial blood. The tension of oxygen in arterial blood is about 100 mm Hg, and in venous blood, about 36 to 38 mm. The tension of carbon dioxide in arterial blood is about 40 to 45 mm, and in venous blood the tension varies directly in relation to muscular activity, but for mixed venous blood the average tension is about 48 to 50 mm.

In the lung the alveoli are separated from the capillaries by thin membranes which are permeable to the gases. Since the pressure gradient for oxygen in alveolar air is high and in the capillary tension low, there is rapid diffusion of oxygen from the alveolar air to the blood. The reverse is true for carbon dioxide: the pressure gradient is high in blood and low in the alveoli—hence equilibrium is rapidly and progressively established between oxygen and carbon dioxide in the blood and alveolar air as blood moves along in the capillary network.

Loss of carbon dioxide during external respiration is a significant factor in maintaining the normal pH of body fluids, as will become apparent in the discussion of acid-base balance (page 533).

Internal Respiration. The exchange of oxygen and carbon dioxide in the tissues constitutes internal respiration and consists of the passage of oxygen from the blood into the tissue fluid and from the tissue fluid into the tissue cells and the passage of carbon dioxide from the cells into the tissue fluid and from the tissue fluid into the blood.

After the exchange of oxygen and carbon dioxide in the lungs, the aerated blood is returned to the heart and distributed to all parts of the body. As blood moves into the somatic and visceral capillaries, oxygen tension is high and carbon dioxide tension is low in the capillary network, and tension of oxygen in tissue fluid and cells is relatively low. Carbon dioxide tension is relatively high in the tissue fluid and cells and relatively low in the capillary. This means that the pressure gradients of the gases favor exchange between tissue fluid and blood. Changes in the pressure gradients cause a disequilibrium between blood plasma and oxyhemoglobin, favor the chemical changes taking place in blood between oxygen and carbon dioxide, and promote a steady, constant flow of oxygen from the blood to tissue fluid and cells and a constant flow of carbon dioxide from the cells and tissue fluid to blood. Complete removal of oxygen from the blood never occurs.

Carriage of Oxygen and Carbon Dioxide. As shown in Figure 19–16, oxygen reaches the cells in three steps: (1) environment to lungs, (2) lungs to blood, and (3) blood to cells.

As the blood flows through the lung capillaries, oxygen diffuses from the alveoli into the plasma and then into the red blood corpuscles and combines with the hemoglobin to form oxyhemoglobin. On leaving the lungs,

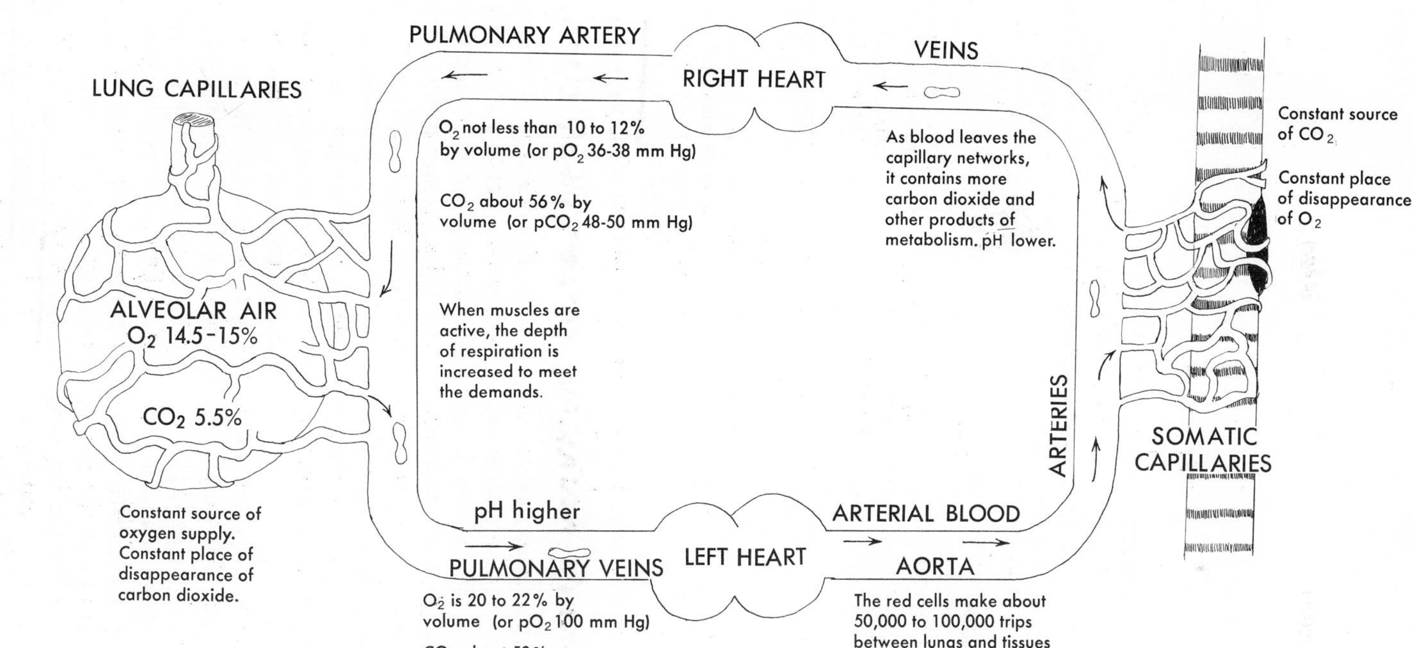

Figure 19–16. Oxygen and carbon dioxide levels in the alveolus and blood as it moves through the circulatory system.

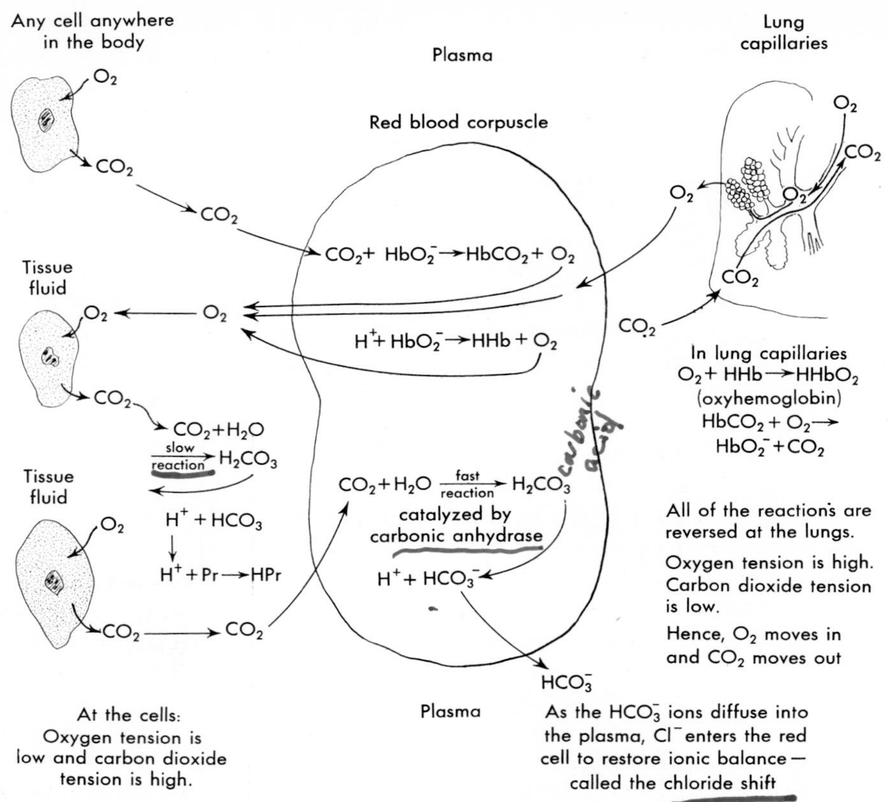

Figure 19–17. Diagram illustrating some of the chemical changes taking place with oxygen and carbon dioxide exchange at the cells and lungs.

practically all the hemoglobin exists as oxyhemoglobin, and the plasma is saturated with oxygen in solution. When the blood reaches the tissue capillaries, there is a continuous diffusion of oxygen from erythrocytes to plasma, plasma to tissue fluid, tissue fluid to cells. The rate of this diffusion of oxygen depends upon the rate of use of oxygen by the cells.

The blood carries *from the lungs* about 20 volumes of oxygen per 100 volumes of blood, more than 19 per cent as oxyhemoglobin (stored as oxyhemoglobin) in the erythrocytes and less than 1 per cent (diffusible) in solution in the water of the blood, hence mainly in plasma. While the blood is flowing through the alveolar capillaries, oxygen diffuses from a place kept relatively high in diffusible oxygen (by breathing) to a place kept relatively low in diffusible oxygen (circulating blood).

The blood leaves in the tissues about 10 volumes of oxygen per 100 volumes of blood. While the blood is flowing through the tissue capillaries, oxygen diffuses from a place kept relatively high in diffusible oxygen (flowing blood) to a place kept relatively low in diffusible oxygen (used in cells).

Carbon dioxide is produced in living cells at varying rates, depending upon activity. Carbon dioxide is believed to enter the blood from the tissue cells by diffusion. Some of it remains in solution in the plasma, but most of it diffuses from plasma into the erythrocytes where the enzyme *carbonic anhydrase* catalyzes the formation of carbonic acid ($H_2O + CO_2 \rightarrow H_2CO_3$). This results in an increase in hydrogen ions and favors the decomposition of oxyhemoglobin ($HHbO_2 \rightarrow HHb + O_2$) and the escape of oxygen to tissue cells. Inasmuch as reduced hemoglobin is a weaker acid than is oxyhemoglobin, this reaction decreases the hydrogen ion concentration within the erythrocyte. A further decrease results from the reaction of carbonic acid with the potassium salts of hemoglobin ($KHb + H_2CO_3 \rightarrow HHb + KHCO_3$). During these reactions the concentration of bicarbonate ions (HCO_3^-) within the red blood cells has increased; consequently these ions diffuse from erythrocytes into the plasma thus building up the sodium bicarbonate concentration in plasma. In compensation for the exit of these anions, chloride ions (Cl^-) diffuse from plasma into the erythrocytes; this adjustment is known as the *chloride shift*. Part of the carbon dioxide which enters the erythrocytes combines directly with hemoglobin to form carbamino hemoglobin; this combination is limited, however, to the availability of free amino groups on the hemoglobin. Thus, various means are provided in erythrocytes and plasma for transportation of a relatively large quantity of carbon dioxide with remarkably little change in the pH of blood. When the blood reaches the lungs, oxygen is available and carbon dioxide can escape. With the entrance of oxygen, the sequence of reactions which took place at the tissue cells is reversed. The *concentration gradients* of the two substances concerned—oxygen and carbon dioxide—are reversed in the blood in the tissue capillaries and in the blood in the alveolar capillaries.

In summary, carbon dioxide is carried in venous blood:

1. As bicarbonate (HCO_3^-), about 90 per cent, one third in the red cell and two thirds in the plasma.
2. As carbamino hemoglobin.
3. As a small percentage dissolved physically in plasma.
4. In other chemical combinations.

Control of Respiration

The respiratory center is located in the medulla oblongata, and this center has connections in the pons. Both centers share in the control of respiration. The medulla is the center for nervous control of depth and frequency of respiration, that is, the quantity of air moved through the lungs during ventilation. In this center are inspiratory and expiratory neurons which are intermixed to a great degree, so that the long-held idea of separate inspiratory and expiratory centers is debatable. There must be inhibition of expiratory neurons when inspiratory neurons discharge, since one cannot inhale and exhale simultaneously. Destruction of the respiratory area in the pons leads to serious interference with the rhythmical discharge of the medullary neurons.

The respiratory center receives impulses from the cerebral cortex (for speaking); from the periphery (for gasping, e.g., when cold water is applied to the skin); and from the vasomotor and cardiac centers. Perhaps the most significant incoming nerve impulses are those from the lung itself. The lung reflex (Hering-Breuer) elicited by inflation of the lung results in deflating the lung, thus helping to maintain rhythmicity of respiration. As the lung is stretched on inspiration, impulses are sent to inhibit the inspiration, thus preventing overstretch. Similarly, with expiration these neurons cease to discharge, permitting inspiration to begin again.

The respiratory center is sensitive to increased acidity, carbon dioxide level, anoxia, and increased temperature of blood, and to increased blood pressure. Of these, carbon dioxide and acidity are the most potent stimuli. Chemoreceptors in the carotid and aortic bodies are stimulated by low pH, high CO_2 level, and anoxia. As arterial pressure rises,

INCREASE IN RESPIRATORY DEPTH AND RATE ON INCREASING CO_2 IN INSPIRED AIR

% CO_2 in Inspired Air	Average Depth of Respiration, cc	Average Respiratory Rate	Minute Lung Volume, liters
Normal (0.04)	673	14	9.4
3.07	1216	15	18.2
5.14	1771	19	33.6

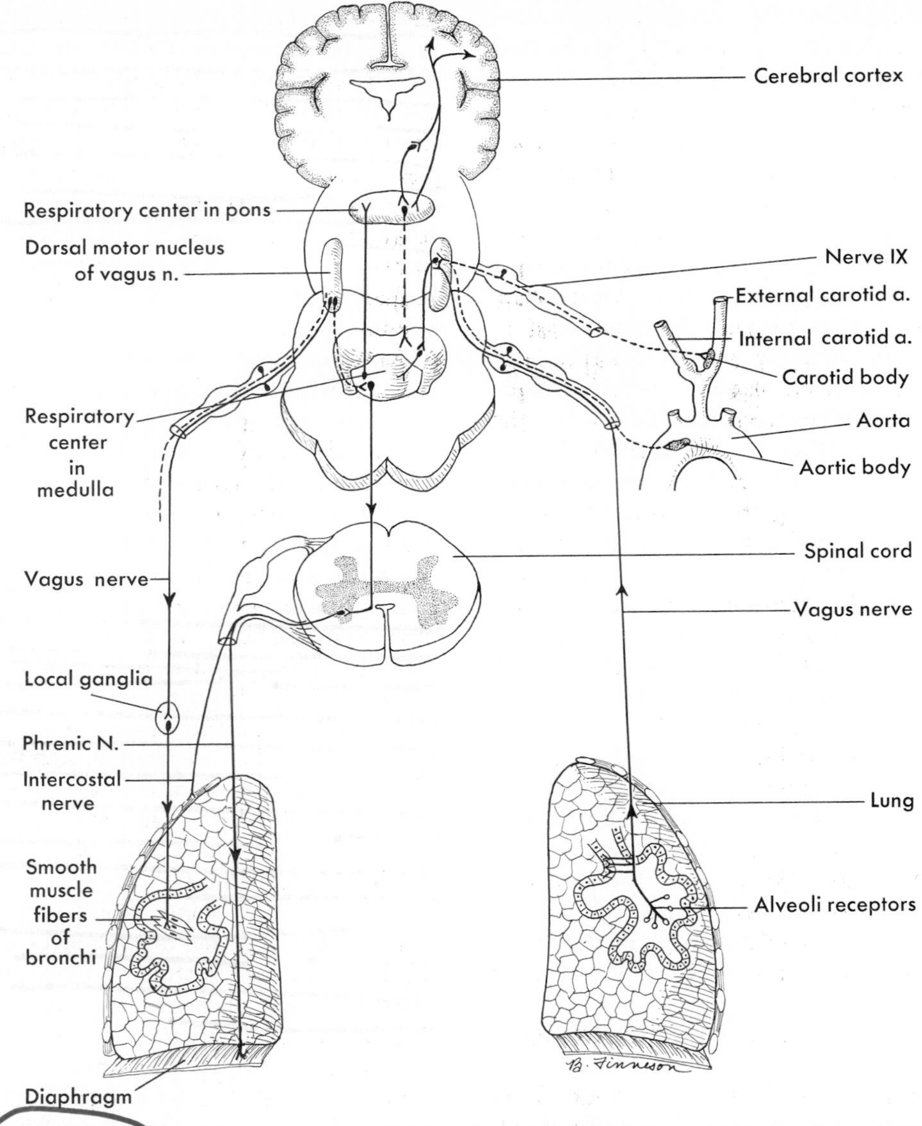

Figure 19–18. Nervous control of respiration, showing connections in the brain. *Arrows* indicate direction of nerve impulses.

receptors in the carotid sinus and aortic arch are stimulated and respiration is inhibited. Stimulation of the chemoreceptors increases the rate and depth of respiration.

From the respiratory center nerve impulses pass via the spinal cord and spinal nerves to the muscles of respiration, and respiration is adjusted to varying body needs. In the table on page 387 it will be noted that the minute ventilation of lungs is multiplied more than three and a half times, mainly by increasing the completeness of contraction of the respiratory muscles rather than by causing them to contract a greater number of times.

Frequency of Respiration. The average rate of respiration for an adult is about 14 to 20 per minute. In health this rate may be increased by muscular exercise or emotion. Anything that affects the heartbeat will have a similar effect on the respirations. Age has a marked influence. The average rate during the first year of life is about 44 per minute, and at the age of five years, 26 per minute. It is reduced between the ages of 15 and 25 to the normal standard. Emotions have a distinct influence on respiratory activity, probably through the hypothalamus and pons.

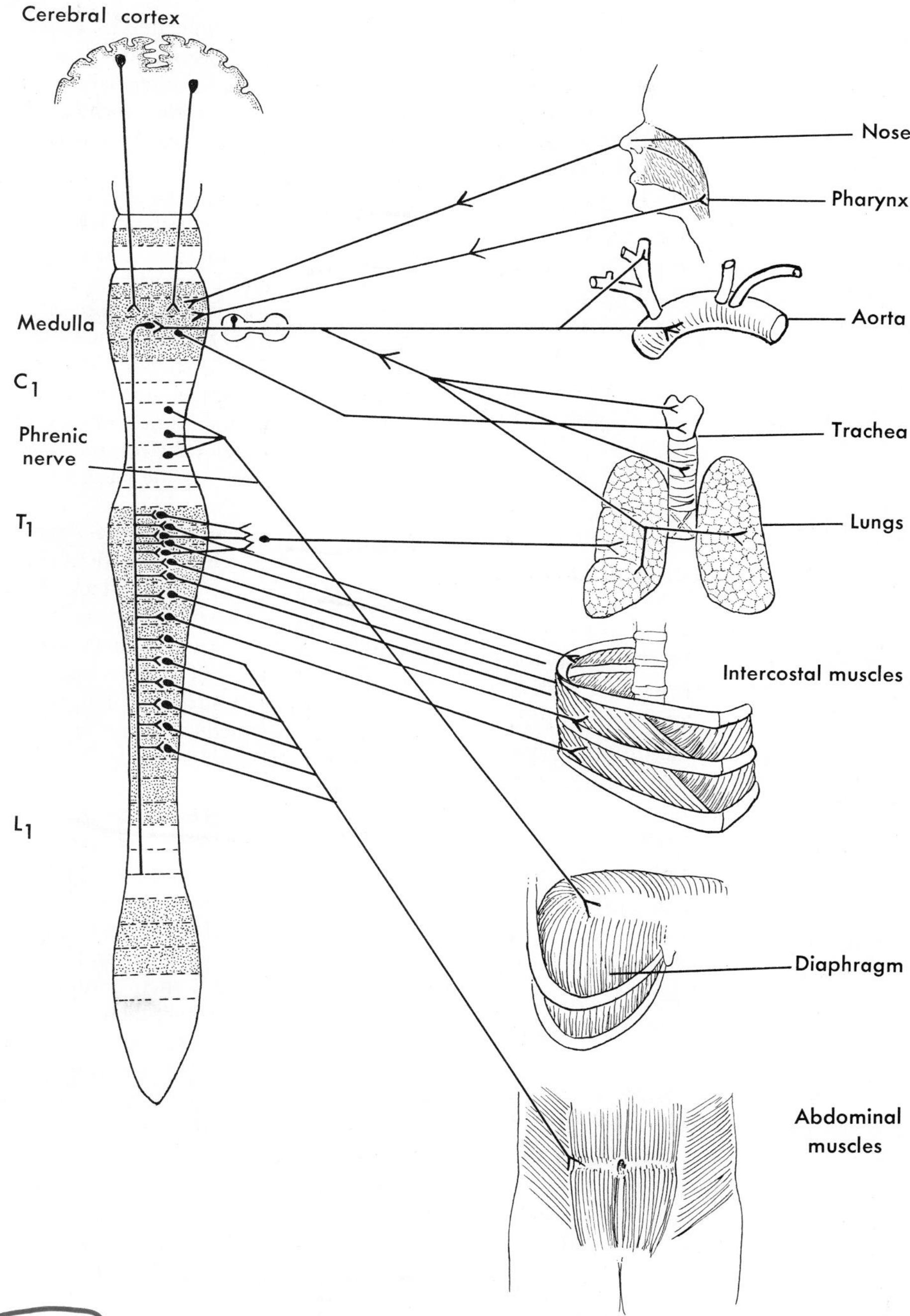

Figure 19–19. Diagram to show nervous control of respiration. (C_1) Spinal cord at first cervical level; (T_1) spinal cord at first thoracic level; (L_1) spinal cord at first lumbar level.

Voluntary Control of Respiratory Rate. It is possible to increase or decrease the respiratory rate within certain limits, by voluntary effort, for a short time. If respirations are arrested or their frequency is diminished, the carbon dioxide concentration in the blood increases, and eventually the stimulus becomes too strong to be controlled. According to some observers, the "breaking point" is reached in 23 to 27 seconds. If, before the breath is held, several breaths of pure oxygen are taken, the breaking point may be postponed; or, if the lungs are thoroughly aerated by forced breathing, so that the carbon dioxide is forced out and more oxygen breathed in, the breaking point may be postponed as long as eight minutes.

Cause of the First Respiration. The human fetus makes respiratory movements while in the uterus, possibly moving amniotic fluid in and out of the lungs. This may play a part in dilation of the future air passages. After birth and the interruption of the placental circulation, the first breath is taken. Three views are held regarding the immediate cause: that it is due to the increased amount of carbon dioxide in the blood, brought about by cutting the umbilical cord; that it is due to stimulation of the sensory nerves of the skin, due to cooler air, handling, drying, etc.; and that it is due to a combination of these causes.

If stimulation through the blood and stimulation through the nerves normally coincide, it may be that the essential cause is the increased tension of the carbon dioxide, and therefore the increased concentration in acidity, following the cutting of the cord.

During intrauterine life, the fetal blood is aerated so well by exchange with the maternal blood that there is not adequate carbon dioxide to act as a stimulus to the fetal respiratory center.

Breath Sounds. Each intake of air is accompanied by a low rustling sound, which can be heard if the ear is applied to the chest wall. It is thought that the dilation of the alveoli produces this sound, and absence of it indicates that the air is not entering the alveoli over which no sound is heard or that the lung is separated from the chest wall by effused fluid. The air passing in and out of the larynx, trachea, and bronchial tubes produces a louder sound, which is called a bronchial murmur. Normally this murmur is heard directly above or behind the tubes; but when the lung is consolidated as in pneumonia, it conducts sound more readily than usual, and the murmur is heard in other parts of the chest. In diseased conditions the normal sounds are modified in various ways and are then spoken of as *rales*.

Eupnea. This term is applied to ordinary quiet respiration made without obvious effort.

Dyspnea. Usually the term *dyspnea* is reserved for painful breathing, in which the expirations are active and forced. Dyspnea may be caused by (1) stimulation of the sensory nerves, particularly the pain nerves, (2) an increase in the hydrogen ion concentration of the blood, and (3) any condition that interferes with the normal rate of the respirations or of the heart action or prevents the passage of air in or out of the lungs.

Hyperpnea. The word *hyperpnea* is applied to an increased rate and/or depth of respirations.

Apnea. The word means a lack of breathing. In physiological literature, it is used to describe the cessation of breathing movements due to lack of stimulation of the respiratory center, brought about by rapid and prolonged ventilation of the lungs. In medical literature, the term is sometimes used as a synonym for asphyxia, or suffocation.

Cheyne-Stokes Respirations. This is a type of respiration which was first described by the two physicians[2] whose names it bears. It is an exaggeration of the type of respiration which is often seen during sleep in normal people. The respirations increase in force and frequency up to a certain point and then gradually decrease until they cease altogether; there is a short period of apnea, then the respirations recommence, and the cycle is repeated. Cheyne-Stokes respirations are associated with conditions that depress the respiratory center, especially in brain, heart, and kidney diseases.

Edematous Respiration. When the air cells become infiltrated with fluid from the blood, the breathing becomes edematous and is recognized by the moist, rattling sounds, or rales,

[2] John Cheyne, Scottish physician (1777–1836). William Stokes, Irish physician (1804–1878).

caused by the passage of the air through the fluid. It is a serious condition because it interferes with aeration of the blood and often results in asphyxia.

Cough. The cough reflex is a critically essential one, for it prevents obstruction of the airway. Foreign material, such as particles or irritating chemicals, stimulate nerve endings and impulses are transmitted to the respiratory center by the vagus nerves. This results in inspiration of a large volume of air; the epiglottis closes tightly; the abdominal muscles and other expiratory muscles contract forcefully. The result is a pressure rise in the lungs of about 100 mm Hg. When the epiglottis opens there is rapid, strong expulsion of air from the lungs, which carries the foreign material outward.

Asphyxia. Asphyxia is produced by any condition that causes prolonged interference with the aeration of the blood, viz., obstruction to the entrance of air to the lungs, depression of the respiratory center, an insufficient supply of oxygen, or a lack of hemoglobin in the blood. The first stages are associated with dyspnea and convulsive movements; then the respirations become slow and shallow and are finally reduced to mere twitches. The skin is cyanosed, the pupils of the eyes dilate, the reflexes are abolished, and respirations cease. If the heart continues to beat, resuscitation is often accomplished by artificial respiration, even after breathing has ceased.

Artificial Respiration. Mouth-to-mouth resuscitation is the most efficient method of ventilating a person who has stopped breathing. This is possible because of the relatively high concentration of oxygen in expired air (see table, page 384). Other methods use manual or machine pressure to alter the size of the thoracic cage.

Hypoxia and Anoxia. Hypoxia is a general term that should be used for oxygen deficiency when arterial oxygen saturation is *not less* than 80 per cent. Anoxia is a marked deficiency or absence of oxygen reaching the tissue cells. It may be due to:

1. Decreased oxygen-carrying capacity of hemoglobin, due to presence of methemoglobin, or carbon monoxide hemoglobin, or low hemoglobin content of blood. This is called *anemic anoxia*.
2. *Anoxic anoxia*—the volume of oxygen in arterial blood is low due to low oxygen tension or inadequate pulmonary ventilation or pulmonary disease.
3. *Stagnant anoxia*—due to disturbances in circulation that slow down circulation in the capillaries, e.g., cardiac disease.
4. *Histotoxic anoxia*—due to interference with cellular respiration, as in cyanide poisoning.

OXYGEN THERAPY

A continuous supply of oxygen is essential for all cells throughout the body. Any shortage of oxygen interferes with production of energy. Hypoxia reduces cell activities and, if severe, endangers the life of cells. The causes of oxygen deficiency are many and varied, but the conditions most frequently requiring oxygen therapy are the acute shortages which result in lowered oxygen tension of blood plasma and a consequent decrease in the rate of oxidation of hemoglobin.

Such conditions may develop during prolonged anesthesia, especially when the respiratory center has been depressed by drugs. With normal lung tissue, such conditions are quickly corrected. The increased need for oxygen is also associated with abnormalities of lung tissue, as in inflammations or destruction of lung tissue from disease. These conditions limit the amount of oxygen crossing the thin membrane which separates the alveoli of the lung from the blood capillaries. Carbon monoxide poisoning interferes with oxygen transportation because hemoglobin combines with carbon monoxide and hence cannot carry oxygen.

The signs of oxygen need are not always clearly defined. Cyanosis may occur. It results from an increase in reduced hemoglobin in the blood and consequently decreased oxyhemoglobin. Various studies indicate that even experienced observers may not detect this sign before the proportion of oxyhemoglobin has dropped from the normal 96 per cent to as low as 85 per cent. A person who is anemic and has a low hemoglobin level will not appear cyanotic although he may lack oxygen. In carbon monoxide poisoning, the skin becomes a cherry red rather than the blue of cyanosis. The earliest symptoms are frequently vague and related to decrease of oxygen to brain cells, which are very sensitive to oxygen shortage.

The purpose of oxygen therapy is to increase the oxygen tension of blood plasma and restore the oxyhemoglobin in the red blood cells to normal proportion, thus supplying oxygen to meet the needs of the tissue cells. This is done by providing oxygen in higher concentration than in air: by enriching the atmosphere in an oxygen tent, by introducing oxygen into the nasopharynx through a nasal tube, or by an oxygen mask. The concentration of oxygen is adjusted by regulating the rate of flow of the gas from a tank where it is stored under pressure. Concentrations of 40 to 60 per cent are usually used although even 100 per cent oxygen can be supplied through the mask technique. Ordinarily the gas is supplied at atmospheric pressure; the increased proportion of oxygen in the mixture increases the tension of oxygen in the alveoli and more oxygen will be absorbed across the alveolar-capillary membrane. Once the hemoglobin has been saturated with oxygen, little or no further advantage is obtained by increasing the oxygen concentration. In carbon monoxide poisoning, increased oxygen concentration in the blood favors release of carbon monoxide from its combination with hemoglobin and the hemoglobin thus released can combine with oxygen. When oxygen therapy is successful, the symptoms associated with hypoxia disappear.

Oxygen leaves the tank as a dry gas, free from water vapor, and as such would be very irritating to the membranes of the trachea, bronchi, and alveoli. Consequently the oxygen must be moistened by bubbling it through water; this is the function of the humidifier. It is also important that the air entering the lungs should be cool and, therefore, the temperature of the tent should be about 20° C (68° F). Increased oxygen concentration in air always increases the danger of fire. The temperature at which burning occurs becomes progressively lower as the oxygen concentration increases. Consequently, it is of utmost importance to safeguard the area where oxygen is in use against possible sources of ignition.

Oxygen Intoxication. Increased oxygen tension in the blood does not significantly increase the amount of oxygen combined with hemoglobin, because the hemoglobin is already saturated; but it does continue to increase the amount of oxygen dissolved in the water of the blood. When this occurs to extreme limits, there is a change in the rates of many chemical reactions within tissue cells (metabolic rates).

The tissue most sensitive is the nervous system. Convulsions may occur or there may be actual brain cell destruction.

In the lungs, since the pulmonary membranes are directly exposed to high oxygen pressure, pulmonary edema may result. Oxygen intoxication will also interfere with the hemoglobin oxygen buffer system.

The alarming incidence of blindness in infants born prematurely has led to a better understanding of the relationship between oxygen and the development of blood vessels of the retina. In the human fetus, these vessels are developing during the fifth, sixth, and seventh months. Hence, they are in a sensitive developmental stage when the baby is born prematurely. Observations indicate that high concentrations of oxygen irritate and destroy the capillary network supplying blood to the retinal cells. The resulting lack of blood supply causes retrolental fibroplasia and blindness. For this reason, oxygen therapy is used very conservatively for the premature infant.

RESPIRATION AND ATMOSPHERIC CHANGES

Low Barometric Pressure. Several changes that take place in the atmosphere as altitude increases affect man's reactions in high-altitude flying or space flight. These may be briefly stated as follows:

Oxygen concentration in air at 40,000 ft is about the same as at sea level, but barometric pressure is lower.

Oxygen begins to decrease at 80,000 ft, and above this height oxygen and nitrogen amounts decrease and the amounts of helium and hydrogen increase. Barometric pressure is also an important factor in high altitudes. At sea level the pressure is 760 mm Hg, while at 18,000 ft pressure is about half, or 380 mm Hg; and as altitude increases, barometric pressure continues to decrease. Another factor is temperature; the higher the altitude the lower the temperature. With every 500 ft of rise in altitude there is about 1° C drop in temperature.

These atmospheric changes affect man considerably as ascent in an airplane is made. Oxygen lack causes anoxia, the barometric pressure changes and extremes of cold also directly affect and modify man's reactions. Above 15,000 ft symptoms of oxygen lack are present. The individual becomes quiet, and the lips, ear lobes, and nail beds become slightly bluish. As a higher altitude is reached the blue color deepens, and weakness and dizziness occur. Since the brain cells are dependent upon oxygen, deprivation causes specific symptoms to become evident. The power of attention is diminished, muscular coordination is lessened, mental confusion is present, and there is interference with perception of objects. Breathing is embarrassed. At still higher altitudes these symptoms become more apparent; the individual may become irritable, the mental confusion increases, and speech is interfered with. Muscular coordination may be so lost that writing is impossible. There is difficulty in understanding written words. There may be drowsiness, headache, apathy, and loss of self-control. Vision and memory are impaired, judgments are unsound, pain sensations are dulled, and appreciation of passage of time is altered. Cyanosis becomes more apparent, dyspnea and vomiting may occur. Each sense is finally lost.

In airplane travel oxygen tension, pressures, and temperature are regulated by artificial means, thus preventing any physiological changes that occur at high altitudes.

High Barometric Pressure. High barometric pressure increases the amount of gases that diffuse from the alveoli into the blood and eventually are dissolved in all body fluids. Increased oxygen absorption will damage tissues. Hemoglobin releases oxygen more rapidly, which results in cellular damage due to deranged cellular metabolism. The brain usually shows early effects which result in twitching, convulsions, and coma. Such an increase in barometric pressure occurs in deep-sea exploration or, less severely, in scuba diving.

Carbon Dioxide. If, for example, a diver's helmet collects high concentrations of carbon dioxide, respiratory acidosis and coma can result.

Nitrogen. It is well known that high concentrations exert an anesthetic effect on the central nervous system. To avoid the problem, nitrogen is frequently replaced with helium, as it does not cause anesthetic effects and also leaves the body fluids rapidly. Nitrogen not only has anesthetic effects, but the gas bubbles in the body fluids when the diver surfaces. This condition is known as decompression sickness, the bends, caisson disease, and diver's paralysis. The most damage is done when bubbles develop in the brain and cord. Serious mental damage or paralysis may occur due to ruptured nerve fibers. Sudden gastrointestinal distention due to gas in the stomach and intestine may also occur. The condition can be prevented by slow ascent or by placing the diver or other worker in a decompression chamber.

QUESTIONS FOR DISCUSSION

1. Discuss the relationship between lung capacity and speech or singing.
2. Discuss Boyle's law and relate it to respiration.
3. Compare the pressure gradients of oxygen and carbon dioxide in the lungs and in the tissues.
4. List and discuss four factors that influence respiratory rate and depth.
5. Discuss the nervous control of respiration.
6. Describe the effects of hyperventilation upon the respiratory center.

SUMMARY

Respiration	All living organisms require continual supply of oxygen Chemical changes in tissue cells dependent upon it Carbon dioxide is one end product of chemical changes in cells, hence need for elimination of excess Exchange of these gases in lungs and cells constitutes respiration
Essentials of Human Respiratory System	1. Air containing a high percentage of oxygen on one side 2. Moist and permeable membrane 3. Moving stream of blood with a high percentage of carbon dioxide on other side

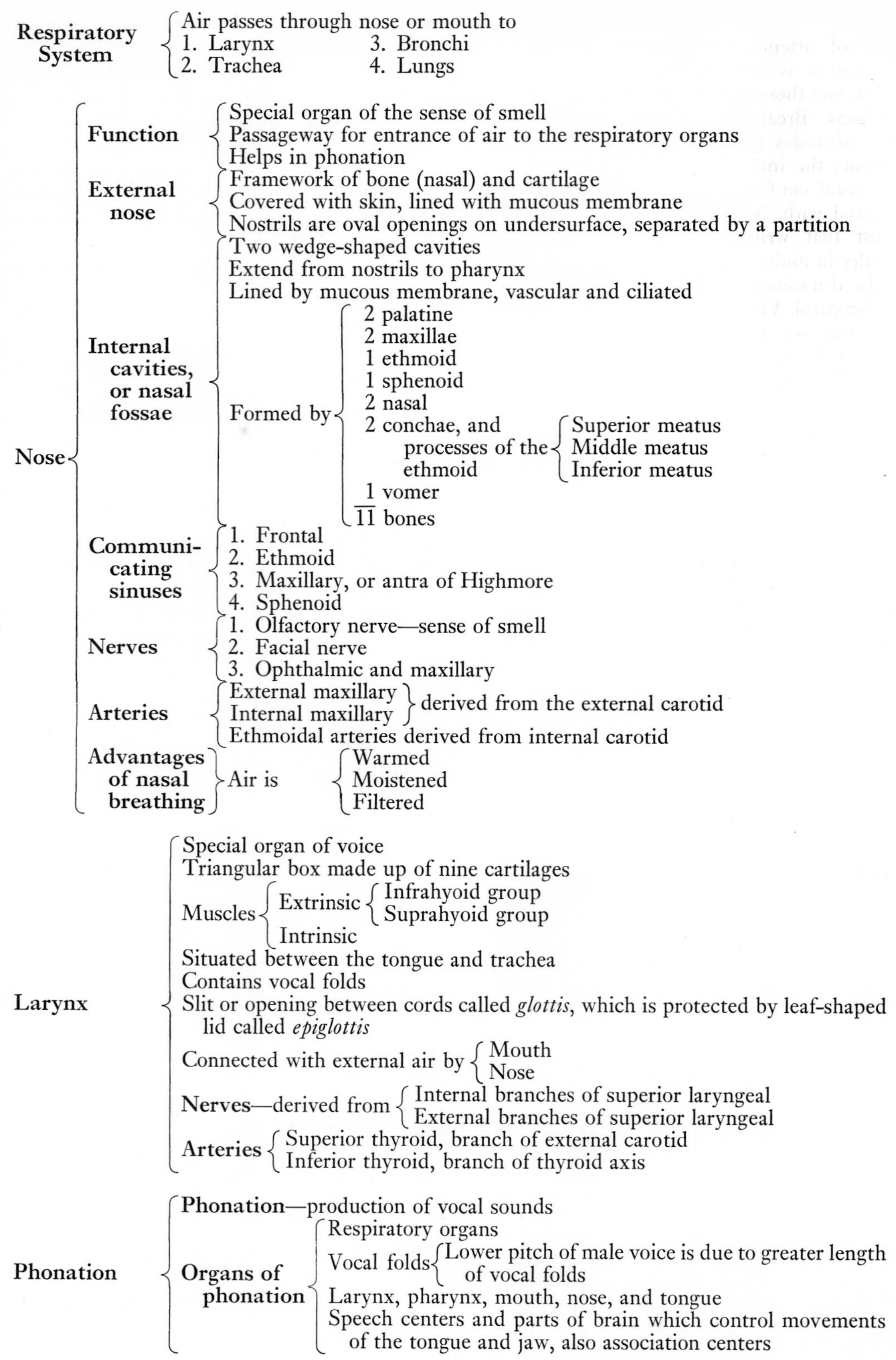

Respiratory System
- Air passes through nose or mouth to
  - 1. Larynx
  - 2. Trachea
  - 3. Bronchi
  - 4. Lungs

Nose
- **Function**
  - Special organ of the sense of smell
  - Passageway for entrance of air to the respiratory organs
  - Helps in phonation
- **External nose**
  - Framework of bone (nasal) and cartilage
  - Covered with skin, lined with mucous membrane
  - Nostrils are oval openings on undersurface, separated by a partition
- **Internal cavities, or nasal fossae**
  - Two wedge-shaped cavities
  - Extend from nostrils to pharynx
  - Lined by mucous membrane, vascular and ciliated
  - Formed by
    - 2 palatine
    - 2 maxillae
    - 1 ethmoid
    - 1 sphenoid
    - 2 nasal
    - 2 conchae, and processes of the ethmoid
      - Superior meatus
      - Middle meatus
      - Inferior meatus
    - 1 vomer
    - 11 bones
- **Communicating sinuses**
  - 1. Frontal
  - 2. Ethmoid
  - 3. Maxillary, or antra of Highmore
  - 4. Sphenoid
- **Nerves**
  - 1. Olfactory nerve—sense of smell
  - 2. Facial nerve
  - 3. Ophthalmic and maxillary
- **Arteries**
  - External maxillary, Internal maxillary } derived from the external carotid
  - Ethmoidal arteries derived from internal carotid
- **Advantages of nasal breathing**
  - Air is
    - Warmed
    - Moistened
    - Filtered

Larynx
- Special organ of voice
- Triangular box made up of nine cartilages
- Muscles
  - Extrinsic
    - Infrahyoid group
    - Suprahyoid group
  - Intrinsic
- Situated between the tongue and trachea
- Contains vocal folds
- Slit or opening between cords called *glottis*, which is protected by leaf-shaped lid called *epiglottis*
- Connected with external air by
  - Mouth
  - Nose
- **Nerves**—derived from
  - Internal branches of superior laryngeal
  - External branches of superior laryngeal
- **Arteries**
  - Superior thyroid, branch of external carotid
  - Inferior thyroid, branch of thyroid axis

Phonation
- **Phonation**—production of vocal sounds
- **Organs of phonation**
  - Respiratory organs
  - Vocal folds
    - Lower pitch of male voice is due to greater length of vocal folds
  - Larynx, pharynx, mouth, nose, and tongue
  - Speech centers and parts of brain which control movements of the tongue and jaw, also association centers

Trachea
- Membranous and cartilaginous tube, 11.2 cm ($4\frac{1}{2}$ in.) long
- Strengthened by C-shaped rings of cartilage
  - Complete in front
  - Incomplete behind
- In front of esophagus—extends from larynx to upper border of fifth thoracic vertebra, where it divides into two bronchi
- **Nerves**
  - Branches of vagus
  - Recurrent nerves
  - Autonomics
- **Arteries**—Inferior thyroid

Bronchi and Bronchioles
- Right and left—structure similar to trachea
- Right—shorter, wider, more vertical than left
- Divide into innumerable bronchial tubes, or bronchioles
- As tubes divide, their walls become thinner. Finer tubes consist of thin layer of muscular and elastic tissue lined by ciliated epithelium
- Each bronchiole terminates in elongated saccule called *atrium*
- Each atrium terminates in small projections known as *alveoli*, or air cells

Lungs
- **Location**—lateral chambers of thoracic cavity, separated by structures contained in mediastinum
- **Cone-shaped organs**
  - Outer surface convex to fit in concave cavity
  - Base concave to fit over convex diaphragm
  - Apex about 2.5 to 4 cm (1 to $1\frac{1}{2}$ in.) above the level of sternal end of first rib
  - Hilum, or depression on inner surface, gives passage to bronchi, blood vessels, lymphatics, and nerves
- **Right**—larger, broader, shorter—three lobes
- **Left**—smaller, narrower, longer—two lobes
- **Anatomy**
  - Porous, spongy organs. Consist of bronchial tubes, atria, alveoli, also blood vessels, lymphatics, and nerves held together by connective tissues
- **Blood vessels**
  - **Pulmonary artery**
    - Blood for aeration
    - Accompanies bronchial tubes
    - Plexus of capillaries around alveoli
    - Returned by pulmonary veins
  - **Bronchial arteries**—supply lung substance

Pleura
- **Closed sac**—envelops lungs, but they are not in it
- **Two layers**
  - Pulmonary, or visceral—next to lung
  - Parietal—outside of visceral
  - (Both:) Normally in close contact—potential cavity; Moistened by serum
- **Function**—to lessen friction

Mediastinum
- Space between pleural sacs. Extends from sternum to spinal column. Contains the heart, large blood vessels connected with heart, trachea, esophagus, thoracic duct, various veins, lymph nodes, and nerves

Respiration
- **Function**
  - Increase the amount of oxygen
  - Decrease the amount of carbon dioxide
  - Help to maintain temperature
  - Help to eliminate water
- **Processes**
  - **Breathing**
    - **Inspiration**—process of taking air into lungs
    - **Expiration**—process of expelling air from lungs
    - **Normal rate**—16–18/minute
  - **External respiration**
    - External oxygen supply
    - External carbon dioxide elimination
    - Takes place in the lungs
  - **Internal respiration**
    - Internal oxygen supply
    - Internal carbon dioxide elimination
    - Takes place in the cells

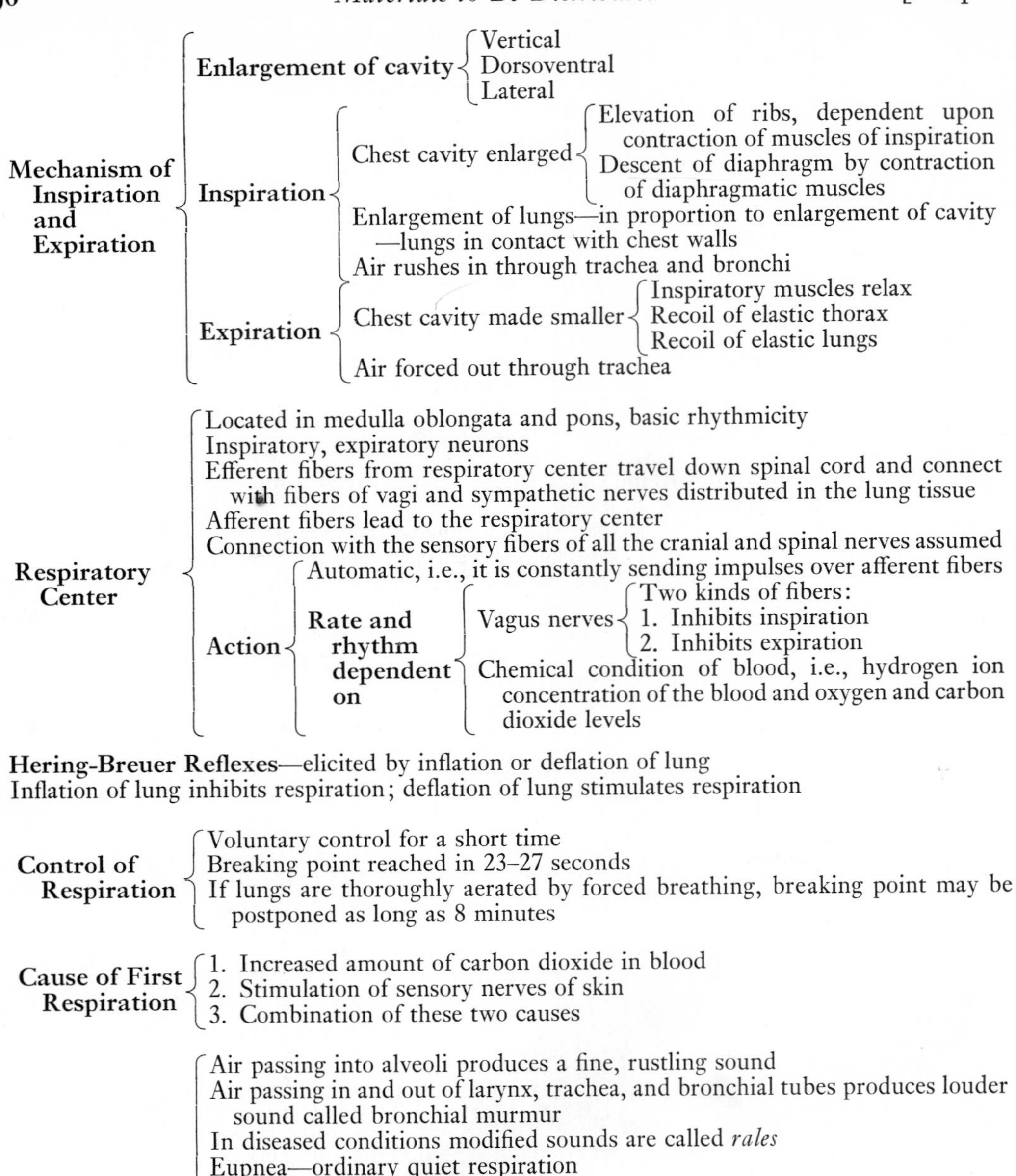

Mechanism of Inspiration and Expiration
- **Enlargement of cavity**
  - Vertical
  - Dorsoventral
  - Lateral
- **Inspiration**
  - Chest cavity enlarged
    - Elevation of ribs, dependent upon contraction of muscles of inspiration
    - Descent of diaphragm by contraction of diaphragmatic muscles
  - Enlargement of lungs—in proportion to enlargement of cavity—lungs in contact with chest walls
  - Air rushes in through trachea and bronchi
- **Expiration**
  - Chest cavity made smaller
    - Inspiratory muscles relax
    - Recoil of elastic thorax
    - Recoil of elastic lungs
  - Air forced out through trachea

Respiratory Center
- Located in medulla oblongata and pons, basic rhythmicity
- Inspiratory, expiratory neurons
- Efferent fibers from respiratory center travel down spinal cord and connect with fibers of vagi and sympathetic nerves distributed in the lung tissue
- Afferent fibers lead to the respiratory center
- Connection with the sensory fibers of all the cranial and spinal nerves assumed
- **Action**
  - Automatic, i.e., it is constantly sending impulses over afferent fibers
  - **Rate and rhythm dependent on**
    - Vagus nerves
      - Two kinds of fibers:
      - 1. Inhibits inspiration
      - 2. Inhibits expiration
    - Chemical condition of blood, i.e., hydrogen ion concentration of the blood and oxygen and carbon dioxide levels

Hering-Breuer Reflexes—elicited by inflation or deflation of lung
Inflation of lung inhibits respiration; deflation of lung stimulates respiration

Control of Respiration
- Voluntary control for a short time
- Breaking point reached in 23–27 seconds
- If lungs are thoroughly aerated by forced breathing, breaking point may be postponed as long as 8 minutes

Cause of First Respiration
1. Increased amount of carbon dioxide in blood
2. Stimulation of sensory nerves of skin
3. Combination of these two causes

Respiratory Phenomena
- Air passing into alveoli produces a fine, rustling sound
- Air passing in and out of larynx, trachea, and bronchial tubes produces louder sound called bronchial murmur
- In diseased conditions modified sounds are called *rales*
- Eupnea—ordinary quiet respiration
- Dyspnea—difficult breathing
- Hyperpnea—excessive breathing
- Apnea—lack of breathing
- Cheyne-Stokes
  - Respirations increase in force and frequency, then gradually decrease and stop. Cycle repeated
- Edematous—air cells filled with fluid, hence moist, rattling sounds
- Asphyxia—oxygen starvation
- Artificial respiration—mouth-to-mouth most efficient
- Cough reflex—protective

Capacity of Lungs
- Exchange dependent on diffusion of gases
- After lungs are once filled, they are never emptied during life
- Vital capacity—quantity of air person can expel by forcible expiration after deepest inspiration possible—averages from 3,500–4,100 ml

Capacity of Lungs (*cont.*)
- **Terms in use**
  - Tidal
  - Inspiratory reserve (complemental)
  - Expiratory reserve (supplemental)
  - Residual
  - Reserve
  - Minimal

Factors Influencing Respiration
- 1. Pressures
  - Intra-alveolar pressure
  - Intrapleural pressure
- 2. Gas laws
  - Boyle's law
    - On inspiration the diaphragm descends, thoracic cavity enlarges, pressure in pleural space decreases. Air rushes into the expanded lung
  - Charles's law
    - As air enters the bronchial tree, it is warmed by the mucous membrane and gases expand slightly
- Rates of gas exchange influenced by
  - Area of contact for exchange
  - Time blood and air are in contact
  - Volume of blood passing through alveolar network
  - Permeability of cells
  - Differences in concentrations (tensions) of gases
  - Rate of chemical reactions
- Tensions
  - Oxygen tension high in blood, low in cells
  - Carbon dioxide tension high in cells, low in tissue fluid and blood

External Respiration
- Takes place in lungs
- Blood
  - Loses about 6% of carbon dioxide
  - Gains about 8% of oxygen
    - Oxyhemoglobin
    - Scarlet color
  - Temperature is slightly reduced

Inspired and Expired Air
- **Changes effected**
  1. Moisture increased. Expired air is saturated with moisture
  2. Temperature increased. Expired air is as warm as blood
  3. Heat to warm air and vaporize moisture taken from body
  4. Oxygen decreased by 4.94%
  5. Carbon dioxide increased by 4.34%

Internal Respiration
- Consists of
  - Exchange of gases in the tissues
  - Passage of oxygen from blood into tissue fluid and from tissue fluid into cells
  - Passage of carbon dioxide from tissue cells into tissue fluid and from tissue fluid into blood
- Important to remember blood does not give up all its oxygen to the tissues or all of its carbon dioxide in the lungs

Oxygen Therapy
- Hypoxia—oxygen lack, not lower than 80%
- Anoxia—oxygen deficiency or absence
- Cyanosis—bluish color due to oxygen need
- General purpose—to increase oxygen tension in blood plasma

Oxygen Intoxication
- Nervous tissue most sensitive
- Pulmonary edema may occur
- High oxygen concentration irritates and destroys capillary networks in the retina of premature infants

Oxygen Lack
- Causes tissue anoxia
- Disturbances of perception
- Diminished power of attention
- Individual becomes irritable
- Mental confusion
- Speech disturbed

High Barometric Pressure	Increases the amount of gases that diffuse from alveoli into the blood Oxygen released rapidly Deranged cellular metabolism
Low Barometric Pressure	Decreases oxygen available for diffusion Many physiological abnormalities

CHAPTER

20

THE DIGESTIVE SYSTEM

Divisions

Structure

Nerve and Blood Supply

ACCESSORY ORGANS OF DIGESTION

PORTAL CIRCULATION

Within the digestive tract is carried on the necessary transformation of ingested complex food substances into the simpler substances which may pass into the blood stream and be distributed to the cells of the body.

The means by which foods are transformed into simple substances are both physical and chemical and constitute the digestive processes; the organs which take part in them form the digestive system.

Processes concerned with such changes can be classified into two groups:

1. Those concerned with the breakdown of food to particles small enough to pass through the wall of the alimentary tract into the body fluids.

Physical comminution brought about by mastication and by various types of muscular activity are described on pages 445 and 446. A subsequent chemical comminution changes large molecules to molecules sufficiently small to pass into the blood. Normal motility of the alimentary tract and proper neuromuscular functioning, by which it is carried on, are essential to health.

2. Those concerned with moving foods along through the alimentary tract with optimum speed. This means slowly enough for all the necessary changes in each organ to be accomplished in preparation for those in the next organ and yet fast enough so that proper absorption shall take place and bacterial decomposition or deleterious changes shall not occur.

The parts of the digestive system are the *alimentary canal*, and the *accessory organs*: tongue, teeth, salivary glands, pancreas, and liver.

The Alimentary Canal. The alimentary canal is a continuous tube and as measured on the cadaver is about 9 m (30 ft) long; it extends from the mouth to the anus. *In the living subject the length of the alimentary canal is much shorter, owing probably to shortening of its longitudinal coats.* The greater part is coiled up in the cavity of the abdomen.

The Peritoneum. The peritoneum, the largest serous membrane in the body, in the male consists of a closed sac (in the female the uterine tubes open into the peritoneal cavity); the *parietal* layer lines the walls of the abdominal cavity, and the *visceral* layer is reflected over the abdominal organs and the upper surface of some of the pelvic organs. The space between the layers, the peritoneal cavity, is under normal conditions a potential cavity only, since the parietal and visceral layers are in lubricated contact. The arrangement of the peritoneum is very complex, for

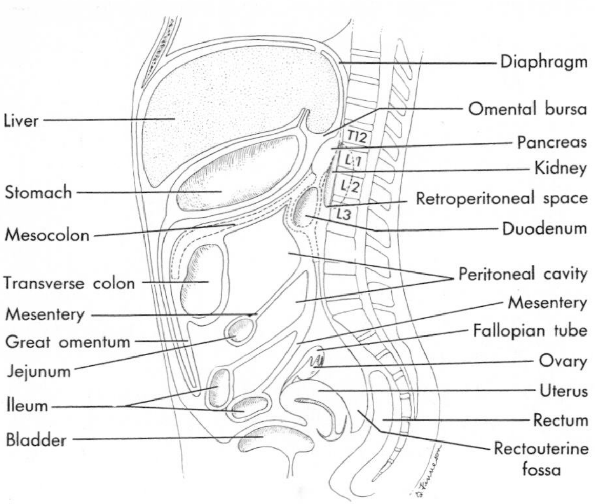

Figure 20–1. Diagram of the side view of the body, showing abdominal cavity, peritoneum, mesentery, and omentum. The *continuous lines* indicate the free surfaces of the peritoneum; the *dotted lines* indicate those parts of the peritoneum in which the free surfaces have disappeared.

elongated sacs and double folds extend from it, to pass in between and either wholly or partially surround the viscera of the abdomen and pelvis. One important fold is the *greater omentum*, which hangs in front of the stomach and the intestines; another is the *mesentery*, which is a continuation of serous coat and attaches the small and much of the large intestine to the posterior abdominal wall. The peritoneum serves to prevent friction between contiguous organs by secreting a serous fluid, which acts as a lubricant. It aids in holding the abdominal and pelvic organs in position. The omentum usually contains fat, sometimes in considerable amounts.

When the abdominal cavity is opened, the intestines appear to lie loosely coiled within it. If a coil is lifted, a clear, glistening sheet of tissue is found attached to it. This is the mesentery, the dorsal portion of which is gathered into folds which are attached to the dorsal abdominal wall along a short line of insertion, giving the mesentery the appearance of a ruffle or flounce. The mesentery supports the blood vessels and lymph vessels supplying the intestine.

The Omentum. The lesser and greater omentum are peritoneal sheets which attach the stomach to the *body wall.* The *lesser* omentum extends from the lesser curvature of the stomach and upper duodenum to the liver. It is continuous with both layers of the peritoneum. The *greater* omentum consists of a thin double layer of peritoneum folded on itself so that four layers are formed, two anterior and two posterior layers, separated by the potential cavity of the omental bursa or lesser peritoneal sac (Figure 20–1). The greater omentum lies between the greater curvature of the stomach and the spleen. From the stomach body wall it hangs as a fat-laden apron down and in front of the small intestine.

There are numerous lymph nodes in the omentum and other parts of the abdominal cavity, and many lymphatic vessels lead from the abdominal cavity into the blood stream, so there is great rapidity with which fluids can leave the cavity. The nodes aid in protecting the peritoneal cavity against infections. (See Figure 18–2, page 356.)

Divisions of the Alimentary Canal

Mouth cavity, containing tongue, orifices of ducts of salivary glands, and teeth
Pharynx
Esophagus
Stomach

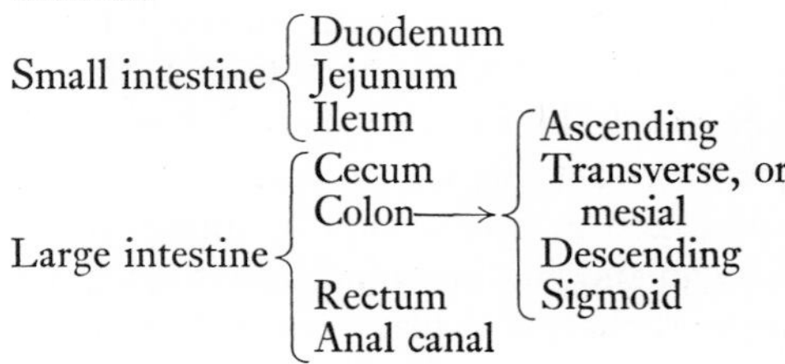

MOUTH CAVITY, PHARYNX, ESOPHAGUS

The Mouth, Oral or Buccal Cavity. This is a cavity bounded laterally and in front by the cheeks and lips; behind, it communicates with the pharynx. The roof is formed by the hard and soft palate, and the greater part of the floor is formed by the tongue and sublingual region and lower jaw. The space bounded externally by the lips and cheeks and internally by the gums and teeth is called the *vestibule.* The cavity behind this is the *mouth cavity proper. The lips*, two musculomembranous folds, surround the orifice of the mouth and are important in speech.

The palate consists of a hard portion in front, formed by processes of the maxillae and palatine bones, which are covered by mucous membrane. Suspended from the posterior border is the soft palate, a movable fold of mucous membrane, enclosing muscle fibers, blood vessels, nerves, adenoid tissue, and mucous glands. Hanging from the middle of its lower border is a conical process called the palatine *uvula.*

The fauces is the name given to the aperture leading from the mouth into the pharynx, or throat cavity. At the base of the uvula on either side is a curved fold of muscular tissue covered by mucous membrane, which shortly after leaving the uvula divides into two pillars; one runs downward, lateralward, and forward to the side of the base of the tongue; the other, downward, lateralward, and backward to the side of the pharynx. These arches are known respectively as the *glossopalatine arch* (anterior pillars of the fauces) and the *pharyngopalatine arch* (posterior pillars of the fauces).

The palatine tonsils are two masses of lymphoid tissue situated, one on either side, in the triangular space between the glossopalatine and the pharyngopalatine arches. The surface of the tonsils is marked by openings called crypts, which communicate with channels that course through the substance of the tissue. They are supplied with blood from the lingual and internal maxillary arteries, which are derived from the external carotid arteries, and receive nerve fibers from both divisions of the autonomic nervous system. Situated below the tongue are masses of lymphoid tissue called the *lingual tonsils*; however, the term *tonsil* as commonly used refers to the palatine tonsils.

The function of the tonsils is similar to that of other lymph nodes. They aid in the formation of white blood cells and help to protect

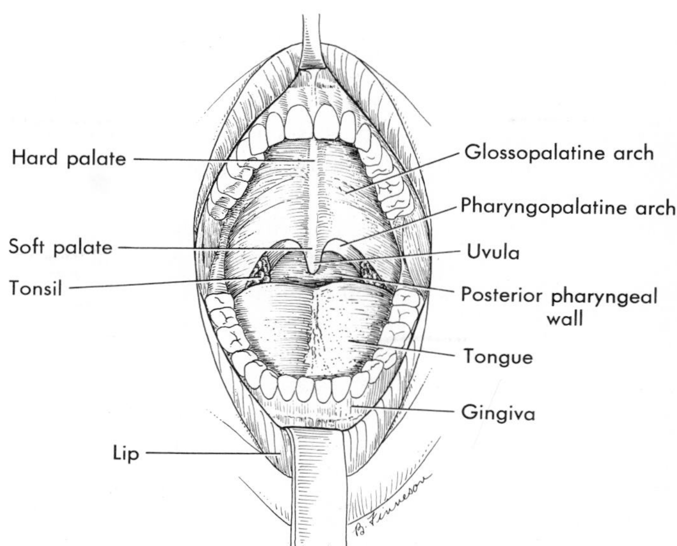

Figure 20–2. Mouth and pharynx viewed from the front.

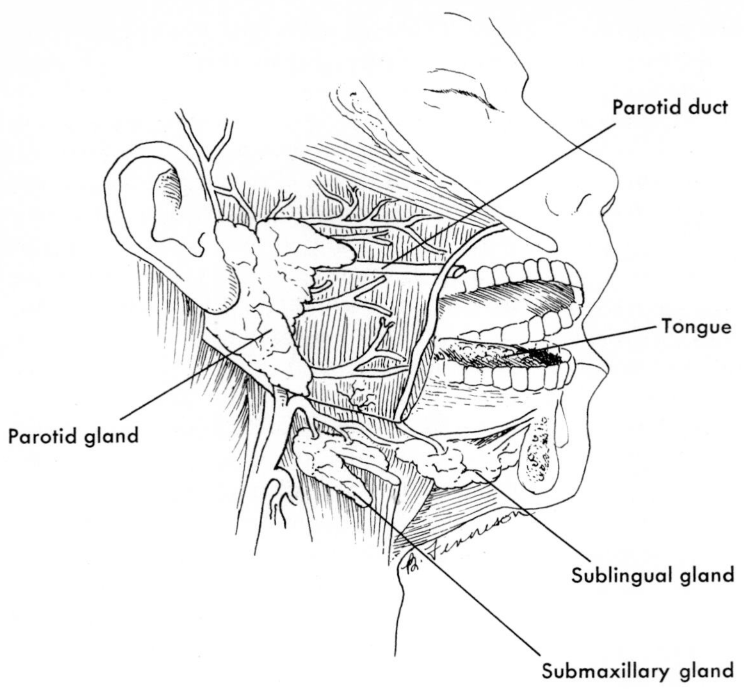

Figure 20–3. The salivary glands and their ducts. These glands manufacture about 1500 ml of saliva in 24 hours.

the body from infection by acting as filters and preventing the entrance of micro-organisms. If they are abnormal, their protective function is reduced, and they may serve as foci of infection, which passes directly into the lymph and so into the blood. Inflammation of the palatine tonsils is called tonsillitis.

The palate, uvula, palatine arches, and tonsils are plainly seen if the mouth is widely opened and the tongue depressed.

The Tongue. The tongue is the special organ of the sense of taste. It assists in mastication, deglutition, and digestion by movements which help to move the food and keep it between the teeth; the glands of the tongue secrete mucus, which lubricates the food and makes swallowing easier; and stimulation of the end organs (taste buds) of the nerves of the sense of taste increases the secretion of saliva and starts the first flow of gastric juices. The sense of taste is mediated over the sensory fibers of cranial nerve VII (anterior two thirds of the tongue) and cranial nerve IX (posterior third of the tongue). Probably more than half of the so-called tastes are due to stimulation of olfactory receptors rather than taste receptors. The tongue is essential for speech.

papilke

The Salivary Glands. The mucous membrane lining the mouth contains many minute glands called *buccal glands*, which pass their secretion into the mouth. The chief secretion, however, is supplied by three pairs of compound saccular glands, the salivary glands, named parotid, submaxillary, and sublingual glands. Each *parotid gland* is placed just under and in front of the ear; its duct, the parotid (Stensen's[1]), opens upon the inner surface of the cheek opposite the second molar of the upper jaw. The *submaxillary* (submandibular) and *sublingual* glands lie below the jaw and under the tongue, the submaxillary being placed farther back than the sublingual. One duct (Wharton's[2]) from each submaxillary (submandibular) and a number of small ducts from each sublingual open in the floor of the mouth beneath the

[1] Nicolaus Stensen, Danish anatomist (1638–1686).

[2] Thomas Wharton, English anatomist (1610–1673).

tongue. The secretion of the salivary glands, mixed with that of the small glands of the mouth, the buccal secretion, is called *saliva*.

Nerves and Blood Vessels. The facial (VII) and glossopharyngeal (IX) nerves supply these glands. The fibers are both secretory and vasomotor and are derived from the craniosacral and thoracolumbar systems. Blood is supplied to the salivary glands by branches of the external carotid artery and is returned, after traveling through many branch arteries and capillaries, via the jugular veins.

The Teeth (Dentes). The alveolar processes of the maxillae and mandible contain *alveoli*, or sockets, for the teeth. Dense connective tissue covered by smooth mucous membrane—the gums, or gingivae—covers these processes and extends a little way into each socket. The sockets are lined with periosteum, which connects with the gums and serves to attach the teeth to their sockets and as a source of nourishment.

Each tooth consists of three portions: the *root*, consisting of one to three fangs contained in the socket; the *crown*, which projects beyond the level of the gums; and the *neck*, or constricted portion between the root and the crown.

Each tooth is composed principally of ivory, or *dentin*, which gives it shape and encloses a cavity, the pulp cavity. The dentin of the crown is capped by a dense layer of

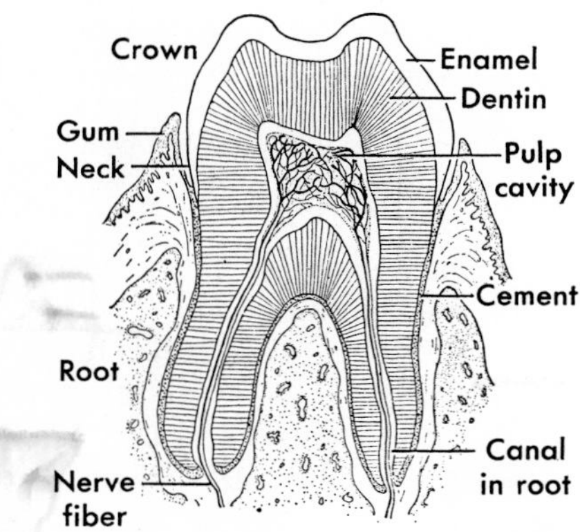

Figure 20–4. Section of human molar tooth. In the pulp cavity are located blood vessels and nerves.

enamel. The dentin of the root is covered by *cement*. These three substances—enamel, dentin, and cement—are all harder than bone, enamel being the hardest substance found in the body. They are developed from epithelial tissue. The pulp cavity is just under the crown and is continuous with a canal that traverses the center of each root and opens by a small aperture at its extremity. It is filled with dental pulp, which consists of connective tissue holding a number of blood vessels and nerves, which enter by means of the canal from the root.

There are two sets of teeth developed during life: the first, deciduous, or milk, teeth; and the second, permanent.

Deciduous Teeth. In the first set are 20 teeth, 10 in each jaw: 4 incisors, 2 canines, and 4 molars. The cutting of these teeth usually begins at six months and ends at about the age of two years. In nearly all cases the teeth of the lower jaw appear before the corresponding ones of the upper jaw.

Deciduous Teeth

	Molars	Canine	Incisors	Canine	Molars
Upper	2	1	4	1	2
Lower	2	1	4	1	2

The deciduous teeth are usually cut in the following order:

Lower central incisors	6–9 months
Upper incisors	8–10 months
Lower lateral incisors and first molars	15–21 months
Canines	16–20 months
Second molars	20–24 months

Another way of expressing the number of teeth is referred to as the "dentition formula." In such cases the formula is written as:

$$\frac{2:1:4:1:2}{2:1:4:1:2}$$

Permanent Teeth. During childhood the temporary teeth are replaced by the permanent. In the second set are 32 permanent teeth, 16 in each jaw. The first molar usually appears between five and seven years of age.

PERMANENT TEETH

	Molars	Premolars	Canine	Incisors	Canine	Premolars	Molars
Upper	3	2	1	4	1	2	3
Lower	3	2	1	4	1	2	3

The permanent teeth appear at about the following periods:

First molars	6 years
Two central incisors	7 years
Two lateral incisors	8 years
First premolars	9 years
Second premolars	10 years
Canine	11–12 years
Second molars	12–13 years
Third molars	17–25 years

The "dentition formula" for permanent teeth would be:

$$\frac{3:2:1:4:1:2:3}{3:2:1:4:1:2:3}$$

According to their shape and use the teeth are divided into incisors, canines, premolars, or bicuspids, and molars. *Incisors*, eight in number, form the four front teeth of each jaw. They have a sharp cutting edge and are especially adapted for biting food. *Canines* are four in number, two in each jaw. They have sharp, pointed edges, are longer than the incisors, and serve the same purpose in biting and tearing. *Premolars*, or *bicuspids*, are eight in number in the permanent set (none in the temporary set). There are four in each jaw, two placed just behind each of the canine teeth. They are broad, with two points or cusps on each crown, and have only one root, which is more or less completely divided into two. Their function is to grind food. *Molars* are 12 in number in the permanent set (eight in the deciduous set). They have broad crowns with small, pointed projections, which make them well fitted for crushing food. Each upper molar has three roots, and each lower molar has two roots, which are grooved and indicate a tendency to division. The 12 molars do not all replace temporary teeth but are gradually added with the growth of the jaws. The hindmost molars are the last teeth to be added. They may not appear until 25 years of age, hence are called *late teeth* or "wisdom teeth."

Long before the teeth appear through the gums their formation and growth are in progress. The deciduous set begins to develop about the sixth week of intrauterine life; and the permanent set, with the exception of the second and third molars, begins to develop about the sixteenth week. About the third month after birth the second molars begin to grow, and about the third year, the third molars, or wisdom teeth, do likewise. Diseases such as rickets retard the eruption of the temporary teeth, and severe illness during childhood may interfere with the normal development of the permanent teeth so that they are marked with notches and ridges. Moreover cavities form in them readily. The diet of the mother during pregnancy and the diet of the child during the first years of life are important factors in determining the quality of the teeth and the development of caries. More recently the addition of fluorine salts to drinking water has been shown to retard caries formation.

The principal functions of the teeth are *biting* with the incisors and *chewing* or *mastication* with the molars. A third function, *grasping* and *tearing* the food with the canines, is frequently employed by children. Mastication of the more solid foods is good for the teeth because they are made to sink and rise in their sockets with a massaging effect upon the gums, which tends to promote circulation in the pulp.

The Pharynx, or Throat Cavity. The pharynx is a musculomembranous tube shaped somewhat like a cone, with its broad end turned upward and its constricted end downward to end in the esophagus. It may be divided from above downward into three parts, nasal, oral, and laryngeal. The upper, or *nasopharynx*, lies behind the posterior nares and above the soft palate, The middle, or *oral*, part of the pharynx reaches from the soft palate to the level of the hyoid bone. The *laryngeal* part reaches from the hyoid bone to the esophagus. The pharynx communicates with the nose, ears, mouth, and larynx by seven apertures: two in front above, leading into the back of the nose, the *posterior nares*; two on the lateral walls of the nasopharynx, leading into the auditory tubes, which communicate with the ears; one midway in front, the *fauces* connecting with the mouth in front; two below—one, the well-defined glottis, opening into the larynx, and the other, the poorly defined, opening into the esophagus.

The mucous membrane lining the pharynx is continuous with that lining the nasal cavities, the mouth, the auditory tubes, and the larynx. It is well supplied with mucous glands. The walls of the pharynx are provided with sensory receptors, which are sensitive to mechanical stimulation and are important in the mechanisms of swallowing. When food or liquid stimulates these touch receptors, the complicated reflex of swallowing is initiated. If these sensory areas are anesthetized, as by swabbing the throat, swallowing becomes difficult. About the center of the posterior wall of the nasopharynx is a mass of lymphoid tissue, the pharyngeal tonsil. When abnormally large it is called *adenoids*.

Usually lymphoid tissue is larger in children than in adults and tends to become smaller with age. Owing to their position, adenoids may become infected or enlarged, block the auditory tubes, and interfere with the passage of air through the nose, as well as impair the hearing.

Nerves and Blood Vessels. Both divisions of the autonomic system supply nerve fibers to the pharynx. There are both sensory and motor fibers within the glossopharyngeal and vagus nerves. Blood is supplied by branches from the external carotid artery.

Functions. The pharynx transmits the air from the nose or mouth to the larynx and serves as a resonating cavity in the production of the voice. It also serves as a channel to transmit food from the mouth to the esophagus. Closure of the mouth and nasopharynx during deglutition, or swallowing, effectively shuts off the pharynx from the outside atmosphere. Contraction of pharyngeal muscles, combined with the thrust caused by other contracting muscles, pushes the food downward and onward into the esophagus.

The Esophagus. The esophagus is a muscular tube, about 23 to 25 cm long and 25 to 30 mm wide, which begins at the lower end of the pharynx, behind the trachea. It descends in the mediastinum in front of the vertebral column, passes through the diaphragm at the level of the tenth thoracic vertebra, and terminates in the upper, or cardiac, end of the stomach, about the level of the xiphoid process.

Structure. The walls of the esophagus are composed of four coats: (1) an external, or fibrous, (2) a muscular, (3) a submucous, or areolar, and (4) an internal, or mucous, coat. The muscular coat consists of an external longitudinal and an internal circular layer. The muscles in the upper part of the esophagus are striated. These are gradually replaced by nonstriated muscle tissues. The lower third of the esophagus is completely nonstriated tissue. Contractions of the layers produce peristaltic waves which propel food to the stomach. The areolar coat serves to connect the muscular and mucous coats and to carry the larger blood and lymph vessels. The mucous membrane is arranged in longitudinal folds which disappear when the esophagus is distended by the passage of food. It is studded with minute papillae and small glands, which secrete mucus to lubricate the canal.

Nerves and Blood Vessels. The nerve fibers from the vagus and the thoracolumbar nervous system form a plexus between the layers of the muscular coat and another in the submucous coat. Blood is supplied to the esophagus by arteries from the inferior thyroid branch of the thyrocervical trunk, which arises from the subclavian; from the thoracic aorta; from the left gastric branch of the celiac artery; and from the left inferior phrenic of the abdominal aorta. Blood is returned via the azygos, thyroid, and left gastric veins of the stomach.

Functions. The esophagus receives food from the pharynx and by a series of peristaltic contractions passes it on to the stomach. Muscle at the lower end of the esophagus acts as a sphincter, preventing reflux of material from the stomach during gastric peristalsis.

THE STOMACH

In the abdominal cavity the esophagus ends in the stomach (gaster), which is a collapsible, saclike dilatation of the alimentary canal serving as a temporary receptacle for food. It lies obliquely in the epigastric, umbilical, and left hypochondriac regions of the abdomen, directly under the diaphragm. The shape and position of the stomach are modified by changes within itself and in the surrounding organs. These modifications are determined by the amount of the stomach contents, the stage of digestion which has been reached, the degree of development and power of the muscular walls, and the condition of the adjacent intestines. It is never entirely empty, but always contains a little gastric fluid and mucin. When the stomach is contracted, its shape as seen from the front is comparable to that of a sickle. At an early stage of gastric digestion, the stomach usually consists of two segments, a large globular portion on the left and a narrow tubular portion on the right. When distended with food, it has the shape shown in Figure 20–6. The stomach presents two openings and two borders, or curvatures, the concave, or *lesser*, and the convex, or *greater* curvatures.

Component Parts. The *cardia* is the portion surrounding the esophageal opening. The upward turn of the stomach forms a J position. The *fundus* is the rounded end of the stomach, above the entrance of the esophagus. The opposite, or smaller, end is the *pyloric portion*. The central portion, between the fundus and the pyloric portion, is called the *body*, or corpus. The part of the stomach adjacent to the pyloric portion is the *antrum*. There are great differences in the posi-

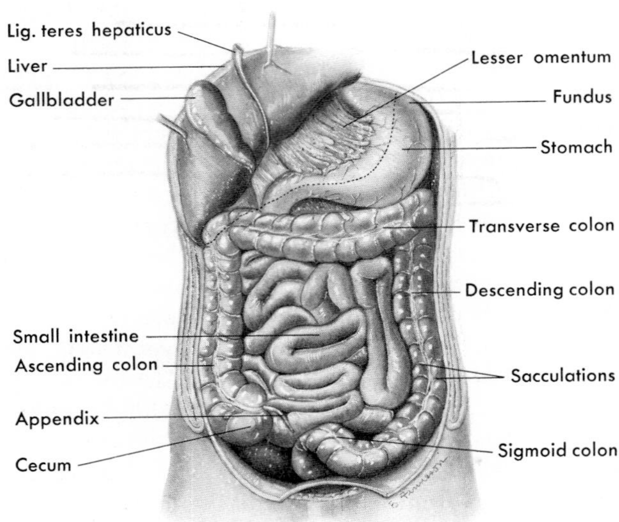

Figure 20–5. The stomach and intestines, front view, the great omentum having been removed and the liver turned up and to the right. The *dotted line* shows the normal position of the anterior border of the liver.

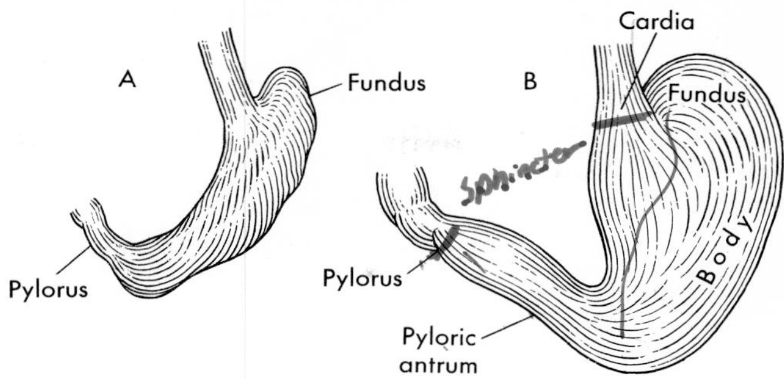

Figure 20–6. Form and outline of the stomach at different stages of digestion when seen from the front. (*A*) Contracted. (*B*) Early stage of digestion.

tion of the stomach. Much depends upon body stature, position, respiratory movement, and content of the stomach.

Openings. The opening by which the esophagus communicates with the stomach is known as the *cardiac*, or esophageal, orifice; the orifice which communicates with the duodenum is known as the *pyloric*. The pyloric aperture is guarded by a ringlike muscle, or sphincteric mechanism, which when contracted keeps the orifice closed. Although a distinct muscle is absent from the cardiac aperture, it is kept closed by the manner in which the muscles are arranged and the diaphragm is attached. Research shows that the pyloric antrum, pyloric sphincteric mechanism, and duodenal bulb function as a unit. The circular fibers of the pyloric sphincter serve to guard against backflow of intestinal contents into the stomach: normally the pyloric sphincter does *not* regulate stomach emptying. The movement of stomach contents into the small intestine is dependent upon the maintenance of a relatively small pressure gradient from the antrum to the pylorus. The food is kept in the stomach until such a pressure gradient is present. The relaxation of this aperture is related to the regular peristaltic waves moving over the stomach on to the duodenum.

Structure. The wall of the stomach consists of four coats: serous, muscular, submucous (or areolar), and mucous.

1. *The serous coat* is part of the peritoneum and covers the organ. At the lesser curvature the two layers come together and are continued upward to the liver as the *lesser omentum.* At the greater curvature the two layers are continued downward as the apronlike *greater omentum,* which is suspended in front of the intestines.

2. *The muscular coat* of the stomach is beneath the serous coat and closely connected with it. It consists of three layers of unstriated muscular tissue: an outer, longitudinal layer; a middle, or circular layer; and an inner, less well-developed, oblique layer limited chiefly to the cardiac end of the stomach. This arrangement facilitates the muscular actions of the stomach by which it presses upon food and moves it back and forth.

3. *The submucous coat* consists of loose areolar connective tissue connecting the muscular and mucous coats.

4. *The mucous coat* is thick, the thickness being mainly due to the fact that it is densely packed with small glands embedded in areolar connective tissue. It is covered with columnar epithelium and in its undistended condition is thrown into folds, or *rugae*. The surface is honeycombed by tiny, shallow pits, into which the ducts or mouths of the glands open. Figure 20–7 and its legend describe the coats and the tissues which compose them.

The Gastric Glands. There are three varieties: cardiac, fundic, and pyloric.

Cardiac glands occur close to the cardiac orifice. They are of two kinds—simple tubular glands with short ducts, and compound racemose glands. *Fundic glands* are simple tubular glands which are found in the body and fundus of the stomach. These glands are lined with epithelial cells, of which there are two varieties. (1) Cells lining the lumen of the tube are called chief cells and secrete pepsinogen. (2) Parietal cells are

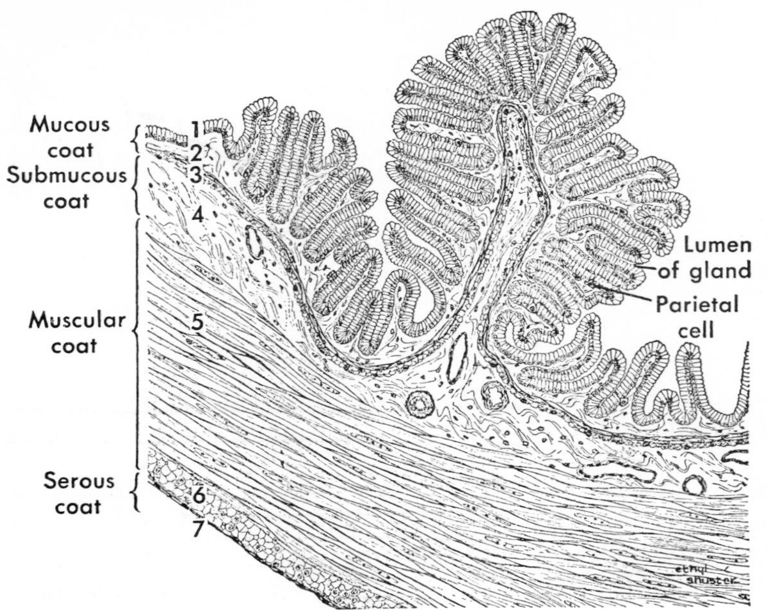

Figure 20–7. Wall of stomach in cross section, highly magnified to show coats. One ruga covered with glands is shown. Parietal cells are shown communicating with the lumen of the glands by clefts between the chief cells which line the lumen. (*1*) Columnar epithelium, (*2*) areolar connective tissues, (*3*) muscularis mucosae, (*4*) areolar connective tissue, (*5*) circular layer of smooth muscle, (*6*) longitudinal layer of smooth muscle, (*7*) areolar connective tissue and mesothelium.

found behind the chief cells. These cells secrete hydrochloric acid into the lumen of the tube through minute ducts. Pepsinogen, in the presence of acid, is converted into pepsin. *Pyloric glands* are branched tubular glands found most plentifully about the pylorus. They secrete pepsinogen and mucin, but not acid.

Nerves and Blood Vessels. The stomach is supplied with thoracolumbar nerve fibers from the celiac plexus. Terminal branches of the right vagus are distributed to the

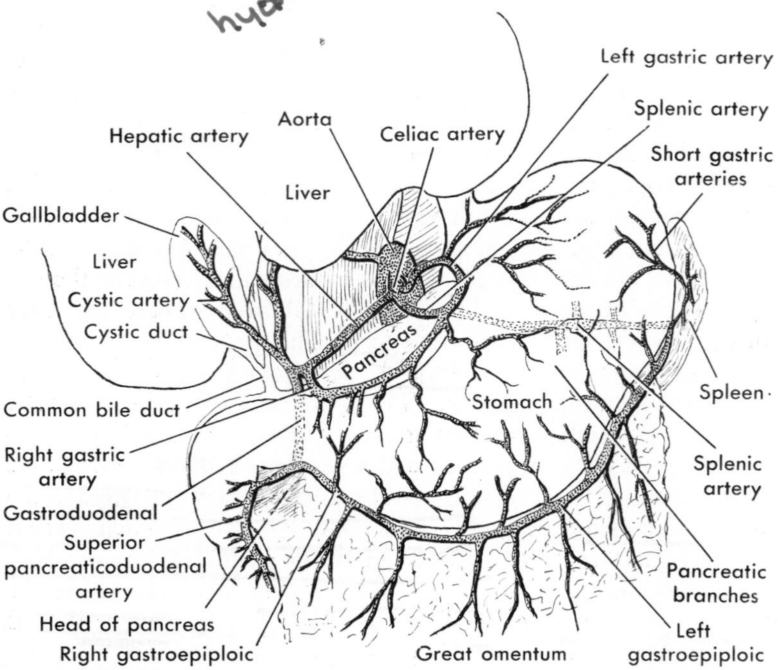

Figure 20–8. The celiac artery and its branches.

posterior part of the organ; branches from the left vagus are distributed to the anterior part. Stimulation of the vagus fibers increases secretion and peristalsis. Stimulation of the thoracolumbar autonomic fibers has just the opposite effect, i.e., inhibits secretion and peristalsis. The blood vessels are derived from the celiac artery. The left gastric artery courses along the lesser curvature of the stomach from left to right, distributing branches to both surfaces. It anastomoses with the esophageal arteries at one end of its course and with the right gastric artery at the other. The right gastroepiploic artery courses from right to left along the greater curvature of the stomach and anastomoses with a branch of the splenic artery, the left gastroepiploic, which courses along the greater curvature from left to right. Blood is returned via the right gastroepiploic, which joins the superior mesenteric, the left gastroepiploic, and several short gastric veins which join the splenic and the left gastric. All of these eventually join the portal vein. A small quantity of blood is returned to the azygos and hemorrhoidal veins instead of entering the portal vessel. (See Figures 20–8 and 20–20, page 420.)

Physiology. Probably the most important function of the stomach is to store food. Without a food reservoir it would be necessary to eat small amounts at frequent intervals. The digestive functions consist of chemical changes of the proteins of food under the action of the enzyme *pepsin* in an acid medium, and of maceration of the food bolus by the mechanics of contractions of the stomach musculature. The mucosa of the fundus of the stomach elaborates a substance called the *intrinsic factor*, which is essential for absorption of vitamin B_{12}. (See page 442.)

THE SMALL INTESTINE

The small intestine extends from the pylorus to the colic valve. It is a folded tube, which in the cadaver is about 7 m (23 ft) in length, and is contained in the central and lower part of the abdominal cavity.

At the beginning the diameter is about 3.8 cm but it gradually diminishes and is hardly 2.5 cm at the lower end. For descriptive purposes the small intestine is divided into three portions: the duodenum, jejunum,

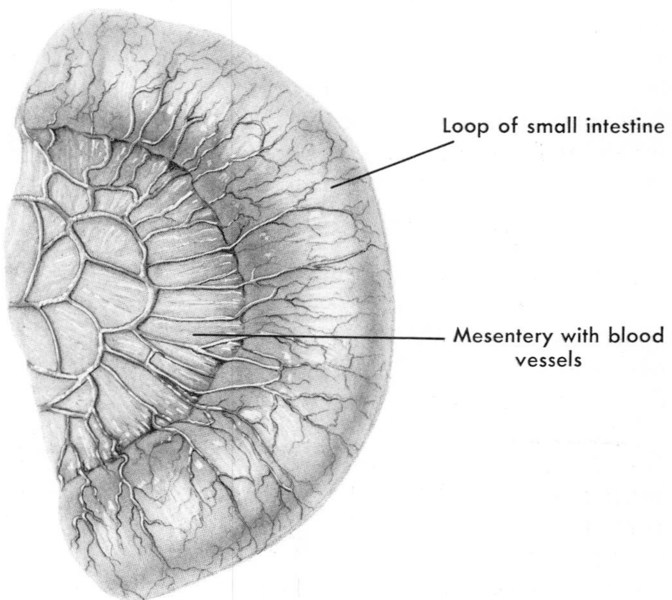

Figure 20–9. Section of small intestine showing mesentery, small intestine, and blood supply.

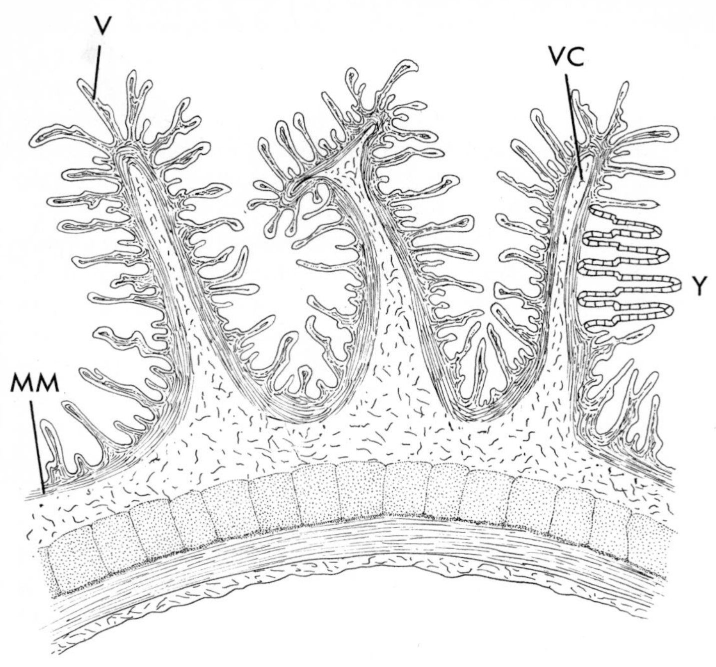

Figure 20–10. Longitudinal section of small intestine. Three valvulae conniventes (*VC*) are shown. Many villi (*V*) are shown on the valvulae and between them. At *Y* four villi with glands between them have been diagrammed. (*MM*) Muscularis mucosae.

and ileum are continuous and show only slight variations.

The Duodenum. The duodenum is 25 cm long and is the shortest and broadest part of the small intestine. It extends from the pyloric end of the stomach to the jejunum. Beginning at the pylorus, the duodenum at first passes upward, backward, and to the right, beneath the liver. It then makes a sharp bend and passes downward in front of the right kidney; it makes a second bend, toward the left, and passes horizontally across the front of the vertebral column. On the left side, it ascends for about 2.5 cm and then ends in the jejunum opposite the second lumbar vertebra.

A musculofibrous band from tissue around the celiac artery and nearby diaphragm attaches to the junction of the duodenum and jejunum, acting as a suspensory ligament (ligament of Treitz[3]).

The Jejunum. This constitutes about two fifths of the remainder, or 2.2 m, of the small intestine and extends from the duodenum to the ileum.

[3] Wenzel Treitz, Austrian anatomist (1819–1872).

The Ileum. This constitutes the remainder of the small intestine and extends from the jejunum to the large intestine, which it joins at a right angle. There is no definite point at which the jejunum ceases and the ileum begins, although the mucous membranes of the two divisions differ somewhat.

The Coats of the Small Intestine. These are four in number and correspond in character and arrangement to those of the stomach. (1) The *serous* coat furnished by the peritoneum forms an almost complete covering for the whole tube except for part of the duodenum. (2) The *muscular* coat of the small intestine has two layers: an outer, thinner layer with longitudinally arranged fibers and an inner, thicker layer with circularly arranged fibers. This arrangement aids the peristaltic action of the intestine. (3) The *submucous*, or loose connective-tissue, coat connects the muscular and mucous coats. (4) The mucosa is thick, glandular, and very vascular.

Circular Folds. About 3 or 4 cm beyond the pylorus the mucous and submucous coats of the small intestine are arranged in circular folds (valvulae conniventes, or plicae circulares) which project into the lumen of the tube (Figure 20–10). Some of these folds extend all the way around the circumference of the intestine; others extend part of the way. Unlike the rugae of the stomach, the circular folds do not disappear when the intestine is distended. About the middle of the jejunum they begin to decrease in size, and in the lower part of the ileum they almost entirely disappear. The major function of these folds is to present a greater surface area for secretion of digestive juices and absorption of digested food.

Villi. Throughout the whole length of the small intestine the mucous membrane presents a velvety appearance due to minute, fingerlike projections called *villi*, which number between 4,000,000 and 5,000,000 in man. Each villus consists of a central lymph channel called a *lacteal*, surrounded by a network of blood capillaries held together by lymphoid tissue. This in turn is surrounded by a layer of columnar cells. After the food has been digested, it passes into the capillaries and lacteals of the villi. Owing to the large number of villi and the presence of microvilli on the absorbing surface of the columnar cells, the surface area of the small intestine is estimated to be about 10 sq m.

Glands and Nodes of the Small Intestine. In addition to these projections, the mucous membrane is thickly studded with secretory glands and nodes. These are known as:

Intestinal glands or crypts of Lieberkühn[4]
Duodenal or Brunner's[5] glands
Lymph nodules—(1) solitary lymph nodules, (2) aggregated lymph nodules

Intestinal glands are found over every part of the surface of the small intestine. They are simple tubular depressions in the mucous membrane, lined with columnar epithelium and opening upon the surface by circular apertures.

Brunner's glands are located chiefly in the submucosa, and pass their secretions by long ducts to the intestinal surface. These glands secrete mucus whereas the cells of other glands in the duodenum secrete an alkaline fluid, mucus, and enzymes. Brunner's glands react

[4] Johann Nathanael Lieberkühn, German anatomist (1711–1756).

[5] Johann Conrad Brunner, Swiss anatomist (1653–1727).

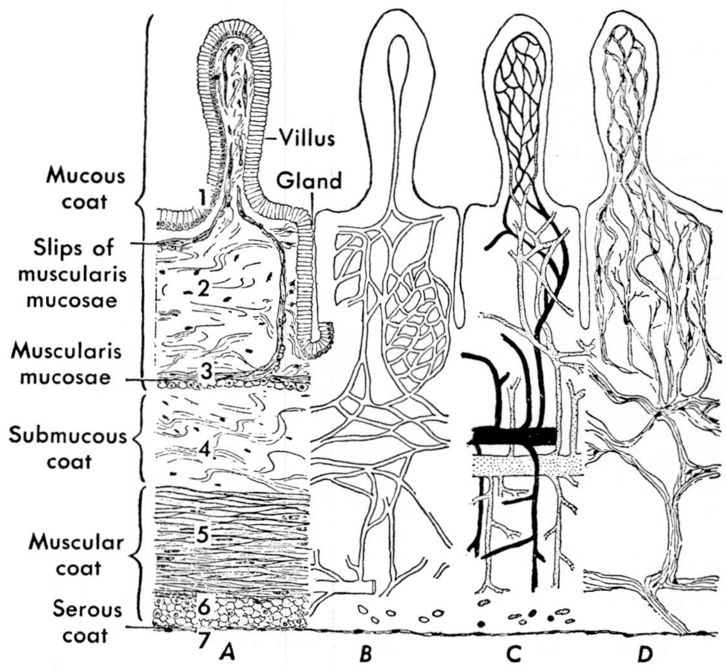

Figure 20–11. Diagram of a cross section of small intestine. *A* shows coats of intestinal wall and tissues of coats, (*1*) columnar epithelium, (*2*) areolar connective tissue, (*3*) muscularis mucosae, (*4*) areolar connective tissue, (*5*) circular layer of smooth muscle, (*6*) longitudinal layer of smooth muscle, (*7*) areolar connective tissue and endothelium. *B* shows arrangement of central lacteal, lymph nodes, and lymph tubes. *C* shows blood supply; arteries and capillaries *black*, veins *stippled*. *D* shows nerve fibers, the submucous plexus lying in the submucosa, the myenteric plexus lying between the circular and longitudinal layers of the muscular coat. (*A* and *C* drawn from microscopic slide of injected specimen; *B* and *D* adapted after Mall.)

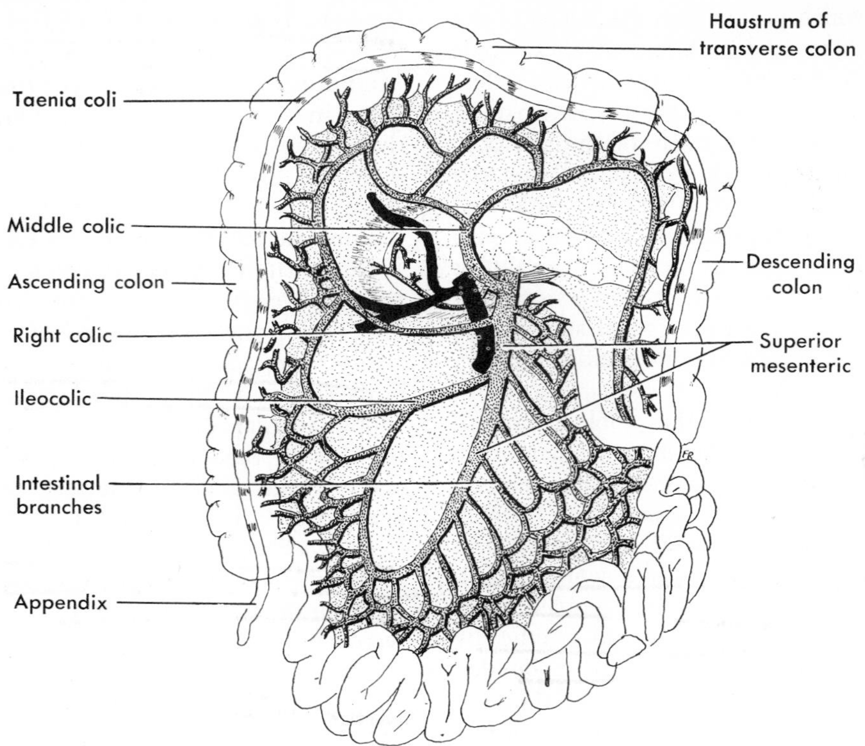

Figure 20–12. Superior mesenteric artery and its branches.

strongly to sympathetic inhibition, which may be a factor in ulcer formation owing to the lack of mucus to protect the mucosa from acid.

Collectively the intestinal secretions are called *succus entericus.*

Lymph Nodules. Closely connected with the lymphatic vessels in the walls of the intestine are small, rounded bodies of the size of a pinhead, called *solitary lymph nodules.* They are most numerous in the lower part of the ileum and consist of a rounded mass of fine lymphoid tissue, the meshes of which are crowded with leukocytes. Into this mass of tissue one or more small arteries enter and form a capillary network, from which the blood is carried away by one or more small veins. Surrounding the mass are lymph channels which are continuous with the lymphatic vessels in the tissue below.

Aggregated Lymph Nodules. These are collections of lymph nodules, commonly called Peyer's[6] patches. These patches are circular or oval, from 10 to 30 in number, and vary in length from about 2.5 to 10 cm. They are largest and most numerous in the ileum. In the lower part of the jejunum they are small and few in number. They are occasionally seen in the duodenum. Peyer's patches may be the seat of local inflammation and ulceration in typhoid fever and intestinal infections, particularly tuberculosis of the intestine.

Figure 20–11 describes the coats of the small intestine and the tissues which compose them and the relationship of blood vessels, lymph vessels, and nerve fibers.

Nerves and Blood Vessels. The vagus nerves supply secretory and motor fibers to the small intestine. Thoracolumbar nerve fibers are derived from the plexuses around the superior mesenteric artery. From this

[6] Johann Conrad Peyer, Swiss anatomist (1653–1712).

source they run to the myenteric plexus (Auerbach's plexus) of nerves and ganglia situated between the circular and longitudinal muscular fibers. Branches from this plexus are distributed to the muscular coats; and from these branches another plexus, the submucous (Meissner's) plexus, is derived (Figure 13–6, page 266). It sends fibers to the mucous membrane. The sensory fibers in the vagus nerve are concerned with intestinal reflexes, and the sensory fibers of the thoracolumbar nerves carry pain sensations. Thus, the pain from an ulcer in the duodenum is reduced after cutting of the thoracolumbar fibers, even though the ulcer is still active.

Blood Supply. The superior mesenteric artery arising from the aorta, just below the celiac artery, supplies all of the small intestine except the duodenum, which is supplied by the gastroduodenal artery and its branch, the superior pancreaticoduodenal. These vessels distribute branches, which lie between the serous and muscular coats and form frequent anastomoses. Blood is returned by the superior mesenteric vein, which unites with the splenic to form the portal tube.

Physiology. It is in the small intestine that the greatest amount of digestion and absorption takes place. It receives bile and pancreatic juice from the liver and the pancreas. The glands of the small intestine secrete succus entericus. The intestinal mucosa, containing glands and covered with villi, is arranged in folds, so that the surface areas for action of digestive juice and absorption are greatly increased. Some of the cells of the mucous membrane (particularly in the duodenum) secrete *secretin*. Secretin is carried by the blood to the liver and pancreas, stimulating them to secretory activity.

THE LARGE INTESTINE

The large, or thick, intestine is about 1.5 m (5 ft) long but is wider than the small intestine, being about 6.3 cm at the cecum. It extends from the ileum to the anus. It is divided into four parts: the cecum with the vermiform appendix, colon, rectum, and anal canal.

The Cecum. The small intestine opens into the side wall of the large intestine about 6 cm above the commencement of the large intestine. This 6 cm of large intestine forms a blind pouch called the cecum. The opening from the ileum into the large intestine is provided with two large projecting lips of mucous membrane forming the colic, or ileocecal, valve, which allows the passage of material into the large intestine but prevents the passage of material in the opposite direction.

The Vermiform Appendix. This is a narrow tube attached to the end of the cecum. The length, diameter, direction, and relations of the appendix are very variable. The average length is about 7.5 cm.

The functions of the appendix are not known. It is most fully developed in the young adult and at this time is subject to inflammatory and gangrenous conditions commonly called appendicitis.

The reasons for this are that its structure does not allow for ready drainage, its blood supply is limited, and its circulation is easily interfered with because the vessels anastomose to a very limited extent.

The Colon. The colon, although one continuous tube, is subdivided into the *ascending*, *transverse*, *descending*, and *sigmoid colon*. The ascending portion ascends on the right side of the abdomen until it reaches the undersurface of the liver, where it turns abruptly to the left (right colic or hepatic flexure) and is continued across the abdomen as the transverse colon until, reaching the left side, it curves beneath the lower end of the spleen (left colic or splenic flexure) and passes downward as the descending colon. Reaching the left iliac region on a level with the margin of the crest of the ileum, it makes a curve like the letter S—hence its name of sigmoid—and finally ends in the rectum (Figure 20–13).

The Rectum. The rectum is about 12 cm long and is continuous with the sigmoid

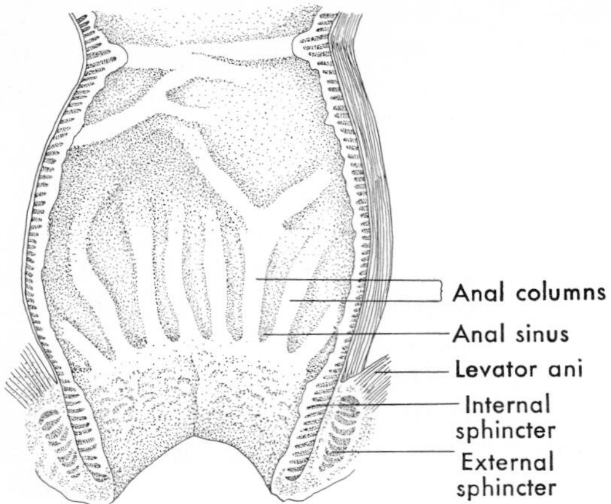

Figure 20–13. Longitudinal section of the anal canal. Shows anal columns, anal sinuses, and sphincter muscles.

colon and anal canal. From its origin at the third sacral vertebra it descends forward along the curve of the sacrum and coccyx and finally turns sharply backward to form the anal canal. In small children the rectum is much straighter than in adults.

The Anal Canal. This is the terminal portion of the large intestine and is about 2.5 to 3.8 cm in length. The external aperture, called the *anus*, is guarded by an internal and external sphincter. It is kept closed except during defecation.

The condition known as *piles*, or *hemorrhoids*, is brought about by enlargement of the veins of the anal canal. They may be *external*, wherein enlargement is of the veins just outside the anal orifice, or *internal*, wherein the enlargement is of veins within the canal.

The Coats of the Large Intestine. These are the usual four, except in some parts where the *serous* coat only partially covers it and in the anal canal, where the serous coat is lacking. The *muscular* coat consists of two layers of fibers, the external arranged longitudinally and the internal circularly. The longi-

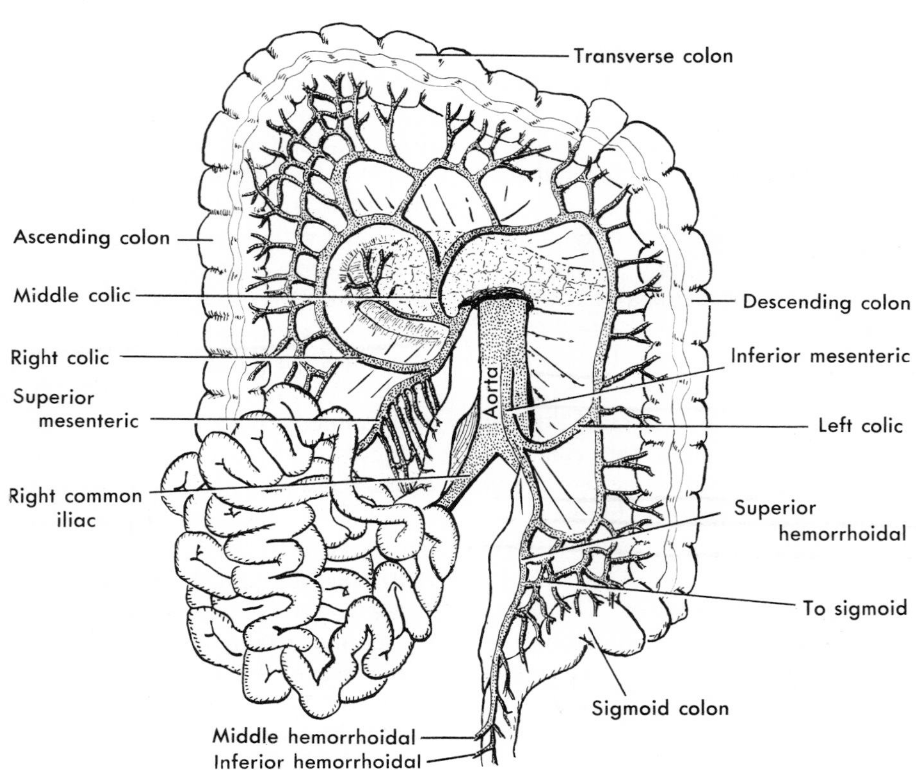

Figure 20–14. Inferior mesenteric artery and its branches.

tudinal fibers form a thicker layer in some regions than in others. The thick areas form three separate bands, the *taeniae coli*, which extend from the cecum to the beginning of the rectum, where they spread out and form a longitudinal layer which encircles this portion. Because these bands (about 5 to 7 mm wide) are about one sixth shorter than the rest of the colon, their walls are puckered into numerous *sacculations*. The third coat consists of *submucous areolar tissue* and the fourth, or inner, coat consists of *mucous membrane*. The mucous coat possesses no villi and no circular folds. It contains intestinal glands and solitary lymph nodules which closely resemble those of the small intestine.

Nerves and Blood Vessels. Fibers from both divisions of the autonomic system reach the large intestine, nerves from the mesenteric and hypogastric plexuses being distributed in a way similar to that found in the small intestine. (See Figure 20–22.)

The arteries are derived mainly from the superior and inferior mesenteric arteries. Branches of the superior mesenteric artery supply the cecum, appendix, and the ascending and right half of the transverse colon. Branches of the inferior mesenteric artery supply the left half of the transverse colon, the descending colon, and the rectum. The rectum also receives branches from the internal iliac arteries. Blood from the large intestine is returned via the superior and inferior mesenteric veins; and blood from the rectum is returned via the superior rectal, which joins the left colic vein, and the middle and inferior rectal, which join the internal iliac vein.

Physiology. Nearly all the processes of food digestion and absorption are completed in the small intestine. Only the indigestible components remain to reach the colon. Perhaps the most important function of the colon is the reabsorption of water and electrolytes. By this process the liquid contents of the colon are dehydrated to form *feces*.

ACCESSORY ORGANS OF DIGESTION

The accessory organs of digestion are: (1) the tongue, (2) the teeth, (3) the salivary glands, (4) the pancreas, (5) the liver, and (6) the gallbladder. The first three have been described.

The Pancreas. The pancreas is a soft, reddish- or yellowish-gray gland which lies in front of the first and second lumbar vertebrae and behind the stomach. In shape it somewhat resembles a hammer and is divided into head, body, and tail. The right end, or head, is thicker and fills the curve of the duodenum, to which it is firmly attached. The left, free end is the tail and reaches to the spleen. The intervening portion is the body. Its average weight is between 60 and 90 gm; it is about 12.5 cm long and about 5 cm wide.

Structure. The pancreas is a compound gland composed of lobules. Each lobule consists of one of the branches of the main duct, which terminates in a cluster of pouches, or lveoli. The lobules are joined together by areolar tissue to form lobes; and the lobes, united in the same manner, form the gland. The small ducts from each lobule open into one main duct about 3 mm in diameter, which runs transversely from the tail to the head through the substance of the gland. This is known as the pancreatic duct or duct of Wirsung.[7] The pancreatic and common bile ducts usually unite and pass obliquely through the wall of the duodenum about 7.5 cm below the pylorus. The short tube formed by the union of the two ducts is dilated into an ampulla, called the *ampulla of Vater*.[8] Sometimes the pancreatic duct and the common bile duct open separately into the duodenum, and there is frequently an accessory duct (duct of Santorini[9]) which opens into

[7] Johann Georg Wirsung, Bavarian anatomist (died 1643).

[8] Abraham Vater, German anatomist (1684–1751).

[9] Giovanni Domenico Santorini, Italian anatomist (1681–1739).

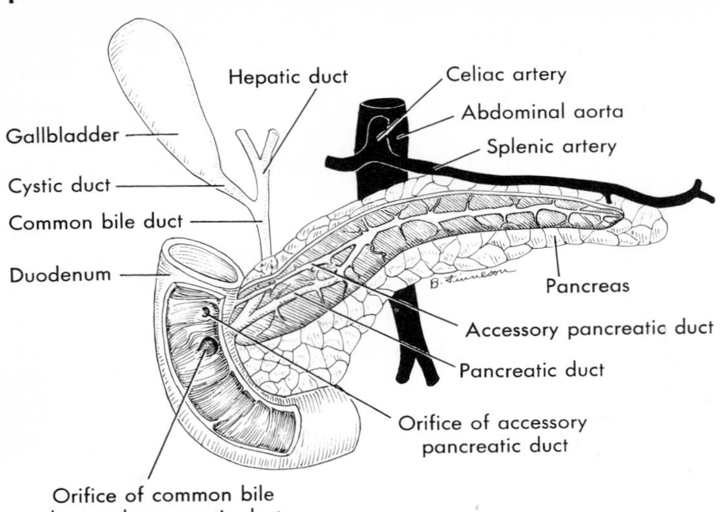

Figure 20–15. Diagram of pancreas showing its relationship to aorta, celiac artery, gallbladder, and hepatic and common bile duct.

the duodenum about 1 in. above the orifice of the main duct.

Islets of Langerhans. Between the alveoli small groups of cells are found, which are termed the islets of Langerhans[10] (interalveolar cell islets). They are surrounded by a rich capillary network and furnish the internal secretion of the pancreas (insulin and glucagon).

Physiology. Two secretions are formed in the pancreas. (1) The pancreatic fluid is an external secretion and is poured into the duodenum during intestinal digestion. (2) The secretions formed by the islets of Langerhans are the internal secretions of insulin and glucagon, which are absorbed by the blood, carried to the tissues, and aid in regulating glucose metabolism. (See page 501.)

The Liver. The liver (hepar) is the largest organ in the body, weighing ordinarily from 1.2 to 1.6 kg. It is located in the right hypochondriac and epigastric regions and frequently extends into the left hypochondriac region. The upper convex surface fits closely into the undersurface of the diaphragm. The under concave surface of the organ fits over the right kidney, the upper portion of the ascending colon, and the pyloric end of the stomach.

[10] Paul Langerhans, German anatomist (1847–1888).

Ligaments. The liver is connected to the undersurface of the diaphragm and the anterior walls of the abdomen by five ligaments, four of which—the falciform, the coronary, and the two lateral—are formed by folds of peritoneum. The fifth, or round, ligament is a fibrous cord resulting from the atrophy of the umbilical vein of intrauterine life.

Fossae. The liver is divided by four fossae, or fissures, into four lobes.

The important fossae are the left sagittal; the portal, or transverse, which transmits the portal blood vessel, hepatic artery, nerves, hepatic duct, and lymphatics; the fossa for the gallbladder; and the fossa for the inferior vena cava.

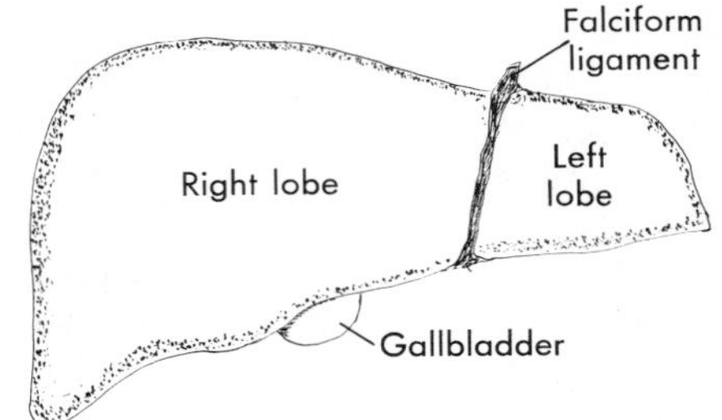

Figure 20–16. Superior surface of liver. The liver measures 20 to 22.5 cm (8 to 9 in.) from side to side, 10 to 12.5 cm (4 to 5 in.) from front to back, and 15 to 17.5 cm (6 to 7 in.) from above downward in its thickest part. It has many diverse functions.

Lobes. The liver is divided into four lobes:

1. Right (largest lobe)
2. Left (smaller and wedge-shaped)
3. Quadrate (square)
4. Caudate (tail-like)

Vessels. The liver has five sets of vessels:

1. Branches of portal vein
2. Bile ducts
3. Branches of hepatic artery
4. Hepatic veins
5. Lymphatics

Nerves and Blood Vessels. The nerve fibers are derived from the left vagus and the thoracolumbar system. They enter at the transverse fossa and accompany the vessels and ducts to the interlobular spaces. From here fibers are distributed to the coats of the blood vessels and ramify between and within the cells.

The blood supply to the liver and pancreas is by way of the hepatic artery, a branch of the celiac. The pancreas receives blood as well from branches of the splenic and superior mesenteric arteries. In addition to the hepatic artery, blood enters the liver by way of the portal vein.

The Portal System. The veins which bring back the blood from the spleen, stomach, pancreas, and intestines are included in the portal system. Blood is collected from the spleen by veins which unite to form the *splenic*, or *lienal*, *vein*. This vein passes back of the pancreas from left to right and ends by uniting with the *superior mesenteric* to form the *portal vein*. Before this union takes place, the splenic receives *gastric veins*, *pancreatic veins*, and usually the *inferior mesenteric vein*, which returns the blood from the rectum, sigmoid, and descending colon. The *superior mesenteric vein* returns the blood from the small intestine, the cecum, and the ascending

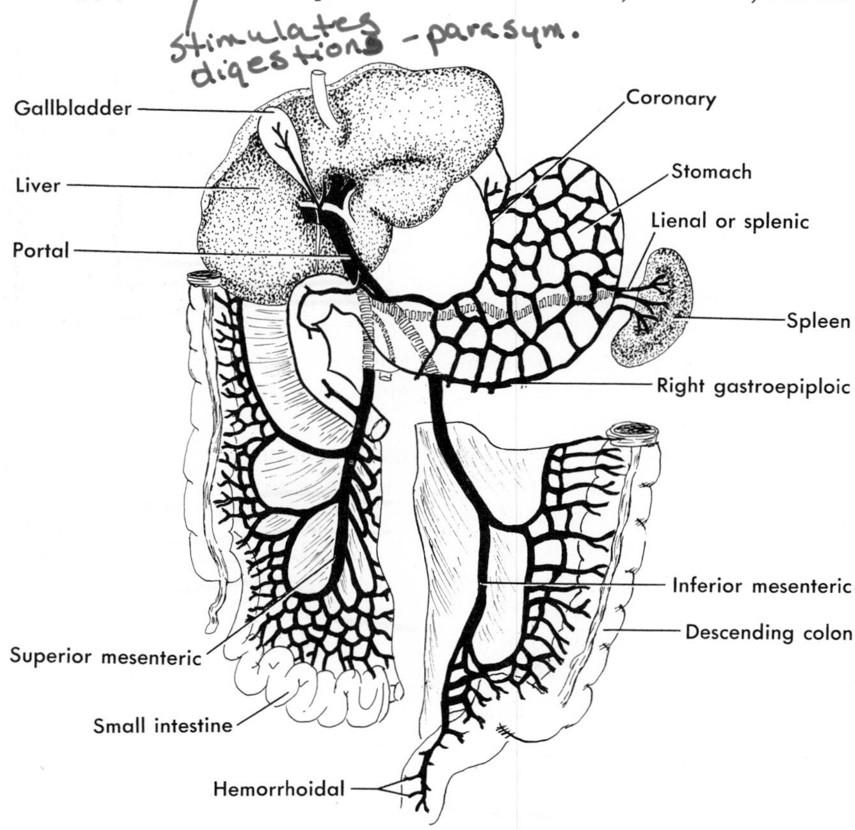

Figure 20–17. Portal system of veins. The liver is turned upward and backward. The transverse colon and most of the small intestine are removed. The veins from the pancreas enter the lienal vein.

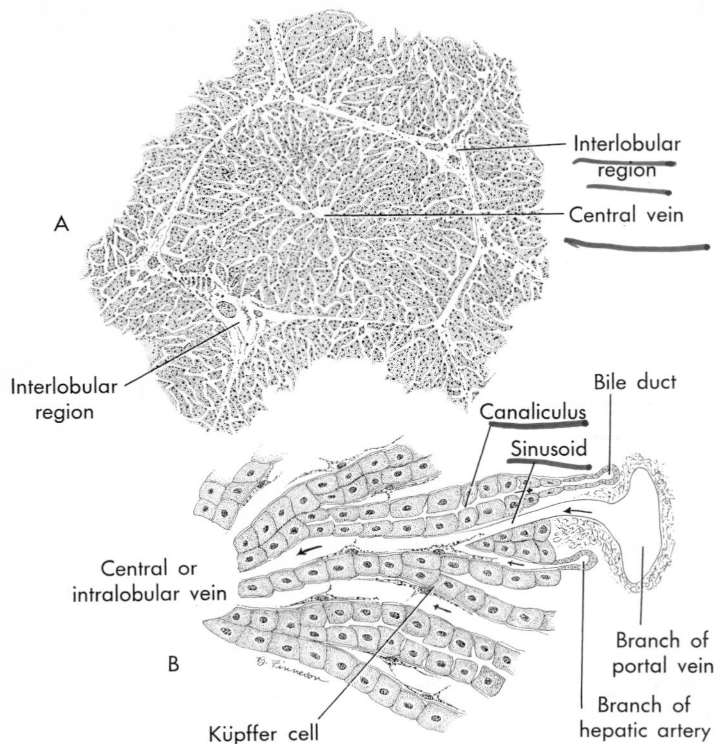

Figure 20–18. Diagram of microscopic views of pig liver. (*A*) Low power, showing one complete lobule in cross section and relation to other lobules. (*B*) High power, cords of liver cells, bile canaliculi, and blood sinusoids. *Arrows* show direction of blood flow and bile flow.

and transverse portions of the colon (Figure 20–17).

The portal vein, formed at the level of the second lumbar vertebra by the union of the splenic and the superior mesenteric, passes upward and to the right to the transverse fissure of the liver. Here it divides into a right and a left branch, which accompany the right and left branches of the hepatic artery into the right and left lobes of the liver. Before entering the liver, the right branch usually receives the cystic vein, which returns blood from the gallbladder. The hepatic artery brings blood direct from the aorta, via the celiac artery to the liver. In the liver, blood from both sets of vessels enters into the interlobular vessels.

Histology of Liver. The liver is made up of many minute units called lobules. Each *lobule* is an irregular body composed of *chains* or *cords of hepatic cells* held together by connective tissue. Between the cords of hepatic cells are capillaries, called *sinusoids*, which are formed from the portal vein and hepatic artery. Kupffer[11] cells are located along the sinusoids. Nerve fibers are also present. The cords of cells are formed by two cells with a bile canaliculus between them, which empties into a bile duct. The cords of cells with their blood and lymph supply are the units of minute structure. Together they give an enormous area of contact between liver cells and capillaries for the volume of tissue concerned. Thus each lobule has all the following: (1) blood vessels in close connection with secretory cells, (2) cells which are capable of forming a secretion, and (3) ducts by which the secretion is carried away.

The *portal vein* brings to the liver blood from the stomach, spleen, pancreas, and intestine. After entering the liver, it divides into a vast number of branches which form a plexus, the interlobular plexus in the spaces between the lobules. From this plexus the

[11] Karl William Von Kupffer, German anatomist (1829–1902).

blood is carried into the lobule by fine branches which converge toward the center. The walls of these small vessels are incomplete, so that the blood is brought in direct contact with each cell. These channels are termed sinusoids, and at the center of the lobule they empty the blood into the intralobular vein. The intralobular veins from a number of lobules empty into a much larger vein, upon whose surface a vast number of lobules rest; and therefore the name *sublobular* (under the lobule) is given to these veins. They empty into still larger veins, the *hepatic*, which converge to form three large trunks and empty into the *inferior vena cava*, which is embedded in the posterior surface of the gland.

The blood brought to the liver by the portal vein is venous blood; arterial blood is brought by the *hepatic artery*. It enters the liver with the portal vein and divides and subdivides in the same manner as the portal vein, with terminations in the sinusoids and interlobular veins. At higher pressures, more arterial blood enters the sinusoids, tending to dilute the portal supply. Blood flow through the liver has been estimated to be about 800 to 1,000 ml per minute, the greater proportion coming from the portal vein.

Pressure in the liver is normally low—near zero in the hepatic vein and about 8 mm Hg in the portal vein. Increased resistance to blood flow, such as with increased amounts of connective tissue in the supporting framework, raises the pressure in smaller vessels, and this eventually raises the portal vein pressure.

The Liver Acinus. Recent investigation of the microcirculation of the liver has resulted in the concept of the *acinus*: a mass of hepatic cells arranged around a central axis of interlobular vessels (portal, hepatic, biliary) and lying between central veins of adjacent lobules. Cells closest to the axis receive the "freshest" blood as compared to those farther away and closer to the central vein. It is known, too, that interlobular vessels do not occur at all the hepatic lobule interdigitating points; thus some cells are relatively far from their interlobular blood supply.

The Accessory Portal System. Some of the veins which are tributaries to the portal vein have small branches whose blood reaches

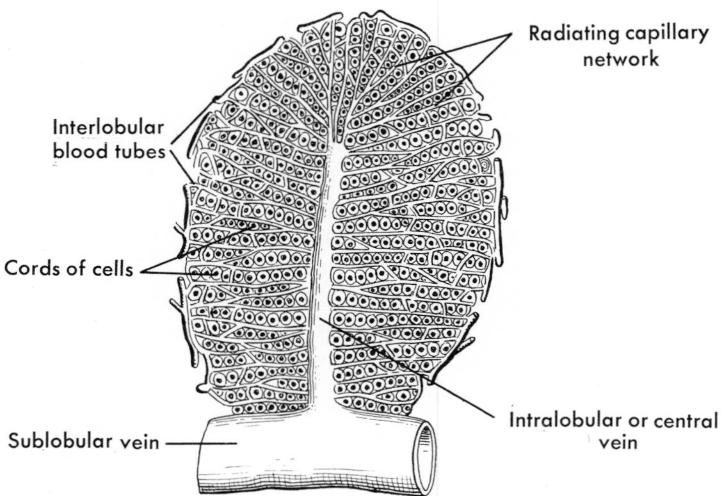

Figure 20–19. Diagram of a hepatic lobule seen in longitudinal section.
Interlobular vessels bring blood in {Branches of hepatic artery / Branches of portal vein}
Intralobular vessels take blood out—Tributaries to hepatic vein

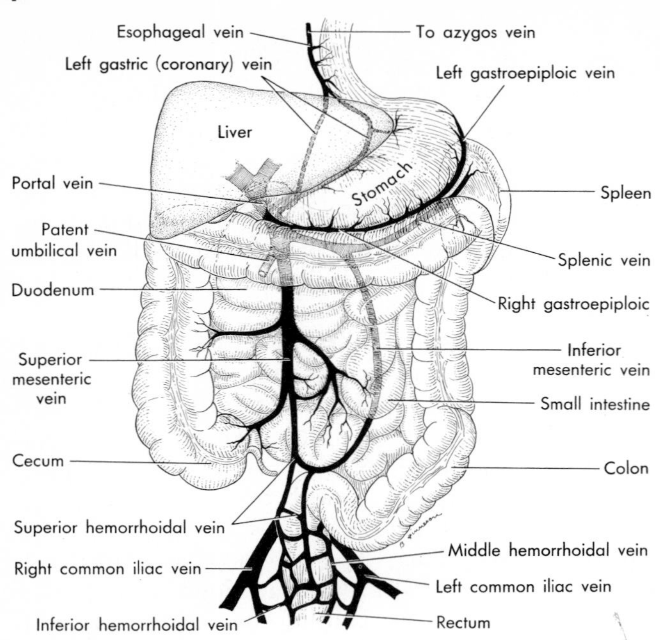

Figure 20–20. Accessory portal circulation. Note anastomosis with systemic circulation (esophageal, umbilical, and hemorrhoidal vessels).

the heart via the superior and inferior venae cavae without going through the liver. For example, branches of the coronary vein of the stomach unite with the esophageal veins which enter the azygos, on its way to the heart, thus bypassing the liver. The inferior mesenteric communicates with the hemorrhoidal veins which empty into the hypogastric veins. There are also small communicating branches that unite the superior and inferior epigastric and internal thoracic veins and through the diaphragmatic veins with the azygos. These communications are called the accessory portal system and are important in returning blood to the superior vena cava when there is interference with portal circulation (Figure 20–20).

Lymphatics. There are a superficial and a deep set of lymphatic vessels. They begin in irregular spaces in the lobules, form networks around the lobules, and run always from the center outward.

The Bile Ducts. The surfaces of the hepatic cells are grooved, and the grooves on two adjacent cells fit together and form a passage into which the bile is poured as soon as it is formed by the cells. These passages form a network between and around the cells as intricate as the network of blood vessels. They are called biliary canaliculi and radiate to the circumference of the lobule, where they empty into the interlobular bile ducts. These unite and form larger and larger ducts until two main ducts, one from the right and one from the left side of the liver, unite in the portal fossa and form the *hepatic duct.*

The hepatic duct passes downward and to the right for about 5 cm and then joins (at an acute angle) the duct from the gallbladder, termed the *cystic duct.* The hepatic and cystic ducts together form the *common bile duct* (*ductus choledochus*), which passes downward for about 7.5 cm and enters the duodenum about 7.5 cm below the pylorus. This orifice usually serves as a common opening for both the common bile duct and the pancreatic duct. It is very small and is guarded by a sphincter muscle, which keeps it closed except during digestion.

The liver is invested in an outer capsule of fibrous tissue called *Glisson's*[12] *capsule.* This capsule is reflected inward at the transverse fossa and envelops the vessels and ducts which pass into the liver. With the exception

[12] Francis Glisson, English anatomist (1597–1677).

of a few small areas, the liver is enclosed in a serous tunic derived from the peritoneum.

Physiology of the Liver. The liver has many functions of a complex nature, some of which are carried on independently of one another. It is possible that one function may be interfered with while other functions proceed normally. The liver functions in a variety of ways to maintain and regulate homeostasis of body fluids.

1. Secretory Functions. The liver forms and secretes daily about 800 to 1,200 ml of bile consisting of bile salts, bile pigments, and cholesterol. The bile salts are important in the intestinal phases of fat digestion (page 452). The bile pigments are formed from blood pigment (hemoglobin) of disintegrated red blood cells. About 90 per cent of the bile salts secreted by the liver are reabsorbed from the small intestine; this *enterohepatic* circulation serves to conserve essential fractions of the bile acids. There is little or no enterohepatic circulation of the other bile constituents.

2. In Relation to Blood. The liver helps to regulate the blood volume by means of a sluice mechanism, which adjusts the volume of blood leaving the liver, via the hepatic vein. Since the liver is an expandable and contractable organ, it has the ability to store large quantities of blood in its vessels.

At birth the ductus venosus gradually becomes completely occluded, more blood flows through the liver, and it gradually assumes the functions characteristic of the normal adult organ. The liver forms red blood cells in the embryo and stores vitamin B_{12}, which is essential for the development of the red blood cells.

It forms prothrombin and fibrinogen, which are concerned with the clotting of blood, and heparin, an anticoagulant of the blood. (Heparin is also found in the spleen, heart, lung, thymus, and muscle. The lung is probably the richest source of heparin.)

The liver also plays a part, along with the spleen, in disposing of the products resulting from disintegration of erythrocytes which are no longer able to function in oxygen transport. A vasodepressor substance (VDM) is formed in the liver during late stages of shock due to hemorrhage.

3. In Relation to Storage. The liver forms vitamin A from carotene. Vitamins A

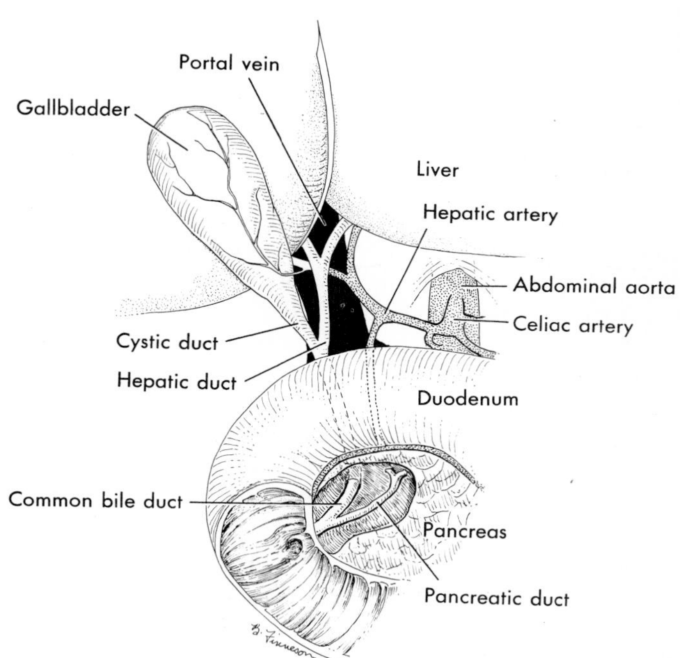

Figure 20–21. Diagram of gallbladder, pancreas, and duodenum to show relationships of bile and pancreatic ducts. Note also circular folds of duodenum.

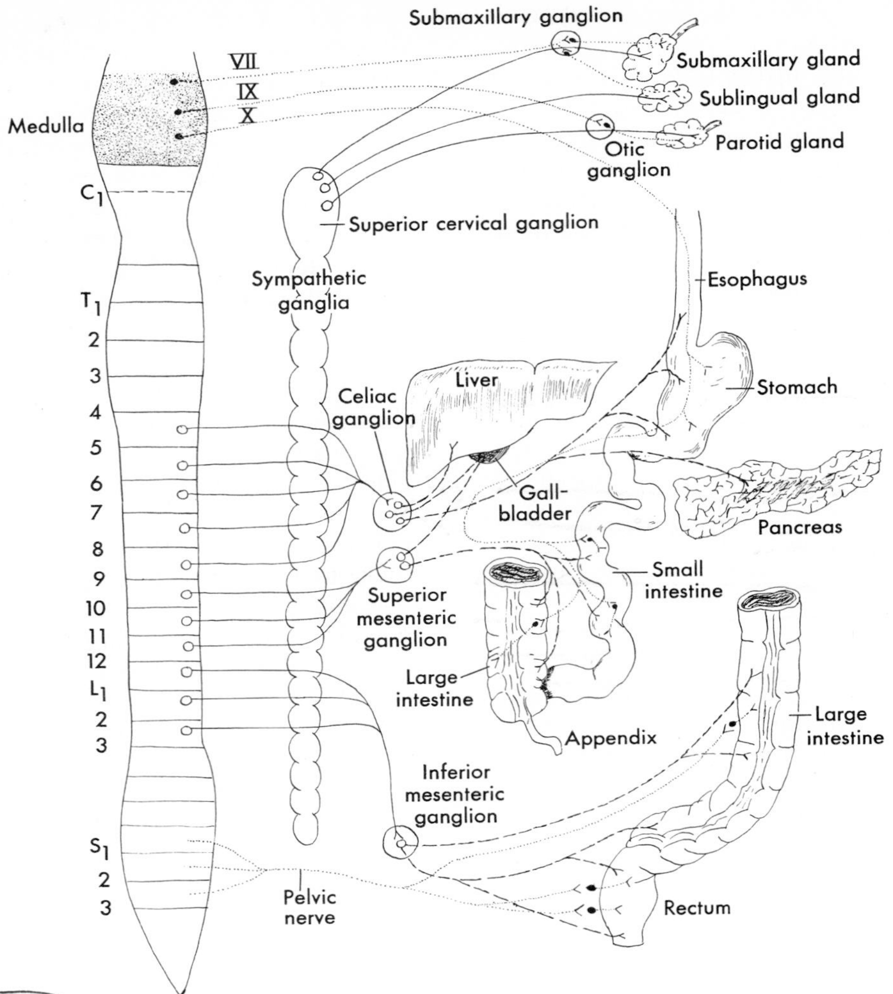

Figure 20–22. Innervation of the digestive pathway. Parasympathetic fibers are *dotted*. The ganglia of the vagus and the pelvic nerves lie in or near the organs.

and D are stored in the liver. Iron, copper, and perhaps other minerals are stored in the liver also. It utilizes vitamin K to form prothrombin.

4. In Relation to Metabolism

a. CARBOHYDRATE. The liver stores glycogen, which is synthesized primarily from glucose, fructose, and galactose (glycogenesis). It synthesizes glycogen from noncarbohydrates (gluconeogenesis) and converts glycogen to glucose (glycogenolysis) to maintain blood sugar constancy.

b. FAT. The liver is a great center for fat metabolism; it oxidizes fatty acids, synthesizes phospholipids and ketones, and synthesizes fats from glucose; it forms lipoproteins. Cholesterol is esterified and excreted in bile or may be transformed to lipoprotein.

c. PROTEIN. The liver deaminizes amino acids and synthesizes urea. It converts acids from other amino acids. It also synthesizes plasma proteins, fibrinogen, and prothrombin. It forms essential nonprotein nitrogen compounds.

5. Detoxification Functions. The importance of the "protective" role of the liver cannot be overemphasized. It not only controls the concentration of various substances, but by a variety of chemical reactions such as oxidation, reduction, conjugation, and by other means, the liver detoxifies harmful chemicals which enter the body and the blood stream. It degrades certain of the hormones and most substances used as anesthetic agents, as well as alcohol.

Through bile the liver eliminates certain drugs and heavy metals such as mercury; morphine and strychnine can be absorbed and stored by the liver and freed slowly so that by dilution their toxicity is diminished. By virtue of the Kupffer cells, which are located in the liver sinusoids, the liver has the ability to detoxify substances. These cells have phagocytic action and hence have an important role in the defense mechanism of the body.

Hippuric acid is synthesized from benzoic acid through conjugation with glycine and is eliminated in the urine. As a result of its many chemical activities the liver provides a great deal of heat for the body. The liver plays an important role in estrogen inactivation and thus helps to maintain the estrogen level in the blood by excreting it into the bile.

The Gallbladder. This is a pear-shaped (when full) sac lodged in the gallbladder fossa on the undersurface of the liver, where it is held in place by connective tissue. It is about 7 to 10 cm long, 2.5 cm wide, holds about 36 ml, and is composed of three coats:

BLOOD SUPPLY TO DIGESTIVE ORGANS OF ABDOMEN

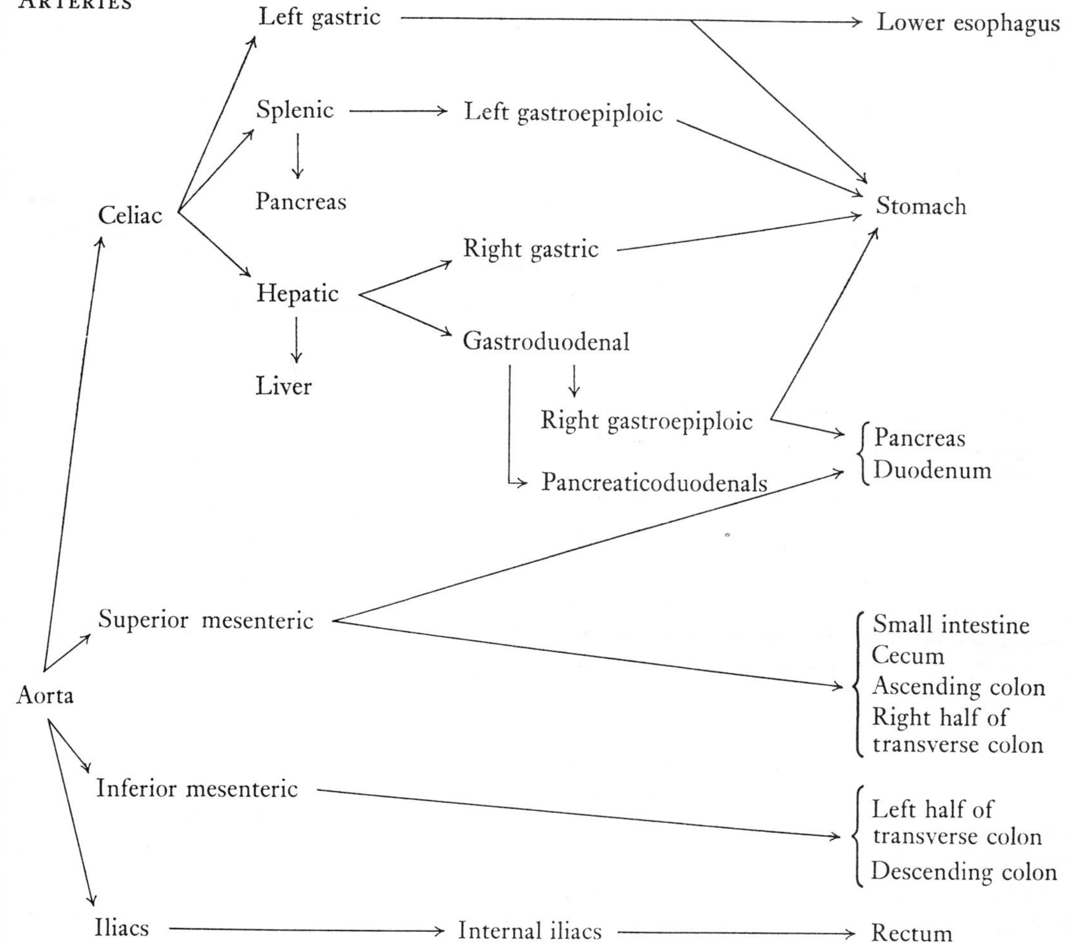

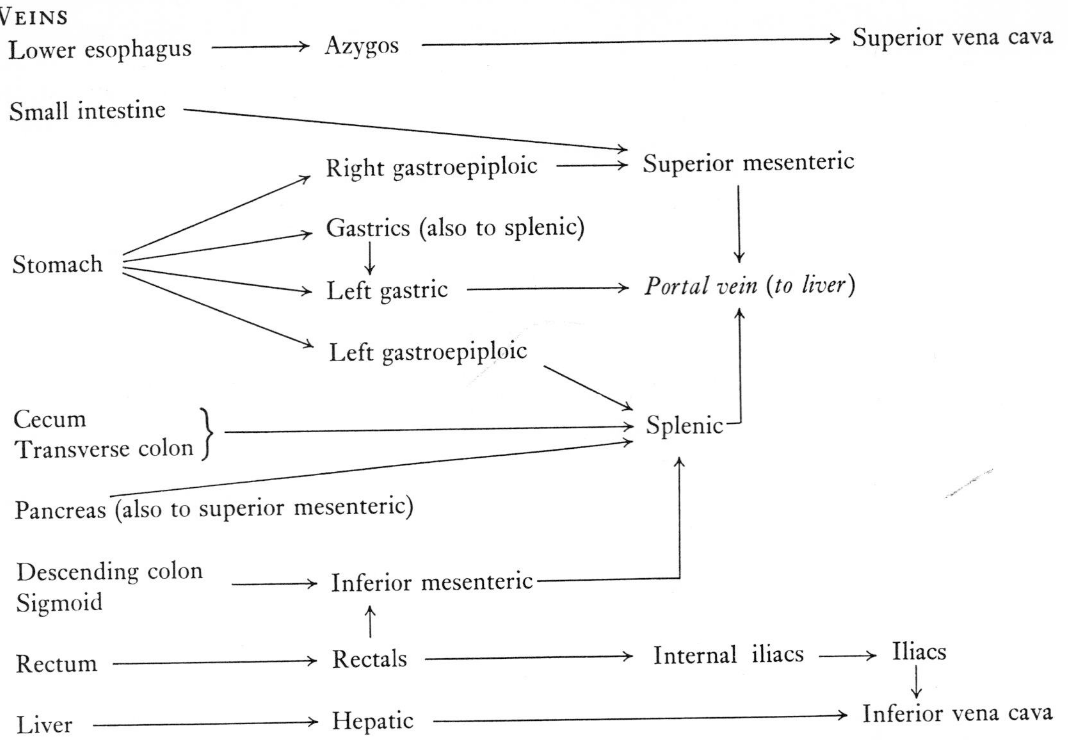

(1) the inner one is mucous membrane; (2) the middle one is muscular and fibrous tissue; and (3) the outer one is serous membrane derived from the peritoneum. It is only occasionally that the peritoneum covers more than the undersurface of the organ.

Most of the bile secreted continuously by the liver enters the gallbladder, where it is concentrated; thus it serves as a reservoir for bile. When required, the gallbladder contracts and expels its bile content into the duodenum. The most potent stimuli for evacuation are the acid gastric juice and fatty foods in the small intestine. A hormone, cholecystokinin, is elaborated by cells of the small intestine in the presence of fat. This hormone causes the gallbladder to contract, thereby emptying its contents of bile into the intestine.

The sphincter of Oddi[13] is relaxed much of the time. However, when pressure in the intestine increases, the sphincter contracts to prevent ascent of intestinal contents into the biliary tract. The sphincteric mechanism must be relaxed when the gallbladder contracts; if not, the contents will not be evacuated, and the resulting distention of the bile duct will cause sharp, unbearable pain called biliary colic. This pain is also produced when the duct is obstructed by so-called "stones."

[13] Ruggero Oddi, Italian surgeon (late nineteenth century).

QUESTIONS FOR DISCUSSION

1. If the duodenum is removed surgically, what other procedure must be done to ensure passage of digestive fluids through the small intestine?
2. What problems would a patient have if the esophagus were removed?
3. There is a similarity in structure of the organs of the digestive tract. What is this?
4. Enlargement of the esophageal veins (varices) may occur in liver disease. Why?
5. Discuss the functions of the liver.

SUMMARY

Digestion. Digestion is dependent on the proper functioning of certain organs that are grouped together and called the digestive system

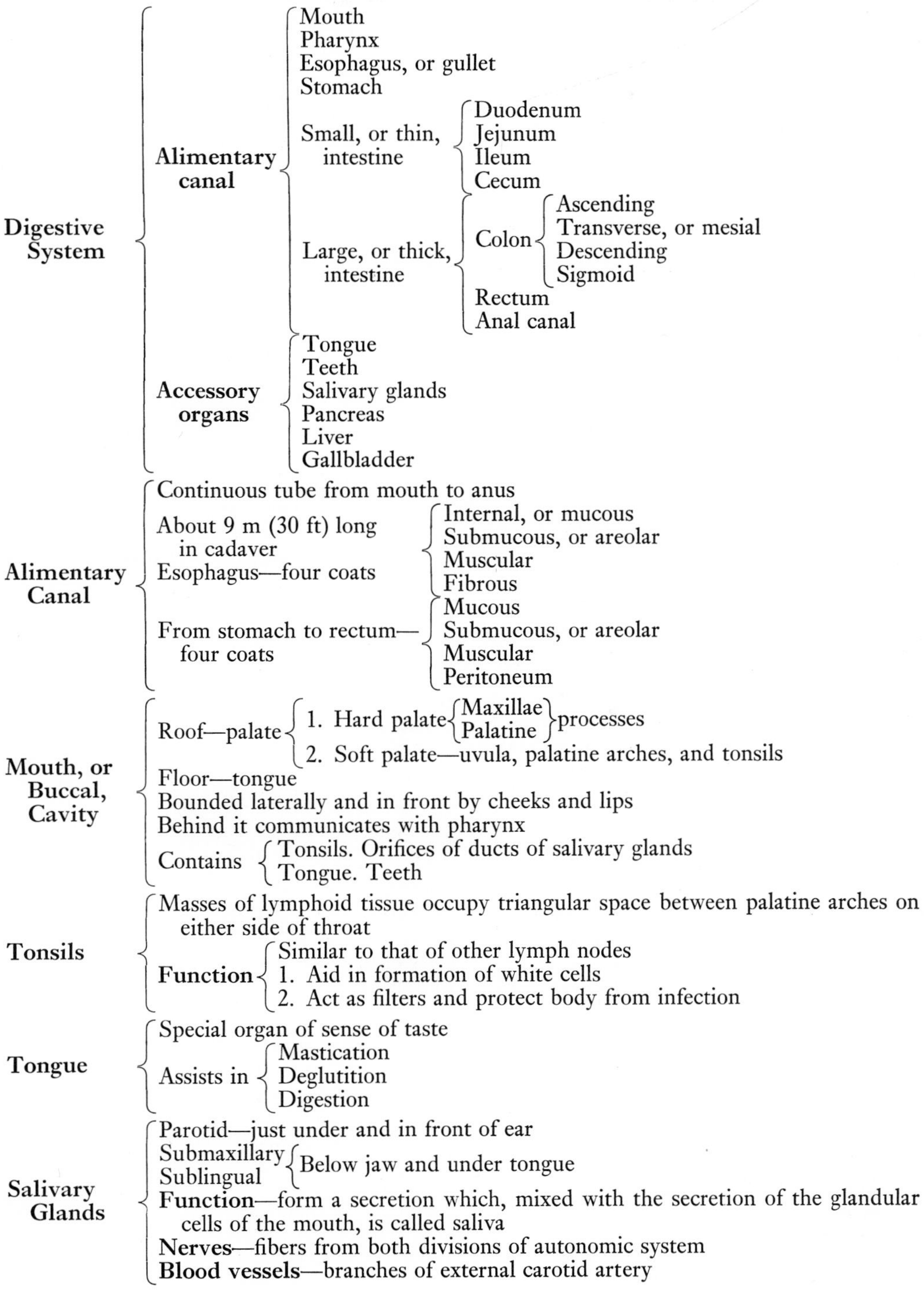

- **Digestive System**
  - **Alimentary canal**
    - Mouth
    - Pharynx
    - Esophagus, or gullet
    - Stomach
    - Small, or thin, intestine
      - Duodenum
      - Jejunum
      - Ileum
      - Cecum
    - Large, or thick, intestine
      - Colon
        - Ascending
        - Transverse, or mesial
        - Descending
        - Sigmoid
      - Rectum
      - Anal canal
  - **Accessory organs**
    - Tongue
    - Teeth
    - Salivary glands
    - Pancreas
    - Liver
    - Gallbladder
- **Alimentary Canal**
  - Continuous tube from mouth to anus
  - About 9 m (30 ft) long in cadaver
  - Esophagus—four coats
    - Internal, or mucous
    - Submucous, or areolar
    - Muscular
    - Fibrous
  - From stomach to rectum—four coats
    - Mucous
    - Submucous, or areolar
    - Muscular
    - Peritoneum
- **Mouth, or Buccal, Cavity**
  - Roof—palate
    1. Hard palate — Maxillae, Palatine processes
    2. Soft palate—uvula, palatine arches, and tonsils
  - Floor—tongue
  - Bounded laterally and in front by cheeks and lips
  - Behind it communicates with pharynx
  - Contains
    - Tonsils. Orifices of ducts of salivary glands
    - Tongue. Teeth
- **Tonsils**
  - Masses of lymphoid tissue occupy triangular space between palatine arches on either side of throat
  - **Function**
    - Similar to that of other lymph nodes
    1. Aid in formation of white cells
    2. Act as filters and protect body from infection
- **Tongue**
  - Special organ of sense of taste
  - Assists in
    - Mastication
    - Deglutition
    - Digestion
- **Salivary Glands**
  - Parotid—just under and in front of ear
  - Submaxillary, Sublingual — Below jaw and under tongue
  - **Function**—form a secretion which, mixed with the secretion of the glandular cells of the mouth, is called saliva
  - **Nerves**—fibers from both divisions of autonomic system
  - **Blood vessels**—branches of external carotid artery

Teeth
- Contained in sockets of alveolar processes of maxillae and mandible
- **Gums**—cover processes and extend into sockets, or alveoli
- **Sockets**—lined with periosteum
  - Attach teeth to sockets
  - Source of nourishment
- Three portions
  - *Root*—one or more fangs contained in alveolus
  - *Crown*—projects beyond level of gums
  - *Neck*—portion between root and crown
- Composed of three substances developed from epithelium
  - *Dentin*—Gives shape. Encloses pulp cavity, which contains nerves and blood vessels that enter by canal from root
  - *Enamel*—caps crown
  - *Cement*—covers root
- Two sets
  - 1. Deciduous—6 months–2 years: Incisors 8, Canines 4, Molars 8 = 20
  - Begin to develop about the sixth week of intrauterine life
  - 2. Permanent—6½ years–25 years of age: Incisors 8, Canines 4, Premolars 8, Molars 12 = 32
  - With the exception of the second and third molars the permanent teeth begin to develop about the sixteenth week of intrauterine life
- **Function**—to assist in the process of mastication

Pharynx
- Muscular, membranous, cone-shaped tube between mouth and esophagus
- Three parts
  - Nasal or nasopharynx—behind posterior nares above soft palate
  - Oral—extends from soft palate to hyoid bone
  - Laryngeal—extends from hyoid bone to esophagus
- **Seven apertures**
  - 2 posterior nares
  - 2 auditory tubes
  - 1 fauces
  - 1 larynx
  - 1 esophagus
- **Nerves**—receives fibers from both divisions of autonomic system
- **Blood vessels**—branches from external carotid artery
- **Function**
  - Transmits air to larynx
  - Serves as a resonating cavity
  - Receives food and passes it to esophagus

Esophagus, or Gullet
- Tube—23–25 cm (9–10 in.) long. Extends from pharynx to cardiac end of stomach
- **Four coats**
  - 1. Internal, or mucous
  - 2. Submucous, or areolar
  - 3. Muscular
    - Internal circular layer
    - External longitudinal layer
  - 4. External, or fibrous
- **Nerves**
  - Vagus
  - Thoracolumbar system
- **Blood vessels**
  - 1. Inferior thyroid branch of thyrocervical trunk
  - 2. Branches from thoracic aorta
  - 3. Left gastric branch of celiac artery
  - 4. Left phrenic branch of abdominal aorta
- **Function**—receives food and passes it on to stomach

Stomach or Gaster
- Dilated portion of canal, size and shape vary
- Oblique position in epigastric, umbilical, and left hypochondriac regions, under diaphragm

- **Stomach or Gaster** (*cont.*)
  - **Openings**
    - Cardiac orifice—connects with esophagus
    - Pyloric orifice—connects with duodenum
    - Guarded by ringlike muscles known as sphincters
  - **Curvatures**
    - Lesser curvature—concave border
    - Greater curvature—convex border
  - **Parts**
    - Fundus—blind end above entrance of esophagus
    - Body—between fundic and pyloric portions
    - Pyloric portion—smaller end
  - **Four coats**
    - 1. Outer—serous—peritoneum
    - 2. Muscular
      - a. Longitudinal layer
      - b. Circular layer
      - c. Oblique layer chiefly at cardiac end
    - 3. Submucous—vascular
    - 4. Mucous-rugae
  - **Glands**
    - Some cells of mucous membrane secrete gastrin
    - Cardiac—secrete mucin
    - Fundus
      - Chief, or central, cells secrete pepsinogen; parietal, or oxyntic, cells secrete acid
    - Pyloric—secrete pepsinogen and mucin
  - **Nerves**
    - Thoracolumbar autonomic nerves from celiac plexus
    - Vagus nerves
  - **Blood vessels** from three divisions of celiac
    - Left gastric
    - Hepatic
    - Splenic
  - **Physiology**
    - 1. Receives food in relatively large quantities about three times a day, holds it while it undergoes mechanical and chemical changes, then passes it on in small portions at frequent intervals
    - 2. Secretes mucin and gastric fluid
- **Small, or Thin, Intestine**
  - Convoluted tube extends from stomach to colic valve. About 7 m (23 ft) long, coiled up in abdominal cavity
  - **Three divisions** (in the cadaver)
    - Duodenum—about 25 cm (10 in.)
    - Jejunum—about 2.2 m ($7\frac{1}{2}$ ft)
    - Ileum—about 4 m ($14\frac{1}{2}$ ft)
  - **Four coats**
    - 1. Serous from peritoneum
    - 2. Muscular
      - Longitudinal layer
      - Circular layer
    - 3. Submucous—connects muscular and mucous coats
    - 4. Mucous
      - Circular folds
      - Villi—contain lacteals and blood capillaries
  - **Glands and nodes**
    - Intestinal glands; Duodenal, or Brunner's — Secrete intestinal fluid
    - Lymph nodules
      - Solitary
      - Aggregated lymph nodules called Peyer's patches
  - **Nerves**
    - Vagi supply sensory and motor fibers
    - Thoracolumbar autonomic nerves derived from plexuses around superior mesenteric artery
  - **Blood vessels**
    - Branches of hepatic
    - Branches of superior mesenteric
      - Distribute arched branches which lie between serous and muscular coats
  - **Function**
    - Digestion
    - Receives bile from liver, pancreatic fluid from pancreas
    - Secretion of succus entericus
    - Absorption
- **Large, or Thick, Intestine**
  - Large in width
  - Length, 1.5 m (5 ft); width, 6.3 cm ($2\frac{1}{2}$ in.) to 3.5 cm ($1\frac{1}{2}$ in.)
  - Extends from ileum to anus

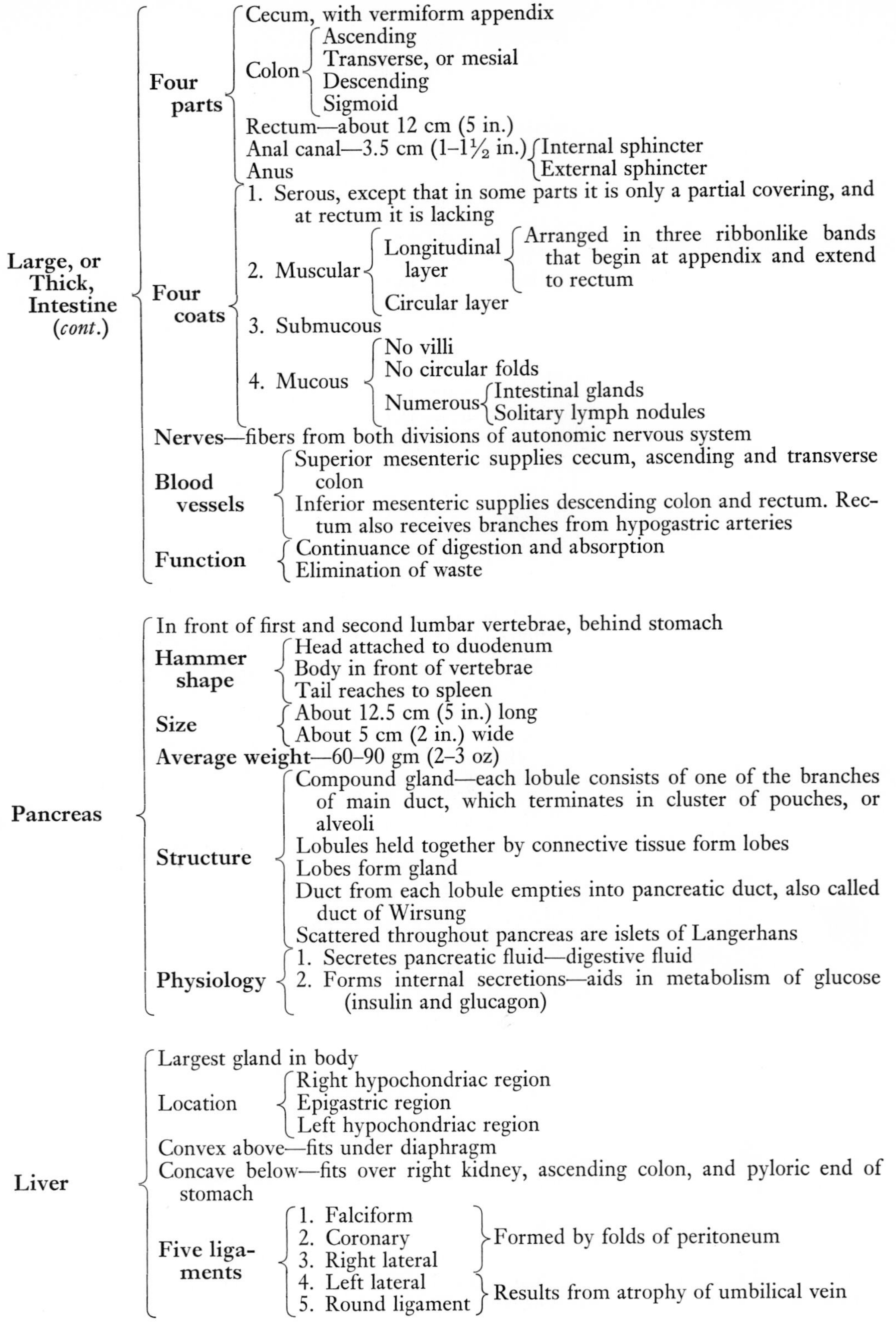

- **Large, or Thick, Intestine** (*cont.*)
  - **Four parts**
    - Cecum, with vermiform appendix
    - Colon
      - Ascending
      - Transverse, or mesial
      - Descending
      - Sigmoid
    - Rectum—about 12 cm (5 in.)
    - Anal canal—3.5 cm (1–1½ in.)
      - Internal sphincter
      - External sphincter
    - Anus
  - **Four coats**
    1. Serous, except that in some parts it is only a partial covering, and at rectum it is lacking
    2. Muscular
       - Longitudinal layer
         - Arranged in three ribbonlike bands that begin at appendix and extend to rectum
       - Circular layer
    3. Submucous
    4. Mucous
       - No villi
       - No circular folds
       - Numerous
         - Intestinal glands
         - Solitary lymph nodules
  - **Nerves**—fibers from both divisions of autonomic nervous system
  - **Blood vessels**
    - Superior mesenteric supplies cecum, ascending and transverse colon
    - Inferior mesenteric supplies descending colon and rectum. Rectum also receives branches from hypogastric arteries
  - **Function**
    - Continuance of digestion and absorption
    - Elimination of waste

- **Pancreas**
  - In front of first and second lumbar vertebrae, behind stomach
  - **Hammer shape**
    - Head attached to duodenum
    - Body in front of vertebrae
    - Tail reaches to spleen
  - **Size**
    - About 12.5 cm (5 in.) long
    - About 5 cm (2 in.) wide
  - **Average weight**—60–90 gm (2–3 oz)
  - **Structure**
    - Compound gland—each lobule consists of one of the branches of main duct, which terminates in cluster of pouches, or alveoli
    - Lobules held together by connective tissue form lobes
    - Lobes form gland
    - Duct from each lobule empties into pancreatic duct, also called duct of Wirsung
    - Scattered throughout pancreas are islets of Langerhans
  - **Physiology**
    1. Secretes pancreatic fluid—digestive fluid
    2. Forms internal secretions—aids in metabolism of glucose (insulin and glucagon)

- **Liver**
  - Largest gland in body
  - Location
    - Right hypochondriac region
    - Epigastric region
    - Left hypochondriac region
  - Convex above—fits under diaphragm
  - Concave below—fits over right kidney, ascending colon, and pyloric end of stomach
  - Five ligaments
    1. Falciform
    2. Coronary
    3. Right lateral
       - (1–3) Formed by folds of peritoneum
    4. Left lateral
    5. Round ligament
       - (5) Results from atrophy of umbilical vein

Liver (*cont.*)

- **Four fossae**
  1. Left sagittal fossa
  2. Portal, or transverse, fossa transmits
     - Portal vein
     - Hepatic artery
     - Hepatic duct
     - Lymphatics
     - Nerves
  3. Gallbladder fossa
  4. Fossa for inferior vena cava
- **Four lobes**
  1. Right (largest lobe)
  2. Left (smaller and wedge-shaped)
  3. Quadrate (square)
  4. Caudate (tail-like)
- **Five sets of vessels**
  1. Branches of portal vein
  2. Branches of hepatic artery
  3. Hepatic veins
  4. Lymphatics
  5. Bile ducts
- **Nerves**—derived from left vagus and thoracolumbar autonomic system
- **Blood vessels**
  - Hepatic artery
  - Portal vein
  - Hepatic veins
- **Anatomy of liver**
  - Cords of hepatic cells are grouped in lobules
  - Lobules 1.0 to 2.5 mm in diameter
  - Branches of portal vessel
    - Interlobular veins (between lobules)
    - Intralobular capillaries (within lobules)
    - Sublobular veins (under lobules)
    - Hepatic veins—exit at portal fossa, empty into inferior vena cava
  - Bile ducts
    - Channels between cells form intercellular biliary passages
    - Interlobular ducts
    - Hepatic duct—exit at portal fossa
  - Branches of hepatic artery
    - Interlobular arteries (between lobules)
    - Intralobular capillaries (within lobules)
    - Course beyond intralobular capillaries same as that pursued by blood from portal vein
  - Lymphatics
    - Begin in lobules, form network, and run from center to periphery
  - Acinus
    - Mass of hepatic cell surrounding interlobular vessels
  - Glisson's capsule invests liver
  - Serous membrane from peritoneum almost completely covers it
- **Physiology**
  - Bile production
  - Forms glycogen which supplies glucose to the blood
  - Gives rise to heparin, or antithrombin
  - Proteins changed into substance that can be eliminated, urea, etc.
  - Finishes disintegration of erythrocytes
  - Secretes into the bile various poisonous substances
  - Regulation of blood volume
  - Manufacture of serum albumin
  - Manufacture of serum globulin
  - Manufacture of fibrinogen, prothrombin
  - Forms blood in embryo
  - Produces heat
  - Forms vitamin A from carotene
  - Storage of iron and copper and vitamins A, D, and B_{12}
  - Detoxification functions
  - Doubtless many other functions in relation to the constancy of the internal environment

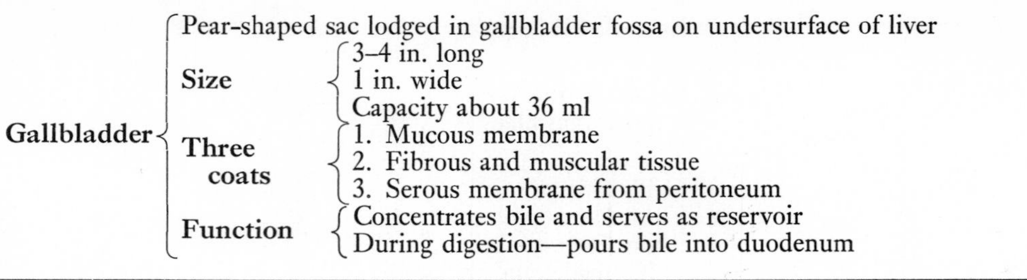

Gallbladder
- Pear-shaped sac lodged in gallbladder fossa on undersurface of liver
- **Size**
  - 3–4 in. long
  - 1 in. wide
  - Capacity about 36 ml
- **Three coats**
  - 1. Mucous membrane
  - 2. Fibrous and muscular tissue
  - 3. Serous membrane from peritoneum
- **Function**
  - Concentrates bile and serves as reservoir
  - During digestion—pours bile into duodenum

CHAPTER

21

FOODS

Carbohydrates, Lipids, and Proteins

Minerals

Vitamins

DIGESTIVE PROCESSES

Mechanical and Chemical

Natural nutrients are in general nondiffusible and held in cells. The cells of plants and animals constitute a natural food supply for man. These foods are taken periodically, digested, absorbed, stored, in general in nondiffusible form in cells, redigested by endoenzymes, and delivered to the cells by the circulatory fluids for use. Food is any substance taken into the body to yield energy, to build tissue, and to regulate body processes.

All the body activities require a certain amount of energy; this energy is supplied by food. The energy released in cells during the interaction of oxygen and food is present in the form of potential, or latent, energy, binding the atoms into molecules and the molecules into larger masses. The splitting of these complex molecules into smaller and simpler ones releases this energy as kinetic energy. Food material, over and above what is needed for this purpose, is stored in the body in the form of glycogen or as fat. This may be regarded as reserve fuel which, when needed, is oxidized to release energy.

Food supplies material for the manufacture of protoplasm, for either growth (increase in the bulk of protoplasm) or repair (replacing the protoplasm incidentally oxidized day by day).

Nutrition and growth are dependent upon certain essential substances called vitamins. Water and inorganic salts are necessary to maintain the normal composition of the tissues. The accompanying table shows the distribution of various food materials in different tissues (page 432).

The chemical composition of various organs in the body is shown here. There is much similarity, particularly in water content.

Classification of Food. Foods may be classified chemically as follows:

Nutrients { Water, Carbohydrates, Lipids, Proteins; Minerals, Vitamins

Water. Water constitutes more than two thirds of the material ingested daily.

The water content of the body comes from three sources: beverages or other liquids; foods, especially vegetables and fruits; and the water formed in the tissues as the result of metabolic activities. (See Chapter 22.)

Carbohydrates. Carbohydrates are the most abundant and most economical sources of energy. All simple sugars and all substances which can be converted into simple sugars by hydrolysis are carbohydrates. The

	% Total Body Wt.	H_2O	Lipids	Protein	Ash*	Ca
Skin	7.8	65	13	22	0.7	tr
Skeleton	15	32	17	19	2.9	11
Teeth	0.06	5	3	23	70	24
Skeletal muscle	32	80	3	16	1	tr
Brain, spinal cord, nerves	2.5	73	13	12	1	tr
Liver	3	71	10	16	0.8	tr
Heart	0.7	74	9	16	0.8	tr
Lungs	4	83.7	1.5	13	1	tr
Spleen	0.2	78	1	18	1	tr
Kidneys	0.5	79	4	15	1	tr
Pancreas	0.2	73	13	13	1	tr
Alimentary tract	2	79	6	13	1	tr
Adipose	14	50	42	7	0.5	tr

* Various chemicals (see page 436).

names of these compounds suggest the number of simple sugar groups they will yield on hydrolysis: monosaccharides, disaccharides, and polysaccharides.

1. Monosaccharides, or Simple Sugars. These contain one sugar group, $C_6H_{12}O_6$. They are soluble and can be absorbed into the body fluids without further change. They are the units from which the more complex carbohydrates are formed.

Monosaccharides
- Glucose, or dextrose, found in fruits, especially the grape, and in body fluids — $C_6H_{12}O_6$
- Fructose, or levulose, found with glucose in fruits — $C_6H_{12}O_6$
- Galactose, obtained by hydrolysis of lactose and certain gums — $C_6H_{12}O_6$

2. Disaccharides. The formula $C_{12}H_{22}O_{11}$ shows that disaccharides consist of two monosaccharide groups. During the process of digestion, they are split into their component monosaccharides, e.g., sucrose into glucose and fructose; lactose into glucose and galactose, and maltose into two molecules of glucose. Only one splitting is necessary, and it utilizes one molecule of water as seen in the following equation.

Sucrose Water Glucose Fructose

$$C_{12}H_{22}O_{11} + H_2O \rightarrow C_6H_{12}O_6 + C_6H_{12}O_6$$

Disaccharides
- Sucrose, or cane sugar, found in vegetables, fruits, and juices of plants — $C_{12}H_{22}O_{11}$
- Lactose, or milk sugar, found in the milk of all mammals — $C_{12}H_{22}O_{11}$
- Maltose is an intermediate product in the digestion of starch, found in the body, in germinating cereals, malts, and malt products — $C_{12}H_{22}O_{11}$

3. Polysaccharides. Polysaccharides are represented by the molecular formula $(C_6H_{10}O_5)_n$. The elements are present in the same proportion, but the value of n may be large and is probably different for the different polysaccharides. For instance, the value of n for the starch molecule is said to be 300 or more, representing as many sugar groups, whereas for the dextrin molecule it is smaller, so that a single molecule of starch when hydrolyzed produces several molecules of dextrin of the same relative composition. Since the polysaccharides are complex, they must pass through several hydrolyses before they are changed to simple sugars. Each splitting of the molecule gives substances with simpler composition, though with the same relative proportion of the constituents, and to each is given a special name. The number of molecules of simple sugar resulting from the hydrolysis of any polysaccharide would depend upon the value of the *n*.

A summary of the hydrolysis of starch to glucose may be expressed as follows.

$$\underset{\text{Starch}}{(C_6H_{10}O_5)_n} + nH_2O \rightarrow \underset{\text{Glucose}}{nC_6H_{12}O_6}$$

Polysaccharides	Starch—found in grain, tubers, roots, etc.	$(C_6H_{10}O_5)_n$
	Cellulose—outside covering of starch grains and basis of all woody fibers	$(C_6H_{10}O_5)_n$
	Glycogen—form in which carbohydrate is stored in the liver and muscles, etc.	$(C_6H_{10}O_5)_n$
	Dextrin—formed from starch by partial hydrolysis	$(C_6H_{10}O_5)_n$

Starch is the principal form in which carbohydrate is stored in plants. During the ripening process in some plants (e.g., apple and banana) starch is changed to glucose; in other plants (e.g., corn and peas) the opposite process occurs.

Cellulose constitutes the supporting tissue of plant cells. When derived from mature plants, cellulose is quite resistant to the action of dilute acids or digestive enzymes and passes through the digestive tract unchanged. The chief value of cellulose in human nutrition is to give bulk to the intestinal contents and thereby facilitate peristalsis.

Glycogen is the form in which reserve carbohydrate is stored in the animal body, in greatest quantity in the liver and muscles.

Dextrins are formed from starch by the action of enzymes, acids, or heat.

Lipids. Lipids are a heterogeneous group of organic compounds which contain fatty acids, usually combined with an alcohol as an ester. They may be divided into two groups—*simple lipids* (fats, oils, and waxes) and *compound lipids* (phospholipids, glycolipids, and sterols). The word *fat* is sometimes used in an anatomical sense and sometimes in a chemical sense. In an anatomical sense, fat denotes adipose tissue. In a chemical sense, fats are glyceryl esters of fatty acids. In other words, fats are hydrolyzed to yield three molecules of fatty acid and one molecule of glycerol. The ordinary fats of animal and vegetable food are not simple substances but are mixtures of simple fats named palmitin, stearin, olein, etc., which are derived from the fatty acids—palmitic, stearic, and oleic acid, and the alcohol glycerol. Oils are chemically similar to fats but are usually liquid at room temperature, whereas fats are usually solid. Oils also contain more unsaturated[1] bonds than fats do. Vegetable oils in particular tend to be highly unsaturated—a fact which may be of medical significance in regard to metabolic utilization of the fat, although the details to date have not been clarified. Experimental evidence indicates the necessity of including some of the unsaturated fatty acids such as linoleic acid and linolenic acid, which are found in most fatty foods.

Fats are compounds of carbon, hydrogen, and oxygen, the same elements found in carbohydrates; but these elements are present in different combinations and proportions. The fats contain proportionately less oxygen and more carbon and hydrogen than the carbohydrates; consequently they make a more concentrated source of energy. Under the influence of lipases, secreted principally by the pancreas, fats and oils are split to glycerol and fatty acids by hydrolysis.

$$\underset{\text{(Stearin)}}{C_3H_5(C_{18}H_{35}O_2)_3} + \underset{\text{(Water)}}{3H_2O} \rightarrow \underset{\text{(Glycerol)}}{C_3H_5(OH)_3} + \underset{\text{(Stearic acid)}}{3H \cdot C_{18}H_{35}O_2}$$

Waxes are esters of fatty acids with high-molecular-weight alcohols. They are not found in the human body and have no nutritional value for humans. They are not hydrolyzed by lipases and are therefore indigestible.

Compound Lipids. These contain other groups in addition to fatty acids and an alcohol in the lipid molecule. These may be phosphate, carbohydrate, or nitrogen-containing radicals.

[1] Carbon compounds having a single bond between the carbon atoms are called *saturated* compounds; those with one or more double or triple bonds between carbon atoms are termed *unsaturated* compounds.

1. *Phospholipids*, or *phosphatides*, contain both phosphorus and nitrogen. The best known are the lecithins, which are abundant in egg yolk and occur in brain and nerve tissue and in all the cells of the body. Cephalins and sphingomyelin are other examples.

2. *Glycolipids*, or *cerebrosides*, are compounds of fatty acids with a carbohydrate and contain nitrogen but no phosphoric acid. Cerebrosides are found in the myelin sheaths of nerve fibers in connection with, possibly in combination with, lecithin.

3. *Sterols* are complex monohydroxyalcohols of high molecular weight, which are found in nature combined with fatty acids. They contain carbon, hydrogen, and oxygen. The best known is cholesterol, which is very widely distributed in the body, being found in the medullary coverings of nerve fibers, in the blood, in all the cells and liquids of the body, in the sebum secreted by the sebaceous glands of the skin, and in the bile. In the blood cholesterol protects the erythrocytes against the action of hemolytic substances, and in the sebum it protects the skin. Cholesterol serves as the precursor of the female sex hormone, pregnanediol; of cholic acid in the bile salts; and of the steroid hormones of the adrenal gland. Under the influence of ultraviolet rays other sterols closely related to cholesterol may be so changed as to acquire the property of an antirachitic vitamin. These are called "provitamin D" sterols.

Proteins. Proteins are more complex than either carbohydrates or fats and differ from them in containing *nitrogen*. Proteins always contain carbon, hydrogen, oxygen, and nitrogen; sometimes sulfur, phosphorus, or iron is present. Proteins are built up of simpler substances called *amino acids*. Amino acids are acids that contain an amino group (NH_2) instead of a hydrogen atom. In acetic acid, which is one of the simplest organic acids, the formula is CH_3COOH. If one of the three hydrogen atoms in the CH_3 group is replaced by NH_2, a substance results which has the formula $CH_2(NH_2)COOH$ and is called aminoacetic acid or *glycine* or glycocoll. Another organic acid is propionic acid, which has the formula C_2H_5COOH; if an atom of hydrogen is replaced by the amino group, $C_2H_4(NH_2)COOH$, aminopropionic acid, or *alanine*, results.

Some 40 or more amino acids have been described as occurring in nature and many more have been synthesized. However, only 23 amino acids have been unequivocally accepted as common "building stones" of the proteins. No one protein contains all of them, but caseinogen of milk yields 17 or more. The proteins of one animal differ from those of another; even the proteins of different tissues are not identical. This is also true of the proteins of plants. The proteins of milk, fish, egg, cereal, and vegetables represent different combinations of amino acids and are therefore different compounds. This means that proteins differ in relation to the numbers of amino acids present, the ratio of one amino acid to another, and the order in which they are linked (see page 435). Among vegetables the legumes—peas, beans, lentils, and peanuts—are especially rich in proteins.

Examples of Protein Constituents of Food

- *Albumin*, the white substance seen when egg is heated, the scum that forms on the top of milk when its temperature is raised above 76° C (170° F), the white coating that forms on meat when it has been in a hot oven for a short time
- *Casein*, the substance that forms a curd when acid or renin is added to milk or when milk sours
- *Glutenin*, the gummy substance in wheat
- *Legumin*, a protein substance contained in the legumes
- *Gelatin*, from intercellular substance of connective tissues, including bones and tendons
- *Organic extracts*, protein substances formed in animals and plants as a result of their metabolism. The flavor of meats and some plant foods is due to extractives

The body can synthesize arginine, but not rapidly enough to meet the demands of normal growth. Histidine may be synthesized

AMINO ACIDS FOUND IN HUMAN TISSUE

Essential	Nonessential*
Valine	Glycine
Leucine	Alanine
Isoleucine	Norleucine
Phenylalanine	Tyrosine
Threonine	Serine
Methionine	Cystine
†Arginine	Aspartic acid
Lysine	Glutamic acid
†Histidine	Hydroxyglutamic acid
Tryptophan	Proline
	Hydroxyproline

* Nonessential means that the body can synthesize in adequate amounts the amino acid listed.
† During growth.

in adult tissues or by intestinal microorganisms.

The following show a few of the many possible combinations of carbon, hydrogen, oxygen, and nitrogen to form amino acids.

Classification. Proteins are classified in two main groups:

1. Simple proteins when hydrolyzed yield only amino acids or their derivatives. Examples are serum albumin, globulin, scleroproteins.

2. Conjugated proteins are substances which contain a simple protein molecule united to some other nonprotein molecule known as the prosthetic group. On hydrolysis they yield amino acids and another molecule. This molecule is nucleic acid in the nucleoproteins, a carbohydrate in the glycoproteins, a phosphate in the phosphoproteins, pigment in the chromoproteins and hemoglobins, and a fatty substance in lipoproteins. Proteins are hydrolyzed to polypeptides and finally to amino acids.

Nutritive Value of Different Proteins. Proteins vary in their constituents and in their nutritive value, depending on their amino acid composition. Because of this they are classed as *adequate* proteins, or those containing all the amino acids for the growth and maintenance of the body, and *inadequate* proteins, which furnish material for energy needs but not for growth and the repair of tissue. In general, the protein of animal origin most nearly meets the essential needs of the human for synthesis of tissue. Gelatin is an

Glycine $CH_2(NH_2) \cdot COOH$

Lysine $CH_2(NH_2) \cdot CH_2 \cdot CH_2 \cdot CH_2 \cdot CH(NH_2) \cdot COOH$

Aspartic acid $COOH \cdot CH_2 \cdot CH(NH_2) \cdot COOH$

Tyrosine

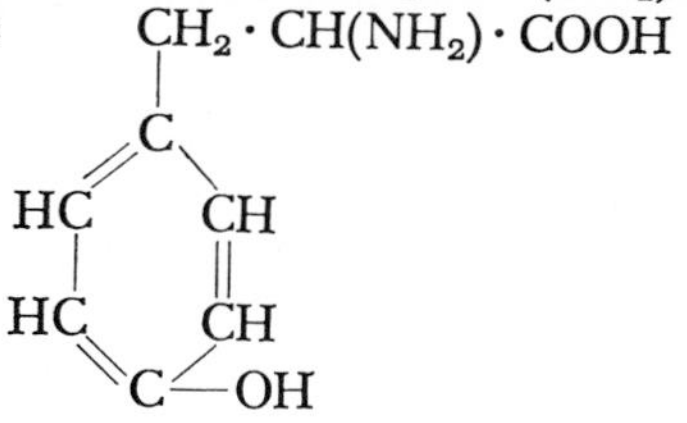

```
   CH2 · CH(NH2) · COOH
   |
   C
 //  \
HC    CH
|     ||
HC    CH
  \\ /
   C—OH
```

Tryptophan

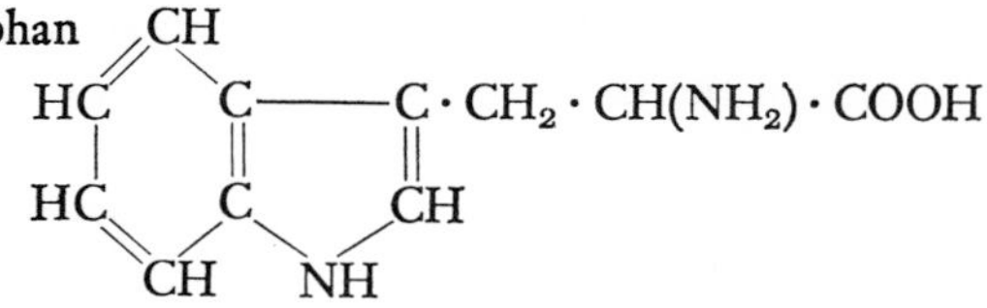

```
   CH
 //  \
HC    C———C · CH2 · CH(NH2) · COOH
|     ||  ||
HC    C   CH
  \\ / \ /
   CH   NH
```

Proline

```
H2C———CH2
|      |
H2C    CH · COOH
   \  /
    NH
```

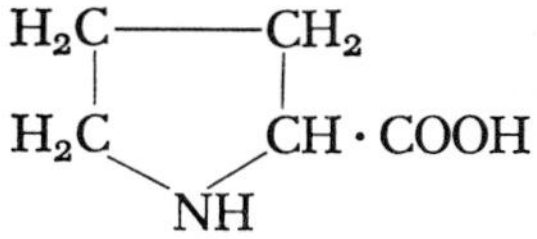

Methionine $CH_3 \cdot S \cdot CH_2 \cdot CH_2 \cdot CH(NH_2) \cdot COOH$

example of an inadequate protein; on the other hand, the casein of milk and the glutenin of wheat contain all essential amino acids and can furnish energy and build tissue. Combinations of incomplete proteins can supplement each other. However, amino acids are not stored to any great degree. If adequate protein is provided but the caloric demands of the body are not being met, amino acids will be used for the production of energy.

Nitrogen Equilibrium. Nitrogen continues to be excreted in the urine even though the diet is devoid of nitrogen. This represents a condition in which the body is oxidizing its own tissues to supply its needs. The nitrogenous portion of the protein molecule of ingested proteins is not stored in the body but is eliminated chiefly in the urine in the form of urea and to a limited extent in the feces. It is therefore important that the body receive daily an amount of protein nitrogen equal to the amount eliminated in the excreta. When this condition exists, the body is said to be in nitrogen equilibrium. If there is a positive balance, it means that protein is being made into body protoplasm; and this is an ideal condition during the period of growth or convalescence from wasting illness. If the balance is negative, it means that the body is oxidizing its own protein. Minimum nitrogen equilibrium can be maintained on about 40 gm of protein or less per day, but it is thought that higher protein intake results in greater resistance to disease and a higher state of physiological efficiency. It is customary to add 50 per cent to the average indicated as the actual requirement based on laboratory experiments, thus bringing the amount up to 60 to 100 gm of protein per day, which is somewhat more than 1 gm per kilogram of body weight.

MINERAL METABOLISM

The mineral elements which enter into the composition of the body are listed on page 23. Mineral constituents form about 4 per cent of the body weight and are primarily located in the skeleton. Since each element enters into the metabolism of body cells, a constant supply of each is necessary to meet the daily loss. These elements are supplied in food. On analysis many of them are classified as ash constituents, since they remain after incineration of the food. These "ash constituents" may function in the body in several ways: as constituents of bone, giving rigidity to the skeleton; as essential elements of all protoplasm associated with enzyme activity; as soluble constituents of the fluids of the body influencing the elasticity and irritability of the muscles and nerves, supplying material for the acidity or alkalinity of all body fluids, helping to maintain the acid-base equilibrium of the body fluids as well as their osmotic characteristics and solvent power; and probably in many other ways. Not only must the body be supplied with certain minerals which are important for its functions, but these must be supplied in readily absorbable form. Thus, only a small fraction, several milligrams, of the ion which is ingested is absorbed daily.

The importance of the optimum concentrations of each of these mineral salts in the tissues and fluids of the body is so great that any considerable change from the normal endangers life.

Calcium is a constituent of all protoplasm and of body fluids and is present in large proportions in bones and teeth. There is more calcium than any other cation in the body. Ninety-nine per cent of body calcium is in bones and teeth. Calcium is essential for all cellular activities. It is related to normal permeability of cellular membranes, excitability of muscle, normal heart action and nerve activity, and must be present in ionic form for normal blood clotting. Children as well as pregnant and lactating animals require large amounts. Milk is the best source of calcium, but calcium is also present in leafy vegetables. The body cannot readily adapt itself to calcium shortage; therefore, a liberal amount is needed daily. It is estimated that an intake of 1 gm of calcium would maintain the body fluids at optimum concentration. Calcium deficiency is a definite problem in the diet of Americans.

Phosphorus is essential to the normal development of bones and teeth. It is a necessary constituent of all cells, particularly nerve and muscle tissue. About 80 per cent of the total is combined with calcium in the bones and teeth. It is in organic combination such as phospholipids, phosphocreatine, and phosphorylated intermediates of carbohydrate metabolism. Blood plasma and body fluids are relatively low in phosphates. The phosphate ester is of great importance in energy transfer. (See page 466.) Phosphorylation is also important in the absorption of carbohydrate from the intestine and in the reabsorption of glucose by the renal tubule. It is also concerned with maintaining enzyme systems and their functioning.

Iron in the adult body amounts to about 4.5 gm, distributed in the hemoglobin of red cells (2.5 gm), myoglobin of skeletal muscle, intracellular enzyme systems (particularly the cytochrome system), and in the tissues as ferritin. This latter is the storage form of iron—bound to protein—and is found primarily in the liver, as well as the spleen, bone marrow, and lymph nodes. In hemoglobin it is the iron-containing part of the molecule to which the oxygen is attached and which carries oxygen to the cells. Traces of copper are essential for utilization of iron in the formation of hemoglobin. Iron absorption occurs only if the iron is in a readily ionizable form. The acid of the stomach ionizes dietary iron; in gastric disease when acid production is reduced, iron absorption is usually impaired.

Storage of iron in the body is limited; therefore, foods containing it should be included in the daily diet. Recent studies indicate that iron deficiency is common among women.

At birth, a baby has a special store of iron in its body, which serves during the period of lactation. During the latter half of the first year, egg yolk and iron-bearing vegetables should be added gradually to the diet, so that as the reserve iron is depleted, fresh supplies will be available. In premature infants this special store of iron is absent; preparations of iron and copper are added to the milk.

Copper is a factor in hemoglobin formation, though it is not a part of the molecule. It must be present for the utilization of iron in hemoglobin synthesis. Since it is not a part of the hemoglobin molecule, it is believed to function as part of an enzyme-catalyzing system necessary for hemoglobin formation.

Magnesium is found in the intracellular fluid of the body and in the extracellular space of skeletal tissue, in about equal amounts in each space. Total magnesium content of the body is approximately 21 to 28 gm. Magnesium is a vital element in cell physiology because it serves as a cofactor in the metabolism of glucose, of pyruvic acid, and of adenosine triphosphate. In excessive amounts it has a depressing action on nerve impulse transmission and nerve tissue functioning in general.

Potassium content of the body is about 125 gm, found primarily inside the cells where it functions in association with various enzymes. It is intimately concerned with transmission of the nerve impulse, with skeletal muscle contraction, and with cardiac contraction. Excess or lack of the normal amount of potassium causes immediate malfunctioning of the heart.

Iodine is utilized by the thyroid gland in the synthesis of thyroxin. To maintain the body store of iodine and meet the loss in metabolism, it is estimated that a normal adult requires 0.15 to 0.30 mg of iodine daily. Regions in which the supply of iodine is insufficient in water report good results in reducing the incidence of goiter by administration of iodine.

Cobalt is a constituent of vitamin B_{12} and is concerned with red-cell formation.

Manganese is an essential element widely distributed in plant and animal tissues. Its specific function in the body is not clear, but it is known that manganese activates several important enzymes.

Zinc is essential in plant nutrition and it is

evident that it is necessary in animal nutrition for it functions in enzyme systems, including carbonic anhydrase. It is universally distributed in plant and animal tissue.

Fluorine is found in bones and teeth and other tissues. In very small amounts it apparently improves tooth structure. Animal research has not provided evidence that it is an essential part of the diet.

"*Trace element*" is the name given to a number of other elements, i.e., molybdenum and strontium, which are found in the body in minute quantities or traces. It is believed that they have important metabolic functions, as in nerve tissue, and may also be involved in some disease processes.

A diet which furnishes sufficient carbohydrate, fat, and protein may be lacking in calcium, phosphorus, iron, iodine, and copper unless vegetables and fruits are added in sufficient quantities to prevent this deficiency. The amount of calcium and phosphorus needed is relatively large, and definite provision must be made for it. The amount of iron needed is minute; but since the quantities in food materials are also minute, the sources of supply must be considered in planning the diet. If the requirements for calcium and iron are met, it is probable that all other minerals will also be supplied in the same foods.

Another aspect of mineral metabolism is its relationship to water and electrolyte balance, which involves sodium, potassium, and hydrogen in particular. This will be discussed in Chapter 25.

THE VITAMINS

Vitamins are organic substances present in small amounts in natural foodstuffs, which are essential for growth and normal metabolism. They are considered to be essential to all cells and are needed in the diet in minute amounts. Several members of the vitamin-B group are known to be components of respiratory enzymes and of other enzymes which act as catalysts for cell processes. Recent experiments emphasize the determination of optimum (as distinguished from merely adequate) amounts of the vitamins and their physiological effects. The vitamins constitute a *nutritional factor*, which has been defined as a single substance or any group of substances performing a specific vital function in nutrition.

The Fat-Soluble Vitamins

The fat-soluble vitamins require the presence of bile in the intestinal tract for absorption. Hence any defect in fat absorption may lead to deficiencies of the fat-soluble vitamins.

Vitamin A. Vitamin A and its provitamins, or precursory substances, called alpha, beta, and gamma carotenes and cryptoxanthin, constitute a nutritional factor essential to growth and to epithelial tissues in particular. The precursory substances occur in yellow pigments of plants such as paprika and carrots. These plants contain no vitamin A but do contain the precursory substances which are transformed to vitamin A, chiefly in the liver and in the wall of the small intestine. They add to the vitamin-A value of the food but not to its vitamin content. Fish-liver oils contain vitamin A as well as the precursory substances; hence, they add to the vitamin content of the foods as well as to their vitamin value.

Two forms of vitamin A are detectable—an acid and an aldehyde. Vitamin-A acid is responsible for the maintenance of epithelial tissues; vitamin-A aldehyde makes up part of the molecule of rhodopsin, the retinal pigment. It is stored in large amounts in the liver, if the diet includes such an amount.

Deficiency results in disturbances associated with nervous and epithelial tissues: (1) retarded growth, (2) susceptibility to xerophthalmia, an eye condition conducive to subsequent infection and resulting blindness, (3) dermatosis or dry skin, (4) generally impaired epithelial tissues and resulting increased susceptibility to infections of the lungs, skin, bladder, sinuses, ears, and alimentary tract, and (5) night blindness, which results from failure of the normal regeneration of visual purple after its light-induced change, and reduced synthesis of thyroxin.

Hypervitaminosis is possible; symptoms include joint pain and loss of hair.

Vitamin D. All of the D vitamins have antirachitic properties, but there is a difference in potency. Irradiated ergosterol (D_2) and irradiated cholesterol (D_3) are powerful antirachitic vitamins. The crystalline form which has been isolated is calciferol.

Role in Physiology. There is a close relationship of action between vitamin D and the hormone of the parathyroid gland in calcium metabolism. Vitamin D is needed for absorption of calcium from the intestine and for reabsorption of phosphates in the renal tubules. It is needed for normal bone growth and is considered a factor in the maintenance of the normal functioning of the respiratory system, in the formation of normal teeth, and in protection against dental caries. Deficiency in vitamin D has long been known to result in rickets, which may be cured by administration of vitamin D, by direct sunlight, by ultraviolet irradiation of the body, or by administration of ergosterol or similar substances produced by irradiation. The effect of ultraviolet irradiation of the skin is through its transformation of provitamin D of skin-gland secretions into vitamin D, which is absorbed by the skin. The effective rays are those that cause tanning. Ingestion of excessive amounts of vitamin D results in elevated calcium levels in blood and tissue fluids and in abnormal calcification of soft tissues.

The Tocopherols. Vitamin E (antisterility) prevents sterility in both male and female rats, but not in humans. However, it may be important in various enzyme transformations in cell respiration.

Vitamin K. Vitamin K possesses antihemorrhagic properties. For this reason, inadequate fat absorption due to lack of bile salts is particularly significant in regard to vitamin K. It is considered a factor essential to normal clotting of blood, as it promotes the synthesis of prothrombin and proconvertin by the liver. The blood of animals having a deficiency of this vitamin shows a lowered content of prothrombin and a delayed clotting time.

Vitamin K is fat soluble and appears to be found in a great variety of foods, but knowledge regarding quantitative requirements of this vitamin is still limited. The newborn infant may have an alimentary deficiency, since the vitamin is not readily passed from mother to fetus, hence the need for giving vitamin K to the newborn and to mothers before delivery. It is also used medically to counteract bleeding effects of drugs which block its formation in the liver.

The Water-Soluble Vitamins

Vitamin B. Vitamin B is of multiple nature and is usually referred to as "the vitamin-B complex." In general, this group of vitamins is necessary for formation of many enzymes, particularly those involved in (1) oxidation-reduction reactions and energy transformation; and (2) formation of red blood cells.

Thiamine (Vitamin B_1). The first B vitamin, thiamine, combines with phosphate to form cocarboxylase, which plays an essential role in carbohydrate metabolism. It is essential for oxidation reactions within the cell and for transformation of the amino acid tryptophan to niacin. An adequate supply of it is necessary for normal appetite and normal motility of the digestive tract.

Beriberi occurs chiefly among Oriental nations that make great use of rice as food. The disease takes a variety of forms, but the symptoms are gastrointestinal disturbances, paralysis, and atrophy of the limbs. This condition is caused by limiting the diet to polished rice. If the polishings are restored to the diet, the condition disappears; or if meat or barley is used with the polished rice, the condition is avoided.

Riboflavin (Vitamin B_2). Riboflavin is somewhat more heat-stable than is B_1. Phosphorylation of riboflavin is essential for its absorption in the intestine. It was first isolated from milk and named *lactoflavin* and is frequently referred to as the "flavin factor." Riboflavin is the essential component of the flavoprotein coenzymes. These coenzymes catalyze hydrogen transfer in various cell reactions leading to the oxidation of hydrogen to water. Riboflavin is thus an important factor in tissue respiration and is essential to normal growth and nutrition at all ages, since it is vital for protein metabolism.

Niacin and Niacinamide (Nicotinic Acid and Nicotinic Acid Amide). These are constituents of two coenzymes which play vital roles in metabolism. These coenzymes function as hydrogen and electron transfer agents in oxidation-reduction reactions. They may be synthesized in man from tryptophan.

Deficiency may result in dermatitis, diarrhea, stomatitis, or glossitis. Niacin is specific for the treatment of acute pellagra.

Pyridoxine (B_6). Vitamin B_6, as pyridoxine, pyridoxal, or pyridoxamine, is important for normal growth and nutrition, and in its active form is essential for the functioning of several enzyme systems. These are the enzymes which catalyze the removal of carboxyl (–COOH) groups from amino acids and those which aid in transfer of amino (NH_2) groups from one substance to another. Pyridoxine also functions in the metabolic reactions involving fatty acids, and in the conversion of tryptophan to niacin. Deficiency produces dermatitis.

Pantothenic Acid. The vitamin pantothenic acid is a constituent of coenzyme A which combines with acetate to form acetyl coenzyme A. It is essential for the intermediate metabolism of fats, carbohydrates, and certain amino acids (see page 474). Acetyl coenzyme A is involved in the formation of cholesterol and the steroid hormones, also of acetylcholine, which is essential to the transmission of nerve impulses. Deficiencies rarely occur in man. In animals the symptoms include growth failure, dermatitis, and nerve involvement.

Cyanocobalamin (Vitamin B_{12}). Cyanocobalamin, so called because of the presence of cobalt in its complex molecule, is also named the antipernicious anemia factor. The absorption of this vitamin in the gastrointestinal tract is dependent upon the presence of a gastric factor, "intrinsic factor." The intrinsic factor is a constituent of gastric mucoprotein. It is found mostly in the cardiac and fundic portions of the stomach. Hence patients who have a total gastrectomy will also develop vitamin B_{12} deficiency and anemia, as absence of the intrinsic factor prevents absorption of vitamin B_{12} from the intestine. It is required for normal metabolism and is essential in the formation of the red blood cell. It is possibly a growth factor for children, but this is uncertain.

Folic Acid (Pteroylglutamic Acid). This vitamin is believed to be concerned chiefly with enzyme systems involved in red cell formation. Its relationship metabolically to B_{12} is close, though as yet unclear. They both stimulate hematopoiesis. It is believed that folic acid can be synthesized by bacteria in the intestine, and that it is concerned with the use of proteins for growth and development.

Biotin, necessary *in very* minute amounts, functions in several systems as a coenzyme. It participates in carboxylation reactions as well as in deamination of certain amino acids.

Other Factors. Lipoic acid aids in decarboxylation of pyruvate before it enters the oxidative cycle. It is not a true vitamin.

Choline. Choline is not a true vitamin; however, its role in nutrition is essential. Choline is a constituent of the lecithins and is also importantly concerned in the metabolism of fats. In the form of acetylcholine, it is essential as the chemical mediator of nerve impulses. Deficiencies in experimental animals show tissue damage and abnormal accumulation of fat in the liver particularly, and also in the heart and blood vessels.

Ascorbic Acid (Vitamin C). Ascorbic acid has long been known to be essential in the prevention of scurvy. Early records of sea voyages reveal many epidemics of scurvy, and it was reported from Austria and Russia during World War I. The cause is lack of fresh fruit and vegetables; the prevention is the use of these. Early cures were through the use of citrus fruit juices. Laboratory experiments on animals and men prove conclusively that scurvy is due to lack of vitamin C in the diet.

Role in Physiology. More recently vitamin C has been shown to be of importance in tissue respiration, which is decreased in scurvy. Shortage of vitamin C is shown to impair general nutrition, to prevent healing of bone wounds, and to be a contributory factor in capillary fragility and the general resistance of the body. Vitamin C is essential for the formation and maintenance of the intercellular cement and collagen. It is necessary for the integrity of capillary membranes and plays an important part in the formation of blood cells in bone marrow. It is also an important factor in the healing of wounds. The adrenal cortex contains a large quantity of vitamin C, which suggests its use in the metabolic synthesis of the steroid hormones. A liberal daily intake of vitamin C throughout life is recommended. The relationship of deficiency to dental caries is undetermined, but the soundness of teeth and their supporting bones and gums is believed to be dependent upon the amount of vitamin C supplied by the food.

Symptoms of scurvy are loss of weight, pallor, weakness, breathlessness, palpitation of the heart, swelling of the gums, loosening of the teeth, pains in the bones and joints, edema, nervousness, and slight hemorrhages appearing as red spots under the skin and forming hidden bleeding places in the muscles and internal organs. The heart hypertrophies and shows degenerative changes, which often cause sudden death.

	Vitamins	Sources	Effects of Cooking	General Effects of Optimum Intake	Evidences of Deficiency
Fat-Soluble	A	Milk, butter, eggs, fish-liver oils, green vegetables, yellow vegetables (provitamins)	Resists heat in absence of air; readily destroyed by oxidation	A factor in— Decreasing susceptibility to skin infections Preserving general health and vigor Effecting chemistry neccessary for vision Promoting growth	Failure to gain weight, susceptibility to xerophthalmia, night blindness, dry skin, impaired epithelial tissues, increased incidence of respiratory diseases and of skin (toad skin), ear, and sinus infections, inflammations and infections of alimentary and urinary tracts, degenerative changes in nervous tissues
	D	Egg yolk, whole milk, butter, fish-liver oils	Slight; relatively stable	A factor in well-developed bone and teeth, calcium and phosphorus metabolism	Rickets (in children) Osteomalacia (in adults), bone demineralization
	E	Seeds of plants, eggs, lettuce, spinach, meat, wide distribution	Unusually heat resistant	A factor in normal gestation in rats	Sterility in rats
	K	Wide distribution, especially green leaves		A factor in normal functioning of liver and normal clotting time	Delayed clotting time

	Vitamins	Sources	Effects of Cooking	General Effects of Optimum Intake	Evidences of Deficiency
Water-Soluble	B_1 Thiamine	Whole-grain cereals, legumes, eggs, pork	Destroyed by prolonged heating, by temperatures higher than boiling	A factor in— Normal carbohydrate metabolism; Maintenance of normal appetite, digestion, absorption	Beriberi, polyneuritis; Stunted growth of children, lowered appetite, reduced intestinal motility
	B_2 Riboflavin	Milk, eggs, green vegetables, liver, heart	Relatively heat stable	A factor in— Tissue respiration; Normal growth and nutrition and vitality at all ages	Dermatitis, pellagra (in part); Well-defined eye lesions
	Niacin	Liver, milk, poultry	Destroyed by high heat	Essential in metabolic processes which release energy	Low nutritional level
	B_6 Pyridoxine Pyridoxal Pyridoxamine	Whole-grain cereals, yeast, milk, eggs, pork, liver, legumes	Unusually heat resistant	A factor in normal metabolism of fats, amino acids	Florid type of dermatitis (experimental pellagra in rats); Nervousness, irritability, and insomnia
	B_{12} Cyanocobalamin	Liver, kidney, lean meat, milk, cheese	Relatively heat stable	A factor in red cell formation	Pernicious anemia
	Pantothenic acid	Egg yolk, kidney, liver, yeast, broccoli, lean meat, heart	Destroyed by high heat	Essential for synthesis of acetyl coenzyme A, metabolism of fats, carbohydrates, and certain amino acids	Rarely occurs in man
	Folic acid	Fresh green leafy vegetables, liver, legumes		A factor in— Functioning of enzyme systems; Essential in metabolic processes—growth and development	Anemia
	C Ascorbic acid	Citrus fruits (raw or canned), tomatoes (raw or canned), broccoli	Readily destroyed by heat, especially slow cooking	A factor in— Red cell formation; Normal integrity of capillaries; Normal development of teeth and maintenance of health of gums; Healing of wounds and protection against infections; Normal cellular chemistry of all tissues	Low nutritional level; Fragility of capillary networks; Scurvy and possibly predisposition to dental caries and systemic type of pyorrhea

As research continues, it is becoming more and more obvious that the major function of all vitamins is in relation to enzyme functioning. For many it is known that they make up part of the molecular structure of coenzymes, or cofactors, which accept atoms or groups of atoms which are removed from a substrate. These are listed in the accompanying coenzyme table:

Coenzyme		Function	Vitamin
(NAD)	Nicotinamide adenine dinucleotide	As hydrogen acceptors in dehydrogenases	Niacinamide
(NADP)	Nicotinamide adenine dinucleotide phosphate		
(FMN)	Flavin mononucleotide	As hydrogen acceptors in aerobic dehydrogenases	Riboflavin
(FAD)	Flavin adenine dinucleotide		
	Pyridoxal phosphate	As transaminases, amino acid decarboxylases	Pyridoxine
(TPP)	Thiamine pyrophosphate	As cocarboxylase	Thiamine
(CoA)	Coenzyme A	In condensing enzymes, fatty acid utilization, acetate transfer	Pantothenic acid

DIGESTIVE PROCESSES

Digestion includes all the changes, physical and chemical, which food undergoes in the body, making it absorbable. In some instances no change is necessary; water, minerals, and certain carbohydrates in fruits are ready to be absorbed. In other instances cooking processes initiate chemical changes in food before it enters the body, for example, changing starch to dextrin, partially splitting fats into glycerol and fatty acids, and changing some proteins to the first stages of their hydrolytic products. Cooking in many instances improves the appearance, odor, and taste of food, and these changes stimulate the end organs of the optic and olfactory nerves and the taste buds, causing a reflex stimulation of the digestive mechanisms. Cooking also tends to destroy microorganisms which would be harmful to the body.

The digestive processes are controlled by the nervous and hormonal systems. Any strong emotion which affects the nervous system unpleasantly inhibits the secretion of the digestive fluids and interferes with digestion, often checking the appetite and even preventing the taking of food. On the other hand, pleasurable sensations aid digestion, hence the value of attractively served food, pleasant surroundings, and cheerful conversation.

THE CRANIAL NERVES RELATED TO DIGESTIVE PROCESSES

Through the olfactory, optic, and cochlear nerves impulses reach the brain and cause reflex stimulation of digestive juices.

The oculomotor, trochlear, and abducens nerves supply the motor fibers to extrinsic and intrinsic muscles of the eye so that adjustment may be made to vision.

The trigeminal and facial nerves are sensory to teeth and mouth and motor to muscles; they are necessary for movement of the jaw in mastication, secretion of saliva (submaxillary and sublingual glands), taste on the anterior part of the tongue, and swallowing.

The glossopharyngeal nerve is concerned with secretion of saliva (parotid gland), taste on the posterior part of the tongue, and general sensation of pharynx and tongue.

The vagus nerve is concerned with taste in the region of the epiglottis; motor to the pharyngeal muscles, sensory to the pharynx; motor to the esophagus, stomach, small intestine, and part of large intestine; secretory to glands of the esophagus, stomach, small and large intestine, liver, and pancreas.

The accessory nerve is motor to muscles of pharynx and is concerned with the act of swallowing.

The hypoglossal nerve is motor to muscles of the tongue for mastication and swallowing.

Mechanical Digestion. This includes the various physical processes that occur in the alimentary canal. It serves the following purposes: taking food in and moving it along through the alimentary canal just rapidly enough to allow the required chemical changes to take place in each part; lubricating the food by adding the mucin and water secreted by the glands of the alimentary canal; liquefying the food by mixing it with the various digestive juices; and grinding the food into small particles, thereby increasing the amount of surface to come in contact with the digestive fluids.

Chemical Digestion. This is essentially a process of hydrolysis which is dependent upon the presence of enzymes. An example of hydrolysis (hydrolytic cleavage) is the splitting of maltose into glucose (also called dextrose) under the influence of maltase.

$$C_{12}H_{22}O_{11} + H_2O \rightarrow C_6H_{12}O_6 + C_6H_{12}O_6$$

Necessity for Chemical Digestion. Chemical digestion is necessary because foods in general cannot pass through animal membranes, and the tissues cannot use them; hence, they must be reduced to small molecules and to such substances as the tissues can use, i.e., (1) simple sugars, resulting from the hydrolysis of all carbohydrate foods; (2) glycerol and fatty acids, resulting from the hydrolysis of fats; and (3) amino acids, resulting from the hydrolysis of proteins.

Agents of Chemical Digestion. Hydrolytic cleavages similar to those of digestion can be brought about in several ways. Boiling foodstuffs with acids, treating with alkali, or subjecting them to superheated steam will accomplish these changes. The *remarkable* fact is that strong acids and high temperatures, or both, are necessary to produce these changes in the laboratory, whereas in the digestive tract they take place at body temperature and are due to the enzymes present in the digestive juices.

Enzyme Functioning in the Digestive Pathway

The enzymes that bring about chemical digestion in the alimentary tract are exoenzymes—organic catalysts which are produced by cells, secreted into the digestive tract where they act. They may be classified as follows:

1. The Sugar-Splitting Enzymes. The glucosidases, which hydrolyze disaccharides to monosaccharides. Examples: maltase splits maltose to glucose; sucrase splits cane sugar to glucose and fructose; and lactase splits milk sugar (lactose) to glucose and galactose.

2. The Amylolytic, or Starch-Splitting, Enzymes. Examples: salivary amylase and pancreatic amylase cause hydrolysis of starch.

3. The Lipolytic, or Fat-Splitting, Enzymes. Examples: lipase found in the pancreatic secretion causes hydrolysis of fat.

4. The Proteolytic, or Protein-Splitting, Enzymes. Examples: pepsin of gastric juice and trypsin and chymotrypsin of pancreatic juice, which cause hydrolysis of the proteins.

The digestive enzymes are found in the secretions of the various organs, in solution with a great deal of water which also contains mucus as well as electrolytes. Thus loss of any large amount of the digestive juices may lead to dehydration and electrolyte imbalance.

Tissue fluid forms the only source of materials for the formation of secretions. The basic materials for the secretions are brought to the tissue fluid by the blood. Energy, together with the necessary nutrients, is used by the cell for the synthesis of organic substances, the secretions. The secretory materials accumulate around the Golgi apparatus and are then extruded through the surface of the cell into the lumen of the gland. At the same time the by-products of glandular cell activity enter the tissue fluid and enter the blood or lymph capillary.

Regulation of Glandular Secretion. Glandular cells are well supplied with nerve fibers from the autonomic nervous system. The stimuli for varying the amount of secretory product may be chemical, nervous, or hormonal. There are secretory as well as vasomotor fibers which, when reflexly stimulated by the sight or smell of food, (1) dilate the blood vessels, increasing the volume of the gland, and (2) cause the glands to produce a secretion that is copious in amount and watery in consistency.

Changes the Food Undergoes in the Mouth

Mastication. When solid food is taken into the mouth, its comminution is immediately begun. It is cut and ground by the teeth, being pushed between them again and again by the muscular contractions of the cheeks and the movements of the tongue, until the whole is thoroughly crushed.

Insalivation. During the process of mastication saliva is poured in large quantities into the mouth and, mixing with the food, lubricates, moistens, and reduces it to a softened mass known as a *bolus*, which can be readily swallowed.

Secretion of Saliva. The nerve supply of the salivary glands is derived in part from the craniosacral and in part from the thoracolumbar divisions of the autonomic system. Both sets of nerves carry secretory and vasomotor fibers. The craniosacral nerves cause the glands to produce a secretion that is copious in amount and watery in consistency.

The consistency of saliva depends in part on the relative number of serous and mucous cells which are secreting. Serous cells produce a thin watery secretion and mucous cells produce a thick secretion. The thoracolumbar nerves carry vasoconstrictor fibers, and perhaps are relatively unimportant for controlling normal function of the salivary glands. However, if the sympathetic fibers are stimulated, vasoconstriction occurs and a scanty, viscid saliva is produced. Under normal conditions, the secretion of saliva is the result of stimulation of the secretory nerves by the smell, taste, or sight of food. Obviously, the taste buds of the tongue, fauces, and cheeks are the sense organs which are stimulated by the presence of food in the mouth.

Saliva. Saliva is secreted by the salivary glands—parotid, submaxillary, and sublingual—and by the numerous minute buccal glands of the mucosa of the mouth.

It consists of a large amount of water (some 99.5 per cent) containing some protein material, mucin, inorganic salts, and *salivary amylase.* It has a specific gravity of about 1.005 and is nearly neutral in reaction (pH about 6.4 to 7.0). Although the amount of saliva secreted per day varies considerably, an average amount is from 1 to 1.5 liters. Substances in saliva include inorganic salts in solution, chlorides, carbonates, and phosphates of sodium, calcium, and potassium.

The other substances are organic, mainly mucin, salivary amylases, serum albumin and globulin, and urea. The calcium carbonate and phosphate in combination with organic material may be deposited on the teeth as tartar, especially if the saliva is alkaline and contains considerable mucin. Occasionally these salts may be also deposited in the ducts of the salivary glands.

The functions of saliva are to soften and moisten the food, assisting in mastication and deglutition; to coat the food with mucin, lubricating it and ensuring a smooth passage along the esophagus; to moisten or liquefy dry and solid food, providing a necessary step in the process of stimulating the taste buds, as taste sensations play a part in the secretion of gastric juice; to digest starch by means of salivary amylase.

Salivary Amylase. Salivary amylase changes starch to dextrins and maltose. The process of reducing starch to maltose is a gradual one, consisting of a series of hydrolytic changes which take place in successive stages and result in a number of intermediate compounds. The change is best effected at the temperature of the body, in a neutral solution. Boiled starch is changed more rapidly and completely than raw, but food is rarely retained in the mouth long enough for the saliva to do more than begin the digestion of starch.

Deglutition, or Swallowing. Deglutition is divided into three stages which correspond to the three regions—mouth, pharynx, and esophagus—through which the food passes. The *first stage* consists of the passage of the bolus of food through the fauces. Contractions of the constrictor muscles of the pharynx force the bolus along. The *second stage* consists of the passage of the bolus through the laryngeal pharynx. During this stage, the respiratory opening into the larynx is closed by the approximation of the vocal folds which close the glottis, by the elevation of the larynx, and by contraction of the muscles of deglutition. The parts are crowded together by the descent of the base of the tongue, the lifting of the larynx, and the coming together of the vocal folds.

The *third stage* consists in the passage of the bolus through the esophagus. Apparently the consistency of the food affects this stage of the process. Solid or semisolid food is forced down the esophagus by a peristaltic movement and requires from four to eight seconds for passage from mouth to stomach. About half of this time is taken up in the passage through the esophagus, and the remainder is spent in transit through the cardiac orifice of the stomach. Liquid or very soft food is shot through the esophagus, which is reflexly inhibited, and arrives at the lower end in about 0.1 second. It may pass into the stomach at once or may be held in the esophagus for moments, depending on the condition of the cardiac sphincter. Repeated deglutition causes the tension of the muscles which function as a cardiac sphincter to diminish progressively, until they become completely relaxed, and food passes into the stomach. Following this, relaxation finally disappears and the sphincter becomes more contracted than usual and remains so for a considerable time.

Summary. During the process of mastication, salivation, and deglutition the food is reduced to a soft, pulpy condition, and any starch it contains may begin to be changed into sugar.

Changes the Food Undergoes in the Stomach

The food which enters the stomach is delayed there by the contraction of the sphincter muscles at the cardiac and pyloric openings. Within a few minutes after the entrance of food small contractions start in the middle region of the stomach and run toward the pylorus. These contractions are regular and in the pyloric region become more forcible as digestion progresses.

Weak rippling peristaltic movements, called *mixing waves*, pass over the stomach about every 15 to 25 seconds. As a result of these movements the food in the prepyloric and pyloric portions is macerated, mixed with the acid gastric fluid, and reduced to a thin liquid mass called *chyme*. At certain intervals the pyloric sphincter relaxes, and the wave of contraction forces some of the chyme into the duodenum. The fundic end of the stomach is less actively concerned with these movements but serves as a reservoir for food. The food at the fundic end may remain undisturbed for an hour or more and thus escape rapid mixture with the gastric fluid, which, therefore, penetrates slowly to the interior of the mass; hence salivary digestion may continue for a time. As the chyme is gradually forced into the duodenum, the pressure of the fundus forces the food into the pyloric end.

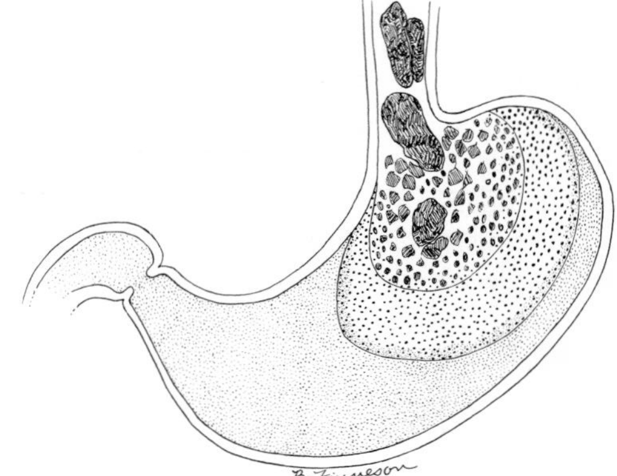

Figure 21–1. Diagram of stomach showing in fine stippling the food which first entered the stomach and has undergone digestive processes. Size of dots indicates progressive physical and chemical breakdown of food particles.

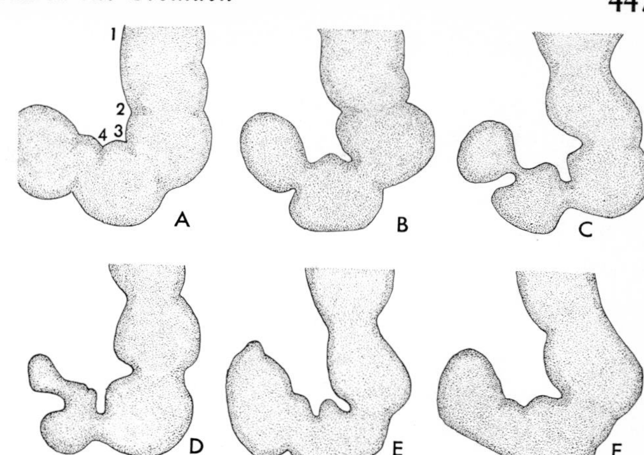

Figure 21–2. Diagrams to show peristalsis in the stomach. Locate *1, 2, 3, 4* in succeeding figures to trace a peristaltic wave over the stomach.

The time required for gastric digestion depends upon the nature of the food eaten. Liquids taken on an empty stomach pass through the pylorus promptly. Small test meals may remain from one to two hours, but average meals probably stay in the stomach from three to four and one-half hours. The shape of the stomach ("fishhook," "steerhorn") is an important factor in determining evacuation time. It has been demonstrated that emptying time was about 50 per cent faster in individuals with a "steerhorn" stomach than those with a "fishhook" (or J-shaped) stomach.

Shortly after ingestion of a meal, peristaltic waves begin to traverse the lower stomach. These waves begin about the middle of the stomach, and sweep downward, usually passing over the pyloric sphincter and often into the duodenum. The fundic part of the stomach contains the meal and functions as a storage chamber. While it shows no peristaltic waves, it does show progressive increase in muscle tension. The increasing tension forces food toward the lower end of the stomach where it comes in contact with the peristaltic waves.

Emptying of the stomach depends *almost entirely* on a pressure gradient between the stomach and duodenum. For material to leave the stomach, the *intragastric* pressure must be greater than the *intraduodenal*. The intragastric pressure is due to (1) gastric tonus changes and (2) head pressure of the peristaltic wave. The pyloric sphincter *does not* control evacuation. The sphincter may actually be relaxed during most of the digestion period *without* emptying occurring. When the intragastric pressure is adequately greater than the intraduodenal, about 2 to 5 ml of gastric content is passed into the duodenum with each peristaltic wave. Meals which are high in fat content delay the emptying time through the action of *enterogastrone*, a hormone which decreases gastric motility.

When the intraduodenal pressure exceeds the intragastric pressure, reflex constriction of the pyloric sphincter prevents the duodenal content from entering the stomach. *The major role of the pyloric sphincter is to prevent regurgitation.* With the exception of the rectal sphincter, the major role of all sphincters of the digestive tract is to prevent retrograde movement of digestive contents.

The secretion of gastric juice is constant. Even in the period of fasting there is a small continuous secretion, but during the act of eating and throughout the period of digestion the rate of secretion is greatly increased.

Gastric juice is produced by the mucous membrane of the stomach. The complete cycle of the activities of the gastric glands is frequently divided into three phases: the *cephalic*, the *gastric*, and the *intestinal*. The *cephalic phase* of gastric secretion refers to reflex stimulation of the gastric glands through the central nervous system by the sight, smell, or taste of food. The *gastric phase* refers to all of the activities of the gastric glands, which are brought about by conditions within the stomach itself. It includes the gastric mechanisms as well as local chemical stimulation by secretagogues (any substance which stimulates secretion by a gland), which occur as a result of the contact of the gastric mucosa with the products of digestion and the stimulation caused by distention of the stomach. During the gastric phase a hormone, *gastrin*, is secreted by cells in the antrum and transported by the blood to fundic cells; it stimulates secretion of both chief and parietal cells. Its secretion is inhibited by excessive acidity of the gastric juice (pH of 2.0).

The *intestinal phase* of gastric secretion is believed to be due to the presence of food in the small intestine, which may stimulate the gastric glands through a hormone or secretagogue. Fats inhibit gastric secretion, by stimulating the production of intestinal hormones, e.g., *enterogastrone*.

Gastric Juice. Gastric juice is secreted by the gastric glands lining the mucous membrane of the stomach. It is a thin, colorless, or nearly colorless liquid with an acid reaction and a specific gravity of about 1.003 to 1.008. The acid which is secreted by the parietal cell has a pH of about 0.9. However, after reaching the lumen of the stomach, the acid is partially neutralized by the gastric mucus, the more alkaline saliva, and the alkaline intestinal content which may be regurgitated into the stomach. This reduction in acidity results in a gastric content of about pH 2.5. The quantity secreted depends upon the amount and kind of food to be digested, possibly an average of 1.5 to 2.5 liters per day. Upon analysis it is found to be a watery secretion containing some protein, some mucin, and inorganic salts; but the essential constituents are hydrochloric acid and one or possibly two enzymes—pepsin and gastric lipase.

Hydrochloric Acid. It is believed that the parietal (acid, or oxyntic) cells of the gastric glands secrete the hydrochloric acid from chlorides found in the blood. The chloride ion combines with the hydrogen ion and is then secreted upon the free surface of the stomach as hydrochloric acid. In normal gastric juice it is found in the proportion of about 0.5 per cent. It serves to activate pepsinogen and convert it to pepsin; to provide an acid medium, which is necessary for the pepsin to carry on its work; to swell the protein fibers, thus giving easier access to pepsin; and to destroy many organisms that enter the stomach.

Excessive secretion of hydrochloric acid, or gastric hyperacidity, is often found associated with peptic ulceration of the duodenum, and with some forms of gastritis, but there is little evidence that there is a cause-effect relationship between hypersecretion and ulcer disease. Secretion of hydrochloric acid below normal, or hyposecretion, is associated with other forms of gastritis and frequently with carcinoma of the stomach. Acid secretion is totally absent in pernicious anemia.

Pepsin is formed in the pyloric glands and the chief cells of the gastric glands. It is present in these cells in the form of a zymogen, an antecedent inactive substance called propepsin or pepsinogen, which is quickly changed to active pepsin by the action of hydrochloric acid.

Pepsin (gastric protease) is a proteolytic enzyme requiring an acid medium in which to function. It has the property of hydrolyzing proteins through several stages into polypeptides. This action is preparatory to the more complete hydrolysis that takes place in the intestine under the influence of trypsin (pancreatic protease) and various peptidases, for polypeptides are not absorbed but undergo a further hydrolysis to amino acids.

Various observers have described other enzymes in addition to the gastric protease, but the evidence regarding these is inconclusive. It is probable that the salivary amylase swallowed with the food continues the digestion of starchy material in the fundus for some time. Regarding the long-chain fats, it is believed that they undergo no digestion in the stomach. They are set free from their mixture with other foods by the digestive action of the gastric fluid; they are liquefied by the heat of the body and are scattered through the chyme as a coarse emulsion by the movements of the stomach, all of which prepare them for digestion. Emulsified fats such as cream may be acted upon to a limited extent by a third enzyme called *gastric lipase*, but the acid condition of the stomach contents prevents any considerable change of this sort. This enzyme is more important in the child than in the adult.

Summary. The stomach serves as a place for temporary storage and maintains a gradual delivery to the intestine; it also serves as a place for the continuation of the salivary digestion of starch, the beginning of the digestion of proteins and perhaps fats, and germicidal activity. While the food is in the pyloric region it is subjected to the acidity of the gastric fluid.

Inhibition of Gastric Digestion. The secretion of gastric fluid is inhibited by stimulation of the thoracolumbar system, so that various emotions and also a distaste for food may delay digestion. Secretion is also inhibited by active exercise soon after a meal, because active exercise increases the amount of blood in the skeletal muscles and decreases the supply to the stomach. When gastric digestion is much delayed, organisms are likely to cause fermentation of the sugars, producing gas which may cause distress.

Vomiting. Vomiting is controlled by a nerve center in the medulla which can be stimulated by chemical and physical qualities of the tissue fluid in the center and by nerve impulses which reach it. Under ordinary circumstances the contractions of the cardiac "sphincter" prevent the regurgitation of food. During vomiting the stomach, esophagus, and esophagogastric junction (so-called cardiac sphincter) are all relaxed. Spasmodic contractions of the abdominal muscles synchronously with contraction of the diaphragm cause phasic increases in intragastric pressure, which results literally in squeezing out the stomach contents in spurts. It is wrong to think that the stomach muscles contract or show reverse peristalsis; the stomach behaves passively like a water-filled rubber bulb which spurts when it is compressed. After the stomach contents have been evacuated, the pyloric sphincter may also relax and permit the duodenal contents to be evacuated. Vomiting is usually preceded by a sensation of nausea and excessive salivation. Vomiting is a reflex act brought about by mechanical irritation of the throat or by irritating substances in the stomach and duodenum, and by pain, motion sickness, and certain emotions such as fear and repulsion.

Changes the Food Undergoes in the Small Intestine

The chyme entering the duodenum after an ordinary meal is normally free from coarse particles of food and is acid in reaction; both the hydrochloric acid and the lactic acid produced by fermentation contribute to this condition. Much of the food is undigested. The proteins are partly digested; some progress has been made in hydrolyzing starch; fats have been liquefied and mixed with other food but probably have not been hydrolyzed themselves. If milk is part of the diet, it will have been curdled and redissolved. It is in the small intestine that this mixture undergoes the greatest digestive changes. These changes, which constitute intestinal digestion, are effected by the movements of the intestine, the pancreatic fluid, the succus entericus, or secretion of the intestinal glands, and the bile.

It is convenient to describe the secretion and digestive action of these three fluids separately, but it must be remembered that they act simultaneously. The pancreatic fluid and the bile enter the intestine about 7 to 10 cm beyond the pylorus, therefore, the foods in the small intestine throughout its length are subjected to a mixture of pancreatic fluid, bile, and small intestinal fluid.

Movements of the Small Intestine. These are described as peristaltic, rhythmical, and pendular.

Peristalsis may be defined as a wave of dilation brought about by the contraction of longitudinal muscles, followed by a wave of constriction caused by the contraction of circular muscles. The purpose is to pass the food slowly forward. *Peristaltic waves* pass very slowly along short distances of the small intestine, with an occasional rapid wave known as the *peristaltic rush*, which moves the food along greater distances. The stimulus

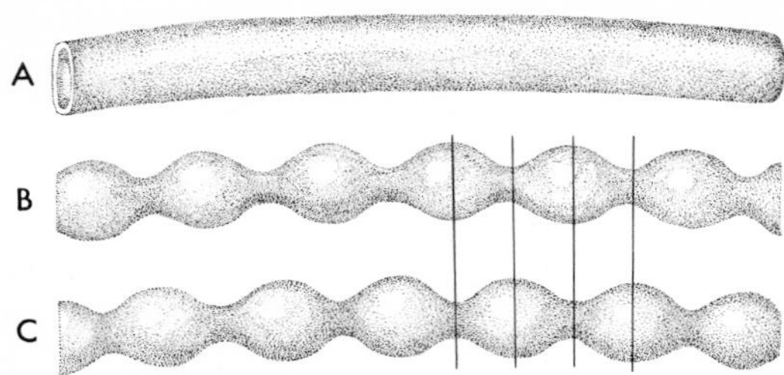

Figure 21–3. Three diagrams of a portion of the small intestine to show rhythmical movements. The small straight lines indicate the same area of the intestine at different intervals.

seems to be partly mechanical, since experimental swallowing of a tube to which a small balloon is attached initiates peristalsis and propulsion of the balloon through the intestine.

The rhythmical movements consist of a series of local constrictions of the intestinal wall which occur rhythmically at points where masses of food lie. These constrictions divide the food into segments. Within a few seconds each of these segments is halved, and the corresponding halves of adjoining segments unite. Again constrictions occur, and these newly formed segments are divided, and the halves re-form. In this way every particle of food is brought into intimate contact with the intestinal mucosa and is thoroughly mixed with the digestive fluids.

Pendular movements are constrictions which move onward or backward for short distances, gradually moving the chyme forward and backward over short distances in the small intestine. These may be seen in the rabbit and other small mammals, but their presence is doubted in the human.

The varied muscular movements of the small intestine increase the blood supply, bringing materials for secretion and removing absorbed materials faster. They assist the minute glands in emptying their secretion, mix the digestive fluids and food intimately, and bring fresh absorbable material constantly to the mucosa, thereby increasing absorption.

Secretion of Pancreatic Juice. Pancreatic secretion, like gastric secretion, consists of two parts: a neurally induced secretion, caused by the secretory fibers in the vagus and splanchnic nerves, and a chemically induced secretion, caused by the action of the hormones *secretin* and *pancreozymin.* The acid gastric fluid and the products of partially digested proteins upon reaching the duodenum and jejunum stimulate the production of these hormones. They are taken by way of the blood to the pancreas where they cause secretion of large quantities of fluid rich in enzymes. It is thought that the neurally induced secretion provides pancreatic fluid in the early stages of intestinal digestion and that the chemical secretion maintains the flow until all the stomach contents reach the duodenum.

Pancreatic Juice. The *nervous secretion* of pancreatic juice is thick, and rich in enzymes and proteins. The *chemical secretion* resulting from pancreozymin activity is thin, watery, and is also rich in enzymes. Pancreatic juice is alkaline and becomes more so with increasing rates of secretion. This is due to an increase in bicarbonates and at the same time a decrease in chloride concentration. These two ions vary in a reciprocal manner, so that the *sum* of the concentrations of these two ions is practically constant.

Pancreatic juice contains three groups of enzymes, pancreatic proteases (carboxypolypeptidase and trypsin), amylase, and lipase. The amount of pancreatic juice secreted each day varies between 600 and 800 ml.

The proteolytic enzyme, trypsin, under favorable conditions may hydrolyze the protein molecule to polypeptides. Trypsin is secreted in an inactive form called *trypsinogen* and is activated by *enterokinase,* an enzyme that is secreted by glands of the small intestine. *Carboxypolypeptidase* breaks polypeptides into component amino acids.

Another proteolytic enzyme, *chymotrypsin,* also is present in pancreatic juice. It is secreted in an inactive form, *chymotrypsinogen,* which is activated by the enzyme, trypsin.

Nuclease is a nucleic acid-splitting enzyme which results in the production of nucleotides

—the subunits which form nucleic acids. There has been some question about its presence in pancreatic juice.

The amylolytic enzyme (*amylase*) is similar to salivary amylase in action. It causes hydrolysis of starch with the production of maltose. The starchy food that escapes digestion in the mouth and stomach becomes mixed with this enzyme and continues under its action until the colic valve is reached. Maltose is further acted upon by the maltase of the intestinal secretion and is hydrolyzed to glucose.

The lipolytic enzyme (*lipase*) is capable of hydrolyzing fats to monoglycerides and some to glycerol and fatty acids. The process of hydrolysis is preceded by emulsification, in which bile salts play a leading role. The lipase splits some of the fats to fatty acids and glycerol; emulsification increases the surface of fat exposed to the chemical action of the lipase and is a mechanical preparation for the further action of lipase. The glycerol and fatty acids produced by the action of the lipase are absorbed by the epithelium of the intestine. It is thought that the fatty acids form soluble and diffusible compounds with the bile salts and are absorbed in this form. After absorption the fatty acids and glycerol again combine to form fat, the triglycerides found in the blood stream as chylomicrons. Lipases are found in blood and in many of the tissues. Although lipases are also secreted by the small intestine, that secreted by the pancreas accounts for about 80 per cent of all fat digestion. For this reason impaired fat digestion is an important result of pancreatic dysfunction.

The Intestinal Secretion (Succus Entericus). This is a clear, yellowish fluid, and amounts to about 2 to 3 liters per day. Its composition varies; in the duodenum and jejunum it is slightly acid. The acidity is greatest in the duodenum, and in the ileum the secretion is practically neutral. In the duodenal bulb and the region down to the ampulla of Vater it is almost entirely mucous. Extracts of the walls of the small intestine have been found to contain four or five enzymes which influence intestinal digestion to a marked extent. The enzymes are to be found in the secretion, and their actions are as follows.

Enterokinase is an enzyme which activates the trypsin of the pancreatic fluid; aminopeptidase, carboxypeptidase, and dipeptidase are enzymes which hydrolyze peptides to amino acids, thus completing the work begun by pepsin and trypsin.

Maltase acts upon the products formed in the digestion of starches, i.e., maltose, and hydrolyzes them to glucose. *Sucrase* acts upon sucrose and hydrolyzes it to glucose and fructose. *Lactase* acts upon lactose and hydrolyzes it to glucose and galactose. This hydrolysis is necessary because disaccharides cannot be used by the tissues, but in the form of simple sugars they are readily utilized.

Nucleases act upon the nucleic acid component of nucleoproteins.

Bile. Bile is formed in the liver and is an alkaline fluid, pH about 6.8 to 7.7, the specific gravity of which varies from about 1.010 to 1.050. Approximately 800 to 1,000 ml are secreted daily. It is usually yellow, brownish yellow, or olive green in color. The color of bile is determined by the respective amounts of the bile pigments, (1) biliverdin and (2) bilirubin, that are present. Bile consists of water, bile pigments, bile acids, bile salts, cholesterol, lecithin, and neutral fats.

The bile acids are glycocholic and taurocholic, occurring as sodium glycocholate and sodium taurocholate. These salts are alternately poured into the duodenum, then reabsorbed, and reappear in the bile. Thus, by continued circulation, the bile salts repeat their function may times. This enterohepatic circulation helps to conserve bile salts, as each circuit is accomplished with only about 10 to 15 per cent loss. Synthesis of new bile salts from materials in the diet makes up the deficit. The mucous membranes of the bile ducts and gallbladder add a mucinlike protein called nucleoalbumin, which, together with some mucin, gives bile its mucilaginous consistency.

Secretion of Bile. Secretion of bile is continuous, but the amount varies, increasing when the blood flow is increased and vice versa. It is thought that the presence of bile in the intestine stimulates secretion in the liver and that this is due to the bile salts, which act as a choleretic. Bile enters the duodenum only during the period of digestion. Between these periods, resistance to the entrance of bile into the duodenum is high, so that the bile is diverted into the gallbladder, where it becomes concentrated by loss of water. The ejection of chyme into the duodenum causes the contraction of the gallbladder and ejection of bile; the hormone cholecystokinin, formed by cells of the duodenal mucosa, mediates this response.

Functions of Bile. Bile salts are essential for the action of lipase. Mixtures of bile and pancreatic fluid split the fats more rapidly than pancreatic fluid alone. Bile salts lower surface tension, which aids in the emulsification of fats with concurrent production of a greater surface area which enables lipase and other enzymes to act more effectively. Bile salts are also important for absorption of fat.

Bile is essential for the absorption of vitamin K and other fat-soluble vitamins. It also stimulates intestinal motility and neutralizes the acid chyme, creating a favorable hydrogen ion concentration for pancreatic and intestinal enzyme activity; bile salts help to keep cholesterol in solution.

In addition, the bile is an excretory medium for toxins, metals, and cholesterol. The liver cells excrete the bile pigments that are brought to them by the blood, just as the kidney cells remove the urea from the blood. The cholesterol of bile is probably a waste product of cellular disintegration.

It is thought that increased putrefaction in the absence of bile is brought about by the action of bacteria on proteins and carbohydrates which have remained undigested because of the protective covering of insoluble fat which is found on them in the absence of bile.

GALLSTONES. Abnormal composition of bile may be such that its constituents become so concentrated in the gallbladder that it tends to crystallize out, and these crystals form gallstones. Inflammatory conditions, which are often due to the typhoid and colon bacilli or to a change in the character of the bile, may cause this crystallization. Gallstones are usually formed in the gallbladder. Their passage through the cystic and common bile ducts often causes severe pain, called gallbladder colic. They may plug the duct and cause obstructive jaundice.

JAUNDICE. When the flow of bile through the bile duct is interfered with, bilirubin is not removed from the blood but is carried to all parts of the body, producing a condition of jaundice, which is characterized by a yellow discoloration of the skin and of the whites of the eyes. The urine is of a greenish hue because of the extra quantity of pigment eliminated by the kidneys, and the stools are grayish in hue, owing to the lack of bile. Jaundice may also be due to the incapacity of the liver cells to eliminate pigments, or to the presence of excessive amounts of bilirubin as in the case of too rapid destruction (hemolysis) of erythrocytes.

Action of organisms in the small intestine hydrolyzes carbohydrates and proteins constantly. Fermentation of the carbohydrates gives rise to organic acids, such as lactic and acetic, but none of the products of this fermentation is considered toxic. On the other hand, the putrefaction of proteins gives rise to a number of end products that are toxic when present in large amounts. Under normal conditions and on a mixed diet, carbohydrate fermentation is the characteristic action of the organisms in the ileum, whereas protein putrefaction occurs in the large intestine. These microorganisms are in many ways beneficial to the body. They synthesize vitamins which may be absorbed; their presence in the intestinal tract is not irritating and at the same time it prevents other, potentially harmful organisms which might be ingested or present in small amounts from multiplying and causing infection.

The time required for digestion in the small intestine is influenced by many factors. It depends largely on the varying proportions of the different foods included in a meal. Twenty to thirty-six hours are required for the passage of ingested food material through the gastrointestinal tract of adults who are on a mixed diet. There is considerable variation among individuals, and usually not all of the residue from a single meal is evacuated at the same time. In diarrheal conditions the time is much shortened.

According to observations made upon a patient with a fistula at the end of the small intestine, food begins to pass into the large intestine from two to five hours after eating, and it requires nine hours or more after eating before the last of a meal has passed the colic valve.

Hormones of the Digestive Pathway

Gastrin is secreted by the pyloric mucosa and excites the fundic glands of the stomach to active secretion of acid.

Enterogastrone is secreted by the duodenal mucosa and inhibits gastric secretion and gastric motility.

Secretin is secreted by the upper intestinal mucosa and excites the pancreas to secrete bicarbonate and water, poor in enzymes.

Pancreozymin is secreted by the jejunal mucosa and stimulates the pancreas to secrete fluid rich in enzymes.

Cholecystokinin is secreted by cells in the upper small intestine and causes contraction of the smooth muscle of the gallbladder, causing it to empty.

It must be remembered that these hormones, like others, are secreted into the blood stream and reach all cells through the circulatory system. However, only *certain* cells respond to each hormone.

Changes the Food Undergoes in the Large Intestine

Movements of the Large Intestine. The opening from the small intestine into the large is controlled by the colic valve and the colic sphincter, which is normally in a state of tone. Food begins to pass into the large intestine within two to five hours after eating. Transit of the meal through the small intestine apparently occurs at a steady rate, so that the total time for the whole meal to pass the colic valve will be determined principally by the gastric evacuation time. As food passes the colic valve, the cecum becomes filled, and gradually the accumulation reaches higher and higher levels in the ascending colon. The contents of the ascending colon are soft and semisolid, but in the distal end of the transverse colon they attain the consistency of feces.

A type of movement characteristic of the large intestine is called *haustral churning*. The pouches, or sacculations, that are present in the large intestine become distended and from time to time contract and empty themselves. Another type of movement is designated as *mass peristalsis*. It consists of the vigorous contraction of the entire ascending colon, which transfers its contents to the transverse colon. Such movements occur only three or four times a day, last only a short time, and are usually connected with eating. When food enters the stomach and duodenum, peristalsis is initiated in the colon through the autonomic nerves of the areas involved. These reflex actions are termed the *gastrocolic* and *duodenocolic reflexes*. They are most noticeable after the first meal of the day and cause increased excitability of the colon, which initiates the defecation reflexes.

The secretion of the large intestine contains much mucin, shows an alkaline reaction, and secretes no enzymes. When the contents of the small intestine pass the colic valve, they still contain a certain amount of unabsorbed food material. This remains a long time in the intestine; and since it contains the digestive enzymes received in the duodenum, the process of digestion and absorption continues.

Action of organisms in the large intestine brings about, in an alkaline reaction, constant putrefaction of whatever proteins are present as the result of not having been digested and absorbed in the small intestine. The splitting of the protein molecules by this process is very complete; not only are they hydrolyzed to amino acids, but these amino acids are deaminized and changed to simpler groups. The list of simple substances resulting from putrefaction is long and includes various peptides, ammonia, and amino acids, and also indole, skatole, phenol, fatty acids,

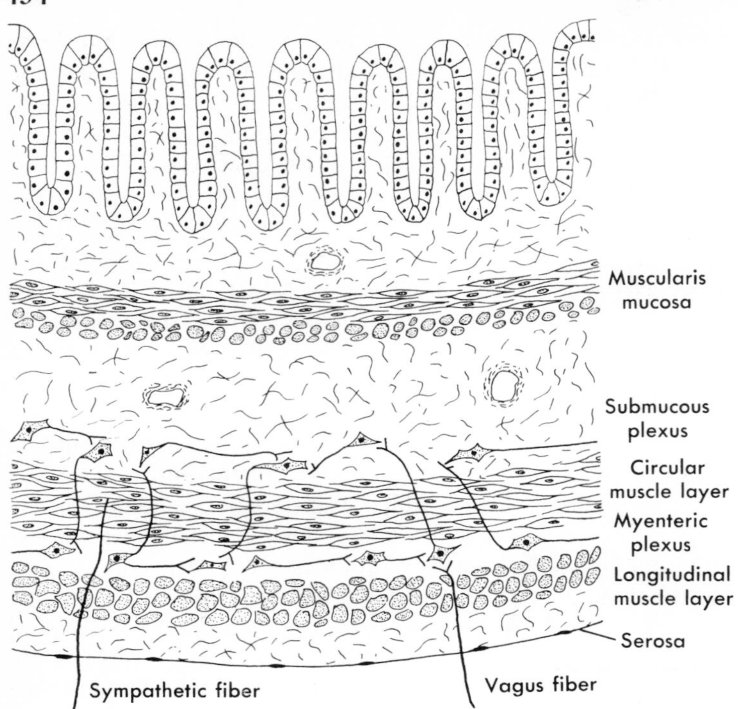

Figure 21–4. Cross section of large intestine, showing muscle layers and autonomic plexuses.

carbon dioxide, and hydrogen sulfide. Some of these are given off in the feces; others are absorbed and carried to the liver, where they are changed to less toxic compounds, and excreted in the urine. Some organisms of the large intestine are useful in that they are capable of synthesizing several of the vitamins needed for normal metabolism. These vitamins include several of the B group and vitamin K.

The Feces. Two classes of material may be mingled in the content of the colon: (1) the residues of the diet with microorganisms and their products, and (2) the excretions of the digestive tube and its glands. The proportion existing between these two is variable. The feces consist of water; the undigested and indigestible parts of the food; pigment due to undigested food or to metallic elements contained in it and to the bile pigments; great quantities of microorganisms of different kinds; the products of bacterial decomposition, i.e., indole, skatole, etc.; the products of the secretions; mucous and epithelial cells from the walls of the alimentary tract; cholesterol or a derivative, which is probably derived from the bile; some of the purine bases; inorganic salts of sodium, potassium, calcium, magnesium, and iron.

Defecation. The anal canal is guarded by an internal sphincter and an external sphincter muscle, which are normally in a state of tonic contraction and protect the anal opening. Normally the rectum is empty until just before defecation. Various stimuli (depending on one's habits) will produce peristaltic action of the colon, so that a small quantity of feces enters the rectum. This irritates the sensory nerve endings and causes a desire to defecate. The voluntary contraction of the abdominal muscles, the descent of the diaphragm, and powerful peristalsis of the colon all combine to empty the colon and rectum.

One of the commonest causes of *constipation* is the retention of feces in the rectum because of failure to act on the desire for defecation. After feces once enter the rectum there is no retroperistalsis to carry them back to the colon. Sensory adaptation occurs and often persists for 24 hours, during which time the feces continue to lose water and become harder and more difficult to expel. A certain amount of indigestible materials in the diet stimulates the lining of the intestines, promotes peristalsis, and as it is pushed along the tube takes with it the less bulky but more toxic wastes. Daily exercise which uses all the muscles, especially the abdominal muscles, aids regularity. Constipation may be due to increased tonicity of the distal part of the colon, which causes a decrease in the lumen of the colon. Onward peristalsis is impaired, haustration is extreme, and hyperirritability and motility with delayed evacuation result. This is called *spastic* constipation. Constipation also may be due to a relaxed state of the muscle layers of the colon. The muscles fail to produce sufficient peristaltic action. The colon becomes relaxed, distended with fecal accumulation. This is called *atonic* constipation. It may follow excessive use of cathartics.

Diarrhea results from irritation of the mucosa of the intestine from bacterial infection usually, or excessive parasympathetic stimulation in stress situations. In these instances large amounts of water and electrolytes are lost in the stool, since normal absorption fails to occur and the glands of the large intestine secrete these materials along with mucus. Diarrhea may also result from pathological conditions which cause malabsorption of certain foodstuffs, notably fats.

SUMMARY OF DIGESTIVE SECRETIONS

Secretion	pH Volume per Day	Proenzyme/ Substance Which Activates	Enzyme	Substrate	End Products
Saliva	6.8 1–1½ liters		1. Salivary amylase	Starch	Maltose
Gastric juice	2–4 1.5–2.5		1. Rennin (infants)	Casein	Paracasein
		Pepsinogen/HCI	2. Pepsin	Proteins, para-casein	Proteoses, peptones, polypeptides
			3. Gastric lipase	Emulsified fats	Fatty acids, glycerol
Pancreatic juice	8–8.4 600–800 ml	1. Trypsinogen/ enterokinase	1. Trypsin	Chymotrypsinogen Proteins, para-casein, peptones, proteoses, poly-peptides	Chymotrypsin Polypeptides, dipeptides
		2. Chymotrypsino-gen/trypsin	2. Chymotrypsin	Proteins, para-casein, peptones, proteoses, poly-peptides	Polypeptides, dipeptides
			3. Pancreatic amylase	Starch, glycogen	Disaccharides
			4. Pancreatic lipase	Emulsified fats	Fatty acids, glycerol
Bile	7.5 800–1,000 ml	Bile salts (not an enzyme—action is physical)		Unemulsified fats	Emulsified fats
Intestinal juice	7–9 2–3 liters		1. Peptidase	Polypeptides, dipeptides	Amino acids
			2. Enteric lipase	Emulsified fats	Fatty acid, glycerol
			3. Sucrase	Sucrose	Glucose, fructose
			4. Maltase	Maltose	Glucose
			5. Lactase	Lactose	Glucose, galactose
			6. Enterokinase	Trypsinogen	Trypsin

QUESTIONS FOR DISCUSSION

1. What are the chemical digestive processes necessary for rendering the food soluble and absorbable?
2. What are the functions of each hormone in the digestive process?
3. A person has had a total gastrectomy. What physiological process will be interfered with and what medication will the person need? Why?
4. Explain the role of vitamins and electrolytes in enzyme systems.
5. Distinguish between a proenzyme and an enzyme. Name three proenzymes and state their function.
6. What roles do the circulatory system and nervous system play in digestion?

SUMMARY

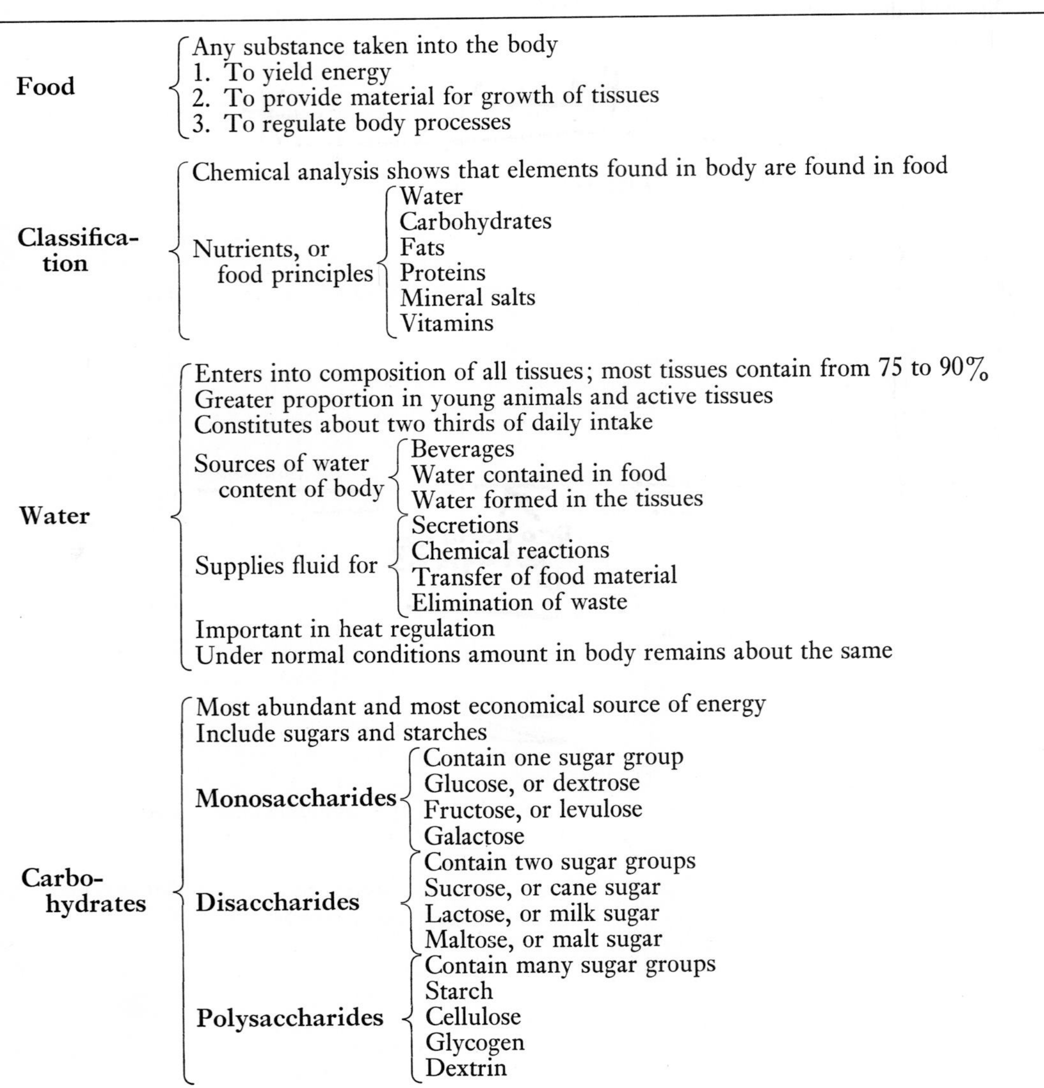

Food
- Any substance taken into the body
- 1. To yield energy
- 2. To provide material for growth of tissues
- 3. To regulate body processes

Classification
- Chemical analysis shows that elements found in body are found in food
- Nutrients, or food principles
  - Water
  - Carbohydrates
  - Fats
  - Proteins
  - Mineral salts
  - Vitamins

Water
- Enters into composition of all tissues; most tissues contain from 75 to 90%
- Greater proportion in young animals and active tissues
- Constitutes about two thirds of daily intake
- Sources of water content of body
  - Beverages
  - Water contained in food
  - Water formed in the tissues
- Supplies fluid for
  - Secretions
  - Chemical reactions
  - Transfer of food material
  - Elimination of waste
- Important in heat regulation
- Under normal conditions amount in body remains about the same

Carbohydrates
- Most abundant and most economical source of energy
- Include sugars and starches
- **Monosaccharides**
  - Contain one sugar group
  - Glucose, or dextrose
  - Fructose, or levulose
  - Galactose
- **Disaccharides**
  - Contain two sugar groups
  - Sucrose, or cane sugar
  - Lactose, or milk sugar
  - Maltose, or malt sugar
- **Polysaccharides**
  - Contain many sugar groups
  - Starch
  - Cellulose
  - Glycogen
  - Dextrin

Fats
- Used in anatomical sense = adipose tissue
- Used in chemical sense = esters of fatty acids and glycerol
- Under influence of body enzymes, split into substances out of which they are built

Compound Lipids
- Esters of fatty acids containing groups in addition
- *Phospholipids*—contain phosphorus and nitrogen, e.g., lecithin
- *Glycolipids*—compounds of fatty acids with a carbohydrate unit
- *Sterols*—solid alcohols of complex structure—e.g., cholesterol

Proteins
- Contain C, H, O, N; usually S, sometimes P and Fe may be present
- Built up of simpler substances called amino acids
- Amino acids are derivatives of ammonia, as indicated by the amino group (NH_2), and of organic acids, as indicated by carboxyl group (COOH). The NH_2 replaces one hydrogen atom
- Acetic acid—CH_3COOH—for H substitute (NH_2) $\rightarrow$ $CH_2(NH_2)COOH$ = aminoacetic acid
- Propionic acid—C_2H_5COOH—for H substitute (NH_2) $\rightarrow$ $C_2H_4(NH_2)COOH$ = aminopropionic acid
- About 40 amino acids have been derived from proteins, and various combinations result in many different kinds of proteins, i.e., milk, meats, fish, egg, peas, beans, lentils, and peanuts
- Amino acids classed as dispensable, indispensable
- **Examples of protein constituents of food**
  - Albumin—found in egg, milk, meat
  - Caseinogen—found in milk
  - Glutenin—gummy substance in wheat
  - Legumin—found in legumes
  - Gelatin—derived from connective tissues, including bone and tendon
  - Organic extracts—flavor of meats and some plant foods due to these
- **Classification**
  - Simple
    - Consist only of amino acids
    - Yield only amino acids or derivatives
  - Conjugated
    - Contain protein molecule united to some other molecule otherwise than as a salt—yield amino acids and some other molecule
    - Nucleoproteins—yield amino acids and nuclein
    - Glycoproteins—yield amino acids and a carbohydrate
    - Phosphoproteins—yield amino acids and phosphates
    - Hemoglobins—yield amino acids and hematin
    - Lecithoproteins—yield amino acids and a fatty substance
  - Derived
    - Primary—involve only slight alterations of the protein molecule
    - Secondary—products of further hydrolytic cleavage, such as proteoses, peptones, and peptides

Chemical Elements
- Fifteen or more elements enter into composition of body
- Five may be furnished by carbohydrates, fats, proteins, and water
- Others to be provided include:
  - Iron, calcium, sodium, potassium, magnesium, phosphorus, chlorine, iodine, fluorine, silicon
- **Function**
  - As constituents of bone
  - As essential elements of soft tissues
  - As soluble salts held in solution in fluids of body

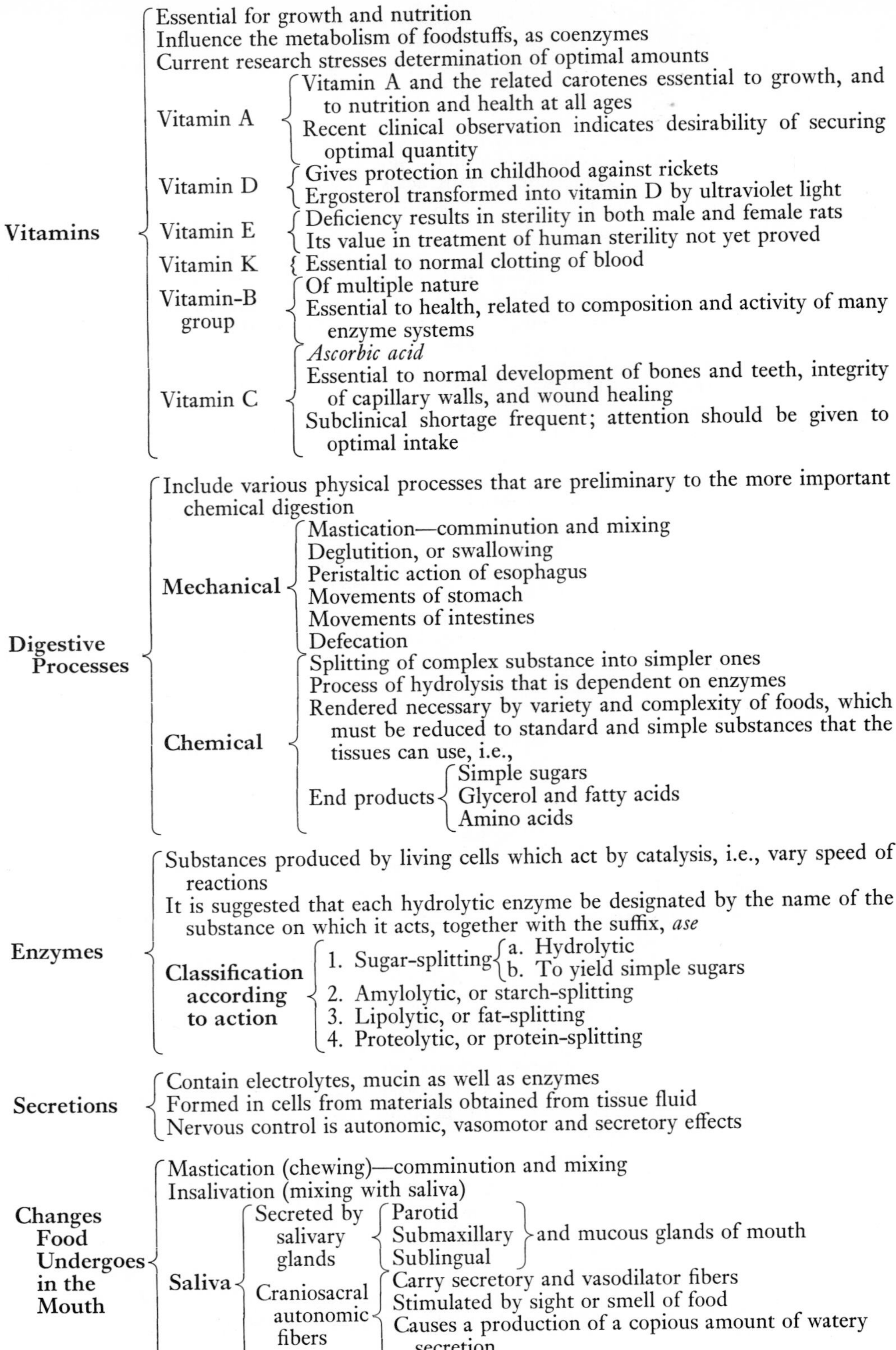

- **Vitamins**
  - Essential for growth and nutrition
  - Influence the metabolism of foodstuffs, as coenzymes
  - Current research stresses determination of optimal amounts
  - Vitamin A
    - Vitamin A and the related carotenes essential to growth, and to nutrition and health at all ages
    - Recent clinical observation indicates desirability of securing optimal quantity
  - Vitamin D
    - Gives protection in childhood against rickets
    - Ergosterol transformed into vitamin D by ultraviolet light
  - Vitamin E
    - Deficiency results in sterility in both male and female rats
    - Its value in treatment of human sterility not yet proved
  - Vitamin K
    - Essential to normal clotting of blood
  - Vitamin-B group
    - Of multiple nature
    - Essential to health, related to composition and activity of many enzyme systems
  - Vitamin C
    - *Ascorbic acid*
    - Essential to normal development of bones and teeth, integrity of capillary walls, and wound healing
    - Subclinical shortage frequent; attention should be given to optimal intake
- **Digestive Processes**
  - Include various physical processes that are preliminary to the more important chemical digestion
  - **Mechanical**
    - Mastication—comminution and mixing
    - Deglutition, or swallowing
    - Peristaltic action of esophagus
    - Movements of stomach
    - Movements of intestines
    - Defecation
  - **Chemical**
    - Splitting of complex substance into simpler ones
    - Process of hydrolysis that is dependent on enzymes
    - Rendered necessary by variety and complexity of foods, which must be reduced to standard and simple substances that the tissues can use, i.e.,
    - End products
      - Simple sugars
      - Glycerol and fatty acids
      - Amino acids
- **Enzymes**
  - Substances produced by living cells which act by catalysis, i.e., vary speed of reactions
  - It is suggested that each hydrolytic enzyme be designated by the name of the substance on which it acts, together with the suffix, *ase*
  - **Classification according to action**
    1. Sugar-splitting
       - a. Hydrolytic
       - b. To yield simple sugars
    2. Amylolytic, or starch-splitting
    3. Lipolytic, or fat-splitting
    4. Proteolytic, or protein-splitting
- **Secretions**
  - Contain electrolytes, mucin as well as enzymes
  - Formed in cells from materials obtained from tissue fluid
  - Nervous control is autonomic, vasomotor and secretory effects
- **Changes Food Undergoes in the Mouth**
  - Mastication (chewing)—comminution and mixing
  - Insalivation (mixing with saliva)
  - **Saliva**
    - Secreted by salivary glands
      - Parotid, Submaxillary, Sublingual — and mucous glands of mouth
    - Craniosacral autonomic fibers
      - Carry secretory and vasodilator fibers
      - Stimulated by sight or smell of food
      - Causes a production of a copious amount of watery secretion

Changes Food Undergoes in the Mouth (*cont.*)
- **Saliva** (*cont.*)
  - Thoracolumbar autonomic fibers
    - Carry secretory and vasoconstrictor fibers
    - Stimulated by food in mouth
    - Produce a smaller amount of thicker secretion
  - Consists of water, some protein material, mucin, inorganic salts, and the enzyme salivary amylase
  - Specific gravity 1.004–1.008. Neutral in reaction—pH 6.6–7.1
  - Amount—1 to 1.5 liters per day
  - **Physiology**
    1. Assists in mastication and deglutition
    2. Serves as lubricant
    3. Dissolves or liquefies the food, thus stimulating the taste buds and indirectly the secretion of gastric fluid
    4. Amylase hydrolyzes starch to dextrin and maltose; maltase changes maltose to glucose
- **Deglutition** (swallowing). Passage of food through (1) fauces, (2) pharynx, and (3) esophagus. Consistency of food affects third stage

Changes Food Undergoes in the Stomach
- Time required—depends on nature of food eaten; average meal of mixed food requires 3–4½ hr
- Food held in stomach by cardiac and pyloric sphincters
- Cavity size of contents—never empty—always few milliliters of gastric fluid in stomach
- When food enters, expands just enough to receive it; contractions start in middle region and run toward pylorus; food in prepyloric and pyloric regions macerated, mixed with gastric fluid, and reduced to *chyme*
- Salivary digestion continues until gastric fluid penetrates bolus of food
- **Gastric juice**
  - Periods of fasting—secreted in small amount
  - While eating and during period of digestion—amount increased
  - Secretion
    - Psychic or appetite, secretion
      - Sensations of eating
      - Taste and odor of food
    - Chemical
      - Secretagogues contained (1) in food and (2) in products of digestion
      - Gastric secretin
  - Secreted by glands of stomach
    - Cardiac
    - Fundus, or oxyntic
    - Pyloric
  - Acid reaction due to free hydrochloric acid
  - Enzymes
    - Pepsin
    - Gastric lipase

Hydrochloric Acid
- Secreted by parietal cells of gastric glands from chlorides found in blood
- Chloride ions combine with hydrogen ions to form hydrochloric acid
- Normal amount about 0.5%
- **Physiology**
  - Activates pepsinogen and converts it to pepsin
  - Provides acid medium for pepsin to carry on its work
  - Swells protein fibers
  - Hypersecretion associated with ulcer formation
  - Germicidal in action

Pepsin
- Formed in pyloric glands and chief cells of gastric glands
- Pepsinogen—zymogen, changed by HCl to active pepsin
- Weak proteolytic enzyme—requires acid medium
- Hydrolyzes proteins through several stages to peptides, which action is preparatory to more complete hydrolysis in intestine

Gastric Lipase—limited action on emulsified fats like cream

Functions of Stomach
- Serves as temporary storage reservoir
- Contractions promote mechanical reduction of food
- Salivary digestion continues until acidity is established
- **Gastric digestion**
  - Pepsin hydrolyzes proteins
  - Gastric lipase may hydrolyze emulsified fats
  - HCl has germicidal action

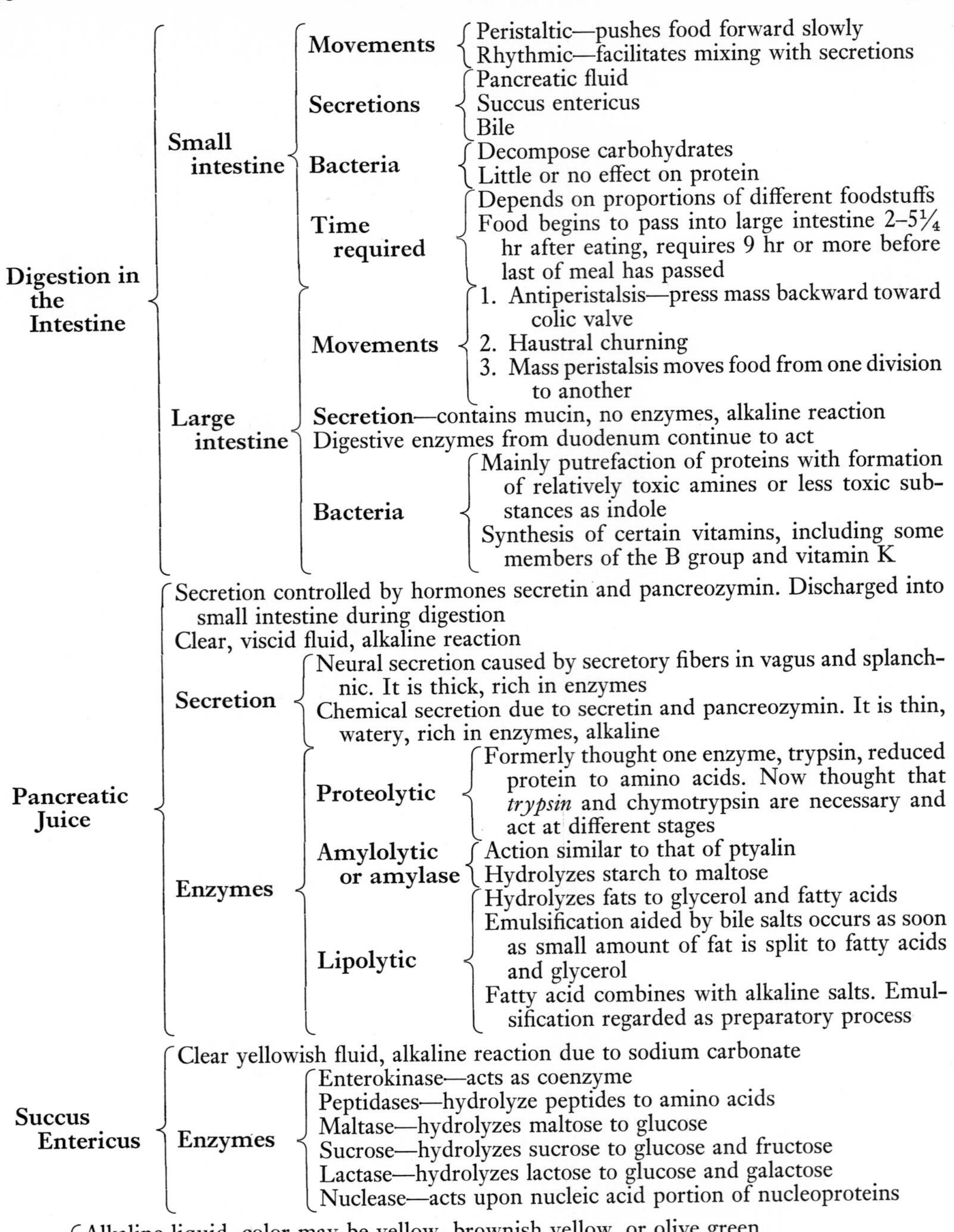

- **Digestion in the Intestine**
  - **Small intestine**
    - **Movements**
      - Peristaltic—pushes food forward slowly
      - Rhythmic—facilitates mixing with secretions
    - **Secretions**
      - Pancreatic fluid
      - Succus entericus
      - Bile
    - **Bacteria**
      - Decompose carbohydrates
      - Little or no effect on protein
    - **Time required**
      - Depends on proportions of different foodstuffs
      - Food begins to pass into large intestine 2–5¼ hr after eating, requires 9 hr or more before last of meal has passed
  - **Large intestine**
    - **Movements**
      1. Antiperistalsis—press mass backward toward colic valve
      2. Haustral churning
      3. Mass peristalsis moves food from one division to another
    - **Secretion**—contains mucin, no enzymes, alkaline reaction
    - Digestive enzymes from duodenum continue to act
    - **Bacteria**
      - Mainly putrefaction of proteins with formation of relatively toxic amines or less toxic substances as indole
      - Synthesis of certain vitamins, including some members of the B group and vitamin K
- **Pancreatic Juice**
  - Secretion controlled by hormones secretin and pancreozymin. Discharged into small intestine during digestion
  - Clear, viscid fluid, alkaline reaction
  - **Secretion**
    - Neural secretion caused by secretory fibers in vagus and splanchnic. It is thick, rich in enzymes
    - Chemical secretion due to secretin and pancreozymin. It is thin, watery, rich in enzymes, alkaline
  - **Enzymes**
    - **Proteolytic**
      - Formerly thought one enzyme, trypsin, reduced protein to amino acids. Now thought that *trypsin* and chymotrypsin are necessary and act at different stages
    - **Amylolytic or amylase**
      - Action similar to that of ptyalin
      - Hydrolyzes starch to maltose
    - **Lipolytic**
      - Hydrolyzes fats to glycerol and fatty acids
      - Emulsification aided by bile salts occurs as soon as small amount of fat is split to fatty acids and glycerol
      - Fatty acid combines with alkaline salts. Emulsification regarded as preparatory process
- **Succus Entericus**
  - Clear yellowish fluid, alkaline reaction due to sodium carbonate
  - **Enzymes**
    - Enterokinase—acts as coenzyme
    - Peptidases—hydrolyze peptides to amino acids
    - Maltase—hydrolyzes maltose to glucose
    - Sucrose—hydrolyzes sucrose to glucose and fructose
    - Lactase—hydrolyzes lactose to glucose and galactose
    - Nuclease—acts upon nucleic acid portion of nucleoproteins
- **Bile**
  - Alkaline liquid, color may be yellow, brownish yellow, or olive green
  - Amount secreted varies with amount of food eaten, estimated at about 800–1,000 ml daily
  - Consists of water, bile pigments, bile acids, bile salts, cholesterol, lecithin, neutral fats, and nucleoprotein
  - Bile salts, i.e., sodium taurocholate and sodium glycocholate, thought to stimulate activity of liver
  - Secreted continuously, enters duodenum during period of digestion
  - Digestive secretion aids action of lipase
  - Excretion—eliminates toxins, metals, and cholesterol
  - Antiseptic—thought to limit putrefaction

Abnormal Conditions
- Gallstones—concentrated cholesterol or bile salts which crystallize out and form gallstones
- Jaundice—due to absorption of bile by blood; bile carried throughout body; pigments deposited in skin and whites of eyes

Feces
- Consist of
  - Residues of diet, microorganisms, and their products
  - Excretions of digestive tube and its glands
- Contain (1) water, (2) the residues of food, (3) pigment, (4) microorganisms, (5) products of bacterial decomposition, indole, skatole, etc., (6) products of secretions, (7) mucous and epithelial cells, (8) cholesterol, (9) purine bases, and (10) inorganic salts

Defecation—term applied to the act of expelling feces from rectum

CHAPTER

22

ABSORPTION AND UTILIZATION OF NUTRIENTS BASAL METABOLISM AND TEMPERATURE REGULATION

The secretory and motor activities of the gastrointestinal tract are all directed toward changing ingested food into substances appropriate for absorption into the blood stream, which then delivers these materials to cells. Food requirements differ in amount according to the individual, although there are basic requirements common to all.

ABSORPTION

Absorption from the gastrointestinal tract consists of transfer of materials across the cell membrane boundary and involves processes previously discussed (Chapter 2), namely, diffusion, hydrostatic pressure, osmosis, and active transport. Particle size and concentration of the materials, as well as lipid solubility, are among the important physical factors which influence these processes.

Conditions which determine the amount of absorption which takes place from any part of the alimentary canal are the area of surface for absorption, the length of time food remains in contact with the absorbing surface, the concentration of fully digested material present, and the rapidity with which absorbed food is carried away by the blood.

Absorption in the Stomach. There is no active transport mechanism in the stomach, so that absorption is limited to materials already of absorbable size which can diffuse across cell membranes. Practically speaking, little absorbs except water.

Absorption in the Small Intestine. It is in the small intestine that conditions are most favorable for absorption; therefore, it is here that the greatest amount of absorption takes place. The circular folds and villi of the small intestine increase the internal surface enormously and food remains in the small intestine for several hours; during this time the most complete digestive changes occur.

The blood flows steadily within the wall of the small intestine. The blood in the capillaries is separated from the digested nutrients in the small intestine by the walls of the capillaries and the intestinal mucosa. On the intestinal side of the wall are the products of digestion and the digestive fluids. Sugars, glycerol, fatty acids, and amino acids are relatively abundant and pass into the blood. The continuous digestion of foods, the muscular activity of the intestinal wall, and the lashing and pumping activities of the villi stir up the intestinal contents and keep relatively high the concentration of absorbable materials in contact with the absorbing membrane. These motions also increase the circulation in the villi, and therefore the absorbed materials are moved on, keeping the concentration in the blood relatively low. Absorption takes place through the membrane from a con-

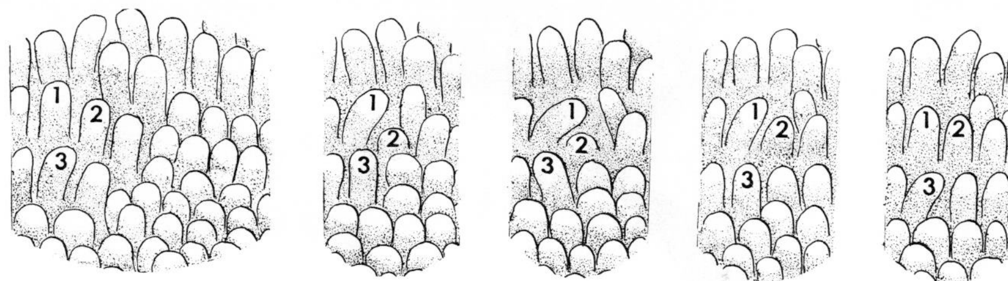

Figure 22–1. Diagram of surface view of the lining of the small intestine as it would be seen if the intestine were opened and stretched under a microscope. Several villi "stand" with tips toward observer. Villus *1* bends to right and then straightens up. Villus *2* telescopes itself and then straightens out. Villus *3*, bent to right, swings to left and over to right again.

stantly higher concentration of absorbable particles to a constantly lower concentration until all digested material is absorbed.

Absorption in the intestine is an active process by which the products of digestion enter the mucosal cells of the villi and thence go into blood capillaries and/or lacteals of the villi.

Absorption in the Large Intestine. When the contents of the small intestine pass the colic valve, they still contain a certain amount of unabsorbed food material. Enzymes are present, and digestion and absorption continue, but to a greatly reduced degree. The consistency is about that of chyme, because the absorption of water from the small intestine is counterbalanced by diffusion or secretion of water into it. In the large intestine the absorption of water continues, so that under usual conditions the formation of semisolid or hard feces occurs.

The Paths of Absorption. *The end products of digestion* are simple sugars, derived from the various carbohydrates; fatty acids and glycerol, derived from the various fats; and amino acids, derived from the various proteins.

The simple sugars pass into the capillaries and thence by way of the portal vein to the liver. In this way simple sugars are absorbed even though the blood sugar is higher in concentration.

The fatty acids and glycerol are absorbed in the small intestine. The bile furnishes bile salts (sodium glycocholate and sodium taurocholate) which aid in the absorption of fatty acids. During their passage through the intestinal mucosa most of the fatty acids and glycerol recombine to form triglycerides. The greater part of the fat is absorbed by the lacteals in the villi and carried to the thoracic duct, which empties into the left brachiocephalic vein. In addition it is considered probable that some of the short-chain fat is absorbed directly as fatty acid and glycerol by the capillaries of the villi and carried by way of the portal vein to the liver, before reaching the general circulation. Fat is present in the blood stream as tiny droplets called chylomicrons, collections of fat molecules.

The amino acids pass into the capillaries of the villi, although there is experimental evidence that, after excessive feeding of protein, a portion may enter the lymphatics. Amino acids are found in the blood, which distributes them to the tissues.

Absorption of water is not appreciable in the stomach. Most of the water of the intestinal contents is absorbed in the small intestine, but the most conspicuous change in the fluidity of the intestinal contents takes place in the large intestine, mainly in the ascending colon and proximal end of the transverse colon.

Absorption of electrolytes is in the small intestine and to a much lesser degree in the larger intestine.

Absorption of mineral salts from any part of the intestines depends on the nature of the salt and the concentration of the solution. Certain salts are readily absorbed, e.g., chlorides and most of the ammonium salts; on the other hand, tartrates, citrates, and some of the sulfates are very slowly absorbed.

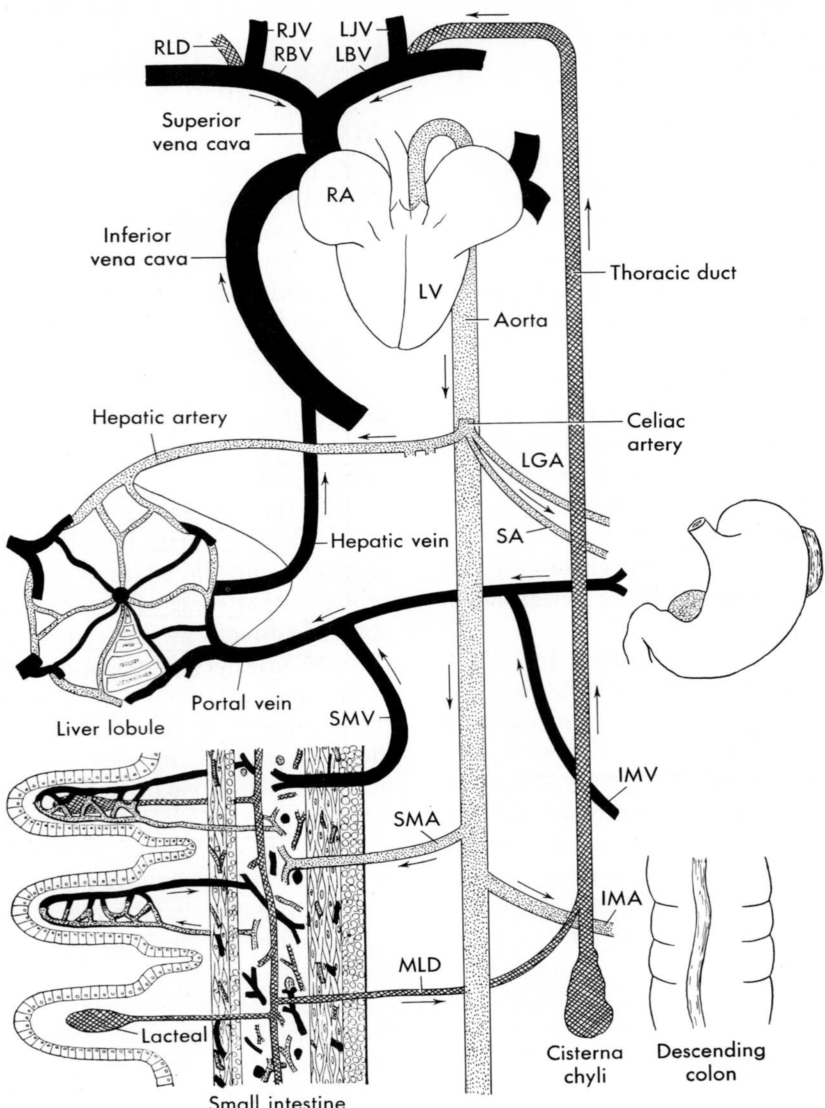

Figure 22–2. Diagram to show absorption. (*IMA*) Inferior mesenteric artery, (*IMV*) inferior mesenteric vein, (*LGA*) left gastric artery, (*LBV*) left brachiocephalic vein, (*LJV*) left jugular vein, (*LV*) left ventricle, (*MLD*) mesenteric lymph duct, (*RA*) right atrium, (*RBV*) right brachiocephalic vein, (*RJV*) right jugular vein, (*RLD*) right lymph duct, (*SA*) splenic artery, (*SMA*) superior mesenteric artery, (*SMV*) superior mesenteric vein.

To be absorbed, salts must be in higher concentration in the intestine than in the blood, with the exception of sodium for which there is active transport.

Cathartic Action of Salts in Solution of Water. The "cathartic" salts are very slowly absorbed from the gastrointestinal tract. For example, the cation magnesium and the anions citrate, tartrate, sulfate, and phosphate, are slowly absorbed. When taken as salts they remain in the intestine for a comparatively long period of time. The tissues between the salts in solution and the blood stream form a semipermeable membrane which is readily permeable to water. Consequently fluid moves from the blood stream to the intestinal cavity, thereby increasing the bulk of the intestinal content. The increased bulk acts as a distention stimulus to promote increased peristalsis and bowel evacuation.

It is important to remember that all materials entering the blood stream from the intestine pass through the liver before reaching the heart and systemic circulation. (See Figure 22–3.) The liver has a significant regulatory influence on the amounts of fat, protein, and carbohydrate appearing in the blood delivered to the cells. It also clears the blood stream of alcohol through oxidation.

Metabolism. The general term *metabolism* refers to all the changes occurring in digested foodstuffs in the body from their absorption until their elimination in the excretions. In actuality metabolism is the *sum total of the chemical changes* taking place within cells. Metabolic changes include both *anabolism*, or constructive process or synthesis, and *catabolism*, which implies the breakdown of large molecules, the products of which are of smaller molecular size.

The changes classified as anabolic include the processes by which cells take food substances from the blood and make them a part of their own protoplasm. This involves the conversion of nonliving material into living material and is a building-up, or synthetic, process. The synthesis of glycogen and of fats within the cells is also anabolism. Anabolism is accompanied by the *storage* of chemical energy.

The changes classified as catabolic consist of the processes by which cells resolve into simpler substances (1) part of their own protoplasm or (2) substances which have been stored in them. This disintegration yields simpler substances, some of which may be used by other cells, though most of them are excreted. *Release* of chemical energy accompanies this process.

In the tissues, the participation of oxygen in the chemical changes of the body forms an integral part of the processes of metabolism.

The chemical reactions occurring within the cell have two overall purposes:

1. Forming molecules which make up the cell itself, e.g., cell membrane, endoenzymes, and cytoplasm, as the cell increases in size or divides; and forming molecules to be secreted from the cell, e.g., hormones, exoenzymes, and serum albumin and globulin.

2. Supplying energy for the synthetic

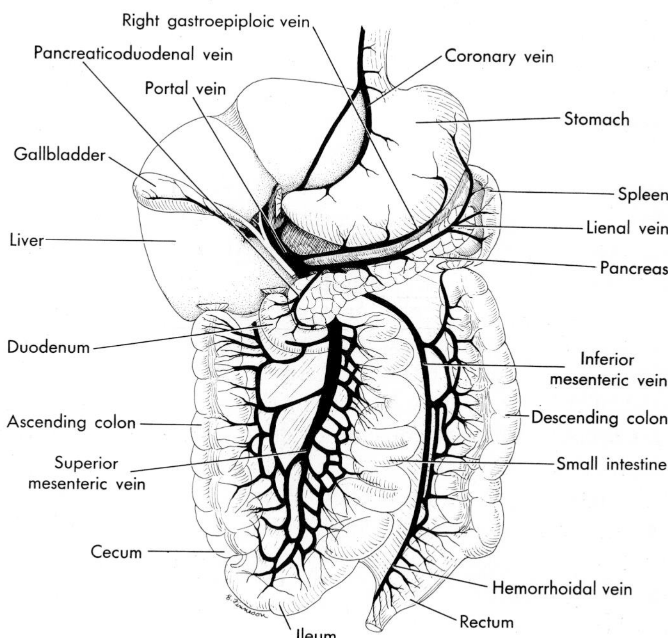

Figure 22–3. Organs of digestion and blood vessels that transport absorbed nutrients to the liver. Which digestive organs are not shown in this diagram?

processes listed above and for such specialized cell activities as muscle contraction, transmission of nerve impulse, ciliary movement, and sperm motility.

Fats and carbohydrates are primarily used for energy supply, although they are also necessary for synthesis of such materials as glycoproteins and cholesterol. Amino acids are primarily utilized in synthesis but may be utilized as energy sources, if fat and carbohydrate supply is inadequate. Energy supply seems to have priority over anabolism.

The chemical reactions within the cell which release energy occur in the mitochondria and are primarily oxidative reactions, that is, transfer of electrons or hydrogen from one substance to oxygen or to another substance. Oxidation may then occur aerobically (utilizing oxygen) or anaerobically. The aerobic oxidative processes yield the largest amount of energy.

Strictly speaking, with the exception of heat produced, energy is not "freed" from a substance but rather transferred. One of the most important substances in the cell in regard to energy transfer is adenosine triphosphate. To synthesize this substance, present in all cells, energy is used to form adenosine from ribose and adenine, and then to attach one, two, or three phosphate groups, adenosine monophosphate (AMP), adenosine diphosphate (ADP), and adenosine triphosphate (ATP). Large amounts of energy are required to attach the second and third phosphate groups; this same amount of energy is released when the phosphate groups, through enzymatic action, are broken off during cell activity. Oxidation in the cell is thus a step-by-step reaction, producing small amounts of energy for storage in ATP molecules which are held in reserve for utilization as needed. At the same time, utilization of ATP is a safety factor, for the release of excessive amounts of energy at one time might destroy the cell.

Muscle cells, in addition to ATP, synthesize another compound with a high-energy phosphate bond, creatine phosphate, which acts as an energy storehouse like ATP until the muscle contracts and energy is needed.

Needless to say, none of the chemical reactions within the cell, energy-transferring, or of a synthetic nature could occur rapidly enough in the absence of the appropriate enzymes. Reference to the enzyme chart on page 29 and the coenzyme chart on page 443 will be helpful in the discussions to follow.

Metabolism of Carbohydrates

During the process of digestion the carbohydrates are changed to simple sugars. Absorption of glucose takes place mainly into the capillaries of the small intestine. These capillaries pour their contents into the portal vein, which carries the blood, rich with glucose, to the liver. The liver cells take this glucose from the blood and convert it to glycogen, which is stored in the liver cells. By the storing up of glycogen and doling out of glucose as needed, the liver helps to maintain the normal quantity of glucose—80 to 120 mg per 100 ml of blood. From the blood stream glucose is taken up by the skeletal muscles and stored as glycogen until needed, or it is utilized by any and all cells as a source of energy or for synthesis of appropriate cell constituents and secretions. Hence the liver functions to help maintain a constant supply of blood glucose to meet the demands of active cells. The percentage of glycogen in a muscle is small, though the total content of all the muscle cells may equal that of the liver. The maximum storage of glycogen in the body is about 400 gm, or nearly 1 lb. The need of the blood for glucose is constant, because it is constantly giving up glucose to the tissues.

The amount of glucose oxidized is determined by the energy needs of the tissues, particularly muscle tissue, for their activity is the principal factor determining the rate of oxidation; naturally the amount of glucose required will be in proportion to the rate at which it is used.

Physiology of Carbohydrate Metabolism. In all cells, the first step in carbohydrate metabolism is the formation of glucose phosphate by transferring a phosphate radical from ATP to glucose, a reaction

Oxidation of Glucose—A Summary

Glycolysis

Glucose + Phosphate

↓

Glucose-1-phosphate*

↓

Glucose-6-phosphate

↓

ATP + Fructose-6-phosphate

↓

Fructose-1,6-diphosphate + ADP

↓ ↓

Dihydroxyacetone phosphate ⇄ Glyceraldehyde-3-phosphate

↓ + NAP + phosphate

1,3-Diphosphoglyceric acid + $NADH_2$

Glycolysis does not require oxygen; the end product is *pyruvic acid.* The energy yield is relatively small

↓ + ADP

3-Phosphoglyceric acid + ATP

↓ + ADP

Lactic acid + NAD ⇄ $NADH_2$ + Pyruvic acid + ATP

↓ + NAD† $NADH_2$‡ +

Carbon dioxide + acetyl coenzyme A enters the citric acid cycle for oxidation to

↓

Carbon dioxide + water

Terminal oxidation to carbon dioxide and water, via the *citric acid cycle*, requires oxygen. The energy yield is relatively large

* In all instances, numbers refer to the carbon atoms which carry the phosphate groups. Thus glucose has 6 carbons:

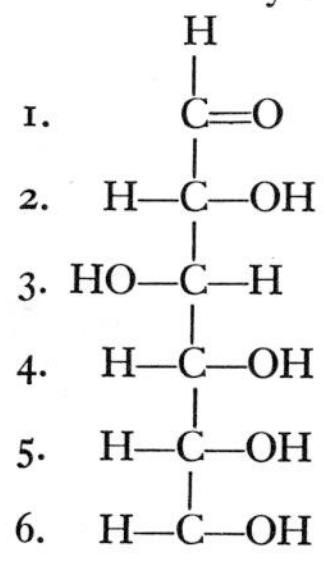

```
         H
         |
1.       C=O
         |
2.    H—C—OH
         |
3.   HO—C—H
         |
4.    H—C—OH
         |
5.    H—C—OH
         |
6.    H—C—OH
```

† NAD = Nicotinamide adenine dinucleotide

‡ $NADH_2$ = Nicotinamide adenine dinucleotide (reduced)

catalyzed by hexokinase. (In the liver fructose and galactose are transformed to glucose.) Glucose phosphate then may be transformed to glycogen (*glycogenesis*) in the case of liver or skeletal muscle cells; or *glycolysis* may occur—breakdown of glucose for energy release. Glycolysis is anaerobic, producing pyruvic acid (and lactic acid in skeletal muscle cells). Further oxidation of lactic acid and pyruvic acid is aerobic, resulting in eventual formation of carbon dioxide and water via the citric acid, or Krebs, cycle—a pathway utilized in oxidation of fats and amino acids as well.

An alternate pathway for oxidation of glucose is the "hexose monophosphate shunt," through which the enzyme NADP (nicotinamide adenine dinucleotide phosphate) is reduced to NADPH as glucose phosphate is transformed to a pentose, then fructose, then fructose phosphate. The reduced form of NADP (NADPH) is essential in synthesis of fatty acids.

Hormones Concerned with Carbohydrate Metabolism. The complex processes by which glucose is utilized, glycolysis, glycogenesis, glycogenolysis (breakdown of glycogen to glucose), and gluconeogenesis (formation of glucose from amino acids and fat), require regulation. Many aspects of the regulatory processes are poorly understood. However, certain hormones are known to be important.

Insulin, secreted by the beta cells of the islets of Langerhans, is concerned with the diffusion of glucose across tissue cell membranes from the extracellular fluids. Potassium enters the cell as glucose does, tending to deplete (temporarily) the plasma level. In the liver, insulin inhibits glycogen formation from noncarbohydrate sources. The alpha cells secrete *glucagon*, a hyperglycemic factor,

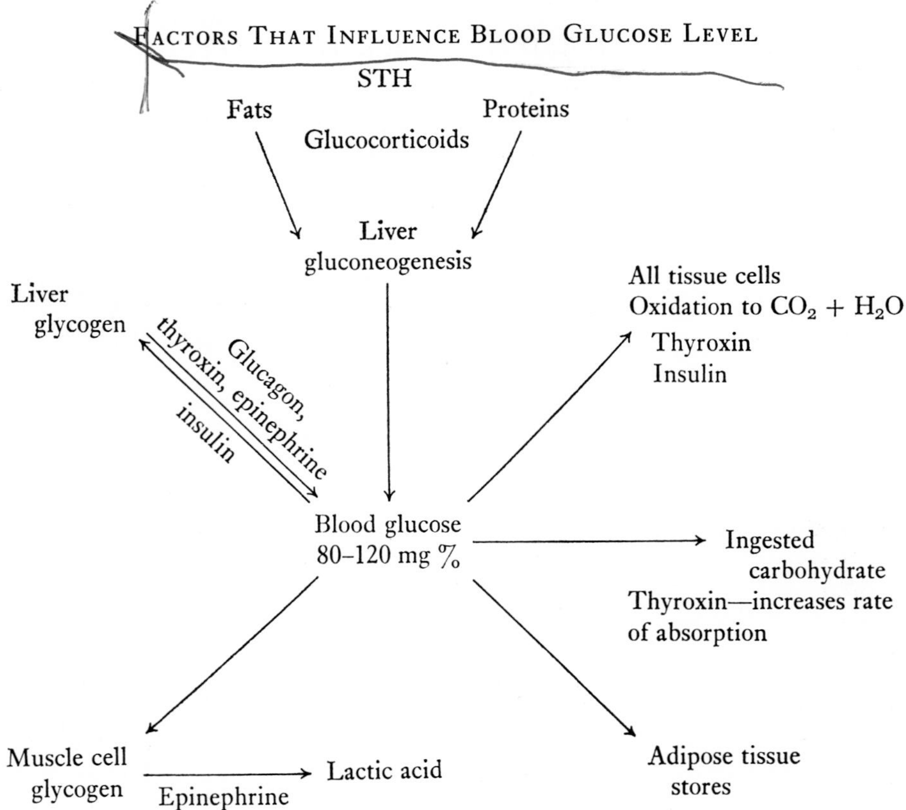

Note that the direction of the arrows (inward and outward) indicates raising and lowering of blood glucose. What organ is the primary regulator of the blood glucose level?

SUMMARY—SOME IMPORTANT STEPS IN CARBOHYDRATE METABOLISM

Sources of Carbohydrates	Role of the Liver	Tissue Cells
Digestion of carbohydrates to monosaccharides in small intestine: glucose, fructose, galactose →	Taken to liver via portal vein and converted to glycogen which is stored and subsequently converted to glucose as needed by cells →	To all cells of the body for oxidation for energy by way of the citric acid cycle
Products of muscle activity: lactic acid, pyruvic acid →	Conversion to glycogen	Stored as glycogen in muscle cells
Liver activities: Conversion of monosaccharides into glycogen	Synthesis of glycogen from noncarbohydrate sources (fats, amino acids) →	(Stored as glycogen in muscle cells)
Conversion of fatty acids into glucose and glycerol	Stored or converted to glucose as needed by cells →	Taken to cells by blood stream
Conversion of amino acids into glucose	Synthesis of fatty acids from glucose →	Stored as adipose tissue
	Glucose →	Synthesis of lactose in mammary glands
	Glucose →	Glycolipids, Glycoproteins, Nucleic acids — All cells

which promotes the conversion of glycogen to glucose in the liver.

Insulin is ineffective when taken by mouth, because it is destroyed in the alimentary canal and because the size of the molecule is too large for intestinal absorption; consequently, it is injected under the skin. The reduction of blood sugar by insulin does not necessarily stop at the normal level; if it proceeds further, prostration may occur. Such reaction is avoided by taking orange juice or sugar when the sensation of weakness is first felt. The improvement of patients receiving insulin is marked, but insulin does not cure diabetes. It is palliative in character, and usually dependence on the insulin continues.

Somatotropin and *adrenocorticotropin* are insulin antagonists and raise the blood sugar level, i.e., they inhibit glucose phosphorylations by inhibiting hexokinase and glucose utilization in the tissues.

The *glucocorticoids* decrease the use of tissue glucose, increase blood sugar, increase gluconeogenesis from amino acids, and increase the production of glucose from glycogen.

Epinephrine causes a rapid conversion of liver glycogen to glucose and increases the rate of use of glycogen in muscle tissue.

Thyroxin influences glucose metabolism by increasing the rate of oxidation in tissue cells. In the liver it increases the rate of glycogen formation from noncarbohydrate sources. At the same time it increases glucose absorption from the intestine, so that its immediate effect is to raise blood sugar level.

Functions of Carbohydrates. The oxidation of glucose serves the following purposes: It furnishes the main source of energy for all cells. The nerve cells use glucose only for energy; thus it is critical for brain functioning. Glucose furnishes an important part of the heat needed to maintain the body temperature. The oxidation of each gram of glucose yields 4 Cal of heat; and since the carbohydrates form the largest part of our diet and are easily oxidized, they must be regarded as specially available material for keeping up body heat. Glucose prevents oxidation of the body tissues, because it constitutes a reserve fund that is the first to be drawn upon in time of need. It is "protein sparing," for protein will be used as the energy source if glucose is not available. Carbohydrates, in excess of the amount that can be stored as glycogen in the liver and muscles, are converted into depot or stored fat.

End Products of Carbohydrate Metabolism. Eventually the glucose derived from the glucose of the blood or from the glycogen of the cell is oxidized by the cell, via the citric acid cycle, to *carbon dioxide* and *water*.

Derangements of Carbohydrate Metabolism. Ingestion of a larger amount of sugar than the liver and muscles can store results in an increased amount in the blood (hyperglycemia). A higher percentage of glucose than normal in the blood is excreted in the urine. This is designated as temporary glycosuria.

Diabetes Mellitus. In mankind derangements of carbohydrate metabolism manifest themselves chiefly in the disease known as diabetes mellitus, the early symptoms of which are excessive secretion of urine (polyuria) containing abnormal amounts of glucose and electrolytes, especially sodium, potassium, and chlorides; an abnormal thirst (polydipsia); and excessive eating (polyphagia). In this disease the daily loss of glucose in the urine may be very large. In severe cases all the carbohydrate of the food may be excreted in the form of glucose; and even when no carbohydrate food is eaten, glucose continues to be excreted in considerable amounts. In the latter case the sugar has as its source the proteins of the food or of the tissues. This disease is caused by lack of secretion of insulin, or perhaps by secretion of a nonusable form of insulin by the islet cells. In addition to the glucose found in the urine in diabetes, this secretion may contain considerable amounts of the acetone bodies. These acetone bodies are intermediary products in the metabolism of fats, and their presence in excess is due to increased utilization of fat. The accumulation of acetone bodies in the blood and tissues of the diabetic is responsible for the condition called *diabetic acidosis*.

Metabolism of Fats

The greater portion of the fat passes into the central lymph channel of each villus (Figure 22–2). From these small lacteals it finds its way through the larger lymphatics in the mesentery to the thoracic duct and then through the thoracic duct to the blood. It seems probable that some of the fatty acid and glycerol is absorbed by the capillaries in the villi, enters the portal vein, and passes through the liver before reaching the general circulation. Fat is carried by the blood to all parts of the body, and the tissues slowly take it out as they need it in their metabolic processes. Within tissues other than nerve tissue, it is oxidized to supply the energy needs of the cells. Nerve cells oxidize glucose only, whereas heart muscle uses a high proportion of fat.

Physiology of Fat Metabolism. Much of the fat absorbed is stored in adipose tissue, although this is not a static storage but a dynamic one with a constant turnover of fat in *lipogenesis* (fat formation) and *lipolysis*. Lipogenesis occurs as triglycerides are formed from fatty acids and glycerol, which are derived either from the degraded neutral fat of the blood stream or from precursors such as glucose and its metabolites. Synthesis from precursors requires the coenzyme NADPH formed in the monophosphate shunt of glycolysis.

Lipolysis involves the breakdown of fat into glycerol and fatty acids, following which oxidation occurs. The glycerol is converted in the liver to glucose or glycogen and then oxidized; the fatty acids are reduced in a series of steps, two carbons at a time until a four-carbon fragment remains. This is then split in half. The two-carbon or acetyl fractions enter the citric acid cycle with eventual formation of carbon dioxide and water.

Liver Metabolism. The liver has many functions in relation to fat metabolism. (1) It synthesizes fatty acids from carbohydrate intermediates; (2) rebuilds fatty acids through lengthening and shortening chains, with saturation or desaturation to provide the lipids characteristic of the human; and (3) oxidizes fatty acids to acetyl fragments, which may be used for synthesis of other substances, such as cholesterol and phospholipids, or oxidized to carbon dioxide and water.

The liver initiates the first steps in the oxidation of fatty acids. During beta oxidation, two carbon units are split off at a time, and in the liver they are condensed to form

SUMMARY—SOME IMPORTANT STEPS IN FAT METABOLISM

Sources of Fat	Blood Stream	Role of the Liver	Tissue Cells
FOODS Digestion of fats to fatty acids and glycerol in the intestine	Found as neutral fats in form of chylomicrons (fat droplets visible under the microscope)	Stores phospholipids and glycerides	Good source of energy by way of citric acid cycle to CO_2 and H_2O—9 Cal per gm of fat
		Oxidation of fatty acids to acetyl fragments	Necessary constituent of all cells, especially muscle cells for use in the citric acid cycle
		Formation of unsaturated fatty acids	Phospholipids and cholesterol essential constituent of all cells
	Phospholipids (lecithin)	Phospholipids formed at a higher rate than in any other organ, except intestinal mucosa during absorption	Lecithin—essential for formation of myelin sheaths
CELLS Mobilization of fat from adipose tissue cells	Cholesterol	Formation of cholesterol	Cholesterol found in all living cells. It is essential for the formation of steroid hormones in the adrenal cortex and gonads
	Cholesterol esters	Cholesterol esters formed and distributed to the cells or excreted in the bile	Cholesterol enters into basic structure of the cell and is essential for the normal permeability of cell membranes
LIVER Synthesis of lipids from: Glucose Acetic acid Amino acid Pyruvic acid	Ketone bodies	Ketone bodies formed in the liver in the course of oxidation of fatty acids Acetate converted to fatty acids for neutral fats and phospholipids	Ketone bodies oxidized in muscle and other cells. Excess excreted by kidney

acetoacetic acid. Acetoacetic acid and beta-hydroxybutyric acid and acetone, the ketone bodies, leave the liver via the hepatic vein and are taken to muscle cells, where they are oxidized by way of the citric acid cycle to carbon dioxide and water with release of energy. Oxaloacetic acid is essential for the oxidation of ketone bodies in the citric acid cycle.

It is evident then that in diabetes mellitus or starvation, when carbohydrate is not available for oxidation, an excess of ketone bodies is produced in the liver. Normally the blood contains 1 mEq per liter of keto acids, but may contain 20 to 30 mEq per liter. This condition is called ketosis.

Synthesis of cholesterol, lipoproteins, and phospholipids and their removal from the blood stream for oxidation occurs in the liver. Certain *lipotropic* factors, such as choline, function in the liver to prevent excessive accumulation of fat in this organ, mainly through the formation of lipoproteins. Choline is obtained in the diet, as well as synthesized from the amino acid methionine.

Hormonal Influences on Fat Metabolism. Somatotropin, adrenocorticotropin, and thyroid-stimulating hormone all increase the energy demands of various tissues, thus requiring the release of fatty acids from adipose tissue. Epinephrine stimulates the breakdown of triglycerides and mobilizes body fat. Insulin has a lipogenic effect; thyroxin is lipotropic.

Functions of Fat. Much of the fat absorbed from the intestine is deposited in fat-storage cells which are widely distributed throughout the body. From these cells fat is constantly being withdrawn to meet the demands of active cells. Some is oxidized to provide energy, some is used for synthesis of lipids for cell use. Each gram of fat yields 9 Cal of heat; thus fat is a valuable source of body heat.

When the food eaten is in excess of the energy requirements of the individual, fat accumulates in the storage cells, thus increasing the amount of adipose tissue. It is a valuable reserve of nutrient and also provides protection and support for organs and insulation for the animal. It is used to form essential tissue and cell components, particularly in the nervous system (myelin and the phospholipids).

Obesity results from ingestion of excessive amounts of nutrients, particularly carbohydrate and fat. It imposes demands on the heart which may be harmful and in general shortens the lifespan. As with many diseases, prevention is easier than cure. Habits formed early in life which match food ingestion to energy needs and the decrease of caloric intake when adulthood is reached (and there is less physical activity) help to prevent this condition.

Experimental work has recently been devoted to the relationship of heart attacks and deposits of lipids, including cholesterol, in the walls of arteries (atherosclerosis). It is known that high levels of serum lipids lead to increased deposits of lipids in the arterial wall. How to decrease these high levels has not been reliably established, although fatty acids containing many "unsaturated" or double bonds between carbon atoms seem more effective than fatty acids that are "saturated" (no double bonds). The essential fatty acids (those that must be present in the diet) are all unsaturated—linoleic, linolenic, and arachidonic acids. Although heart attacks do appear to be related to the deposits of lipids in arterial walls, there still is no concrete evidence that changing from a diet high in "saturated" fatty acids to one high in "unsaturated" fatty acids is beneficial.

Metabolism of Proteins

As a result of digestion, proteins are hydrolyzed to amino acids, which are absorbed by the blood capillaries of the villi, pass into the portal vein, are carried through the liver into the blood of the general circulation, and are distributed to the tissues. The tissues select and store certain of these substances; and in each organ they are either synthesized into new tissue or used to maintain and repair tissue. Such synthesis of tissue protein, or of materials to be secreted from the cell such as lipoproteins, is under the direction of RNA.

Amino acids not used in synthesis of protoplasm are broken down or deaminized in the liver. In deaminization, the amino groups are removed from amino acid molecules; transamination involves the transfer of the amino group from an amino acid to another organic acid. These NH_2 groups may be used for synthesis of other amino acids or for formation of urea by the liver. In the kidney, ammonia is formed from certain amino acids and is used for the production of ammonium salts, thus sparing the sodium ions of the blood in maintaining acid-base balance (page 538).

In skeletal muscle amino acids are utilized to form creatine and creatine phosphate, substances which have an active role in muscle contraction.

The nonnitrogenous portion of the amino acid molecule which is left after deaminization is oxidized to furnish energy (see citric acid cycle, page 474) or is synthesized into glycogen or into fat. Therefore, this portion of the amino acid molecule may be regarded as a source of energy.

Certain amino acids have physiological roles that are distinctive. *Glycine* is used by the liver in detoxification of benzoic acid, a food preservative, and in formation of hemoglobin, one of the bile acids, purines, and fatty acids. *Methionine* reacts with niacin and participates in formation of phospholipids, ergosterol, and histamine and in the detoxification of certain poisons such as chloroform and carbon tetrachloride. *Tryptophan* is a precursor of niacin and of serotonin, a vasoconstrictor.

Nucleoproteins. These conjugated proteins are found in the nuclei of cells, as well as in the cytoplasm, and are abundant in the nucleated cells of the glandular organs, such as the liver, pancreas, and thymus. Digestion of nucleoproteins releases the purines in the molecule which are oxidized to uric acid and excreted in urine.

Hormones Influencing Protein Metabolism. Somatotropin stimulates cell and tissue formation, with a resultant positive nitrogen balance. Androgens, particularly testosterone, have a similar action; this is noticeable at puberty when the muscles increase in size, and when the overall size increases. Insulin is necessary for somatotropin effect; thyroxin's metabolic effect also influences the action of these hormones in building tissue.

Hormones causing a catabolic effect on protein synthesis are the adrenal steroids and excessive amounts of thyroxin. The glucocorticoids of the adrenal gland cause gluconeogenesis and deamination of amino acids, thus potentiating the oxidation of the glucose residues.

SUMMARY—SOME OF THE IMPORTANT STEPS IN PROTEIN METABOLISM

Sources of Protein	Role of the Liver	Tissue Cells
Digestive processes Digestion of protein foods to amino acids →	Taken to liver via portal vein Amino acids →	To all cells of body for maintenance, growth, and repair of tissues Nucleoproteins in cytoplasm and in nucleus of all cells
	Synthesis of: Serum albumin Serum globulin Fibrinogen Prothrombin	→ Synthesis of certain hormones and enzymes
	Synthesis of essential nitrogen containing nonproteins: Choline Purines Creatine Pyrimidines	
	Deaminization of amino acids, conversion of amino acids into glucose and fats	
	Synthesis of amino acids from other amino acids	Excess amino acids oxidized by way of citric acid cycle to carbon dioxide and water
	Formation of keto acids →	Oxidized by way of citric acid cycle to carbon dioxide and water

Common Metabolic Pool

The concept of a common metabolic pool is helpful in understanding the interrelationships of metabolism. Protein, lipids, and carbohydrates may be interconverted because of the similarity in chemical composition (C, H, O). With the availability of NH_2 radicals amino acid synthesis is possible, as seen below.

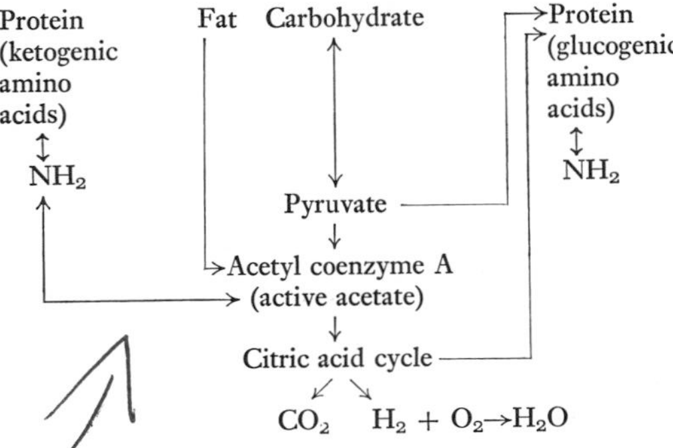

The term *metabolic pool* includes in reality all the substances in the body which enter into metabolic reactions. Thus various minerals, even calcium, which is stored in bones, are included.

Citric Acid Cycle

The final stage in oxidation of glucose, fatty acids, and amino acids is the citric acid cycle—a complex series of chemical reactions in which acetyl fragments are first activated by combination with coenzyme A. The acetyl coenzyme A then reacts with oxaloacetic acid to form citric acid, releasing coenzyme A. By a series of steps hydrogen and carbon dioxide contained in the original acetyl radical are released with eventual formation of oxaloacetic acid. Hydrogen is combined with oxygen in the presence of cytochrome enzymes.

Ketogenic amino acids (which form ketone bodies on oxidation) and glucogenic amino acids (forming pyruvic acid) enter the cycle as acetyl fragments, as do fatty acids and their ketone bodies. Lactic acid is transformed to pyruvic acid before entering the cycle. Thus pyruvic acid and the acetyl radical in particular are crucial intermediary products in oxidation and provide the means by which carbohydrates can be synthesized from non-carbohydrate sources, since much of the pathway is reversible.

The citric acid cycle, however, is not merely a cycle which eventually forms carbon dioxide and water. Its *purpose* is the release of energy in the acetyl radical; formation of carbon dioxide and water is incidental. The large amount of energy is transferred to adenosine as phosphate radicals are attached to it, with eventual formation of ATP.

Measurement of Food Energy

The energy of food is not used directly as heat, but it is customary to measure it in heat units. To determine the amount of energy produced by the oxidation of food, the amount of heat produced on oxidation is measured by a calorimeter in terms of calories. A large calorie is the amount of heat required to raise the temperature of 1 kg of water 1° C. The large calorie (Cal) is the one referred to in physiology. When undergoing complete oxidation in the bomb calorimeter, the foodstuffs yield the following:

Carbohydrate	1 gm—4.10 Cal
Fat	1 gm—9.45 Cal
Protein	1 gm—5.65 Cal

The oxidation of protein in the body is never quite complete, for the urea, creatinine, uric acid, etc., eliminated in urine still contain about 113 Cal per gram of protein catabolized by the cells. Hence, protein yields to body cells only 4.35 Cal (5.65 less 1.3 Cal) per gram of protein received by them. The cells oxidize the carbon and the hydrogen completely but only partially oxidize the nitrogen of the proteins which they receive. It is said that on the average about 98 per cent of the carbohydrates, about 95 per cent of the fats, and about 92 per cent of the proteins ingested are absorbed and reach the body cells. Some deductions are made for what are called *losses in digestion*. The practical figures

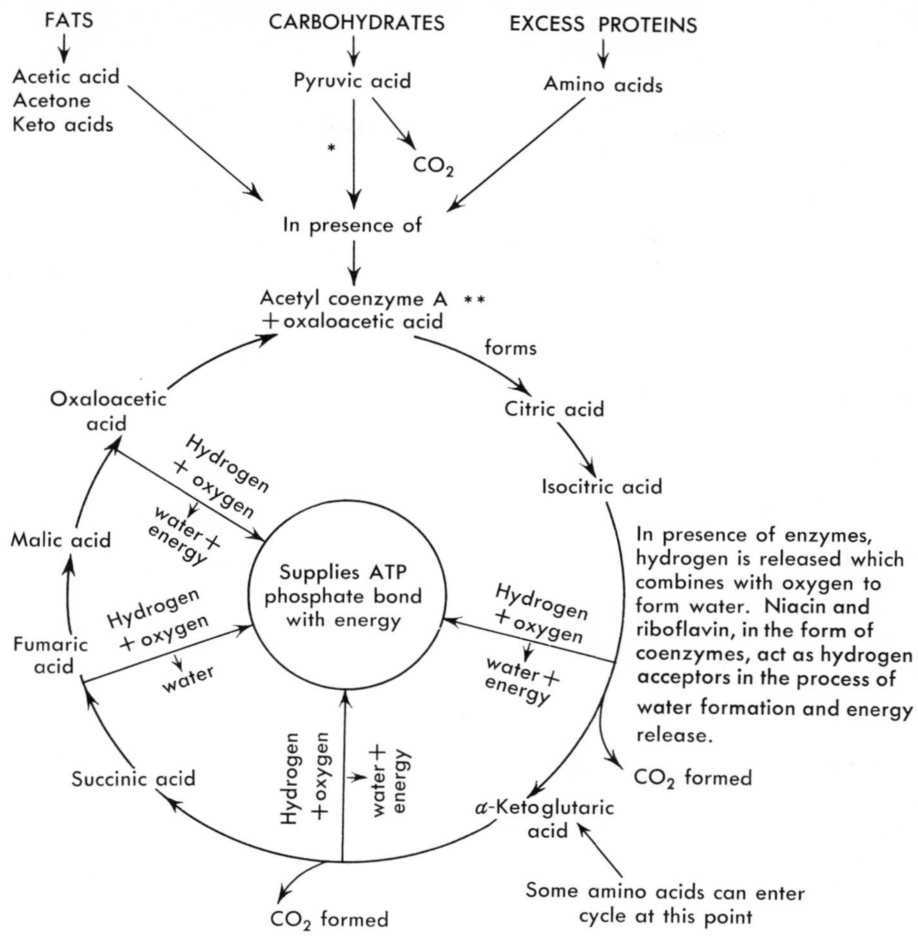

Figure 22–4. Citric acid cycle. Using fats, carbohydrates, and excess amino acids as fuel, the citric acid cycle supplies energy-rich bonds to adenosine triphosphate. A series of acids are converted one to another by enzymes with release of carbon dioxide and transfer of hydrogen to oxygen, forming water. The energy released is used to form *ATP* and to provide body heat. *ATP* is essential for all muscle contraction and is also found in all cells of the body. The B vitamins in the form of coenzymes are an integral part of the cycle.

used in estimating the fuel value of food are therefore:

Carbohydrate	1 gm—4 Cal (98% of 4.10 Cal)
Fat	1 gm—9 Cal (95% of 9.45 Cal)
Protein	1 gm—4 Cal (92% of 4.35 Cal)

Basal Metabolism

Basal metabolism is the rate of energy metabolism required to keep the body alive. The term *basal metabolism* is used clinically to indicate the rate of energy metabolism of the body when the subject is lying quiet and relaxed in a room of comfortable temperature in what is called "postabsorptive" state, i.e., 12 to 18 hours after the last meal. The digestion and absorption of the meal should be completed, and only such expenditure of energy should occur during the test as is required to maintain body warmth, minimal cell activity, respiration, and circulation; or, briefly, conditions should represent *functional activity at a minumum.* The basal rate of energy metabolism is used as a starting point for the calculation of total energy requirements in food under varying conditions and as a basis for diagnosis.

Basal metabolism may be determined by *the direct method,* in which the subject is placed in a respiratory chamber and the amount of heat evolved is measured, or *the indirect method,* in which the heat given off is computed from the respiratory exchange. Metabolism rates determined by the indirect method are based on the respiratory quotient, which is the ratio between the volume of carbon dioxide excreted and the volume of oxygen consumed. It is found by dividing the former by the latter. It has been demonstrated that energy calculated from the amount of carbon dioxide excreted and oxygen absorbed by a subject is equivalent to the heat given off by the body.

The amount of oxygen required to oxidize a given amount of carbohydrate, fat, or protein is not the same. In the oxidation of carbohydrate, the volume of carbon dioxide produced is equal to the volume of oxygen absorbed. The respiratory quotient (or RQ) is, therefore,

$$\frac{\text{Volume } CO_2 \text{ produced}}{\text{Volume } O_2 \text{ consumed}}, \text{ or RQ} = 1$$

There are slight variations in the respiratory quotients for different fats, owing to differences in molecular weight. For human fat, the quotient is 0.703. For protein, the quotient is 0.8 to 0.82. These figures show that the carbon dioxide produced is generally less than the oxygen which has disappeared in the exchange.

If the combustion of carbohydrate alone were possible, the respiratory quotient would be 1; if only protein were burned, it would be 0.80 to 0.82; if fat, about 0.7.

Under ordinary conditions, the respiratory quotient is about 0.85, but it may vary within rather wide limits, depending on the diet.

Basal metabolism calculated on the basis of surface area of the body is more nearly accurate than that determined in terms of body weight, because heat loss increases in proportion to surface rather than weight. A table for this purpose has been worked out. According to this table, a woman standing 5 ft, 4 in. tall and weighing 56 kg with 1.6 sq

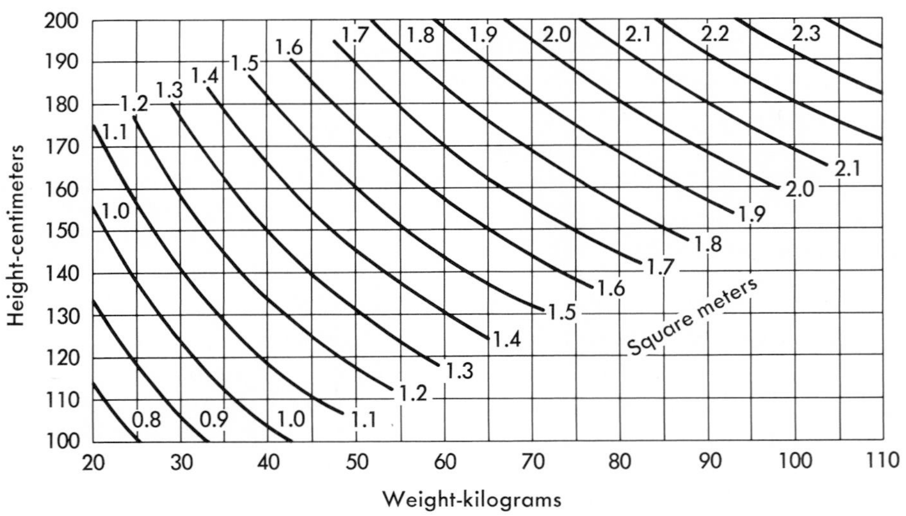

Figure 22–5. Chart for determining surface area of adults from weight and height. Height in inches divided by 0.393 gives height in centimeters. Weight in pounds divided by 2.2 gives weight in kilograms. (Courtesy of Dr. Eugene Du Bois and the *Archives of Internal Medicine.*)

m of body surface will have a basal metabolism of about 36.9 Cal per square meter per hour with a total basal metabolism of 1,400 Cal per day (1.6 × 24 × 36.9). Likewise, a man of 50 years of age, weighing 70 kg and measuring 5 ft, 8 in. in height, will have a body surface of 1.83 sq m, and his basal metabolism will be about 1,700 Cal per day (1.83 × 24 × 39.7).

Variations in Basal Metabolism. A number of factors, such as age, sex, sleep, and thyroid hormone, influence the basal metabolic rate. In women the rate is a little lower than in men; it gradually decreases with age; it may be increased by systematic exercise over a long period; prolonged undernourishment reduces it. All the preceding relate in great degree to the amount of muscle tissue in the individual, which has a higher metabolic rate than adipose tissue; certain races appear to have a slightly higher rate than others.

Emotional tension increases it, but the individual then is not basal—i.e., not completely relaxed. Temperature has a marked effect on the metabolic rate. Fever causes an increase—often beyond the energy supplied in the diet, and body tissues are utilized for energy. Similarly, a decrease in body temperature decreases metabolic rate and therefore decreases the amount of oxygen required.

Daily Calorie Requirement

If constant weight is to be maintained, showing neither gain nor loss, the daily output of calories (as determined by calorimeter tests) must be balanced by calories taken in. On such data the daily food requirement in terms of calories is based. Since basal metabolism represents the heat given off when physiological work is at a minimum (in the morning after a comfortable night's rest, relaxed in bed, before breakfast), it is obvious that any increase in physiological activity, even the slightest (sitting up under the same conditions), increases the metabolic rate over the minimum. Comparison of the basal metabolic rate with the metabolic rates during various types of work shows that work results in an increment in the amount of heat eliminated. Such increases have been estimated and graded for the average individual according to the calories required as follows:

	Calories Per Hour
Very light work, or sitting at rest	100
Light work	120
Moderate work	175
Severe work	350

Total Calorie Requirement. The metabolic rate is reduced about 10 per cent beyond the basal level during sleep. Allowance is made for this in estimating the total daily calorie requirement of an individual. On the other hand, the process of digestion of food itself brings about a need for an increase of 6 to 10 per cent of the calorie intake. This is called the *specific dynamic action of food* (S.D.A.), and allowance must be made for it. Protein S.D.A. is higher than that for fat or carbohydrate; thus weight-losing diets contain a high proportion of protein.

After consideration of all these factors the total calorie requirement of the average man will be found to be about as follows:

	Calories
8 hours of sleep at 65 Cal	520
2 hours of light exercise at 120 Cal	240
8 hours of moderate work at 175 Cal	1,400
6 hours sitting at rest at 100 Cal	600
	2,760
6–10 per cent for S.D.A.	250
Total requirement for 24 hours	3,010

In a diet of 3,000-Cal energy value, the proportions of the main constituents should be approximately as shown below.

	Calories	Approximate % of Total Calories	Grams
Carbohydrate	1,440	48	380
Fat	1,200	40	133
Protein	360	12	90

It is obvious that increased calorie need occurs in the growing child and in pregnancy.

Physiology of Body Temperature

From the standpoint of heat control, animals may be divided into two great classes:

Constant-temperature (homeothermic) animals, or those whose temperature remains practically constant whether the surrounding air is hotter or cooler than the body. Birds and mammals (including human beings) are in this class.

Variable-temperature (poikilothermic) animals, or those whose temperature varies with that of the surrounding medium, e.g., reptiles, frogs, fishes. In winter their temperature is low, and in summer their temperature approximates that of their surroundings. The human fetus is in this class.

At birth the heat-regulating mechanism is not functioning optimally, and infants are not able to regulate their body temperature, hence the importance of keeping them warm. Premature infants are even less able to regulate their body temperature, hence the need of special means to keep them warm, but they should not be kept at the temperature of the adult.

Between the two groups are various classes of hibernating animals.

The great difference between these two classes of animals is in their reactions to external temperature. A cold environment reduces the temperature of the cold-blooded creature, reduces the metabolism of all its tissues, and thus reduces its heat production. The warm-blooded animal reacts in the opposite way. In a cold environment its temperature remains fairly constant. As shivering occurs, metabolism increases and thus heat production increases.

Distribution of Heat. The blood permeates all the tissues and serves as an absorbing medium for the heat. Wherever oxidation takes places and heat is generated, the temperature of the blood circulating in these tissues is raised. Wherever, on the other hand, the blood vessels are exposed to conditions which are cool because of heat lost by evaporation, etc., as in the moist membranes in the lungs or the more or less moist skin, the temperature of the blood is lowered. But these changes are not effected instantaneously, and consequently the temperature of some internal parts must always be higher than that of others. This is particularly true of the liver because its blood vessels are well protected against loss of heat. Because of this the temperature of the blood in different parts of the body varies slightly; but the circulation, moving through warmer and then through cooler parts, tends to keep the average temperature of the blood at about 38° C.

Regulation of Body Temperature

The constant temperature of the body is maintained by means of a balance between heat production (thermogenesis) and heat loss (thermolysis). The body must control the production and the loss of heat (thermotaxis). It is important to remember that although heat production may be increased by increasing the rate of metabolism, it is not possible to decrease metabolic rate as a means of producing less heat. Experimental work indicates that the accurate *balance* between heat production and heat loss is controlled by nerve fibers connected with a temperature-regulating center in the hypothalamus (page 215).

Thermogenesis. The heat produced within the body represents the difference between the energy used in the anabolic processes and the energy provided by the catabolic processes. The heat produced in the

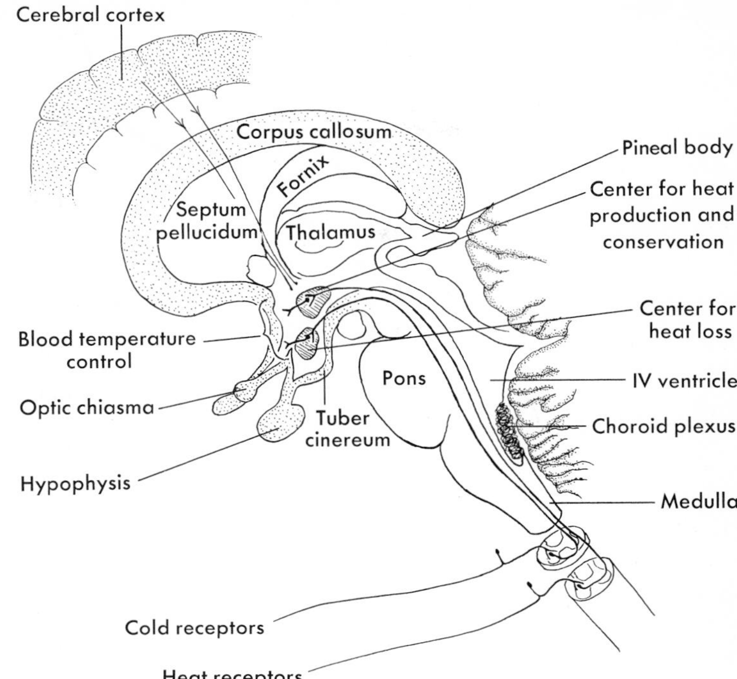

Figure 22–6. Nervous control of body temperature.

body is varied by increasing or decreasing the physiological oxidations. This end is effected in part by *taking food* and by *muscular exercise*. In this connection the action of enzymes and some of the internal secretions (e.g., thyroxin—and possibly epinephrine) is important. *Thyroxin* increases the metabolism of the body and stimulates all of the metabolic processes. During digestion heat is produced partly by the peristaltic action of the intestines and partly by the activity of the various digestive glands, particularly the liver. *Cold weather* stimulates the appetite; and an increased amount of food, usually accompanied by an increase of fats, increases heat production. Cold causes the muscles to contract and speeds up the processes of oxidation. Muscular contractions give rise to heat; therefore, muscular activity counteracts the effects of external cold.

Thermolysis. To a small extent heat loss is facilitated through an increase in the respiratory rate. The increased respirations associated with muscular activity aid somewhat in eliminating the excess heat produced, although this factor is not as important as sweating and flushing of the skin. In man respiration plays only a small part in temperature regulation; but in animals that do not perspire, respiration is an important means of regulating the temperature.

During muscular activity or when the external temperature is high, receptors for heat are stimulated, and impulses are transmitted over sensory fibers to the nerve centers controlling the motor fibers of the sweat glands. The motor fibers stimulate the activity of the sweat glands, and an increased amount of perspiration occurs. An increased amount of heat is required to vaporize this perspiration, and thus heat is lost. Excessive humidity interferes with the evaporation of water and thus interferes with the loss of heat, hence the discomfort experienced on hot, humid days.

The receptors for heat not only transmit impulses that stimulate the sweat glands to activity but at the same time transmit impulses that result in the depression of the vasoconstrictor center leading to the arterioles of the skin. In consequence the arterioles dilate, and more blood is sent to the surface to be cooled. This tends to increase the temperature of the skin and hence increases the heat lost by conduction and radiation. When the external temperature is low, the receptors for cold transmit impulses which result in stimulation of the vasoconstrictors and consequent contraction of the arterioles of the skin. This lessens the amount of blood in the skin arterioles, reduces the temperature of the skin, and so lessens the amount of heat loss.

LOST FROM SKIN	2,156 Cal, or 87.5%
1,792 Cal, or 73.0%, by radiation and conduction	
364 Cal, or 14.5%, by evaporation of perspiration	
LOST IN EXPIRED AIR	266 Cal, or 10.7%
182 Cal, or 7.2%, vaporization of water	
84 Cal, or 3.5%, warming air	
LOST IN URINE OR FECES	48 Cal, or 1.8%
Total heat loss per 24-hour day	2,470 Cal, or 100.0%

The flow of blood through the skin tends to raise skin temperature, whereas the loss of heat to the environment tends to lower it. The nervous system adjusts the flow of blood in the skin in relation to environmental temperature at the skin surface in such a way that the body maintains a constant temperature. Temperature and heat-dissipating capacities of the environment at the skin surface are modified by clothing (amount, texture, style, color, etc.) and by ventilation of rooms.

Thermal comfort seems to be closely related to skin temperature, and optimal average skin temperature seems to be about 33° C (91.4° F).

Variations in Temperature

The temperature of the human body is usually measured by a thermometer placed in the mouth, axilla, or rectum. Such measurements show slight variations. The normal temperature by mouth is about 37° C (98.6° F), by axilla the temperature is lower, and by rectum it is usually 1° higher.

Normal Variations. These depend on such factors as time of day, exercise, meals, age, sex, season, climate, and clothing. The temperature is usually lowest between 3 and 5 A.M. It rises slowly during the day, reaches its maximum at about 4 P.M., and falls again during the night. This corresponds to the usual temperature ranges in fever, when the minimum is in the early morning and the maximum is in the evening. Muscular activity and food cause a slight increase in temperature. This probably accounts for the increase in temperature during the day. In the case of nightworkers who sleep during the day, the increase in temperature occurs during the night, which is the period when food is eaten and work performed. Age has some influence. Infants and young children have a slightly higher temperature (about 1°) than adults. Their heat-regulating mechanism is more easily disturbed, and rise of temperature is caused by slight disturbances of digestion or metabolism and usually is less significant than the same increase in adults. Continual slight reduction in basal metabolic rate and decrease in heat production result in lower body temperature with aging.

Subnormal Temperature. In order to carry on the activities essential to life, the body must maintain a normal temperature. If the temperature falls much below normal, to about 35° C (95°F), life may be threatened. Subnormal temperature may be due to excessive loss of heat, profuse sweating, hemorrhage, and lessened heat production, as in starvation. In cases of starvation the fall of temperature is very marked, especially during the last days of life. The diminished activity of the tissues first affects the central nervous system; the patient becomes languid and drowsy, and finally unconscious; the heart beats more and more feebly, the breath comes more and more slowly, and the sleep of unconsciousness passes insensibly into the sleep of death.

Hypothermia. It is possible to decrease body temperature by giving sedatives to depress the hypothalamic thermostat and then using ice packs or a cooling mattress. Temperature can be maintained considerably below 32.2° C (90° F). Artificial cooling of the body is used during heart surgery so that the heart can be stopped for several minutes at a time without apparent untoward physiological results, since the metabolic rate decreases and oxygen need is less.

Factors Influencing Temperature Regulation

It has been suggested that the *concentration of the blood* is a factor to be considered. The water of the body holds heat; and when the external temperature is low, water is withdrawn from the blood to the tissues, leaving the blood more concentrated. When the external temperature is high, water is withdrawn from the tissues to the blood. When the blood is dilute, an increased amount of water is brought to the surface, and an increased loss of heat results; but when the water is withheld in the interior of the body, less heat is lost. Other factors to be considered are size, age, and constitution.

Size. The quantity of heat produced by well-nourished animals, including man, is relatively constant; but the larger the surface of the body exposed to a cooler medium, the greater must be the loss of heat, since the heat lost is related to the *area of surface.* Small animals present a proportionately larger surface to the surrounding medium than larger animals; hence, the loss per unit of weight is greater, and this must be compensated for by a greater heat production. Skin secretions of different animals have varied effects in relation to heat insulation, and account must be taken of this also.

Age. In children the heat production is relatively large, because they are active and growing. Moreover, young children have not the constancy of temperature which is an evolved characteristic of adult life. On the contrary, they are subject to changes of body temperature which would be of grave import in an adult.

Constitution. Individuals differ greatly in their power of heat loss. Apart from differences in size and in the faculty of perspiration, there exist differences in compactness of shape, in the amount of adipose tissue protecting the viscera, etc.

Clothing. Clothing aids in the maintenance of heat, though, of course, clothes are not in themselves usually sources of heat. Clothing of any kind captures a layer of warm and moist air between it and the skin and thus diminishes greatly the loss by evaporation, conduction, and radiation.

Fever. An elevation of body temperature above the normal range is a fever. This may be caused by an abnormality of the brain, such as a tumor, or manipulation of the brain during surgery; or it may be due to toxins produced by bacteria and by certain breakdown products of protein. These substances, known as pyrogens, act by "resetting" the hypothalamic center for temperature, so that temperature regulation is at a higher level. Destruction of leukocytes, as in infection, releases a substance which is known to be pyrogenic. Dehydration is also a cause of fever, presumably by its effect on the hypothalamus. A temperature above 41° C is extremely hazardous to life. During the fever, particularly the early stages, "chills" often occur. Since the "thermostat" is set at a higher level than the temperature of the circulating blood, the normal mechanisms for thermogenesis come into play—excessive shivering, peripheral vasoconstriction—and the person feels cold. This continues until the blood and tissues of the body are at the elevated temperature of the thermostat.

Fever has a beneficial effect in many infectious diseases because the high temperature kills the causative organism. Inability to produce a fever during an infection has a negative effect as far as recovery is concerned.

Heat Stroke. Heat stroke occurs when the individual is exposed to extremely high atmospheric temperature for a long period, and when the humidity is high so that heat loss is difficult. As the body temperature rises, the hypothalamic center becomes damaged, and heat regulation is impossible.

QUESTIONS FOR DISCUSSION

1. What are the normal end products of digestion, and how do they reach the blood stream?
2. If the quantity of food from a meal is in excess of immediate energy needs, what will become of the excess? Through what metabolic process might this be accomplished?
3. Since the body does not use the food directly for energy, what is the function of the citric acid cycle?
4. Which hormones influence the level of blood glucose? What other factors are involved?
5. What is the role of the liver in relation to metabolism of carbohydrates, fats, and proteins?
6. Differentiate between metabolism and basal metabolism and explain three factors that will affect each one.
7. How can you determine your metabolic needs? Why is "calorie counting" important (a) for growing children, (b) for energy production, (c) for individuals who have a tendency to put on weight, and (d) for "senior" individuals with a "heart condition"?

SUMMARY

- **Absorption**
  - Passage of digested food material from the cavity of the alimentary canal to the blood
  - **Determining conditions**
    1. Area of surface for absorption
    2. Length of time food is in contact with absorbing surface
    3. Concentration of digested material present
  - **Small intestine**
    - Above conditions are realized in small intestine
    1. Circular folds and villi increase internal surface
    2. Food remains for several hours
    3. Products of digestion higher in intestine, lower in blood
  - **Paths of absorption**
    1. Capillaries of villi absorb sugars, amino acids, and some of the glycerol and fatty acids, carry them to portal vein, then to liver
    2. Central lymph channel of villus absorbs glycerol and fat, empties into larger lymph vessels, then into thoracic duct, superior vena cava, and right atrium of heart
  - **Stomach**
    - Alcohol and alcoholic solutions absorbed
    - Small amounts of sugar, amino acids may be absorbed
    - Water passively absorbed
  - **Large intestine**
    - Limited absorption of digested foodstuffs, marked absorption of water
- **Place of Absorption of Digested Foodstuffs**
  - Water—absorbed in small intestine but loss made good by secretion, marked absorption in large intestine
  - Salts—absorption may take place from any part of intestines, depends upon concentration of solution and nature of salt
  - Simple sugars—pass into capillaries and then by way of portal vein to liver
  - Fatty acids and glycerol—absorbed by lacteals in villi, synthesized to form fat. Fat carried to thoracic duct, which empties into left subclavian vein
  - Amino acids—pass into capillaries of villi
- **Metabolism**
  - May include all processes involved from time food enters the body until waste is excreted
  - In this chapter metabolism is limited to include only changes that occur in cells
  - **Consists of**
    - **Anabolism**—processes by which living cells take food substances from the blood and make them into protoplasm and stored products

Metabolism (*cont.*)

- **Consists of** (*cont.*)
  - **Catabolism**—processes by which living cells change into simpler substances (1) part of their own protoplasm, (2) stored products, or (3) absorbed nutrients
  - Catabolic processes
    1. Simple splitting of complex molecules into simpler ones
    2. Hydrolysis, or the splitting of complex molecules into simpler ones through reaction with water
    3. Oxidation, with the production of carbon dioxide and water
- **Purpose**
  - Growth and repair of tissue
  - Release of chemical energy in the form of heat, nervous activity, muscular activity, etc.
- **Factors**
  1. Oxygen absorbed from lungs
  2. Enzymes secreted by tissue cells
  3. Hormones secreted by ductless glands
  4. Vitamins furnished by food
  5. The nervous system

Metabolism of Carbohydrates

- Supply regulated by diet
- Storage provided temporarily, by liver, muscles, and cells of tissues. Carbohydrates stored as glycogen
- Consumption controlled by energy needs of tissues
- **Processes**
  - Glycogenesis, or the production of glycogen in the liver
  - Glycogenolysis, or the conversion of glycogen to glucose according to body needs
  - Glycolysis, or the anaerobic oxidation in the tissues
  - Glyconeogenesis, formation of glycogen or glucose from noncarbohydrate sources
  - Glycosuria, or loss of glucose in the urine
- **Regulation of blood glucose**
  - Hormonal:
  - Pancreas—produces *insulin* for metabolism of glucose
    - a. Concerned with phosphorylation of glucose
    - b. Inhibits glycogen formation in liver from noncarbohydrate sources
    - c. Decreases plasma glucose level
  - Glucagon—favors glycogenolysis
  - Anterior pituitary—opposes action of insulin in glucose phosphorylation, increases glucose formation from noncarbohydrate sources
  - Adrenal cortex—glucocorticoids decrease tissue utilization of glucose, increase blood glucose and gluconeogenesis, promote formation of oxygen
  - Adrenal medulla—epinephrine stimulates glycogenolysis in liver and muscle
  - Thyroid—thyroxin increases oxidative rate, therefore, utilization of glucose, increases glyconeogenesis
- **Purpose**
  - Furnish main source of energy for muscular work and all the nutritive processes
  - Help to maintain body temperature
  - Protect body tissues by forming reserve fund for time of need (glycogen)
  - Excess carbohydrates are converted into depot fat
  - May be used in constructive processes
- **End products**
  - When completely oxidized, the waste products are carbon dioxide and water
- **Derangements of**
  1. Glycogenesis breaks down, giving rise to alimentary glycosuria
  2. Plasma glucose level rises and renal threshold is exceeded

Metabolism of Fats

- **Reconstruction**—in act of passing through epithelial cells of villi, glycerol and fatty acids combine to form triglycerides
- **Purpose**
  - Yield heat and other forms of energy
  - Stored as adipose tissue
  - Synthesized to form compound fats and fatlike substances; lecithin, cholesterol
  - Glycerol may be converted to glucose
- **Terms**
  - Lipogenesis—formation of lipids
  - Lipolysis—breakdown of lipids
- **Oxidation**
  - Fatty acids split; 2-carbon units enter citric acid cycle; eventually oxidized to carbon dioxide and water
- **Factors affecting**
  - Choline and methionine essential for synthesis of phospholipids in the liver
  - Hormones—epinephrine and norepinephrine, ACTH, and glucagon stimulate release of fatty acids from depot fats
- **Body fat**
  - Formed from fats, carbohydrates, and proteins of food in order named
- **Obesity**
  - May be caused by eating more food than body needs, by lack of exercise, or both

Metabolism of Proteins

- Absorbed as amino acids. From villi pass to portal vein, thence to liver, and general circulation
- Tissues select amino acids
  1. To build new tissue and serum proteins
  2. To maintain cell activity
- Amino acids not used in the synthesis of protoplasm are deaminized and split into nonnitrogenous and nitrogenous portions
- Nonnitrogenous portion oxidized to carbon dioxide and water, or converted into glycogen
- Nitrogenous portion passes through a series of changes—end product, urea, or ammonium salts
- **Classification**
  - Endogenous, includes building up of amino acids to tissue protoplasm and final disintegration to creatinine and urea
  - Exogenous, includes reactions affecting uncombined amino acids, formation of urea from nitrogenous portion, and glucose from nonnitrogenous portion, also secondary production of glycogen
- **Nucleoproteins**
  - Protein separated from nucleic acid and hydrolyzed to amino acids
  - Nucleic acid gives rise to purine bodies of which uric acid is waste product
  - Endogenous uric acid from nucleoproteins of tissue cells
  - Exogenous uric acid from nucleoproteins of food
- **Nutritive value**
  - **Adequate** proteins contain all the amino acids for maintenance and growth of tissue
  - Proteins may yield energy
- **Hormones**
  - Somatotropin, testosterone, insulin are anabolic
  - Glucocorticoids, excessive thyroxin are catabolic

Citric Acid Cycle

- A complex series of chemical reactions whereby glucose, fatty acids, and amino acids enter the final stage of oxidative reactions and energy is released, to form ATP. Formation of carbon dioxide and water is incidental

Basal Metabolism

- Food source of energy for tissue building or work
- **Calorie**
  - Unit of measurement of heat production
  - Large calorie = quantity of heat necessary to raise temperature of 1 kg (2.2 lb) of water 1° C
- **Carbohydrates** 1 gm—4 Cal
- **Fat** 1 gm—9 Cal
- **Protein** 1 gm—4 Cal
- **Basal metabolism**—energy necessary to keep body alive

- **Basal Metabolism** (*cont.*)
  - **Respiratory quotient**
    - Ratio between carbon dioxide excreted and oxygen absorbed
    - Ratio between the two is figured by dividing the volume of carbon dioxide by the volume of oxygen
  - **Variations** in basal metabolism influenced by age, sex, internal secretions

- **Daily Calorie Requirement**
  - **Factors to consider**—body surface, work, sleep
  - **Distribution**
    - Proteins—10–15%
    - Nitrogen equilibrium maintained on about 40 gm of protein per day
    - Fats—about 25–35%
    - Carbohydrates—depends upon form in which taken, also on amount of fat

- **Nutritional Need**
  - Considers supplying kinds and concentration of all essential nutrients, adequate amounts of all essential chemical elements, adequate caloric intake, selection of proteins from standpoint of suitability for construction of body tissues

- **Body Heat**
  - Animals divided into two classes
    1. Homeothermic, or those which have an almost constant temperature. Birds and mammals (including human beings) are in this class
    2. Poikilothermic, or those whose temperature varies with that of their environment, e.g., snakes, frogs, and fishes. The human fetus is in this class
  - **Derived from**
    1. In the process of **oxidation** every body cell produces heat, but the most important heat-producing organs are the **muscles** and **liver**
    2. Minor sources
       - Friction of muscles, blood
       - Hot substances ingested
       - Radiation from sun and heat appliances
  - **Distributed**—by the blood circulating through the blood vessels
  - **Lost by**
    - Skin—2,156 Cal, or 87.5%
      - Offers large surface for radiation, conduction, and evaporation of sweat
      - Contains large amount of blood
    - Lungs—266 Cal, or 10.7%, is lost by warming the inspired air and in the evaporation of the water of respiration
    - Urine and feces—48 Cal, or 1.8%, is lost in the urine and feces

- **Regulation of Body Heat**
  - Due to maintenance of *balance* between heat production and heat dissipation
  - **Heat production**
    - By physiological oxidations, due to
      - Food intake and utilization
      - Muscular exercise
  - **Heat loss**
    1. The respiratory center
    2. The sweat center and sweat nerves
    3. The vasomotor center and nerves
    4. The water content of the blood
  - Coordinated by heat-regulating centers in the hypothalamus
  - **Other factors**
    1. Size
    2. Age
    3. Constitution

- **Variations in Temperature**
  - The normal temperature by mouth is about 37° C (98.6° F)
  - **Normal**
    1. Depends on where temperature is taken
       - Mouth
       - Axilla
       - Rectum
    2. Depends on time of day
       - Lowest in early morning, between 3 and 5 A.M.
       - Highest in late afternoon, about 4 P.M.
    3. Slightly increased by muscular activity and the digestive processes
    4. Age. Higher and more variable in infants; lower in aged

Variations in Temperature (*cont.*)

- **Normal** (*cont.*)
  - 5. Sex
  - 6. Season
  - 7. Climate
  - 8. Clothing
- **Subnormal due to**
  - Excessive loss of heat
  - Profuse sweating and hemorrhage
  - Lessened heat production, as in starvation
- **Abnormal**
  - **Fever**
    - Due to resetting of hypothalamic thermostat by brain damage or pyrogens
    - Is protective in infection
    - Temperature of 41° C serious

CHAPTER

23

HORMONES

Classification, Structure, and Physiology

Physiological organization is brought about by higher centers (hypothalamus) of the nervous system and by chemical substances in the circulatory fluids which are carried everywhere in the body, bringing about local changes in equilibrium of physical and chemical conditions and affecting correlations of these changes in a bodywide way.

The functions of the body are regulated by the nervous system and by hormones. In general, the nervous system regulates the rapidly changing activities such as skeletal movements, smooth-muscle contraction, and many glandular secretions. The hormonal system regulates the many *metabolic functions* of the body and the varying rates of chemical reactions. Hormones influence transport of substances through cell membranes and various aspects of cell metabolism. In some instances there are specific interrelationships between nervous stimuli and hormonal secretion. There are also many interactions between hormones, so that a disturbance in one endocrine gland can interfere with activities of other hormones. Hormones are specific in action, i.e., specific cells respond.

General Hormones. These are secreted into extracellular fluids and have effect in distant organs.

Local Hormones. Some physiologically active substances are released from specific sites in tissue. These function at the point of origin and are normally destroyed rapidly. (See page 503.)

Mechanism of Hormone Action. Research indicates that formation of a cyclic form of adenosine monophosphate within the cell is the trigger which initiates the chemical reactions characteristic of a cell's response to a hormone. Hormones act at receptor sites on the cell surface to activate an enzyme present in cell membranes which promotes formation of cyclic AMP. Cyclic AMP is known to be the common intermediate in actions of several hormones (insulin and those of the adrenal cortex) and is presumed to be the intermediate for others not yet studied.

Control of Hormone Secretions. The secretion of hormones is controlled by "feedback" mechanisms. Each gland has a tendency to oversecrete its specific hormone, but when physiological effects are achieved, the feedback mechanisms in some way check secretion. If there is undersecretion, the blood level falls and the gland is stimulated to active secretion. In this way the levels of concentration of each hormone in the blood stream are controlled in relation to body needs.

The methods of study of hormones are (1) observation of conditions caused by disease or removal of the glands, (2) administration of glands, extracts, synthetic preparations, or active principles, and (3) injection

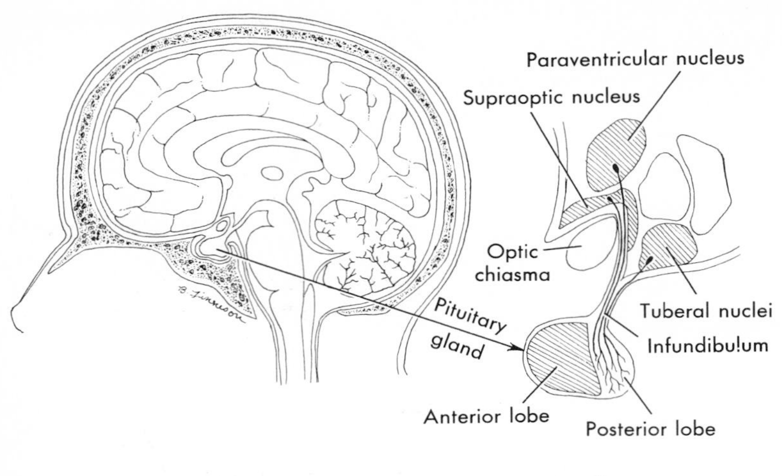

Figure 23–1. (*A*) Diagram showing brain, brain case, and location of pituitary gland. (*B*) Diagram to show fibers from hypothalamus to the neurohypophysis.

of glandular extracts into normal animals and animals from which the glands have been removed.

Hormones are *destroyed* by metabolic inactivation in tissues, mainly in the liver, and excreted by the kidney. The rate of inactivation may be altered by changes in liver function.

The Hypophysis. The hypophyseal gland weighs about 0.5 to 0.7 gm and is located in the sella turcica of the sphenoid bone. The infundibular stem attaches the gland below and the hypothalamus above. The hypophysis is highly vascular and receives its blood supply from the *superior* and *inferior* hypophyseal arteries. These are branches of the internal carotid artery and from the posterior communicating artery.

The *superior* hypophyseal artery extends medially to the upper part of the hypophyseal stalk and divides into the anterior and posterior branches. These branches anastomose and supply the upper part of the infundibular stem. Another branch supplies the superior surface and connective tissue of the pars distalis. This artery does not supply the glandular tissue. Branches of the inferior hypophyseal artery divide into the medial and lateral branches and supply the *posterior lobe*. The blood supply to the *anterior lobe* is mainly through a portal system of veins. Branches of the internal carotid arteries break up into capillaries in the median eminences of the hypothalamus and in the lower infundibular stalk. The capillaries form portal vessels which then terminate in blood capillaries and sinusoids in the pars distalis (anterior lobe) of the pituitary gland. The capillaries and sinusoids finally empty into the hypophyseal veins, which enter the circular and cavernous sinuses.

The neurohypophysis is well supplied with

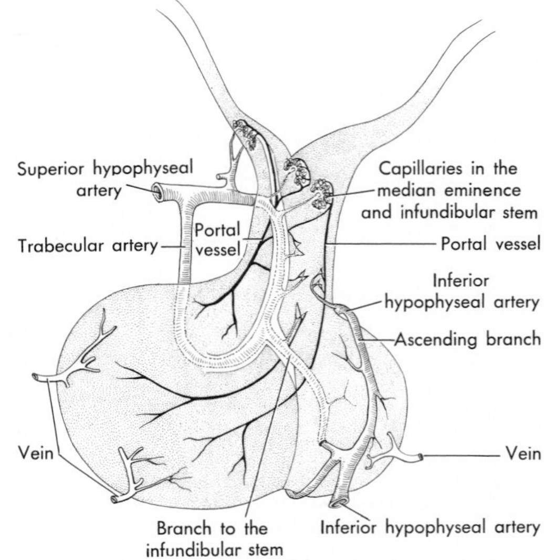

Figure 23–2. Blood supply to the hypophysis. (Modified from Crosby, Humphrey, and Lauer.)

nerve fibers which descend in the hypophyseal tract; there is no nerve supply to the pars distalis. The nerve supply from the sympathetic plexus terminates around the internal carotid artery and is vasomotor in its function.

The hypophysis consists of two main lobes; the larger anterior lobe is derived embryologically from the primitive pharyngeal epithelium; the posterior lobe is derived from neural ectoderm.

Adenohypophysis
- Pars tuberalis, Pars distalis — Anterior lobe
- Pars intermedia — Intermediate lobe has no known function in mammals

Neurohypophysis (pars nervosa)
- Infundibular process
- Infundibular stem
- Median eminence
- Posterior lobe
- Pituitary stalk

There are hypothalamic "hormones" called "releasing factors" that control the secretions of the hypophysis: Corticotropin-releasing factor (CRF) releases corticotropin; thyrotropin-releasing factor (TRF) releases thyrotropin; somatotropin-releasing factor (SRF) releases somatotropin; gonadotropin-releasing factor for control of secretion of the follicle-stimulating hormone (FSH) and the luteinizing hormone (LH), but not the luteotropic hormone (LTH).

The Adenohypophysis (Pars Distalis). This consists of glandular tissue, the cells of

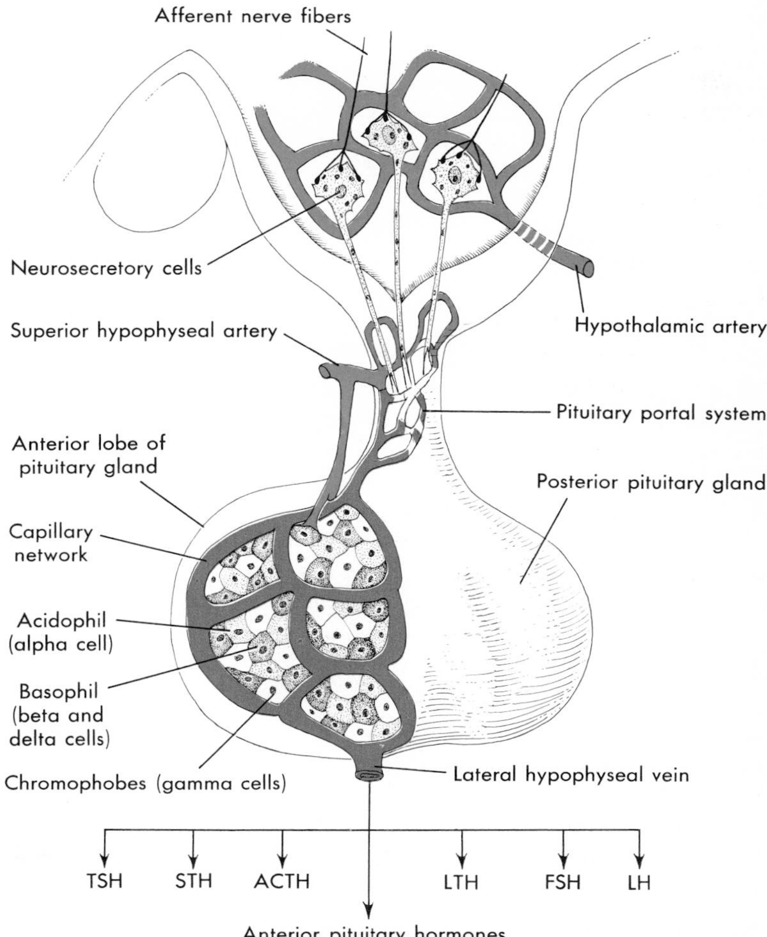

Figure 23–3. The pituitary portal system. Note the relationship of capillaries in the hypothalamus and adenohypophysis.

which give characteristic staining (chromophobic, indifferent to dyes; acidophilic, taking red stain called alpha cells; and basophilic cells [beta cells], taking blue stain). The tissue is composed of irregular branching cords of epithelial cells, supported by fine reticular fibers. Between the cords of cells are many blood sinuses which form a plexus. The pars distalis, influenced by hypothalamic releasing factors (page 489), forms hormones which have their primary site of action on other endocrine glands, "target glands." These are known as tropic hormones and exert specific influence on the activity of the target gland.

1. CORTICOTROPIN. Corticotropin (adrenocorticotropin, ACTH) is secreted by the chromophobic cells and has influence on the integrity of adrenal cortex. Its greatest effect is to stimulate the secretion of the glucocorticoid hormones.

2. SOMATOTROPIC HORMONE (STH) OR GROWTH HORMONE (GH). Somatotropic hormone is secreted by the acidophils

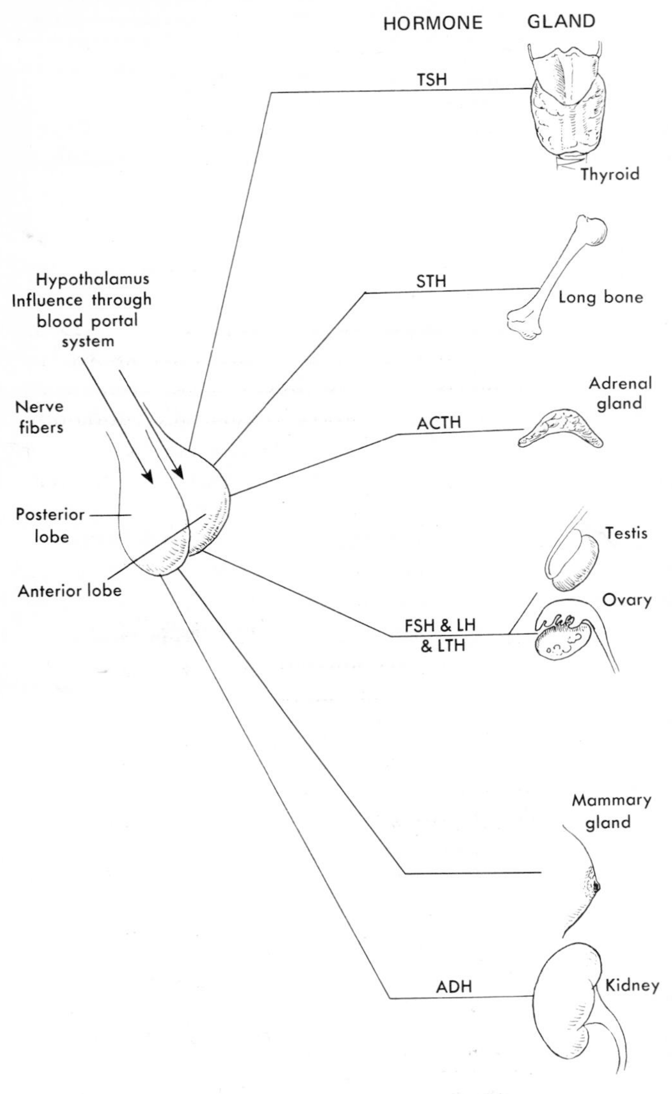

TSH (thyroid-stimulating hormone) influences structure and secretory activity of the thyroid. The thyroid influences metabolic rate. Hypothalamic releasing factor is *thyrotropin-releasing* factor (TRF). Feedback level of thyroxin in the blood stream.

STH (somatotrophic hormone) influences growth of long bones, muscles, and viscera. In some way it is related to protein metabolism. It acts directly on all tissues. Hypothalamic releasing factor is *somatotropin-releasing* factor (SRF).

ACTH influences the activities of the *adrenal* cortex. Two hormones, the *mineralocorticoids,* influence Na^+, Cl^-, K^+ reabsorption in the kidney. *Glucocorticoids* influence carbohydrate, protein, and fat metabolism. Hypothalamic releasing factor is called *corticotropin-releasing* factor (CRF). Feedback—level of cortisone in the blood stream.

FSH (follicle-stimulating hormone) influences ripening of follicles, production of estrogen, and activity of the seminiferous tubules. Feedback is level of estrogen in the blood stream.

LH (luteinizing hormone) influences secreting cells of the ovaries and testes and maintains their normal activity. In the male, stimulates secretion of testosterone. The hypothalamic releasing factors, *gonadotropin-releasing* factors, control the secretion of FSH and LH but not LTH. Feedback—level of progesterone or testosterone in blood stream.

Oxytocin is secreted during parturition—causes uterine contraction and active ejection of milk.

ADH (antidiuretic hormone) controls water reabsorption in the kidney tubules and in this way regulates water and electrolyte balance of body fluids. Secreted by cells in the hypothalamus, trickles down nerve fibers to posterior pituitary where it is stored. Feedback mechanisms–osmolarity of blood stream on osmoreceptors in hypothalamus.

Figure 23–4. Diagram showing some of the functions of the pituitary hormones on physiological activities.

of the pars distalis. It has a specific effect on the growth of tissues, especially of bone, muscle, and viscera. It is essential for growth and development and promotes both increased mitosis and increased sizes of cells. STH has effect on metabolic processes; these include increased rate of protein synthesis in tissue (Chapter 22), decreased rate of carbohydrate utilization in striated muscle and adipose tissue, increased mobilization of stored fat, and increased use of fats for energy. Selye believes that STH has a proinflammatory effect on tissues.

Excess of the growth hormone in early life results in giantism; the result of hyperactivity of the gland in later life is acromegaly, in which the jaws, bones, hands, and feet show overdevelopment and the features become enlarged and coarse. Hypoproduction of the growth hormone results in dwarfism. Growth of the body and sexual development are arrested. In the adult, the result is called Simmonds' disease, in which emaciation, muscular debility, loss of sexual function, and general apathy occur.

3. THYROTROPIN (TSH). Thyrotropin influences both the *structure* and all *secretory activity* of the thyroid gland. An increase in concentration of thyroxin and triiodothyronine in body fluids has an inhibitory effect on the rate of secretion of thyrotropin, and this feedback mechanism prevents overactivity of the thyroid gland. A decrease in thyroxin stimulates its secretion.

4. GONADOTROPIC HORMONES (FSH, LTH, LH, and ICSH). These hormones influence the activity of the gonads, the development of the mammary gland during pregnancy and the subsequent secretion of milk.

Follicle-stimulating hormone (FSH) causes proliferation and maturation of the follicle cells of the ovary. It also has a stimulating effect on these cells to secrete estrogens. FSH is essential for ovulation.

In the male, FSH influences spermatogenesis by its action on the seminiferous tubules.

Luteotropin (LTH, prolactin) stimulates the corpus luteum to produce progesterone and estrogens. It also has a stimulating effect on the mammary glands, influencing the final development of glandular tissue and promoting secretion of milk.

Luteinizing hormone (LH) functions along with FSH and influences maturation of the ovarian follicles, initiates rupture of the ripe follicle, and stimulates formation of corpus luteum and production of progesterone. LH also functions in the male and influences the interstitial cells of the testis to secrete testosterone. Hence this hormone is frequently called the interstitial-cell-stimulating hormone (ICSH). In turn testosterone causes masculinizing effects in the male and is necessary for spermatogenesis.

The reciprocal relationship between these hormones and the hormones of the gonads is discussed in detail in Chapter 26.

The Neurohypophysis. This consists of the infundibular process and stem and the median eminence. The infundibular process (posterior pituitary) is composed of numerous nerve fibers and glial-like cells known as pituicytes. Nerve fibers arise from cells located in the paraventricular and supraoptic nuclei of the hypothalamus and descend in the hypothalamohypophyseal tract and terminate on capillaries in the posterior pituitary (Figure 23–1). The hormones of the posterior pituitary are formed in these hypothalamic nuclei and trickle down the nerve fibers into the infundibular process (posterior pituitary), where they are stored in the pituicytes or enter the blood stream directly.

Two hormones are stored in the infundibular process (posterior lobe): the *antidiuretic hormone* and *oxytocin.* Both hormones are polypeptides and have been synthesized in the laboratory.

ANTIDIURETIC HORMONE (ADH or VASOPRESSIN). Antidiuretic hormone increases the permeability of the cells of the distal tubule and collecting ducts in the kidney, hence decreases urine formation. In the absence of ADH large amounts of urine with a very low specific gravity are eliminated (polyuria); at the same time fluid intake is increased (polydipsia).

Secretion of ADH is regulated by the

osmolality of the blood. Cells in the supraoptic nuclei function as osmoreceptors which are sensitive to the concentration of solutes in plasma. A rise in osmotic pressure increases the secretion of ADH and increases water reabsorption. (See Chapter 25.) In other words, concentrated body fluids stimulate the osmoreceptors and increase secretion of ADH, whereas dilute concentrations of body fluids inhibit ADH secretion.

Diabetes insipidus, a disease in which the urinary output is greatly increased, was formerly thought to result from hyposecretion of the posterior lobe; but it has been shown that a similar polyuria results from injury to the hypothalamic region (supraoptic nuclei) of the brain. It is therefore probable that involvement of either the posterior lobe of the pituitary or the hypothalamus will cause the disease.

OXYTOCIN. Oxytocin has a stimulating effect upon smooth muscles of the pregnant uterus; physiological concentrations have no effect upon the nonpregnant uterus. Oxytocin is secreted in increased amounts during parturition, thereby increasing the contraction of the uterus. Oxytocin is also secreted during the process of lactation and causes ejection of milk from the alveoli into the ducts so that the infant can obtain it by suckling. The suckling stimulus increases the secretion of oxytocin.

The Thyroid Gland. The thyroid gland consists of two lobes, situated at the sides of the trachea and thyroid cartilage. These lobes are connected by strands of thyroid tissue called the isthmus, ventral to the trachea. The external layer of the thyroid is connective tissue which extends inward as trabeculae and divides the gland into closed follicles of irregular size. Centrally, each of these follicles contains a colloid or jellylike substance which is secreted by the columnar epithelial cells which line the follicle. Thyroxin combines with the colloidal substance and is stored in the follicle. The thyroid gland contains numerous lymphatics.

An abundant blood supply is derived from the external carotids and the subclavian arteries and is returned via the superior, middle, and inferior thyroid veins to the jugular and left brachiocephalic veins. It has been estimated that about 4 to 5 liters of blood pour through the gland per hour.

The nerves are derived from the second to fifth thoracic spinal nerves through the superior and middle cervical ganglia of the thoracolumbar system and from the vagus and glossopharyngeal nerves of the craniosacral system.

The hormones of the thyroid are thyroxin and triiodothyronine. The latter is more active than thyroxin, but its action is not as sustained. The thyrotropic hormone of the pituitary stimulates the growth and activity of the follicular cells of the thyroid, and in this way the formation of thyroxin is controlled.

Ingested iodides are absorbed from the intestinal mucosa into the blood and are selectively removed from the blood by cells of the thyroid gland and used in the synthesis of thyroxin, triiodothyronine, and diiodothyronine, all of which are stored in the center of the follicle in a protein combination known as *thyroglobulin*. When these hormones are released into the blood, they combine with plasma protein to form protein-bound iodine (PBI). The measurement of the protein-bound iodine in blood provides a reliable means for determining the activity of the thyroid gland. This value is closely related to the rate of the basal metabolism. The normal range for PBI is between 4 and 7.5 μg per 100 ml of blood serum.

Functions of Thyroxin

1. Thyroxin regulates the metabolic and oxidative rates in tissue cells, hence it is involved in maintaining body temperature. It increases the rate of glucose absorption from the intestine and increases the rate of glucose utilization by cells. These effects are believed to be through enzyme systems in mitochondria.

2. Thyroxin stimulates the growth and differentiation of tissues in young persons.

3. Thyroxin influences conversion of glycogen from noncarbohydrate sources and conversion of glycogen to glucose, thus raising blood sugar.

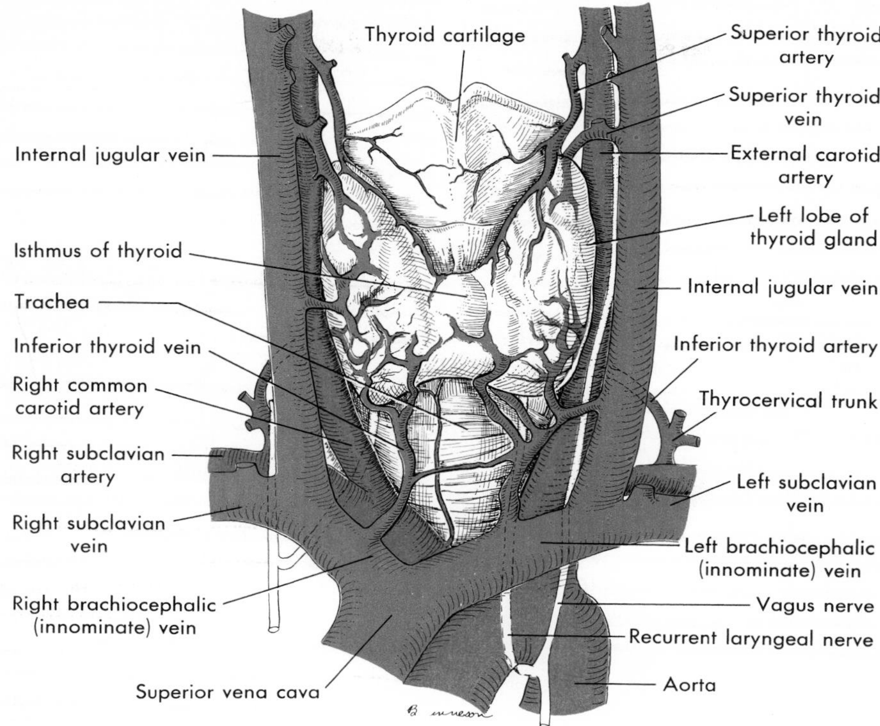

Figure 23–5. The thyroid gland and related blood vessels. (Modified from Pansky and House.)

4. Thyroxin increases quantities of certain oxidative enzymes in the mitochondria.

5. Thyroxin increases osteoclastic activity more than it increases osteoblastic activity in bones.

6. Thyroxin influences the rate of metabolism of lipids, proteins, carbohydrates, water, vitamins, and minerals.

7. Thyroxin increases protein synthesis as indicated by (1) increased turnover of RNA, and (2) increased incorporation of amino acids into protein by the mitochondria.

8. Thyroxin has action on enzyme systems and influences the quantity of enzymes; hence it increases the need for vitamins, especially B_{12}. Since the rate of metabolism directly affects cardiac output, heart rate and arterial pressure are increased.

9. In the young person both physical and mental development are influenced and in the adult thyroxin stimulates mental processes.

10. Thyroxin is believed to increase the rate of parathyroid secretion, which in turn influences bone resorption of calcium.

One milligram of thyroxin increases the metabolic rate about 2.5 per cent. Carbohydrates, proteins, and fats are all oxidized in increased amounts. The thyroid hormones regulate cell metabolism primarily by controlling the activities of oxidizing enzymes within the mitochondria. This in turn increases the activity of carbohydrases, amidases, transferases, and proteolytic enzymes.

When thyroxin is given experimentally to animals or human beings, nitrogen loss exceeds intake. Glucose tolerance is decreased and stored glycogen is also decreased, although blood glucose may be normal or below. The thyroid gland is believed to influence calcium and phosphorus, since, when the hormone is given experimentally, an increased amount of calcium and phosphates is eliminated in the feces and urine. Blood levels remain constant, which indicates that calcium is being lost from bone. Cases of hypoactivity of the gland may show as much as 50 per cent decrease in the metabolic rate; cases of hyperactivity may show an increase up to 60 to 100 per cent and more. Injection or feeding of thyroid tissue results in increased basal metabolism, loss of weight, increase in elimination of nitrogen, increased heart rate —which results at times in an abnormality called tachycardia—and nervous excitability.

The size of the thyroid varies with age, sex, and general nutrition. It is relatively larger in the young, in women, and in the well-nourished. Removal of the gland does not cause death but, unless the hormone is replaced, brings about marked changes, such as lowered basal metabolism and general malnutrition. Disturbances in the secretion of thyroxin are classed under two headings: (1) hypothyroidism, or decreased secretion, and (2) hyperthyroidism, or excess secretion. The liver removes excess thyroxin from the blood stream.

Goiter is an enlargement of the gland. It may result from increased functional activity due to a decrease in the iodine content of the gland. This in turn is usually due to a decrease or lack of iodine in water and food. Goiter occurs frequently in adolescent girls, but its incidence is greatly reduced if iodine is given. A goiter may be due to the presence of a tumor or increased thyroxin secretion.

Hypothyroidism. In man certain pathological conditions are caused by hypothyroidism, i.e., cretinism and myxedema.

Cretinism is caused by congenital defects of the thyroid or by atrophy in early life. The growth of the skeleton ceases, although the bones may become thicker than normal and there is marked arrest of mental development. Children so afflicted are called cretins. They are not only dwarfed but ill-proportioned, having large heads, protruding abdomens, weak muscles, and slow speech.

Myxedema is a condition that results from atrophy or removal of the thyroid in adult life. The most marked symptoms of this condition are slowness of both body and mind, usually associated with tremors and twitchings. The skin becomes rough and dry, owing to lack of cutaneous secretions, and assumes a yellow, waxlike appearance. There is an overgrowth of the subcutaneous tissues, which in time is replaced by fat; the hair grows coarse and falls out; the face and hands are swollen and puffy; the metabolic rate is low and the mental activities apathetic. Cretinism and myxedema are both caused by insufficient secretion of thyroxin, which may be supplied by feeding the thyroid of other animals. The treatment must be kept up throughout the patient's life.

Hyperthyroidism. Overactivity of the thyroid gland, i.e., increase in the amount of the internal secretion, produces a condition called Graves' disease or exophthalmic goiter. It is characterized by protruding eyeballs, quickened and sometimes irregular heart action, elevated temperature, nervousness, and insomnia. The appetite may be excessive, but this is accompanied by loss of weight due to increased metabolism and digestive disturbances. This condition is sometimes remedied by removing part of the gland.

The Parathyroid Glands. The parathyroids, usually four in number and arranged in pairs, are independent of the thyroid both in origin and in function but are usually located on its dorsal surface. These small reddish glands are about 6 to 7 mm long and 2 to 3 mm thick. Accessory nodules are sometimes found surrounding the glands or embedded in connective tissue. The glands consist of closely packed epithelial cells richly supplied with capillaries from branches of the inferior and superior thyroid arteries. The nerve supply is from the vagus and glossopharyngeal nerves of the central nervous system and from the cervical autonomics of the thoracolumbar system. It is not influenced by ACTH.

Physiology. The parathyroids secrete a hormone, parathyroid hormone, or parathormone, protein in nature, which plays an important role in the maintenance of the normal calcium level of the blood. It also regulates phosphorus metabolism and increases the rate of calcium reabsorption in the renal tubules. *Calcitonin*, produced by cells in the thyroid gland, is another hormone controlling calcium ion concentration in the body. Its action is to prevent excessive calcium levels in the blood.

Parathormone in the presence of vitamin D influences the absorption of calcium in the intestine and of phosphate in the renal tubules. Parathormone exerts action on bone and stimulates osteoclastic activity. This may be a phagocytic action whereby bony particles are digested with a final release of calcium and phosphate into the body fluids.

Acute symptoms of hypoparathyroidism, known clinically as tetany, may result from removal of the parathyroids or may possibly occur spontaneously; the concentration of blood calcium falls and increased nerve irritability causes muscle spasms that may result in death if untreated. Symptoms are relieved by giving solutions of calcium.

In hyperparathyroidism there are muscular weakness, pain in the bones, and an increase in the calcium in blood and urine. The bones show decalcification and deformity, and spontaneous fractures may occur. These symptoms are often caused by a parathyroid tumor, the removal of which brings about a reduction in the blood calcium; and considerable resolidification of the bones occurs. Deposits of calcium may occur, especially in the kidney, and nitrogenous wastes may become excessive in blood and lymph.

The Thymus. Although the thymus is considered to be part of the lymphatic system (page 361), efforts have long been made to identify an endocrine function for this gland. At present, the evidence is conflicting. It is possible that a hormone from the thymus is involved in initiating antibody formation by the plasma cells and lymphocytes.

Adrenal Glands. The adrenal glands are two small bodies which lie at the superior pole of each kidney. The right adrenal gland is somewhat triangular in shape and the left one more semilunar. They vary in size, and the average weight of each is about 5 to 9 gm. Each gland is surrounded by a thin capsule and consists of two parts known as the cortex, or external tissue, and the medulla, or chromophil tissue. These parts differ in origin and function.

Embryologically the adrenal cortex develops from mesoderm; the medulla has the same embryological origin as the thoracolumbar division of the autonomic nervous system, namely, from an outgrowth from the neural ectoderm. It is also functionally related to the sympathetic nervous system.

At birth the adrenal glands weigh about 8 gm, which is proportionately 20 times greater than in the adult. They gradually decrease in size, and by one year of age the two adrenals weigh 4.5 gm. The more mature the infant, the more adequately the adrenal cortex responds to stress.

Blood Supply. The arteries supplying this highly vascular gland are derived from the aorta, the inferior phrenics, and the renal arteries. Blood is returned via the suprarenal veins. It has been estimated that a quantity of blood equal to about six times each gland's weight passes through it per minute.

Nerves. The nerve fibers are derived

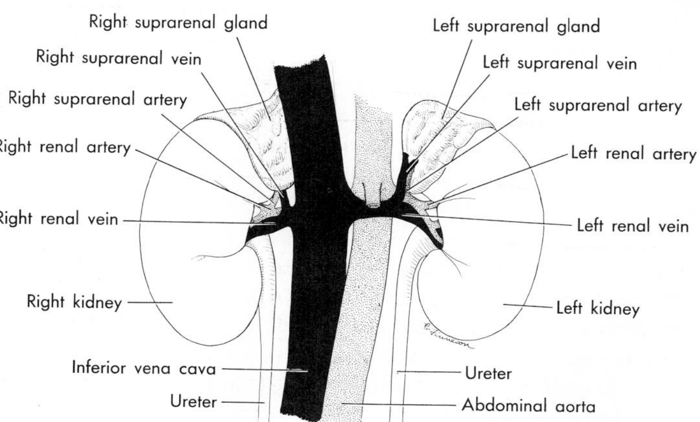

Figure 23–6. Diagram showing position of adrenal glands and kidneys. Note blood vessel arrangement.

from the celiac and renal plexuses (splanchnic nerves). Removal of the gland has long been known to be followed by prostration, muscular weakness, and lowered vascular tone, with subsequent death in a few days. These symptoms are caused by the removal of the adrenal cortex. Removal of the medulla causes no serious disturbance.

Hormones of the Adrenal Cortex. The adrenal cortex secretes a group of hormones called corticosteroids. These include the *mineralocorticoids* and the *glucocorticoids.* It also secretes small amounts of androgenic hormones and minute quantities of estrogenic hormones.

The hormones of the adrenal cortex include *cortisol*, *corticosterone*, *aldosterone*, *androgens*, *estrogens*, and *progesterone*. Cortisol and corticosterone are called glucocorticoids because they have a specific effect on glucose metabolism. *Aldosterone* has been called a *mineralocorticoid* because its chief action is to promote sodium retention and potassium excretion.

THE MINERALOCORTICOIDS. The salt or mineral hormone aldosterone functions at the renal tubule and stimulates the reabsorption of Na^+ which then attracts Cl^- and causes its reabsorption into the blood. In this way the Na^+ and Cl^- content of the extracellular fluids is maintained. Water is reabsorbed with the salt as the result of increased osmotic pressure. The reabsorption of K^+ is depressed and hence the Na^+/K^+ ratio is controlled in body fluids. Fluid balance is also controlled through regulation of these electrolytes. Aldosterone secretion is increased by

1. A decrease in extracellular volume
2. An increase in extracellular potassium
3. A decrease in extracellular sodium
4. An increase in angiotensin formation

Any of these conditions excites the adrenal cortex to activity. Conversely, high extracellular volume, low extracellular potassium, and high extracellular sodium decrease aldosterone secretion. Decreased secretion of aldosterone promotes acidosis through its effect on sodium blood levels, whereas an increased secretion promotes alkalosis.

THE GLUCOCORTICOIDS. The actions of the glucocorticoids are chiefly from cortisol (hydrocortisone or compound F). The glucocorticoids are hormones whose predominant action is the regulation of metabolism of carbohydrate, protein, and fat.

1. *Effect on Carbohydrate Metabolism.* These hormones stimulate gluconeogenesis by the liver. The liver forms glycogen from noncarbohydrate sources and decreases the rate of glucose utilization by the cell.

2. *Effects of Protein Metabolism.* The glucocorticoids reduce protein stores by decreased anabolism of protein, a decreased rate of protein synthesis, and mobilization of amino acids from the tissues. Liver protein is increased, and in turn plasma proteins are released into the blood. Glucocorticoids increase permeability of the liver cells to amino acids and decrease the permeability of muscle cells to amino acids.

3. *Effects on Fat Metabolism.* As need arises, the glucocorticoids either promote fat mobilization from fat depots (adipokinesis) or increase the rate of storage of fat deposition as adipose tissue (lipogenesis).

4. *Effect on Lymph and Blood.* The corticosteroids influence the activity of lymphoid tissue and the number of eosinophils in circulating blood. Administration of adrenocortical hormones decreases the number of circulating eosinophils and the size of lymphoid tissue. Large doses of the glucocorticoids reduce or may completely block antibody formation in lymphoid tissue. Cortisone and hydrocortisone are the two widely known hormones in this group.

5. *Stress Situations.* The adrenal cortex in some way aids the body to cope more effectively with adverse environmental situations, or what is commonly known as stress situations. See discussion and diagram, page 499.

6. *Gonadal Hormones.* Several hormones have been isolated from the adrenal cortex that have influence on the sex organs, for example, androgen, estrogen, and progestins.

When the adrenal cortex, ovaries, or testes are removed, certain physiological changes take place. Removal of the ovaries or testes results in an enlargement of the adrenal cortex. If the adrenal glands fail to function and blood level of cortisol falls, corticotropin, secreted by the pituitary gland, is greatly increased. This is believed to explain why there is decreased production of the gonadal hormones. On the other hand, sex hormones can affect adrenocortical function. Estrogens from the ovary inhibit the formation of FSH by the pituitary; however, at the same time corticotropin is increased.

Cortical hypofunction is recognized as the cause of Addison's disease, which, if untreated, is fatal within from one to three years.

Symptoms of Addison's disease are muscular weakness and general apathy, gastrointestinal disturbances, pigmentation of the skin and mucous membranes, loss of weight, and depressed sexual function. The pigmentation is the outstanding symptom and is due to excessive deposition of the normal cutaneous pigment, melanin. Treatment with cortical extract gives favorable results.

Cortical hyperfunction appears to be associated with cortical tumors. It results in the young in precocious sexual development with profuse growth of hair, and in the case of adult females, in the development of secondary male characteristics.

Hormones of the Adrenal Medulla. The adrenal medulla consists of large, granular cells arranged in a network. It secretes two hormones, amine in nature, called epinephrine (Adrenalin) and norepinephrine (noradrenalin).

Epinephrine affects all structures of the body innervated by the sympathetic nervous system and thereby reinforces its action.

The hormones *epinephrine* and *norepinephrine* belong to a group of chemicals known as *catecholamines* and are referred to as *sympathomimetic amines* because they have the same physiological effect as the sympathetic nervous system. Through the glycogenolytic effect of *catecholamines*, these hormones provide the body with a means of sparing carbohydrates for the brain during periods of hypoglycemia. They also have ability to stimulate the release of free fatty acids from adipose tissue. These, in turn, are used by muscle tissue of the body in place of glucose, thereby providing another physiological means of conserving circulating glucose. On the whole, norepinephrine is more effective in vasoconstriction and epinephrine has a more pronounced effect on carbohydrate metabolism.

The differences in effect of epinephrine and norepinephrine are believed to be due to type of receptor on the effector cell, one class having alpha receptors, the other beta receptors. Norepinephrine affects only the

COMPARISON OF EFFECTS OF EPINEPHRINE AND NOREPINEPHRINE

Epinephrine Affects Beta and Alpha Receptors	Norepinephrine Affects Only Alpha Receptors
1. Cardiac acceleration	Cardiac acceleration
2. Vasoconstriction	Vasodilation in muscle
3. Increased myocardial strength	About the same
4. Increased cardiac output and venous return	Slight effect
5. Systolic pressure raised	Pressor effects marked, raises both systolic and diastolic pressure
6. Hypoglycemic effects marked	Much less effect
7. Marked increase in basal metabolic rate	Much less effect
8. Lipolytic effects, liberates nonesterified fatty acids from fat depots	Slightly greater effects
9. Excitation of central nervous system	No effect
10. Myometrial relaxation	Pilomotor contraction
11. Dilation of iris	
12. Bronchial relaxation	

effector cells that contain alpha receptors; epinephrine can affect both.

Examples of the use of epinephrine in medicine are to bring about vasoconstriction, which prolongs the action of local anesthetics and reduces the absorption of the substance producing the anesthesia; to relax the bronchioles in asthma; to constrict arterioles of the mucous membranes and of the skin, thus reducing the loss of blood in minor operations.

Cannon and his associates noted that the supply of epinephrine to the blood by the adrenal medulla is increased under emotional stress. This increase results in a more rapid and forceful heartbeat; a greater flow of blood to the muscles, central nervous system, and heart; an increased output of glucose from the liver; inhibition of the intestinal muscle coat; and closure of the sphincters. The muscle coat of the bronchi is relaxed and there is contraction of the splenic capsule, which gives more blood to circulation. By means of these reactions the stable environment of cells is maintained during periods of great functional demands. Whether these reactions are in direct response to the increased secretion of the medulla or are brought about by the action of the sympathetic nervous system alone is undetermined. Nevertheless, it may be said that the medulla in normal physiological activities carries on certain emergency functions such as constriction of skin and splanchnic blood vessels, vasodilation in skeletal and cardiac muscle, a rise in general blood pressure and increased output of the heart, the liberation of glucose supplies from the liver, the contraction of both smooth and striated muscles, decrease in the coagulation time of the blood, discharge of red blood cells from the spleen, and an increase in the depth and rate of respiration. These and other accompanying reactions, such as emotional responses, result in equipping the individual to meet the emergency at hand.

STRESS

The anterior pituitary and adrenal glands play an important role in aiding the body to deal effectively with stress.

In *any type of injury* to tissues or cells, exposure to intense cold or heat, hemorrhage, excessive exercise, deprivations such as starvation, or infections or in emotional stress, there is a definite pattern of physiological response. Selye found that no matter what the stressor was, including physical restraint, certain changes always occurred in the animal. These were atrophy of the thymus gland, marked enlargement of the adrenal cortex, and hemorrhage into the gastric mucosa. The reasons for all these changes have not been clarified. It is known that the stress situation calls out ACTH and the response is an increased production of adrenocortical hormones. There is also increased sympathetic nervous system activity with a calling out of epinephrine, which in turn stimulates production of ACTH as well as bringing about the usual body adjustments for emergency physiology. The following chart indicates many of the physiological adjustments necessary for survival of the individual.

The term "general adaptation syndrome" is used to explain the three stages of physiological changes to stress according to Selye.

1. The Alarm Stage. Sodium and chloride levels in extracellular fluids fall, while potassium rises. Blood glucose falls, but later rises.

2. Stage of Resistance. The body fights back. Blood levels return to normal. More ACTH is released, and the body tries to combat factors causing stress. The adrenal cortex increases in size.

3. Stage of Exhaustion. If the original stress is not removed, the adrenal gland becomes depleted of cholesterol, there is hemorrhage into the cortex, and ACTH fails to be formed. Sodium and chloride and glucose levels in blood fall, potassium and phosphate levels rise, and death results from exhaustion. It is evident that prompt, skilled care is necessary if the individual is to survive severe stress.

On the other hand, the helpful properties of stress should be remembered. For instance, normal bone needs the stress of weight bearing if it is to retain its mineral content. In fact, all tissues of the body need moderate stress to maintain normal functioning. The aim should not be to eliminate stress from life situations, but effort should be made to understand and moderate stress before it becomes excessive.

The Gonads. The *ovary* produces two internal secretions whose actions are understood. (1) Follicular hormone, or estrogen, is

Know

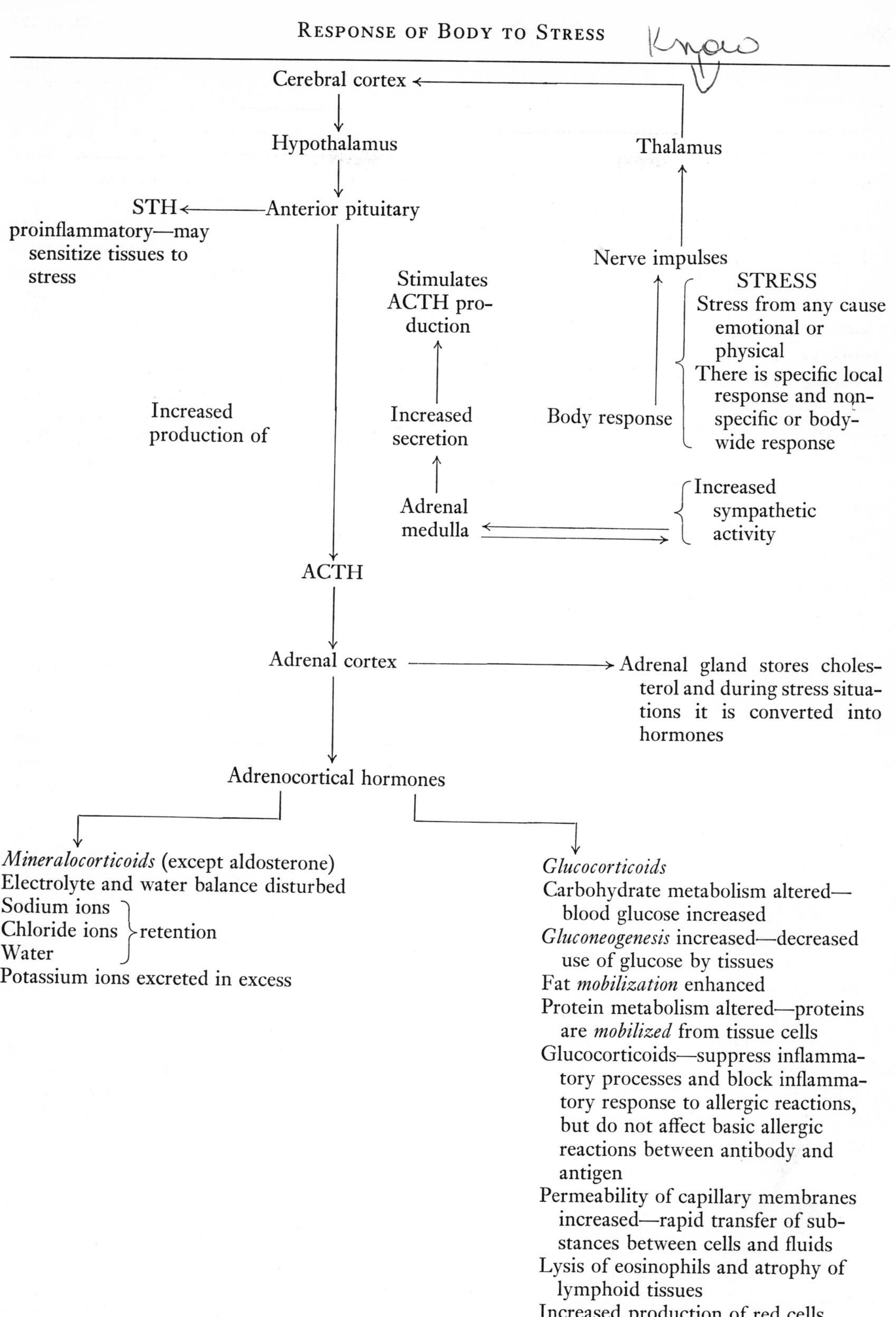
Cerebral cortex
Hypothalamus
Thalamus
STH
proinflammatory—may sensitize tissues to stress
Anterior pituitary
Nerve impulses
Stimulates ACTH production
STRESS
Stress from any cause emotional or physical
There is specific local response and nonspecific or bodywide response
Increased production of
Increased secretion
Body response
Adrenal medulla
Increased sympathetic activity
ACTH
Adrenal cortex
Adrenal gland stores cholesterol and during stress situations it is converted into hormones
Adrenocortical hormones
Mineralocorticoids (except aldosterone)
Electrolyte and water balance disturbed
Sodium ions
Chloride ions
Water
retention
Potassium ions excreted in excess
Glucocorticoids
Carbohydrate metabolism altered—blood glucose increased
Gluconeogenesis increased—decreased use of glucose by tissues
Fat *mobilization* enhanced
Protein metabolism altered—proteins are *mobilized* from tissue cells
Glucocorticoids—suppress inflammatory processes and block inflammatory response to allergic reactions, but do not affect basic allergic reactions between antibody and antigen
Permeability of capillary membranes increased—rapid transfer of substances between cells and fluids
Lysis of eosinophils and atrophy of lymphoid tissues
Increased production of red cells

secreted by the ovary and acts on the uterus and fallopian tubes, the vagina, and the mammary glands in their changes throughout the phases of the menstrual cycle. Estrogen is present in the blood of females from puberty to the menopause, reaching its highest concentration just before ovulation. It is present in large amounts in the blood during pregnancy. It is also present in the urine of males and has been found in the tissues of growing plants and animals. Several different kinds of estrogens have been isolated from human blood plasma. Three are present in significant amounts: β-estradiol, estrone, and estriol. β-estradiol is the most important and most potent. The liver plays an important role in estrogen excretion. (2) The corpus luteum hormone, or progesterone, supplements the action of estrogen, promoting further development of the uterine mucosa in preparation for implantation of the developing ovum. It suppresses estrus and ovulation and is essential for the growth of the mammary glands. It is essential to the complete development of the maternal portion of the placenta and to the development of the mammary glands during pregnancy.

In the nonpregnant female most of the progesterone is secreted during the latter half of each ovarian cycle. It is secreted in larger

Name	Where They Function	Effect
Estrogens	Fallopian tubes and endometrium	Cause glandular cells to proliferate Increase number of ciliated epithelial cells Activity of cilia enhanced
	Breasts	Initiate growth of breast Cause fat deposition and development of stromal tissues. Lobules and alveoli develop to slight extent
	Skeleton	Cause osteoblastic activity at puberty. There is a rapid growth rate which causes early uniting of the epiphyses with the shafts of long bone
	Pelvis	Broaden pelvis and size of vagina
	Calcium and phosphate in blood stream	Cause retention to promote bone growth
	Metabolism	Apparently have no effect on metabolic rate but do cause greater deposition of fat and increase total body proteins
	Skin	Cause skin to develop a soft, smooth texture and increase its vascularity
	Electrolyte balance	Cause Na^+ and Cl^- and H_2O retention by the kidney
Progesterone	Uterus	Promotes secretory changes and storage of nutrients in the endometrium, thus prepares it for implantation of the fertilized ovum Inhibits contractibility of the myometrium
	Fallopian tubes	Promotes secretions of mucosa
	Breasts	Promotes final development of lobules and alveoli; causes proliferation of cells and causes cells to become secretory. Enlarges breasts
	Electrolyte balance	Enhances Na^+, Cl^-, and H_2O reabsorption from distal tubules of kidney
	Protein	Has a mild catabolic effect

See Chapter 26 for details.

quantities than is estrogen. It is rapidly changed to other steroids that have no progesteronic effect. The liver is important for these metabolic changes. The end product is pregnanediol.

The chart on facing page summarizes the effects of estrogens and progesterone.

Relaxin, present in the blood of pregnant mammals, is believed to bring about relaxation of the pelvic ligaments in preparation for parturition.

The androgens are *androsterone* (from male and also female urine) and *testosterone* and *androstenedione* (from the testicle). Testosterone promotes the development of the male sex organs, the development of masculine characteristics, and retention of nitrogen, leading to increase in growth of tissues and muscular vigor. It increases the total quantity of bone matrix and deposition of calcium salts and increases the size and strength of bone.

Both the male and female sex hormones are produced in both sexes. The sex of the animal determines whether male or female hormones will be secreted in preponderance.

The adrenal cortex is also a source of androgens, estrogens, and progestational substances found in normal urine and is the only source of the substances in urine after ovariectomy or castration.

The 17-Ketosteroids. The androgens provide a clinical test for determining the degree of activity of the adrenal cortex. Some of the steroid compounds are secreted in the urine; therefore, the quantity of 17-ketosteroids secreted in the urine gives an index to the activity of the adrenal cortex.

The Placenta. The placenta is a source of many hormones, including estrogen and progesterone, and of chorionic gonadotropin, which has similar action to the gonadotropic principles of the anterior pituitary hormones (LH). The placenta is also a source of a rich supply of immune bodies and of a blood coagulant. See Chapter 27 for complete discussion.

The Pancreas. Deep within the pancreas are special groups of cells, the *islets of Langerhans*. These cells form an internal secretion, protein in nature, called *insulin*, which is essential for normal glucose metabolism. Several types of cells are in the islet group. The beta cells secrete *insulin*, and the alpha cells secrete *glucagon*. Insulin increases cell permeability to glucose and in some way influences phosphorylation.

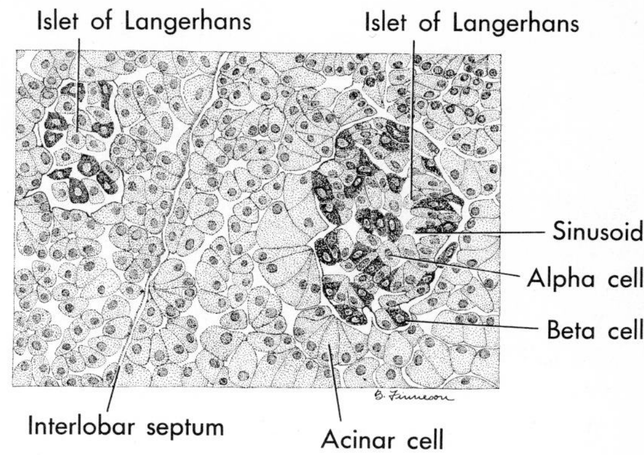

Figure 23–7. Diagram of microscopic view of a thin section of pancreas showing islet of Langerhans. Alpha cells light, beta cells dark.

Insulin promotes the utilization of glucose in tissue cells and thereby decreases blood glucose concentration. In the liver it inhibits glycogen formation from noncarbohydrate sources; it promotes glycogen storage. *Glucagon functions* in the liver and aids in the conversion of glycogen to glucose.

Insulin is essential for the maintenance of normal levels of blood glucose. Hypoglycemia results from increased insulin secretion (hyperinsulinism) or from the injection of insulin. Marked decrease in the blood sugar level leads to coma, convulsions, and death. Hyperglycemia and glycosuria may result from insufficient secretion of insulin. Marked increased levels of blood sugar, if untreated, lead to coma and death. This condition is known as diabetes mellitus (see Chapter 22).

Internal Secretions of the Gastric and Intestinal Mucous Membranes. *Gastrin* is a hormone secreted into the blood by the parietal cells of the mucous membrane lining the stomach. This hormone is carried by the blood to the peptic and pyloric glands, which it stimulates. It is believed that the mucous membrane of the intestine, particularly the duodenum, contains cells which secrete a

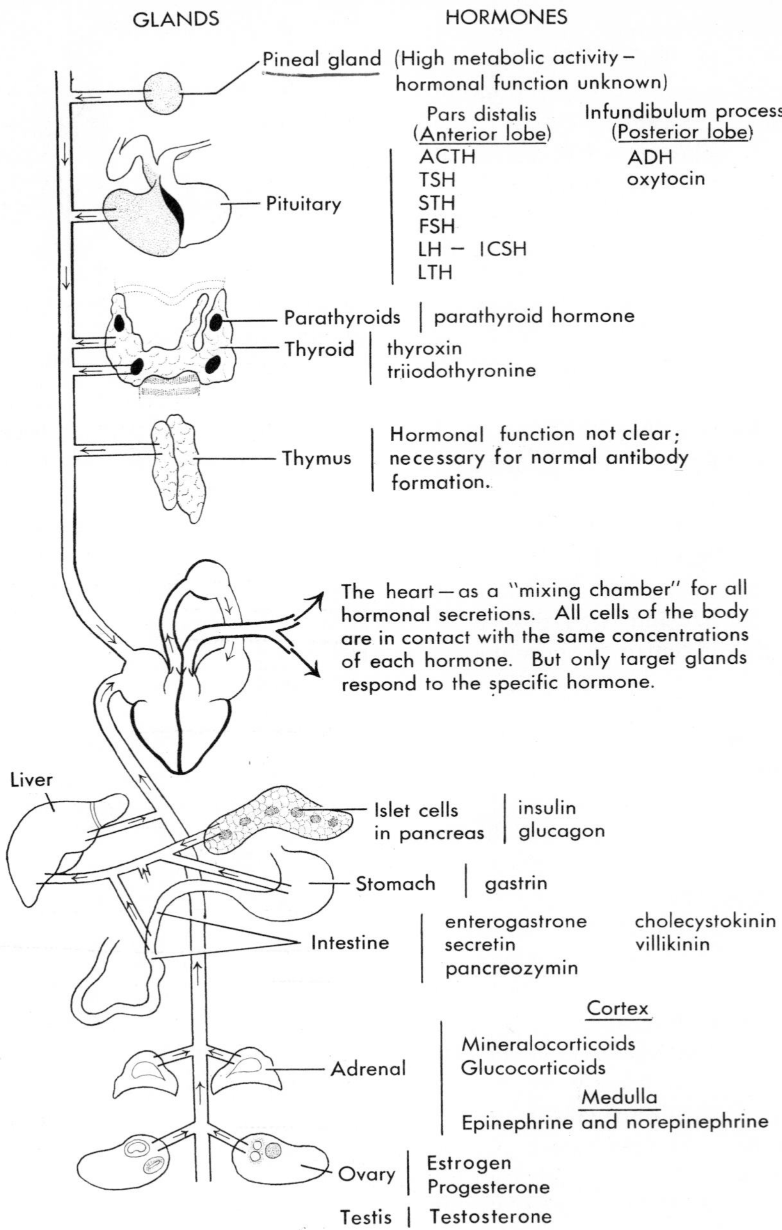

Figure 23–8. Diagram showing relationship of endocrine glands to the blood stream. The blood stream is always moving, so that small quantities of hormones enter the blood continuously.

substance known as *prosecretin*, which is inactive until the medium is acid. When the acid chyme from the stomach enters the duodenum, prosecretin is liberated, changed to *secretin*, absorbed by the blood, and carried to the pancreas, stimulating it to secretory activity. There are other hormones produced in the intestinal mucosa. See Chapter 22.

Prostaglandins. The prostaglandins are a group of chemicals derived from the fatty acid arachidonic acid and are found in a wide variety of tissues. These include male and female reproductive tracts, heart, lung, thymus, brain, intestine, liver, kidney, and pancreas. The type of prostaglandin varies slightly according to tissue and species. Prostaglandins have an important effect on lypolysis of fat depots and blood level of fatty acids; on activity of smooth muscle of the digestive tract, cardiovascular system, and respiratory system; and on organs of the reproductive system (see page 548). It is too early yet to know the exact action of each of the prostaglandins; however, their wide distribution signifies their metabolic importance.

Local or tissue substances should be recognized as a factor in the complex chemical system of the body fluids. These substances act in the area of their release. They function at point of origin and are normally destroyed rapidly. Two important ones are:

1. Acetylcholine is secreted at the parasympathetic and skeletal nerve endings. It is a chemical transmitter and also may be necessary for rhythmical activities in the heart.

2. Norepinephrine is secreted at most endings of postganglionic sympathetic nerve fibers. Important exceptions are the sympathetic fibers to sweat glands and certain of the fibers to striated muscle arterioles.

The Pineal Gland, or Epiphysis. The pineal gland is part of the epithalamus and is located in the brain between the superior quadrigeminate bodies. It has been the subject of active investigation for many years. In rats removal of the gland before sexual development produces gonadal precocity. However the significance of the gland in man is not known.

Studies with radioactive substances show that the gland has high metabolic activity. Recent studies show that the gland produces many active physiological agents, but to date there is no evidence of hormonal secretion.

QUESTIONS FOR DISCUSSION

1. Name the hormones of the anterior pituitary and explain the function of each.
2. Explain the anatomical relationship between the hypothalamus and the hypophysis.
3. What is the hypothalamic-portal system?
4. List the hormones of the pars distalis and explain their function.
5. Explain the feedback mechanism for control of the secretion of one hormone.
6. Which of the adrenal hormones are essential for life? Explain.
7. Differentiate between the actions of epinephrine and norepinephrine.
8. Explain briefly the physiological response to stress.

SUMMARY

- **Endocrine Glands**
  - **General hormones**
    - Secreted into extracellular fluids
    - Have effect on distant organs
  - **Local hormones**
    - Function at point of origin
    - Normally rapidly destroyed
  - **Control of hormonal secretion**
    - *Hypothalamic releasing factors*
      - Corticotropin-releasing factor (CRF)
      - Thyrotropin-releasing factor (TRF)
      - Somatotropin-releasing factor (SRF)
      - Gonadotropin-releasing factor for FSH, LH, but not LTH
  - **Feedback mechanisms**—High blood level of hormone from target-gland checks secretion of stimulating hormone
  - **Method of study**
    - Observations of conditions caused by disease
    - Administration of gland extracts, synthetic preparations, or active principles
    - Removal of glands in animals
  - **Endocrine glands**—Hypophysis, thyroid, parathyroid, thymus, adrenals, gonads

Name of Gland	Location	Secretion	Probable Function	Diseases Associated with It
Pituitary, or Hypophysis Cerebri Mass of reddish-gray tissue about 1 cm in diameter. Consists of an anterior and posterior lobe and a tuberal part containing colloid	Lodged in the sella turcica of the sphenoid bone	Hypothalamus—stored in posterior lobe *ADH*	Antidiuretic—controls water reabsorption in the distal kidney tubule Pressor effects unimportant physiologically	**Hypofunction** (or hypothalamic lesion) results in *diabetes insipidus*
		Oxytocin	Oxytocic effect—muscles of pregnant uterus contract	
		Pars distalis (anterior lobe) *Several hormones*	ACTH influences adrenal cortex secretion STH influences growth of tissues TSH influences structure and secretory activity of thyroid gland Gonadotropic hormones FSH, LTH, LH, ISCH influence gonadal functions	**Hypofunction** may result in Simmonds' disease, dwarfism, polyuria, depressed sexual function, and scanty growth of hair **Hyperfunction** may result in gigantism (early life), acromegaly (adult life), and glycosuria
Thyroid Weighs about 1 oz Consists of two lobes connected by an isthmus	In front of trachea and beside thyroid cartilage	*Thyroxin*—contains 65% of the body iodine *Triiodothyronine*	Influence the general rate of oxidation in the body, also growth and development in the young Influence through enzyme systems	**Hypothyroidism** may result in cretinism (early life) and myxedema (adult life) **Hyperthyroidism** may result in Graves' disease (exophthalmic goiter)
Parathyroids Four small glands	Between the posterior borders of the lobes of the thyroid gland and its capsule	*Parathyroid hormone* (*parathormone*)	Regulates the blood-calcium level and the irritability of the nervous system and muscles Increases excretion of inorganic phosphate in the renal tubule	When the parathyroids are removed, **tetany** develops **Hyperparathyroidism** may result in muscular weakness and high blood calcium
The Thymus has two lobes	Upper chest cavity	*Unnamed hormone* in youth	Hormonal action unknown at present	Unknown except for failure to produce antibodies
Adrenal Glands Two small glands, each surrounded by a fibrous capsule and consisting of two parts {cortex, medulla}	Placed above and in front of the upper end of each kidney			
Cortex consists of epithelial cells arranged in columns. These cells are derived from the part of the mesoderm that gives rise to the kidneys		*Several hormones* (glucocorticoids, mineralocorticoids)	Regulate electrolyte and water balance. Influences fat, carbohydrate, and protein metabolism; activity of lymphoid tissue and sexual organs. Aids body to cope more effectively with stress situations	Removal causes death **Hypofunction** results in Addison's disease and poor response to stress **Hyperfunction** may cause precocious sexual development (Cushing's syndrome) and virilism in the adult female

Name of Gland	Location	Secretion	Probable Function	Diseases Associated with It
Medulla consists of a network of large granular cells which when treated with chromic acid give a yellow or brown reaction. Derived from neural crest of ectoderm		Medulla—*Epinephrine*	Constitutes a reserve mechanism that comes into action at times of stress. Epinephrine augments the response of sympathetic nerves, increases the heartbeat, increases blood supply to muscles, nervous system, and heart, and increases output of glucose from liver. Raises B.P.	Removal of the medulla causes no serious physiological disturbance
		Norepinephrine	Vasoconstriction, elevates blood pressure	
Gonads *Ovaries* Two almond-shaped bodies which weigh 2–3.5 gm	One on each side of the uterus, attached to the broad ligament and below the uterine tubes	*Estrogen*	Seems to act by maintaining nutrition and mature size of female reproductive organs	Excessive ovarian function produces precocious puberty. Diminished ovarian function characterized by late onset of menstruation, faulty development of genital organs, delayed menstruation
		Progesterone	Sensitizes the mucous membrane of the uterus so that it responds to the contact of the developing ovum and assists in implantation	
Testes Two glandular organs which weigh 10.5–14 gm	In the scrotum	*Testosterone*	Influences the development of secondary sex characteristics in the male	The tendency to become obese after castration
Placenta	Pregnant uterus	*Estrogen, progesterone, chorionic gonadotropin*	Similar action to the anterior pituitary gonadal hormones	See Chapter 27 for details of gonadal hormones
Pancreas A compound gland which weighs between 2 and 3 oz	In front of the first and second lumbar vertebrae behind the stomach	Islets of Langerhans furnish two hormones *Insulin*	1. Restores the power to utilize the glucose of the blood 2. Accelerates the synthesis of sugar to glycogen and the storage of glycogen 3. Restricts production of glucose in liver from protein and fat	**Diabetes mellitus**—results from insufficient secretion of insulin
		and *Glucagon*	Aids in the conversion of glycogen to glucose in the liver	
	Various tissues	*Prostaglandins* (several types)	Not clearly understood at present	Unknown
Gastric Mucosa	Stomach	*Gastrin* is hormone of internal secretion	Carried by blood to fundic and pyloric glands and stimulates secretion of pepsin and HCl	
Intestinal Mucosa	Intestine-duodenum	Cells of duodenum produce *prosecretin*, changed by acid to *secretin*	Secretin stimulates the pancreas to activity	

UNIT VI
Maintaining Homeostasis of Body Fluids

Claude Bernard, a French physiologist, first stated in the late nineteenth century that the constancy of the internal environment was the prime essential for cell life. When materials enter the body in excessive amounts, the excess must be removed as must the waste products of cell metabolism. Only thus can the chemical characteristics of the internal environment remain within the narrow limits of efficient cell functioning. This vital role belongs to the kidney.

CHAPTER

24

URINE FORMATION AND EXCRETION THE URINARY SYSTEM

Kidney, Ureters, and Bladder—Blood Supply, Nervous and Hormonal Controls

Nutrients added to the blood stream by the digestive organs and oxygen from the lungs are utilized by cells of the body for growth and repair, for synthesis of hormones or other secretions, and as a source of energy for these and other cell activities. As a result of the complex chemical reactions taking place within the cell, certain products are formed which tend to alter the normal internal and external environment of the cell. Unless these are kept within the normal range, cell functioning will deteriorate, causing eventual death of the cell and possibly of the individual. The kidney is the organ most responsible for maintaining homeostasis of body fluids.

MATERIALS FOR ELIMINATION

1. Liquid—water
2. Gas—carbon dioxide
3. Metabolic end products of protein metabolism—e.g., urea, creatinine, uric acid, sulfates
4. Heat

To these may be added the nonabsorbable and unabsorbed materials of the diet and the dead and living microorganisms constantly excreted in large numbers in the feces.

Substances eliminated are classed as excreta and the process by which they are removed from the body as excretion, or elimination.

EXCRETORY ORGANS

The organs that function as excretory organs and the products they eliminate may be tabulated as follows:

Excretory Organ	Essential	Incidental
Lungs	Carbon dioxide	Water, heat
Kidneys	Water and soluble salts, resulting from metabolism of proteins, neutralization of acids, etc.	Carbon dioxide, heat
Alimentary canal	Solids, secretions, etc.	Water, carbon dioxide, salts, heat
Skin	Heat	Water, carbon dioxide, salts

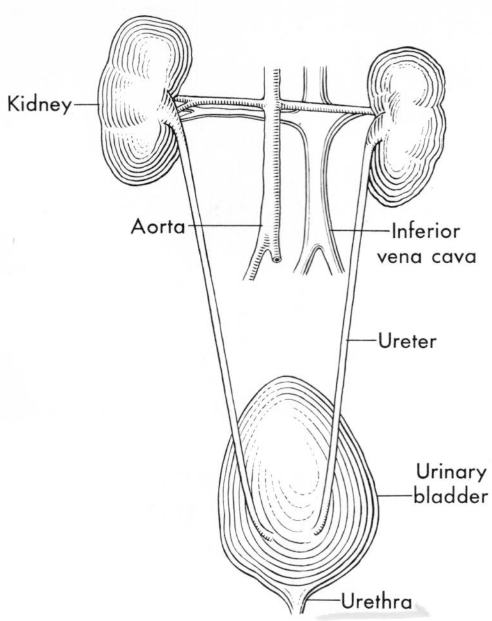

Figure 24–1. The urinary system viewed from behind.

Since the function of the lungs, the alimentary system, and the skin in elimination has been discussed in previous chapters, attention is now turned to the urinary system.

Urinary System	2 kidneys	Form urine from materials taken from the blood
	2 ureters	Ducts which convey urine from kidney to bladder
	1 bladder	Reservoir for urine
	1 urethra	Tube which conveys urine from bladder to external environment

Anatomy of the Kidneys

The kidneys are compound tubular glands, placed at the back of the abdominal cavity, one on each side of the spinal column and behind the peritoneal cavity. They correspond in position to the space included between the upper border of the twelfth thoracic and the third lumbar vertebrae. The right kidney is a little lower than the left, because of the large space occupied by the liver.

Each kidney with its vessels is embedded in a mass of fatty tissue termed an *adipose capsule.* The kidney and the adipose capsule are surrounded by a sheath of fibrous tissue called the *renal fascia.* The renal fascia is connected to the fibrous tunic of the kidney by many trabeculae, which are strongest at the lower end. The kidney is held in place partly by the renal fascia, which blends with the fasciae on the quadratus lumborum and psoas major muscles and also with the fascia of the diaphragm, and partly by the pressure of neighboring organs.

The kidneys are bean-shaped, with the medial or concave border directed toward the medial line of the body. Near the center of the concave border is a fissure called the *hilum* (hilus), which serves as a passageway for the ureter, and for the blood vessels, lymph vessels, and nerves going to and from the kidney. Each kidney is covered by a thin but rather tough envelope of fibrous tissue. At the hilum of the kidney the capsule becomes continuous with the outer coat of the ureter. If a kidney is cut in two lengthwise, it is seen that the upper end of the ureter expands into a basinlike cavity, called the *pelvis* of the kidney. The substance of the kidney consists of an outer portion called the cortical substance (cortex) and an inner portion called the med-

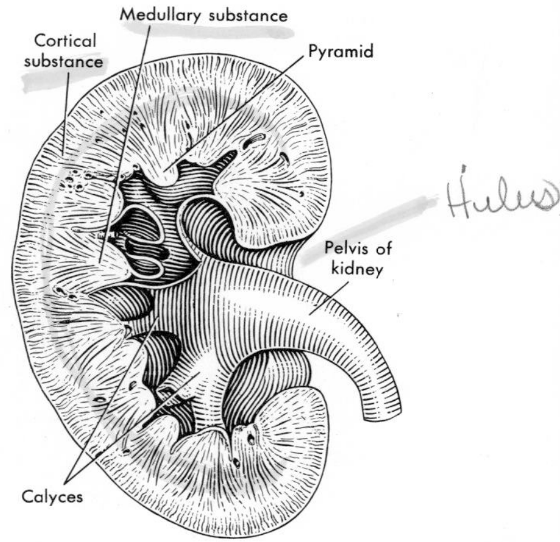

Figure 24–2. Diagrammatic longitudinal section of the human kidney. Each kidney is about 11.25 cm long, 5.0 to 7.5 cm broad, and 2.5 cm thick, and weighs about 135 gm. (Modified from Henle.)

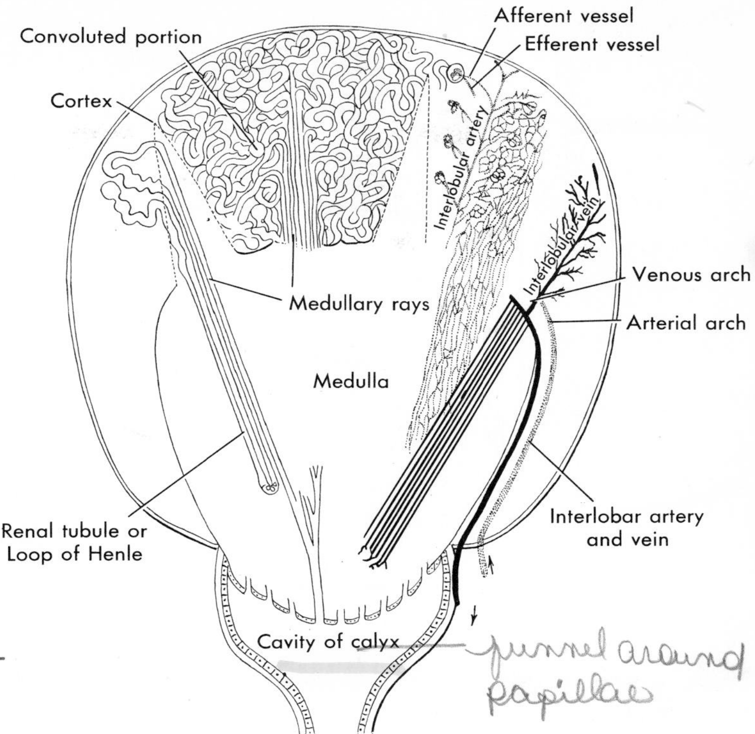

Figure 24–3. Diagram of a longitudinal section of a lobe of the kidney showing the arrangement of tubules and blood vessels in the lobe. The calyx embraces the apex of the pyramid. It is lined with epithelium, which continues from it over the apex, the latter being perforated with many apertures of collecting tubules. Note the arrangement that gives the granular and radial striations in the cortex. Nephron, arteriole, and venous units are diagrammed separately; in actuality they all occur in each pyramid and cortex section. (Modified from Gerrish.)

ullary substance (medulla). Between cortex and medulla are the arterial and venous arches.

The Medulla. The medulla is red and consists of from 8 to 18 radially striated cones, the renal pyramids, which have their bases toward the circumference of the kidney, whereas their apices converge into projections called papillae which are received by the cuplike cavities, or calyces, of the pelvis of the kidney.

The Cortex. The cortex is reddish brown and contains the glomeruli and convoluted tubules of the nephron and blood vessels. It penetrates for a variable distance between the pyramids, separating and supporting them. These interpyramidal extensions are called the *renal columns* and support the blood vessels. A glance across the shiny surface of a freshly cut kidney discloses both a granular structure and also areas showing radial striations. In general these alternate with each other. The granular areas contain the renal capsules, glomeruli, and convoluted areas of the tubule. The radially striated areas contain other parts of the tubule. (See Figures 24–2 and 24–3.)

The bulk of the kidney substance, in both cortex and medulla, is composed of minute tubes, or tubules, closely packed together, having only enough connective tissue to carry a large supply of blood vessels and a number of lymphatics and nerve fibers. The appearance of the cortex and medulla is due to the arrangement of these tubules, the *nephrons*, or functional units.

The Nephron. The nephron, the unit pattern of the kidney, consists of a glomerulus, its tubule, and its blood supply. Tubules vary in length, and the glomeruli vary in size. The largest ones are found nearest the medulla.

The *renal tubule* begins as a closed, invaginated layer of epithelium, the *glomerular capsule*, or capsule of Bowman.[1] The inner layer of this globelike expansion closely

[1] Sir William Bowman, English anatomist and ophthalmologist (1816–1892).

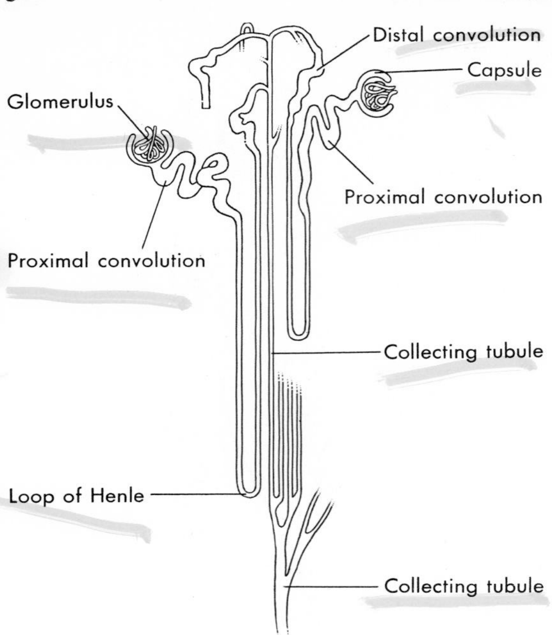

Figure 24–4. Diagram of the course of two renal tubules.

invests a capillary tuft called a renal *glomerulus*. The glomerulus consists of a few capillary loops which do not anastomose and which are completely encapsulated by the expansion of the tubule except at the point where an *afferent vessel* enters and an *efferent vessel* leaves the capillary tuft. The glomerulus, a basement membrane, and the enveloping capsule make up a renal corpuscle, or malpighian[2] body. More than 1,000,000 of these corpuscles are said to be in the cortex of each kidney.

There is bulging of the nuclei of the endothelial cells into the lumen of the glomerular capillaries. Around each bulged area the cytoplasm of each endothelial cell spreads out into a very thin film, so that the capillary walls are formed by a thin film of cytoplasm. In this thin wall are actual pores varying in size which are believed to play an important role in the filtration process.

The cells in the visceral layer of Bowman's (glomerular) capsule have numerous large arms of cytoplasm, called major processes, extending from its cell body which terminate as "feet" on the membrane of the glomerular capillary wall. These cells are called *podocytes* (Figure 24–5, page 513). Smaller processes and "feet" interdigitate with the major processes around the glomerular capillaries, leaving tiny spaces between them. It has been suggested that these podocytes may have contractile or elastic power. The renal capsule joins the rest of the tubule by a constricted *neck*; the tubules, after running a very irregular course, open into collecting ducts which pour their contents through their openings on the pointed ends, or papillae, of the pyramids into the calyces of the kidney. About 20 of these collecting ducts empty into the calyces from each papilla.

The epithelial lining of the renal tubule varies in different parts of the tubule. A distinctive characteristic of cells of the proximal convoluted tubule is the presence of microvilli forming a "brush border" which projects into the lumen. In the convoluted tubules and ascending limb of Henle's[3] loop the cells are columnar, while in the glomerular capsule and descending limb of Henle's loop they are thin, squamous cells. The collecting tubules have well-defined colum-

[2] Marcello Malpighi, Italian anatomist (1628–1694).

[3] Friedrich Gustav Jakob Henle, German anatomist (1809–1885).

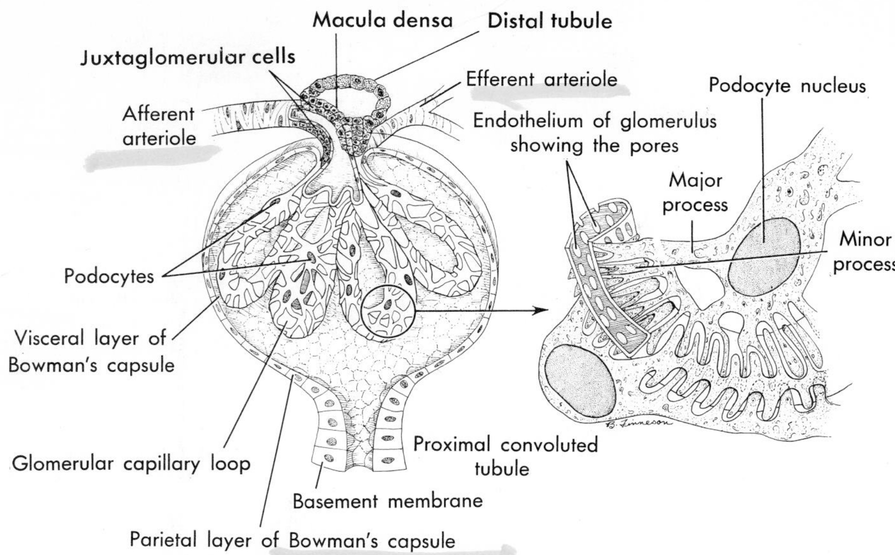

Figure 24–5. Schematic diagram from an electron micrograph of the glomerulus. (*A*) Renal malpighian corpuscle. Parietal and visceral layers of endothelium of Bowman's capsule are continuous. Note that the afferent artery is wider than the efferent artery. Is there capillary anastomosis in the glomerulus? (Modified from Bailey.) (*B*) Enlarged microscopic section of *A*. Note the many processes of podocytes and their relation to the glomerular capillary pores. (Modified from Harris.) Note the juxtaglomerular cells and macula densa and distal tubule.

nar cells, definitely resembling those of excretory ducts. The ascending limb of the loop of Henle returns to the glomerulus at the point of the afferent and efferent vessels before continuing as the distal convoluted portion. At this point it is in contact with both blood vessels and particularly with the afferent because there is no basement membrane between cells of the tubule (the *macula densa*) and those of the afferent arteriole, granular cells termed *juxtaglomerular* cells (Figure 24–5). The macula densa cells are peculiarly different in that the Golgi apparatus is between the nucleus and the juxtaglomerular cell, rather than toward the lumen as is usual in the tubular cell.

The Blood Supply of the Kidney. (Figure 24–6.) The kidney is abundantly supplied with blood by the *renal artery*, which is a branch of the abdominal aorta. Before or immediately after entering the kidney at the hilum, each artery divides into several branches, which enter the renal parenchyma separately. These branches travel up the renal columns as interlobar arteries.

When these arteries reach the boundary zone between the cortex and medulla, they divide laterally and form the *arch*, or *arcuate arteries*. From the convexity of these arches, the *interlobular arteries* (cortical) enter the cortex, giving off at intervals minute *afferent arterioles*, each of which branches out as the *capillaries of a glomerulus*. These capillaries reunite to form an *efferent arteriole* much smaller than the afferent arteriole. The efferent arteriole breaks up in a close meshwork, or *plexus*, of capillaries, which are in close approximation with both the convoluted tubule in the cortex and the loop of Henle in the medulla. These capillaries unite to form the *interlobular veins* (cortical) and *medullary veins*, which pour their contents into the *arcuate veins* lying between the cortex and the medulla. The arcuate veins converge to form the *interlobar veins*. These merge into the *renal vein*, which emerges from the kidney at the hilum and opens into the inferior vena cava.

The Nerves of the Kidneys. These are derived from the *renal plexus*, which is

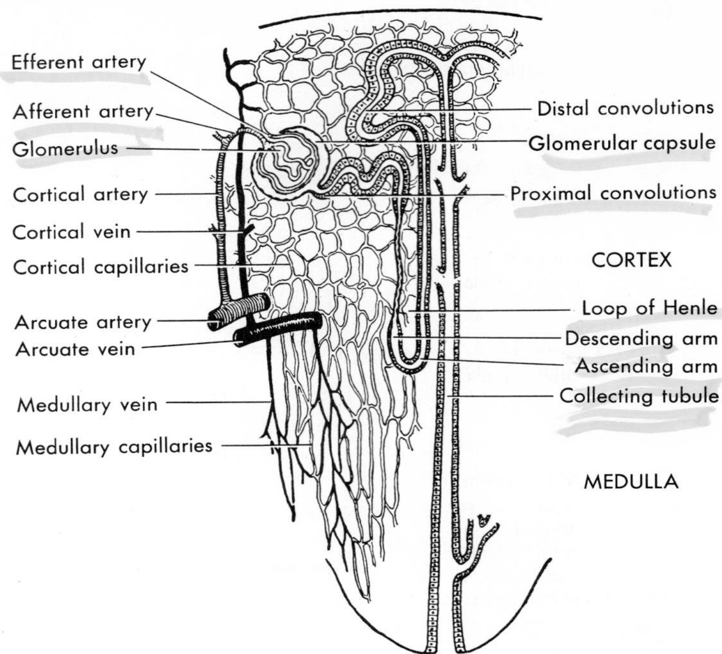

Figure 24–6. Nephron and its blood supply. Length of tubule is approximately 35 to 40 mm; diameter, about 0.02 mm; diameter of capsule, about 0.2 mm.

formed by branches from the celiac plexus, the aortic plexus, and the lesser and lowest splanchnic nerves. They accompany the renal arteries and their branches and are distributed to the blood vessels. They are vasomotor nerves, and by regulating the diameters of the small blood vessels, they control the circulation of the blood in the kidney.

Kidney Function. The functions of the kidneys include:

1. Regulation of Osmotic Pressure of Extracellular Fluids. This is accomplished by the relative amounts of water and sodium chloride excreted. If large quantities of fluids are ingested, more water will be eliminated, and the ratio between water and electrolytes will change. This is evidenced by change in specific gravity (s.g.) of urine. Conversely, ingestion of excess sodium chloride without an increase of fluid intake will raise the s.g. of urine.

2. Regulation of the Electrolytic Pattern of Extracellular Fluids. The kidneys not only regulate the total concentration of water and electrolytes, but also regulate the concentration of each electrolyte. The regulation is complex and is accomplished by tubular reabsorption and tubular secretion. The processes are under the influence of hormones produced in the hypothalamus and adrenal cortex.

3. Excretion of Metabolic Wastes. The kidney excretes metabolic wastes, particularly those arising in protein metabolism, such as urea, uric acid, creatinine, and ammonia.

4. Regulation of pH. By regulating the rate of excretion of hydrogen ions and electrolytes, the kidney helps to keep the pH of the plasma within normal limits. This is discussed more fully in the next chapter.

5. Regulation of the Volume of Extracellular Fluid. The kidneys aid in the regulation of the volume of extracellular fluid by elimination of water.

6. Secretion of Renin. Certain cells located in the juxtaglomerular apparatus (JGA) of the afferent arterioles respond to pressure changes and secrete an enzyme substance called *renin.* Renin enters the blood and functions as a proteolytic enzyme which activates a plasma globulin known as angiotensinogen to form angiotensin I. Under the influence of another plasma enzyme, two amino acid units are split off from angiotensin I to form angiotensin II, an extremely potent vasopressor substance. In addition, angiotensin II stimulates the release of aldosterone from the adrenal cortex.

How Kidney Functions Are Implemented. Three processes are involved in urine formation: filtration by the glomerulus, reabsorption, and secretion by the tubular cells.

The *glomerulus* functions as an ultrafilter, permitting particles smaller than the size of the endothelial pores to escape, thus filtering small colloidal and noncolloidal substances of plasma into the plasma. There is no selectivity to this filtration, other than that of particle size; so composition and concentration of materials in the filtrate are the same as those of plasma. The filtrate is generally spoken of as "protein free," although small amounts of low-molecular-weight plasma proteins do filter through the glomerular membrane and are reabsorbed in the tubules by pinocytosis.

The filtering process in the glomerulus is directly related to blood pressure. Hydrostatic pressure in the glomerulus is about 75 to 80 mm Hg and the protein osmotic (oncotic) pressure is about 25 mm Hg. This means that the effective hydrostatic pressure, or filtration pressure, is about 50 or more mm Hg. This pressure is essential for the filtration of 170 to 180 liters of the protein-free filtrate. The pressure must also be adequate to overcome resistance to movement of fluid within the tubule. This back pressure has been estimated to be about 7 mm Hg. The total filtration pressure is therefore equal to the glomerular hydrostatic pressure, minus the oncotic pressure and the back pressure within the tubules. Back pressure in the tubules is increased by intraureteral pressure, which is transmitted upward through the renal pelvis and inhibits the onward movement of filtrate. Pressure in the ureter rises if urine flow is impeded by obstruction of the ureteral openings into the bladder, or of the urethra.

Although systemic blood pressure may vary, the pressure in the glomerulus is maintained by alterations in the lumen of the efferent arteriole as compared with the afferent arteriole. Thus filtration continues until blood pressure falls to very low levels; and when hypertension is present, filtration continues at the normal rate. The average rate of filtration is about 120 ml per minute. This means that about 170 to 180 liters are filtered in 24 hours into the tubules. Urine output is about 1 ml per minute, or about $1\frac{1}{2}$ liters in 24 hours. As the protein-free filtrate passes through the tubule, it is changed in both volume and composition by the reabsorption of about 168 or 169 liters of water and certain of its constituents.

The *tubular cells* are responsible for reabsorbing materials to approximate normal blood levels of each. In addition secretion occurs, particularly in relation to maintaining acid-base balance, although secretion of other materials, such as creatinine also occurs. Much of the reabsorption is an active process involving "carriers" within the tubular cell to aid in transporting the substance across the membrane. There is a limit to the rate at which the active transport system can operate; when this limit is reached, the material, e.g., glucose, which is present in excessive amounts in filtrate, then fails to be reabsorbed and is excreted in the urine. The term *threshold* is also used in relation to reabsorption of transport substances. The threshold of a particular substance is that point above which the substance will appear in urine, and below which it will not. In addition to active transport, there is passive transport across the membrane by diffusion and osmosis. All three are involved in reabsorption.

Tubular reabsorption varies in different parts of the tubule:

---

1. Proximal tubule and descending limb	Glucose, amino acids, vitamins and protein, bicarbonate, and sodium (largely under influence of aldosterone) are actively reabsorbed; chloride, sulfate, phosphate ions, and urea are passively reabsorbed; water is

	reabsorbed with these substances, leaving the filtrate osmotic pressure unchanged. Eighty per cent of the water is reabsorbed in this way and is known as obligatory water reabsorption (a must)
2. Loop of Henle	Sodium is actively transported from the filtrate in the ascending limb into the medullary interstitial fluid, thus raising its osmotic pressure. This causes more water to be reabsorbed from the descending limb and the collecting duct and results in the concentration of the urine
3. Distal tubule and collecting ducts	Active reabsorption of sodium (in exchange for secreted potassium or hydrogen) and reabsorption of water. Filtrate is progressively more concentrated and volume greatly reduced as water continues to be reabsorbed, under the influence of ADH, depending on body needs. This is known as facultative reabsorption (optional). About 10 to 15 per cent of the water may be absorbed in this way

Countercurrent Mechanism. The ability of the kidney to conserve water for the body by forming concentrated urine, and to permit water loss by forming dilute urine, is a function of the loop of Henle and its associated capillaries. The mechanism for effecting dilution and concentration has been termed the *countercurrent mechanism*. In the ascending limb of the loop sodium is actively transported out of the filtrate into the surrounding interstitial fluid, with chloride ions moving out also. Since the ascending limb is highly impermeable to water without the influence of the antidiuretic hormone, the filtrate becomes more and more dilute as sodium is pumped out and the water remains. As NaCl increases in the interstitial fluid, it diffuses back into the descending limb, increasing the osmolality of the filtrate moving down toward the tip of Henle's loop, hence countercurrent. A similar phenomenon occurs in the capillary loops nearby. NaCl diffuses into the section of capillary near the ascending limb and out of the capillary loop near the descending limb. Blood flow through the capillaries in the medulla, where the countercurrent mechanism is operating, is sluggish, and only about 5 per cent of the total renal blood flow is in this area. Ninety-five per cent of the blood flow is in the cortex where the glomeruli lie and where the distal convoluted tubules are functioning to reabsorb (or fail to reabsorb) water. Thus the effect of the countercurrent mechanism is to alter filtrate concentration before it reaches the cortex with its favorable blood supply. In addition, body electrolyte concentrations are not appreciably altered.

Hormonal Control of Kidney Function. The reabsorption of water in the distal tubules of the kidney is promoted primarily by the antidiuretic hormone ADH, also called vasopressin. ADH increases the size of the pores in the epithelial cells of the distal tubule and collecting ducts, permitting reabsorption of water from the filtrate. The

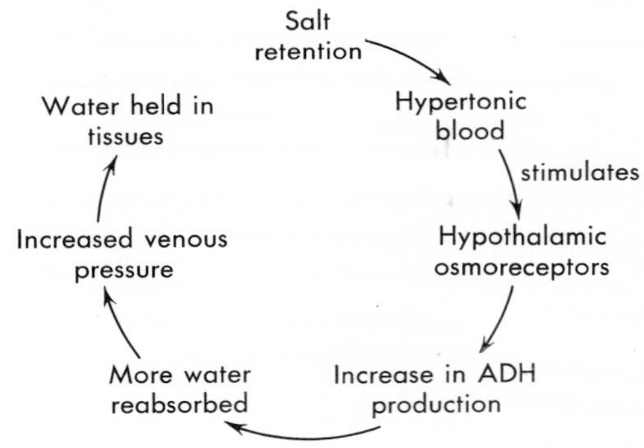

regulation and production of the ADH are under the influence of the hypothalamus. There are receptor cells in the hypothalamus called *osmoreceptors* that are sensitive to the osmotic pressure of the plasma. A rise causes an increased secretion of ADH and inhibition of normal water diuresis. This is represented in the above diagram, which at the same time illustrates how water may be held in the tissues.

The mineralocorticoids of the adrenal cortex (aldosterone) promote the excretion of potassium ions and the reabsorption of sodium ions, which then electrostatically attract chloride ions and cause their reabsorption throughout most of the tubule. In this way, water and sodium reabsorption and elimination by the kidneys are rigorously controlled. Eighty per cent of the tubule water is reabsorbed by osmosis as a result of decreased osmolality created by the reabsorption of these electrolytes and, to a lesser extent, other solutes.

Result of Kidney Function. The table below compares the concentrations of the various substances in blood plasma and in urine and indicates the number of times *each substance is concentrated by the kidney.* It will be noted that proteins, fats, and other colloids are not filtered.

When the kidney is unable to secrete nitrogenous wastes and to regulate pH and electrolyte concentrations of the plasma (as in kidney disease) artificial control may be instituted. *Hemodialysis* by means of artificial kidney involves removal of blood from an artery, transporting it through a lengthy coiled cellophane tube immersed in a "water bath," and returning the blood to the body via a vein. The radial artery and the cephalic or basilic veins are often used. The cellophane tube functions as a semipermeable membrane, and the mixture of ions in the water bath is calculated so that materials *diffuse out* of the plasma. If, for example, the patient has a high serum potassium or urea level, there will be little or no potassium and *no* urea in the water bath. Since the substances are in higher concentration in blood plasma than they are in the water bath, they dialyze *out* of the plasma into the bath, thereby lowering plasma concentrations. Conversely, low calcium blood levels may be raised by adding calcium to the water bath.

Peritoneal dialysis may be used instead of the artificial kidney. In this technique the *peritoneal cavity* is used, the dense capillary network of the entire peritoneal cavity functioning as a dialyzing membrane. A sterile solution of the desired mixture of substances is introduced into the abdominal cavity by means of a tube inserted through a small incision in the abdominal wall. The fluid usually remains for 30 to 45 minutes to allow for sufficient time for dialysis and is then permitted to flow out through the tube. The process may be repeated any number of times until normal plasma concentrations of the various substances have been attained.

An understanding of the physiology of urine formation, with filtration of deproteinized blood plasma through the glomerular capsule and concentration in the renal tubule, helps to explain symptoms of glomerular nephritis. When the glomerulus is impaired, proper filtration does not occur; nonprotein nitrogenous substances are retained in the blood, edema may be present, and a small amount of highly concentrated urine containing albumin may be passed.

Substance	Blood Plasma %	Urine %	Number of Times Concentrated by Kidney
Water	90–93	95	—
Proteins, fats, and other colloids	7–9	—	—
Glucose	0.1	—	—
Urea	0.03	2	60
Creatinine	0.001	0.075	75
Uric acid	0.004	0.05	12
Sodium ions	0.32	0.35	1
Potassium ions	0.02	0.15	7
Ammonium ions	0.001	0.04	40
Calcium ions	0.008	0.015	2
Magnesium ions	0.0025	0.006	2
Chloride ions	0.37	0.6	2
Phosphate ions	0.009	0.15	16
Sulfate ions	0.002	0.18	90

Diuretics are substances which increase the volume of urine excreted, causing a condition known as *diuresis.* For example, mercurial diuretics prevent reabsorption of sodium ions by the tubular cells, which in turn causes water to remain in the filtrate. Careful regulation of these drugs is necessary to prevent fluid and electrolyte imbalance.

Urine

Physical Characteristics of Urine. Normal urine is usually a yellow, transparent liquid with an aromatic odor. Cloudy urine is not necessarily pathological, for turbidity may be caused by mucin secreted by the lining membrane of the urinary tract; this, however, if present in excess does denote abnormal conditions. If urine is alkaline, especially after a meal, turbidity may be due to phosphates and carbonates. The color of urine varies with the changing ratios of water and substances in solution and may, of course, be affected by the presence of abnormal materials such as those produced by disease or certain drugs.

Urine is usually slightly acid, though its pH may vary between 5.5 and 7.5. Diet affects this reaction; a high-protein diet increases acidity, and a vegetable diet increases alkalinity. This variation is due to the difference in the end products of metabolism in each case. If human urine is allowed to stand, it will eventually become alkaline due to the decomposition of urea with production of ammonia, and many solutes will precipitate.

In health the specific gravity of urine may vary from 1.008 to 1.030, depending upon the relative proportions of solids and water. When the solids are dissolved in a large amount of water, the specific gravity will naturally be lower than when urine is more concentrated. The ability to concentrate urine when water is lost from the body by other means, as in sweating, is an important characteristic of the kidney and depends on adequate numbers of tubular cells. When disease destroys them, the individual excretes dilute urine.

The average quantity of urine excreted by a normal adult in 24 hours varies from 1,200 to 1,500 ml (40 to 50 oz). Much wider variations may occur for short periods of time without pathological significance, as, for example, when a rise in environmental temperature or unusual muscular activity increases perspiration and so lessens the urinary output. The quantity of urine may be affected by the amount of fluid taken in by the body; the amount of fluid lost in perspiration, respiration, or in vomiting, diarrhea, or hemorrhage; the health of the organs concerned, the kidneys, heart, blood vessels; and the action of certain drugs such as diuretics.

The amount of urine excreted by children in 24 hours is great in proportion to their body weight.

Age	Weight	Amount
6 months–2 years	17–26 lb	540–600 ml
2–5 years	26–38 lb	500–780 ml
5–8 years	38–55 lb	600–1,200 ml
8–14 years	55–103 lb	1,000–1,500 ml

Thus fluid intake in children must be closely observed for adequacy.

Chemical Composition of Urine. Water forms about 95 per cent of urine. The solutes (on chemical examination, precipitated as solids—some 60 gm in 1,500 ml of urine) are organic and inorganic waste products.

Urine 1,500 ml daily	Organic wastes 35 gm	Urea	30 gm
		Creatinine	1–2 gm
		Ammonia	1–2 gm
		Uric acid	1 gm
		etc.	1 gm
Solutes (solids) 60 gm	Inorganic salts 25 gm	Chlorides, sulfates, phosphates of	Sodium Potassium Magnesium Calcium

Sodium chloride is the chief inorganic salt, about 15 gm being excreted daily by the kidneys; however, sodium chloride excretion will vary with intake. Substances found in

NITROGEN OUTPUT AS INFLUENCED BY LEVEL OF PROTEIN INTAKE

	High-Protein Diet (Free from Meat)	Low-Protein Diet (Starch and Cream)
Total nitrogen	16.8 gm	3.6 gm
Urea nitrogen	14.7 gm, or 87.5%	2.2 gm, or 61.7%
Ammonia nitrogen	0.49 gm, or 2.9%	0.42 gm, or 11.3%
Uric acid nitrogen	0.18 gm, or 1.1%	0.09 gm, or 2.5%
Creatinine nitrogen	0.58 gm, or 3.6%	0.60 gm, or 17.2%
Undetermined nitrogen	0.85 gm, or 4.9%	0.27 gm, or 7.3%
Water output	Normal	Diminished

Note that urea nitrogen decreased 12.5 gm when the low-protein diet was used. The creatinine nitrogen varied only 0.02 gm. These diets were similar in all respects, except for protein intake.

urine are both exogenous and endogenous, i.e., they are derived from the diet as well as from the metabolism of intracellular components.

Nonprotein Nitrogen Constituents of Normal Urine. These are creatinine, urea, ammonia, hippuric acid, and purine bodies.

Creatinine. Creatinine is always present in the urine, and in amounts independent of the proteins of the diet. It is thought, therefore, to be an endogenous substance resulting from cellular metabolism of certain protoplasmic constituents. About 1 to 2 gm of creatinine are excreted in the urine daily, the amount being stable for the individual. Thus it serves as a check for the adequate recording of urine output. The source of creatinine in urine is creatine and creatine phosphate of muscle. It is not yet known whether this change from creatine to creatinine, which involves a loss of water, is accomplished in the blood or in the kidney. *Creatine* is not excreted as such in the urine of the adult male, but it is constantly present in the urine of children and perhaps in that of women after menstruation, during pregnancy, and in the puerperium. Creatine is also present in the urine during starvation or fever, probably because the body tissues are being utilized at a rate too high for all the creatine to be changed to creatinine. It is markedly increased in the urine of individuals who have muscular diseases.

Urea. Urea constitutes about one half (30 gm daily) of all the solids excreted in the urine. It is made by the liver cells from NH_2 radicals released on the deaminization of amino acids. Normally 27 to 28 mg of urea are contained in each 100 ml of blood. The kidneys constantly remove the urea as it is formed, keeping the amount in the blood stream at its normal level.

Ammonia. Ammonia in the urine is formed by the kidney from amino acids, especially glutamine. The amount of ammonia produced by the kidney may depend upon the general need of the body for conserving sodium ions to offset acid substances in the blood and tissues.

Hippuric Acid. Hippuric acid is thought to be the means by which benzoic acid, a toxic substance occurring in food and from body processes, is eliminated from the body. A vegetable diet increases the quantity of hippuric acid excreted, probably because fruit and vegetables contain benzoic acid.

Purine Bodies (Uric Acid, Etc.). Purine bodies are derived from foods containing nucleic acid (exogenous) and from the catabolism of the body cells (endogenous). The exogenous purines excreted depend upon the quantity eaten of purine-containing foods such as meat; the endogenous purine waste depends upon the health and activities of the body and is normally fairly constant.

Some Abnormal Constituents Appearing in Urine. These include albumin, glucose, indican, acetone bodies, casts, calculi, pus, blood, and bile pigments.

Albumin. Serum albumin is a normal

constituent of the blood plasma, but it is not usually filtered into the renal capsule. Its presence in the urine is spoken of as *albuminuria* and is usually due to increased permeability of the glomerular membrane.

Glucose. Normal urine contains so little sugar that for clinical purposes it may be considered absent. In health the amount of glucose present in the blood varies from 80 to 120 mg per cent. When the blood level of glucose rises above 180 mg per cent, it "spills" into the urine; that is, the tubules fail to reabsorb it.

Indican. Indican (indoxyl potassium sulfate) is a potassium salt that is formed from indole. Indole results from the putrefaction of protein food in the large intestine. It is absorbed by the blood and carried to the liver, where it is probably changed to indican. Traces of indican are found in normal urine, but its presence in larger amounts is abnormal.

Ketone Bodies. The ketone bodies, acetoacetic acid, beta hydroxybutyric acid, and acetone, normally appear in the urine in very small amounts. But, when excessive quantities of fatty acids are oxidized in the liver, as in acute starvation, or in insulin deficiency of diabetes, these "ketones" are excreted in the urine in appreciable quantities. In normal individuals they may appear in the urine during periods of fasting.

Casts. In some abnormal conditions the kidney tubules become lined with substances which harden and form a mold or cast inside the tube. Later these casts are washed out by the urine, and their presence can be detected with the aid of a microscope. They are named either from the substances composing them or from their appearance. Thus there are pus casts, red cell casts, epithelial casts from the walls of the tubule, granular casts from cells which have decomposed and form masses of granules, fatty casts from cells which have become fatty, and hyaline casts which are formed from coagulable elements of the blood.

Calculi. Mineral salts in the urine may precipitate and form calculi, or stones. Calculi may be formed in any part of the urinary tract from the tubules to the external orifice of the urethra. The causes which lead to their formation are an excessive amount of salts, a decrease in the amount of water, and abnormally acid or abnormally alkaline urine.

Pus. In suppurative conditions of any of the urinary organs, pus cells are present in the urine.

Blood. In cases of acute inflammation of any of the urinary organs blood may be present in the urine, a condition known as *hematuria*. Blood imparts a smoky or reddish color to urine.

Bile Pigments. Bile pigments in the urine may be caused by obstructive jaundice, when bile has been reabsorbed from the biliary tract into the blood stream, or by diseases in which an abnormal number of erythrocytes are destroyed. Bile pigments give the urine a greenish-yellow or golden-brown color.

Elimination of Toxic Substances. It is the function of the kidneys to eliminate toxic substances that find their way into the blood, whether these substances result from defective metabolism, from bacterial activity, or from chemical poisons.

The Ureters

The ureter is a tube which conveys the urine from the renal pelvis to the bladder. Each commences as a number of cuplike tubes, or *calyces*, which surround the renal papillae. The calyces (varying in number from 7 to 13) join and form two or three short tubes, which unite and form a funnel-shaped dilatation called the *renal pelvis*. The ureter is about 25 to 30 cm long, about 4 to 5 mm in diameter, and consists of three coats: an outer fibrous coat, a muscular coat, and an inner mucous lining. The contractions of the muscular coat produce peristaltic waves, which commence at the kidney end of the ureter and progress downward.

The Bladder

The bladder is a hollow muscular organ situated in the pelvic cavity behind the pubes, in front of the rectum in the male, and in front of the anterior wall of the vagina, and

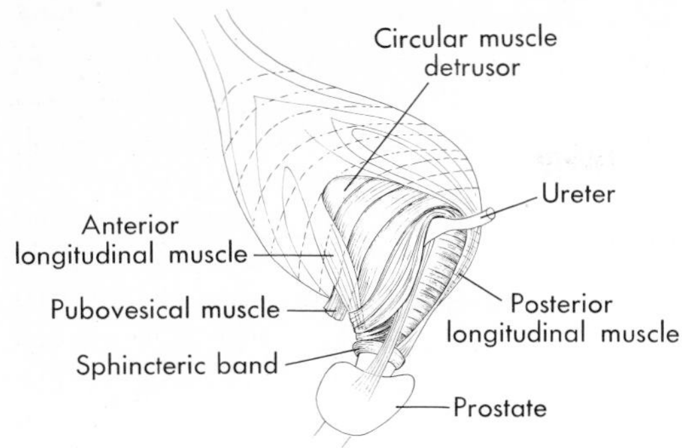

Figure 24–7. Lateral view of male bladder. (Modified from McCrea.)

the neck of the uterus, in the female. It is a freely movable organ but is held in position by folds of peritoneum and fascia. During infancy it is conical and projects above the upper border of the pubes into the hypogastric region. In the adult, when quite empty, it is placed deeply in the pelvis; when slightly distended, it has a round form; but when greatly distended, it is ovoid and rises to a considerable height in the abdominal cavity. It has four coats: (1) The *serous* coat is a reflection of the peritoneum and covers only the superior surface and the upper part of the lateral surfaces. (2) The *muscular* coat has three layers, an inner longitudinal, middle circular, and outer longitudinal. The fibers of the outer layer are arranged in a more or less longitudinal manner, up the inferior surface of the bladder, over its vertex, and descending along the fundus. They are attached in the male to the prostate, and in the female in front of the vagina. At the sides of the bladder the fibers are arranged obliquely and intersect one another. This layer is called the *detrusor* muscle. The circular fibers are collected into a layer of some thickness around the opening of the bladder into the urethra. These circular fibers form a sphincter muscle, which is normally in a state of contraction, relaxing only when the accumulation of urine within the bladder renders its expulsion necessary. (3) The *submucous* coat consists of areolar connective tissue and connects the mucous and muscular coats. (4) The *mucous* membrane of transitional epithelium lining the bladder is like that lining the ureters and the urethra. This coat is thrown into folds, or rugae, when the bladder is empty, with the exception of a small triangular area formed by the two orifices and the internal orifice of the urethra where the mucous membrane is firmly attached to the muscular coat. This area is called the trigone.

There are three openings into the bladder. The two ureters open into the corners of the trigone, $\frac{1}{2}$ in. from the midline. The ureters take an oblique course through the wall of the bladder, downward and medialward. The urethra leads from the bladder, its vesical opening lying in the midline below and in front of the openings of the ureters.

Nerve Supply. The bladder is supplied by nerves from both the craniosacral and thoracolumbar divisions of the autonomic nervous system. The sacral fibers bring about contraction of the muscles of the bladder and relaxation of the internal sphincter. It is believed that the reflex centers for these fibers are located in the midbrain, anterior pons, and posterior hypothalamus. The function of the thoracolumbar fibers seems to be primarily related to blood supply to the bladder wall. Spinal nerves are important as well, because they innervate the muscles of the pelvic floor and perineum and aid in conscious control of the external sphincter.

Blood Supply. The superior, middle, and inferior vesical arteries (branches of the hypogastric artery) supply the bladder. In the female, branches of the uterine and vaginal arteries also supply the bladder.

Function. The bladder serves as a reservoir for urine. Its capacity varies. When moderately distended, it holds about $\frac{1}{2}$ liter (about 1 pt).

The Urethra. In the female the urethra is a narrow membranous canal which extends from the bladder to the external orifice, the meatus. It is placed behind the symphysis pubis and is embedded in the anterior wall of the vagina. Its diameter, when undilated, is about 6 mm ($\frac{1}{4}$ in.), and its length is about 3.8 cm ($1\frac{1}{2}$ in.). Its direction is obliquely

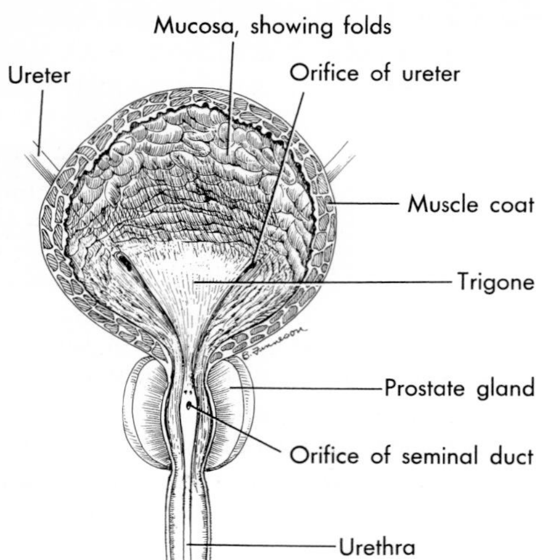

Figure 24–8. Diagram of the bladder opened ventrally to show bladder wall, orifices of ureters, and urethra. The orifices of the ureters and urethra form a triangle—the trigone. Note that the ureters enter the bladder wall from the posterior and run obliquely downward for about 2 cm. (Modified from Pansky and House.)

downward and forward, its course being slightly curved, with the concavity directed forward and upward. The meatus is the narrowest part and is located between the clitoris and the opening of the vagina.

The walls of the urethra consist of three coats: (1) an outer muscular coat, which is continuous with that of the bladder; (2) a thin layer of spongy tissue, containing a plexus of veins; and (3) a mucous coat, which is continuous internally with that lining the bladder and externally with that of the vulva.

The male urethra is about 20 cm long. It is divided into three portions: (1) the prostatic, which runs vertically through the prostate; (2) the membranous, which extends between the apex of the prostate and the external sphincter; and (3) the cavernous portion, which extends from the membranous to the urethral meatus.

The male urethra is composed of (1) mucous membrane, which is continuous with the mucous membrane of the bladder and is prolonged into the ducts of the glands that open into the urethra; and (2) a submucous tissue, which connects the urethra with the structures through which it passes.

Physiology of Micturition. The act by which the urine is expelled from the bladder is called micturition. The desire to urinate is due to stimulation of pressure receptors in the bladder itself caused by pressure of urine. As the bladder fills, pressure is exerted against the detrusor muscle. This reflexly causes the muscle to contract, and the internal sphincter to relax. The reflex is sustained until the bladder is completely empty. The act of micturition is started by voluntary relaxation of the external sphincter and surrounding muscles of the perineum.

While the emptying of the bladder is reflexly controlled, it may be initiated voluntarily and may be started or stopped at will.

Involuntary Micturition, or Incontinence. In young infants incontinence of urine is normal. The infant voids whenever the bladder is sufficiently distended to arouse a reflex stimulus. Children vary markedly in the ease with which they learn to control micturition and defecation. During the first year, some children can be taught to associate the act with the proper time and place. By the second year, regular training in habit formation and proper feeding should enable the child to inhibit the normal stimulus and control of micturition, at least during the day. Control of micturition at night is a habit

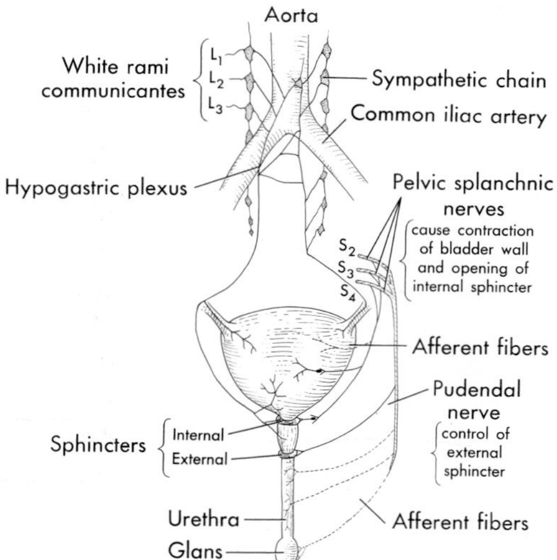

Figure 24–9. Innervation of bladder and urethra. (Modified from Grant.)

requiring longer practice and is usually formed by the end of the second year. When involuntary voiding occurs at night with any degree of regularity after the third year, it is called enuresis. If this is not caused by emotional stress or irritation of the bladder, it will usually yield to proper training.

Involuntary micturition may occur as the result of a lack of consciousness or as the result of injury to the spinal centers which control the bladder. If the spinal cord is transected, all bladder controls are abolished and loss of voluntary control is permanent. If there is injury to the sympathetic fibers, no significant effects result, but frequency may be present for a short time. There may be difficulty in initiating the act of voiding, where there is injury to the brain cortex.

Involuntary micturition may also result from some irritation due to abnormal substances in the urine, or to disease of the bladder (cystitis). Emotional stress may provoke the desire to urinate when there is only a small amount of urine in the bladder, owing to failure of the detrusor muscles to relax. This desire may also be aroused by visual and auditory impressions, such as the sight and sound of running water.

Retention of Urine. Retention, or failure to void urine, may be due to: (1) some obstruction in the urethra or in the neck of the bladder, (2) nervous contraction of the urethra, or (3) lack of sensation to void. In the last two conditions retention is often overcome by measures which induce reflexes, i.e., pouring warm water over the vulva, or the sound of running water. If micturition does not occur and the bladder is not catheterized, distention of the organ may become extreme, and there is likely to be constant leakage, or involuntary voiding of small amounts of urine without emptying the bladder. This condition is described as retention with overflow.

Anuria. A far more serious condition than retention is the failure of the kidneys to form urine. This is spoken of as suppression, or *anuria.* Unless anuria is relieved, a toxic condition known as uremia will develop. When the secretion of urine is decreased below the normal amount, the condition is spoken of as *oliguria.*

QUESTIONS FOR DISCUSSION

1. Explain the functions of the glomerulus and renal tubule in relation to volume and composition of urine.
2. Which hormones affect kidney function? What is the specific action of each?
3. Explain the relationship of arterial blood pressure to kidney function.
4. What is the trigone? How does it differ from the rest of the bladder? Is this important?
5. Explain how the two divisions of the autonomic nervous system regulate micturition.
6. What is the normal composition of urine?
7. Would it be possible to remove excessive fluid from an edematous patient by use of the artificial kidney? Explain the principles involved.

SUMMARY

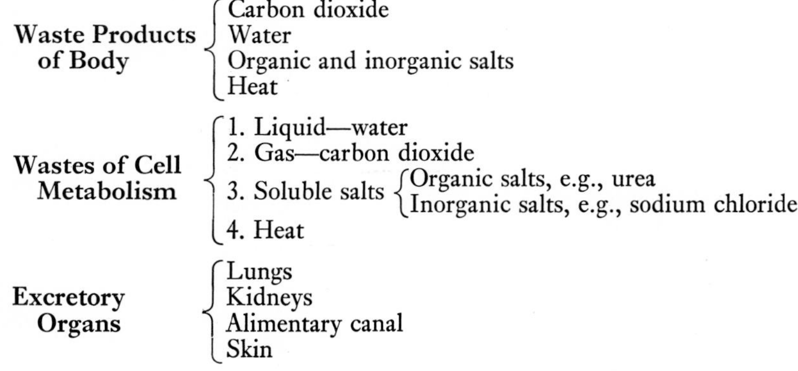

Waste Products of Body
- Carbon dioxide
- Water
- Organic and inorganic salts
- Heat

Wastes of Cell Metabolism
- 1. Liquid—water
- 2. Gas—carbon dioxide
- 3. Soluble salts
  - Organic salts, e.g., urea
  - Inorganic salts, e.g., sodium chloride
- 4. Heat

Excretory Organs
- Lungs
- Kidneys
- Alimentary canal
- Skin

Urinary System
- **Kidneys** (2)—form urine
- **Ureters** (2)—ducts which convey urine from kidneys to bladder
- **Bladder** (1)—reservoir for urine
- **Urethra** (1)—tube through which urine is voided

Kidneys
- **Location**
  - Posterior part of lumbar region, behind peritoneum
  - Placed on either side of spinal column and extend from upper border of twelfth thoracic to third lumbar vertebra
- **Covering and support**
  - Embedded in a mass of fatty tissue, adipose capsule
  - Surrounded by fibrous tissue called renal fascia
  - Held in place by renal fascia which blends with fasciae on
    - quadratus lumborum, psoas major, and diaphragm
  - Also by pressure and counterpressure of neighboring organs
- **Size and shape**
  - About 4.5 in. long, 2–3 in. broad, and 1 in. thick
  - Weight about 4.5 oz (135 gm)
  - Bean-shaped organs
  - Concave border directed toward median line of body
  - Hilum—fissure near center of concave side serves for vessels to enter and leave
- **Gross structure**
  - **Pelvis**—upper expanded end of ureter
  - **Calyces**—cuplike cavities of the pelvis that receive papillae of pyramids
  - **Medulla**—inner striated portion, made up of cone-shaped masses
    - **Pyramids**—8–18
    - **Bases** directed toward circumference of kidney
    - **Papillae**—apices of pyramids, directed into pelvis
  - **Cortex**—outer portion of kidney
    - **Renal columns**—extensions of cortical substance between pyramids
- **Unit pattern**
  - **Nephron**—consists of a renal tubule with its blood supply
  - **Renal tubules**—begin as capsules enclosing capillary tufts—glomeruli—in the cortex, and after a tortuous course open into straight collecting tubes which pour their contents into calyces of kidney pelvis
- **Blood supply**
  - **Renal artery**—direct from aorta
  - Before entering kidney divides into several branches
  - **Arterial arches**
    - Lateral branches at the boundary zone between cortex and medulla
    - Send branches to cortex
  - **Venous arches**
    - Lateral branches at level of base of pyramids
    - Receive blood from cortex
    - Receive blood from medulla
  - Veins empty into renal vein, leave kidney at hilus, and empty into inferior vena cava
- **Autonomic nerves**
  - Nerves derived from renal plexus, and from the lesser and lowest splanchnic nerves
  - Vasomotor, by regulating size of blood vessels, influences blood pressure
- **Functions of kidneys**
  - Regulation of osmotic pressure of extracellular fluids
  - Regulation of electrolytic pattern of extracellular fluids
  - Excretion of metabolic wastes
  - Regulation of acid-base ratio
  - Regulation of the volume of extracellular fluid
  - In shock the kidneys produce a vasoexcitatory material—renin
- **Hormonal control**
  - ADH—reabsorption of water in the kidney tubule
  - Mineralocorticoids (aldosterone)

Physiology of Urine Formation
- Efferent vessel is smaller than afferent, making blood pressure in glomerulus high
- Deproteinized plasma filters through capsule into tubule
- Efferent vessel, with others, forms plexuses about tubule
- Urine is concentrated in tubule by diffusion of water and some salts back into the blood
- Secretion of H^+, NH_4^+, or K^+, reabsorption of Na^+
- Countercurrent mechanism functions in loop of Henle to alter concentration of filtrate

- **Urine**
  - **Physical characteristics**
    - An aqueous solution of organic and inorganic substances
    - **Color** and **transparency** depend upon concentration, diet, etc.
    - **Reaction**, usually slightly acid, pH 5.5–7.5
    - **Specific gravity** 1.010–1.030, depending upon proportions of solids and water
    - **Quantity**—1,200–1,500 ml daily. Affected by:
      - Amount of fluid ingested
      - Amount of fluid lost in other excretions than urine, e.g., perspiration
      - Ability of organs to function—heart, blood vessels, kidneys, etc.
      - Action of specific substances, as diuretics
  - **Composition of urine**
    - 95% water
    - Remainder, about 3.7% organic and 1.3% inorganic wastes
      - May be exogenous or endogenous
    - **Exogenous**, e.g., urea
      - Amount excreted varies with diet
    - **Endogenous**, e.g., creatinine
      - Amount excreted does not vary with diet

- **Some Constituents of Normal Urine**
  - **Inorganic** — Chlorides, sulfates, phosphates of Sodium, Potassium, Magnesium, Calcium
  - **Organic**
    - **Creatinine**
      - 1–2 gm excreted daily
      - From endogenous metabolism, probably from creatine formed in metabolism of striated muscle tissue
    - **Urea**
      - About 30 gm excreted daily
      - Constitutes one half of all solids excreted in urine
      - Is made by liver cells
    - **Ammonia**
      - 0.7 gm daily
      - Is made by the kidney from amino acids. Amount made may depend upon body's need for conserving sodium ions
    - **Hippuric acid**
      - About 1 gm daily
      - Amount increased on diet of foods containing benzoic acid
    - **Purine bodies**
      - End products resulting from metabolism of nucleoproteins of food (exogenous) and tissues (endogenous) — Eventually appear in urine as uric acid

- **Some Abnormal Constituents of Urine**
  - **Albumin** (albuminuria)—Caused by disease of kidneys
  - **Sugar** (glycosuria)
    - Normal urine contains no sugar
    - Glycosuria may be temporary, as after ingestion of much sugar, or persistent, as in diabetes mellitus
  - **Indican**
    - Indican is indoxyl potassium sulfate
    - **Caused by**
      - Excessive putrefaction of proteins in intestines
      - Putrefaction in body itself
  - **Ketone bodies**—result of excessive oxidation of fats
  - **Casts**
    - Substances which harden and form a mold inside of tubules
    - Named from substances composing them or from their appearance
    - Varieties
      - Pus casts, red cell casts, epithelial casts, granular casts, fatty casts, hyaline casts
  - **Calculi**
    - Deposits of solid matter precipitated from the urine, vary in shape and size
    - **Causes**
      - Increase in slightly soluble constituents of urine
      - Decrease in amount of water secreted
      - Abnormally acid or abnormally alkaline urine

Some Abnormal Constituents of Urine (*cont.*)

- **Pus**—due to suppurative conditions of urinary organs
- **Hematuria**
  - Blood in urine
  - Inflammation of urinary organs, tuberculosis, cancer, renal stone
- **Bile pigments**
  - In obstructive jaundice
  - In diseases in which many erythrocytes are destroyed
  - Give urine greenish-yellow or golden-brown color

Ureters

- Excretory ducts. Connect kidneys with bladder and serve as passageway for urine
- Commence as calyces which surround renal papillae. These join to form two or three short tubes, and these unite to form renal pelvis
- Duct is 25–30 cm long
- **Three coats**
  1. Mucous—lining
  2. Muscular
     - Inner, longitudinal layer
     - Outer, circular layer
  3. Fibrous—carries blood vessels and nerves
- **Function**—conduct urine to the bladder

Bladder

- Hollow muscular organ
- Situated in pelvic cavity behind the pubes
  - In front of rectum in male
  - In front of anterior wall of vagina and neck of uterus in female
- Freely movable. Held in position by folds of peritoneum and fascia
- Size, shape, and position depend upon age, sex, and whether bladder is full or empty
- **Four coats**
  1. Mucous—lining
  2. Areolar—connects mucous and muscular
  3. Muscular
     - Inner layer—longitudinal
     - Middle layer—circular
     - Outer layer—longitudinal, forms detrusor muscle
  4. Serous—partial covering derived from peritoneum
- **Three openings**
  - Ureters run obliquely downward through the bladder wall opening into lower part, about ½ in. from median plane
  - Urethral opening is below and in front of the opening of the ureters

Nerve Supply

- **Cranio-sacral**
  - Contraction of muscle of bladder
  - Relaxation of internal sphincter
- **Thoracolumbar**—Primarily related to blood supply of bladder wall
- **Spinal nerves**—Conscious control of external sphincter
- **Function**
  - Serves as a reservoir for the reception of urine
  - When moderately distended, holds about 500 ml

Urethra

- Membranous canal, extends from the bladder to the meatus urinarius
- 3.8 cm long in female, about 20 cm long in male
- In female behind symphysis pubis, and embedded in the anterior wall of vagina
- **Three coats**
  1. Mucous—lining
  2. Submucous—supports network of veins
  3. Muscular
     - Inner—longitudinal
     - External—circular
- Meatus urinarius—external orifice located between clitoris and vagina

Micturition

- Act of expelling urine from bladder
- Reflex act—controlled by voluntary effort

Retention
- Failure to void urine
- Due to
  1. Obstruction in urethra or neck of bladder
  2. Nervous contraction of urethra
  3. Lack of sensation
- May be accompanied by constant leakage, or involuntary voiding of small amounts

Anuria—Failure of the kidneys to secrete urine
Oliguria—Deficient secretion of urine

CHAPTER

25

PHYSIOLOGY OF WATER AND ELECTROLYTE BALANCE ACID-BASE REGULATION

Water is the universal medium in which all of the complex metabolic processes of life take place. Water is the largest single constituent of living cells; life itself depends upon a constant source of, and utilization of, water in the body. Enzyme activity and electrolyte balance are closely related to water balance—each being dependent upon and influencing the other.

WATER

Water constitutes more than two thirds of the material ingested daily.

The water content of the body comes from three sources: beverages or other liquids; foods, especially vegetables and fruits; and the water formed in the tissues as the result of metabolic activities.

Water enters into the composition of all the tissues within the cell as well as in tissue fluid, most tissues containing between 75 and 90 per cent water by weight, although there are exceptions (see chart, page 432). Bone, which makes up a large percentage of the body weight, contains little water (less than 20 per cent). Thus the total body water is less than 70 per cent in most individuals. Adipose tissue water content is also low and, as this tissue increases in the body, the overall body water decreases; this accounts for the sex differences in adults. Women characteristically are less muscular than men and have a thicker layer of subcutaneous fat; body water content is about 50 per cent for women and 60 per cent for men. Age is another variable. Seventy to seventy-five per cent of infant body weight is water (extracellular water content is higher); after the first few months of life this gradually decreases. As tissues continue to age, they become relatively dehydrated, so that the total body water may be around 40 or 50 per cent in those over 65 years. However, the greatest change is in childhood.

Water supplies fluid for the secretions and serves as a medium for the chemical changes occurring in digestion. Its most obvious functions are in connection with the absorption of food in solution and the removal of dissolved products of metabolism. By its evaporation from the skin and the respiratory passages, it helps to keep the body temperature from rising above normal.

Under normal conditions the amount of water in the body remains about the same, even though the intake may vary considerably. If the intake of water is increased, the excretion of urine is increased. If the intake of water is decreased, more water is reabsorbed by the tubular cells of the kidney and less urine (more concentrated) is excreted. In addition the individual feels thirsty.

Distribution of Water in the Body.

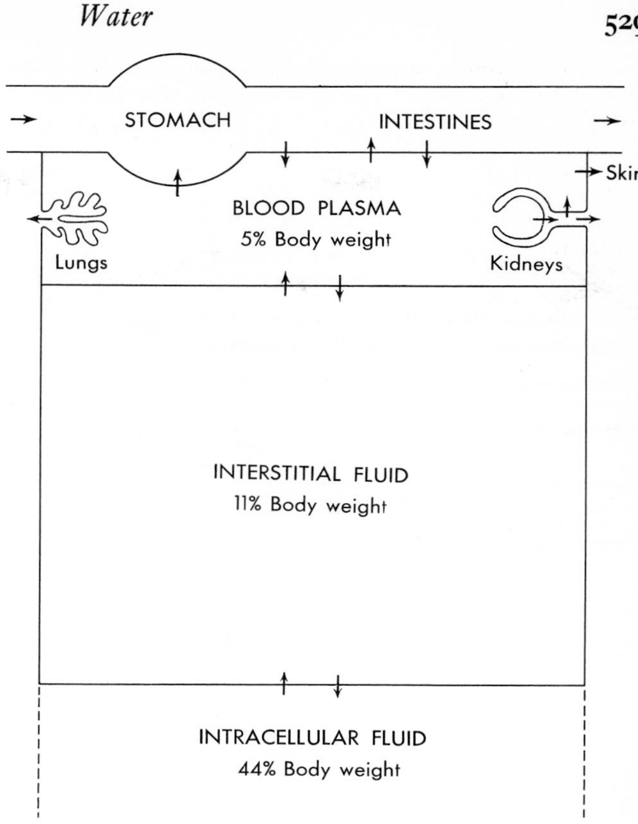

Figure 25-1. Diagram illustrating distribution of water in the body and exchange of water between compartments, normal sources of body fluid, and fluid loss. Figures are average for lean muscular adult. (Reprinted by permission of the publishers from James Lawder Gamble, *Chemical Anatomy, Physiology and Pathology of Extracellular Fluid: A Lecture Syllabus.* Cambridge, Mass.: Harvard University Press, Copyright, 1942, 1947, 1954, by The President and Fellows of Harvard College.)

Water is distributed in the body in three main compartments (figures are in terms of adult male):

1. Blood plasma 5% of body weight
2. Interstitial fluid 11% of body weight
3. Intracellular fluid 44% of body weight

This means that if an individual weighs about 70 kg there are about 3.5 liters of water in the plasma compartment, 7.7 liters of water in the interstitial compartment, and 30.8 liters of water within the cells. This makes a total of 42 liters of water. The amount of fluid in each compartment may be measured with relative accuracy, and the measurement of plasma volume is done frequently prior to surgery.

Plasma volume may be measured by giving a known quantity of the blue dye T 1824 (Evans blue). It is nontoxic, soluble in water, but not in fat; it does not readily pass through the capillaries, for it unites with plasma proteins; hence it may be used as a measure of plasma volume.

The dye is given intravenously and after it has had opportunity to be mixed well in the blood stream, samples of blood are taken. Plasma is separated from the cells and matched against samples of similar known dye dilutions. These values are considered along with hematocrit readings, i.e., the ratio of cells to plasma.

Radioactive chromium also is used to measure blood volume; in this case the red cells are the significant component, not the protein. A small amount of blood is removed, mixed with radioactive chromium for a half-hour; then the cells are washed, the degree of radioactivity is determined (from the chromium which has entered the cell), and the cells are reintroduced into the blood stream. The degree to which these cells have been diluted, as determined by the degree of radioactivity of a second sample, gives an estimate of the total blood volume.

The extracellular fluid volume can be measured with radioactive sodium; the total body water, with "heavy water" (containing deuterium, the isotope of hydrogen). In these instances the amount remaining in a plasma sample is the index of measurement.

Movement of water between compartments takes place freely. At the blood capillaries, which is the functional boundary between plasma and interstitial fluid, all solutes in these two fluids except protein are almost freely diffusible across the capillary membrane. The cell membrane, however, regulates the movement of electrolytes into and out of the cell so that sodium and chloride remain in high concentration outside the cell and potassium is high inside. This membrane is very permeable to the solutes—glucose, amino acids, urea, carbon dioxide, bicarbonate ions, but not to proteins.

In reality interstitial fluid functions as the "middleman" between plasma and cells. Plasma volume and cell volume are kept relatively constant by temporary reduction or increase in the amount of fluid in the interstitial compartment. Movement of fluid in the *extra*cellular compartments takes place through the cardiovascular system and the lymph channels.

The total forces that hold fluid in the various compartments are not completely understood. However, in the plasma compartment the blood proteins, especially

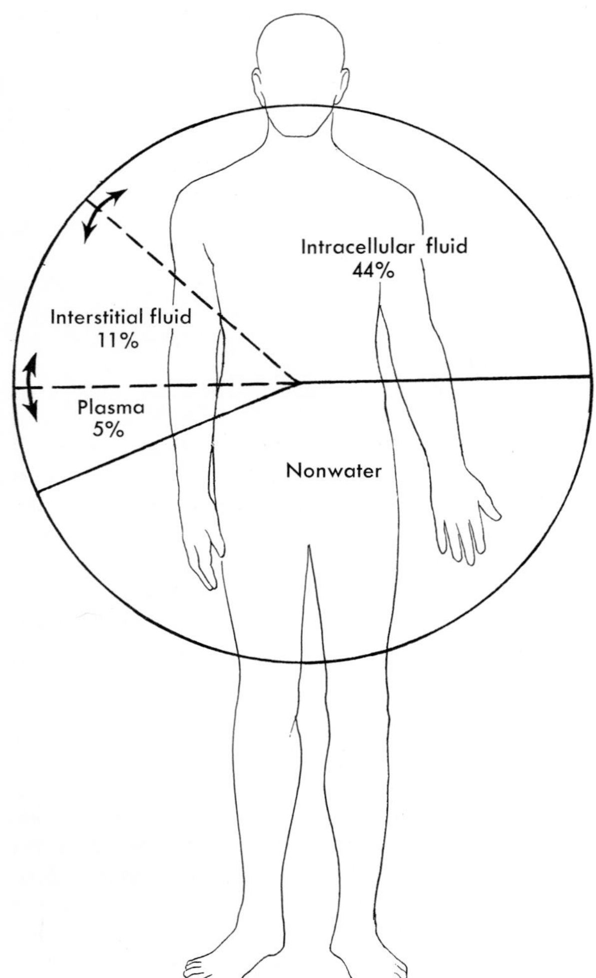

Figure 25–2. Diagram to illustrate fluid balance in the fluid compartments of the body. *Arrows* indicate direction of movement of the fluids. If fluid output exceeds intake, dehydration results.

serum albumin, play a large part in the control; and the large percentage of protein within the cell forms an osmotic relationship which holds water within the cells.

Regulation of Body Water. Controls for total fluid volume are incompletely understood but involve both hormonal and neural regulation.

A decrease in blood volume, such as following hemorrhage, (1) stimulates secretion of aldosterone, which, acting through tubular cells of the kidney, results in increased sodium and water reabsorption, therefore bringing back to normal the total fluid volume; aldosterone also stimulates secretion of ADH; and (2) stimulates the "thirst" center of the hypothalamus, which causes a voluntary increase in water intake, as well as increased secretion of ADH; increased tubular reabsorption of water under stimulus of ADH and increased voluntary water intake effect an increase in total body water.

A decrease in total body water includes decrease of circulating fluid volume. The accompanying decrease in cardiac output and in arterial blood pressure results in decrease in glomerular filtration rate, thus preventing excessive loss of body water. Similarly increase in circulating blood volume and in arterial pressure affects glomerular filtration. Since such large amounts of fluid are filtered normally, only slight increases or decreases of filtration rate effect relatively large changes in urinary output.

Increased osmolality of body fluids as in dehydration and excessive sweating similarly results in compensatory conservation of water through ADH secretion and increased fluid intake through stimulation of the "thirst" center.

The question of *volume receptors* is much debated at present and is still unresolved. It is possible that there are such receptors (still unidentified) in the cardiovascular system which are sensitive to an increase in blood volume.

In severe stress situations, such as burns and hemorrhage, ACTH secretion and its effect on adrenal cortex secretion play an important role in conservation of body fluids.

Fluid Exchange. Under normal conditions fluid enters the body via the mouth. In the stomach, fluid moves from the blood plasma to the cells of the gastric glands for the manufacture of about 1,500 ml of gastric juice in 24 hours. This fluid moves, along with ingested foods and fluids, to the intestine. Here again large quantities of water move from the blood plasma to gland cells for the manufacture of large quantities of digestive fluids, and finally the fluids and end products of digestion are returned to the blood stream. Small amounts of fluid (about 150 to 200 ml) are lost in feces daily. This describes the tremendous exchange of fluids between plasma and secreting cells and back to the plasma again.

The fluid in the plasma compartment also loses water via the lungs, the skin, and the kidneys. During respiration, as blood circulates through the lungs, plasma loses about 350 ml of fluid in 24 hours. Water loss via the skin in the form of perspiration varies; but, under ordinary circumstances, about 600 ml or more is lost as insensible perspiration in 24 hours. Increased amounts are caused by increased temperature or humidity, exercise, nervousness, pain, diaphoretic drugs, nausea, and certain diseases. Sodium chloride is also lost from the body in perspiration. The skin prevents water loss from tissues and capillaries by the protective covering formed by stratified squamous epithelium. Excessive loss of water through perspiration from any cause may deplete the body fluids.

Through the kidney, plasma normally loses about 1,500 ml of water in 24 hours. Since water loss through the kidney is rigorously controlled, urine output varies with fluid intake. The kidney also rigorously regulates the kinds and amounts of substances in solution in the water lost in the form of urine.

Fluid Intake. Fluid intake is in the form of water, other liquids or beverages, and foods. Normally water furnishes about a third or so of the required need, and the rest is furnished by other liquids and foods. Some foods have a much higher water content than do others. Another source of water to the body

FLUID MOVEMENT DURING A 24-HOUR PERIOD
(EXCHANGE AND LOSS)

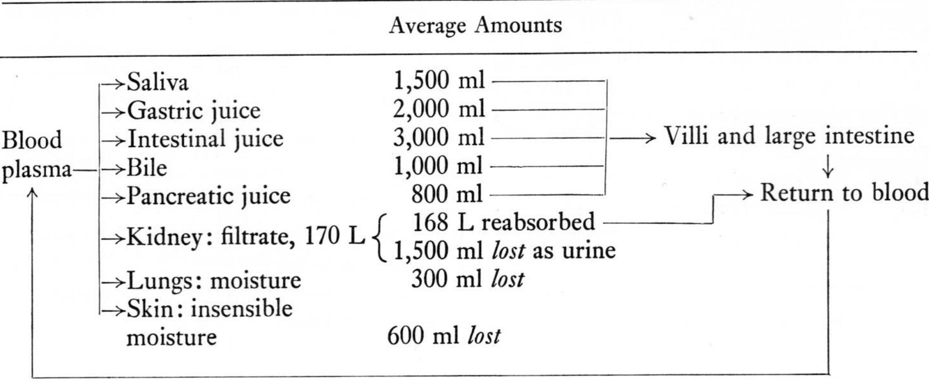

From the above figures it can be seen that the kidney has an important function in maintaining water and electrolyte balance. What is the composition of each of the above fluids?

fluids is the water of metabolism. An ordinary mixed diet yields about 250 ml in 24 hours. On the whole, 100 gm of starch yields 55 gm of water, 100 gm of fat yields 107 gm of water, and 100 gm of protein yields 41 gm of water.

The amount of fluid needed is related to size, weight, and activities of an individual. This means that fluid intake may vary from 1,800 to 3,000 ml in 24 hours.

When excess amounts of fluids are taken by mouth, water is rapidly absorbed into the plasma compartment. If large quantities are taken with no food, absorption is complete in about 30 to 40 minutes. Blood volume may be temporarily increased, as well as cardiac output. However, there is rapid adjustment to the increased water load by the opening of capillary networks to increase the vascular bed; the sinusoids of the liver and spleen open to hold more blood, and fluid is rapidly transferred to the interstitial compartment. The kidneys eliminate excess water and balance is restored within two or three hours.

Fluid Output. Normally fluid output is directly related to fluid intake. Water loss via the kidneys is rigorously controlled and varies from 1,000 to 1,500 ml in 24 hours. As a rule water loss through feces is about 100 to 150 ml. Through insensible perspiration about 450 to 800 or so milliliters of water is lost in 24 hours and via the lungs about 250 to 350 ml. There is a relationship between water loss through kidneys and through the skin. Usually when large quantities of water are lost via the skin, urine volume is decreased.

It is readily understandable that excessive loss of fluid by diarrhea, vomiting, or perspiration, excess loss by the kidneys, loss due to burns, or loss of fluid through hemorrhage causes fluid loss from the plasma and interstitial compartments. Failure to ingest sufficient quantities of fluid may also deplete the fluid in the interstitial compartment, and eventually the plasma compartment may be disturbed.

"Reserve" Body Water. It is useful in considering water balance to think in terms of the individual's water "reserve"—his ability to withstand water loss. That is, should he be faced with a stress such as lack of water for drinking, or unusual loss as in vomiting and diarrhea, or excessive perspiration, how good is his reserve? Obviously the person with the greatest percentage of body water, other things being equal, has the best reserve. Obesity is the commonest cause of decreased body water. The very obese person's body water content may be as little as 25 to 30 per cent of his body weight.

Infants also have poor reserve. Although they have more body water in terms of percentage than most adults, they also lose relatively more in urinary output each 24 hours; thus their reserve is poor. Under normal conditions this large water loss is matched by a large water intake. Stressful situations such as those mentioned above easily cause severe dehydration in infants.

The Electrolytes

Acids, bases, and salts are known as electrolytes because, when in water solution, they conduct an electric current. Such solutions owe their chemical activity to the presence of dissolved ions. In general, the higher the concentration of the ions, the more active the solution. Some electrolytes ionize freely and provide a high concentration of ions; these are known as strong electrolytes. Some electrolytes maintain a reserve of neutral molecules in the solution, consequently, a low ion concentration; these are known as weak electrolytes. Both weak and strong electrolytes are important physiologically.

Within the body, electrolytes (especially sodium, potassium, chloride, and bicarbonate ions) function in various ways to hold fluid within compartments, and to maintain the acid-base relationship essential for enzyme activities. A study of Figure 25–3 illustrates the distribution of various ions within the blood plasma, interstitial fluid, and cells. The concentrations of the various ions are expressed in milliequivalents per liter, the measuring unit which provides a basis for comparing relative concentrations of ions.

To transpose values recorded in milligrams per 100 ml of blood to milliequivalents per liter, it is necessary to know the equivalent weight of the ion. This is obtained by dividing the atomic weight of the element or formula weight by its valence. Thus, for sodium with an atomic weight of 23 and a valence of one, the equivalent weight of the sodium ion is $\frac{23}{1} = 23$. To transpose from milligrams per 100 ml to milliequivalents per liter:

Na^+ 330 mg per 100 ml blood plasma
3,300 mg per 1,000 ml blood plasma (1 liter)

Therefore, $\frac{3,300}{23} = 143$ milliequivalents of Na^+ per liter, expressed 143 mEq/L.

Study of the chart (Figure 25–3) shows that sodium and chloride ions are in higher concentration in plasma and interstitial fluid than in intracellular fluid. Sodium ion concentration, to a large degree, controls the movement of water between cells and the interstitial fluids. Potassium ions are in much higher concentration within cells than in the extracellular fluids. The distribution of negatively charged ions is also of significance. Phosphates, sulfates, and proteinates predominate within cells where their presence is attributed to metabolic activities in the cells. The electrolytes function in the control of osmotic pressures in the various compartments and thereby help to regulate water balance. They help to maintain the acid-base balance essential for normal cell activities. In addition many of these electrolytes have specific functions, which have been discussed in Chapter 21.

The Acid-Base Balance. Within the body as a whole, the balance between acid and alkaline components is maintained within a remarkably constant range. This is strikingly illustrated by the range within blood plasma which normally varies only between pH 7.35 and 7.45, with an average value of pH 7.4. (See Figure 25–4.) Extremes beyond 7.0 and 7.8 are life threatening.

The sources of acids and bases in the body are (1) the cells and (2) the ingestion of food. The cells continuously form carbon dioxide through the metabolism of carbohydrates, fats, and proteins. This forms carbonic acid by combination with water. Lactic acid is a product of carbohydrate metabolism; acetoacetic acid is formed in the liver from fatty acids; the sulfate ion is formed from certain amino acids and is a potential source of sulfuric acid. These substances escape from

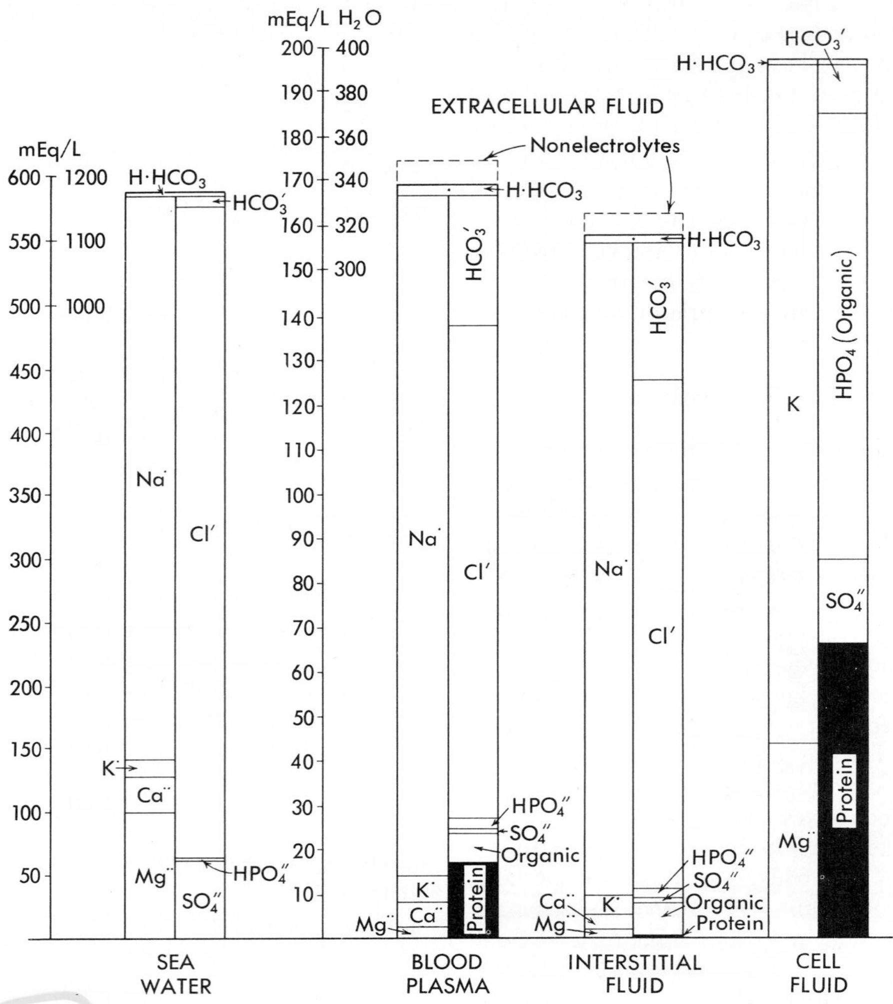

Figure 25–3. Chart illustrating the distribution of electrolytes and nonelectrolytes in the body. It will be noted that blood plasma and interstitial fluid are almost identical. Comparison with sea water is very interesting. (Reprinted by permission of the publishers from James Lawder Gamble, *Chemical Anatomy, Physiology and Pathology of Extracellular Fluid: A Lecture Syllabus.* Cambridge, Mass.: Harvard University Press, Copyright, 1942, 1947, 1954, by The President and Fellows of Harvard College.)

the cells and, when ionized, tend to increase the hydrogen ion concentration of blood and tissue fluids.

Various organic acids enter with the food, for instance, acetic, citric, and tartaric acids. Fatty acids are also absorbed from the intestine as end products of fat digestion. These tend to increase the hydrogen ion concentration of blood. Plant cells contain salts, chiefly potassium salts of weak acids. Sodium salts, such as sodium chloride and sodium bicarbonate, are frequently added to foods during preparation.

The constancy with which the hydrogen ion concentration of blood is regulated is due to three well-integrated mechanisms. These are the presence of buffer systems in extracellular fluids and within cells, the removal of carbon dioxide in the lungs, and renal regulation of the bicarbonate buffer system.

1. The Buffer Systems of the Body. These consist of weak acids accompanied by their sodium or potassium salts. The three important buffer systems are:

In Plasma:	
Carbonic acid / Sodium bicarbonate	H_2CO_3 / $NaHCO_3$
Sodium dihydrogen phosphate / Sodium monohydrogen phosphate	NaH_2PO_4 / Na_2HPO_4
Hydrogen proteinate / Sodium proteinate	

The efficiency of the buffers is determined by the ratio of acid to its salt.

IN CELLS. The same buffers occur but the salts are potassium salts.

A buffer system acts through an exchange of ions which results in reduction of H^+ ion concentration through the formation of molecules of a weaker electrolyte. This may be illustrated by reference to the functioning of the carbonic acid–sodium bicarbonate buffer system.

When any acid stronger than carbonic acid enters the blood, it will be buffered by the reaction with the sodium bicarbonate salt. Hydrogen ions will be removed to form

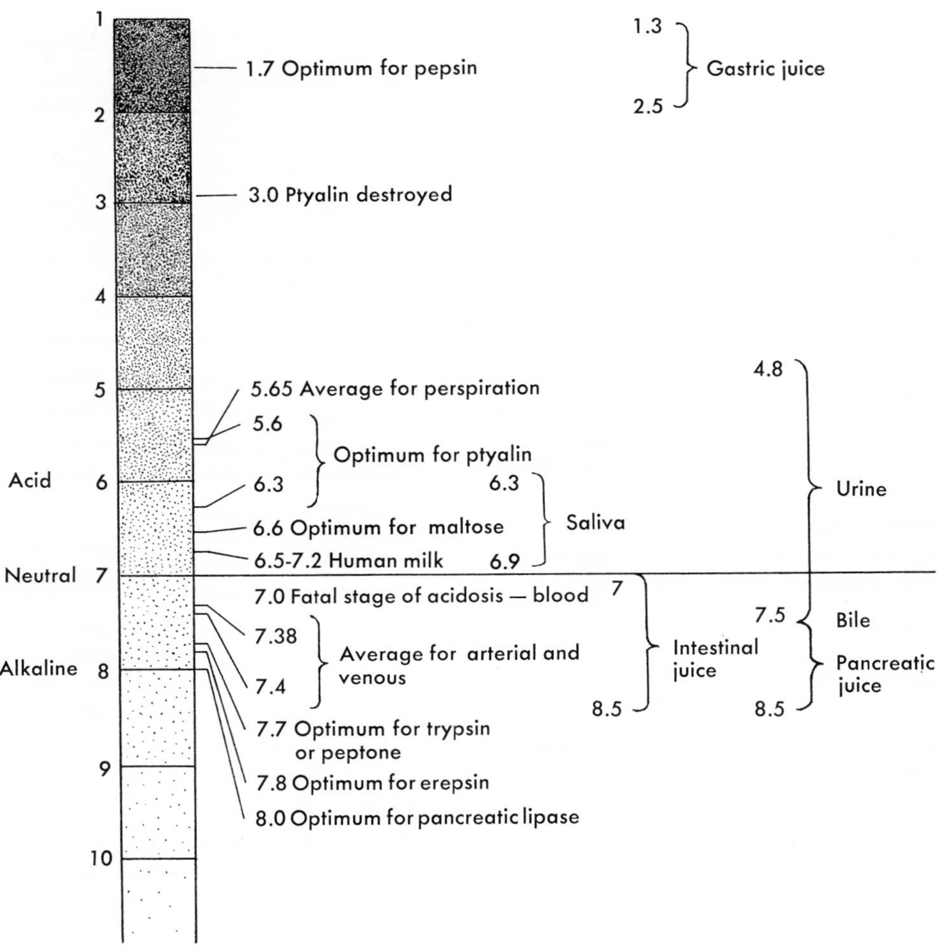

Figure 25-4. The pH scale runs from 1 to 14. In physiology the pH range is comparatively narrow; in tissue fluids it is more restricted. Buffer systems maintain the range optimum for cellular enzyme activity. Figures represent average values.

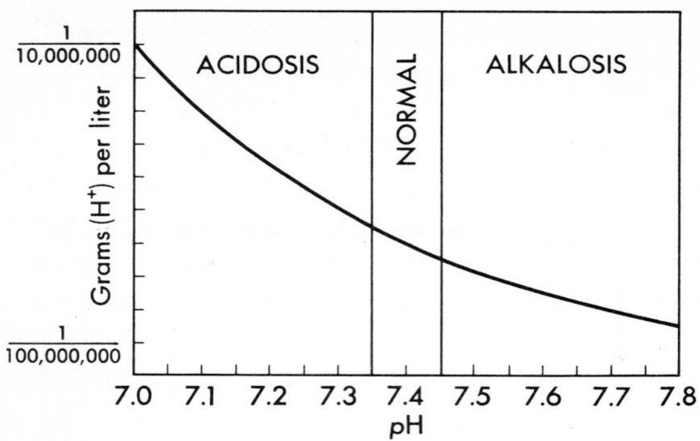

Figure 25–5. Diagram illustrating the range of hydrogen ion concentration compatible with life. It will be noted that the physiological range lies on the alkaline side of neutrality. In health the hydrogen ion range is between pH 7.35 and 7.45. (Reprinted by permission of the publishers from James Lawder Gamble, *Chemical Anatomy, Physiology and Pathology of Extracellular Fluid: A Lecture Syllabus.* Cambridge, Mass.: Harvard University Press, Copyright, 1942, 1947, 1954, by The President and Fellows of Harvard College.)

molecules of carbonic acid and a sodium salt of the stronger acid. For example:

Lactic acid + Sodium bicarbonate →
Sodium lactate + Carbonic acid

The carbonic acid thus formed can be buffered by both the phosphate salt buffers or the protein. In fact, the most important buffer for carbonic acid is the potassium salt of hemoglobin within the erythrocytes. Most of the carbon dioxide which enters the plasma goes into the red blood cells. Part of it then combines with water and forms carbonic acid (page 386), which in turn reacts with the hemoglobin salts to make the hemoglobin acid, a much weaker acid than is carbonic acid. In this way, respiration plays an important role in buffer systems.

Strong bases such as sodium hydroxide and potassium hydroxide are not usual components of food, nor are they products of cell metabolism. Nevertheless, intake of substances that tend to increase the salt of the buffer pair will influence the pH because the relative amount of each salt determines the degree of ionization of its appropriate acid. For example, as the sodium bicarbonate increases, there is less ionization of the carbonic acid and vice versa. The various buffering mechanisms of cells, tissue fluids, and plasma thus serve to maintain the pH within rather narrow limits whether metabolic end products tend to lower or raise the pH.

The bicarbonate buffer system is the most significant aspect of acid-base regulation because the body has efficient means of altering the relative concentrations of carbonic acid and sodium bicarbonate.

2. Respiratory Regulation. The normal ratio of carbonic acid to sodium bicarbonate is 1:20. At this ratio the ionization of carbonic acid is such that the free hydrogen ions are equivalent to a pH of 7.4. When the ratio changes to increase carbonic acid, there is more free hydrogen; when the relative amount of carbonic acid is less, there is less free hydrogen. *Increasing* the hydrogen ion concentration lowers the pH (and increases the acidity); *decreasing* the hydrogen ion raises the pH (increasing the alkalinity, or decreasing the acidity).

From this it is obvious that as respiratory rate and depth increase, more carbon dioxide is lost, thus decreasing carbonic acid concentration in the blood. As respiratory rate and depth decrease, as with shallow breathing, less carbon dioxide is removed, more carbonic acid is retained in the blood, and there is a change in the ratio of carbonic acid to sodium bicarbonate. Since low pH is a stimulus to the respiratory center, it is difficult to alter the pH voluntarily. However, drugs which depress the respiratory center, such as barbiturates, prevent normal removal of carbon dioxide since respirations are shallow and slow and cause a decrease in blood pH. Voluntary hyperventilation has the opposite effect but is self-limiting and is followed by a period of apnea during which the carbon dioxide content (and carbonic acid level) of the blood rise to a normal level. Normal elasticity of lung tissue is a requisite for efficient removal of carbon dioxide from the lungs. Any disease which decreases this elasticity results in retention of carbon dioxide and of carbonic acid, thus causing acidosis—a lower than normal pH.

3. Renal Regulation of pH. In the tubular cells of the kidney, as carbon dioxide is formed during cell activity in the citric acid cycle, it combines with water under the influence of carbonic anhydrase as in other cells, and carbonic acid is formed. Hydrogen ions from this acid are secreted into the filtrate in exchange for a sodium ion. The secreted hydrogen ion replaces the sodium in the phosphate molecule and is lost in the urine. If the sodium were combined in sodium bicarbonate, the resulting H_2CO_3 in the filtrate is not all lost in the urine, for carbonic acid breaks down to CO_2 and water, and the carbon dioxide diffuses back into the tubular cell and is returned to the capillaries as bicarbonate ion or sodium bicarbonate.

Secretion of ammonia is a second means the tubular cell uses to regulate pH. When the acidity of body fluids is low, glutamine is metabolized, from which NH_3 results. When ammonia is secreted into the filtrate, again a sodium ion is returned to the tubular cell and blood stream. Ammonia secretion does not occur when body fluids are not acidic.

Secretion of hydrogen ions and of ammonia in exchange for sodium in the filtrate results in return of sodium bicarbonate to the blood, thus tending to increase the bicarbonate fraction of the carbonic acid: sodium bicarbonate buffer pair.

CONSERVATION OF SODIUM BY THE KIDNEY

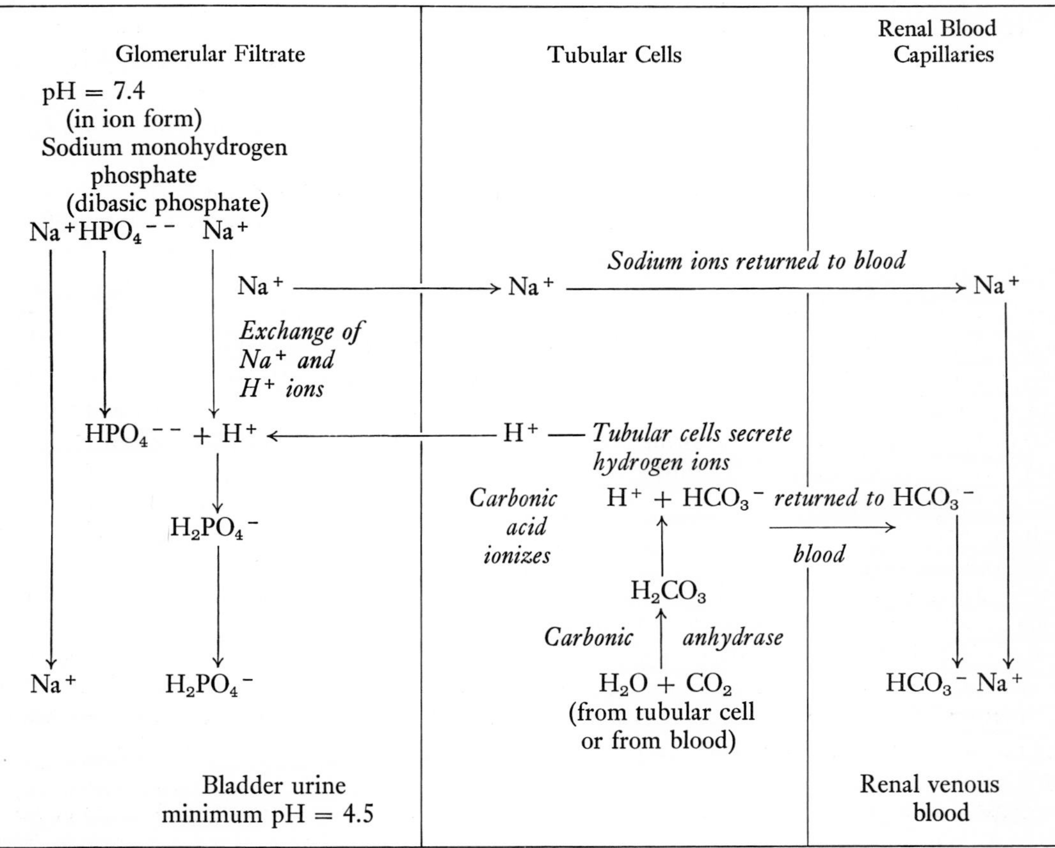

Modified from Davenport.

FORMATION OF AMMONIA BY THE KIDNEY

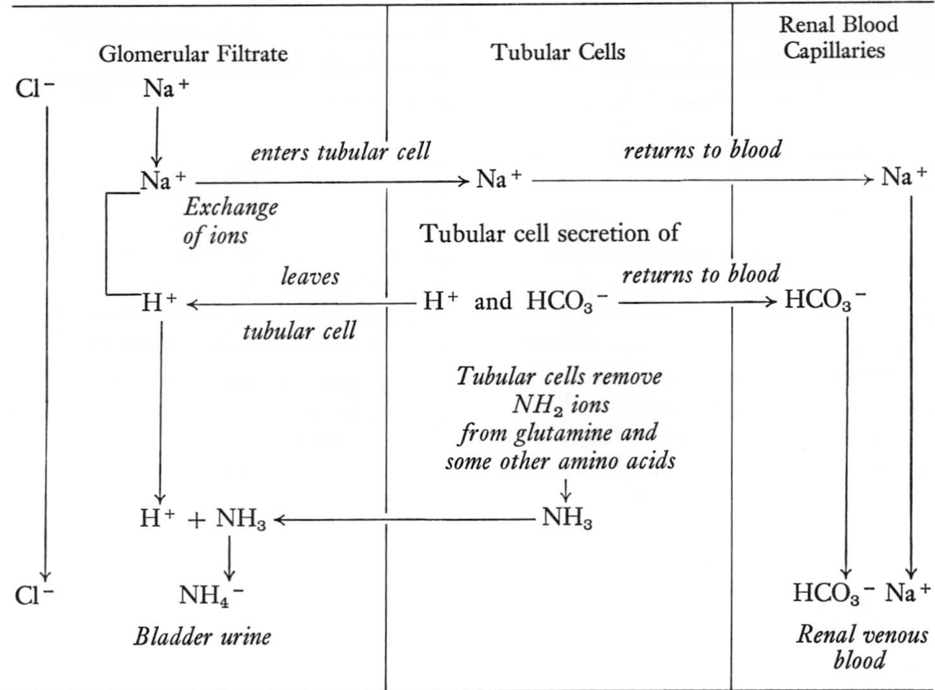

Modified from Davenport.

In spite of the remarkable adjustments thus made among the electrolytes, if abnormal demands are made on the system, disturbance of the acid-base balance does occur and acidosis or an alkalosis may result, although blood pH in these conditions is still alkaline, i.e., above 7.0.

In *acidosis* the lower-than-normal blood pH may be of metabolic or respiratory origin. Respiratory acidosis results from inadequate removal of carbon dioxide from the body, thus preventing the usual regulation of carbonic acid level and altering the 1:20 ratio. Metabolic acidosis (see Figure 25–6) results from production of substances which are acidic and "tie up" temporarily sodium ions so that the net effect is to lower the sodium bicarbonate portion of the 1:20 ratio. Such substances are produced in excessive fat oxidation, as in starvation or diabetes mellitus. Another means of decreasing sodium bicarbonate is the loss from the body of positively charged ions, potassium and sodium both, as occurs in diarrhea.

Alkalosis is present when the pH of body fluids is higher than normal, and less free hydrogen ion is present in the blood stream. Voluntary hyperventilation has already been mentioned as a possible cause. Others include excessive vomiting, with loss of hydrogen ion in the hydrochloric acid of the gastric juice, gastric drainage, which has a similar effect, and excessive ingestion of sodium bicarbonate as a medicament.

Acidosis and alkalosis occur only when the compensatory mechanisms of the body have been exhausted, or when they are incompetent from disease processes involving the lung and kidney. Compensatory mechanisms in acidosis include hyperventilation, and renal excretion of hydrogen and ammonia with reabsorption of sodium ions. The urine may be more acid than normal (pH 5.5 to 7.5) depending on the amount of ammonium

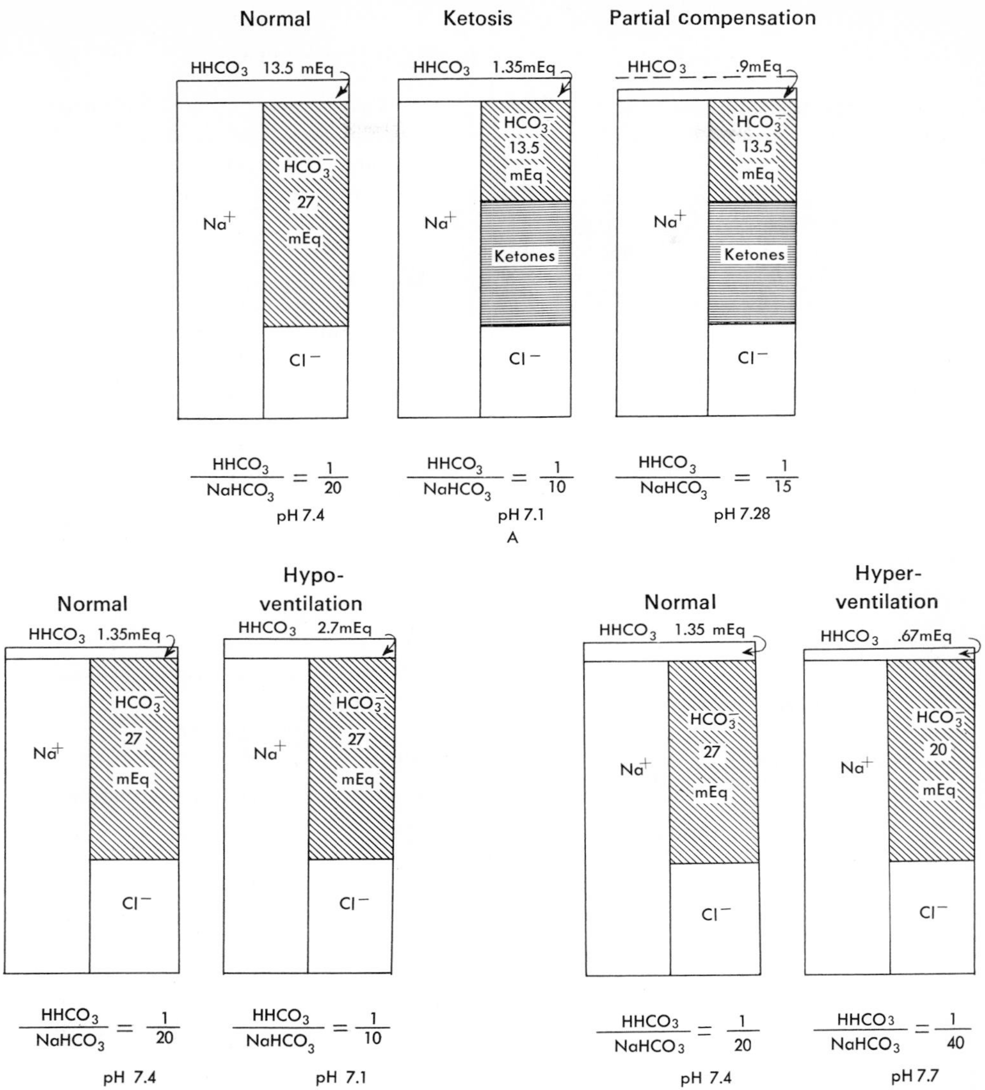

Figure 25–6. *A.* Diagram illustrating metabolic acidosis with partial compensation. Note the decrease in bicarbonates and the increase of ketones. Compare with *B* below.

B. Comparison of the ratios of carbonic acid and bicarbonate in respiratory acidosis. Compare with *C* below.

C. Figure to illustrate the ratios of carbonic acid and bicarbonate in the development of respiratory alkalosis caused by hyperventilation.

salts present. In alkalosis the kidney does not secrete hydrogen ions, permits sodium to be lost, and ventilation is shallow. By these means the blood pH is kept within its narrow range, in spite of varying dietary pattern and cellular activity.

QUESTIONS FOR DISCUSSION

1. An adult female was admitted to the hospital with a history of vomiting for two days. Urine output was scant. The doctor's orders included nothing by mouth and 3,000 ml of physiological saline with 5 per cent glucose, to be given within the first 18 hours, measure and record intake and output of all fluids.
   a. What electrolytes were being lost by vomiting?
   b. What is the usual amount of gastric juice formed each 24 hours?
   c. Would there be a tendency for this patient to develop acidosis or alkalosis? Explain.
   d. Why was the urine output decreased in amount? Explain in detail.
   e. Discuss why sodium chloride and glucose solution was ordered.
   f. What is meant by acid-base balance?
   g. What are the fluid compartments of the body? What factors hold fluid in each compartment?
2. When an individual perspires profusely (e.g., during a baseball game on a hot day), how is total body fluid kept within normal limits?
3. Which organs and hormones are essential for maintaining the constancy of body fluids in relation to electrolytes?
4. When faced with acute lack of water, which would suffer most: the mother, the father, or a six-month-old infant? Which least? Explain.
5. When an individual takes one large teaspoonful of bicarbonate of soda in water for indigestion, what happens to the blood pH?

SUMMARY

Water Balance	**Distribution of water in the body**	1. Blood plasma 5% of body weight 2. Interstitial fluid 11% of body weight 3. Intracellular fluid 44% of body weight
	Movement of water	Water and solutes move freely between compartments
	Water intake, 1,800 to 3,000 ml in 24 hours	Water Other fluids Foods Water metabolism 300–350 ml in 24 hours
	Water output	Feces 100 to 150 ml Skin 450 to 800 ml Lungs 250 to 350 ml Urine 1,000 to 1,500 ml
	Adjustment to excess fluid intake	Fluid rapidly absorbed into blood stream Blood volume may be temporarily increased Cardiac output may be increased Capillary networks open, vascular bed increased Sinusoids of liver and spleen hold more blood Fluid rapidly transferred to interstitial compartment Kidney eliminates excess water and balance is restored in several hours
	Regulation by hormones	ADH regulates water reabsorption in the kidney tubule Aldosterone of the adrenal cortex regulates Na^+–K^+ ratio in plasma and their elimination by the kidney, thus aiding in the regulation of water balance
	Stress situations	ACTH and the adrenal-cortex hormones respond to stress situations and play a large role in maintaining homeostasis of the body fluids
	Reserve body water	Ability of individual to withstand water loss from any cause Person with greatest percentage of body water has best reserve Obesity reduces water reserve Infants have poor reserve

- **Electrolyte Balance**
  - An electrolyte may be an acid, base, or salt which, in solution, has the power to conduct an electric current. Some are chemically more active than others
  - **Distribution**
    - In extracellular fluids
      - Chiefly Na^+, Cl^-, HCO_3^-; small quantities of K^+, Ca^{++}, HPO_4^{--}, SO_4^{--}, Mg^+
    - Intracellular fluids
      - Chiefly K^+, Mg^{++}, HPO_4^{--}; small quantities of SO_4^{--}, HCO_3^-, Na^+
  - **Milliequivalents**
    - Concentrations expressed in terms of milliequivalents
      - Shows relative magnitudes and interrelationships
  - Important cations—
    - Na^+ 142 mEq/L
    - Ca^{++} 5 mEq/L
    - Mg^{++} 3 mEq/L
    - K^+ 5 mEq/L
  - Important anions—
    - Cl^- 103 mEq/L
    - HCO_3^- 27 mEq/L
    - HPO_4^{--} 2 mEq/L
    - SO_4^{--} 1 mEq/L
    - Organic acids 6 mEq/L
    - Protein 16 mEq/L
- **Electrolyte Regulation**
  - Electrolyte concentrations controlled most effectively by the kidneys and by elimination of carbon dioxide in the lungs
- **Acid-Base Balance**
  - Normal pH range: 7.35–7.45
  - Depends on degree of hydrogen ion concentration, which is determined by carbonic acid:sodium bicarbonate ratio of 1:20
  - **Buffering**
    - Potassium salts buffer within the cells
    - Sodium salts buffer in the extracellular fluids
    - Cell proteins, especially hemoglobin, are effective buffers
    - Buffering is accomplished through exchange of ions
    - Acids react with buffer salts to form weaker acids
    - Bases react with buffer acids to form water and salts
  - **pH regulated by**
    1. Secretion of acid urine, removing hydrogen ions
    2. Production of ammonia in kidney cells with conservation of sodium ions in blood
    3. Elimination of carbonic acid in lungs
  - **Sources of acid and base**
    1. The cell. Products of metabolism of
       - Carbohydrates
       - Fats
       - Proteins
       - → Carbon dioxide and water, lactic acid, acetoacetic acid, and from protein, sulfate and phosphate ions
    2. From foods. The average diet provides various acids and salts of organic acids
       - Ions
         - Citrate
         - Lactate
         - Acetate
         - Fatty acid
       - Potassium salts
       - Sodium bicarbonate
  - **Acidosis, alkalosis**
    - Pathological conditions when compensatory mechanisms are inadequate

UNIT VII
Structural and Functional Relationships for Human Reproduction and Development

Human sexual functions have as a goal reproduction of the individuals involved, and additionally a larger goal—reproduction of the human species. The male is responsible for sex determination; the female is responsible for nourishment of the fertilized ovum following conception and during gestation. Male and female together contribute inherited traits and characteristics determined by the chromosomes in the sperm and ovum. During the gestational period cell division and differentiation result in formation of distinctly different tissues and organs typical of the human. Thus characteristics of one individual are transmitted from generation to generation.

CHAPTER

26

MALE AND FEMALE ORGANS OF REPRODUCTION

Structure and Function

HORMONAL CONTROLS MENSTRUATION

Sex cells, or *gametes*, grow and develop within the ovaries and testes. These organs are especially adapted for the maturation of spermatozoa in the male and ova in the female. Gonadal, hypophyseal, and thyroid hormones are essential influences in all aspects of reproduction. Once the ovum has been fertilized by a spermatozoon, it travels to the uterus, where it implants. Slowly and intricately the *zygote* develops into an *embryo* and then a *fetus* and finally enters the external world, takes its first breath of air, and becomes a newborn baby.

MATURATION OF THE REPRODUCTIVE ORGANS

Although the sex of the embryo is determined at the time of fertilization, the reproductive organs do not acquire their morphological characteristics until the end of the second month of embryological development. Functional maturity is attained at the time of puberty. *Puberty* may be defined as the period when the gonads or sex glands attain normal adult function. In temperate climates, the age at which boys usually attain puberty is between 14 and 16 years; in girls, puberty is signaled by the beginning of the menses and occurs between the ages of 11 and 14. In warmer climates, puberty often occurs earlier, and in the Arctic regions, one or two years later. However, the time of puberty varies from individual to individual. Psychological factors producing stress at the time of puberty may cause physiological changes that induce early puberty or impede its progress. It is believed that increased secretion of gonadotropic hormones several years before the onset of puberty brings about gonadal maturation.

The onset of puberty is signaled in the male by production of functional spermatozoa and in the female by the beginning of ovulation and menstruation. At birth, the testes contain thousands of immature spermatocytes and the ovaries contain thousands of partially developed germ cells, but these cells do not mature until the onset of puberty. Puberty is also marked by the gradual appearance of the secondary sex characteristics induced by the increasing amounts of circulating sex hormones in the body. In the male, increased secretion of testosterone by the testes causes the increased development of skeletal muscle, enlargement of the external genitalia, and hair growth in the axillae and on the face, pubes, and to a varying degree on the extremities. The male larynx increases in size and accentuates the prominence called the "Adam's apple." The vocal folds thicken, and the male voice becomes lower. The girl undergoes a gradual change of figure; the pelvis widens, and fat deposits increase around the hips, thighs, and buttocks. Hair grows on the pubes and in the axillae. Subcutaneous fat deposition increases in the breasts. The menstrual cycle is initiated, and rhythmical changes begin to occur in the ovaries, uterus, and vagina. Increased production of estrogens and progesterone by the ovaries and their feedback effects upon pituitary gonadotropic secretion bring about these changes in the female figure and reproductive organs.

These secondary sex alterations begin at puberty and continue to develop over a number of years. This period is known as *adolescence*, and it extends from puberty until the age of 17 to 20 years in the female and until the age of 18 to 21 years in the male. At the age of 20 to 21, in the average man and woman the rapid increase in height characteristic of adolescence comes to an end owing to the closure of the epiphyseal bone plates. The complete development of all secondary characteristics has also been achieved.

MALE ORGANS OF REPRODUCTION

The male reproductive organs include two *testes* that produce spermatozoa and testosterone and the following bilateral accessory organs: the *seminal vesicles*, *seminal ducts* (vas or ductus deferens), *ejaculatory ducts*, *epididymides* (singular *epididymis*), *bulbourethral* (Cowper's[1]) *glands*, as well as the following single structures: the *prostate gland*, the *penis*, the *urethra*, and the *scrotum*.

[1] William Cowper, English anatomist (1666–1709).

The Testes. The testes are two glandular organs suspended from the inguinal region by the *spermatic cord*. The *spermatic cord* is made up of sheets of fascia derived from the abdominal muscles and contains the ductus or vas deferens, spermatic artery and veins,

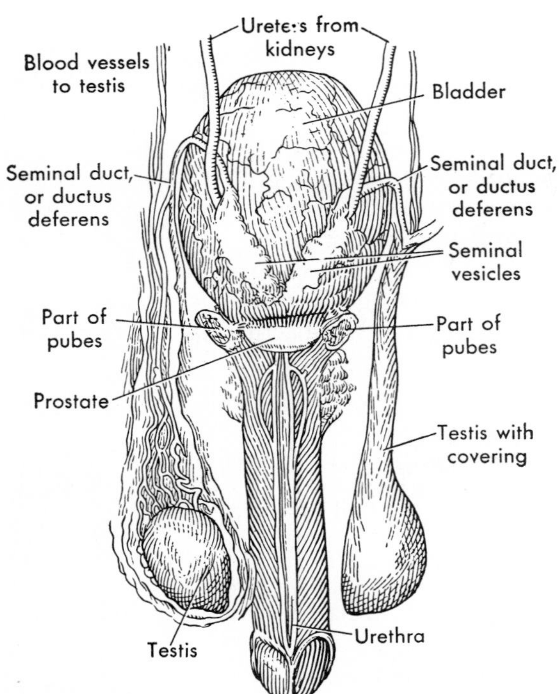

Figure 26–1. Male reproductive organs, dorsal view.

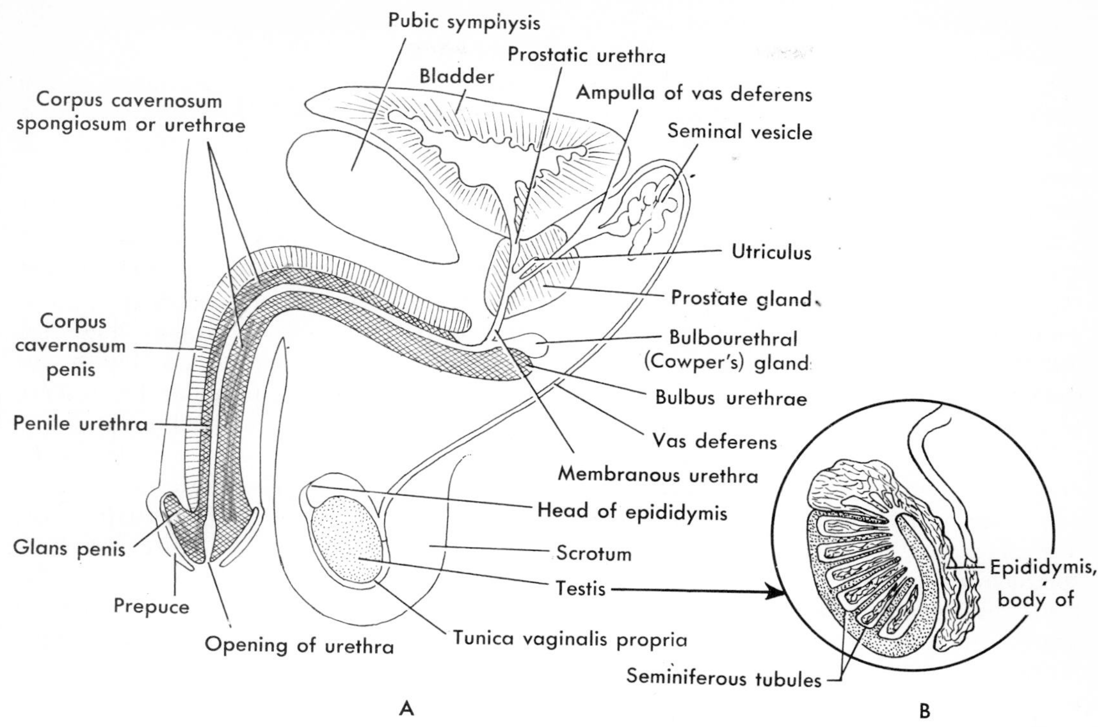

Figure 26–2. (*A*) Diagram of midsagittal section of male reproductive organs to show glands, ducts, and corpora cavernosa. (*B*) Detail of testis structure.

lymph vessels, and autonomic nerve fibers. It is formed just above the internal inguinal ring and passes through the inguinal canal into the scrotum. Each testis is about the shape and size of a small egg and is attached to an overlying structure called the epididymis. It is covered by fibrous tissue which sends incomplete partitions into the central portion of the gland, dividing it into communicating cavities. In these cavities are winding seminiferous tubules surrounded by blood vessels and supported by interstitial tissue. The *seminiferous tubules* provide for production of spermatozoa, and the interstitial or Leydig cells produce testosterone. These tubules intertwine and join together in a meshwork of exiting small ducts called the rete testis and finally all unite in the epididymis.

The *epididymides* are long bilateral narrow bodies that lie upon the superior portions of the testes and are composed of 15 to 20 tortuous tubules which eventually open into a single convoluted tubule. These tubules contain smooth muscle cells in their walls and are lined with mucous membrane. They connect the testes with the seminal ducts and serve as areas for final maturation of the spermatozoa.

Descent of the Testes. The testes are formed and develop in the abdomen slightly inferior to the kidneys but within the peritoneal cavity. During growth and development of the fetus, they migrate downward and through the inguinal canal into the scrotum. Shortly before birth or soon afterward, the testes are found in the scrotum. Sometimes, particularly in premature infants a testis has not descended and is found in the inguinal canal or even in the abdominal cavity. As a rule, it soon descends, but if it does not, the condition is referred to as *cryptorchidism* and may be either unilateral or bilateral. If the testis remains inside the abdomen after puberty, spermatogenesis is depressed owing to the slightly higher intra-abdominal temperature, and eventually it ceases altogether. It can be treated successfully prior to puberty by a simple surgical procedure.

The Scrotum. The scrotum is a thin pouch of skin, muscles, and fascia that contains and supports the testes, the epididymides, and parts of the spermatic cords. The smooth-muscle layer of the scrotum that is covered by a thin layer of skin disposed in folds or rugae is called the *dartos muscle*. It contracts reflexly with the cord to raise the testes closer to body warmth. The tissues of the scrotum are continuous with those of the groin and perineum.

The Seminal Ducts (Vas Deferens or Ductus Deferens). The seminal ducts, which are bilateral continuations of the epididymides, are important storage sites for spermatozoa and are the excretory ducts of the testes. Each duct conveys the spermatozoa along a devious course, from the scrotum through the layers of the inguinal ligament known as the inguinal canal into the pelvic cavity, where eventually the duct joins with the duct of a seminal vesicle to form an ejaculatory duct.

The Seminal Vesicles. These are two membranous pouches located posterior to the bladder, between this organ and the rectum. Recently it has been shown that the seminal vesicles produce secretions containing fructose, amino acids, mucus, and small amounts of some vitamins. During ejaculation, these substances are added to the semen at the time spermatozoa are transported to the ejaculatory ducts from the vas deferens. The fructose and other substances contained in the seminal fluid provide nutrients and protection for the spermatozoa. All the various secretions added to the semen increase its bulk.

The Ejaculatory Ducts. These are narrow bilateral passageways less than an inch long formed by the union of the seminal vesicles with the vas deferens. They descend between the lobes of the prostate gland to the urethra, into which they open and discharge their contents.

The Prostate Gland. The prostate gland is situated immediately inferior to the bladder and internal urethral orifice. It surrounds the first portion of the urethra, referred to as the *prostatic urethra*, and is comparable to a chestnut in shape, size, and consistency. The prostate is covered by a dense fibrous capsule and consists of glandular units surrounded by fibromuscular tissue that contracts only during ejaculation. The glandular tissue consists of tubules which communicate with the urethra by minute orifices. The function of the prostate gland is to secrete a thin, milky alkaline fluid that enhances spermatic motility. Fluid in the vas deferens is quite acidic owing to the presence of the metabolic end products of the stored sperm. The secretions of the female vagina are also quite acidic. Therefore, it is probable that alkaline prostatic fluid neutralizes the acidity of the semen and vaginal secretions and thereby greatly increases the motility and fertility of the spermatozoa. Seminal fluid also contains prostaglandins, which have little, if any, effect on the sperm, but do influence the tone and contractility of the uterus and fallopian tubes.

Age Changes in the Prostate. The prostate enlarges during adolescence along with the other reproductive organs owing to the effect of androgens secreted by the interstitial cells of the testes. It attains full size during the twenties. In older age, for reasons not yet understood, frequently the prostate increases in size so that two out of every three men reaching the age of 70 suffer from some degree of obstruction to urination. This can be serious because of the obstructive effect on ureteral pressure.

The Bulbourethral Glands (Cowper's Glands). These are two small bodies about the size of peas situated on either side of the membranous portion of the urethra a little inferior to the prostate gland. Each small gland is provided with a short duct which empties its mucous secretion, a viscid alkaline fluid, into the urethra. The secretion of these glands precedes ejaculation and adds lubricating and protective mucus to the semen.

The Semen. The semen is the fluid that is ejaculated during the male sexual act. It is composed of the combined fluids from the testes, epididymides, seminal vesicles, prostate gland, and bulbourethral glands—a grayish-white viscid liquid that contains carbohydrates, mucin, proteins, salts, and about 100,000,000 spermatozoa per milliliter. At each ejaculation, 2 to 5 ml of semen are usually expressed through the urethra. *Ejaculation*, or the discharge of semen to the exterior, is initiated by peristaltic waves

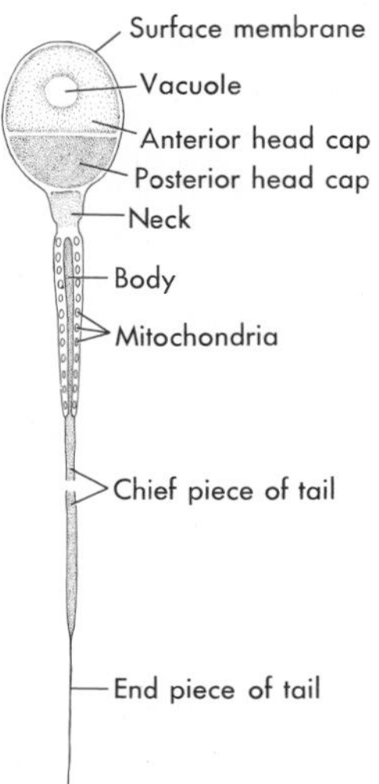

Figure 26–3. Diagram of spermatozoon.

moving along the tubes leading from the testes and by rhythmical contractions of the smooth muscle layers of the testes, epididymides, seminal vesicles, and prostate gland. Increased pressure upon all these structures causes expulsion of the semen. The bulbourethral glands discharge additional quantities of mucus into the urethra at this time. The process to this point is called *emission* and is brought about by rhythmical sympathetic impulses which leave the spinal cord at L_1 and L_2 and then pass through the hypogastric plexus to the genital organs. Ejaculation proper is brought about by contraction of the skeletal muscles that encase the base of the erectile tissue of the penis and that are innervated by fibers traveling in the pudendal nerves. In some stages of sexual life, especially during the teens, the male may have nocturnal emissions during dreams.

The Penis. The penis, or organ of copulation of the male, is a short, cylindrical, pendulous body that is suspended from the front and sides of the pubic arch. It is composed of three cylindrical masses of cavernous erectile tissue bound together by fibrous strands and covered with skin. The lateral two masses are known as the *corpora cavernosa penis*. The third, known as the *corpus cavernosum urethrae* or *spongiosum*, makes up the ventral surface and contains the urethra. The term *cavernous* is used because of the relatively large venous spaces present within its structure. It is also described as erectile tissue because the venous spaces may become distended with blood during sexual excitement, and the penis then becomes firm and erect. *Erection* is the first effect of male sexual stimulation, and it is brought about by parasympathetic impulses that pass from the sacral portion of the spinal cord via the *nervi erigentes* (pelvic splanchnic nerves) to the penis. These impulses cause dilatation of the penile arteries which results in compression of the exiting veins. Increased blood supply that is under high pressure and unable to leave the area results in filling of the venous spaces and erection of the organ.

At the end of the penis there is a slight enlargement known as the *glans penis* that contains the external urethral orifice (meatus) and the sensory end organs that are stimulated during sexual intercourse. These end organs convey impulses to the spinal cord via the pudendal nerves. Their endings synapse on the sacral preganglionic cell bodies of the parasympathetic nervous system to produce erection and upon preganglionic cell bodies of the sympathetic nervous system to produce emission of the semen. The loose integument of the penis forms the *prepuce*, or *foreskin*. Sometimes the foreskin may cover the glans too tightly causing restricted circulation to the area and collection of the sebaceous secretion, called *smegma*, which provides a good environment for microbial multiplication and inflammation. Constriction of the foreskin is known as *phimosis* and is often prevented and treated by the operation known as *circumcision*, surgical removal of the foreskin.

The *male urethra* is an S-shaped tube lined with mucous membrane, about 17.5 cm long, extending from the internal to the external urethral orifice. It serves at separate times as conveyor of both urine and semen to the exterior. There are three parts: the *prostatic*, the *membranous*, and the *cavernous*, or *penile*.

Blood Supply to the Pelvis. When the descending aorta reaches the body of the fourth lumbar vertebra, it divides into the two *common iliac* arteries. These arteries pass downward and outward for about 5 cm (2 in.), and then each divides into the hypogastric, or internal, and external iliac arteries.

The internal iliac arteries send branches to the pelvic walls, pelvic viscera, the external genitalia, the buttocks, and the medial side of each thigh.

The external iliacs are larger than the internal iliacs and extend from the bifurcation of the common iliacs to a point halfway between the anterior superior spines of the ilia and the symphysis pubis. They enter the thigh and become the femoral arteries.

The external iliacs send small branches to the psoas major muscles and to the neighboring lymph nodes, and each gives off the *inferior epigastric* and the *deep iliac circumflex*. These arteries are of considerable size and distribute branches to the abdominal muscles and peritoneum, also to the region of the pubes. The external spermatic arteries branch from the inferior epigastric arteries.

The internal spermatic arteries arise from the front of the aorta, a little below the renal arteries. They supply the testes (Figure 15–10, page 306).

The veins of the pelvis correspond to the arteries with one exception. The right spermatic vein empties into the inferior vena cava; the left, into the left renal vein.

Spermatogenesis. Beginning at about the age of 12, spermatozoa begin to be produced in the seminiferous tubules of the testis of the male under the influence of the pituitary gonadotropic hormones. Spermatogenesis, or the production and maturation of sperm, continues throughout adult life. Germ cells called spermatogonia, formed during fetal life, now begin to proliferate and differentiate through definite stages to form spermatozoa. As these cells divide, increase in number, and move toward the center of the tubule, they become *primary spermatocytes*. Primary spermatocytes then go through a meiotic, or reduction, division, consisting of two maturation divisions, during which the number of chromosomes of the developing cells is halved from 46, the diploid number, to 23, the haploid number. The process and significance of meiosis are discussed in detail in the following chapter. Each primary spermatocyte divides into two *secondary spermatocytes*, each of which contains 23 double chromosomes. The secondary spermatocytes each divide again to form two *spermatids* with 23 single chromosomes contained within each one. In summary, then, from every primary spermatocyte, four spermatids are derived. The process of meiosis apportions the sex chromosomes so that each spermatozoon receives one. One half of the spermatozoa carry the X chromosome, and one half carry the Y chromosome. The sex of the fertilized ovum is determined by the sex chromosome contributed by the spermatozoon because all ova normally contain one X chromosome. When a spermatozoon enters an ovum at fertilization, the original complement of 46 chromosomes is re-established.

The *spermatid* develops into a *spermatozoon* when a tail or flagellum is formed, and the cytoplasm has contracted around the cell nucleus to form the head. Between the head and the tail, the neck and the body are found. The body contains many mitochondria that produce large amounts of adenosine triphosphate. ATP provides energy for movement of the flagellum. A small sac at the tip of the head bursts on contact with the ovum, extruding the enzyme hyaluronidase. This enzyme is thought to facilitate penetration of the ovum by the sperm.

Two other factors besides the gonadotropins, FSH and LH (called ICSH in the male), seem necessary for normal spermatogenesis to take place. The first factor is the presence of *Sertoli*, or *sustentacular*, *cells*, which line the basement membrane of the seminiferous tubules. They contain considerable amounts of glycogen in their cytoplasm and in some way are thought to serve as nutrient cells for the germinal epithelium during the formation of spermatozoa from spermatids. The second factor is the production of adequate amounts of *testosterone*. Under the influence of LH (ICSH) *testosterone* is secreted by the interstitial Leydig cells of the testis. These cells are found interspersed in groups between the seminiferous tubules. The specific role of this androgen in spermatogenesis is not clear, but without normal adult levels of this hormone, adequate formation of spermatozoa cannot take place.

Spermatozoa are formed at the edge of the lumen of the seminiferous tubules and reach the epididymis via a series of excretory ducts called the *tubili recti*, the *rete testes*, and the *efferent ductules*. They are conveyed by the motion of ciliated epithelium, for at this stage of their development they are nonmotile. Sperm most probably mature within the epididymis, since after they have remained there for one-half day or more, they have developed the power of motility and the capability of fertilizing the ovum. They are stored in the seminal ducts, where they remain dormant within the acid medium resulting from their own metabolism. Viable sperm may be stored in the epididymis and vas deferens for as long as six weeks, but once ejaculated to the exterior, they survive at normal body temperature for only 48 to 72 hours.

Male Fertility. Approximately 100 million spermatozoa are contained in each milliliter of ejaculated semen. These are highly uniform in size and shape, with occasional sperm having two heads or two tails or being otherwise abnormal. When the percentage of abnormal spermatozoa is greater than 25 percent, or the sperm count is less than 35 million per milliliter the fertility is greatly decreased. Even though only one spermatozoon fertilizes each ovum, a large number of normal ones is necessary to ensure fertilization.

Male Climacteric. Sexual function usually does not significantly decline at a particular period in the life of the male as it does in the female. If and when testosterone production by testicular Leydig cells does decrease, symptoms may appear that are similar to those observed in menopausal women.

FEMALE ORGANS OF REPRODUCTION

The female organs of reproduction include the bilateral *ovaries*, the bilateral *uterine* (*fallopian*) *tubes*, or *oviducts*, the *uterus*, the *vagina*, and the *external genitalia*.

The Ovaries. The ovaries produce the ova and the sex hormones, progesterone and estrogens. Each ovary is a slightly flattened, almond-shaped body measuring from 1.5 to 3 cm in width and about 8 mm in depth. One is located on each side of the pelvis, lateral to the uterus, inferior to the uterine tube, and attached to the posterior surface of the broad ligament. The *broad ligament* is a reflection of the peritoneum that supports the uterus and extends from each side of the uterus laterally to the pelvic wall. Each ovary is attached to the lateral angle of the uterus by a short *ovarian ligament*, a fibrous cord within the broad ligament, and to the tubal end of the uterine tube by the largest of the fringelike processes of the tubal fimbriated extremity, the ovarial fimbria.

The Uterine (Fallopian) Tubes, or Oviducts. These are bilateral muscular ducts, lined with mucosa containing ciliated epithelium, that pass from the upper angles of the uterus in a somewhat tortuous course between the folds and along the superior margin of the broad ligament toward the sides of the pelvis. They are about 4 in. long, and the margin of the dilated end, or ampulla, is surrounded by a number of fringelike processes called *fimbriae*.

The functions of the uterine tubes are to convey the ova from the ovaries to the uterus, to aid in the upward passage of the spermatozoa, and to provide circular folds within which the ovum is nourished and delayed for fertilization. The sequestration of the fertilized ovum within these tubes allows adequate

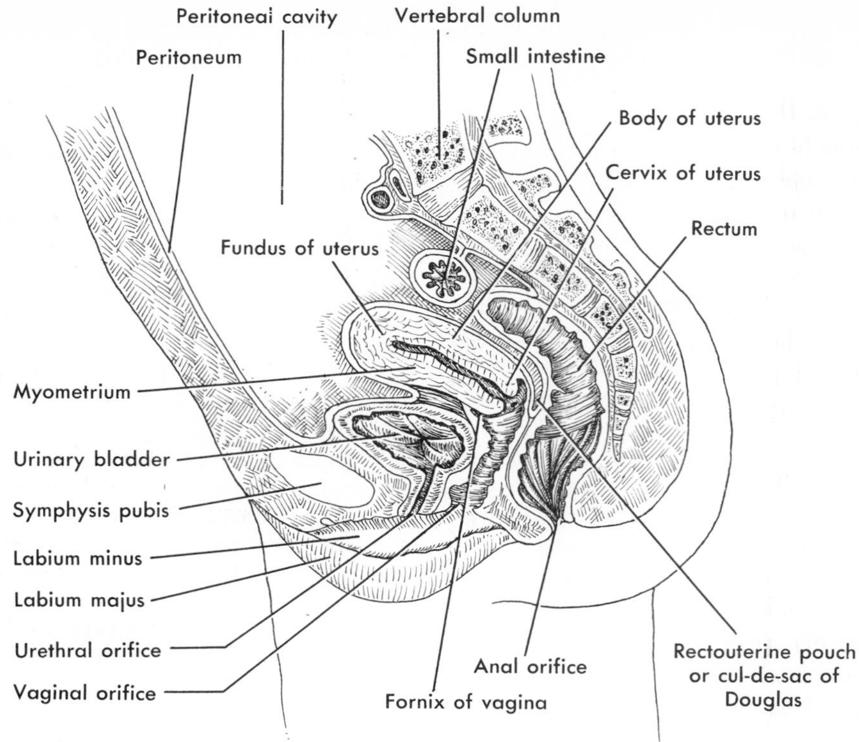

Figure 26–4. Median sagittal section of female pelvis.

time to elapse between fertilization and implantation so that the uterine wall will be properly prepared for growth and development of the embryo.

The Uterus, or Womb. The uterus is a hollow, thick-walled, pear-shaped muscular organ about 3 in. long, situated in the pelvic cavity between the rectum and the bladder. Three parts of the uterus can be distinguished: (1) the *body*, or *corpus uteri*, with its superior expanded portion called the *fundus* extending above the entrance of the uterine tubes; (2) the *isthmus*, or middle, slightly constricted portion; and (3) the cervix, or cylindrical lower part, that surrounds the *cervical canal* and projects into the vagina. The short (2.5-cm) cervical canal extends from the *internal orifice*, or *os*, of the uterus to the *external os* at the termination of the cervix.

The cavity of the uterus is small because of the thickness of its walls. The part of the cavity within the body is triangular and has three openings, one very small one at each upper angle communicating with the fallopian tubes, and the third, the *internal os*, opening into the cervical canal. The uterus is the organ of the reproductive tract in which the embryo grows and develops until the time of delivery.

Structure of the Uterus. The walls of the uterus are thick and consist of three layers:

1. The External, or Serous, Layer. This is derived from the peritoneum and covers the superior part of the uterus. It adheres intimately to the outer surface of the fundus and surfaces of the uterine body and is reflected from the body to the bladder as the *vesicouterine* pouch. Posteriorly it may descend as far as the upper part of the vagina before reflection to the rectum as the *rectouterine pouch* (*cul-de-sac* of Douglas). Laterally it becomes the broad ligament.

2. The Middle, or Muscular, Layer. This is about 2 cm thick, forms the bulk of the uterine wall, and is called the

myometrium. It consists of three ill-defined layers of smooth muscle disposed longitudinally, circularly, and spirally. Peristaltic-like movements of the muscles are thought to be increased around the time of ovulation. It is believed that these contractions assist the ascension of spermatozoa by the suction they produce within the organ. The larger blood vessels are found deep within the myometrium.

3. THE INNER, OR MUCOUS, LAYER. Called the *endometrium,* this layer is continuous with the mucous membrane that lines the vagina and uterine tubes. The endometrium is highly vascular and is provided with numerous uterine glands. It is lined with ciliated and secretory epithelium, except for the lower third of the cervical canal, where it gradually changes to stratified squamous epithelium similar to that lining the vagina. In the sexually mature, nonpregnant female, the uterine mucosa is subject to cyclical menstrual changes that are influenced by ovarian hormonal secretions. Three phases of activity can be identified in the endometrial cycle: (1) the follicular, or growth, phase, which makes up the first half and is concurrent with the developing graafian follicle; (2) the lutein, or secretory, phase, which is associated with the actively secreting corpus luteum and endometrial glands; and (3) the menstrual, or sloughing-off, stage, which is associated with involution of the corpus luteum and the extravasation and expulsion of the necrotic mucosa into the vagina.

The *blood supply of the uterus* is abundant and reaches it by means of the *uterine arteries*, branches from the internal iliac (hypogastric) arteries, and the *ovarian arteries*, which are branches from the abdominal aorta. The arteries are remarkable for their tortuous course and frequency of anastomoses. The veins are large and correspond to the arteries in size and frequency of anastomoses. The uterine veins empty into the internal iliac (hypogastric) veins. The right ovarian vein empties into the inferior vena cava but the left one empties into the left renal vein.

Position of the Uterus. The uterus is not firmly attached or adherent to any part of the skeleton. It is suspended in the pelvic cavity by fibrous cords and folds of peritoneum called *ligaments.* Normally the fundus is inclined forward, and the general line of the uterus is almost at right angles to that of the vagina. A full bladder tilts it backward, and a full rectum pushes it forward. During gestation the uterus becomes enormously enlarged and extends into the epigastric region of the abdominal cavity.

If the uterus becomes fixed or rests habitually in a position beyond the limits of normal variation, it is said to be displaced. *Retroversion* signifies a backward turning of the whole uterus without a change in the relationship of the body to the cervix. *Retroflexion* signifies a bending backward of the body on the cervix at the level of the internal os. *Anteversion* means a forward turning of the whole uterus, and *anteflexion*, a forward bend of the body at the isthmus which brings the fundus under the symphysis pubis.

Ligaments. (See Figure 26–5.) The main support of the uterus is supplied by the *levator ani* and *coccygeus muscles*. Several fibrous cords covered with mesothelium and peritoneal folds, all called *ligaments,* assist in holding the internal reproductive organs in normal position and in anchoring them to the wall and floor of the pelvis. The ligaments of the uterus are two *broad ligaments*, two *round ligaments*, two *cardinal ligaments*, two *uterosacral*, and one *anterior* and one *posterior ligament*. The *broad ligaments* are the largest and the most important, and they provide the reproductive organs with the greatest support. They are wide peritoneal folds that are slung over the anterior and posterior surfaces of the uterus, ovaries, and uterine tubes, and extend laterally to the walls of the pelvis. Other important structures found between the layers of the broad ligaments are the ligaments of the ovary, nerves, blood vessels, and lymphatics and the cardinal and round ligaments. The part of the broad ligament containing the ovarian vessels is called the *suspensory ligament of the ovary. The round ligaments* are flattened fibrous cords that extend from the lateral borders of the uterus within the broad ligaments to the connective

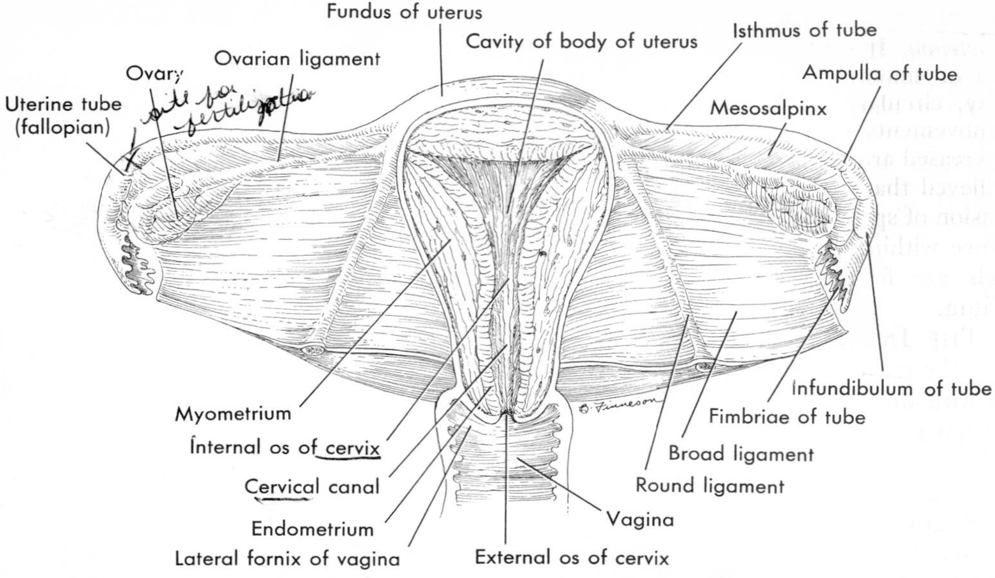

Figure 26–5. Uterus in section showing relation to ovary, uterine tube, and ligaments. Anterior view. (Modified from Pansky and House.)

tissue and skin of the labia majora via the inguinal canals of their respective sides. They help to hold the fundus forward in a slightly anteflexed position. The *uterosacral ligaments* are peritoneal folds that pass from the cervix to the sacrum, one extending on each side of the rectum. The *cardinal*, or *Mackenrodt's*, *ligaments* are less important supporting structures of the uterus. They are enveloping bands of fascia that surround the uterine blood vessels as they pass to the vagina and cervix from the lateral pelvis. Folds of peritoneum that contribute little or no support to the pelvic viscera, but which are frequently included in the list of ligaments, are the *anterior* and *posterior ligaments*. The sheath of peritoneum that extends from the urinary bladder to the anterior surface of the uterus is called the *anterior ligament*. The *posterior ligament* is the reflection of the peritoneum from the anterior surface of the rectum upon the posterior surface of the uterus and vagina. The *cul-de-cac*, or *pouch of Douglas*, is the deep recess formed by this peritoneal reflection between the uterus and the rectum.

The Vagina. The vagina is a fibromuscular tube, 7.5 to 10 cm in length, situated anterior to the rectum and anal canal and posterior to the bladder and urethra. It is parallel to the direction of the urethra; that is to say, it is directed upward and backward. It is the organ of copulation, for the deposition of semen in the female, and during parturition it serves as the exit from the uterus. The cervix projects into the vault of the vagina, and the vaginal recesses are formed around it. These recesses are known as the *anterior*, *posterior*, and *lateral fornices* (singular, *fornix*).

The vaginal wall consists of fascial, muscular, and mucous coats. The mucous coat is composed of stratified squamous epithelium with glycogen stored within its cells. Estrogen secretion during the menstrual cycle and pregnancy seems to cause an increase in glycogen stores and keratinization of the surface epithelium. The inner surface of mucous membrane is thrown into two longitudinal folds and transverse folds, or rugae. The circular and longitudinal smooth-muscle layers hypertrophy during pregnancy, and these layers, together with the rugae of the mucous coat and the interstitial elastic connective tissue, allow for extreme distensibility of the canal during parturition.

The vagina normally has a pH of between 4 and 6. This acidic environment impedes the growth of microorganisms and thus functions to prevent infection of the pelvic organs. The mucus that lubricates the vagina originates from the glands of the cervix. This mucus is acidified by the fermenting action of the vaginal bacteria, mainly lactobacilli, upon the glycogen from the vaginal epithelium. Striated muscle fibers form a ring-shaped sphincter around the introitus, or external orifice of the vagina. This opening may be partially occluded in the virgin by a fold of mucous membrane containing squamous epithelium with a thin connective tissue core called the *hymen.*

Vaginal Cells. The cells found in the vaginal secretion may be studied microscopically to determine hormonal balance of the individual, since there is a cyclic change during the menstrual cycle, and to identify cancerous cells. These vaginal cells are derived from the endometrium, the inner and outer surfaces of the cervix, and the lining of the vagina.

The External Female Genitalia. The external organs, often grouped together under the name of *vulva*, include the *mons pubis*, the *labia majora*, the *labia minora*, the *clitoris*, the *vestibule of the vagina*, and the *greater vestibular glands* (Bartholin's glands). These are shown in Figure 26-6.

The mons pubis is a pad of fat making up an eminence situated anterior to the symphysis pubis. After puberty it is covered with hair.

The labia majora are two prominent longitudinal folds which begin at the mons pubis anteriorly and extend posteriorly to within 1 in. of the anus. The labia majora are homologues of the scrotum in the male and, like the scrotum, contain large sebaceous glands and become pigmented after puberty. They protect the perineum and help to maintain its secretions. Within their substance lie the terminations of the round ligaments.

The labia minora are two thin longitudinal folds of skin bordering the vestibule of the vagina. They are situated between the labia majora, are united anteriorly in the hood or prepuce of the clitoris, and form the boundaries of the vestibule, which is the area between them.

The clitoris is a small protuberance more or less hidden by the folds of skin called the

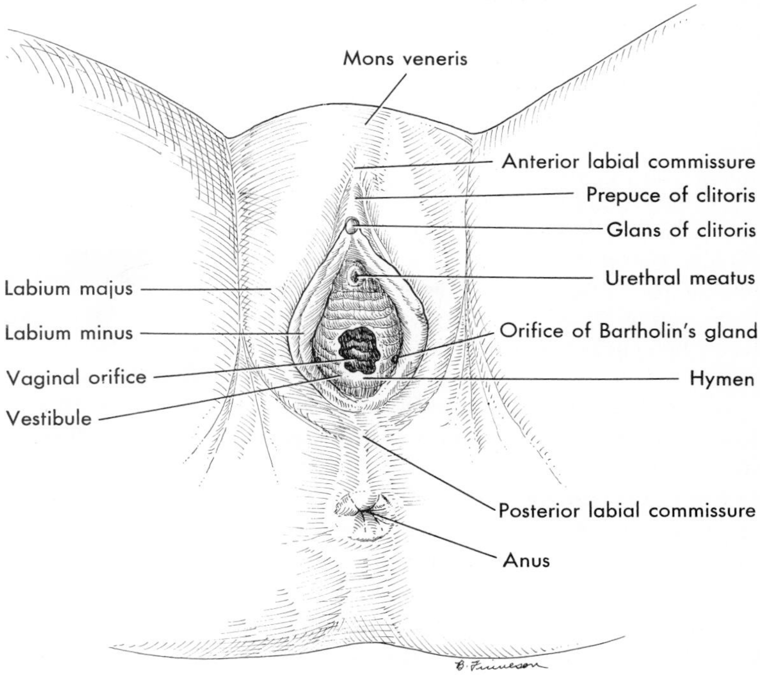

Figure 26-6. External female genitalia.

prepuce, situated at the apex of the triangle formed by the junction of the labia minora. It is the homologue of the penis in the male and, like it, contains erectile tissue, venous cavernous spaces, and specialized sensory corpuscles that are stimulated during coitus.

The vestibule of the vagina is the area situated posterior to the clitoris and between the labia minora. The urethra opens into this space anteriorly, and the vagina opens into it posteriorly. Several glands open into the floor of the vestibule.

Bartholin's glands, or the *greater vestibular glands*, open on either side of the vaginal orifice. These glands together with the smaller lesser vestibular glands and paraurethral glands have a moistening function and are of clinical diagnostic importance because they may become infected with microorganisms, particularly the gonococcus, which causes the venereal disease known as gonorrhea.

The Perineum. The perineum is the external surface of the floor of the pelvis, extending from the pubic arch to the coccyx and including the underlying muscles and fascia. In the female it is perforated by the vagina as well as by the urethra and anus. A wedge-shaped upward extension of the perineum, forming a septum between the vagina and rectum, is called the perineal body.

The perineum is distensible and is stretched to a remarkable degree during parturition. Nevertheless, it may be lacerated during delivery and, if not surgically repaired, may cause weakening of the muscular and fascial supports of the pelvic floor. Without adequate support the bladder may prolapse with the anterior vaginal wall to form a hernia known as a *cystocele*. The herniation of the bowel through prolapse of the posterior vaginal wall is known as a *rectocele*.

Blood Supply. Arteries and veins of the female pelvis are similar to those in the male (page 550).

The ovarian arteries in the female arise from the same portion of the aorta as the spermatic arteries in the male. They supply the ovaries and send small branches to the ureters and uterine tubes. One branch unites with the uterine artery (a branch of the hypogastric) and assists in supplying the uterus. During pregnancy the ovarian arteries become considerably enlarged. The right ovarian vein empties into the inferior vena cava, and the left into the left renal vein.

The uterine arteries have been described on page 553.

Histology of the Ovary. The ovaries embryologically are derived from the bilateral germinal ridges located in close proximity to the kidneys on the posterior wall of the abdominal cavity. The ovaries move into the pelvis during fetal life but descend a shorter distance than do the testes.

The peripheral layer, or cortex, of the ovary is covered by germinal epithelium which is derived from the epithelium of the germinal ridges. The primordial ova are believed to be differentiated from the germinal epithelium during fetal life, undergo mitosis, and migrate, together with surrounding epithelioid granulosa cells, into the ovarian cortex. There they make up the approximately 2 million primary oocytes that are present in the two ovaries at birth. During the sexual life of the female only about 400 of these follicles become mature, and the rest regress in size throughout life. At menopause they are hard to find and only the scars remain. The medulla or central part of the ovary consists of loose connective tissue that contains a large number of blood vessels.

The Menstrual Cycle. At the time of puberty the ovaries enlarge and become very vascular, and the normal sex life of the female, characterized by cyclical hormonal, ovarian, uterine, and vaginal changes, begins. This cycle is regulated by hormonal feedback and averages 28 days, although its length may vary greatly from one individual to another.

The adenohypophysis begins secreting more and more hormones beginning at the age of about seven years until the beginning of adult sexual life at puberty. At this time *follicle-stimulating hormones* (FSH) from the anterior pituitary begins to be secreted in large quantity. This causes growth and development of the *primordial follicle* and of its surrounding layer of cells, the *theca interna*, which then begins to produce increasing amounts of *estrogens*. FSH causes the ovum to enlarge with concurrent development of follicular fluid encompassing it. Several follicles begin to develop under this stimulation, but normally only one fully matures while the theca interna produces estrogens. *Estrogenic hormones* cause increased development of the inner lining of the uterus, the endometrium, and increases its vascularity and glandular secretions. This stage continues over approximately one half of the menstrual cycle and is often referred to as the *estrogenic*, *follicular*, or *proliferative phase*. As the blood level of estrogens rises, this has a feedback effect on the adenohypophysis by stimulating the secretion of *luteinizing hormone* (LH). This hormone, together with luteotropic or lactogenic hormone (LTH) also secreted by the adenohypophysis, seems to be necessary for final follicular growth and for ovulation. Secretion of FSH, LH, and LTH is regulated by hypothalamic factors (page 489). No matter how long the menstrual cycle, ovulation is believed to occur between the thirteenth and fifteenth day before the beginning of menstrual bleeding.

Ovulation can be defined as the extrusion of the ovum surrounded by a mass of granulosa cells, into the peritoneal cavity. As the fluid content of the follicular antrum increases, the blood supply is decreased, and it is perhaps, although by no means certain, for this reason that the follicle ruptures and releases the ovum. In its mature state the follicle is known as the *graafian follicle* and is about 10 to 12 mm in diameter.

At birth the primordial follicles are already formed and the *primary oocytes* have begun the first maturation division of meiosis. They then enter a resting stage until puberty, at which time approximately 500,000 primary oocytes remain. Under the influence of FSH, during the first portion of the menstrual cycle, the *primary oocyte* finishes its first maturation division which was started a long time previously during prenatal life, and a thick membrane, the *zona pellucida*, develops around it. From the first meiotic division two daughter cells of unequal size, each with 23 double chromosomes, are formed. The larger of the two cells is known as the *secondary oocyte*, and the second, much smaller cell, containing very little cytoplasm, is called *the first polar body*. The secondary oocyte then begins a second maturation division. A *mature ovum* containing 23 single chromosomes and another polar body result from this division. The secondary oocyte is extruded from the ovary before the second maturation division is completed. This division may never be terminated unless fertilization takes place. The first polar body may or may not undergo a second division. Three or four polar bodies may be formed during the two maturation divisions, but they are reabsorbed and do not serve any

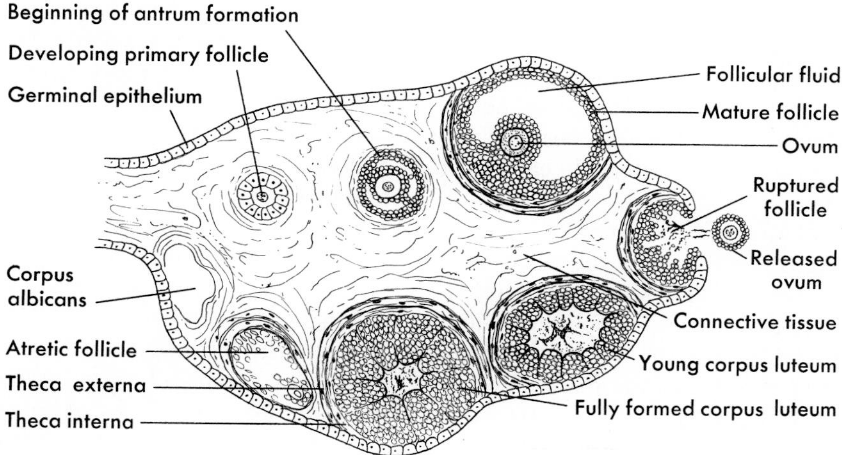

Figure 26–7. Microscopic view of the ovary showing ovum in various stages of maturation.

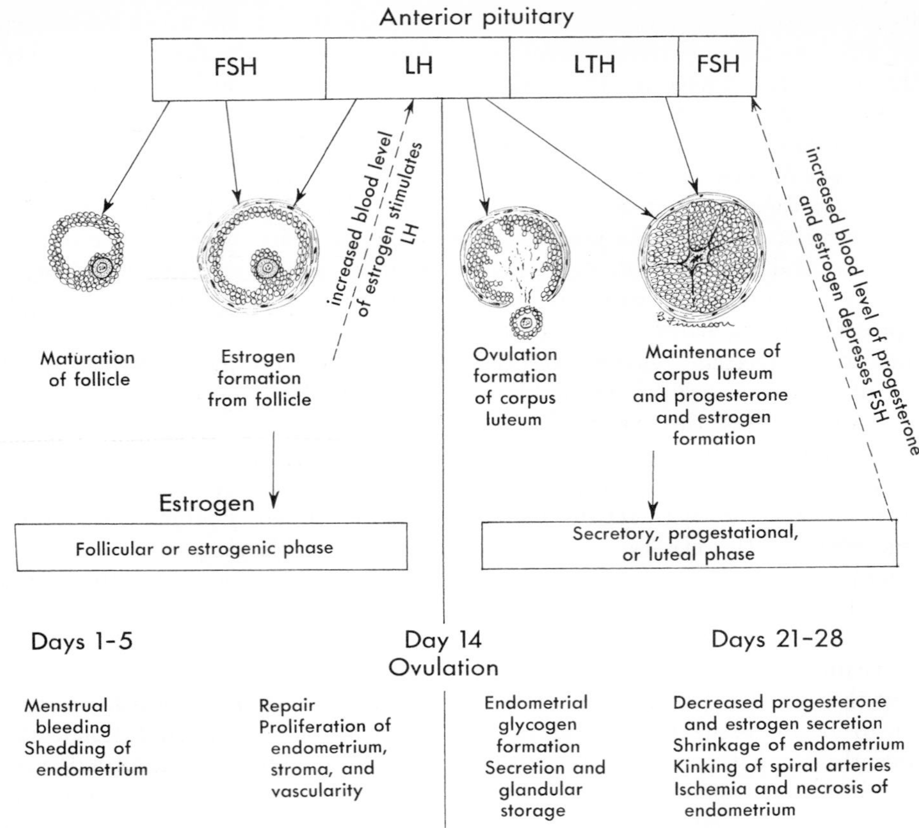

Figure 26–8. Summary of hormonal effects upon the ovary and uterus.

reproductive function. (See Figure 27–1, page 568.) The mature ovum is globular, almost 0.2 mm in diameter. It is much larger than the spermatozoon, whose elliptical head is only about 0.003 mm long and whose tail measures about 0.06 mm in length, or one half the diameter of the human ovum. If it is not fertilized within approximately 24 hours, it is no longer viable and is usually reabsorbed from the peritoneal cavity or genital tract.

After ovulation the remaining granulosa and theca cells of the follicle and the cells of the theca interna undergo a process of luteinization, or cellular accumulation of yellow, lipid inclusions. Under the continued stimulation of LH and LTH the mass of lutein cells becomes the *corpus luteum*, a secretory organ producing a large quantity of progesterone and, to a lesser degree, some estrogens. This phase of the menstrual cycle, usually comprising the 13 to 15 days before the commencement of menstrual bleeding, is most commonly referred to as the *progestational*, or *secretory*, stage.

The function of *progesterone* secreted under the influence of LH and LTH is to increase the secretory function of the endometrium, and to bring about the formation of glycogen and lipid stores within its structure. It also inhibits contractility of the uterine smooth-muscle layers, the myometrium, thereby preventing expulsion of the embryo. In these ways progesterone functions to prepare the uterus for the implantation, early growth, and development of the fertilized ovum or zygote. High blood levels of progesterone also prepare the breasts for lactation, inhibit the secretion of FSH, and therefore inhibit the development of other follicles, while there is feasibility of fertilization of the extruded ovum.

The increasing production of progesterone toward the end of the cycle has a feedback inhibitory effect on the anterior pituitary production of LH and perhaps upon the production of LTH. This causes the corpus luteum to involute and become a *corpus albicans,* or scar, and results in decreasing production of progesterone and estrogens. About two days before the end of the cycle the ovarian hormone secretion decreases sharply to low levels and *menstruation* ensues. Inadequate amounts of ovarian hormones probably are the cause of vasospasm of blood vessels to the mucosal layers of the endometrium, and necrosis, or death, of the inner layers of endometrium. The dead tissues and released blood initiate uterine contractions which expel the sloughed-off uterine contents. Approximately 40 ml of blood and about the same amount of serous fluid are lost during menstruation. Small amounts of *fibrinolysin* released from the desquamated tissues prevent clotting of this blood and fluid. Menstruation usually ceases after four to six days and the endometrium becomes completely re-epithelialized. FSH secretion, no longer inhibited by progesterone and estrogens at this time, resumes in increasingly larger amounts, the endometrium proliferates, another follicle begins to mature, and a new menstrual cycle has begun.

If fertilization of the ovum occurs, menstruation does not take place. The fertilized ovum completes its second maturation division, and male and female pronuclei unite, forming a zygote which implants within the uterus after about a week following fertilization. The developing placenta secretes a hormone called *chorionic gonadotropin* which has much the same function as the pituitary hormones, LH and LTH. It prevents the involution of the corpus luteum at the end of the menstrual cycle, causing it to enlarge considerably and to continue to secrete large amounts of progesterone and estrogens. Desquamation of the endometrium, or menstruation, is thus prevented if pregnancy occurs.

Summary of Hormonal Changes and Influences During the Menstrual Cycle

1. The anterior pituitary begins the secretion of *FSH* during the time of menstrual flow. This causes follicles to grow and develop in the ovary. At the end of about two weeks *one follicle* reaches maturity. Under the influence of FSH the *theca interna* begins to secrete gradually increasing amounts of *estrogens.* This is often referred to as the *estrogenic* or *proliferative phase of the cycle* and it lasts, usually, about two weeks.

2. The estrogens aid in the repair and proliferation of the endometrium of the uterus. They cause an increased thickening, keratinization, and glycogen storage of the vaginal epithelium and also probably aid *libido.* The rising blood levels of estrogens stimulate the secretion of *LH* toward the end of the two-week period.

3. LH in some way helps to cause ovulation or rupture of the mature follicle and release of the ovum about 13 to 15 days

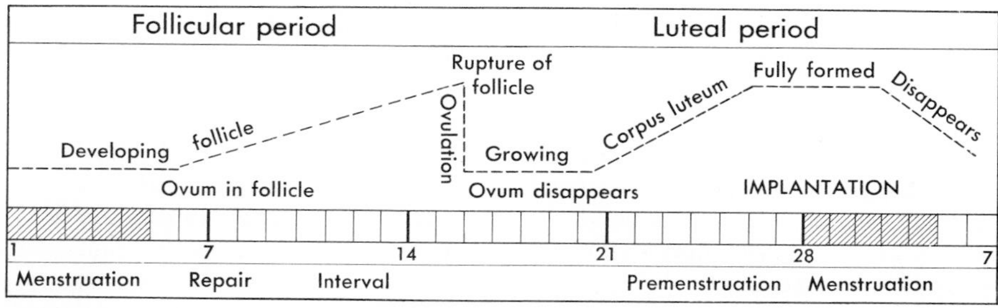

Figure 26–9. Diagram to show sequence of events in ovary and in uterus in human menstrual cycle. (Modified from Corner.)

before the beginning of the next menstrual flow. Together with *LTH*, now also released from the anterior pituitary, it causes the remains of the ruptured follicle to be transformed into an endocrine gland known as a *corpus luteum* that secretes increasingly large amounts of *progesterone* and some *estrogens* during the second, *progestational* or *secretory*, phase of the cycle.

4. *Progesterone* has a secretory effect on the uterine endometrium. That is to say, it causes increased secretions and a nutrient storage within the uterine mucosa in preparation for the reception and nourishment of a fertilized ovum. It also appears to have a quieting effect upon uterine musculature which favors implantation of the embryo. As the level of *progesterone increases* toward the end of the cycle, it appears to have a feedback effect upon the anterior pituitary by causing it to secrete *less* and *less LH* and *LTH*. When the production of LH and LTH is thus inhibited, the *corpus luteum involutes* and ceases to secrete progesterone.

5. *Menstruation* is believed to be caused by the resulting low levels of progesterone and estrogens. Lack of sufficient amounts of estrogens is thought to cause vasospasm of the spiral arteries to the endometrium. This results in inadequate nutrition of the superficial layers of endometrium, which then become necrotic and slough off.

6. The *decreased* blood level of *progesterone* is no longer sufficient to *inhibit* the anterior pituitary production of *FSH*; so it is *again secreted* and the cycle resumes.

7. If *fertilization* and *implantation* occur, the *corpus luteum persists* and continues to secrete large amounts of *estrogens* and *progesterone* under the stimulating influence of *chorionic gonadotropin* produced by the developing placenta.

Parturition takes place, normally, at about 280 days from the beginning of the last menstrual period and results in the birth of the child. At the time of labor and delivery intense rhythmical contractions of the myometrium, probably under the influence of the posterior pituitary hormone, *oxytocin*, result in cervical effacement and dilatation and, in combination with maternal efforts, expulsion of the fetus through the vaginal canal.

Involution is the process of rapid decrease in the size of the uterus. It is brought about by a gradual autolysis, or "self-digestion," of the uterine wall and requires approximately six weeks. During this time the uterus resumes its normal nonpregnant position in the pelvic cavity and approximately its original size.

Menopause. The menopause, or female climacteric, is the period during which there is a physiological cessation of the menstrual flow, the termination of development of the follicles in the ovaries, a decrease in estrogen production, and consequently the end of the childbearing period. It is usually marked by atrophy of the breasts, uterus, uterine tubes, and ovaries. The onset of menopause usually occurs somewhere between the ages of 45 and 50 and may or may not be indicated by a number of troublesome symptoms that include insomnia, irregular menstruation with its eventual cessation, nervous irritability, palpitations, increased sweating, periods of depression, and intolerance to heat. The exact cause of these symptoms has been ill-defined, although they presumably follow the reduction of blood and tissue levels of estrogens. It is probable that the estrogen deficiency itself is not the sole cause of emotional disturbances that may become evident at this time, but rather that the events associated with the climacteric amplify or bring about latent potentialities.

Other menopausal problems resulting from estrogen deficiency may include obesity, believed to result from decreasing caloric expenditure, and *osteoporosis*, due to decreasing protein anabolism, causing a loss of protein matrix particularly of the vertebral column with resultant softening and decalcification.

Female Fertility. The ovum is capable of being fertilized for only a short period, probably about 24 hours. Sperm can remain viable up to about 72 hours; therefore, the period of possible conception is only a few days, if the time of ovulation is known. Ovulation is thought to occur 14 days prior to menstruation, whether the menstrual cycle is 28 days or longer or shorter, and is accompanied by a sharp rise of about a half degree in temperature (F). The most common cause of sterility in women is the failure to ovulate. This may be diagnosed by tests for presence of progesterone breakdown products in the urine, and by physical examination of the

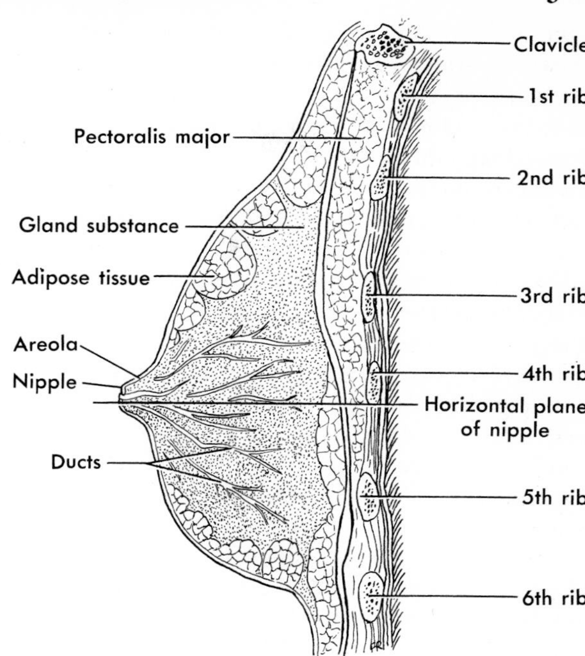

Figure 26–10. Right breast in sagittal section, inner surface of outer segment.

uterine lining, cervix, and vaginal epithelium for lack of progesterone effect.

Mammary Glands. The two mammary glands, or breasts, are structurally and developmentally closely related to the integument but function as accessory organs of the reproductive system since they secrete milk for nourishment of the infant.

The mammary gland is contained entirely within the superficial fascia and is composed of 15 to 20 glandular tissue lobes, divided by connective-tissue bands and arranged radially about the centrally located *nipple.* The glandular tissue occupies only a small portion of the breast in the nonpregnant or nonnursing breast. A variable but usually considerable amount of adipose tissue is contained between and around the lobules and makes up most of the peripheral part of the structure.

Each breast covers a nearly circular space anterior to the pectoralis muscles extending from the second to the sixth ribs and from the sternum into the axilla. The increase in the size and the shape of the mammary glands at the time of puberty and adolescence is due to increased amount of glandular tissue and adipose tissue brought about under the influence of estrogens and progesterone. The glandular tissue remains underdeveloped unless conception takes place.

The nipple is perforated at the tip by the 15 to 20 minute openings of the lactiferous ducts, each one of which is an excretory duct from one of the lobules to the surface. The skin of the nipple extends outward on the surface of the breast for 1 to 2 cm to form a pink or brown *areola.* The areola contains numerous large sebaceous glands that secrete a lipoid material which protects and lubricates the nipple during nursing of the infant.

During pregnancy *estrogens* probably stimulate the growth of the glandular duct system, whereas *progesterone* is considered to be the stimulus for glandular cell or acini formation. Complete development of the mammary system for lactation requires the concerted action of estrogens, progesterone, lactogenic hormone, and somatotropin. Before parturition lactation is presumably held in abeyance by the high titers of placental sex steroids which suppress secretion of *lactogenic* or *luteotropic hormone*, otherwise known as *prolactin*. After delivery and the expulsion of the placenta, the anterior pituitary is no longer inhibited by progesterone and estrogens, and lactogenic hormones begin to be secreted in increasingly large amounts. These hormones are especially important for their major role in the initiation and maintenance of lactation.

Oxytocin is secreted by the posterior pituitary by a reflex action induced by the infant's sucking on the breast. The milk letdown principle of this hormone causes contraction of the myoepithelial cells of the mammary alveoli and ductules, which forces the milk into collecting ducts to be expelled.

The mammary glands are well supplied with blood brought to them by the thoracic branches of the axillary, internal mammary, and intercostal arteries. The nerve fibers are derived from the ventral and lateral cutaneous branches of the fourth, fifth, and sixth thoracic nerves.

An understanding of the *lymphatic drainage* of the breasts is of the greatest importance in relation to malignant conditions of the breast. Malignant cells may readily spread from the affected breast to other areas of the body via the lymphatic vessels and nodes that drain the adjacent regions. Direct paths of lymph drainage follow the blood vessels and are primarily to the nodes within the pectoral muscles, the axillary nodes, and the internal mammary nodes. Some lymph also drains into the subcutaneous plexus and into the deep cervical nodes posterior to the clavicle.

In the surgical removal of malignant disease of the breast, the entire breast, all of the underlying subcutaneous tissue, the pectoralis muscles of that side, and all of the aforementioned lymph nodes are removed with the hope of preventing the spread of the tumor to other areas of the body, either by direct extension into adjacent tissue, or by spread of some of the cells via lymph or blood systems.

QUESTIONS FOR DISCUSSION

1. Define the terms *puberty* and *adolescence*. In temperate climates at what age do they occur in the male? In the female? Discuss secondary sex changes and their causes in the male and in the female.
2. Describe the pathway of the descent of the testes before or soon after birth. If the testis remains within the abdominal cavity, how will its function be affected? Explain.
3. What stimulates the production of LH? What are the functions of LH and LTH?
4. Where is progesterone produced and what are its functions? What is believed to be the cause of menstruation? Why does menstruation not take place if the ovum becomes fertilized?
5. Explain the pathway of the spermatozoa from the seminiferous tubules to the urinary meatus. What secretions are added to the semen and what are thought to be the special functions of each fluid that is added?

SUMMARY

Reproduction	Means by which new life is brought into existence Sexual type depends upon the union of two cells, one of which is produced by the male and one by the female organism
Puberty	Age at which sex organs attain normal adult function Male begins to produce functional spermatozoa in temperate climates between ages 14–16 years Female begins to ovulate and menstruation commences in temperate climate between ages 11–14 years Period marked by gradual appearance of secondary sex characteristics in both sexes

Adolescence
- Period from puberty to early twenties during which complete development of all secondary sex characteristics have been achieved—epiphyseal plates close at age of 20–21 years
- Physical growth accompanies psychological growth to maturity

Male Organs of Reproduction and Functions
- 2 testes—contained in the scrotum—produce spermatozoa and testosterone
- 2 epididymides (singular, epididymis)—lie superior and posterior to testes —spermatozoa mature here
- 2 seminal ducts (vas or ductus deferens)—storage sites for spermatozoa—convey them from epididymides to seminal vesicles
- 2 seminal vesicles—membranous pouches—lie posterior to bladder—produce nutritious secretions added to semen
- 2 ejaculatory ducts—short passageways within prostate gland—convey semen from seminal ducts to urethra
- Prostate gland—size of chestnut situated immediately inferior to internal urethral sphincter—surrounds proximal urethra—secretes alkaline fluid —increases motility of spermatozoa—prostate may increase in size in old age causing urinary retention
- 2 bulbourethral glands (Cowper's)—small bodies on either side of membranous urethra—secrete lubricating and protective mucus—remove urine residues prior to ejaculation
- Penis—organ of copulation suspended from front and sides of pubic arch—consists of 3 bodies of cavernous tissue—2 lateral corpora cavernosa penis —and 1 corpus cavernosum urethrae—these erectile bodies become distended with blood to produce erection of organ—glans penis, expansion at lower portion of penis, contains sensory end organs and urethral orifice—covered by foreskin or prepuce
- Blood supply—abdominal aorta, internal and external iliacs, spermatic arteries. Corresponding veins
- **Semen**
  - Fluid derived from the various sex glands in the male—contains approximately 100,000,000 spermatozoa per milliliter. Fertility depends on number and quality
- **Nervous control**
  - Parasympathetic nerves (sacral 2, 3, 4) control erection of penis
  - Sympathetic nerves (lumbar 1, 2, 3) control emission and ejaculation of semen

Spermatogenesis—begins at about age 12—continues throughout adult life
Spermatogonia—formed in seminiferous tubules of testes during fetal life
Primary spermatocytes—at puberty primary spermatocytes develop from spermatogonia

Primary spermatocytes undergo first maturation division of meiosis—46 or diploid number of chromosomes reduced to 23 double chromosomes in each of two secondary spermatocytes formed

Secondary spermatocytes—each secondary spermatocyte undergoes second maturation division of meiosis to form a spermatid containing 23 single chromosomes

Spermatids—a spermatid develops into a spermatozoon when it develops a head and tail, or flagellum

Spermatozoa—half of the spermatozoa contain X chromosomes; other half contain Y chromosomes

At fertilization original complement of 46 chromosomes is re-established—sex chromosome of spermatozoon determines sex of fertilized ovum

Male Urethra
- S-shaped tube—extends from internal urethral orifice to external urethral orifice of glans penis—17.5 cm in length—divided into 3 parts: prostatic, membranous, and penile urethra

Female Organs of Reproduction and Functions
- **2 ovaries**
  - Almond-shaped bodies measuring from 2.5–5 cm (1–2 in.) in length located one on each side of pelvic cavity—are attached to posterior surface of broad ligament, to uterus by ligament of the ovary, to ovarian tubes by fimbriae—functions are to produce ova and the sex hormones, progesterone and estrogens

Female Organs of Reproduction and Functions (*cont.*)

- **2 uterine or fallopian tubes (oviducts)**
  - Muscular ducts lined with mucosa—containing ciliated epithelium—enclosed in layers of broad ligament—extend from upper angles of uterus to sides of pelvic cavity
  - Divisions
    - Isthmus—inner constricted portion near uterus
    - Ampulla—dilated portion which curves over ovary
    - Infundibulum—trumpet-shaped extremity—fimbriae
  - Coats
    - External, or serous
    - Middle, or muscular
    - Internal, or mucous, arranged in longitudinal folds—lined with ciliated epithelium
  - Function
    - To convey ova to uterus, provide environment for fertilization and early development of fertilized ovum
- **Uterus**
  - Hollow, pear-shaped, muscular organ placed in pelvic cavity between bladder and rectum
  - Divisions
    - Body—superior part, upper rounded portion above entrance of tubes called fundus
    - Isthmus—middle or slightly constricted portion
    - Cervix—lower and smaller portion extends into vagina—contains internal and external os
  - Three coats
    - External, or serous, derived from peritoneum, covers intestinal surface and anterior surfaces to beginning of cervix
    - Muscular or myometrium
      - Circular layer
      - Longitudinal layer
      - Spiral layer
      - (Interlaced)
    - Mucous membrane, or endometrium
      - Lines internal aspect
  - Blood vessels
    - Uterine arteries from hypogastrics
    - Ovarian arteries from aorta
    - Remarkable for tortuous course and frequent anastomoses
  - Ligaments
    - Broad—two large layers of serous membrane—from uterus to walls of pelvic cavity
    - Round—two fibromuscular cords from sides of uterus to labia majora
    - Anterior—peritoneal fold from bladder to uterus
    - Posterior—peritoneal fold from uterus to rectum
    - Uterosacral—two partly serous, partly muscular ligaments from cervix to sacrum
    - Cardinal, or Mackenrodt's—fascia surrounding uterine vessels from pelvic wall to cervix and vagina
  - Function
    - To receive fertilized ovum, provide for implantation, nourishment, and environment for growth and development of fetus until parturition

Female Organs of Reproduction and Functions (*cont.*)

- **Vagina**
  - Extends from uterus to vulva—about 7.5–10 cm (3–4 in.)
  - Coats
    - Internal mucous lining arranged in rugae
    - Layer of submucous connective tissue
    - Muscular coat
  - Location—placed anterior to rectum, posterior to bladder and urethra
  - Function—for deposition of semen, serves as exit of birth canal
- **External genitalia**
  - Mons pubis—cushion of areolar, fibrous, and adipose tissue in front of pubic symphysis, covered with skin and after puberty covered also with hair
  - Labia majora—two folds that extend from mons pubis to within an inch of anus—protect perineum—maintain secretions
  - Labia minora—two folds situated between labia majora
  - Clitoris—small protuberance at apex of triangle formed by junction of labia minora—well supplied with nerves and blood vessels
  - Vestibule—cleft between labia minora
  - Hymen—fold of mucous membrane partly covering and surrounding vaginal orifice
  - Glands—greater vestibular or Bartholin's—oval bodies situated on either side of vagina—secretions have moistening function
  - Perineum—external surface of floor of pelvis, extends from pubic arch to coccyx

Histology of the Ovary

- **Embryonic development**
  - Ovaries derived from bilateral germinal ridges located in close proximity to the kidneys
  - Descend into pelvis during fetal life
  - Primordial ova are differentiated from germinal epithelium, migrate into ovarian cortex, approximately 2 million primary oocytes present at birth
- **Structure**
  - Outer layer of germinal epithelium
  - Inner layer of connective tissue or stroma, also containing developing graafian follicles that are derived from primordial follicles—one graafian follicle matures during each menstrual cycle from puberty to menopause
- **Development of ovum**
  - Primary oocyte, present at birth, finishes first maturation division of meiosis under influence of FSH, and zona pellucida develops
  - From this division, secondary oocyte and first polar body develop, each with 23 double chromosomes
  - Secondary oocyte undergoes second maturation division forming mature ovum with 23 single chromosomes and another polar body
  - Ovum is extruded from ovary before second maturation division is completed
  - If ovum is not fertilized, division may not terminate; ovum is viable for 24 hours

Menstrual Cycle

- **Menstruation** or desquamation of the endometrium is thought to be due to ischemia of this tissue following drop in blood levels of progesterone and estrogens prior to beginning of cycle. In menstruation about 40 ml of blood and about the same amount of serous fluid are lost—cycle begins on first day of menstruation
- *FSH* secreted at beginning of cycle causes development of a graafian follicle and production of estrogens by follicle and theca interna

Menstrual Cycle (*cont.*)

- Estrogenic follicular or proliferative stage
  - *Estrogens* cause increase in thickness, vascularity, and secretions of endometrium—high blood levels of estrogens stimulate production of LH
  - *LH* assists production of ovulation or extrusion of ovum into peritoneal cavity usually between 13th–15th day before beginning of menstrual bleeding. One mature ovum derived from each primary oocyte. Each ovum contains 22 + one X chromosomes. Polar bodies disintegrate
- Progestational, luteal, or secretory stage
  - *LH and LTH* stimulate luteinization of follicle after ovulation with formation of a corpus luteum, a secretory body that produces large quantities of progesterone and smaller amount of estrogens
  - *Progesterone* increases secretory function of endometrium, causes formation of glycogen, and lipid stores within endometrium, inhibits contractility of uterine smooth muscle. Increased blood levels of progesterone depress production of FSH by anterior pituitary. Corpus luteum involutes as a result of diminished FSH, and menstruation ensues
- **Hormonal changes in pregnancy**
  - If fertilization occurs, menstruation does not take place—placenta secretes hormone called chorionic gonadotropin which causes continuation and enlargement of corpus luteum—large amounts of estrogens and progesterone are secreted, and thick, vascular secretory endometrium is maintained for implantation and development of embryo

Menopause

- Female climacteric—the period of physiological cessation of menstrual flow, termination of follicular development, decrease in sex hormones, and the end of the childbearing period—occurs between the ages of 45–50 and may or may not cause troublesome symptoms such as increased irritability, hot flushes, insomnia, depression, and osteoporosis

Mammary Glands

- Composition
  - Made up of 15–20 lobes of glandular tissue divided by connective tissue bands and embedded in superficial fascia
- Location
  - Anterior to pectoralis muscles, extending from 2nd–6th ribs and from sternum into the axilla
- Size and shape
  - Increased size at puberty under influence of increased hormones produced, especially estrogens and progesterones
- Pregnancy and postpartum
  - Increase in size and numbers of glands mainly under influence of pituitary hormones and estrogens and progesterone. Lactation depends on concerted action of progesterone, estrogen, prolactin, and somatotropin
  - After delivery and expulsion of placenta, decrease in female sex steroids allows prolactin to be released from anterior pituitary. Milk letdown principle of oxytocin causes expulsion of milk
- Blood supply—from thoracic branches of axillary, internal mammary, and intercostal arteries
- Nerve supply—from lateral and cutaneous branches of fourth, fifth, and sixth thoracic nerves
- Lymphatic drainage—follows pathway of blood vessels—drains into nodes within pectoral muscles, into axillary nodes and internal mammary nodes. Some lymph drains into deep cervical nodes

CHAPTER

27

CONCEPTION AND DEVELOPMENT OF THE EMBRYO MATURATION OF GERMINAL TISSUES INHERITANCE FETAL CIRCULATION

The human organism begins life as a single cell derived from the fusion of two parental cells, the ovum and the spermatozoon. This fertilized egg, or zygote, undergoes mitotic cell division and cells become differentiated into tissues, organs, and systems forming the multicellular, highly organized replica of its species. The purpose of this chapter is to discuss the maturation of the sex cells, the process of fertilization, and the development of a fetus from the zygote, or fertilized egg.

DEVELOPMENT OF GERMINAL TISSUES

In an embryo of about six weeks the germinal tissues that will develop into reproductive glands may be distinguished from the somatic tissues that will form the remaining portions of the body. The germinal tissues make their appearance as a pair of genital folds in the dorsal region of the embryo, and by about the tenth or eleventh week these are differentiated into the reproductive organs called *gonads*. Primordial germ cells that have migrated to the gonads during their embryological development remain dormant in a resting stage from birth until puberty when, under the influence of gonadotropic hormones, their further growth and maturity are achieved.

Maturation of the germ cells is the process whereby the male and female reproductive cells grow and are prepared for fertilization. The process of egg formation is referred to as *oogenesis* and the process of sperm formation is termed *spermatogenesis*.

Spermatogenesis. Spermatogenesis has been discussed in detail in the previous chapter. Four spermatozoa are formed from each primary spermatocyte produced by the spermatogonium. Two of these cells carry X chromosomes, and the other two carry Y chromosomes, as has been previously stated. Some crossing over (see below) has undoubtedly taken place during the first maturation division.

Formation of the Oogonia and Primary Oocytes. In the embryo, once the primordial germ cells enter the developing ovary, they divide rapidly and form the most primitive female germ cells, the *oogonia*. The oogonia are arranged in clusters and are located in the cortical part of the ovary. They are surrounded by a layer of flat epithelial cells. It is believed that each group or cluster is formed by the descendants of a single primordial germ cell and that the cells that surround them are derived from the surface

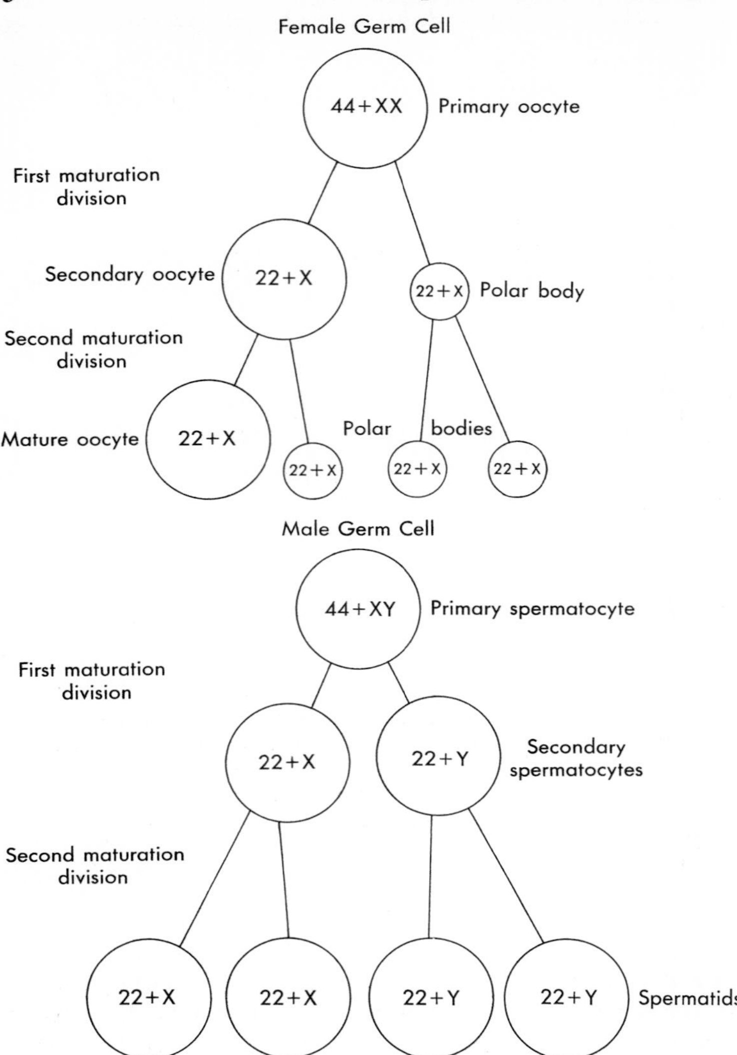

Figure 27–1. Diagrams to show the two maturation divisions in the male and female germ cells. Note that one ovum is formed from one primary oocyte, and four spermatids are formed from one primary spermatocyte. Two of the spermatids have X chromosomes, and two have Y chromosomes.

epithelium. From the fourth through the seventh months of fetal development each *oogonium*, or primitive sex cell, may differentiate into a larger cell known as a *primary oocyte* (page 559), which then enters the prophase of meiosis in the first maturation division.

Meiosis. Meiosis is a special kind of cell division which achieves a reduction to half the number of chromosomes and genes within the germ cell. Otherwise, with the fusion of sex cells, or *gametes* in fertilization, each carrying a full complement of chromosomes, there would be a doubling of chromosomes each generation. The number of chromosomes before meiosis is 46 and is referred to as the *diploid* number. The reduced number following meiosis is 23, or the *haploid* number.

As a sex cell goes into the prophase of the *first maturation division*, there is an important difference from the prophase of a typical mitotic division. The chromosomes begin to pair. *Homologous chromosomes* face each other and often entwine around one another in the center of the cell. This is referred to as a *synapsis*. Each chromosome duplicates itself so that it becomes doubled. Such doubled

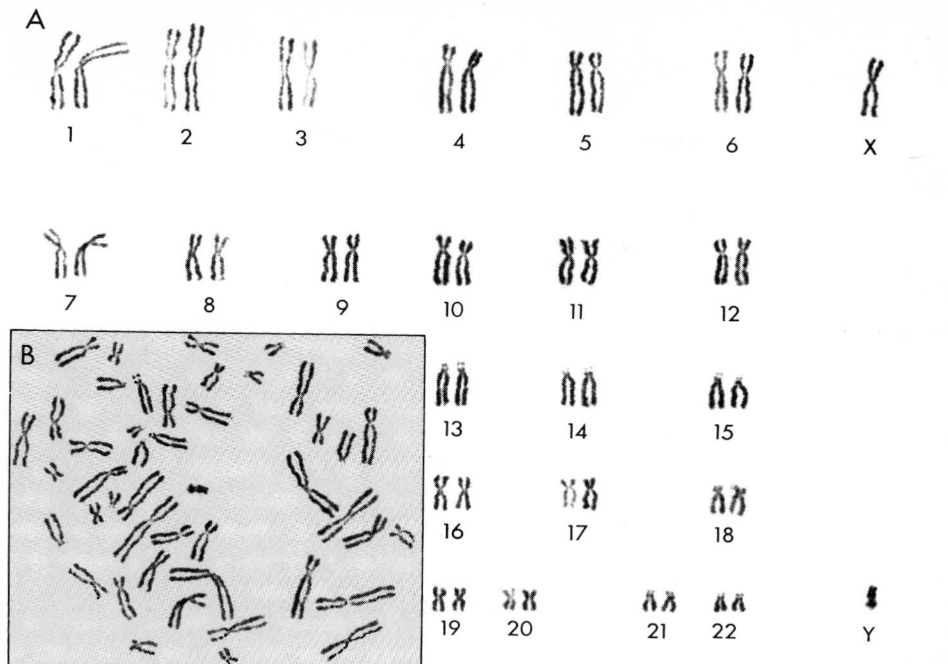

Figure 27–2. Normal human male chromosomes as they appear during metaphase. Cell division has been arrested by treatment with colchicine; hypotonic salt solution then is added to swell and disperse the chromosomes and make them more visible. (*B*) Inset: chromosomes as they appear under the microscope following this treatment. (*A*) Karyotype: chromosomes are paired and arranged according to a standard classification based on the size, position of the centromere, and other characteristics. The normal human has 22 somatic pairs plus two sex chromosomes (an X and Y in males, two X's in females). (Courtesy of Dr. James L. German, III, Cornell University Medical College, New York City.)

chromosomes are termed *dyads* and are held together by a band called the *kinetocore* or *centromere.* In the late prophase, these paired, doubled chromosomes can be seen as four *chromatids* grouped together to form *tetrads.*

The work of Bateson[1] and Punnet[2] has shown that during the first maturation division of meiosis there is some method of transfer and recombination of genes that lie on *homologous chromosomes.* As the tetrads are formed there may be simultaneous breakage and reattachment between *homologous chromatids.* This process creates a new association of genes and is known as *crossing over.* As the chromosomes go into the later part of the prophase and separate from one another slightly, it is possible to see crosses between chromatids of the homologous chromosomes, forming *chiasmata.* It is generally concluded that the chiasmata (singular, chiasma) represent regions where crossing over has taken place.

Each tetrad in the cell undergoing its first maturation division goes into typical metaphase, anaphase, and telophase, and then the cell divides. Each daughter cell has 23 dyads, or *double chromosomes.* The reduction in chromosome number has been achieved, but the chromosomes are still double. There is a *second maturation division* of meiosis, to be discussed later, which permits separation of these dyads into single chromosomes and provides for increased numbers of cells.

Significance of Meiosis. What is the

[1] William Bateson, British naturalist (1861–1926).

[2] Reginald C. Punnet, English geneticist (1875–).

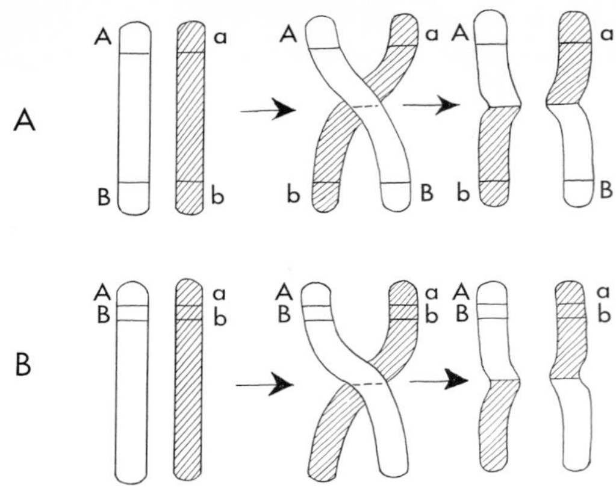

Figure 27–3. Diagrams to illustrate the phenomenon of *crossing over*. (*A*) Shows the breakage and reattachments between homologous chromosomes where genes *A* and *B* on one chromosome and *a* and *b* on its mate are located at opposite ends of the chromosomes. When the chromosomes are reattached, *crossing over* has taken place, with an exchange of the depicted genes, between the two chromosomes. (*B*) Shows the adjacent location of *A* and *B* genes on one chromosome and *a* and *b* on the other. When *crossing over* occurs, the genes, because of their close relationship on the chromosome, are not exchanged between the two partners.

significance of this process of selection and exchange of genes during meiosis? The reducing divisions of meiosis separate each pair of chromosomes; thus it halves the number of chromosomes, but chance alone decides the actual distribution of the maternal or paternal member of any pair to any particular daughter cell. Meiosis also provides an opportunity for reshuffling of the genes from one chromosome to another as the result of the *crossing over* or interchange of chromosome parts. In man, reduction to the haploid number of chromosomes during meiosis makes possible in each gamete one of eight million final combinations of chromosomes. A further increase in new heredity combinations is made possible by the phenomenon of *crossing over*. Each child carries the genes inherited from his parents and their ancestors, but each child has a different inheritance and different appearance from every other person in the world because of the infinite variety provided by reduction and the recombination of chromosomes produced during meiosis.

Fertilization, or Conception. Fertilization occurs when the nucleus of the spermatozoon, or male gamete, fuses with the nucleus of the ovum, or female gamete, to form the *zygote*. Soon after extrusion into the peritoneal cavity, the ovum, surrounded by the follicular cells that make up the corona radiata, passes into the fallopian, or uterine, tube. It is apparently carried into the infundibulum, or funnel, of the tube by currents in the peritoneal fluid created by the fimbriae and the cilia of the infundibulum and tubular mucosa. It is possible that an ovum from one ovary can pass to the opposite uterine tube. Rhythmical muscular contractions of the uterine tube also aid the passage of the ovum toward the uterus.

Fertilization normally occurs in the ampulla of the uterine tube or at least in the distal third. It is believed that tubular and uterine musculature contractions cause aspiration of spermatozoa into the uterus and tubes. The flagella, or tails, of the sperm probably contribute only slightly to their ascent into the female reproductive tract, since they enable them to move only from 1 to 4 mm per minute. The main function of these flagella seems to be to aid in the penetration of the corona radiata and the surrounding membranes of the ovum, the zona pellucida, and the vitelline membrane.

Only one spermatozoon of the 200 to 300 million spermatozoa deposited in the female reproductive tract is necessary for fertilization of the ovum. It is believed that other surrounding spermatozoa release enzymes such as hyaluronidase that detach the layer of corona radiata and thereby aid the penetration of the fertilizing cell. In the human being both the head and tail enter the ovum. If two ova mature at the same time and both are fertilized, fraternal twins result.

As soon as the spermatozoon enters the ovum, the female germ cell finishes its second maturation division, and its 22 plus 1 X chromosomes make up the *female pronucleus*. The spermatozoon moves toward the female pronucleus, and its swollen head becomes the *male pronucleus.* The two pronuclei meet and join, thus restoring the complete 46, or diploid number of, chromosomes in the human somatic cell. The tail that had been detached from the head immediately following fertilization contributes to the formation of the centrosome, which soon divides into two halves, each half moving to the opposite pole of the spindle, thus forming two new cells. Each cell of the rapidly forming individual contains 46 chromosomes, that is, the original diploid number.

Fertilization determines the sex of the zygote, restores the diploid number of chromosomes, and causes the initiation of mitotic, cleavage division, all of which result in the formation of the embryo.

Inheritance. Heredity is a term applied to the transmission of potential traits, physical or mental, from parents to their offspring. An individual receives one chromosome of each pair from each of his parents. Each member of the pair (except the sex chromosomes) carries the same general set of hereditary genes as its mate and is called an *autosome.* For example, each of the paired chromosomes may carry a gene for eye color, for hair form, or for length of fingers. These genes may be the same or different, depending on the genetic contribution of each parent. If the offspring has received a gene for brown eyes from each parent, we say he is *homozygous* for brown eyes. On the other hand, if he has received a gene for brown eyes from one parent and a gene for blue eyes from the other, we say he is *heterozygous* for eye color, and his eye color will be brown. Some traits, such as brown eye color, are *dominant* under usual conditions, and are bound to appear. Other traits are *recessive*, such as blue eye color, and will not *usually* appear unless two recessive genes are received by the offspring.

Two genes are *alleles* when they carry the same trait and occupy the same position or locus on the chromosome and will come together when the two chromosomes enter into synapsis during the first maturation division of

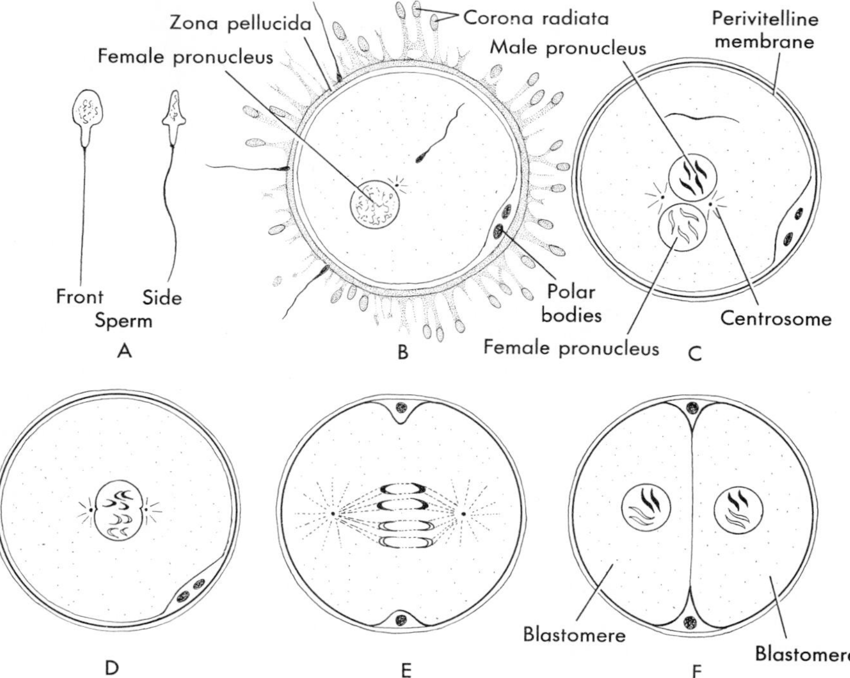

Figure 27–4. Diagrams showing the fertilization of the ovum, the joining of the male and female pronuclei, the chromosomes organized on the spindle, and the two-cell stage of blastomeres.

meiosis. Homologous genes, or alleles, may be alike alleles, producing the same effect, or nonalike alleles, producing differing effects.

The system of using letters as symbols for genes as well as the whole development of the gene concept was devised by the Austrian monk Gregor Mendel,[3] the "father of modern genetics," and it is utilized almost universally today. A small letter stands for a recessive gene, the capitalized form of the same letter for the gene which is dominant over this recessive. For instance, *B* might represent the dominant brown eye color and *b* the recessive color blue. The term *genotype* means the type of genes present in the individual. *Phenotype* refers to the expression of the genes. The person with one gene for blue eyes and one for brown eyes might be said to have the heterozygous genotype for brown color, but the phenotype of brown, since this is the color of this individual's eyes.

Dominance may be complete, partial, or absent. A gene that is dominant to one gene may be recessive to another one. Certain abnormalities are inherited as dominants over the normal condition, e.g., extra digits or excessively short digits. Others such as albinism may be recessive to the normal. Some abnormalities appear as sex-linked recessives, becoming evident in males with a single recessive factor but in females only when there are two, e.g., red-green color blindness and hemophilia.

It used to be thought that all characteristics were caused by either heredity or environment. Modern genetic understanding has shown that there is rarely a clear-cut line of distinction between inherited and environmentally induced characteristics. It is the blending of heredity and environment that results in the final expression of an individual's characteristics.

DEVELOPMENT OF THE EMBRYO

Formation of Morula and Blastocyst. Cleavage consists of a number of rapid mitotic divisions which result in the production of a number of increasingly smaller cells that are known as *blastomeres*. Cleavage is not really a growth process since there is no increase in protoplasmic volume despite the progressive increase in cell number.

As the zygote passes down the fallopian tube, cleavage continues. When the 16- to 20-cell stage is attained, it is known as a *morula* (a hollow ball of cells). The morula is divided into two parts, the inner cell mass, which is composed of a group of centrally located cells, and the surrounding single-cell layer of trophoblast cells, called the outer cell mass. The inner cell mass gives rise to the tissues that make up the embryo itself, but it also contributes to the formation of embryonic membranes called the amnion and yolk sac. The outer cell mass forms the trophoblast from which the outer embryonic membrane known as the *chorion* and the *placenta* are developed. The morula reaches the uterine cavity about three to four days after ovulation, the zona pellucida disappears, and the zygote produces a fluid-filled cavity between the inner and outer cell masses, resulting in the formation of the *blastocyst*.

Occasionally, as the inner cell mass develops in this early period prior to tissue differentiation, it separates into two groups of cells, each of which then matures in the normal fashion as described below. Should this occur, *identical* twins result—"identical" because each has developed from one fertilized ovum, and therefore they have the same genetic inheritance.

Implantation of the Blastocyst. *Implantation*, or uterine attachment, of the blastocyst probably occurs between the seventh and ninth days after ovulation. It is thought that the penetration and erosion of the epithelial cells of the uterine mucosa necessary for implantation result from the combined effects of proteolytic enzymes produced by the trophoblast and by the vascular

[3] Gregor Johann Mendel, Austrian monk and geneticist (1822–1884).

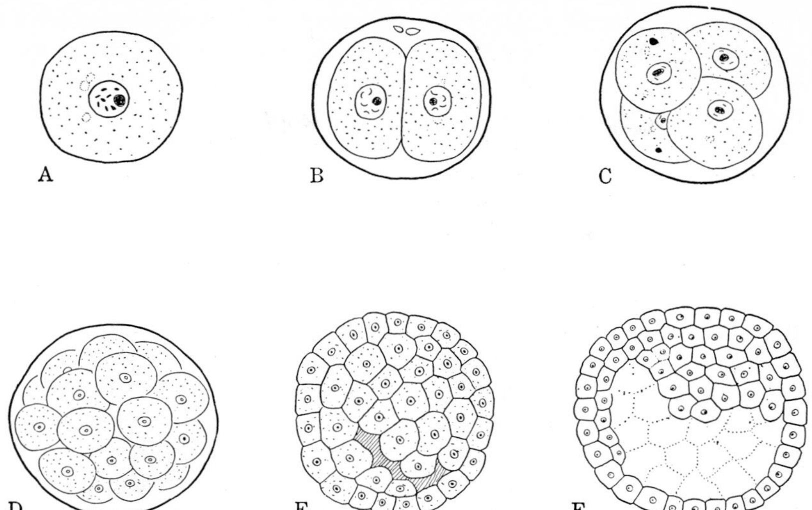

Figure 27–5. Diagram to show very early stages of mammalian development. (*A*) One-celled embryo; (*B*) two-celled embryo; (*C*) four-celled embryo; (*D*) berrylike ball of cells or *morula*; (*E*) beginning formation of the blastocyst; (*F*) well-developed blastocyst, consisting of a hollow ball of *trophoblast* cells and an inner mass of cells known as formative cells.

changes in the endometrium. In any case, the blastocyst normally implants in the endometrium of the body of the uterus. The erosion in the uterine mucosa brought about by the penetration of the blastocyst is gradually obliterated by the growth of adjacent epithelium and by the formation of a *fibrin coagulum*. If the blastocyst implants abnormally in close proximity to the cervical internal os, a condition known as *placenta previa* occurs and causes severe bleeding in the latter part of pregnancy and during delivery. Implantation in the uterine tube results in a tubal pregnancy, which is dangerous because it causes rupture of the tube, severe internal hemorrhage, and death of the embryo during the second or third month of pregnancy. Implantations anywhere outside the uterus are known as *extrauterine*, or *ectopic*, *pregnancies*.

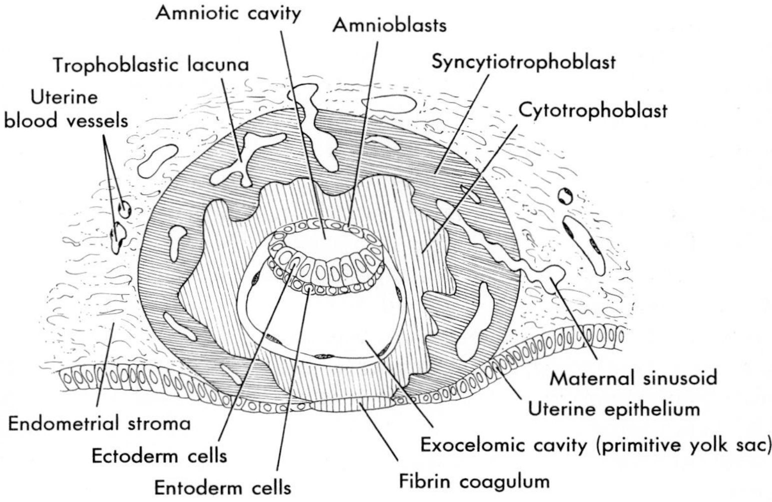

Figure 27–6. Diagram of a 9- to 12-day blastocyst to show developing ectoderm, entoderm, layers of the trophoblast, and the beginning of the uteroplacental circulation. The amniotic cavity is well defined, and the original uterine surface defect is closed by a fibrin coagulum. (Modified from Langman.)

During pregnancy, the uterine mucosa is highly modified and is called the *decidua*. The glands become extremely convoluted and hyperactive, and stromal cells become differentiated into decidual cells which possess variable amounts of glycogen, lipids, and increasing numbers of mitochondria. After implantation of the blastocyst and until the fourth month of gestation, three parts of the decidua can be recognized: the *decidua basalis* underlying the implanted ovum, the *decidua capsularis* that surrounds the surface of the implanted chorionic sac, and that portion that lines the rest of the uterus, the *decidua parietalis*, or *vera*.

Major Events in the Development of the Blastocyst. The blastocyst becomes firmly embedded in the uterine mucosa during the second and third weeks of development and its two parts, the *embryoblast* and the *trophoblast*, begin to grow and differentiate. The embryoblast gives rise to the three basic layers of the embryo proper, the *ectoderm*, the *entoderm*, and the *mesoderm*. The cells of the trophoblast grow deeply into the endometrium and form the *placenta*.

By the eighth day of development, the embryoblastic cells differentiate into two distinct cell layers, the inner *entodermal* germ layer, which is composed of flattened polyhedral cells facing the lumen of the blastocyst, and the outer *ectodermal* germ layer, which is composed of a layer of tall columnar cells.

The trophoblast forms an inner pale layer, the *cytotrophoblast*, and an outer darker zone referred to as the *syncytiotrophoblast*, or *syncytium*. The endometrial stroma at the implantation site is highly vascular and edematous, and its enlarged glands secrete mucus and glycogen. Between the ectoderm cells and the trophoblast an opening begins to form, called the *amniotic cavity*, and its outer portion is lined with flattened cells, the *amnioblasts*. The amniotic cavity becomes filled with a thin, clear fluid which serves as a protective cushion to absorb shock, to maintain fetal environmental temperature, to prevent adherence of the embryo to the surrounding surface, and to allow for fetal movements. The gradually enlarging cavity extending toward the lumen of the uterus forms the *exocelomic* cavity, or *primitive yolk sac*.

Maternal capillaries become dilated and congested and begin to extend into the syncytiotrophoblast. Maternal blood begins to enter the *lacunar system* as the syncytial cells begin to erode the endothelial lining of the maternal sinusoids. Thus the future uteroplacental circulation begins to be established. Owing to the great differences in blood pressures between the arterial and venous capillaries, maternal blood begins to flow through the trophoblastic lacunar system. Bleeding may occasionally occur at the implantation site around the thirteenth day of development owing to increased blood flow into the trophoblastic lacunar spaces at this time, although the epithelial surface has usually healed by then. This bleeding may be confused with normal menstrual bleeding since it occurs at about the twenty-eighth day of the menstrual cycle and the anticipated delivery date may be estimated inaccurately.

Cells of the inner surface of the cytotrophoblast delaminate and differentiate to form the loose network of tissue known as the *extraembryonic mesoderm*. This mesoderm fills the expanding space between the amnion and primitive yolk sac internally and the trophoblast externally. When large cavities develop in this tissue and become confluent, a new space, the *extraembryonic celom*, is formed. This cavity surrounds the blastocyst except between the germ disk and trophoblast, where the attachment remains.

The extraembryonic celomic cavity enlarges, and by the twentieth day the embryo is attached to the surrounding trophoblast by a narrow *connecting body stalk*, which later develops into the *umbilical cord* and attaches the embryo to the placenta.

During the second and third weeks, ectodermal cells in the caudal region of the germ disk begin to multiply and to migrate toward the midline, forming a narrow groove, the *primitive streak*. It is believed that modified ectodermal cells proliferate and migrate between the ectodermal and entodermal germ layers and spread laterally at this time, forming the intermediate cell layer known as the *mesoderm*. The *notochord* now is formed along a longitudinal axis and the entodermal layer establishes firm contact with the ectoderm making up the *posterior cloacal membrane* from which *urogenital* and *anal membranes* are derived. The *buccopharyngeal* membrane is later developed from the *prochordal* plate, which now begins to appear at the anterior ectodermal attachment. An outpocketing called the *allantois*, or *allantoenteric diverticulum*, appears about the sixteenth day and extends from the posterior wall of the yolk sac into the connecting stalk. This structure in some lower vertebrates becomes a large reservoir for urine storage, but in man it is normally rudimentary and gradually disappears during further embryonic development.

The Embryonic Period. The first two months of development are known as the *embryonic period*. During this interval, the shape and the appearance of the embryo are greatly altered, and by the end of the second month of development, all the important features of the external body may be recognized. Each germ layer starts a course of differentiation into specific tissues, organs, and systems, and by the end of the embryonic period, all the major body systems have been formed.

Ectodermal Germ Layer. The ectoderm gives rise to the formation of the *central nervous system* during the *somite period*. During the third and fourth week the *neural* plate, posterior to the *notochord*, is formed from ectoderm cells, and it soon invaginates to form the *neural groove* lined by the *neural fold*. When the folds approach each other and fuse, the groove becomes the *neural tube*. This fusion begins in the future neck region and proceeds simultaneously in cephalic and caudal directions. The tube does not close off entirely at this time but temporarily remains open for some time at the anterior and

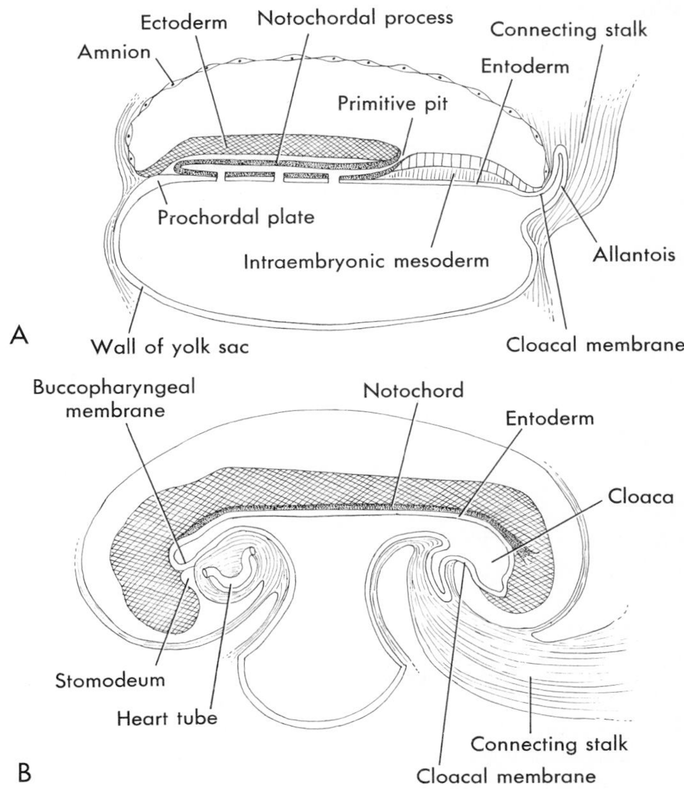

Figure 27–7. Diagrams of midsagittal sections through embryos to show: (*A*) Extension of notochordal process and fusion with the entoderm in 18-day embryo. The newly formed intermediate mesodermal layer is shown. It is thought to be derived from modified ectodermal cells. (*B*) Fourteen-somite embryo with developing heart and buccopharyngeal and cloacal membranes.

posterior neuropores. The brain begins to enlarge and develop at the cephalic end of the neural tube, and the spinal cord and peripheral nerves develop from the remainder of the tube. At the end of the first month the *otic vesicle* and *optic vesicle*, outpocketings of the brain, are formed. From the former, parts of the ear are derived, and from the latter, the retina and optic nerve develop.

From the ectodermal germ layer the following parts of the body are derived: (1) the central nervous system and hypophysis, (2) the peripheral nervous system including the autonomic nervous system, (3) the sensory epithelium of the sense organs, (4) the enamel of the teeth, and (5) the epidermis including hair, nails, and subcutaneous glands.

Mesodermal Germ Layer. The mesoderm is formed between the ectoderm and the entoderm. The mesodermal cells form a thin layer on each side of the midline, until the end of the third week when the mass begins to thicken immediately lateral to the notochord, to become the *paraxial mesoderm* (the future somites), the *intermediate mesoderm* (the future excretory units), and the *lateral plate*, which splits into somatic and visceral layers.

By the end of the third week, the paraxial mesoderm becomes segmented into approximately 40 pairs of somites. These *somites* mold the contours of the embryo, and from them are formed the *mesenchyme*, which gives rise to connective tissue, cartilage, and bone, and *myoblasts*, which give rise to striated muscle cells. Some of the cells from the somites become mesenchymatous and spread under the ectoderm to form the subcutaneous tissue of the skin (integumentary system).

The *cardiovascular system* is derived from the mesodermal germ layer during the third week. Blood islands, lined by endothelial cells, become arranged in isolated clusters which then fuse and give rise to small blood vessels. During the fourth week, a single *primitive heart tube* is formed and is suspended in the pericardial cavity. *Extraembryonic blood vessels* are also formed in a similar manner during this time and become the *umbilical* and *vitelline vessels*, which, as they

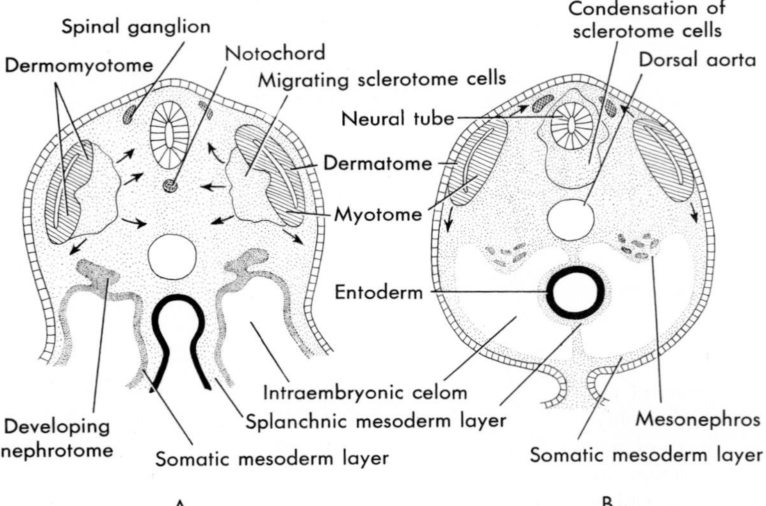

Figure 27–8. (*A*) Transverse section through a 26-day embryo to show migration of cells of *sclerotome*, or ventromedial part of the somite. The remaining cells form the *dermomyotome*. The intermediate mesoderm has proliferated to form *nephrotomes*, the excretory units of the urinary system. The *arrows* indicate the direction of the migrating cells of the *dermatome* and *sclerotome*.
(*B*) Transverse section through a 28-day embryo to show condensation of sclerotome cells around the neural tube to form the axial skeleton. (J. Langman, *Medical Embryology*. Courtesy of Williams & Wilkins Co.)

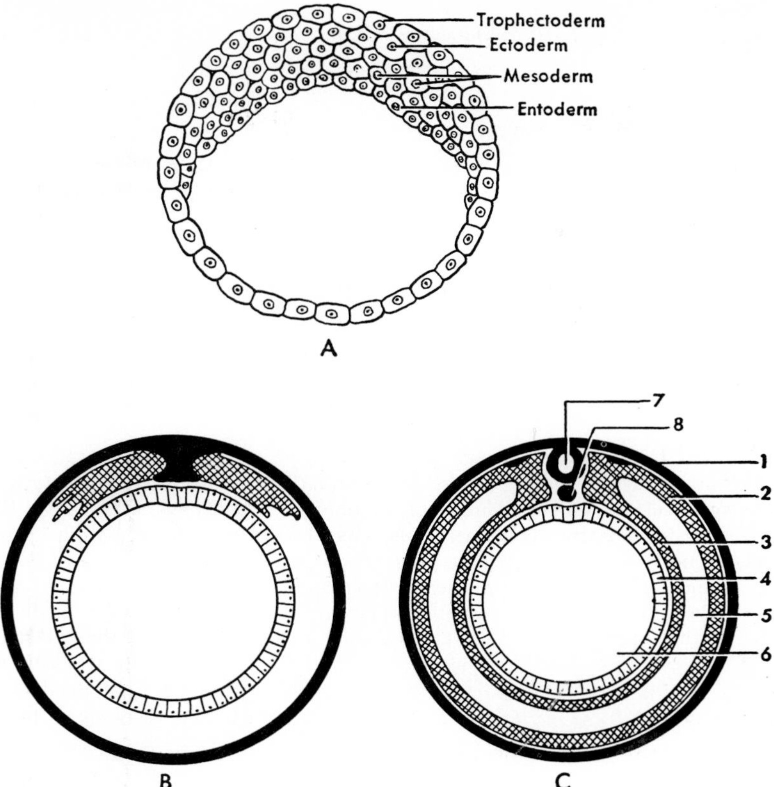

Figure 27–9. Diagram of a section of an embryo, showing the beginning of tissue formation. (*A*) The embryonic disk shows the cells arranged in layers. (*B*, *C*) Two diagrams of sections of embryos showing later stages of tissue formation. *Ectoderm* is shown in black, *entoderm* as cells; the two layers of *mesoderm* are cross-hatched. (*1*) Ectoderm, (*2*) parietal mesoderm, (*3*) visceral mesoderm, (*4*) entoderm, (*5*) future body cavity, (*6*) enteron, (*7*) neural tube, (*8*) notochord.

develop, begin to penetrate the embryo proper where they reach the independently developing intraembryonic vascular system. The pharyngeal arches give rise to the maxillary, mandibular, hyoid bones, and ossicles of the ear, as well as other ligaments, muscles, and bones.

The lateral plate of the mesoderm separates into two layers, the *somatic*, or *parietal*, *layer* lying next to the ectoderm, and the *splanchnic*, or *visceral*, *layer* lying next to the entoderm. The ectoderm and the somatic mesoderm form the *somatopleure*, and from this the body wall is developed. The entoderm and the splanchnic mesoderm form the *splanchnopleure*, and from this the viscera are developed. The *celom* is a cavity between the two layers of mesoderm which develops into the body cavity. The peritoneal, pleural, and pericardial cavities develop from the celom and are lined with mesothelium derived from mesoderm encompassing them.

The important structures that are considered to be derivatives of the mesodermal layer are (1) cartilage, joints, and bones; (2) connective tissue; (3) blood and lymph cells, walls of blood and lymph vessels, and the heart; (4) the spleen; (5) serous membranes; and (6) kidneys, gonads, and their ducts.

Entodermal Germ Layer. As the embryo folds and its head comes closer to the tail, a portion of the yolk sac, lined with entoderm, becomes incorporated into the embryo proper and forms the *primitive foregut* and *hindgut*,

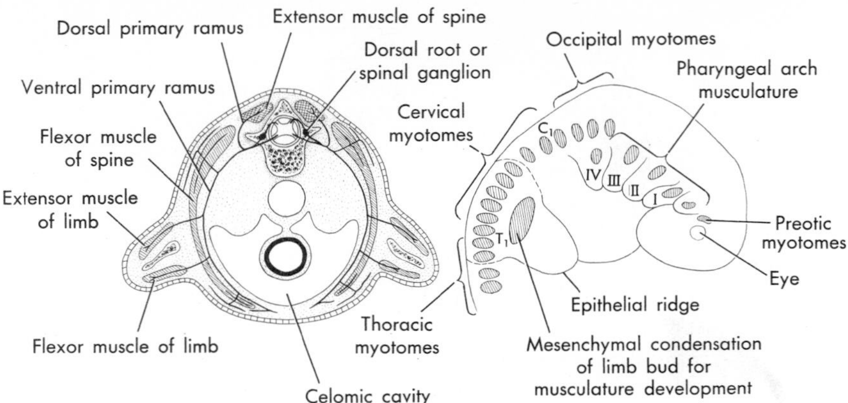

Figure 27–10. (*A*) Cross section through embryo in region of the limb bud attachment. Muscle tissue has penetrated limb bud and has divided into ventral (flexor) portion and dorsal (extensor) components. The spinal nerves follow a similar orientation but eventually unite to form large dorsal (radial) and ventral (median and ulnar) nerves in upper extremity. (*B*) Longitudinal view to show *myotomes* in head, neck, and thoracic regions of embryo at seven weeks. The tissue of the somite that remains after the migration of the cells of the *sclerotome* and *dermatome* makes up the *myotome*. *Myoblasts* of three of the four *occipital myotomes* migrate forward to form muscles of the tongue. The upper extremity is budding opposite the lower cervical and upper thoracic segments. (Modified from Langman.)

which are lined with epithelium of entodermal origin. The *buccopharyngeal* membrane ruptures at the end of the third week, and thus an open connection between the primitive gut and the amniotic cavity is established. The primitive gut located between the fore- and hindgut remains temporarily in open connection with the yolk sac by way of a wide duct, the *omphalomesenteric* or *vitelline duct*.

Important structures that are subsequently derived from the entodermal germ layer are (1) the epithelial lining of the digestive and respiratory tracts and part of the bladder and urethra, (2) the epithelial lining of the tympanic cavity and eustachian tube, and (3) the main cellular portions of the tonsils, parathyroids, thymus and liver, pancreas, and gallbladder.

Development of the Extremities. The fore- and hindlimbs appear as buds at the beginning of the second month. The *forelimb buds* arise quite high, at the level of the fourth cervical to the first thoracic somites, and this explains their subsequent innervation by the *brachial plexus*. The *hindlimbs* appear at the level of the lumbar and sacral somites just below the attachment of the umbilical stalk and are later innervated by nerves from the *lumbosacral plexus*. As the limb buds grow, they undergo a 90-degree rotation but in opposite directions, so that the elbow points dorsally and the knee points ventrally.

The Fetal Period. The interval from the beginning of the third month to the end of intrauterine life is known as the *fetal period*. During this time some differentiation of tissues does continue, but the major changes are brought about by the rapid growth of the body. At the beginning of the third month the head constitutes approximately one half of the crown-rump (CR) length, or sitting height, but at birth the proportion has diminished to one fifth. The eyes are initially directed laterally, but during the third month the eyes are located on the ventral aspect of the face, the ears reach their final position, and the limbs their relative length in comparison to the rest of the body, although the lower limbs remain a little shorter and slightly less developed than the upper extremities. The *external genitalia* have usually developed by the end of the second month, so that the sex of the fetus can be determined by external appearance.

During the fourth and fifth months, at the end of the first half of intrauterine life, the fetus lengthens rapidly and its CH, or crown-heel length, is approximately 23 cm. This is about one half the total length of the full-term newborn.

There are many presumptive signs of pregnancy, but the three positive signs occur during the fetal period and include hearing the fetal heart between the eighteenth and twentieth weeks, visibility of the fetal skeleton by x-ray during the fourteenth to sixteenth weeks, and the physician's observance of fetal movement during the fifth month. The mother is usually able to discern fetal movements during the fifth month (quickening).

The weight of the fetus increases considerably during the second half of intrauterine life, from 500 gm at the end of the fifth month to 3,200 gm by the end of the ninth month. Subcutaneous fat is formed during the last months before birth so that the fetus loses much of its former wrinkled appearance. At birth the fetus is approximately 50 cm long, and the skull still has the largest circumference of the body. At birth the testes have usually descended through the inguinal canal and into the scrotum.

The Placenta, Its Development and Functions. The placenta is composed of an embryonic portion, the *chorion frondosum*, and a maternal portion, the *decidua basalis*. Each portion has its own blood supply, and there is no direct connection between them. Exchange of substances between the two systems takes place by diffusion.

The *trophoblast* develops a great number of *secondary villi* or *cytotrophic projections* that extend into and are attached to the *maternal decidua*. They are now referred to as the *chorionic villi*. The portion of the chorion that contains the expanding villi and is adherent to the decidua basalis is called the *chorion frondosum* (bushy chorion), and the portion projecting into the lumen of the uterus is smooth and almost nonvascular and is known as the *chorion laeve*.

The *decidua basalis*, the endometrial layer adjacent to the embryonic *chorion frondosum*, consists of a compact layer that is tightly connected to the chorion and a spongy layer that contains dilated glands and the spiral arteries. The compact layer is often referred to as the *decidual plate*. The *decidua capsularis* is the decidual layer adjacent to the chorion laeve which projects into the uterine lumen. During the third month, as the fetus increases in size, the decidua capsularis degenerates, and the *chorion laeve* fuses with the *decidua parietalis* on the opposite side of the uterus. Most of the uterine cavity is now obliterated and the chorion frondosum remains the only functional part of the chorion. The *placenta*

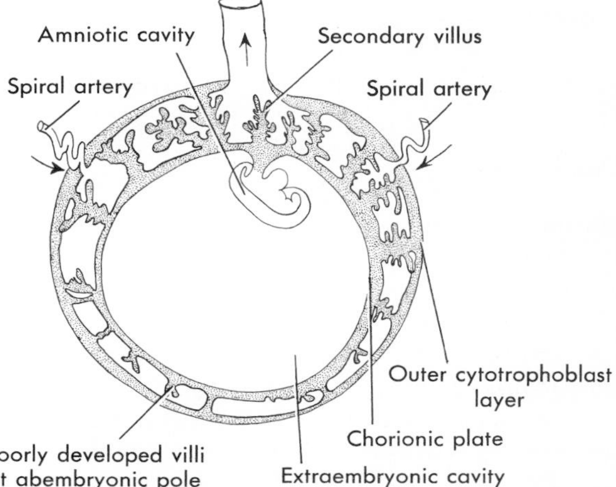

Figure 27–11. Diagram of embryo at beginning of second month of development to show numerous well-formed secondary villi. (Modified from Langman.)

is composed of the chorion frondosum, its fetal portion, and the decidua basalis, its maternal portion. The placenta enlarges greatly as the fetus and uterus increase in size, and it amounts to about 25 per cent of the internal surface of the uterus. The main functions of the placenta are the exchange of gaseous and metabolic products as well as nutrients between the maternal and fetal blood streams, and the production of hormones to maintain pregnancy.

There are intervillous spaces between the chorionic and decidual plates. These spaces are filled with maternal blood and are lined with *syncytium* of fetal origin. Fetal villous capillaries from umbilical veins project into these intervillous spaces, where they are bathed by approximately 150 ml of oxygenated blood from the maternal spiral arteries. Blood from the intervillous lakes is returned to the maternal circulation via venous openings from these spaces. It is estimated that from 500 to 600 ml of maternal blood circulates through the intervillous spaces every minute, thus permitting a replacement of 150 ml in the intervillous spaces every two to three minutes.

The placental barrier, or dividing membrane, is made up entirely of fetal tissue. Until the fourth month the barrier is composed of four layers, but then it becomes much thinner and retains only two, the endothelial lining of the capillaries and the syncytial covering that lies in intimate contact with them. The thinner layer allows for more rapid exchange of substances such as nutrients, gases, and other metabolic products between the two blood systems. Hormones and antibodies also pass across the placental barrier, although it is not known just how the high-molecular-weight substances such as proteins and maternal gamma globulins can pass through the barrier. The fetus acquires some of the antibodies that the mother has produced against such infectious diseases as scarlet fever, measles, smallpox, and diphtheria. The precise mechanism whereby these antibodies reach the fetus is unknown, but

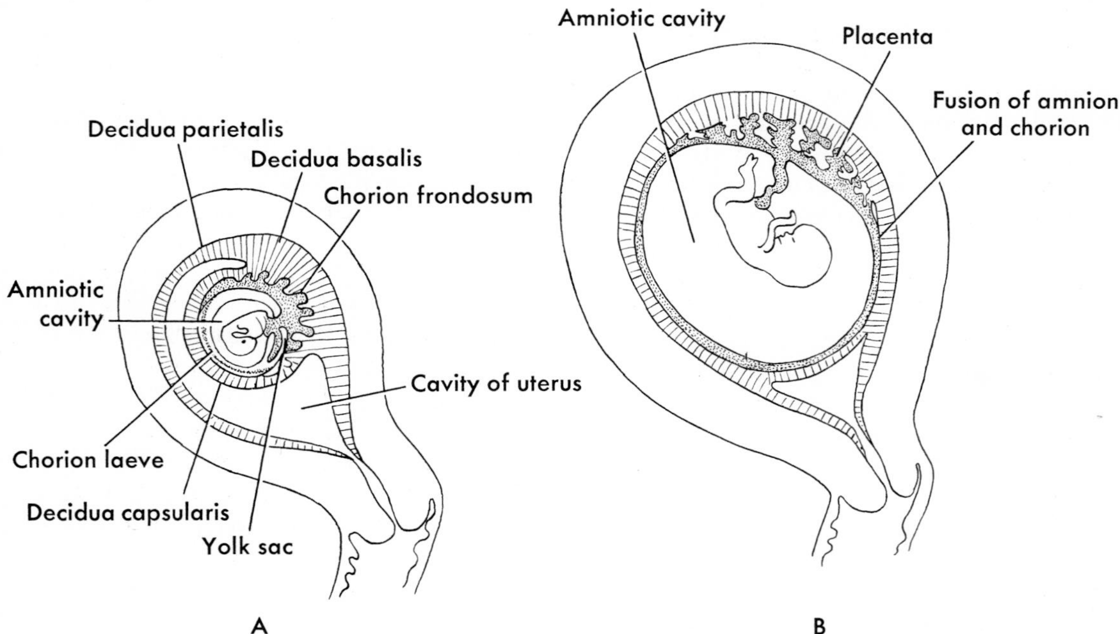

Figure 27–12. (*A*) Schematic drawing to show the decidua and fetal membranes in embryo at the end of the second month. Villi have disappeared at the abembryonic pole. (*B*) Schematic drawing of embryo at the end of the third month to show obliteration of the decidua capsularis and chorion laeve. Fusion of the amnion and chorion has also occurred.

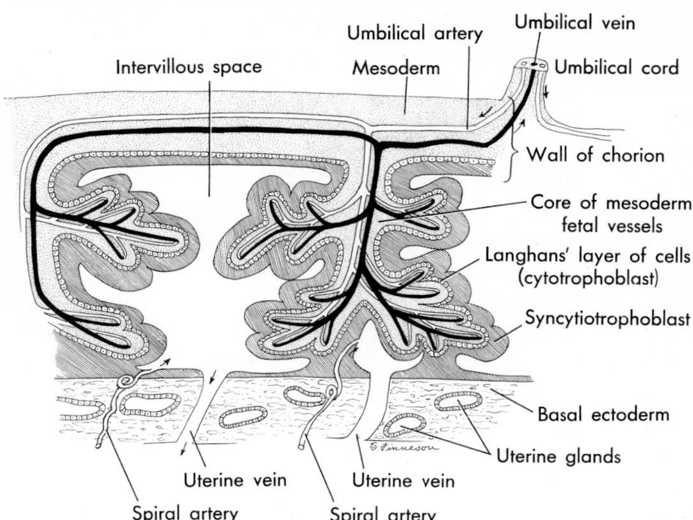

Figure 27–13. Schematic drawing of the structure of the villi at an early stage of development. The capillaries of the fetal circulation are separated from maternal blood in the intervillous spaces by surrounding layers of mesoderm, cytotrophoblast, and syncytiotrophoblast. After the fifth month only a single layer, that of the syncytiotrophoblast lies between the fetal capillary wall and the maternal blood. Note the umbilical cord containing one umbilical vein and two arteries. Two uterine spiral arteries emptying into the intervillous spaces and two veins returning maternal blood are shown.

it has been suggested that they may be transferred by the process of *pinocytosis*.

The placenta produces sufficient amounts of gonadotropins, progesterone, and estrogens by the end of the fourth month of pregnancy so that the ovarian corpus luteum is no longer needed and it therefore begins to degenerate. Estrogenic hormones are produced in increasing amounts until a maximum level is reached just before the end of pregnancy.

The presence of chorionic gonadotropin in the urine early in pregnancy is used as an indicator in some varieties of pregnancy tests. When this urine is injected into the immature mouse, it causes ovarian hyperemia, and in the young female rabbit it causes ovulation. If young male frogs are injected with urine or blood serum containing these gonadotropins, it will cause their ejection of spermatozoa. More recently immunological tests have been used—gonadotropin in the urine showing agglutination when antiserum is added.

Fetal Circulation Before Birth. The umbilical cord unites the placenta with the navel of the fetus. The cord is made up of two arteries and one large vein. These vessels are surrounded and protected by soft mucous connective tissue known as *Wharton's jelly*. Nutrients and oxygenated blood are conveyed to the fetus via the umbilical vein, which travels to the liver within the anterior peritoneal attachment, the *falciform ligament*. The main portion of the blood to the fetus bypasses the liver. It flows from the umbilical vein into the short vessel called the *ductus venosus* and from there into the inferior vena cava. Since the liver, at this time, is only partially functional, there is no need for the major portion of blood to perfuse it. Only a small amount of blood enters the sinusoids of the liver and mixes with the blood from the portal circulation. There is a sphincter mechanism in the ductus venosus near the entrance of the umbilical veins. When venous return is too great because of the additional pressure caused by a uterine contraction, this sphincter, it is believed, closes so that the heart will not be overloaded with blood.

Blood from the inferior vena cava enters the right atrium and is directed toward the *foramen ovale* by the valve of the inferior vena cava. As a result the largest portion of the returning blood bypasses the nonfunctioning lungs and passes directly into the left atrium. This blood will supply the coronary vessels of the heart and the carotid arteries to the brain with well-oxygenated blood.

A small portion of blood from the inferior vena cava joins the desaturated blood from the superior vena cava which flows into the right ventricle and out into the pulmonary

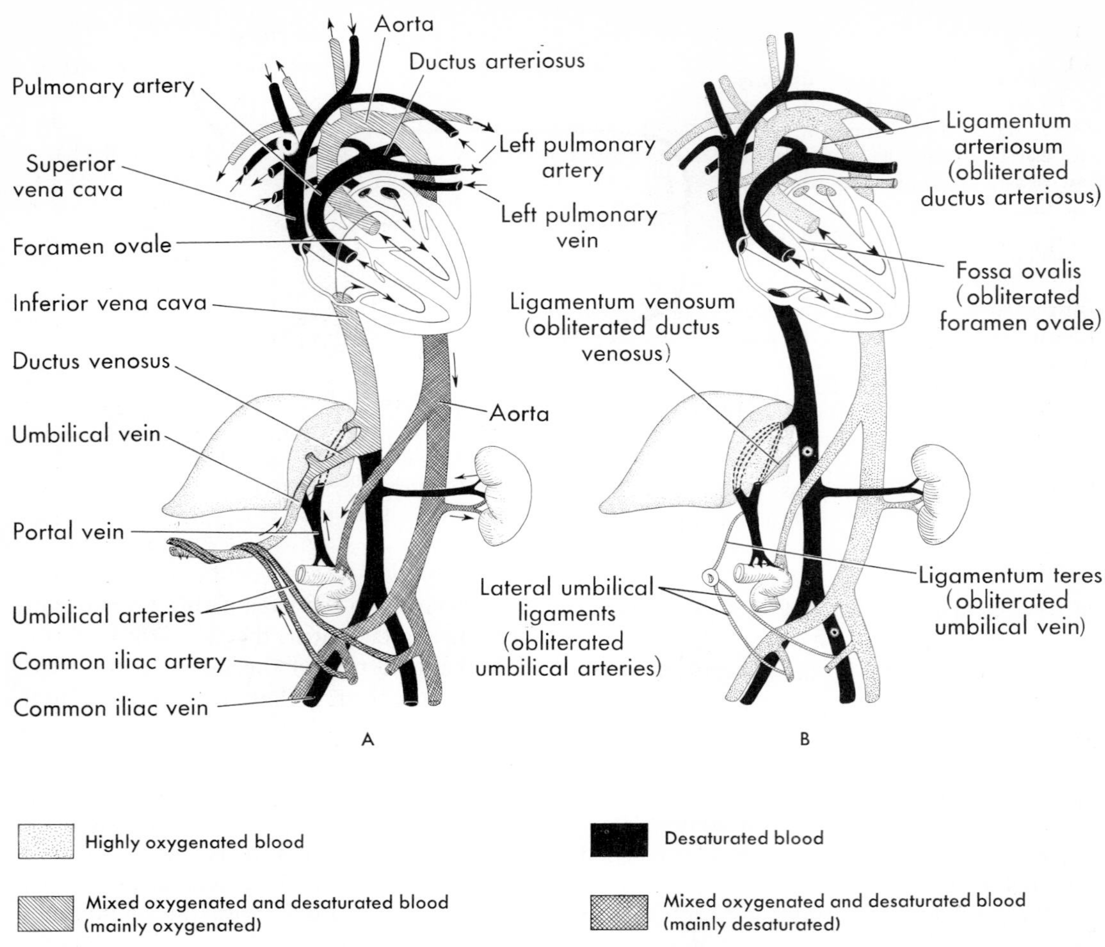

Figure 27–14. (*A*) Fetal circulation. (*B*) Circulation after birth.

artery. During fetal life resistance in the pulmonary vascular system is very high, causing the blood to pass through the *ductus arteriosus* into the descending thoracic aorta, where it mixes with blood from the left heart. The *umbilical arteries*, branches of the hypogastric arteries, return the fetal blood to the placenta, where it is reoxygenated, receives nutrients diffused from the mother's blood, and discharges the excess carbon dioxide and nitrogenous metabolic wastes into her circulation. The capillary networks of fetal and maternal circulation are not directly connected, as has previously been stated, but are in close association within the placenta so that diffusion of products between the two separate systems is feasible. At the end of pregnancy a small portion of blood may be carried by the pulmonary artery through the fetal lungs.

Changes in the Blood Circulation After Birth. At birth a number of changes occur in the newborn due to the cessation of the placental flow and the beginning of lung respiration. When the amniotic fluid in the alveolar sacs and bronchial tree is replaced by air at birth and when the pressure in the right atrium decreases as a result of interruption of the placental blood flow, many of the fetal vascular structures are no longer needed and they cease functioning. The *ductus arteriosus* closes because of muscular contraction of its wall. The amount of blood flowing through the lung increases as the fluid is expelled and as breathing fills the lungs with air. Since the blood pressure within the right atrium has decreased as a result of the interrupted placental flow and the pulmonary pressure increases as a result of the increased pulmonary blood flow, the pressure becomes equalized on both sides of the *foramen ovale*. The *septum primum* is then apposed to the *septum secundum*, and the interatrial opening closes functionally. In 20 per cent of all adults perfect anatomical closure of the foramen ovale may never be obtained, although there may be no flow of blood from one atrium directly into the other. Anatomic fusion of the two septa is usually completed at the end of the first year of life.

The umbilical arteries, umbilical vein, and ductus venosus close shortly after birth owing to contraction of smooth muscle of the vessel walls as a result of the ligation of the umbilical cord and the thermal and mechanical stimuli, as well as a change in oxygen tension. Following their obliteration, the umbilical arteries become the *lateral vesicoumbilical ligaments*, and the umbilical vein becomes the connective tissue band, the *ligamentum teres hepatis*, in the margin of the *falciform ligament*. The ductus arteriosus closes almost immediately after birth following the contraction of its muscular wall and becomes the fibrous band known as the *ligamentum arteriosum*. If either the foramen ovale or the ductus arteriosus does not become entirely obliterated, the affected child may suffer from inadequate oxygenation of his blood, resulting in a bluish appearance of the skin, known as cyanosis, especially after exertion.

Complete anatomical closure of all these structures by proliferation of vessel wall intima and fibrous tissues takes anywhere from several months to a year.

Some Congenital Malformations and Their Causes. Congenital malformations, or "gross structural defects," present at birth may be caused by a great variety of viral infections or chromosomal and genetic factors. It is estimated that approximately 10 per cent are caused by environmental factors, 10 per cent are due to genetic and chromosomal factors, and the remaining 80 per cent are due to some combination of both genetic and environmental factors.

Malformations of the fetus have been known to follow maternal infection with measles, mumps, chickenpox, hepatitis, poliomyelitis, and German measles (rubella). At present it is well established that rubella virus affecting pregnant women during the first three and perhaps four months of gestation can cause malformations of the eye, internal ear, and heart and may also be responsible for some cases of mental retardation and brain abnormalities. Damage to the nervous system, cleft palate, damage to fetal extremities, or mutations which may later lead to the occurrence of congenital malformations in succeeding generations may result from treating pregnant women with large doses of roentgen rays or radium. Mothers who have taken thalidomide, an antinauseant and hypnotic, have had babies with total or partial absence of the extremities. Other defects produced by thalidomide are intestinal atresia and cardiac anomalies. Other drugs such as quinine and the antimetabolite aminopterin and excessively large amounts of progestins may cause congenital malformations. Factors such as nutritional deficiencies, abnormal maternal antibodies, hypoxia, and maternal diabetes are under investigation for their role in the incidence of congenital abnormalities.

An abnormal number or configuration of chromosomes of the fetus may result in congenital malformation. Individuals with mongolism have three number 21 chromosomes. Mental retardation, congenital heart defects, deafness, cleft lip and palate, or other defects may be found in the child with extra chromosomes numbers 13 to 15 and 17 to 18.

Abnormalities in the sex chromosomes may cause congenital defects. If, during meiosis of the female sex cell, the two homologous X chromosomes fail to separate and move instead into one daughter cell, the resultant ovum has either two X chromosomes or none. If an ovum with two X chromosomes combines with a sperm containing a Y chromosome, the result is a male with an XXY complement (Klinefelter's syndrome). Some of the important features of this syndrome are testicular atrophy, sterility, and mental retardation. If the ovum without sex chromosomes is fertilized by a sperm containing an X chromosome, the result is an individual with an XO complement (Turner's syndrome).

This condition found in women is characterized by the absence of ovaries. Last, if an ovum containing two X chromosomes combines with an X sperm, the result is an XXX individual. Women with the triple-X syndrome have some degree of mental retardation, are infantile, and have scant menses.

Many congenital malformations in man are inherited and in many cases may be due to a change in a single gene. Malformations may be caused by autosomal dominant or recessive inheritance or by abnormal genes carried by the X chromosome. A mutation or sudden and persistent change in the expression of a gene may also cause congenital malformation.

Many factors may cause congenital malformations, and they must be considered in the plan for pregnancy and maternal care during gestation, especially during the first four months of embryonic differentiation of tissues. The importance of adequate prenatal care cannot be overemphasized.

QUESTIONS FOR DISCUSSION

1. Explain why no two children in the same family (unless they are identical twins) have exactly the same physical appearance despite the fact that every child has received 23 chromosomes from each of his parents.
2. Explain how the diploid number of chromosomes is reduced to the haploid number of single chromosomes during meiosis.
3. How many spermatozoa are formed from one primary spermatocyte? What percentage of the spermatozoa will carry X chromosomes?
4. What is crossing over and when may it occur?
5. How many ova are produced from each primary oocyte? When do the first and second maturation divisions occur? What are polar bodies and what happens to them after meiosis is completed?
6. If one parent is homozygous for brown eyes (B brown, B brown) and the other parent is heterozygous for brown eyes (B brown, b blue), can any of their children have blue eyes? Explain.
7. What important structures are developed from the embryoblast and from the trophoblast of the blastocyst?
8. Explain the development and functions of the placenta. What is the placental barrier, how is it formed, and what are its functions?
9. Describe fetal circulation before birth. Explain the causes of circulatory changes in the newborn infant.
10. What important parts of the body are developed from the ectoderm? The mesoderm? The entoderm?
11. Name several factors which may prevent fertilization of the ovum.

SUMMARY

Development of Germinal Tissues	Germinal tissues can be distinguished in six-week embryo, become genital folds in dorsal region of embryo Gonads are formed from genital folds at 10–11 weeks Primordial germ cells that have migrated to gonads remain dormant until puberty
Maturation of Germ Cells	Process whereby male and female reproductive cells grow, develop, reduce their number of chromosomes to 23, and are prepared for fertilization **Oogenesis**—process of egg formation **Spermatogenesis**—process of sperm formation
Spermatogenesis	Four spermatozoa formed from each primary spermatocyte Two of these cells carry an X chromosome Two of these cells carry a Y chromosome Two maturation divisions of meiosis take place in the formation of spermatozoa from primary spermatocytes Some crossing over undoubtedly occurs during first maturation division

Oogenesis

- Primitive female germ cells, oogonia, formed in embryo
- Oogonia located in clusters in ovarian cortex, surrounded by layer of flat epithelial cells
- Fourth to seventh month of fetal life—oogonium differentiates into primary oocyte which enters prophase of meiosis
- First maturation division—one secondary oocyte, one polar body
- Second maturation division—one mature oocyte (ovum), three polar bodies
- Ovum contains 23 chromosomes, polar bodies degenerate

Meiosis

- Special type of cell division which achieves a reduction in chromosomes from 46, or diploid number, to 23, or haploid number. Meiosis is composed of two maturation divisions
- **First maturation division**
  - Chromosomes begin to pair; synapsis—entwining of homologous chromosomes in center of cell
  - Each chromosome duplicates itself and becomes doubled, or dyad
  - Kinetocore or centromere—band binding dyad, constriction in chromosome
  - Tetrad-paired double chromosomes or chromatids
  - Crossing over—transfer and recombination of genes that lie on homologous chromosomes
  - Chiasmata—represent regions where crossing over has occurred
  - Cell completes prophase, metaphase, anaphase, and telophase
- **Second maturation division**
  - Each cell now has single set of 23 chromosomes
  - Polar bodies degenerate, have no role in reproduction

Significance of Meiosis

- Halves number of chromosomes
- Provides opportunity for crossing over and reshuffling of genes
- Provides offspring with infinite variations resulting in greater individuality

Fertilization

- Ovum conveyed to uterine tube by currents created in peritoneal fluid by fimbriae and cilia of tubular mucosa
- Flagella of spermatozoa propel them only 1–4 mm per minute, their ascent in female tract believed to be assisted by aspiration following tubular and uterine contractions
- Only one out of 200–300 million deposited sperm necessary for fertilization—penetration of ovum assisted by enzyme, hyaluronidase, released by one or more sperm
- Head and tail of sperm enter ovum
- Fertilization—normally occurs when nucleus of spermatozoon fuses with nucleus of ovum to form *zygote*; occurs in distal third of uterine tube
- Pronuclei of sperm and ovum join to restore 46 or diploid number of chromosomes

Inheritance

- Heredity—term applied to transmission of potential traits, physical or mental, from parents to their offspring; offspring receives one chromosome of a homologous pair from each of his parents
- Autosome—chromosome that carries same general set of genes as its mate, 44 in man
- 22 pairs of homologous, one pair of sex chromosomes
- Heterozygous—having alternate genes for the same trait, e.g., one gene for blue and one for brown eyes
- Homozygous—having two similar genes for the same trait, e.g., two genes for brown eyes
- Dominant gene—gene whose trait is bound to appear under normal circumstances

Inheritance (*cont.*)

- Recessive gene—gene whose trait will not appear usually unless two of them are present or dominance is not complete
- Capital letter used to denote dominant trait, small letter for recessive trait
- Dominance may be complete, partial, or absent
- Alleles—genes that carry the same trait and occupy the same position or locus on the chromosomes—come together during synapsis
- Gregor Mendel—"father of modern genetics," responsible for whole development of the gene concept
- Genotype—refers to type of genes present in individual
- Phenotype—refers to expression of genes present
- Total final expression of individual's characteristics due to blending of hereditary and environmental factors
- **Genetic abnormalities**
  - Abnormalities may be inherited as dominants over normal condition, e.g., extra digits or excessively short digits, or may be recessive to the normal, e.g., albinism
  - Some abnormalities appear as sex-linked recessives evident in males with only one factor, but in females only when two factors are present, e.g., red-green color blindness or hemophilia
  - Abnormal number of chromosomes, especially of sex chromosomes, results in abnormality

Early Development of the Embryo—Cleavage Formation of Morula and Blastocyst

- Cleavage—consists of a number of rapid mitotic divisions which result in an increasing number of smaller cells known as *blastomeres*
- Morula—16–20-cell stage of cleavage resulting in hollow ball of cells—inner cell mass forms embryo and embryonic membranes, the amnion and yolk sac—outer cell mass forms the trophoblast from which the chorion is developed
- Morula reaches uterine cavity 3–4 days after ovulation
- Blastocyst—formed when cavity appears between inner and outer cell masses

Implantation of Blastocyst

- Implantation—uterine attachment of the blastocyst—occurs 7–9 days after ovulation and normally in the endometrium
- Decidua—modified uterine mucosa during pregnancy—can be divided into three parts: *decidua basalis* at base of placenta, *decidua capsularis* portion surrounding surface of chorionic sac, and *decidua parietalis* that lines the rest of the uterus

Major Events in Development of Blastocyst

- Blastocyst—made up of *trophoblast* and *embryoblast*
- Embryoblast gives rise to *ectoderm*, *entoderm*, and *mesoderm*
- Trophoblast has inner layer, *cytotrophoblast*, and outer layer, *syncytiotrophoblast*
- Amniotic cavity—forms between trophoblast and ectoderm—fills with fluid to protect and nourish the embryo
- Connecting stalk—later becomes umbilical cord, attaches embryo to placenta
- Primitive streak and notochord (embryonic backbone) formed in midline from modified ectodermal cells; notochord later replaced by segmented vertebral column
- Posterior cloacal membrane—formed from joining of ectoderm and entoderm, urogenital and anal membranes formed from it
- Prochordal plate—appears at anterior ectodermal attachment—buccopharyngeal membrane formed from this plate
- Allantois and yolk sac—pocketlike extensions of ventral side of embryo—they can be seen in umbilical cord of young embryo
- Neural tube—developed from ectoderm—gives rise to brain, spinal cord, autonomic and spinal nerves
- Embryonic period—the first two months of development during which all major body systems are formed

Portions of the Body Derived from Ectoderm

1. Central nervous system and hypophysis
2. Peripheral nervous system
3. Sensory epithelium of sense organs
4. Enamel of teeth
5. Epidermis including hair, nails, and subcutaneous glands

Portions of the Body Derived from Mesoderm

1. Cartilage, joints, and bones
2. Connective tissue
3. Heart, blood, and lymph cells and vessels
4. Spleen
5. Serous membranes
6. Kidneys, gonads, and their ducts

Portions of the Body Derived from Entoderm

1. Epithelial lining of digestive and respiratory tracts and parts of bladder and urethra
2. Epithelial lining of tympanic cavity and eustachian tube
3. Main cellular portions of tonsils, parathyroids, thymus, liver, pancreas, and gallbladder

Development of Extremities

Fore- and hindlimbs appear as buds at beginning of second month—as buds grow, they undergo 90° rotation in opposite directions—elbow points dorsally, knee ventrally

The Fetal Period

Interval from beginning of third month to end of intrauterine life—major changes are brought about by rapid body growth—at end of 4th–5th month the CH length is approximately 23 cm and the weight 500 gm

At birth the fetus is approximately 50 cm long and the weight is about 3,200 gm

Placental Development and Functions

Chorion frondosum—embryonic portion of placenta

Decidua basalis—maternal portion of placenta

Chorion laeve—portion of chorion that is smooth, almost nonvascular, and projects into uterus

Main functions of placenta—exchange of gaseous and metabolic products between fetus and mother and production of hormones

Development of Blood Circulation Within Placenta

Intervillous spaces between chorionic and decidual plates are filled with maternal blood and are lined with syncytium of fetal origin

Fetal villous capillaries derived from umbilical arteries and veins project into these spaces where they are bathed with oxygenated blood from maternal circulation

Placental barrier—is made up of fetal tissue starting with four layers, but retaining only two after fourth month—endothelial lining of capillaries and syncytial covering—thinner layer allows for more rapid exchange of nutrients, gases, metabolic products, hormones, and antibodies

Fetal Circulation

Umbilical cord—unites the placenta with the navel of the fetus—contains *two umbilical arteries*, extensions from fetal hypogastric arteries, and one umbilical vein that travels in falciform ligament of fetus to the ductus venosus—these vessels are surrounded by soft mucous connective tissue called *Wharton's jelly*

Direct communication between right and left atrium by means of *foramen ovale*

Direct communication between pulmonary artery and aorta known as *ductus arteriosus*

Direct communication between umbilical vein and inferior vena cava through *ductus venosus*

Oxygen and nutritive substances diffuse from maternal blood in placenta across placental barrier to fetal blood. Carbon dioxide and metabolic wastes diffuse from fetal capillaries in placenta across the same barrier into maternal blood

Changes in Circulation of Infant Following Birth	Infant respiration stimulates pulmonary circulation; this causes a rise in blood pressure in left atrium—pressure is equalized across atrial septum and connective tissue begins to close over foramen ovale—will become *fossa ovalis* Ductus arteriosus becomes fibrous cord—*ligamentum arteriosum* Umbilical vein becomes fibrous cord—*ligamentum teres*, or round ligament, in edge of falciform ligament Ductus venosus becomes fibrous cord—*ligamentum venosum* Umbilical arteries are obliterated to become *lateral vesicoumbilical ligaments*, their most proximal portions remain as *hypogastric* arteries Complete anatomical closure of all these structures takes from several months to a year

REFERENCE BOOKS AND BOOKS FOR FURTHER STUDY

GROSS ANATOMY

Cunningham's Textbook of Anatomy, 10th ed., edited by G. J. Romanes. New York: Oxford University Press, 1964.

GRANT, J. C. B.: *An Atlas of Anatomy*, 5th ed. Baltimore: The Williams & Wilkins Company, 1962.

——, and BASMAJIAN, J. V.: *A Method of Anatomy*, 7th ed. Baltimore: The Williams & Wilkins Company, 1965.

Gray's Anatomy of the Human Body, 28th ed., edited by C. M. Goss. Philadelphia: Lea & Febiger, 1966.

LOCKHART, R. D.; HAMILTON, G. F.; and FYFE, F. W.: *Anatomy of the Human Body*. Philadelphia: J. B. Lippincott Company, 1965.

Morris' Human Anatomy, 12th ed., edited by B. J. Anson. New York: The Blakiston Division, McGraw-Hill Book Company, 1966.

NETTER, FRANK H.: "The Digestive System." *The Ciba Collection of Medical Illustrations*. Summit, N.J.: Ciba Pharmaceutical Products, Inc., 1957. Vol. 3, parts 1, 2, 3.

PANSKY, BEN, and HOUSE, EARL L.: *Review of Gross Anatomy*, 2nd ed. New York: The Macmillan Company, 1969.

——, and ——: *Study Wheels in Human Anatomy*. New York: The Macmillan Company, 1965.

QUIRING, D. P.: *Collateral Circulation. Anatomical Aspects*. Philadelphia: Lea & Febiger, 1949.

——: *The Extremities*, 2nd ed. Philadelphia: Lea & Febiger, 1960.

——: *The Head, Neck and Trunk*, 2nd ed. Philadelphia: Lea & Febiger, 1960.

SOBOTTA, J., and FIGGE, F. H.: *Atlas of Human Anatomy*. New York: Hafner Publisher, 1963. 3 vols.

WISCHNITZER, SAUL: *Outline of Human Anatomy*. New York: The Blakiston Division, McGraw-Hill Book Company, 1963.

WOODBURNE, RUSSELL T.: *Essentials of Human Anatomy*, 3rd ed. New York: Oxford University Press, 1965.

ZUCKERMAN, SIR SOLLY: *A New System of Anatomy*. New York: Oxford University Press, 1962.

HISTOLOGY—MICROSCOPIC ANATOMY

AREY, LESLIE BRAINERD: *Human Histology*, 3rd ed. Philadelphia: W. B. Saunders Company, 1968.

Bailey's Textbook of Histology, 15th ed., edited by W. M. COPENHAVER and D. D. JOHNSON. Baltimore: The Williams & Wilkins Company, 1964.

BLOOM, W., and FAWCETT, D. W.: *Textbook of Histology*, 9th ed. Philadelphia: W. B. Saunders Company, 1968.

CARPENTER, A. M.: *Human Histology*. New York: The Blakiston Division, McGraw-Hill Book Company, 1968.

Ciba Foundation: *Cell Differentiation*. Boston: Little, Brown & Company, 1968.

COWDRY, E. V., and FINERTY, J. C.: *A Textbook of Histology*, 5th ed. Philadelphia: Lea & Febiger, 1960.

CRUICKSHANK, BRUCE; DODDS, T. C.; and GARDNER, D. L.: *Human Histology*. Baltimore: The Williams & Wilkins Company, 1968.

GREEP, ROY O.: *Histology*, 2nd ed. New York: The Blakiston Division, McGraw-Hill Book Company, 1965.

HAM, A. W., and LEESON, T. S.: *Histology*, 5th ed. Philadelphia: J. B. Lippincott Company, 1969.

NEUROANATOMY AND NEUROPHYSIOLOGY

ALPERS, BERNARD J.: *Clinical Neurology.* Philadelphia: F. A. Davis Company, 1963.

ALVAREZ, W. C.: *Nervousness, Indigestion and Pain.* New York: Paul B. Hoeber, Inc., 1954.

BURN, H. J.: *The Autonomic Nervous System.* Philadelphia: F. A. Davis Company, 1968.

CROSBY, E. C.; HUMPHREY, T.; and LAUER, E. W.: *Correlative Anatomy of the Nervous System.* New York: The Macmillan Company, 1962.

ELLIOTT, H. C.: *Textbook of Neuroanatomy.* Philadelphia: L. B. Lippincott Company, 1963.

EYZAGUIRRE, C.: *Physiology of the Nervous System.* New York: Year Book, 1969.

GARDNER, E.: *Fundamentals of Neurology*, 4th ed. Philadelphia: W. B. Saunders Company, 1963.

HOUSE, E. LAWRENCE, and PANSKY, BEN: *A Functional Approach to Neuroanatomy.* New York: The Blakiston Division, McGraw-Hill Book Company, 1967.

MAGOUN, H. W.: *The Walking Brain*, 2nd ed. Springfield, Ill.: Charles C Thomas, Publisher, 1963.

MILLEN, J. W., and WOOLLAM, D. H. M.: *The Anatomy of Cerebrospinal Fluid.* New York: Oxford University Press, 1962.

NETTER, F. H.: *The Nervous System*, 5th ed. Summit, N.J.: Ciba Pharmaceutical Products, Inc., 1962. Vol. I.

PENFIELD, W., and RASMUSSEN, T.: *The Cerebral Cortex of Man.* New York: The Macmillan Company, 1950.

RANSON, S. W., and CLARK, S. L.: *Anatomy of the Nervous System*, 10th ed. Philadelphia: W. B. Saunders Company, 1959.

RASMUSSEN, A. T.: *Principal Nervous Pathways*, 4th ed. New York: The Macmillan Company, 1952.

Strong and Elwyn's Human Neuro-anatomy, 5th ed., revised by R. C. Truex and M. B. Carpenter. Baltimore: The Williams & Wilkins Company, 1964.

WYBURN, G. M.: *The Nervous System.* New York: Academic Press, Inc., 1960.

DEVELOPMENTAL ANATOMY AND GENETICS

ALLAN, FRANK D.: *Essentials of Human Embryology.* New York: Oxford University Press, 1960.

AREY, L. B.: *Developmental Anatomy*, 6th ed. Philadelphia: W. B. Saunders Company, 1965.

BEADLE, GEORGE and MURIEL: *The Language of Life.* Garden City, N. Y.: Doubleday, 1966.

COLIN, E. C.: Elements of Genetics: *Mendel's Laws of Heredity with Special Application to Man*, 3rd ed. New York: McGraw-Hill Book Company, 1956.

GUTTMACHER, A. F.: *Birth Control and Love.* New York: The Macmillan Company, 1969.

HAMILTON, W. J.; BOYD, J. D.; and MOSSMAN, H. W.: *Human Embryology* (*Prenatal Development of Form and Function*), 3rd ed. Baltimore: The Williams & Wilkins Company, 1962.

KEMPTHORNE, O.: *Biometrical Genetics.* New York: The Macmillan Company, 1960.

KORMONDY, EDWARD J.: *Introduction to Genetics.* New York: The Blakiston Division, McGraw-Hill Book Company, 1964.

LANGMAN, JAN: *Medical Embryology.* Baltimore: The Williams & Wilkins Company, 1963.

LEVINE, R. P.: *Genetics.* New York: Holt, Rinehart and Winston, Inc., 1962.

LI, C. C.: *Human Genetics.* New York: The Blakiston Division, McGraw-Hill Book Company, 1961.

MOORE, JOHN A.: *Heredity and Development.* New York: Oxford University Press, 1963.

PATTEN, BRADLEY M.: *Foundations of Embryology*, 2nd ed. New York: The Blakiston Division, McGraw-Hill Book Company, 1964.

REISMAN, L. E., and MATHENY, A. P., Jr.: *Genetic Counseling in Medical Practice.* St. Louis: The C. V. Mosby Company, 1969.

ROBERTS, J. A.: *An Introduction to Medical Genetics*, 4th ed. New York: Oxford University Press, 1967.

THOMPSON, J. S., and THOMPSON, M. U.: *Genetics in Medicine.* Philadelphia: W. B. Saunders Company, 1966.

WINCHESTER, A. M.: *Heredity. An Introduction to Genetics.* New York: Barnes and Noble, 1961.

PHYSIOLOGY

BEST, C. H., and TAYLOR, N. B. (eds.): *The Physiological Basis of Medical Practice*. Baltimore: The Williams & Wilkins Company, 1966.

BROWSE, NORMAN L.: *The Physiology and Pathology of Bed Rest*. Springfield, Ill.: Charles C Thomas, Publisher, 1965.

CANNON, W. B.: *Bodily Changes in Pain, Hunger, Fear, and Rage*, 2nd ed. New York: Appleton-Century-Crofts, Inc., 1929.

——: *The Wisdom of the Body*. New York: W. W. Norton and Company, 1963.

DAVSON, HUGH (ed.): *Principles of Human Physiology*, 13th ed. London: J. & A. Churchill, Ltd., 1962.

EXTON-SMITH *et al.*: *Vitamins in the Elderly*. Baltimore: The Williams & Wilkins Company, 1968.

FINNESON, B. E.: *Diagnosis and Management of Pain Syndrome*, 2nd ed. Philadelphia: W. B. Saunders Company, 1969.

GANONG, WILLIAM F.: *Review of Medical Physiology*. Los Altos, Calif.: Lange Medical Publications, 1969.

GUYTON, A. C.: *Textbook of Medical Physiology*. Philadelphia: W. B. Saunders Company, 1971.

HORROBIN, D. F.: *Medical Physiology and Biochemistry*. Baltimore: The Williams & Wilkins Company, 1968.

KORENCHEVSKY, V.: *Physiological and Pathological Aging*. New York: Hafner Publishing Company, 1961.

LEAVELL, BYRD, and THORUP, OSCAR: *Fundamentals of Clinical Hematology*, 2nd ed. Philadelphia: W. B. Saunders Company, 1966.

MCDOWALL, R. J. S.: *Handbook of Physiology*, 43rd ed. New York: The Blakiston Division, McGraw-Hill Book Company, 1960.

MONTAGNA, W., *et al.*: *Advances in Biology of Skin*. Vol. II. *Blood Vessels and Circulation*. New York: The Macmillan Company, 1961.

MOUNTCASTLE, V. B. (ed.): *Medical Physiology*. St. Louis: The C. V. Mosby Company, 1968.

REEVE, E. B., and GUYTON, A. C.: *Physical Basis of Circulatory Transport*. Philadelphia: W. B. Saunders Company, 1967.

RUCH, T. C., and FULTON, J. F. (eds.): *Medical Physiology and Biophysics*, 19th ed. of Howell's *Textbook of Physiology*. Philadelphia: W. B. Saunders Company, 1965.

RUSHMER, R. F.: *Cardiovascular Dynamics*. Philadelphia: W. B. Saunders Company, 1961.

SELKURT, EWALD E. (ed.): *Physiology*. Boston: Little, Brown & Company, 1965.

SODEMAN, WILLIAM A., and SODEMAN, W. A., Jr. (eds.): *Pathologic Physiology*, 4th ed. Philadelphia: W. B. Saunders Company, 1967.

STARLING, E. H., and LOVATT, EVANS: *Principles of Human Physiology*, 14th ed., by Hugh Davson and M. Grace Eggleton. Philadelphia: Lea & Febiger, 1968.

WINTON, F. R., and BAYLISS, L. E.: *Human Physiology*, 5th ed. London: J. & A. Churchill, Ltd., 1962.

WRIGHT, S.: *Applied Physiology*, 11th ed., revised by Cyril A. Keele and Eric Neil. New York: Oxford University Press, 1965.

YOUMANS, WILLIAM B.: *Fundamentals of Human Physiology for Students in the Medical Sciences*, 2nd ed. Chicago: Year Book Medical Publishers, Inc., 1961.

STRESS

SELYE, HANS: *The Story of the Adaptation Syndrome*. Montreal: Acta, Inc., 1952.

——: *Stress*. Montreal: Acta, Inc., 1950.

——: *The Stress of Life*. New York: McGraw-Hill Book Company, 1956.

ENDOCRINOLOGY

GROLLMAN, ARTHUR: *Principles of Endocrinology*. Philadelphia: J. B. Lippincott Company, 1964.

HARRIS, R. S.: *Vitamins and Hormones*. New York: Academic Press, Inc., 1968.

WILLIAMS, R. H. (ed.): *Textbook of Endocrinology*, 3rd ed. Philadelphia: W. B. Saunders Company, 1968.

CELLS AND BODY FLUIDS

American Association for the Advancement of Science: *Cell and Protoplasm*, edited by F. R. Moulton. Publication No. 14. New York: Science Press, 1940.

ANDREW, W.: *Cellular Changes with Age*. Springfield, Ill.: Charles C Thomas, Publisher, 1952.

ASIMOV, ISAAC: *The Living River*. New York: Abelard-Schuman, 1959.

——: *The Wellsprings of Life*. New York: The New American Library, 1960.

BLAND, JOHN H.: *Clinical Metabolism of Body Water and Electrolytes*. Philadelphia: W. B. Saunders Company, 1963.

BOWSHER, DAVID: *Cerebrospinal Fluid Dynamics in Health and Disease*. Springfield, Ill.: Charles C Thomas, Publisher, 1960.

BUTLER, J. A. V.: *Inside the Living Cell*. New York: Basic Books, Inc., 1959.

CHRISTENSEN, H. N.: *Body Fluids and the Acid-Base Balance: A Learning Program for Students of the Biological and Medical Sciences*. Philadelphia: W. B. Saunders Company, 1964.

DEROBERTS, E. D.; NOWINSKI, W. W.; and SALY, F. A.: *Cell Biology*, 4th ed. Philadelphia: W. B. Saunders Company, 1965.

FREEMAN, JAMES A.: *Cellular Fine Structure*. New York: The Blakiston Division, McGraw-Hill Book Company, 1964.

GAMBLE, J. L.: *Chemical Anatomy, Physiology and Pathology of Extracellular Fluid: A Lecture Syllabus*, 6th ed. Cambridge, Mass.: Harvard University Press, 1954.

GERARD, R. W.: *Unresting Cells*, new ed. New York: Harper & Brothers, 1949.

GIESE, ARTHUR C.: *Cell Physiology*. Philadelphia: W. B. Saunders Company, 1967.

HUTCHINS, CARLEEN M.: *Life's Key—DNA*. New York: Coward-McCann, Inc., 1961.

LOEWY, ARIEL G., and SIEKEVITZ, PHILIP: *Cell Structure and Function*. New York: Holt, Rinehart and Winston, 1963.

MCELROY, WM. D.: *Cell Physiology and Biochemistry*, 2nd ed. Englewood Cliffs, N.J.: Prentice-Hall, Inc., 1964.

MAZIA, DANIEL, and TYLER, ALBERT (eds.): *General Physiology of Cell Specialization*. New York: The Blakiston Division, McGraw-Hill Book Company, 1963.

Readings from the Scientific American: *The Living Cell*. San Francisco: W. H. Freeman Company, 1965.

SNIVELY, WILLIAM D., Jr.: *Sea Within: Story of our Body Fluid*. Philadelphia: J. B. Lippincott Company, 1960.

STATLAND, HARRY: *Fluid and Electrolytes in Practice*, 3rd ed. Philadelphia: J. B. Lippincott Company, 1963.

SWANSON, CARL P.: *The Cell*. Englewood Cliffs, N.J.: Prentice-Hall, Inc., 1960.

WILSON, G. B., and MORRISON, J. H.: *Cytology*. New York: Reinhold Publishing Corporation, 1961.

CHEMISTRY, BIOCHEMISTRY, AND NUTRITION

BELL, G. H.; DAVIDSON, J. N.; and SCARBOROUGH, H.: *Textbook of Physiology and Biochemistry*, 5th ed. Baltimore: The Williams & Wilkins Company, 1961.

CHRISTENSEN, H. N., and PALMER, G. A.: *Enzyme Kinetics* (A Learning Program for Students of the Biological and Medical Sciences). Philadelphia: W. B. Saunders Company, 1967.

Hawk's Physiological Chemistry, 14th ed., edited by Bernard L. Oser. New York: The Blakiston Division, McGraw-Hill Book Company, 1965.

HODGMAN, CHARLES D. (ed.-in-chief): *Handbook of Chemistry and Physics*, revised annually. Cleveland, Ohio: Chemical Rubber Publishing Co.

KINLEER, ISRAEL S., and ORTEN, JAMES M.: *Biochemistry*, 6th ed. St. Louis: The C. V. Mosby Company, 1962.

TAYLOR, C. M., and PYE, O. F.: *Foundations of Nutrition*, 6th ed. New York: The Macmillan Company, 1966.

WEBER, G.: *Regulation of Enzyme Activity*. New York: The Macmillan Company, 1965.

WEST, E. S.; TODD, W. R.; MASON, H. S.; and VAN BRUGGEN, J. T.: *Textbook of Biochemistry*, 4th ed. New York: The Macmillan Company, 1966.

WHITE, ABRAHAM; HANDLER, P.; SMITH, E.; and STETTEN, D., Jr.: *Principles of Biochemistry*, 3rd ed. New York: McGraw-Hill Book Company, 1964.

WOHL, MICHAEL, and GOODHART, ROBERT: *Modern Nutrition in Health and Disease*, 3rd ed. Philadelphia: Lea & Febiger, 1964.

LABORATORY MANUALS—ANATOMY AND PHYSIOLOGY

BENSLEY, B. A.: *Practical Anatomy of the Rabbit*, revised ed., by E. Horne Craigie. New York: The Blakiston Division, McGraw-Hill Book Company, 1957.

GREENE, E. G.: *Anatomy of the Rat*. Philadelphia: American Philosophical Society, 1935.

REIGHARD, Jr.; JENNINGS, H. S.; and ELLIOTT, R.: *Anatomy of the Cat*, 3rd ed. New York: Henry Holt and Company, 1935.

TUTTLE, W. W., and SCHOTTELIUS, B. A.: *Physiology Laboratory Manual*. St. Louis: The C. V. Mosby Company, 1963.

VISSCHER, M. B., *et al.*: *Experimental Physiology*, 2nd ed. Minneapolis: Burgess Publishing Company, 1950.

ZOETHOUT, W. D.: *Laboratory Experiments in Physiology*, 6th ed. St. Louis: The C. V. Mosby Company, 1963.

DICTIONARIES

ASIMOV, ISAAC: *Words of Science*. Boston: Houghton Mifflin Company, 1959.

Blakiston's New Gould Medical Dictionary, 2nd ed. New York: The Blakiston Division, McGraw-Hill Book Company, 1956.

Dorland's Illustrated Medical Dictionary, 24th ed. Philadelphia: W. B. Saunders Company, 1965.

JAEGER, EDMUND C.: *A Source-Book of Biological Names and Terms*, 3rd ed. Springfield, Ill.: Charles C Thomas, Publisher, 1962.

Stedman's Medical Dictionary, 21st ed. Baltimore: The Williams & Wilkins Company, 1966.

METRIC SYSTEM

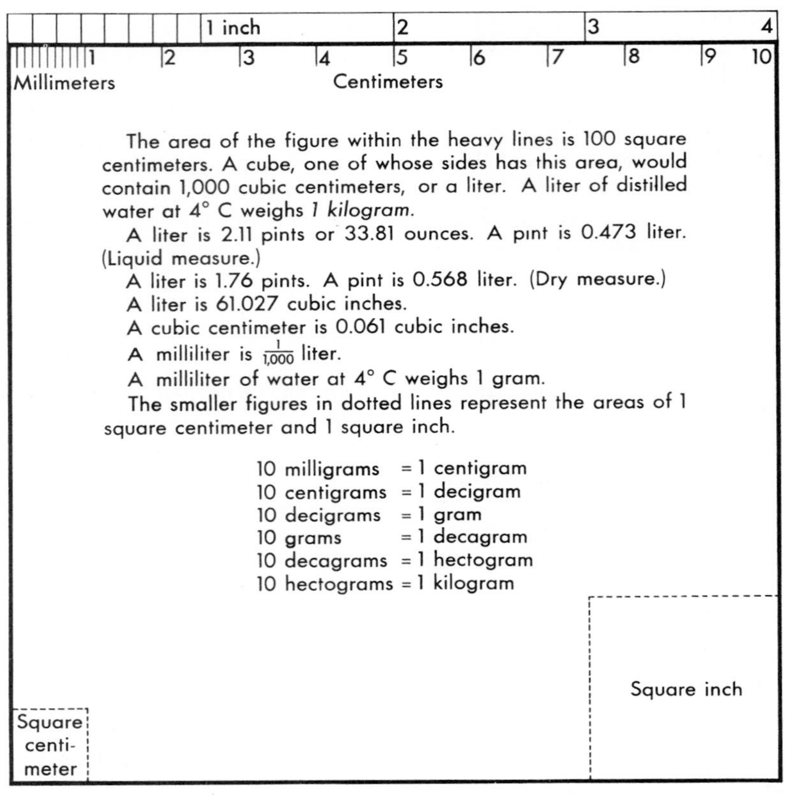

1 millimeter = 0.039 inch
1 centimeter = 0.393 inch
1 decimeter = 3.937 inches
1 meter = 39.370 inches

1 milligram = 0.015 grain
1 centigram = 0.154 grain
1 micron (μ) = 0.001 millimeter
1 millimicron ($m\mu$ or $\mu\mu$) = 0.000001 millimeter
1 Å, or Angstrom unit = 0.0001 μ, or 10^{-7} millimeters

1 decigram = 1.543 grains
1 gram = 15.432 grains
1 decagram = 154.323 grains
1 hectogram = 1,543.235 grains
1 kilogram = 15,432.350 grains
1 kilogram = 35.274 ounces
1 kilogram = 2.204 pounds

Avoirdupois weights are used in weighing the organs of the body. One ounce avoirdupois = 28.35 grams. For the sake of simplicity in converting figures in the text from one system to the other, we have assumed

1 in. to equal 25 mm
1 in. to equal 2.5 cm
1 in. to equal 25,000 microns (μ)
1 cm to equal 0.4 in.
1 ml to equal 15 minims
30 ml to equal 1 oz

GLOSSARY

Terms adequately defined in the body of the text are not always included in the Glossary. They may be located through the Index.

acetab′ulum. "Shallow vinegar cup"; the depression in the innominate bone which receives the head of the femur

ac′etone. $(CH_3)_2CO$. A simple ketone with a sweetish odor, present in blood and in body excretions whenever fats are used in metabolism without the presence of sufficient carbohydrate

acro′mion. Point of the shoulder. The spine of the scapula terminates in the acromion process

adsorption. The attachment of one substance to the surface of another

adventi′tia. The outermost layer of the organs which are not bounded by a serous coat, the outer areolar connective tissue being continuous with that of the other organs; e.g., blood vessels have no outer limiting membrane but lie in the common areolar tissue. Often called the *externa*

agglu′tinins. Substances which induce adhesion or clumping together of cells

agglutin′ogen. Substances (ABO) in the red blood cells which when in contact with agglutinins (Aa, Bb) will cause agglutination

al′binism. Congenital absence of the pigment melanin in the skin, iris, and hair. It may be partial or complete

albu′mins. Thick, viscous substances containing nitrogen; soluble in water, dilute acids, dilute salines, and concentrated solutions of magnesium sulfate and sodium chloride. They are coagulated by heat. Examples: egg albumin and serum albumin of blood

ampul′la. A flasklike dilatation of a canal

an′aerobe. Any microorganism which is able to live with free air or oxygen

an′kylose. Immobilization of a joint by pathological or surgical process

anom′aly. Anything unusual, irregular, or contrary to the general rule

an′tigens. Name given to foreign proteins and certain other substances which upon entering the blood stream cause the formation of antibodies in the serum

antimetab′olite. A substance which resembles chemically a normal metabolite but is foreign to the body and competes with, replaces, or antagonizes the latter. These substances may be used to prevent growth of cancer cells

a′pex. The top or pointed extremity of a body

arach′noid. Resembling a cobweb

arboriza′tion. A branching distribution of veinlets or of nerve filaments, especially the branched, terminal ramifications of neurofibrils

au′ricle. Ear. The *pinna* of the ear which with the *external meatus* constitutes the external ear

autonom′ic. Performed without the will; automatic

az′ygos. Without a fellow; single; unpaired

bas′al metab′olism. Rate of energy metabolism of a person at rest 12 to 18 hours after eating, as measured by the calorimeter or a BMR machine

bas′ilar. Pertaining to the base of an object; e.g., basilar artery located at the base of the brain

bicip′ital. Referring to the biceps

blas′tula. A hollow sphere of embryonic cells; the last stage in development before the embryo divides into two layers

brachiocephal′ic. Pertaining to both the upper arm and head, as the brachiocephalic (innominate) artery and veins

cal′cify. Harden by deposit of salts of calcium; petrify

cal′culus, pl., **cal′culi.** A stone

cal′orie. The Calorie is the amount of heat required to raise the temperature of 1 kg of water 1° C. The small calorie is the amount of heat required to raise the temperature of 1 gm of water 1° C

canalic′ulus, pl., **canalic′uli.** A minute channel or vessel

car′dia. The heart. The esophageal orifice of the stomach

castra′tion. Removal of the testes in the male or the ovaries in the female

catacrot′ic. Referring to an irregularity of the

pulse in which the beat is marked by two or more expansions of the artery. A tracing of this pulse shows one or more abnormal elevations on the downward stroke

catal'ysis. A changing of the speed of a reaction, produced by the presence of a substance which does not itself enter the final products

celluli'tis. Inflammation of connective tissue, most commonly of superficial fascia

chi'asm. An X-shaped crossing or decussation, especially that of the fibers of the optic nerve

choa'na. Any funnel-shaped cavity, such as the posterior nares

cholere'tic. Any substance that stimulates secretion and flow of bile

choles'terol. A sterol, $C_{27}H_{43}OH$, found in small quantities in the protoplasm of all cells, especially in nerve tissue, blood cells, and bile. Same as cholesterin

chor'da tym'pani. The tympanic cord, a branch of the facial (seventh cranial) nerve, which traverses the tympanic cavity and joins the gustatory (lingual) nerve

chro'maffin. Certain cells, occurring in the adrenal medulla, along the sympathetic nerves, and in various organs, stain deeply with chrome salts (brownish-yellow), hence the name chromaffin. The whole system of such tissue throughout the body is named the chromaffin or chromaphil system

chro'matin. Portions of the nucleus which stain deeply with basic dyes, e.g., methylene blue

chro'mosomes. Segments of chromatin in the nuclei of cells, concerned with the transmission of hereditary characteristics and the direction of the embryo's development

cica'trix. The mark or scar left after the healing of a wound

cister'na mag'na, or **cister'na cerebel'lo med'ullaris.** That portion of the subarachnoid cavity between the cerebellum and the medulla

clea'vage. The process of division of the fertilized ovum before differentiation into layers occurs

co'don. A triplet of three bases in a DNA or RNA molecule which codes for a specific amino acid

coen'zymes. Nonprotein substances produced by living cells, which are essential for action of certain enzymes

col'loid. A state of matter in which particles having a diameter of 0.1 to 0.001 μ are dispersed in a medium such as water

com'missure. A joining. A bundle of nerve fibers passing from one side of the brain or spinal cord to the other side. The corner or angle of the eyes or lips

congen'ital. Existing from or before birth

cor'acoid. Shaped like a crow's beak; a process of the scapula

cor'pus. A body or mass

cor'tex. The bark or outer layer; the outer portion of an organ

cre'nated. Notched on the edge (indented)

crepita'tion. A grating or crackling sound or sensation, like that produced by fragments of a fractured bone rubbing together

crib'riform. Perforated like a sieve

cu'neiform. Wedge-shaped

cyano'sis. Blueness of the skin, resulting from insufficient oxygenation of the blood

cysti'tis. Inflammation of the bladder

deaminiza'tion. Removal of the amino group, NH_2, from an amino compound

dec'ibel. Unit of loudness, tenth of a bel. Used for measuring loudness, differences of sounds

decid'uous. That which falls off; not permanent

dehydra'tion. Removal of water as from a tissue

delamina'tion. Separation of cells into layers

del'toid. Triangular; resembling in shape the Greek letter Δ, delta

detri'tus. Waste matter from disintegration

diapede'sis. Passing of any of the formed elements of the blood through vessel walls without rupture

diath'esis. A predisposition to certain kinds of disease

dichot'omous. Divided into two; consisting of a pair or pairs

diffu'sion. Continual movement of molecules among each other in liquid or in gases. The passage of a substance through a membrane. The diffusing substance always diffuses from an area of high concentration to an area of lesser concentration (of that particular substance)

dura mater. "Hard mother"; the tough outer membrane enveloping the brain and spinal cord

dyne. Unit of force which, when acting on a mass of 1 gm for 1 second, will cause an acceleration of 1 cm per second

dyspha'gia. Difficulty in swallowing

ectop'ic. Out of place. *Ectopic gestation* refers to pregnancy when the fecundated ovum, instead of entering the uterus, remains in either a fallopian tube or the abdominal cavity

ede'ma. Swelling due to abnormal effusion of serous fluid into the tissues

empir'ical. Founded on experience; relating to the treatment of disease according to symptoms alone, without regard to scientific knowledge

emul'sion. A mixture of two fluids insoluble in each other, where one is dispersed through the other in the form of finely divided globules

endergon'ic. A reaction characterized by absorption of energy; this is characteristic of many anabolic processes, such as synthesis

endochon'dral ossifica'tion. Ossification in which cartilage is formed first and then is gradually replaced with bone

endog'enous. Originating within the organism. Opposite of exogenous

endother'mic. In a reacting system, if heat is absorbed the reaction is said to be endothermic

en'ergy. Capacity or ability to do work, activity, exertion of power

equilib'rium. The balanced condition resulting when opposing forces are exactly equal. The term may refer to the maintenance of correct concentration of constituents of the body fluids or to the harmonious action of the organs of the body as in standing

erg. A unit of work. The work done in moving a body 1 cm against a force of 1 dyne

eth'moid. Resembling a sieve

evagina'tion. Protrusion of some part or organ from its normal position

evapora'tion. The changing of a liquid into a vapor. Heat is necessary for evaporation, and if not otherwise applied it is taken from near objects. Thus, the heat necessary for the evaporation of perspiration is taken from the body

exergon'ic. A reaction characterized by release of free energy; this is characteristic of catabolic reactions

exog'enous. Originating outside the organism; opposite of endogenous

exophthal'mic. Pertaining to abnormal protrusion of the eyeball

exother'mic. In a reacting system if heat is formed, the reaction is said to be exothermic

exten'sile. Capable of being stretched

ex'udate. A fluid or semifluid which has oozed through the tissues into a cavity or upon the body surface

fal'ciform. Sickle-shaped

fal'ciform ligament. Fold of peritoneum between the liver and the anterior abdominal wall in which the umbilical vein (ligamentum teres) is contained

fascic'ulus, pl., **fascic'uli.** A bundle of close-set fibers, usually muscle or nerve fibers

fecunda'tion. Fertilization; impregnation

fenes'trated. Having windowlike openings; perforated

fibril'la, pl., **fibril'lae.** A small fiber or filament

fim'bria, pl., **fim'briae.** A fringe

flat'ulence. Distention due to generation of gases in the stomach and intestine

fontanelle'. "Little fountain"; the rise and fall of the pulse can be observed through the membranous interspaces of fontanelles in the infant's cranium

gastrocne'mius. "Belly of the leg"; one of the calf muscles

gas'troepiplo'ic. Pertaining to the stomach and greater omentum

gen'erative. Having the power or function of reproduction

genes. The factors on chromosomes which determine certain hereditary characteristics believed to be the sequence of bases in the DNA molecule

genu. Any structure with the shape of the flexed knee

ger'minal. Cells or tissue from which new ones arise

gesta'tion. Pregnancy

gli'a. Neuroglia

glob'ulins. Protein substances (myosin, fibrinogen, etc.) similar to albumins but insoluble in water and soluble in dilute solutions of neutral salts

glycogen'esis. The production of glycogen

glycogenol'ysis. Splitting of glycogen into glucose by the liver, or into pyruvic or lactic acid in other tissues

glycol'ysis. Splitting of glucose into carbon dioxide and water

glyconeogen'esis. Formation of glucose or glycogen from noncarbohydrate substances

gon'ad. Gamete-producing gland; e.g., testis, ovary

hem'atin. An iron-containing compound derived from heme, the colored nonprotein constituent of hemoglobin

hemorrhoi'dal. Pertaining to hemorrhoids, small tumors caused by dilation of the veins of the anal region

hi'lus or **hi'lum.** The depression, usually on the concave surface of a gland, where vessels and ducts enter or leave

homeosta'sis. Constancy of the internal environment

homoge'neous. Of the same kind or quality throughout; uniform in nature; the reverse of heterogeneous

hy'aline. Glassy; translucent

hydrostatic pressure. A pressure exerted uniformly and perpendicularly to all surfaces as by a homogeneous liquid

hy'oid. Y- or U-shaped

hyperglyce'mia. An abnormally high amount of glucose in the blood

in'guinal. Pertaining to the groin

interme'diary meta'bolism. Refers to metabolism taking place after absorption and before excretion from the excretory organs, that is, either in cells or in the body fluids—tissue fluid, lymph, or blood

internun'cial. Acting as a medium between two nerve centers

intersti'tial. In the interspaces of a tissue; refers to the connective-tissue framework

intro'itus. An entrance to a cavity or space

ionize. To form ions which are atoms, or groups of atoms, bearing electric charges

ische'mia. Local anemia due to mechanical obstruction (mainly arterial narrowing) to the blood supply

is'chium, pl., **is'chia.** The lower portion of the os innominatum; that upon which the body is supported in a sitting posture

isoagglu'tinin. A substance present in the blood serum which can agglutinate or clump together the erythrocytes of other individuals of the same species

isoagglutin'ogen. A substance in blood cells which stimulates the action of agglutinins

i'sotope. Isotopes are atoms that have different numbers of neutrons in their nuclei, but have the same number of protons. They weigh differently but behave alike chemically. Some of them are radioactive and can be used as tracers in the body; for instance, iron, iodine

ketogen'ic. Tending to produce "ketone bodies," acetone, acetoacetic acid, and beta hydroxybutyric acid

lacer'tus fibro'sus. Aponeurotic band from biceps tendon to fascia of forearm

lacta'tion. The secretion of milk

lacu'na, pl., **lacu'nae.** A minute, hollow space

lambdoi'dal. Resembling the Greek letter Λ, lambda

lamel'la, pl., **lamel'lae.** A thin plate, or layer

lam'ina. A thin plate; a germinal layer

laryn'goscope. The instrument by which the larynx may be examined in the living subject

libi'do. Conscious or unconscious sexual desire

lin'ea as'pera. A rough, longitudinal line on the back of the femur

lymphangi'tis. Inflammation of a lymphatic vessel

ly'sin. Lysis, "to dissolve." An antibody which can dissolve cells

macera'tion. The softening of the parts of a tissue by soaking

macroscop'ic. That which can be viewed with the naked eye

manom'eter. An instrument for measuring the pressure or tension of liquids or gases

maras'mus. Progressive wasting and emaciation, especially in young infants

matura'tion. Cell division in which the number of chromosomes in the germ cells is reduced to one half the number usual for the species

medul'la. The central portions of an organ. Marrow. The medulla oblongata of the spinal cord

mesoco'lon. A process of the peritoneum by which the colon is attached to the posterior abdominal wall

methemoglo'bin. A transformation product of oxyhemoglobin found in the circulating blood after poisoning with acetanilid, potassium chlorate, etc.; the iron is oxidized from ferrous to ferric form; this compound does not carry oxygen

microceph'alus. Congenitally defective fetus with a very small head

micro'villi. Fine protoplasmic extensions at the apical surface of a columnar epithelial cell

mononu'clear. Having but one nucleus

mo'tor. Producing or subserving motion. A muscle, nerve, or center that affects or produces movement

mu'cin. A glycoprotein, a constituent of mucus

muta'tion. A distinctive character appearing for the first time in a pure line which is transmitted through succeeding generations. It is due to some change in the chromosomes

my'elocyte. A bone-marrow cell giving rise to granulocytes

myogen'ic. Originating in muscular tissue
myoneu'ral. Pertaining to both muscle and nerve
my'osin. A globulin, chief protein substance of muscle
na'ris, pl., **na'res.** A nostril
navic'ular. Boatlike
ner'vus er'igens, pl., **ner'vi erigen'tes.** A nerve fiber supplying the bladder, genitalia, and rectum; derived from the second and third sacral nerves
neurogen'ic. Originating in nerve tissue
no'tochord. The primitive backbone in the embryo
nystag'mus. Rhythmical oscillation of the eyeballs, either horizontal, rotary, or vertical. A symptom seen sometimes in disease of the inner ear or cerebellum
odon'toid. Toothlike
o'ocyte. The primitive ovum in the cortex of the ovary, before maturation takes place
os, pl., **o'ra.** A mouth
os, pl., **os'sa.** A bone
osmo'sis. The passage of fluids and solutions, separated by a membrane or other porous septum, through the partition, so as to become mixed or diffused through each other
os'sa innomina'ta, pl. of **os innomina'tum.** "Unnamed bones." The irregular bones of the pelvis, unnamed on account of their nonresemblance to any known object
os'teoblasts. The cells forming or developing into bone
os'teoclast. A large cell found in the bone marrow, believed to be capable of absorbing bone
o'tic. Pertaining to the ear
o'toliths. Particles of calcium carbonate and phosphate found in the internal ear on the hair cells
papil'la, pl., **papil'lae.** A small eminence; a nipplelike process
paranas'al si'nuses. Sinuses which communicate with the cavity of the nose. They are often called air sinuses of the head
paren'chyma. The essential or specialized part of an organ, e.g., hepatic cell, as distinguished from the supporting tissue
parturi'tion. Act of giving birth
patel'la. A small pan; the kneecap
ped'icle. A stalk
pedun'cle. A narrow part acting as a support
pet'rous. Stonelike
phlebot'omy. The surgical opening of a vein; venesection
phren'ic. Pertaining to the diaphragm
pi'a ma'ter. "Tender mother"; the innermost membrane closely enveloping the brain and spinal cord
pir'iform. Pear-shaped
pis'iform. Pea-shaped
polar'ity. Tendency of a body to exhibit opposite properties in opposite directions; referring to the possession of positive and negative poles
poles. Points having opposite properties, occurring at the opposite extremities of an axis. Either end of a spindle in mitosis
precip'itins. Antibodies in the blood serum which are capable of precipitating antigens
psy'chical. Pertaining to the mind
ptery'goid. Wing-shaped
pyogen'ic. Producing pus
pyrex'ia. Elevation of temperature; fever
quadrigem'inal. Consisting of four parts
recep'tor. This word is used with various meanings. One dictionary defines it as a sense organ; another as "nerve endings in organs of sense." Others would define it as the "ends of an afferent nerve fiber." It should be used and interpreted with care
rec'tus, pl., **rec'ti.** Straight. Name given to certain straight muscles of the eye and abdomen
regurgita'tion. The casting up of undigested food from the stomach. A backward flowing of blood through a cardiac valve because of imperfect closure of a valve leaflet
rhe'obase. Minimal electric current required to excite a tissue, e.g., nerve or muscle
rhom'boid. A quadrilateral figure whose opposite sides and angles are equal but which is neither equilateral nor equiangular
saliva'tion. An excessive secretion of saliva
saphe'nous. Superficial, as the saphenous veins of the body
saponifica'tion. Alkaline hydrolysis; when fats are thus hydrolized, soaps are produced
sig'moid. Shaped like the letter S
ska'tole. A strong-smelling crystalline substance from human feces, produced by decomposition of proteins in the intestine
sol'ute. A dissolved substance
sol'vent. A substance, usually liquid, which is capable of dissolving another substance
somat'ic. Pertaining to the body, especially the body wall
specif'ic grav'ity. A comparison between the weight of a substance and the weight of an

equal volume of some other substance taken as a standard. The standards usually referred to are air for gases and water for liquids and solids. For instance, the specific gravity (s.g.) of carbon dioxide (air standard) is 1.5, meaning that it is 1.5 times as heavy as an equal volume of air. Again, the specific gravity of mercury (water standard) is 13.6, meaning that mercury is 13.6 times as heavy as an equal volume of water. The specific gravity of solutions, as a salt solution, will necessarily vary with the concentration

sphe'noid. Wedge-shaped

sphinc'ter. A circular muscle which contracts the aperture to which it is attached

splanch'nic. Pertaining to the viscera

summa'tion. Addition; finding of total or sum

suppura'tion. Formation of pus

sur'face ten'sion. The force which exists in the surface film of liquids which tends to bring the contained volume into a form having the least superficial area. It is due to the fact that the particles in the film are not equally acted on from all sides but instead are attracted inward by the pull of molecules below them

su'ture. That which is sewn together, a seam; the synarthrosis between two cranial bones

syner'gic or **synerget'ic.** Acting in harmonious cooperation, said especially of certain muscles

ten'do achil'lis. "Tendon of Achilles." The tendon attached to the heel, so named because Achilles is supposed to have been held by the heel when his mother dipped him in the river Styx to render him invulnerable

tet'any. A disease characterized by painful tonic and symmetrical spasm of the muscles of the extremities

the'nar. Mound at base of thumb

thermogen'esis. The physiological process of heat production in the body

thermol'ysis. Loss of body heat by evaporation, radiation

thermotax'is. The normal adjustment of the bodily temperature. The movement of organisms in response to heat

trabec'ula, pl., **trabec'ulae.** A supporting fiber; a prolongation of fibrous membrane which forms septa or partitions

troch'lear. Pertaining to a pulley. The trochlear nerve supplies the superior oblique muscle

u'vula. "Little grape"; the soft mass which projects downward from the posterior middle of the soft palate

vac'uole. A space or cavity within the protoplasm of a cell, containing nutritive or waste substances

vas'cular. Latin, *vasculum*, a small tube. Refers to tubes conveying liquids, as blood vascular and lymph vascular systems

ve'na co'mes, pl., **ve'nae com'itantes.** A deep vein following the same course as the corresponding artery

ver'miform. Worm-shaped

vo'lar. Pertaining to the palm of the hand or the sole of the foot

INDEX